Lov

Love
me
4-Life

BIOLOGY
THE STUDY OF LIFE

BIOLOGY
THE STUDY OF LIFE
Second Edition

William D. Schraer

Chairperson, Science Department
Middletown High School
Middletown, NY

Herbert J. Stoltze

Professor of Biology
Northeastern Illinois University
Chicago, IL

CEBCO · ALLYN AND BACON, INC.
Newton, Massachusetts

STAFF CREDITS

Editorial Development   Lois B. Arnold, Patricia M. Dambry, Thomas M. Frado, Natania Mlawer
Preparation Services   Martha E. Ballentine
Book Design/Production   Jonathan B. Pollard
Book Manufacturing   Annie Puciloski
Art Direction   L. Christopher Valente

OUTSIDE CREDITS

Editorial/Writing Services   Mary Alice Alexander, Dori Smith, Dotty Burstein, Hubert M. Vining, Lee Drummond, Sandra Gottfried
Design/Production Services   S. Stuart Wallace, Betty Fiora
Photo Research   Laurel Anderson/Photosynthesis
Cover Design   Ligature, Inc., Chicago
Book Design   George A. Bakacs/Associated Designers, Joseph Weiler/The Flack Studio
Illustrations   George A. Bakacs, Mark Lefkowitz, ANCO/Boston, John Hamberger, Leslie Farnsworth, Denise Dunn

Printed in the United States of America

ISBN 0-205-09614-X

2 3 4 5 6 7 8 9   93 92 91 90 89 88 87

ACKNOWLEDGMENTS

CONSULTANTS

Critical and Creative Thinking

Robert J. Swartz,
Codirector of Critical and Creative Thinking Program
University of Massachusetts,
Boston, Massachusetts

Science Content

Donald W. Deters (*Respiration*)
Dept. of Biological Sciences
Bowling Green State University
Bowling Green, Ohio

Gary B. Ellis (*Vertebrates*)
Office of Technology Assessment for the
U.S. Congress
600 Pennsylvania Avenue, S.E.
Washington, D.C.

Kenneth R. Miller (*Photosynthesis*)
Biology Dept., Brown University
Providence, Rhode Island

M. V. Parthasarathy (*Plant structure and function*)
Biology Dept., Cornell University
Ithaca, New York

Irwin Rubenstein (*The cell*)
Dept. of Genetics and Cell Biology
University of Minnesota
Minneapolis, Minnesota

Charles F. Stevens (*Nervous and endocrine systems*)
Section of Molecular Neurobiology
Yale University Medical School
New Haven, Connecticut

Daryl Sweeney (*Invertebrates*)
Dept. of Biology, University of Illinois
Champaign-Urbana, Illinois

Marjorie B. Zucker (*Circulatory systems*)
Pathology Dept.
New York University School of Medicine
New York, New York

TEACHER REVIEWERS

Cathy Banks, Wheeler High School Marietta, Georgia;
Cathy Bennett, Dunbar High School Dunbar, West Virginia;
Carole Brenkacz, West Seneca East Senior High School, West Seneca, New York;
Brenda L. Dorsey, York Community High School, Elmhurst, Illinois;
Karen L. Fout, Fenwick High School, Middletown, Ohio;
Richard L. Gaume, Plain Local Schools, Canton, Ohio;
Norm Grimes, Columbian High School, Tiffin, Ohio;
Emiel Hamberlin, Du Sable High School, Chicago, Illinois;
Sister M. Francis Hopcus, Pomona Catholic High School, Pomona, California;
Mic Jaeger, East Union High School, Manteca, California;
Nevin Longenecker, John Adams High School, South Bend, Indiana;
Harold Pratt, Jefferson County Schools, Lakewood, Colorado;
Helen Louise Shafer, Science and Technology Magnet School, Dallas, Texas;
Russell H. Stanhope, Worcester Public Schools, Worcester, Massachusetts;
Harlow B. Swartouf, Woodstock High School, Woodstock, Illinois;
Robert C. Wallace, formerly Reavis High School, Burbank, Illinois;
Melanie Wojtulewicz, Whitney M. Young Magnet High School, Chicago, Illinois.

TABLE OF CONTENTS

1 Introduction to Biology

2 Animal Maintenance

7 Cellular Respiration 108

8 Nutrition 124

9 Transport 144

10 The Blood 162

11 Respiration   178

12 Excretion   194

13 Support and Locomotion   208

14 Nervous Regulation   224

15 The Human Nervous System   242

16 Chemical Regulation 266

3 Plant Maintenance

17 Plant Nutrition 284

18 Plant Structure 298

19 Plant Maintenance 314

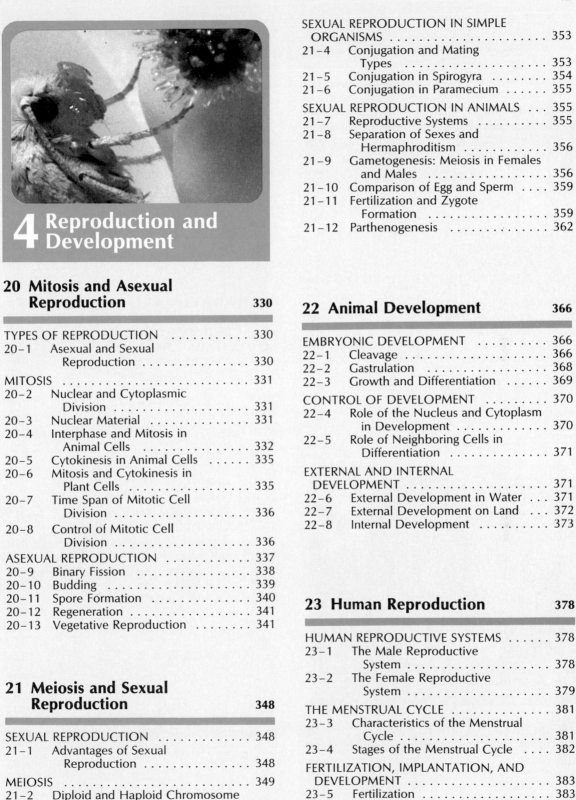

4 Reproduction and Development

5 Genetics

25 Mendelian Genetics   410

26 Modern Genetics   426

27 Molecular Genetics   442

29 The Modern Theory of Evolution

6 Evolution

28 Evidence of Evolution

7 Diversity of Living Things

8 Ecology

37 Organization in the Biosphere 670

38 Biomes of the Earth 690

39 Human Ecology 706

FEATURES

Frontiers of Biology

Careers

Sidelights

Issues in Biology

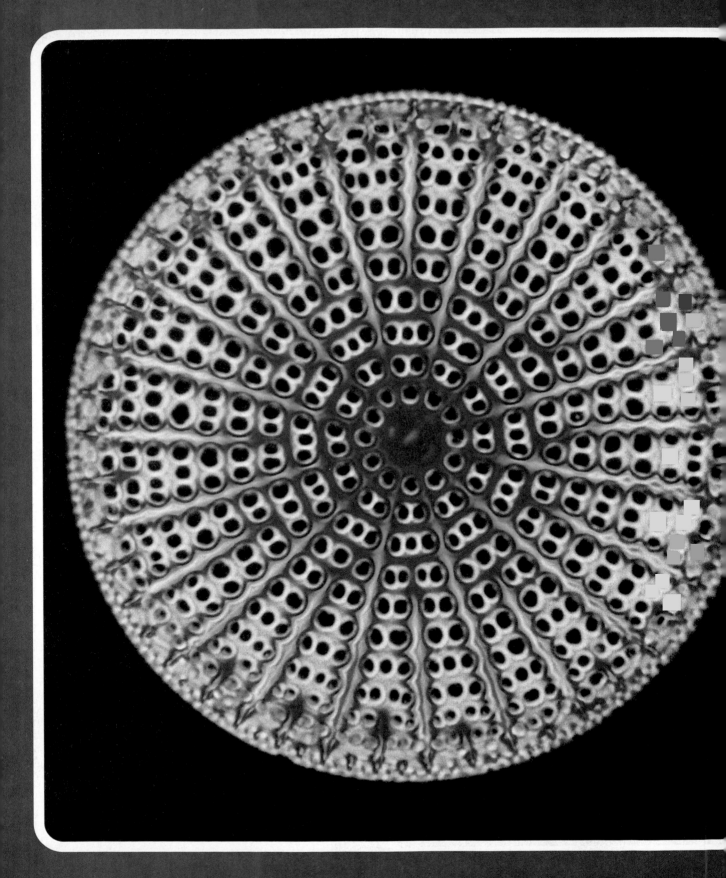

UNIT 1

INTRODUCTION TO BIOLOGY

Examine a drop of sea water under a microscope and you may catch a glimpse of this tiny one-celled organism known as a diatom. Diatoms exist in incredible numbers in the world's oceans. They are different from other organisms, even other one-celled organisms. But, like all life forms, the diatom must be adapted for carrying out its essential life processes. In this Unit, you will consider the many traits that all organisms have in common, despite the amazing diversity they display. You will see that at the cellular and molecular level, the similarities become even more striking.

Chapter 1

THE NATURE OF LIFE

When a cougar chases its prey, it displays the ability to respond to its environment.

DESCRIBING LIFE

Objective:
List nine general characteristics that distinguish living from nonliving things.

The word **biology** is easy to define. It is the study of living things. Let us consider what this might mean. Think for a minute or two about the different kinds of living things you know by sight. You may want to jot them down under various headings, such as domestic animals, wild animals, ocean life, insects. Don't forget the plants you know—for example, trees, wildflowers, garden flowers, house plants, weeds. If you take the time to do it, you may come up with quite a long list— probably 100 kinds, at least.

Suppose you wanted to find out everything you could about the living things you know. You might expect it to take quite a long time. Yet, the living things you know are only a tiny fraction of all that exist. Biologists have found more than a million different kinds of life on earth. You may wonder how you can possibly learn very much about a million different things in one year of biology.

Actually, you are going to learn a great deal about every one of them by reading just a few pages of this chapter. The reason is that despite the great *diversity* of life, there is also a great *unity* of life. All living things are alike in many ways. We are going to begin the study of biology by talking about these similarities.

Figure 1-1. Temperate Forest in Summer.

1-1 Characteristics of Life

Just what do we mean when we say that something is alive? Look at Figure 1-1. It is a fairly common sight—the edge of a woods. Do you see a dead tree in the picture? What makes you think so?

Now look at Figure 1-2. This is a similar scene during the winter in one of the colder parts of the country. Are all these trees dead? They certainly look like the dead tree in Figure 1-1. But they are probably not dead. In the spring, tiny buds at the ends of twigs will grow into leaves. The trees will once again show signs of life.

Figure 1-2. Temperate Forest in Winter.

The growth of new leaves on a tree is a sign of life. What other signs of life can you think of? Biologists have not been able to agree on a simple definition of life that fits all cases. But they have agreed on what the "signs of life" are. Taken together, these characteristics or activities become the definition of life.

Each individual living thing is called an **organism** (*or*-guh-nih-zum). All organisms have the following characteristics.

1. Living things are highly organized and contain many complex chemical substances.

2. Living things are made up of one or more **cells,** which are the smallest units that can be said to be alive.

3. Living things use energy.

4. Living things have a definite form and a limited size.

5. Living things have a limited life span.

6. Living things grow.

7. Living things respond to changes in the environment.

8. Living things reproduce.

9. Groups of living things *evolve*, or change over time.

Nonliving objects may show one, or even a few, of these characteristics, but they never show all of them.

1-2 Borderline Cases

It is a human trait to try to define and classify the things we find in the world around us. But the world doesn't seem to be made to suit our wishes. Our definitions and classifications often have fuzzy edges. There are usually borderline cases that fit partly into one category and partly into another. This is especially true of our attempts to define life. There are things in the world that cannot clearly be called "living" or "nonliving." One example is the *viruses*—objects that can be stored like chemicals in a bottle, but when inside a living cell can reproduce more of themselves. Viruses can reproduce, but they do not otherwise carry on any of the processes of life. Another example is a plant seed. Many seeds can be kept in a package for years without undergoing any change. When supplied with water and other suitable conditions, they develop into living plants. Is the seed in the package alive?

The best answer to the question may be that it doesn't really matter whether we say a seed is living or not. There is a far more important and, we think, more interesting question: How does a seed develop into a living plant? You will be trying to answer this kind of question in your study of biology.

THE LIFE PROCESSES

Objectives:

1. Name and define eight general processes by which the life of organisms is maintained.

2. Define the term *metabolism*.

We have mentioned some of the general characteristics of living things. Living things carry on certain activities that are also characteristics of life. In this section we will briefly describe the functions or processes that organisms perform in order to stay alive. These life processes are nutrition, transport, respiration, synthesis and assimilation, growth, excretion, regulation, and reproduction. We will find as we go along that everything we learn about living things is related in some way to these life processes. No matter how different individual organisms may be, they all must carry out these activities. This is the common thread that ties all living things together and makes them basically alike.

1-3 Nutrition

Every organism takes materials from its environment and changes them into forms it can use. This activity is called **nutrition** (noo-*trish*-un). Substances that an organism needs for energy, growth, repair, or maintenance are called **nutrients** (*noo*-tree-unts).

There are two basic types of nutrition. In one kind of nutrition, the organism can produce its own complex nutrients from simple substances in the environment. All the green plants and some bacteria and other one-celled organisms are able to make their own nutrients in this way.

Organisms that cannot make their own nutrients must obtain them in the form of food from the environment. All animals must find their nutrients already made in their environment (see Figure 1-3).

The taking in of food from the environment is called **ingestion** (in-*jes*-chun). Generally, the nutrients in food are not in forms that the organisms can use directly. The nutrients are chemically too complex, and the organism must first break them down into simpler forms. The breakdown of complex food materials into simpler forms that can be used by an organism is called **digestion** (dy-*jes*-chun). The elimination of indigestible material from the digestive tract is called **egestion** (ih-*jes*-chun).

1-4 Transport

Transport is the process by which substances taken into the organism (absorption) or produced within the organism are distributed throughout the organism (**circulation**). Nutrients, wastes, and other products of the life processes are transported from one place to another within the organism. In the smallest organisms there is no real transport system. Usable materials are absorbed directly into the organism from the environment. Wastes pass from the organism directly back to the environment. In most animals, there is a specialized circulatory system for carrying needed materials to all parts of the organism and carrying wastes away. In plants, there are specialized conducting structures that carry substances from the roots and leaves to all parts of the plant.

Figure 1-3. Nutrition in Animals. All animals must obtain food from the environment.

1-5   Respiration

All the life processes require a constant supply of energy. Organisms obtain their energy by releasing the chemical energy stored in certain nutrients. The process by which this is accomplished is called **respiration** (res-puh-*ray*-shun).

Respiration involves a complex series of chemical reactions. In one type of respiration, sugar is broken down to produce water and carbon dioxide. This is called **aerobic** (er-*roh*-bik) **respiration** because it requires oxygen from the air. Some simple organisms carry on **anaerobic** (an-uh-*roh*-bik) **respiration**, which does not require oxygen.

1-6   Synthesis and Assimilation

Organisms are able to combine simple substances chemically to form more complex substances. This process is called **synthesis** (*sin*-thuh-sis). The substances used in synthesis are generally products of the digestion of complex food materials.

One of the results of synthesis is to produce materials that can become part of the structure of an organism. In this way, the organism can repair or replace worn-out parts and can also grow. The incorporation of materials into the body of the organism is called **assimilation** (uh-sim-uh-*lay*-shun).

1-7   Growth

Growth is the process by which living organisms increase in size. It is one result of assimilation of nutrients. In one-celled organisms, growth is simply an increase in the size of the cell. In organisms made up of many cells, growth is usually the result of an increase in both the number and size of cells. Growth in multicellular organisms is accompanied by **differentiation,** the process whereby initially similar and unspecialized cells become specialized for specific functions. In animals, growth generally follows a particular pattern and ends after a certain period of time. Some plants, on the other hand, continue growing throughout life.

1-8   Excretion

Every organism produces waste substances that it cannot use and that may be harmful if allowed to accumulate in the body. The removal of these wastes is called **excretion** (ek-*skree*-shun).

1-9   Regulation

Regulation is the process by which an organism maintains a stable internal environment in a constantly changing external environment. The condition of a stable internal environment is called **homeostasis** (hoh-mee-oh-*stay*-sis).

In animals, regulation is accomplished primarily by the *nervous system,* the *endocrine* (*en*-duh-krin) *system,* and the *excretory system.* The nervous system consists of a network of specialized cells that carry messages, or impulses, throughout the organism. The endocrine system consists of a number of glands that secrete chemicals called *hormones.* Hormones act as chemical messengers. Both nerve impulses and hormones can bring about changes in the organism in response to changes in either the internal or the external environment. There is no nervous system in plants, but there are parts of the plant that produce hormones. These hormones enable the plant to respond to various changes in the environment. The excretory system eliminates metabolic wastes from the body, helping to maintain the body's internal chemical balance.

1-10 Reproduction

Reproduction is the process by which living things produce new organisms of their own kind. Unlike the other life processes, reproduction is not necessary for the continued life of an individual organism. However, it is necessary for the continued existence of that kind of organism.

There are two types of reproduction—**asexual** (ay-*sek*-shuh-wul) **reproduction** and **sexual** (*sek*-shuh-wul) **reproduction** (see Figure 1-4). In asexual reproduction there is only one parent, and all offspring are identical to that parent. In sexual reproduction there are two parents, and the offspring are not identical to either parent.

1-11 Metabolism

All the chemical reactions occurring within the cells of an organism are called its **metabolism** (muh-*tab*-uh-liz-um). Metabolism includes processes that build complex substances from simpler ones and processes that break down complex substances into simpler ones. Metabolism also involves the continuous release and use of energy. Many biologists consider metabolic activity to be the single most important characteristic of life.

Figure 1-4. Types of Reproduction. In one type of asexual reproduction, the plantlets on the edge of the leaf (top) fall off and grow into new plants. In sexual reproduction, two parents share in the reproductive process. Some parents, like these swans (bottom), also share the task of raising the young.

Chapter Review

SUMMARY

- Biology is the study of living things. There are more than a million different kinds of living things on earth. Although they vary in many respects, they all show certain basic characteristics that distinguish them from nonliving things.

- A few things, including viruses and seeds, are difficult to classify as either living or nonliving because they show characteristics of both.

- Living things carry on certain activities that are characteristics of life. These activities include nutrition, transport, respiration, synthesis and assimilation, growth, excretion, regulation, and reproduction. Metabolism includes all the chemical reactions of the life processes.

KNOW THE TERMS

absorption	circulation	ingestion	respiration
aerobic respiration	differentiation	metabolism	sexual reproduction
anaerobic respiration	digestion	nutrient	synthesis
asexual reproduction	egestion	nutrition	transport
assimilation	excretion	organism	
biology	growth	regulation	
cell	homeostasis	reproduction	

SECTION QUESTIONS

Describing Life

1. Define the term *organism*.
2. What is the smallest unit of life?
3. Name one characteristic of life.

The Life Processes

4. What life process involves obtaining material and changing it into useful forms?
5. Which process accounts for the absorption and distribution of materials in organisms?

6. Name the process by which organisms release chemical energy from nutrients.
7. What is the process by which organisms form complex substances?
8. Define the term *growth*.
9. What life process is involved with removing body wastes?
10. What is homeostasis?
11. Name two types of reproduction.

KNOW THE FACTS

Copy the numbers from Column 1 on a sheet of paper. Select the letter for the term or phrase from Column 2 that matches each numbered item, and write it beside the number.

Column 1

1. growth
2. life span
3. assimilation
4. nutrients
5. reproduction
6. absorption
7. egestion
8. metabolism
9. regulation
10. digestion

Column 2

a. produces others of its own kind
b. taken into the organism
c. increase in size
d. elimination from digestive tract
e. incorporation of materials into the body
f. length of life
g. substances used for energy
h. breakdown of foods
i. chemical reactions of life processes
j. distribution throughout the organism
k. stable internal environment

UNDERSTAND THE CONCEPTS

11. Explain the relationships among the processes of ingestion, digestion, and egestion.
12. How does aerobic respiration differ from anaerobic respiration?
13. How does growth occur in many-celled organisms?

14. List the eight characteristics of living things.
15. How is growth related to assimilation?
16. How do the nervous and endocrine systems function in regulation?
17. Explain the difference between sexual and asexual reproduction.

THINK CRITICALLY

18. In what sense is a moving automobile like a living thing?
19. Why might biologists consider metabolic activity to be the single most important characteristic of life?
20. It could be said that viruses represent a transition between the nonliving and living states. Explain.

THINK CREATIVELY

21. How would you decide whether a newly discovered object is living or nonliving?
22. Offer as many reasons as you can why living things show a fundamental unity in life processes as well as a tremendous diversity in appearance.

FOR FURTHER INVESTIGATION

1. What are the products of aerobic respiration? To find out, exhale against the surface of a small hand mirror. What do you observe on the mirror? Now pour some lime water into a drinking glass, put a straw in the glass, and take a deep breath through your nose and mouth. Exhale by blowing through the straw into the glass of lime water. What do you observe?
2. Write a report on the life and contributions of one of the following scientists:
   a. Margaret Morse Nice
   b. Ethel Browne Harvey
   c. James Monroe Joy
   d. Kono Yasui
3. Prepare a report for the class on one of the career opportunities listed below. If possible, interview an individual who is working in the field. Be sure to prepare your questions in advance. You may wish to inquire about training, future opportunities, and the daily routine. A tape recorder will be very helpful.
   a. Biologist
   b. County agricultural agent
   c. Dietitian

FOR FURTHER READING

Asimov, Isaac, *How Did We Find Out About the Beginning of Life?* Walker Publishing Co., Houston, TX, 1982.

Attenborough, David, *Life on Earth*, Little Brown & Co., Boston, 1979.

Carson, Rachel, *The Sea Around Us*, Oxford University Press, New York, 1970.

Durrell, Gerald, *A Practical Guide for the Amateur Naturalist*, Knopf, New York, 1983.

Hutchins, Ross E., *Nature Invented It First*, Dodd, Mead & Co., New York, 1980.

Wunderlich, Klaus, and Gloede, Wolfgang, *Nature as Constructor*, Arco Publishing, Inc., New York, 1981.

Chapter 2

BIOLOGY AS A SCIENCE

Careful observation and recording of experimental data are important aspects of any scientific investigation.

THE NATURE OF SCIENCE

Objectives:
1. State the essential steps of a scientific investigation.
2. Explain what is meant by a controlled experiment.
3. Define the terms *hypothesis* and *theory*.

2-1 The Scientific Method

Broadly speaking, all science is an attempt to understand the world we live in. By this we mean that science goes beyond simple observation and description of objects and events. It tries to find general principles that explain why things are as they are and why things happen the way they do. There are so many different kinds of phenomena to be explained, and so many unanswered questions, that scientists have had to become specialists—physicists, chemists, astronomers, earth scientists, biologists, and so on. Within each of these major fields, there are numerous subdivisions. Today, few scientists have the knowledge or the time to make investigations beyond a narrow field of interest.

Scientists in all fields approach their problems in the same way. When a scientist announces a finding or proposes a new idea, other scientists may repeat the work or test its conclusions. This universal approach to scientific problems is called the **scientific method.** Its main features are the same in all areas of science.

Defining the problem. The scientific method begins when a person chooses to investigate a particular phenomenon or set of facts. The subject may be one about which little is known, or it

Figure 2-1. Observation. Biologists often observe organisms in nature. Such studies provide information that cannot be obtained in a laboratory setting.

may even be a well-understood one. In either case, the scientist consciously defines a specific problem for investigation.

This decision is usually followed by a thorough search in the literature for information relevant to the topic. Most of the information is derived from the data of experiments performed by other scientists and reported in scientific journals. By becoming familiar with existing knowledge about a phenomenon, the scientist not only avoids duplicating work already accomplished, but is also able to plan the best approach to the problem.

Formulating a hypothesis. In analyzing a problem, the investigator may discern from the existing data a specific pattern of events, or some definite relationships between certain factors. However, these observations do not by themselves explain anything. What scientists really want to know is why a particular pattern is observed, i.e., what causes the pattern. It is here that reasoning, guesswork, and inspiration enter. At this stage in the scientific method, the scientist usually formulates a **hypothesis,** a possible explanation of an observed set of facts. This is a critical step in the scientific method.

Testing the hypothesis—Experimentation. Although a hypothesis may offer a theoretical explanation for everything that is known about a certain problem, until it is tested by new experiments, it remains only a hypothesis—a logical guess. A hypothesis cannot be tested just by carrying out more experiments of the same kind. That would only verify the known pattern, rather than confirm the explanation offered by the hypothesis. But since a good hypothesis will predict other kinds of patterns or interactions that have not yet been observed, the scientist must test a hypothesis by designing experiments which will either verify or disprove the predictions of the hypothesis. A hypothesis is accepted as probably correct if all its predicted effects in experiments are observed, and if these effects are repeatable. A hypothesis can never be completely proved. However, it may at any time be disproved by a single experiment! (Of course, that experiment, like all experiments, must be repeated and checked to make sure its results are correct.)

The design of an experiment is critical to the success of an investigation. In an experiment, the investigator sets up a situation in which a particular kind of observation can be made. The investigator makes certain changes in the situation and observes the results. In biology, research often involves the use of **controlled experiments.** In a controlled experiment, a situation is set up in duplicate. A single factor is then changed in one setup, but not in the other. Any difference in the results of the two setups can be assumed to be caused by the factor that was changed. The setup in which no change was made, and which serves as a reference, is called the *control* (see Figure 2-2).

Observations and measurements. Since the goal of science is to explain what is observed, every investigation must include *observations.* (see Figure 2-1). In the early history of science,

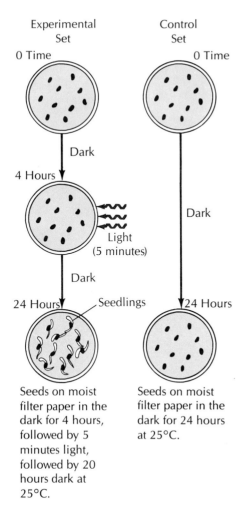

Experimental Set

Control Set

0 Time

0 Time

Dark

4 Hours

Dark

Light
(5 minutes)

Dark

24 Hours — Seedlings   24 Hours

Seeds on moist filter paper in the dark for 4 hours, followed by 5 minutes light, followed by 20 hours dark at 25°C.

Seeds on moist filter paper in the dark for 24 hours at 25°C.

Figure 2-2. A Controlled Experiment. The experiment illustrated here was used to determine if the seeds of a particular plant species required light to germinate. The only difference between the two sets of seeds was the five minutes exposure to light in the experimental set.

observations were generally imprecise. One thing might be described as larger than another, or an event might be described as more likely to happen at warm temperatures than at cold temperatures. Today we recognize that such vague generalizations are not very useful. The heart of modern science is accurate measurement and the statement of results in numerical, or quantitative, form. To obtain precise, quantitative results, scientists use many special tools and instruments.

Recording and reporting observations. For progress to occur in any field of science, there must be no secrecy, no withholding of information. The materials and procedures used in all investigations, as well as all observations and results, must be recorded accurately and reported in full detail. If an experiment cannot be repeated by other investigators, the reported results of the original investigation cannot be considered valid.

When a research project has been completed, the investigator may write a paper describing the project and submit the paper to a scientific journal. These journals are usually publications of scientific societies specializing in a particular branch of science. The journals serve as a source of information on recent developments in various scientific fields. Before a research paper is accepted by a journal for publication, it is reviewed by several scientists. The reviewers are usually scientists working in an area of science the same as, or related to, that of the research paper. Reviewers look to see that correct scientific methodology is used, that results are reported clearly, and that conclusions are supported by the experimental data. If they find deficiencies, their criticisms and suggestions are passed on to the original investigator, who can then perform additional experiments, analysis, and/or interpretation of data to correct and improve the paper before it is resubmitted for publication. In this way the quality of science that is reported is maintained at a high level.

Theories As hypotheses are tested through experimentation, new and better hypotheses are proposed. In fact, scientists are constantly trying to refine hypotheses, i.e., to have them more accurately describe nature. While hypotheses are obviously important, each is usually an idea limited to observations in a particular investigation. Explanations that apply to a broad range of phenomena are called **theories.** Theories are much harder to come by and to establish than hypotheses. An example of a well-tested theory is the germ theory of disease, developed from the work of Louis Pasteur. According to this theory, diseases are the effects of microscopic organisms living and reproducing inside the body of the diseased individual. The nature of disease had been completely misunderstood before this theory was proposed. The theory led to methods of treating and preventing many human diseases. However, it is a theory with limits. Many diseases are not caused by germs. The world is still waiting for a theory that will account for the so-called

mega-	one million	1,000,000
kilo-	one thousand	1,000
deci-	one-tenth	0.10
centi-	one-hundredth	0.01
milli-	one-thousandth	0.001
micro-	one-millionth	0.000001

Table 2-1. Some Prefixes of the Metric System.

degenerative diseases, such as arthritis, diabetes, cancer, and heart disease.

2-2 Scientific Measurement

Measurements in scientific investigations are usually expressed in units of the **metric system.** In this system, the basic unit of length is the meter (m); the unit of mass or weight is the gram (g); the unit of volume is the liter (L); the unit of time is the second (s); and the unit of temperature is the Celsius degree, or kelvin. In the customary system of measurement used in daily life in the United States, units of different size have different names. For example, inches, feet, yards, and miles are all units of length. For a particular measurement we choose the unit that is most convenient. Thus we express the size of a sheet of paper in inches; the dimensions of a room in feet; and the distance between cities in miles. In the metric system, a simpler method is used to make units of convenient size. A prefix is attached to the basic unit name to make it larger or smaller. The basic most commonly used prefixes are defined in Table 2-1. The measurements of some familiar objects in metric units are shown in Figure 2-3.

The biologist has a need for small units because of the small size of the structures in living cells. Many of these structures are no more than a few millionths of a meter (micrometers) in length or diameter. Since so many measurements in biology are in this range, biologists often use a shorter name, the micron, in place of the micrometer. One micron (symbol, μ) is the same as one micrometer, or one-millionth of a meter. It is also equal to one-thousandth of a millimeter (0.001 mm).

Another small unit of length sometimes used for cell structures is the Angstrom unit (symbol, Å). One Angstrom unit is one ten-thousandth of a micron.

Figure 2-3. Some Representative Metric Units

TOOLS OF THE BIOLOGIST

Objectives:

1. State why instruments are necessary for scientific research.
2. Name and state the function of the parts of a compound microscope.
3. Explain how to find the magnification of a compound microscope.
4. Define and state the importance of *resolution* in a microscope.
5. Describe the steps in preparing a specimen for examination with a microscope.
6. State the special characteristics and uses of the stereomicroscope, the phase-contrast microscope, and the electron microscope.

2-3   The Need for Instruments

Observation and measurement are the backbone of scientific investigation. The observations that can be made by the unaided senses are quite limited. Therefore, every branch of science makes use of instruments that increase the range and accuracy of the human senses. Even in daily life we use instruments to help our senses. Eyeglasses are an obvious example. But we also use thermometers, measuring cups, scales, and rulers. We seldom think of these things as scientific instruments, but that is what they are. In this section of the text we will describe a few of the important instruments that are used in biological research.

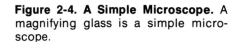

Figure 2-4. A Simple Microscope. A magnifying glass is a simple microscope.

2-4   The Optical Microscope

A **microscope** is any device that enables us to see small details in an object by apparently enlarging it. What we see when we use a microscope to examine an object is called an *image.* The ratio of the image size to the object size is the **magnification,** or *magnifying power*, of the instrument. Microscopes that make use of light to produce enlarged images are called **optical microscopes.** Optical microscopes depend on the fact that light rays change direction when they pass from one transparent medium into another. Optical microscopes contain lenses, which are pieces of glass with curved surfaces. The lenses cause light rays from an object to bend in such a way as to produce an enlarged image.

2-5   The Simple Microscope

The **simple microscope** is what we know as a magnifying glass (see Figure 2-4). It consists of a single lens. Lenses of this type were used as early as the tenth century. They are still used by biologists to identify specimens in the field and for quick observations not requiring the high magnifications of a laboratory instrument.

2-6   The Compound Microscope

A **compound microscope** is one that uses two lenses (see Figure 2-5). One lens produces an enlarged image that is further magnified by the second lens. A compound microscope has an optical system, a mechanical system, and a light system. Its use has led to dramatic advances in nearly all fields of science (see Figure 2-6).

The optical system. The lenses make up the **optical system** of the compound microscope. The two lenses of the optical system are the *objective* and the *ocular* (ahk-yuh-ler), or *eyepiece*. In modern microscopes, the objective and the ocular each consist of several lenses combined to give the desired optical properties. However, as far as the operation of the instrument is concerned, each set of lenses acts like a single lens.

A compound microscope usually has two or more objective lenses of different magnifying powers. A *low-power objective* is used first to locate the region of the specimen to be examined. A *high-power objective* is then moved into position if further magnification is wanted. Usually the ocular can be removed and replaced by another of different power.

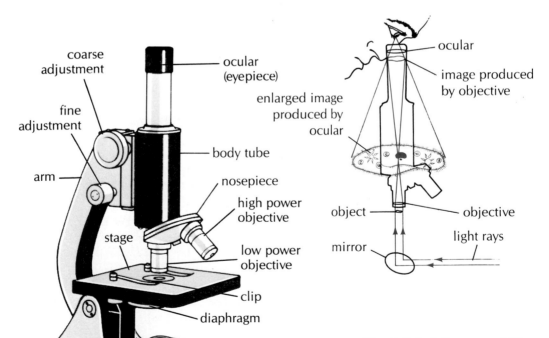

Figure 2-5. A Compound Microscope. The objective produces an enlarged image of the specimen. When this image is viewed through the ocular, a still larger image of the specimen is seen.

The mechanical system. The **mechanical system** consists of the structural parts that hold the specimen and lenses and permit focusing of the image.

The *base* is the structure on which the microscope stands. Most of the other mechanical parts are attached to the *arm.* The *stage,* which is a platform coming out from the arm, has a round opening over which the specimen is placed. The specimen is usually mounted on a glass or plastic *slide* for observation. Two *clips* attached to the stage hold the slide in place. Attached to the top of the arm is the cylindrical *body tube,* which holds the lenses. The eyepiece, which you look through when using the microscope, is at the top of the body tube. At the bottom of the body tube is a revolving *nosepiece,* which holds the objective lenses. The objectives are changed by turning the nosepiece.

To focus the microscope, two adjustment knobs are used. The large knob is the *coarse adjustment,* which is used for approximate focusing of the low-power objective. The smaller knob is the *fine adjustment,* which is used for final focusing of the low-power objective and for all focusing of the high-power objective. Both adjustment knobs vary the distance between the objective and the specimen by moving either the body tube or the stage. The specimen is in focus when the image is sharpest for the observer. When the high-power objective is in position, it generally lies very close to the slide on which the specimen is mounted. For this reason, only the fine adjustment knob should be used in focusing the high-power objective.

The light system. The **light system** consists basically of a mirror and a diaphragm. In some microscopes there is also a substage illuminator and a condenser. The *mirror,* which is under the opening in the stage, can be adjusted to direct light up through the specimen into the objective. In some microscopes, light is supplied directly by a *substage illuminator,* which is a small electric light. The amount of light reaching the objective is regulated by the *diaphragm* (*dy*-uh-fram), which is mounted below the stage. There are two types of diaphragms: the *disc diaphragm* consists of a flat plate with different-sized holes in it; the *iris diaphragm* is made up of overlapping plates that can be adjusted to increase or decrease the size of the central opening. Some microscopes have *condensers* located in or below the stage. Condensers are lenses that concentrate the light on the specimen.

2-7 Magnification

Magnification refers to enlargement in one direction, such as length, not a change in area or "size." If a microscope has a magnification of 100×, the image of a line 1 millimeter long will appear to be 100 millimeters long. The area of an image is increased by the square of the magnification. For example, the image of a square 1 millimeter × 1 millimeter will be 100

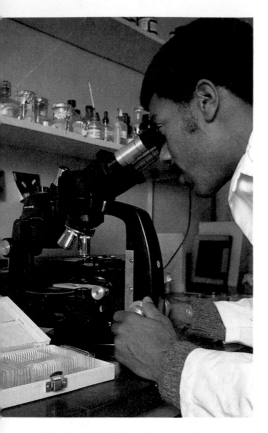

Figure 2-6. The Modern Compound Light Microscope. Work in numerous fields of science and technology is dependent on the use of the light microscope.

millimeters × 100 millimeters. The square has an area of 1 square millimeter. Its image has an area of 10,000 square millimeters. Students are sometimes confused by this difference between the enlargement of a line and the enlargement of an area.

In a compound microscope, the total magnification can be found by multiplying the magnifying power of the objective by the magnifying power of the ocular. In student microscopes, the power of the high-power objective is often 43×, and that of the ocular is 10×. With the high-power objective in use, the total magnifying power of the microscope is 43 × 10, or 430×. This means that the distance between two points in the image is 430 times greater than it is in the actual object.

2-8   Resolution

The microscope does not add detail to objects. The details are always there. What the microscope does is to spread the details apart so the human eye can make them out. To the unaided eye, two tiny spots close together blend into one. We cannot see them as separate spots. Under the microscope, these two spots are seen farther apart. Now we can see them separately.

The ability of a microscope to show two points that are close together as separate images is called its **resolution** (rez-uh-*loo*-shun), or *resolving power*. Resolution is another term for sharpness of an image. It does no good to increase the magnifying power of a microscope if its resolving power is not also increased. If only the magnification is increased, the image gets larger, but you cannot make out any more detail. Small blurred spots simply become larger blurred spots.

Up to a point, the resolving power of a microscope depends on the precision and quality of the lenses. However, there is a limit to the resolving power of any optical lens system. An optical microscope cannot distinguish two points that are less than 0.2 micrometers apart. This limit of resolving power is the result of the properties of light. Light is not affected by spacing that small, so it carries no information about the spacing. The two points might just as well be one. This property of light sets a limit on what can be discovered through the optical microscope about the structure of cells. This limit remained until the development of electron microscopes in the 1930s. The electron microscope is described later in this chapter.

2-9   Fixation, Embedding, Sectioning, and Staining

A specimen to be observed under the compound microscope must be thin enough so that light can pass through it. Most biological materials are too thick to allow the passage of light. For this reason they must first be fixed, embedded, and then sliced into thin sections. *Fixation* is done by first cutting the material into relatively small pieces, and then allowing it to soak

Figure 2-7. A Microtome. A microtome is used to slice thin sections of material.

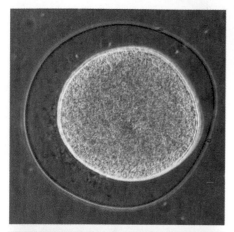

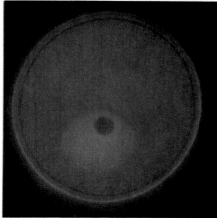

Figure 2-8. Staining. Unstained (top) and stained (bottom) preparations of a sea urchin egg are seen through a light microscope.

Figure 2-9. The Stereomicroscope.

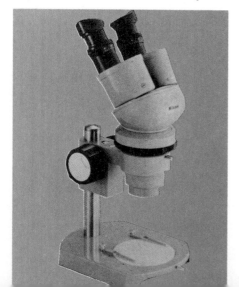

in a fixative, such as formalin. The fixed material is then *embedded* in liquid wax or plastic, which is allowed to harden. The wax or plastic holds the material in place so that it can be sliced, or *sectioned.* The instrument used for slicing thin sections is called a *microtome* (see Figure 2-7).

The thin sections are then usually attached to a glass slide and stained. Without staining, relatively little structural detail of biological specimens can be observed with the compound microscope. However, by using one or more colored stains, which are taken up only by certain structures in the section, the details can be seen (see Figure 2-8). There are some stains, called *vital stains*, that can be used with living tissues. They are taken in by the tissue, but they do not kill it, and the structural details can be seen with the microscope.

2-10   The Stereomicroscope

The **stereomicroscope** has an ocular and an objective for each eye. It provides a three-dimensional image of the specimen being viewed. The magnifying power of stereomicroscopes varies from about 6 × to about 50 ×. This type of microscope is used mainly in studying the external, or surface, structure of specimens. In laboratories, dissections may be carried out under the stereomicroscope (see Figure 2-9).

2-11   The Phase-Contrast Microscope

The reason we are able to use our eyes to distinguish one object from another is that the objects affect light waves in different ways. The eyes and the brain then use the differences in the light waves to "see" the two objects separately. One difficulty with the ordinary optical microscope is that the different structures in living cells are nearly transparent to light. The structures have the same effect on the color or brightness of light passing through them. As a result, we cannot distinguish the structures.

As already mentioned, one solution to this problem is staining. But staining usually kills living organisms. There is another solution. Structures may have the same effect on the color and brightness of light, but different effects on the *speed* of light passing through them. This difference causes the light waves to become "out of phase." The eye cannot detect a difference in the phase of light waves, but an optical system can be made that will make such differences visible. This is the basis of the **phase-contrast microscope.** This instrument is quite complex, but it makes structures in living cells visible that cannot be seen with ordinary light microscopes (see Figure 2-10).

2-12 The Electron Microscope

With the **transmission electron miscroscope** it is possible to obtain magnifications of more than 250,000 times with useful resolution (see Figures 2-11, 2-12). In place of the light beams and optical lenses of the light microscope, the electron microscope has an electron beam and electromagnetic lenses. The electron beam is directed through a vacuum chamber containing a series of electromagnets, which serve as lenses to focus the electron beam. When the electrons hit the specimen, some pass through, some are absorbed, and some are scattered. Those that are transmitted through the specimen are focused on a screen similar to a television screen for viewing. Denser portions of the specimen will absorb more electrons than less dense portions, and will thus appear darker on the viewing screen. Electron microscopes also contain cameras, which can photograph the image of the specimen.

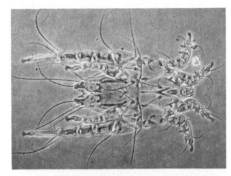

Figure 2-10. Phase-Contrast Microscopy. A feather mite is shown as it appears through an ordinary light microscope (top) and through a phase-contrast microscope (bottom).

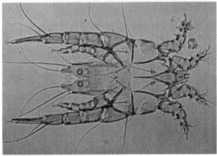

Figure 2-11. A Transmission Electron Microscope.

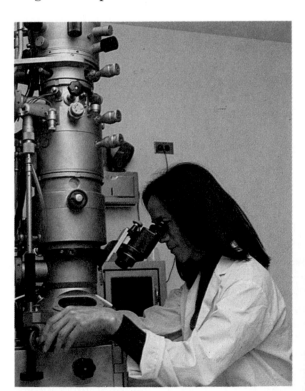

Figure 2-12. Electron Microscopy. The ultrastructure of a plant cell is shown in this thin-section electron micrograph.

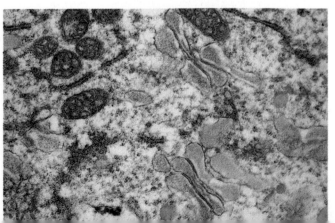

Figure 2-13. Black Fly Seen with Scanning Electron Microscope.

Sidelight

A computer-processed image from a scanning electron microscope of a sea urchin sperm.

Image-Processing Computers

Scientists have found that the images produced by various kinds of microscopes can be greatly enhanced by introducing video cameras and computers into the systems. The image from the microscope is picked up by the video camera, processed by an image-processing computer, and displayed on a screen. This technique was originally developed to handle photographs from space satellites. The image-processing computer can be adjusted to sharpen blurred images or to increase the contrast between light and dark areas.

Specimens to be viewed in an electron microscope must be completely dried, embedded in plastic, and sliced into very thin sections (no more than 1 micron in thickness). The sections are then mounted on fine grids. Often, the specimen is coated with a very thin layer of heavy metal to provide increased contrast.

The *scanning electron microscope* operates in a somewhat different way. This microscope uses an electron beam that has been focused to a fine point. The beam is then passed back and forth over the surface of the specimen. Electrons reflected or ejected from the surface are collected and used to produce an image of great depth (see Figure 2-13). The scanning electron microscope does not have great magnifying power. However, it can reveal very fine details of the surface structure of whole specimens. There are many scanning electron microscope photographs in this text.

2-13 Other Special Techniques

Centrifugation (sen-truh-fyoo-*gay*-shun) is a process by which materials of different densities can be separated from one another. The instrument used to do this is called a **centrifuge** (*sen*-truh-fyooj). The material that is to be separated into its component fractions is suspended in liquid in a test tube, which is put into the centrifuge. The centrifuge spins the tube around. The heaviest particles in the liquid settle to the bottom the fastest. The next-heaviest form a layer on top of the heaviest, and so on. The lightest layer is left on top. Each layer, or fraction, can then be removed by itself from the tube.

The *ultracentrifuge* is much more powerful than a regular centrifuge. It spins at rates of from 40,000 to 100,000 revolutions per minute. It can be used to separate very light particles, including the various parts of the cell, from one another.

In **microdissection** (my-kroh-dis-*ek*-shun), very small instruments are used to perform various operations on living cells (see Figure 2-14). This work must be done under a microscope. First, a *micromanipulator* (my-kroh-muh-*nip*-yuh-layter) is attached to the microscope stage. This apparatus controls the tiny tools used in microdissection. Among the tools that can be used with the micromanipulator are *microelectrodes,* which are used to measure or produce electrical currents in the cell; *microknives* or *microneedles,* which are used to remove cell structures; and *micropipettes* (my-kroh-py-*pets*), which are used to introduce materials into, or remove materials from, the cell.

Tissue culture is a technique for maintaining living cells or tissues in a culture medium outside the body. Cells from living organisms are placed in culture tubes and bathed in fluid containing all necessary nutrients, oxygen, etc. Cells grown in tissue culture are used in many types of biological and medical research.

Chromatography (kroh-muh-*tog*-ruh-fee) and **electrophoresis** (ih-lek-truh-fuh-*ree*-sis) are both sensitive processes used for separating and analyzing mixtures of chemical substances. In chromatography the mixture to be separated is placed on a solid material to which it adheres. A solvent is then introduced. Those substances that adhere most loosely to the material will be carried away first in the solvent. Those substances that adhere most tightly will be carried away last. In this way the different substances in the mixture separate. If the test substances are colored, they will form colored bands or spots. If they are colorless, they can be sprayed with chemicals that give them a color. The rate at which a given substance moves in a given solvent is a characteristic of that substance. By comparing the distance that the test substances have moved with the pattern of known substances, the test substances can be identified.

Electrophoresis is a technique used to separate substances whose particles have an electrical charge. An electric current is run through a trough of liquid containing the test mixture. Different substances move at different rates in the electrical field. In this way the substances that make up the test mixture are separated. Again, the rate at which each substance moves is a characteristic of that substance.

Spectrophotometry (spek-trah-fah-*tah*-mah-tree) is a method routinely used by scientists to identify and quantify substances. An instrument measures the amount of light at different wavelengths, i.e., colors, that is absorbed by a substance. From the pattern of light absorption, the substance can be identified, since each substance has its own unique absorption pattern. Also, the amount of substance present can be determined from the amount of light absorbed at any given wavelength.

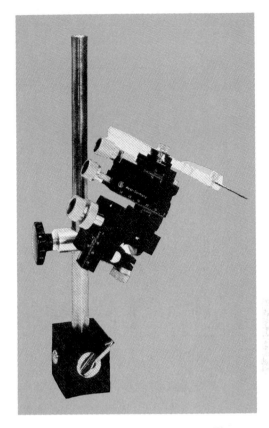

Figure 2-14. A Micromanipulator Fitted with a Microneedle.

Frontier of Biology

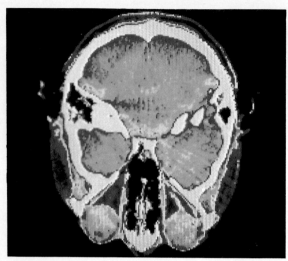

A CAT scan image of a human skull and brain.

Seeing Through the Skin

In recent years, a number of important new instruments have been developed that allow scientists and physicians to "see" through the surface of a living organism and view its internal structures without surgery. New techniques use X rays, sound, and other forms of radiation to pass the barrier of the skin.

The CAT (computerized axial tomography) scan uses a rotating beam of X rays to provide a detailed view of a particular part of the human body. The different tissues of the body vary in density and therefore absorb different amounts of X rays. The greater the amount of X rays absorbed, the less is transmitted by, or passes through, the tissue. Sensors detect the X rays that pass through the tissues. A computer uses the information from the sensors to produce an image of the tissues being examined. The CAT scanner is very sensitive and can distinguish between tissues of very similar densities. It has become widely used in the diagnosis of a number of types of disorders, particularly those involving the brain and spinal cord, kidneys, lungs, and liver. CAT scans make it possible to avoid a number of more dangerous diagnostic tests and give the physi-

cian a clear picture of internal structures without surgery.

Another technique that achieves images comparable in many ways to those from CAT scans is called NMR (nuclear magnetic resonance) imaging. This method requires that a patient be placed inside a special chamber that contains a large electromagnet. The strong magnetic field causes the atomic nuclei of certain elements in the patient's tissues to orient in one direction. Radio waves are produced inside the chamber and are absorbed selectively by the magnetically oriented atomic nuclei, causing them to change their orientation. When the radio waves are turned off, the atomic nuclei realign with the magnetic field and, in so doing, emit signals that are detected by a special sensor in the chamber. As with CAT, a computer uses the information from the sensor to produce an image on a video screen.

NMR imaging has the advantage over CAT scanning of not exposing the patient to harmful kinds of radiation. Also, NMR imaging reveals certain conditions more clearly than CAT scanning. However, many conditions not revealed by NMR can be seen with CAT scans.

A third technique, called sonography, uses ultrasound to detect underlying tissues. Ultrasound is sound whose frequency is above that which can be detected by the human ear.

Diagnostic techniques using ultrasound are employed in cases where exposure to X rays could be harmful, most frequently in viewing a developing baby in the uterus of a pregnant woman. Waves of ultrasound beamed at the mother's body strike the various internal structures, which vary in density. Some of the sound waves are reflected off the surfaces of these structures. Sensors detect the returning sound waves, and, using this information, a computer generates an image of the internal structures that is displayed on a viewing screen. From this image, a physician can tell the size and position of the baby and whether it is developing normally.

Chapter Review

SUMMARY

- The approach to problems used by scientists is called the scientific method. According to this method, the investigator must follow a series of steps to find a solution to a problem. This often involves the use of controlled experiments.

- Experimental observations may include precise measurements, which are made with special instruments. All materials, procedures, and observations must be accurately recorded.

- The results of an experiment may lead to the development of a hypothesis. Once accepted, a hypothesis may lead to the development of a theory.

- In scientific investigations, measurements are usually expressed in metric units.

- Some of the instruments most commonly used by biologists include simple microscopes, compound microscopes, stereomicroscopes, phase-contrast microscopes, and electron microscopes.

- A number of techniques used in biological research are centrifugation, microdissection, tissue culture, chromatography, and electrophoresis.

KNOW THE TERMS

centrifuge
—centrifugation
— chromatography
compound microscope
controlled experiment
— electrophoresis
hypothesis

light system
magnification
mechanical system
metric system
microdissection
microscope
optical microscope

optical system
— phase-contrast microscope
—resolution
scientific method
simple microscope
— spectrophotometry
—stereomicroscope

— theory
tissue culture
—transmission electron
microscope

Scanning-electron micro

SECTION QUESTIONS

The Nature of Science

1. Name the principal steps in the scientific method.
2. Define the term *hypothesis*.
3. List the basic units of measurement in the metric system.

Tools of the Biologist

4. How do instruments improve observations?
5. What is magnification?
6. What is a simple microscope?

7. How many lenses does a compound microscope have?
8. List the systems of a compound microscope.
9. Define the term *resolution*.
10. What is the usefulness of staining in light microscopy?
11. What focuses the beam of electrons in an electron microscope?
12. What method is used to keep alive for research purposes cells that have been removed from an organism?

KNOW THE FACTS

Copy the numbers of the following statements on a sheet of paper. Beside each number, show whether the statement is true or false. If the statement is false, replace the italicized word(s) with a term that will make the statement true.

1. In research, the set-up to which the experimental set-up is compared is called the *control*.
2. A theory applies to a *narrow* range of phenomena.
3. The coarse adjustment is used with the *low power* objective.
4. The magnification of a microscope with a 5x ocular and a 43x high power objective is *430x*.
5. Tissues are sectioned by a *microtome*.
6. Staining cells *improves* the visibility of different structures.
7. The stereomicroscope provides a *two-dimensional* image.
8. The electron microscope has high magnification with *poor resolution*.
9. In a centrifuge, materials of different densities can be *fused to* each other.
10. Chromatography *separates* different substances in a mixture or solution.

UNDERSTAND THE CONCEPTS

11. Explain the function of a control.
12. What is the difference between a centimeter and a millimeter? How many millimeters are in four centimeters?
13. Describe the procedure for focusing a compound microscope.
14. How is the total magnification of a compound microscope calculated?
15. In microscopy, what is meant by the term resolution?
16. Explain the steps involved in preparing materials that are to be viewed with a light microscope.
17. What advantage does a phase-contrast microscope have over an ordinary compound microscope?
18. Describe how a transmission electron microscope produces an image of a specimen.
19. Explain how a micromanipulator can be used to study cells.
20. Explain the principle by which different substances are separated from each other in chromatography.

THINK CRITICALLY

21. What assumptions do scientists make about the world that they are attempting to understand?
22. Why are careful observations and recording of experimental data so important to scientific investigations?
23. Why is there a need for a universal language among scientists?
24. Hypotheses can never be completely proved. Explain.
25. Why is biology a science?
26. In Figure 2-2 an experiment is illustrated. Use this illustration to recreate the actual experiment in your own words. Begin by identifying the problem. Then formulate a hypothesis and describe any experimentation that you think may have occurred. Speculate about what instruments would have been used, what the control group consisted of, what data were recorded, and what conclusions could have been drawn from an analysis of the data.

THINK CREATIVELY

27. A biology student wants to study the effects of vitamin A deprivation on hamsters. Draw up guidelines that this student should follow when using animals for experimentation.
28. Scientists are the practitioners of science. List the attributes that you think scientists should possess in order to be successful in their work.
29. Louis Pasteur said, "Chance favors only the mind that is prepared." Explain this statement by relating it to the practice of science by scientists.

FOR FURTHER INVESTIGATION

1. Set up a controlled experiment in which you study the effect of various levels of sunlight on seedling growth. Keep accurate records detailing the growth and physical appearance of the seedlings. The seeds may be purchased from a biological supply house or garden center.
2. Write a brief report on the life and contributions of one of the following scientists.
   a. Katherine J. Bush
   b. Mary Jane Guthrie
   c. Andreas Vesalias
   d. Chien-Shiung Wu
3. Prepare a report for the class on one of the career opportunities listed below. See suggested procedures, p. 9, "For Further Investigation" Activity 3.
   a. Electron microscopist
   b. Laboratory technician
   c. Microbiologist

FOR FURTHER READING

Goldberg, Joan Rachel, "Jonas Salk," *Science Digest*, June, 1984.

Gould, Stephen J., "On Heroes and Fools in Science," *Natural History*, August/September, 1974.

Haskell, Ann, "A Poet of Science Who Saw the World in a Grain of Sand," *Smithsonian*, March, 1984.

Jenkins, Edward S., ed., *American Black Scientists and Inventors*, National Science Teachers Association, Washington, DC, 1975.

Lederman, Leon, "The Value of Fundamental Science," *Scientific American*, November, 1984.

McCullough, David, "The Queen of Fleas," *Smithsonian*, June, 1985.

Chapter 3

BASIC CHEMISTRY

Water is an essential substance in the chemistry of living things.

ATOMIC THEORY OF MATTER

Objectives:
1. Define the terms *element* and *compound*.
2. Recognize the names and chemical symbols of the most common elements.
3. Describe the structure of the atom.
4. Define the terms *atomic number, isotope,* and *atomic mass*.
5. Briefly describe the process of radioactivity, and explain how radioisotopes and other isotopes are used in biological and chemical research.
6. Describe the arrangement of electrons in the space around the nucleus.

In this century, great progress has been made in understanding the processes of life. Because these processes are chiefly chemical, the biology student must know basic chemistry. Living systems, from the smallest organism to a forest filled with living things, are made of the same atoms found in nonliving systems. The various substances within a living system react according to the same laws of chemistry that other substances obey. Yet some substances in living systems display distinctive properties associated with the large, complex combinations of atoms found in living organisms. Some, for example, transform and store energy for use when needed. Others code information for the traits of the species and the individual organism. Still others combine to perform the functions that keep organisms alive. In this chapter and the next, you will study the chemistry that will enable you to comprehend the basic processes of life.

3-1 Elements and Compounds

As you can see just by looking around you, the world is made of many different substances. Hundreds of thousands of different substances are known. Hundreds of thousands of others can probably exist. Chemistry tells us that all of these different kinds of matter are made of **atoms** combined in various ways. We will have more to say later about atoms.

In spite of the very large number of different substances, there are only about 100 different kinds of atoms. Some substances are made entirely of one kind of atom. These substances are called **elements.** Iron, for example, is an element. All iron consists entirely of iron atoms. Oxygen is an element made entirely of oxygen atoms. Since there are about 100 different kinds of atoms, there are about 100 different elements.

Most substances are **compounds.** In a compound, there are two or more kinds of atoms combined in definite proportions. For example, water is a compound made of hydrogen atoms and oxygen atoms in the proportion of 2 to 1. In water, there are always two hydrogen atoms for each oxygen atom.

There is no way of knowing, just by inspecting a substance, whether it is an element (made of a single kind of atom) or a compound (made of two or more kinds of atoms) (see Figure 3-1). For example, the gas oxygen is an element; the gas carbon dioxide is a compound. However, there are chemical means of deciding whether something is a compound. Compounds can be separated into the elements that make them up. Carbon dioxide, for example, can be separated into carbon and oxygen. Carbon and oxygen cannot be separated into anything else. They are pure elements in themselves.

Chemists have given names and symbols to all the elements. The symbols are a convenient shorthand for showing the makeup of compounds and for showing what happens during chemical reactions. Table 3-1 lists the names and symbols of the elements that are important in biological processes. You

Figure 3-1. Elements and Compounds. Glass (top) can look very much like diamond (bottom). However, diamond is a crystalline form of the element carbon. Glass is a mixture of compounds consisting chiefly of sodium, silicon, and oxygen.

Table 3-1. Elements of Importance in Biology. The Latin name is given when the symbol is derived from it.

Name of element	Symbol	Atomic number	Name of element	Symbol	Atomic number
hydrogen	H	1	phosphorus	P	15
carbon	C	6	sulfur	S	16
nitrogen	N	7	chlorine	Cl	17
oxygen	O	8	potassium (*kalium*)	K	19
sodium (*natrium*)	Na	11	calcium	Ca	20
magnesium	Mg	12	iron (*ferrum*)	Fe	26

will find it useful to learn these symbols. Notice that most of them are abbreviations or initials of the name of the element in English. The others come from the Latin names of the elements. These are elements that were known to scientists several hundred years ago, when Latin was used for most scholarly writing. Names of elements are not capitalized, but the first letter of the symbol is capitalized.

3-2 Structure of Atoms

The idea that matter is made of atoms is a very old one, going back about 2500 years to the philosophers of ancient Greece. The early concept of an atom was that it was an extremely small particle that could not be changed in any way. Research in the twentieth century has shown that atoms are not the hard, solid balls they were first imagined to be. They consist of still smaller particles. Each atom has a very small central portion called the **nucleus.** The nucleus contains particles called **protons** (*proh*-tahnz) and **neutrons** (*noo*-trahnz). In the space outside the nucleus, there are other particles called **electrons** (ih-*lek*-trahnz).

Electrons. The electrons are the parts of an atom that determine its chemical properties. When atoms combine to form compounds, they do so by shifting some of their electrons. An important feature of an electron is that it carries an electric charge. There are two kinds of electric charge—positive and negative. The electron has a negative charge. All electrons have the same amount of electric charge. This is usually called one unit of charge.

Protons. The nucleus of every atom contains one or more protons. A proton has a positive charge of one unit. That is, it has the same amount of charge as an electron, but of opposite sign. However, a proton has almost 2,000 times as much mass, or weight, as an electron.

Neutrons. With the exception of the hydrogen atom, every atomic nucleus also contains neutrons. A neutron has almost exactly the same mass as a proton, but no electric charge.

3-3 Atomic Number

The number of protons in the nucleus of an atom is called its **atomic number.** Each different atomic number represents a different element. For example, an atom of hydrogen has 1 proton in its nucleus (see Figure 3-2). Therefore, the atomic number of hydrogen is 1. The nucleus of an oxygen atom has 8 protons. Therefore, the atomic number of oxygen is 8. Each atom has the same number of electrons as protons. The hydrogen atom has 1 electron; the oxygen atom has 8 electrons. In each atom, the total positive charge of the protons is balanced by the equal number of negative charges of its electrons. Therefore, an atom is normally electrically neutral.

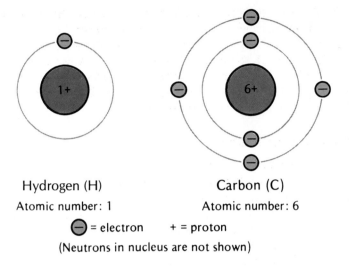

Hydrogen (H)
Atomic number: 1

Carbon (C)
Atomic number: 6

Oxygen (O)
Atomic number: 8

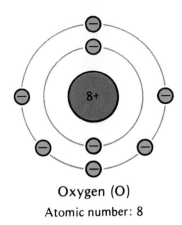

⊖ = electron   + = proton
(Neutrons in nucleus are not shown)

Figure 3-2. Diagrams of Some Atoms. The atomic number of an atom equals the number of protons in its nucleus. It also equals the number of electrons surrounding the nucleus. These diagrams are not supposed to be pictures of what atoms would look like if they could be seen.

3-4 Isotopes

The number of neutrons in an atom does not have a definite relation to its atomic number. Atoms of an element may have different numbers of neutrons. For example, most hydrogen atoms have no neutrons. The nucleus is simply a single proton (see Figure 3-3). However, there are also hydrogen atoms with 1 neutron in the nucleus, and others with 2 neutrons. Although these atoms are not exactly alike, they behave the same chemically. That is true because they all have only one electron, and it is the electrons in an atom that determine its chemical properties. Therefore, these three kinds of atoms are all considered to be atoms of the element hydrogen. These varieties of hydrogen, which differ only in the number of neutrons in their atomic nuclei, are called **isotopes** (*i*-suh-tohps) of hydrogen.

All elements have isotopes. For example, the most common variety of oxygen atom has 8 neutrons in its nucleus. But there are other varieties that occur naturally with 9 and 10 neutrons. Other isotopes of oxygen, with 6, 7, and 11 neutrons, have been produced artificially.

Figure 3-3. Isotopes of Hydrogen. The atomic number is the same for all isotopes of the same element. Only the number of neutrons in the atomic nucleus is different for each isotope.

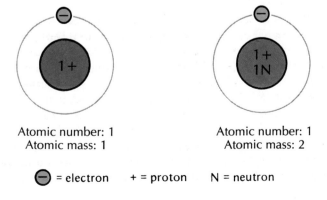

Atomic number: 1
Atomic mass: 1

Atomic number: 1
Atomic mass: 2

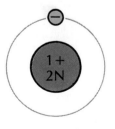

Atomic number: 1
Atomic mass: 3

⊖ = electron   + = proton   N = neutron

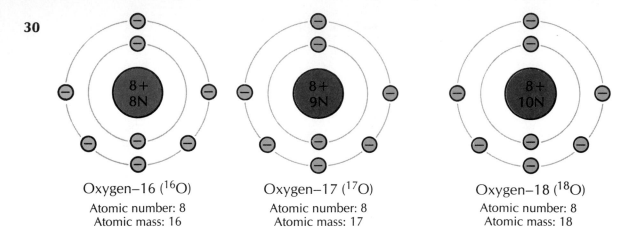

Oxygen–16 (^{16}O)
Atomic number: 8
Atomic mass: 16

Oxygen–17 (^{17}O)
Atomic number: 8
Atomic mass: 17

Oxygen–18 (^{18}O)
Atomic number: 8
Atomic mass: 18

Figure 3-4. Isotopes of Oxygen. The atomic mass, or mass number, of each isotope of an element is different. The atomic number remains the same.

3-5   Atomic Mass

Recall that protons and neutrons have about the same mass, and that this mass is about 2,000 times as large as the mass of an electron. Since the protons and neutrons are packed into the nucleus, just about all the mass of an atom is in its nucleus. If we think of each proton and neutron as having one unit of mass, the mass of an atom is equal to the sum of its protons and neutrons. This sum is called the *atomic mass* of the atom, or its **mass number.** The mass number of an atom with 9 protons and 10 neutrons is 19. Isotopes of the same element have the same atomic number, but different mass numbers (see Figure 3-4). The three isotopes of hydrogen have mass numbers of 1, 2, and 3. The three natural isotopes of oxygen have mass numbers of 16 (8 + 8), 17 (8 + 9), and 18 (8 + 10).

3-6   Symbols of Isotopes

Before the discovery of isotopes, the symbol of a chemical element was used to represent any atom of that element. Since all atoms of an element were thought to be exactly alike, this was considered enough to identify the atom. The symbol O, for example, was used to represent an atom of oxygen. This is still done when it does not matter which isotope of oxygen is meant. When it is necessary to distinguish one isotope from another, a small number is placed next to the chemical symbol to show the mass number of the isotope. The number is written as a superscript; that is, it is placed slightly above the symbol, either to the left or to the right. For example ^{18}O or O^{18} stands for the oxygen isotope of mass 18. In recent years, the preference has been to put the superscript at the left of the symbol, and this is the practice used in this book. When the name of the element is spelled out, the isotope is identified by means of a hyphen and the mass number. For example, the isotope ^{18}O would be spelled out as oxygen-18.

3-7   Radioactive Isotopes

The nuclei of many isotopes are unstable. The number of protons or neutrons in the nucleus suddenly changes, and the nucleus gives off charged particles and radiation. In this pro-

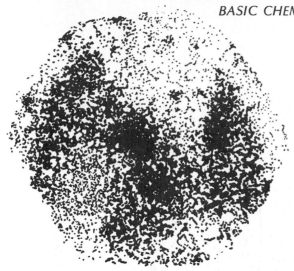

Figure 3-5. Use of Radioactive Iodine in Diagnosing Thyroid Disorders. Iodine is specifically taken up by the cells of the thyroid gland. This photo of an autoradiogram shows where iodine has been concentrated in thyroid cells (dark spots).

cess the atom changes to another isotope, usually an isotope of a different element. The process is called **radioactivity** (ray-dee-oh-ak-*tiv*-uh-tee). It was discovered in 1896 during experiments with minerals containing the element uranium.

All the isotopes of the heaviest elements (those with atomic numbers greater than 83) are radioactive. These elements have no stable forms. But even the elements that do have stable isotopes also have some radioactive isotopes. Most of these are made artificially in nuclear reactors or by bombardment of the elements with high-speed atomic particles.

Radioactivity is not a chemical process. We mention it here because radioactivity is an important means of studying biological processes. The reason for this is that radioactive isotopes, or **radioisotopes** (ray-dee-oh-*i*-suh-tohps), can be detected and their amounts measured by instruments sensitive to the radiations they emit. Radioisotopes can thus be used to follow materials in the body and to detect abnormalities in the size, shape, or function of organs (see Figure 3-5). They can also be used to study biochemical reactions in living organisms. The atoms of the radioisotope act as *tracers*, or tagged atoms. They can be detected and followed as they move from one compound to another. Thus the detailed chemical steps of a process can be determined.

Isotopes need not be radioactive to serve as tracers. They can be detected by their different masses in an instrument called a *mass spectrometer* (spek-*trahm*-uh-ter). Oxygen-18, a stable isotope, has been used in this way to study the process of photosynthesis.

3-8   Electron Structure of Atoms

The electrons in an atom are located in the space surrounding the nucleus. They are arranged in **energy levels** at different distances from the nucleus. Modern atomic theory states definite rules for the distribution of an atom's electrons. We need not go into the details of this theory. However, we must know

Career

Radiologist and Radiologic Technician

Radiology, or nuclear medicine, is a field of medicine in which radioisotopes and various forms of radiation are used in the diagnosis and treatment of disease. A radiologist is a medical doctor who has completed several years of additional training in this field.

Radiologists are often assisted by technicians, who actually carry out many of the tests. Radiologic technicians must be high school graduates and have at least two years of specialized technical training.

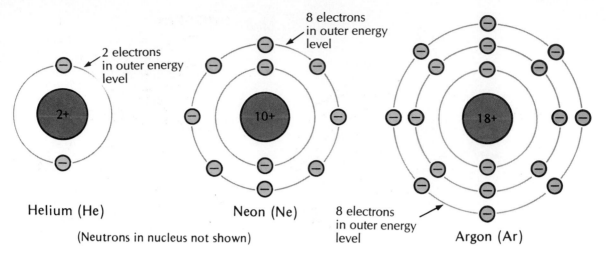

2 electrons in outer energy level

8 electrons in outer energy level

Helium (He)

Neon (Ne)

(Neutrons in nucleus not shown)

8 electrons in outer energy level

Argon (Ar)

Figure 3-6. Inert Elements. In the inert elements, the outer energy levels are filled to capacity.

that the first energy level can hold only 2 electrons. When it has 2 electrons, it is said to be filled. An atom with more than 2 electrons has more than one energy level. In all such atoms, the outside level can hold only 8 electrons. If the outside level has fewer than 8 electrons, it is unfilled.

A filled outer energy level is a very stable arrangement. Elements that already have filled outer levels are chemically inactive. Except for a few special cases, they do not form compounds with other elements. They are all gases under ordinary conditions. Examples are helium, neon, and argon. The structures of these atoms are shown in Figure 3-6.

Atoms that do not have filled outer energy levels can form compounds with other elements. When atoms combine to form compounds, their outside electrons are rearranged to give each atom a filled outer level. The ways in which this can happen are described in the next section.

CHEMICAL BONDING

Objectives:
1. Describe the formation of covalent and ionic bonds.
2. Define the term *diatomic molecule,* and give several examples of diatomic molecules.

3-9 Covalent Bonds

Water is a compound of the elements hydrogen and oxygen. It consists of chemical units in which two atoms of hydrogen and one atom of oxygen are joined together. A unit of this kind, in which two or more atoms are combined and act as a single particle, is called a **molecule** (*mahl*-ih-kyool). Let us see how a molecule of water is formed.

The structures of a hydrogen atom and an oxygen atom are shown in Figure 3-7. The hydrogen atom has 1 electron. This electron occupies energy level no. 1. This level can hold 2 electrons. One more electron can be added to the level to fill it. The oxygen atom has 8 electrons. Two of its electrons are in

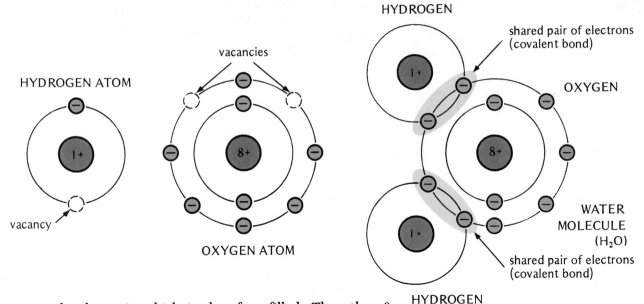

HYDROGEN ATOM

vacancy

vacancies

OXYGEN ATOM

HYDROGEN

shared pair of electrons
(covalent bond)

OXYGEN

WATER
MOLECULE
(H₂O)

shared pair of electrons
(covalent bond)

HYDROGEN

energy level no. 1, which is therefore filled. The other 6 electrons are in level no. 2. This level, being the outer energy level, can hold 8 electrons. Two more electrons can be added to the level to fill it.

Figure 3-7 includes a diagram of a water molecule, showing two hydrogen atoms combined with one oxygen atom. Each hydrogen atom is sharing its electron with the oxygen atom. At the same time, the oxygen atom is sharing one of its electrons with each hydrogen atom. In this arrangement, the outer levels of all three atoms are filled (2 electrons in each hydrogen atom, 8 in the oxygen atom).

The sharing of a pair of electrons by two atoms produces a force of attraction that holds the atoms together. This force of attraction is called a **chemical bond.** When a chemical bond is formed by the sharing of electrons, it is called a **covalent** (koh-*vay*-lent) **bond.** In a molecule of water there are two covalent bonds holding the molecule together.

Figure 3-8 shows the electron structure of the element chlorine. The outer energy level of a chlorine atom has 7 electrons. The chlorine atom needs only one more electron to fill its outer level. It can fill this level by sharing a pair of electrons with a hydrogen atom. When this happens, a molecule of the compound hydrogen chloride is formed. This molecule is held together by a covalent bond between the chlorine atom and the hydrogen atom (see Figure 3-8).

Figure 3-7. Electron Shells of Hydrogen and Oxygen. The hydrogen atom can accept one electron in its outer energy level. The oxygen atom can accept two electrons in its outer energy level. By sharing two pairs of electrons, the outer levels of the three atoms in the water molecule are filled. Each pair of shared electrons forms a single covalent bond.

Figure 3-8. Structures of the Chlorine Atom and Hydrogen Chloride. Chlorine needs one electron to fill its outer energy level. In hydrogen chloride, a covalent bond is formed by the sharing of one pair of electrons.

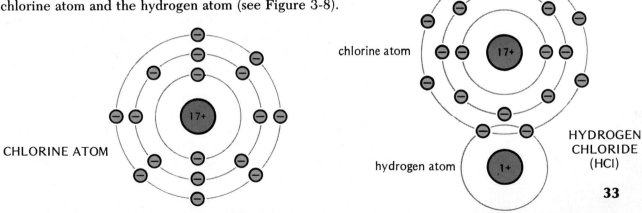

CHLORINE ATOM

chlorine atom

hydrogen atom

HYDROGEN
CHLORIDE
(HCl)

33

3-10 Ionic Bonds

Figure 3-9 (top) shows the electron structures of a sodium atom and a chlorine atom. The outer energy level of a sodium atom has only 1 electron. To fill this level, 7 more electrons would be needed. Could a sodium atom fill its outside energy level by combining with a chlorine atom and sharing electrons? No, there is no way for this to happen. Electrons are usually shared in pairs, one from each atom. The sodium atom has only one outside electron to contribute, and could therefore share in only one pair.

However, the sodium atom can *transfer* its outer electron to a chlorine atom altogether. This will fill the outer energy level of the chlorine atom. At the same time, the sodium atom, having lost its outer electron, will be left with a new outer energy level of 8 electrons. Thus, the outer level of the sodium atom will also be a filled energy level (see Figure 3-9).

When the chlorine atom acquires an extra electron from the sodium atom, the chlorine atom acquires an excess negative charge of 1 unit. An atom that acquires an excess charge in this way is called an **ion** (*i*-ahn). The chlorine atom has become a chlorine ion with a negative charge of 1 unit. The chlorine ion (also called the chlor*ide* ion) is represented by the symbol Cl^-.

When a sodium atom gives up an electron, it is left with an excess positive charge of 1 unit. It becomes a sodium ion, represented as Na^+.

One of the laws of electric charge is that particles with opposite charges attract each other. When a sodium atom loses an electron to a chlorine atom, the two ions that form are attracted to each other. The force of attraction between two ions is called an **ionic** (i-*ahn*-ik) **bond.** The compound of

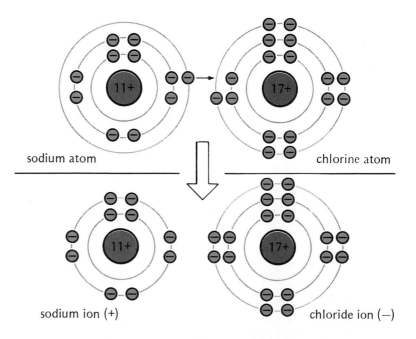

Figure 3-9. Forming Ionic Bonds. Chlorine needs one electron to fill its outer energy level (top). If sodium transfers its one outer electron to chlorine, each atom acquires a filled outer level and becomes a charged ion. The sodium ion has a single positive charge. The chlorine atom has a single negative charge. An ionic bond is formed between them (bottom).

sodium atom   chlorine atom

sodium ion (+)   chloride ion (−)

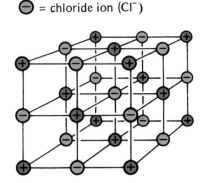

= sodium ion (Na^+)

= chloride ion (Cl^-)

sodium and chlorine, called sodium chloride, consists of sodium and chlorine ions held together by ionic bonds. Note, however, that the sodium and chlorine ions do not form molecules (see Figure 3-10). Molecules are formed only when atoms share electrons and form covalent bonds. In sodium chloride, the ions remain separate. Each sodium ion is attracted to several chlorine ions around it. Each chlorine ion is attracted to several sodium ions around it. Materials with this type of structure are called *crystals*. No distinct molecules are present in crystals.

3-11 Diatomic Molecules

Atoms of the same element sometimes form covalent bonds with each other, forming molecules consisting of two atoms. These are called **diatomic** (dy-uh-*tahm*-ik) **molecules**. Most elements that form diatomic molecules are gases under ordinary conditions. They include hydrogen, oxygen, nitrogen, and chlorine (see Figure 3-11).

SODIUM CHLORIDE (NaCl)

Figure 3-10. Structure of Sodium Chloride. Ionic compounds do not form molecules. Each ion is attracted to several oppositely charged ions around it.

Figure 3-11. Diatomic Molecules of Some Gases. Two chlorine atoms form one covalent bond in a diatomic molecule, as do two hydrogen atoms. Two oxygen atoms form two covalent bonds in a diatomic molecule.

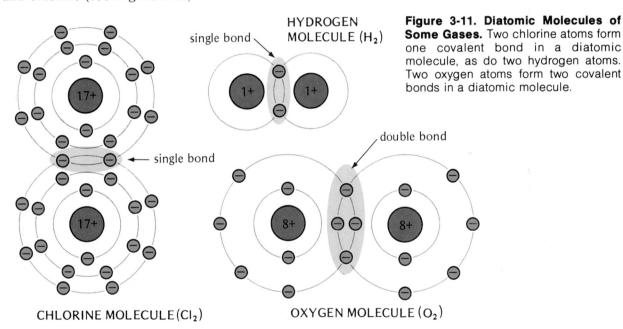

HYDROGEN MOLECULE (H_2)

single bond

single bond

double bond

CHLORINE MOLECULE (Cl_2)

OXYGEN MOLECULE (O_2)

CHEMICAL REACTIONS

Objectives:
1. Define and give examples of the following: *empirical formula, molecular formula,* and *structural formula.*
2. Describe the types of changes that occur when a chemical reaction takes place.
3. Write out a simple balanced chemical equation and label the reactants and the products.

3-12 Chemical Formulas

Every compound consists of atoms combined in definite proportions. In water, for example, the proportion is 2 hydrogen atoms to 1 oxygen atom. In sodium chloride, the proportion is 1 sodium atom to 1 chlorine atom. This information about a compound can be given by its chemical formula. In a chemical formula, each element is represented by its chemical symbol. The proportions in which the atoms combine are shown by subscripts—small numbers written after the symbol and slightly below the line. The subscript 1 is not written in the formula, but is understood when no other subscript is shown. For example, the formula for water is H_2O, while the formula for sodium chloride is NaCl.

A formula that shows the simplest proportions of atoms in the compound is called an **empirical** (em-*pih*-rih-kul) **formula.** A formula that shows the composition of a molecule of a compound is called the **molecular** (muh-*lek*-yuh-ler) **formula** of the compound. In many cases the molecular formula is the same as the empirical formula. For example, H_2O is the molecular formula as well as the empirical formula of water. It shows the composition of a molecule of water—2 hydrogen atoms combined with 1 oxygen atom.

There are, however, many compounds that are chemically different, yet have the same empirical formula. This is especially true of compounds of carbon. The carbon atom can form four covalent bonds with other atoms, including other carbon atoms. As a result, carbon is the base of many very complex molecules. Many of these molecules have the same *proportions* of atoms, but the atoms are arranged in entirely different ways and in entirely different numbers. As a simple example, consider the two compounds acetylene and benzene. Each of these compounds consists of carbon atoms and hydrogen atoms in a proportion of 1:1. The empirical formula of both compounds is CH. However, the molecular formula of acetylene is C_2H_2, while that of benzene is C_6H_6. To identify a molecular compound by its formula, the molecular formula must be given. (In ionic compounds, such as sodium chloride, there are no molecules. Therefore, the only formula that can be written is the empirical formula.)

3-13 Structural Formulas

A **structural formula** is a kind of molecular formula that shows not only the number and kind of atoms in a molecule, but also how they are bonded to one another. In a structural formula, each pair of shared electrons—that is, each covalent bond—is shown by a short line joining the atoms that are connected by the bond. The structural formulas of water, acetylene, and benzene are shown in Figure 3-12, along with the structural formula of glucose. Glucose is one of the sugars

WATER (H_2O)

ACETYLENE (C_2H_2)

BENZENE (C_6H_6)

GLUCOSE ($C_6H_{12}O_6$)

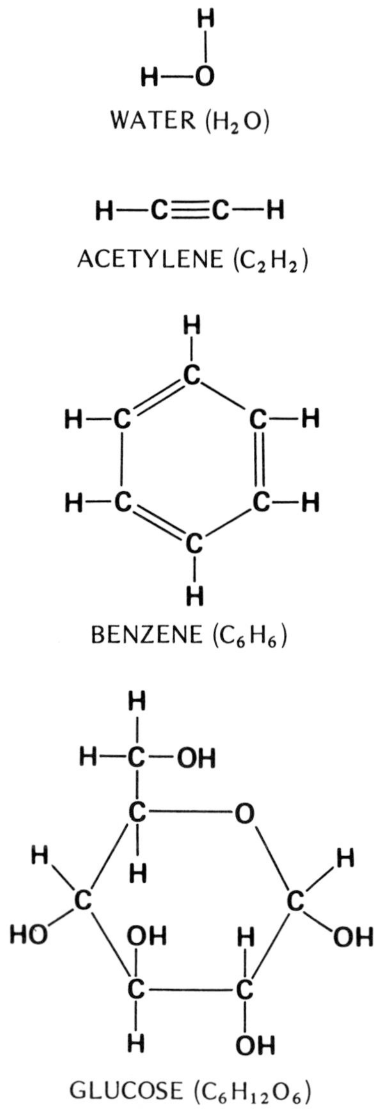

Figure 3-12. Structural Formulas. Note that every carbon atom in a structural formula has four bonds connected to it.

made by plants during photosynthesis. It is the chief source of energy for living things.

Note that the formula of glucose includes several OH symbols. The covalent bond between the O and the H has been omitted. This is often done to simplify structural formulas that contain certain common groups of atoms.

3-14 Chemical Equations

Every compound is a combination of atoms of certain elements bonded to one another in definite proportions and patterns. Chemical bonds can be broken, and atoms can form new bonds in new combinations, forming different substances. Whenever this happens, we say that a *chemical change,* or **chemical reaction,** has occurred (see Figure 3-13). The substances that were present before the reaction started are called the **reactants** (ree-*ak*-tunts). The new substances produced by the reaction are called the **products.**

A chemical reaction can be represented by a **chemical equation.** In a chemical equation, the formulas of the reactants are shown at the left and the products at the right. Plus signs are used to join the reactants and to join the products. An arrow points from the reactants to the products.

As an example, consider the equation for the formation of water from hydrogen and oxygen. The reactants are hydrogen (H_2) and oxygen (O_2). Note the use of the molecular formulas rather than the atomic symbol alone. The reason for this is that hydrogen and oxygen, when uncombined with other elements, exist in the form of diatomic molecules. The product is water (H_2O). We can start writing the equation as follows:

$$H_2 + O_2 \longrightarrow H_2O$$

This equation says that 1 molecule of hydrogen (H_2) reacts with 1 molecule of oxygen (O_2) to produce 1 molecule of water (H_2O). However, if we examine this equation carefully, we see that there is something wrong with it. There are 2 atoms of oxygen in the molecule O_2 on the left, but only 1 atom of oxygen in H_2O on the right. One atom of oxygen is missing. The equation cannot be telling the whole story. A more accurate equation is the following:

$$2H_2 + O_2 \longrightarrow 2H_2O$$

This equation says that 2 molecules of hydrogen react with 1 molecule of oxygen to produce 2 molecules of water. In this equation all the atoms are accounted for. There are 4 H's and 2 O's on the left, and 4 H's and 2 O's on the right.

An equation in which the numbers of atoms of each kind are the same on both sides of the reaction is called a *balanced equation.* Chemical equations are almost always written in balanced form. The numbers placed in front of the formulas in

Figure 3-13. A Familiar Chemical Reaction. Whenever chemical bonds are broken or formed, energy is involved. Some chemical reactions absorb energy. Others, like the burning of wood, release energy.

order to balance the equation are called *coefficients* (koh-uh-*fish*-ents). A coefficient applies to the entire formula. It multiplies all the atoms shown in the formula.

Here is the balanced equation for the breakdown of glucose, the chemical reaction that provides most of the energy for living organisms:

$$\underset{\text{glucose}}{C_6H_{12}O_6} + \underset{\text{oxygen}}{6O_2} \longrightarrow \underset{\substack{\text{carbon} \\ \text{dioxide}}}{6CO_2} + \underset{\text{water}}{6H_2O}$$

We will discuss this reaction in some detail in a later chapter.

SOLUTIONS AND SUSPENSIONS

Objective:

Define the following terms and give an example of each: *mixture, solution, solvent, solute, suspension, colloidal dispersion.*

3-15   Mixtures

In every compound, the atoms or ions are joined by chemical bonds. The atoms or ions are present in fixed proportions and in a definite arrangement in space. It is possible, however, for substances to be physically mingled, but without forming new chemical bonds. The result is called a **mixture.** The substances in a mixture may be present in any proportions, and the proportions can change as one of the substances is added to or removed from the mixture. Another characteristic of mixtures is that the different substances in the mixture retain their usual properties.

Consider, for example, a mixture of table salt (sodium chloride) and iron filings. If this mixture is placed in water, the salt will dissolve, as it normally does. The iron filings will remain undissolved. On the other hand, a magnet will attract the iron filings in the mixture and remove them, leaving the salt behind (see Figure 3-14).

The substances in a mixture may be spread uniformly throughout the mixture. Such a mixture is said to be *homogeneous* (hoh-muh-*jee*-nee-us). Air, for example, is a homogeneous mixture of several different gases, including nitrogen, oxygen, carbon dioxide, water vapor, and a few others.

3-16   Solutions

Broadly speaking, any homogeneous mixture can be called a **solution.** However, the term is usually used for mixtures that are liquid. The liquid substance that makes up the bulk of the solution is called the **solvent.** The other substances, which are dissolved in the solvent, are called **solutes** (*sahl*-yoots). Solutes may be solids, liquids, or gases before they are dissolved in

Figure 3-14. A Mixture. In a mixture of salt and iron filings, each substance retains its own properties. A magnet can remove the iron filings from the dry mixture. If the mixture is placed in water, the salt will dissolve, leaving the iron filings behind.

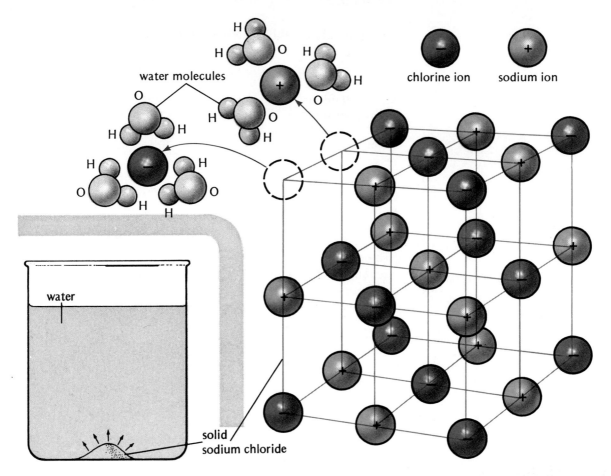

the solvent. The most common solvent is water, and most solutions are made with water.

When molecular substances dissolve in a liquid, the substance separates into its individual molecules. The solute is spread through the solvent in the form of separate molecules. When ionic substances dissolve, the compound breaks up into its ions. Thus, when sodium chloride dissolves in water, it breaks up into sodium and chlorine ions (see Figure 3-15). This process is called *dissociation* (dis-soh-see-*ay*-shun). It can be represented by the following equation:

$$NaCl \longrightarrow Na^+ + Cl^-$$

We will see in later chapters that many important processes in living cells and tissues depend upon the presence of ions.

3-17 Suspensions

There are, as you know, many substances that do not dissolve in water to any noticeable extent. For example, sand is insoluble in water. If you put some in a pail of water and stir the water vigorously, the sand will form a cloudy mixture with the water. If you let this mixture stand, the particles of sand will gradually settle to the bottom of the pail. A mixture that

Figure 3-15. Dissociation of an Ionic Compound. When sodium chloride is placed in water, the structure of the salt breaks down. The compound separates into its individual ions, which become surrounded by water molecules. A solution of sodium chloride in water is formed.

separates on standing is called a **suspension** (suh-*spen*-shun) (see Figure 3-16).

3-18 Colloidal Dispersions

In a true solution, the particles of the solute are either molecules or ions. They remain distributed through the solvent indefinitely. In a suspension, the particles are large enough to give the liquid a cloudy appearance, and the force of gravity gradually causes them to settle out. There is an intermediate type of mixture called a **colloidal dispersion** (kuh-*loyd*-ul dis-*per*-zhun). In a colloidal dispersion, the particles are larger than molecules or ions, but still too small to settle out.

The medium in which a colloidal dispersion forms need not be a liquid. It can be a gas, or even a solid. The dispersed substance may likewise be a solid, liquid, or gas. Smoke, for example, is a colloidal dispersion of carbon particles in air. Milk and mayonnaise are colloidal dispersions of several liquids. Whipped cream is a colloidal dispersion of a gas (air) in a liquid.

Solutions, suspensions, and colloidal dispersions are all present in living cells and tissues. The activities of life depend upon the special properties of these different types of mixtures.

Figure 3-16. Suspensions and Solutions. Note the cloudiness of the suspension (left). The solution (right) is completely transparent, but it contains some undissolved particles of the solute.

ACIDS, BASES, AND SALTS

Objectives:
1. Define and compare the terms *acid* and *base,* and give an example of each.
2. Describe what happens in a neutralization reaction.
3. Explain the meaning of the pH scale and what is indicated by pH values of 1, 7, and 14.
4. Explain how indicators are used.

3-19   Acids

There are many compounds that are molecular in the dry state, but form ions when dissolved in water. An important group of these compounds is the **acids** (*as*-idz). All acids contain hydrogen covalently bonded to another atom or group of atoms. When these compounds are dissolved in water, the hydrogen breaks loose as a hydrogen ion, H^+. The rest of the molecule forms a negative ion.

A simple example of an acid that is important to our life activities is hydrochloric acid, HCl. In its dry state, this compound is a gas consisting of HCl molecules. However, when it dissolves in water, it separates into H^+ and Cl^- ions:

$$HCl \xrightarrow[\text{water}]{\text{in}} H^+ + Cl^-$$

Any substance that produces hydrogen ions in solution is called an acid. It is the presence of hydrogen ions that gives acids their particular properties (see Figure 3-17).

3-20 Bases

A compound that produces *hydroxyl* (hy-*drahk*-sul) *ions* (OH^-) when dissolved in water is called a **base.** Many bases in the dry state are ionic compounds. Sodium hydroxide (NaOH) is an example. This is a solid compound consisting of sodium and hydroxyl ions. When it is dissolved in water, it separates into its ions.

$$NaOH \xrightarrow[\text{water}]{\text{in}} Na^+ + OH^-$$

A few bases are not ionic compounds in the dry state, but they do produce hydroxyl ions when dissolved in water. Ammonia, for example, is a molecular gas, NH_3. When dissolved in water, it reacts with the water to produce OH^- ions:

$$NH_3 + H_2O \longrightarrow NH_4^+ + OH^-$$

The positive ion, NH_4^+, is called the ammonium ion. The solution of ammonia in water is called ammonia water, or ammonium hydroxide. You are probably familiar with this base as a cleaning agent.

Notice that one of the H's in NH_4^+ comes from the water molecule. This H is detached from the water molecule without its electron. It therefore carries a positive charge, and it is this that gives the ammonium ion its positive charge. The part of the water molecule left behind is an O and an H with an extra electron. It is a hydroxyl ion (OH^-). If the formula for water is written HOH, the reaction with NH_3 is a little easier to understand:

$$NH_3 + HOH \longrightarrow NH_4^+ + OH^-$$

3-21 Neutralization

When solutions of an acid and a base are mixed, a reaction occurs. The hydrogen ions from the acid combine with the hydroxyl ions from the base to form molecules of water:

$$H^+ + OH^- \longrightarrow HOH \text{ (or } H_2O)$$

If the quantities of acid and base are just right, all the H^+ and OH^- ions will combine, and there will be no excess of either one in the solution. The solution will be neither an acid nor a base. It is said to be neutral. The process of reacting an acid and a base to produce a neutral solution is called **neutralization** (noo-truh-luh-*zay*-shun).

Figure 3-17. Acid Rain Damaged Trees. When fossil fuels are burned, sulfur and nitrogen oxides are often produced. These compounds dissolve in rain water, snow, and fog, producing acids. When acid rain falls, it contaminates water and soil, and damages plants. These spruce trees, marked by environmentalists' crosses, show the effects of acid rain.

Acids and bases are both caustic; that is, in concentrated solutions they can damage living tissue, as well as nonliving materials. When an acid or a base is accidentally spilled, the best way to reduce or prevent harm is to neutralize the substance with its opposite. An acid can be neutralized with a base; a base can be neutralized with an acid.

3-22 Salts

When an acid and a base react, their hydrogen and hydroxyl ions combine to form water molecules. These two ions are therefore removed from the solution; that is, they are no longer present as separate ions. However, the negative ions of the acid and the positive ions of the base are still present. For example, when hydrochloric acid reacts with sodium hydroxide, sodium and chlorine atoms remain in the solution. In other words, this neutralization reaction produces a solution of sodium chloride.

$$HCl + NaOH \longrightarrow Na^+ + Cl^- + HOH$$

The sodium chloride can be obtained from the solution by evaporating the water.

The compound produced by a neutralization reaction between an acid and a base is called a **salt.** Sodium chloride, or table salt, is actually only one of many different salts that can be formed. Most of the substances in food that are called minerals are salts. Salts provide many essential ions for body processes.

3-23 Dissociation of Water

We have said that water is a molecular compound, H_2O. However, at any given moment a small fraction of the molecules in water are dissociated into hydrogen and hydroxyl ions:

$$H_2O \longrightarrow H^+ + OH^-$$

Since each water molecule furnishes one hydrogen ion and one hydroxyl ion, the number of ions of each kind in pure water is the same. Water is therefore neutral; it has no excess of either H^+ or OH^- ions. However, it does have a certain concentration of H^+ ions (and the same concentration of OH^- ions).

3-24 The pH Scale

If an acid is dissolved in water, the concentration of H^+ ions increases. At the same time, the concentration of OH^- ions decreases. This happens because some of the excess H^+ ions combine with OH^- ions, forming undissociated water molecules. (Remember that there are always some H^+ and OH^- ions in water.) If a base is dissolved in water, the OH^- ion concentration increases. This causes a reduction in H^+ ion

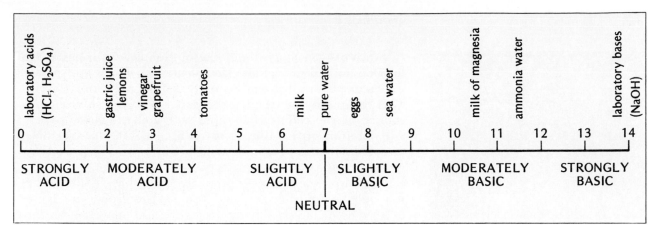

```
0    1    2    3    4    5    6    7    8    9    10   11   12   13   14
```

| STRONGLY ACID | MODERATELY ACID | SLIGHTLY ACID | SLIGHTLY BASIC | MODERATELY BASIC | STRONGLY BASIC |

NEUTRAL

concentration. This means that in acid solutions the H^+ concentration is greater than it is in pure water. In basic solutions, the H^+ concentration is smaller.

The H^+ concentration is indicated by a unit called **pH.** The pH scale has been set up in such a way that high concentrations of H^+ (acid solutions) correspond to low values of pH (see Figure 3-18). Low concentrations (basic solutions) correspond to high pH values. The pH scale runs from 0 (highly acid) to 14 (highly basic). A neutral solution has a pH of 7. This is the pH of pure water.

Whether a solution is acid or basic can be determined by means of indicators. An **indicator** is a substance that changes color when the pH goes above or below a certain value. *Litmus* (*lit*-mus) *paper*, for example, turns red when the pH is moderately acid (below 5); it turns blue when the pH is at least slightly basic (above 8) (see Figure 3-19). *Methyl orange* changes from yellow to red in fairly acid solutions (pH below 3). *Phenolphthalein* (*feen*-ul-*thal*-leen) changes from colorless to red in fairly basic solutions (pH above 10).

Figure 3-18. The pH Scale. Each change of one unit on this scale is a change of ten times in the degree of acidity. For example, a pH of 4 is ten times as acid as a pH of 5.

Figure 3-19. Common Indicators. Litmus (left) turns red in acid solutions and blue in basic solutions. Phenolphthalein (center) changes from colorless to red in basic solutions. Methyl orange (right) is red in strong acids, changing to yellow in weaker acids.

Figure 3-20. Soil Chemistry. Soil can be acidic, neutral, or basic. Most plants grow best in soil that is neutral or only slightly acidic. However, some plants, like blueberries, flourish in acid soil that has a pH of about 5.

Indicators can show whether a solution is acid or basic, but they do not tell the actual value of the pH. There are special indicator papers that can be used to find pH more closely. This is done by moistening the paper with the solution and comparing the color of the paper with a chart. These papers will determine pH within a few tenths of a unit. More accurate measurements can be made with pH meters, which work by measuring the electrical properties of the solution.

If you are a gardner, you probably know that the pH of the soil must be right for the plants you want to grow (see Figure 3-20). The pH levels of body tissues are also important for the body's activities. For example, the contents of the stomach must be slightly acid for digestion to proceed normally. Maintaining the right pH levels in different parts of the body is part of homeostasis.

Chapter Review

SUMMARY

- All matter is made up of atoms. Atoms contain protons, neutrons, and electrons. Electrons and protons have an electrical charge. Neutrons bear no electrical charge. Atoms form two kinds of matter: elements and compounds.

- Each element has a different atomic number. All atoms of an element have the same number of protons, but the number of neutrons can vary. Atoms of an element that have a different number of neutrons are called isotopes. The atomic mass of an atom is equal to the sum of its protons and neutrons. Many elements have radioactive isotopes.

- The electrons of an atom are found at various distances from the nucleus in different energy levels. If the outermost energy level is not filled, the atom can form compounds with other elements. A chemical bond may be formed between atoms. There are two types of chemical bonds: ionic bonds and covalent bonds.

- In a chemical formula each element is represented by its chemical symbol. There are three types of formulas: empirical formula, molecular formula, and structural formula. A chemical equation shows what happens in a chemical reaction. In mixtures no new chemical bonds are formed. Mixtures are divided into solutions, suspensions, and colloidal dispersions.

- A substance that produces hydrogen ions when dissolved in water is an acid. A base produces hydroxyl ions when dissolved in water. A reaction between an acid and a base is called neutralization. Hydrogen ion concentration is indicated by a unit called pH. Indicators display different colors in acids and bases due to changes in pH values.

KNOW THE TERMS

acid	covalent bond	mixture	radioactivity
atom	diatomic molecule	molecular formula	radioisotope
atomic mass	electron	molecule	reactant
atomic number	element	neutralization	salt
base	empirical formula	neutron	solute
chemical bond	energy level	nucleus	solution
chemical equation	indicator	pH	solvent
chemical reaction	ion	product	structural formula
colloidal dispersion	ionic bond	proton	suspension
compound	isotope		

SECTION QUESTIONS

Atomic Theory of Matter

1. What is an element?
2. Define the term *compound*.
3. Which atomic particles possess electrical charges?
4. What is the atomic number of an atom?
5. What is the atomic mass of an atom?
6. How are electrons arranged in an atom?

Chemical Bonding

7. Name two types of chemical bonds.
8. What kind of chemical bonding forms molecules?

Chemical Reactions

9. List three types of chemical formulas.

10. Where is the product side of a chemical equation?

Solutions and Suspensions

11. What is a mixture?
12. What are substances called that dissolve in a solvent?
13. What happens to particles in a suspension?

Acids, Bases, and Salts

14. When acids are dissolved in water, what positive ion is released?
15. When bases are dissolved in water, what negative ion is released?
16. What substance is formed from the reaction of an acid and a base?

KNOW THE FACTS

Copy the number of each sentence below on a sheet of paper. Beside each number, write the term(s) that correctly complete(s) the sentence.

1. A neutron has the same mass as a proton, but no _____ charge.
2. The electrons determine an atom's _____ properties.
3. Atoms of an element may have different numbers of _____.
4. Radioisotopes can act as _____ to study biochemical reactions.
5. Atoms with unfilled outside shells combine to form _____.
6. A chemical bond formed by the sharing of electrons is said to be _____.
7. The force of attraction between two ions is called a(n) _____ bond.

8. Diatomic molecules consist of two atoms of the same _____.
9. A formula that shows the composition of a molecule is called the _____ formula.
10. In a structural formula, a pair of shared electrons is shown by a _____.
11. In a colloidal dispersion, the particles are larger than _____.
12. The reaction between an acid and a base is called a _____ reaction.
13. As pH changes beyond a certain value, a(n) _____ changes color.
14. On the pH scale, 7 indicates a(n) _____ solution.

UNDERSTAND THE CONCEPTS

15. How can you determine whether a substance is a compound or an element?
16. Describe the structure of an atom.
17. How do you determine the atomic mass of an element?
18. Write the symbols for the isotopes of oxygen having mass numbers 16, 17, and 18.
19. What changes occur when a radioactive isotope disintegrates?
20. Describe the arrangement of electrons around the nucleus of an atom.
21. Describe a covalent bond.
22. What is an ion?
23. Describe an ionic bond.
24. What is the difference between an empirical formula and a molecular formula?
25. What is a balanced equation?
26. What happens when a molecular substance dissolves in a liquid?
27. What happens when an ionic compound dissolves in a liquid?
28. How does a colloidal dispersion differ from a suspension?
29. What ions are formed by the dissociation of water?
30. What is the pH scale?

THINK CRITICALLY

31. If all atoms are composed of electrons, protons, and neutrons and if each elementary particle is itself identical to other elementary particles of its kind, what accounts for atoms of the different elements being different from each other?
32. Plants combine carbon dioxide and water to make glucose and oxygen. Write and balance the chemical equation that describes this process.
33. Water is an essential substance in the chemistry of living things. Why?
34. An oversecretion of stomach acid can cause the stomach wall to become irritated. Would milk of magnesia aid in reducing the acidity level in the stomach? Why or why not?

THINK CREATIVELY

35. You are given two clear, colorless liquids and told that one is a compound and the other is a mixture. How might you determine which is the compound and which is the mixture?
36. What steps could be taken to reduce the increased acidity of rivers and lakes that have been damaged by acid rain?

FOR FURTHER INVESTIGATION

1. Gather four clear glass jars and the following substances: one packet of unflavored gelatin; one-half teaspoon food coloring; one tablespoon cornstarch; and one tablespoon garden soil. To each jar, add one-half cup of warm water and one of these substances. (For the gelatin, use hot water.) Mix each thoroughly, and observe for ten minutes without touching. Decide in each case whether you have created a mixture, a solution, a suspension, or a colloidal dispersion.
2. Radioactive isotopes play an important role in the diagnosis of disease. Select three isotopes for study, and find out which diseases they are used to detect. Determine how physicians use them for diagnosis and how they are traced in the body.
3. Prepare a report for the class on one of the career opportunities listed below. See suggested procedures, p. 9, "For Further Investigation" Activity 3.
   a. Chemist   c. Toxicologist
   b. Pharmacologist

4. Write a report on the life and contributions of
   one of the following scientists:
   a. Samuel Proctor Massié
   b. Emma Perry Carr
   c. Gladys Anderson Emerson
   d. Sarah Ratner

FOR FURTHER READING

Asimov, Issac, *How Did We Find Out About Atoms?* Avon Books, New York, 1982.

Boslough, John, "Worlds Within the Atom," *National Geographic*, May, 1985.

Mascetta, Joseph, *Chemistry* (Easy Way Series), Barron's Educational Series, Inc., Woodbury, NY, 1983.

Thomsen, Dietrick E., "A Matter of Energy Levels," *Science News*, March, 1982.

Trefil, James, "Closing In on Creation: How the Universe Began," *Smithsonian*, May, 1983.

Chapter 4

CHEMICAL COMPOUNDS OF LIFE

The chameleon's well-known color changes are due to organic compounds called pigments.

ORGANIC COMPOUNDS

Objectives:
1. List the major elements found in organic compounds.
2. Explain why organic compounds are generally larger and more complex than inorganic compounds.
3. Name the four major types of organic compounds found in living cells.

At one time it was believed that there was something special about the chemistry of life. Many chemists were sure that the substances found in living things could never be made in a laboratory. They thought, in other words, that the laws of ordinary chemistry did not apply to the chemistry of organisms. Today we know that this was a false idea. There is nothing going on in a cell that cannot be explained by the same principles that apply to chemistry in a test tube. The only difference is that most of the compounds in living cells are enormously complex. The reactions among these compounds are also very complicated. In this chapter you will become familiar with the kinds of compounds that play an important part in life processes. This will help you understand these processes when they are discussed in later chapters.

4-1 Definition of Organic Compounds

Organic compounds are carbon compounds that occur naturally only in the bodies of living organisms or in their products and remains. Many organic compounds can also be produced in chemical laboratories. Organic compounds almost always contain hydrogen and usually contain oxygen and nitrogen. They may also contain phosphorus and sulfur as well as small amounts of iron, calcium, sodium, chlorine, and potassium.

Living organisms also contain **inorganic compounds** (all compounds that are not organic). Inorganic compounds do not usually contain carbon. (Carbon dioxide, CO_2, and carbonate compounds like calcium carbonate, $CaCO_3$, are exceptions.) Some common inorganic compounds in organisms are water, carbon dioxide, various salts, and inorganic bases and acids like hydrochloric acid.

4-2   Structure and Types of Organic Compounds

The big difference between the organic compounds of living organisms and the inorganic compounds found in the nonliving world is the size and complexity of many organic molecules. The reason for this is found in the electron structure of the carbon atom. The carbon atom has 6 electrons. Two of these electrons occupy the first energy level, leaving 4 electrons for the second level (see Figure 4-1). This means that the carbon atom can fill its outer energy level with 8 electrons by forming 4 covalent bonds with other atoms. Each bond involves the sharing of one electron from the carbon atom and one electron from another atom bonded to the carbon. The atoms bonded to a carbon atom may be other carbon atoms. The carbon atoms may be bonded into long chains, with other groups of chains of atoms branching from the main chain. Carbon atoms may also be bonded into rings with side branches, or with connections to other rings. The possible size and variety of these arrangements is unlimited.

In organic compounds, each carbon atom forms four bonds with other atoms. In many cases the bond is double; that is, there are two bonds between the same pair of atoms. In a few cases a pair of carbon atoms are joined by a triple bond. Figure 4-2 illustrates simple examples of single, double, and triple carbon-to-carbon bonds.

Although the total number of organic compounds is very large, they can be classified into a fairly small number of types. Four types of organic compounds will be discussed in this chapter—carbohydrates, lipids, proteins, and nucleic acids.

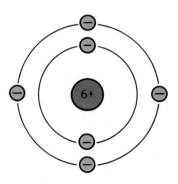

Figure 4-1. Structure of the Carbon Atom. The four electrons in the outer energy level allow a carbon atom to form four covalent bonds. This special characteristic accounts for the unlimited variety of organic compounds.

Figure 4-2. Bonds Between Carbon Atoms. Carbon atoms can form single bonds (top), double bonds (middle), and even triple bonds (bottom).

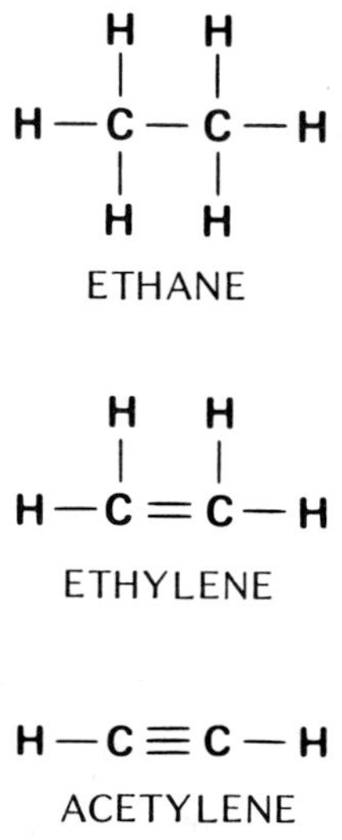

ETHANE

ETHYLENE

ACETYLENE

CARBOHYDRATES

Objectives:

1. Describe the basic chemical makeup of carbohydrates.
2. Name three monosaccharides and give their empirical and molecular formulas.
3. Describe the process of dehydration synthesis.

Figure 4-3. Structures of Some Mono-saccharides. Glucose, fructose, and galactose have the same molecular formula ($C_6H_{12}O_6$), but their atoms are arranged differently.

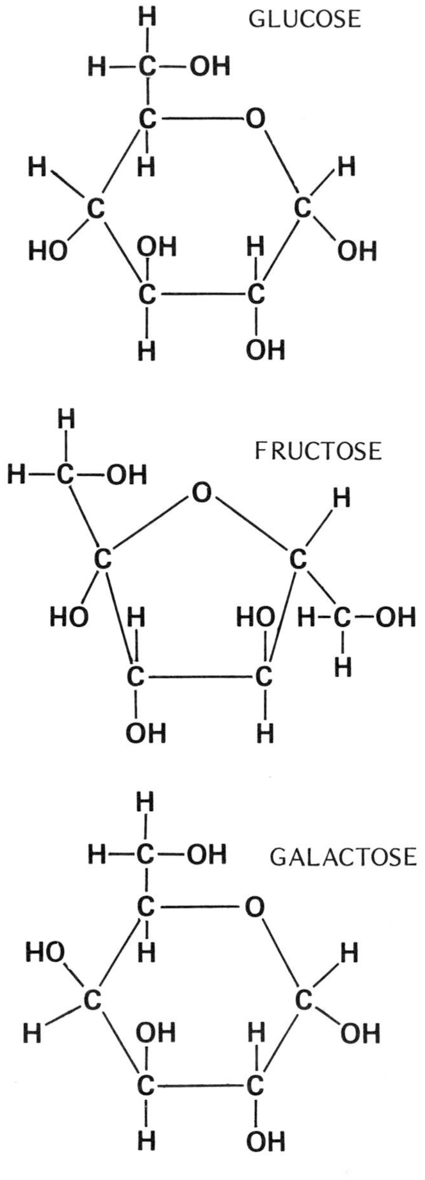

GLUCOSE

FRUCTOSE

GALACTOSE

4. Define the terms *disaccharide, polysaccharide,* and *polymer.*
5. Name three polysaccharides found in living organisms and explain the function of each.
6. Describe the process of hydrolysis.

4-3 Characteristics of Carbohydrates

Carbohydrates (kar-boh-*hy*-drayts) are compounds of carbon, hydrogen, and oxygen in which the ratio of hydrogen to oxygen is the same as in water (2 atoms of hydrogen to 1 atom of oxygen). The simplest carbohydrates are the simple sugars, or **monosaccharides** (mahn-uh-*sak*-uh-ryds). They have the empirical formula CH_2O, but no sugar molecule is actually that simple. The most common monosaccharides have the molecular formula $C_6H_{12}O_6$. However, the atoms of the molecule may be arranged in several different structures, each corresponding to a different sugar. Figure 4-3 shows the structural formulas of three of these sugars—glucose, fructose, and galactose. Simple sugars with 5 carbons ($C_5H_{10}O_5$) and 4 carbons ($C_4H_8O_4$) also exist. The names of sugars end in *-ose.*

The sugars are biologically important because they contain large amounts of energy. This energy can be released by breaking the sugars down, in the presence of oxygen, to carbon dioxide and water. Nearly all organisms use glucose as a source of energy.

4-4 Dehydration Synthesis

Sugar molecules can be bonded together by a process called **dehydration synthesis** (dee-hy-*dray*-shun *sin*-thuh-sis). The

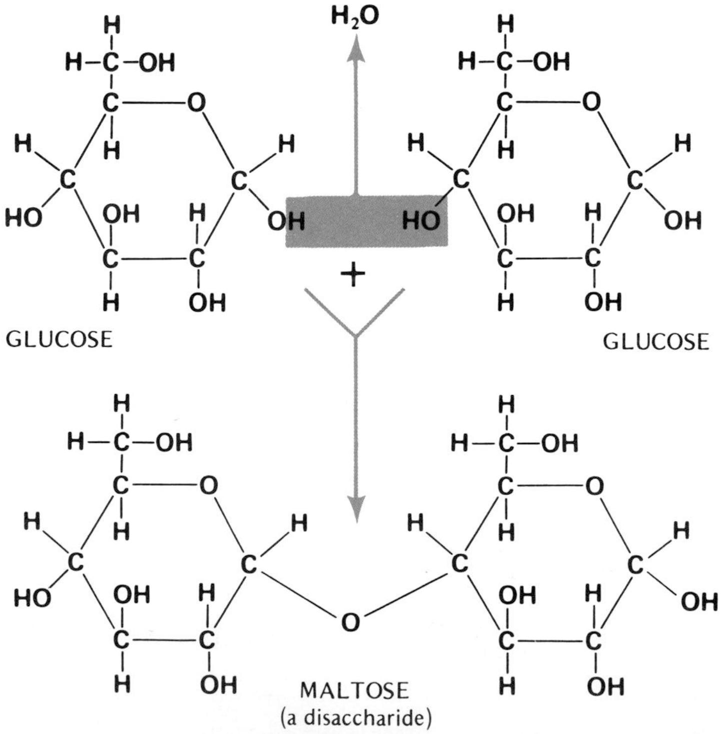

Figure 4-4. Dehydration Synthesis. In dehydration synthesis, two simple molecules bond together to form a more complex molecule, with the release of water. Many of the organic compounds in organisms are synthesized in this way.

H_2O

GLUCOSE

+

GLUCOSE

MALTOSE
(a disaccharide)

bond forms where an OH group is present in each molecule. One OH combines with the H from the other OH, forming a molecule of water, and the two molecules become joined through the remaining O (see Figure 4-4).

Synthesis means "putting together" and *dehydration* means "removing water." Thus, *dehydration synthesis* means "putting together by removing water." In living cells, dehydration synthesis is brought about by the action of *enzymes*. (Enzymes are discussed on p. 59.) It is an important process in making many organic compounds that the organism needs.

The molecule formed by joining two simple sugars is called a double sugar, or **disaccharide** (dy-*sak*-uh-ryd). The disaccharide formed by the dehydration synthesis shown in Figure 4-4 is maltose.

4-5 Polysaccharides

Simple sugars can be joined together by dehydration synthesis to form **polysaccharides** (pahl-ee-*sak*-uh-ryds), or long chains of repeating sugar units. Large molecules consisting of chains of repeating units are called **polymers** (*pahl*-uh-merz). The polysaccharides are examples of sugar polymers.

Organisms store excess sugar in the form of polysaccharides. In plants, this form of stored sugar is called **starch.** Starch is found in seeds and in roots and stems specialized for food storage. In humans, surplus sugar is stored in the liver as the polysaccharide **glycogen** (*gly*-kuh-jen), sometimes called "animal starch." Other types of polysaccharides form tough structural parts of organisms. For example, *cellulose* (*sel*-yuh-lohs), is a polysaccharide found in plants, while *chitin* (*kyt*-un) is a polysaccharide that makes up the shells of insects.

4-6 Hydrolysis

Chains of sugar molecules may be broken apart by the process called **hydrolysis** (hy-*drahl*-uh-sis). In this type of reaction, a water molecule is returned to the place from which it was removed in dehydration synthesis (see Figure 4-5). The bond between the two molecules is broken, and the original

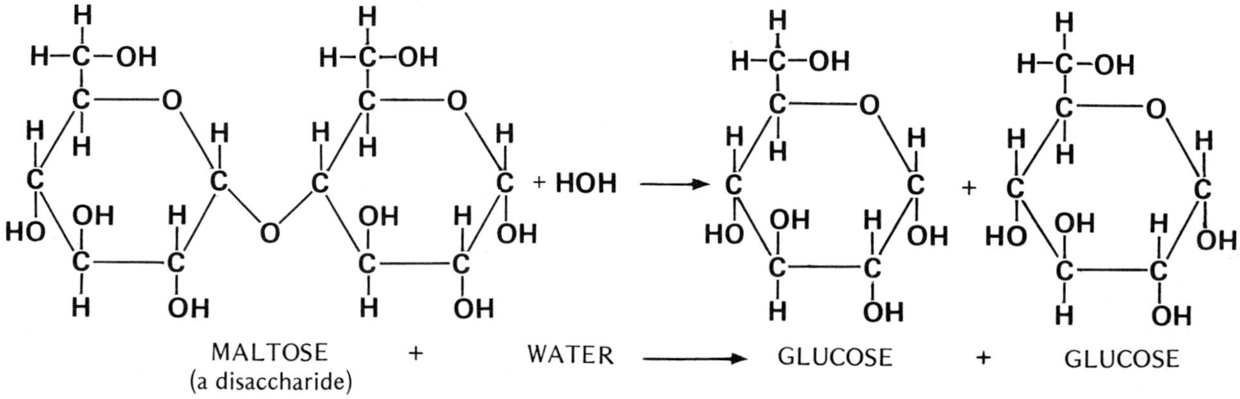

Figure 4-5. Hydrolysis. A complex molecule can be broken down into smaller, simpler molecules by the addition of a water molecule. Hydrolysis is the most common process by which organisms change organic compounds into more usable forms.

MALTOSE + WATER ⟶ GLUCOSE + GLUCOSE
(a disaccharide)

OH groups are restored. Hydrolysis can be repeated on long chains until an entire polysaccharide has been split into its simple sugars.

LIPIDS

Objectives:
1. Name the three most common types of lipids.
2. Describe the basic chemical structure of a fatty acid molecule.
3. Explain what is meant by a saturated, unsaturated, and polyunsaturated fat.
4. Explain the relationship between saturated fats in the diet, cholesterol, and circulatory disorders.
5. Describe the functions of lipids in plants and animals.

4-7   Chemical Composition of Lipids

Lipids (*lip*-idz) include the substances commonly called fats, oils, and waxes. Like carbohydrates, they are made up of carbon, hydrogen, and oxygen. However, in lipids there is relatively less oxygen than in carbohydrates. One result of this difference is that gram for gram, fats yield more energy than carbohydrates when they are broken down.

Fats and oils are formed from the combination of fatty acids and glycerol. A **fatty acid** molecule consists of a chain of carbon atoms to which hydrogen atoms are bonded. At one end of the chain there is a **carboxyl** (kar-*bahk*-sul) **group**, COOH.

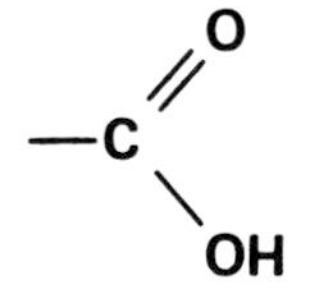

$$-C \overset{\displaystyle O}{\underset{\displaystyle OH}{<}}$$

Fatty acids and other compounds containing carboxyl groups are called *organic acids*. Like the inorganic acids discussed in Chapter 3, these acids release hydrogen ions in solution. However, organic acids are much weaker than inorganic acids. The structure of a typical fatty acid is shown in Figure 4-6.

Alcohols are organic compounds that resemble bases in having one or more OH groups in their molecules. However, they do not release OH⁻ ions and are therefore not true bases. **Glycerol** (*glis*-uh-rohl) is an alcohol that has three OH groups in its molecule.

A molecule of fat is produced by the combination of three fatty acid molecules with one glycerol molecule (see Figure 4-7). Each fatty acid molecule becomes attached to the glycerol at one of the OH groups by dehydration synthesis. Three molecules of water are released for each molecule of fat that is formed.

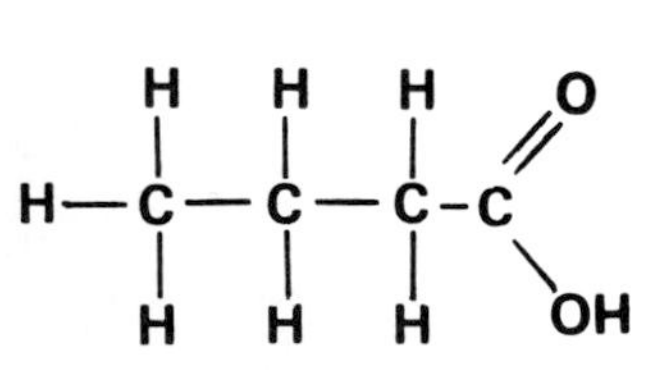

Figure 4-6. Structure of a Fatty Acid. A fatty acid consists of a chain of carbon and hydrogen atoms with a carboxyl group at one end.

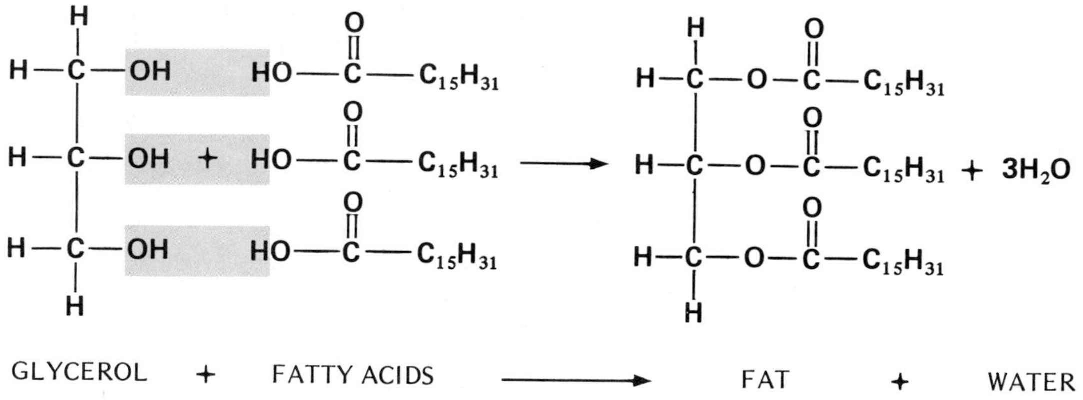

GLYCEROL + FATTY ACIDS ⟶ FAT + WATER

Fats as they occur in nature are almost always combinations of two or three different fatty acids with glycerol. Some fats are liquids at ordinary temperatures. These are usually called *oils* (animal oils or vegetable oils, depending on their source). *Waxes* are lipids formed by the combination of fatty acids with alcohols other than glycerol.

Figure 4-7. Synthesis of a Fat. A molecule of fat is formed by the dehydration synthesis of three fatty acid molecules and one glycerol molecule.

4-8 Saturated and Unsaturated Fats

If all the carbon-to-carbon bonds in a fatty acid are single bonds, the acid is said to be saturated. Fats formed from such acids are called **saturated** (*satch*-uh-rayt-ed) **fats.** In **unsaturated fats,** one or more pairs of carbon atoms in the fatty acid molecules are joined by a double bond, or even a triple bond. A fat that has just one unsaturated bond in its molecule is called *monounsaturated*. A fat that has chains with more than one double or triple carbon bond is called *polyunsaturated*. A typical unsaturated fatty acid is illustrated in Figure 4-8.

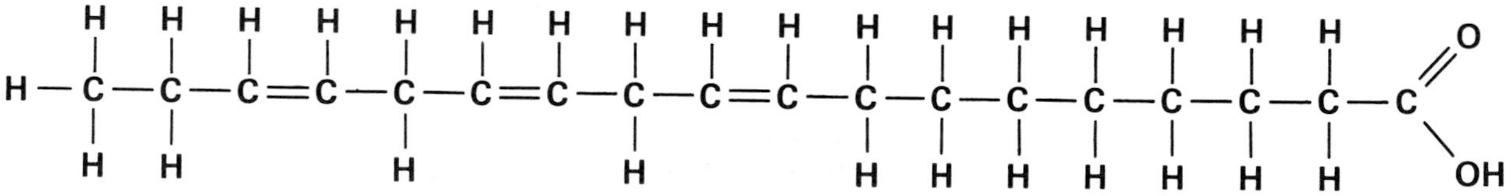

In a saturated fatty acid, each carbon atom along the chain is bonded to two hydrogen atoms. (The carbon at the start of the chain is bonded to three hydrogens.) An unsaturated acid of the same length will have fewer hydrogen atoms. Unsaturated fats can be changed to saturated fats by adding hydrogen to them. This process is called *hydrogenation* (hy-drahj-uh-*nay*-shun).

Cholesterol (kuh-*les*-tuh-rohl) is an essential compound found in most animal tissues. However, it plays an important part in the buildup of deposits that harden and narrow the arteries. This condition can lead to heart attacks and strokes. There is evidence that saturated fats, such as those found in butter and meat, tend to increase the amount of cholesterol

Figure 4-8. Structure of an Unsaturated Fatty Acid. An unsaturated fatty acid contains at least one double, or even triple, carbon bond.

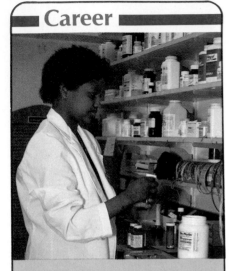

■ **Career** ■

Pharmacist

Pharmacists, or druggists, are people who prepare and dispense drugs prescribed by physicians and dentists. Because some drugs are beneficial when prescribed alone but become toxic when taken along with certain other drugs, pharmacists will often inquire about a patient's total medication, and inform doctors about potentially dangerous combinations of medication. They also advise people on the use of nonprescription drugs and other health-related items.

In the past, pharmacists actually made up the drugs prescribed. However, modern drugs are produced mostly by large manufacturers.

Pharmacists must be graduates of an accredited college of pharmacy. The pharmacy course is generally five years long, and includes courses in biology and chemistry, as well as pharmacology, which is the study of drugs and their effects. To become a licensed pharmacist, graduates of pharmacy schools must serve a one-year internship under the supervision of a registered pharmacist and must also pass a state board examination.

produced in the body. Many medical authorities therefore recommend reduced intake of saturated fats in the diet to lower the cholesterol levels in the blood.

4-9   Functions of Lipids

Lipids are important in many life activities. They are a component of cell structures, especially the cell membranes. They also serve as a reserve energy supply. They furnish about twice as much energy as the same amount of carbohydrate. Plants store oils in seeds. Some familiar oils are peanut oil, corn oil, and castor oil. Mammals store fat under the skin, where it also cushions the body and insulates it against heat loss. Although animal fats are storage products, they are not stored for long periods of time. Instead, they are constantly being broken down and replaced. Investigations have shown that mice, for example, replace about one-half of their stored fat each week.

PROTEINS

Objectives:
1. List the functions of proteins in living organisms.
2. Illustrate the general molecular structure of an amino acid.
3. Describe the formation of a peptide bond.
4. List three shapes that protein molecules can have, and describe in general how polypeptide chains can form such shapes.

4-10   The Nature of Proteins

Proteins (*proh*-teenz) are compounds that contain nitrogen in addition to carbon, hydrogen, and oxygen. The number of possible proteins is virtually unlimited, and they have an astonishing range of properties. The reasons for this variety will become clear when we examine the way in which proteins are constructed.

It is the existence of proteins that makes life possible in its present degree of complexity. A few examples of the countless functions of proteins are:

1. *Structural parts* of cells and of body tissues, such as hair and nails, and the tough materials of cartilage and connective tissue.

2. *Pigments* in animal blood, skin, and eyes, and chlorophyll in green plants.

3. *Hormones,* the chemical messengers that regulate body functions in plants and animals.

4. *Contractile material* of muscle tissues.

5. *Antibodies,* which protect animal bodies against foreign substances and disease organisms.

6. *Enzymes*, which enable complex chemical reactions to take place with precision and speed.

To understand how proteins are able to do all this and much more, let us examine their chemical structure.

4-11 Amino Acids

Amino (uh-*mee*-noh) **acids** are the structural units of proteins. An amino acid is a relatively simple compound (see Figure 4-9). It consists of a central carbon atom to which are bonded:

1. A carboxyl group, COOH.
2. An **amino group**, NH_2.
3. A single hydrogen atom.
4. A side chain, symbolized by the letter R, which is different in each amino acid. In the simplest amino acid, glycine, the side chain is just another H. In alanine, it is a CH_3 group. Other side chains are more complex, and some contain sulfur and phosphorus. But none of the amino acid molecules is especially large. There are 20 different amino acids that are found as parts of proteins.

4-12 The Peptide Bond

Two amino acids may be bonded together by dehydration synthesis. The bond forms between the amino group of one amino acid and the carboxyl group of the other, with the loss of one water molecule. The bond is called a **peptide** (*pep*-tyd) **bond,** and the resulting molecule is called a **dipeptide.** The formation of a dipeptide is illustrated in Figure 4-10.

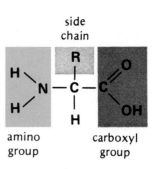

Figure 4-9. Structure of an Amino Acid. The side chains of the 20 amino acids give each its special chemical properties.

Figure 4-10. Formation of a Peptide Bond. A dehydration synthesis reaction between two amino acids links them together in a peptide bond. The molecule is called a dipeptide.

| AMINO ACID | + | AMINO ACID | ⟶ | DIPEPTIDE | + | WATER |

peptide bond

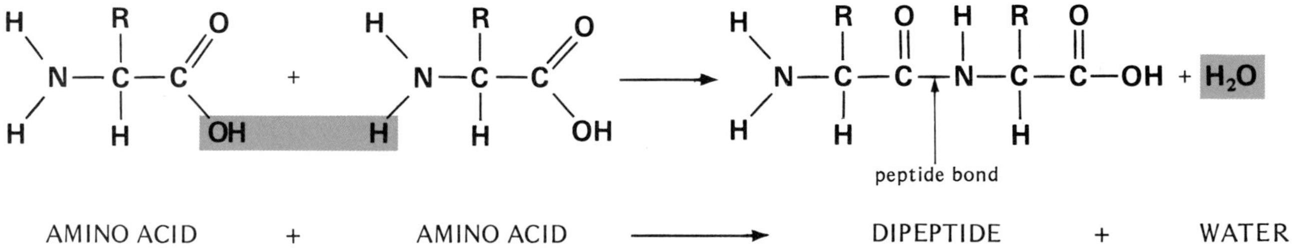

Amino acids can be added on at either end of a dipeptide in the same way, forming a chain of amino acids. Such a chain is called a **polypeptide.** All proteins are made of polypeptides.

4-13 The Structure of Proteins

Amino acids can be linked together in any sequence whatever and in chains of varying length. Each different sequence makes a different protein. Furthermore, the chains can fold and twist in space, making structures of many different shapes. Typical shapes of protein molecules are coils or helixes, pleated sheets, and globules. Often, adjacent sections of a folded chain become bonded to each other by what are called *cross-links*. The variations in shape and formation of cross-links make possible an enormous variety of proteins.

All protein molecules are large in terms of the number of atoms and amino acid units they contain. The smallest protein molecules have about 50 amino acids, or about 1,000 atoms. The largest have over 100,000 amino acids and millions of atoms.

Determining the actual sequence of amino acids in a particular protein is obviously a difficult task. The first protein structure to be determined was that of insulin. It was accomplished by Frederick Sanger, at Cambridge University, England, in 1954. Sanger later received the Nobel Prize for this work. The molecular structures of several hundred proteins have since been worked out by painstaking methods. These methods include breaking the molecule chemically into successively smaller pieces and identifying the amino acid at the end of each broken section. Machines are now being developed that will automatically analyze a protein and print out its amino acid sequence.

NUCLEIC ACIDS

Objectives:
1. Name the two types of nucleic acids found in cells.
2. Describe where the two types of nucleic acids are found and give their functions.
3. Describe the structure of each type of nucleic acid, including the type of sugar each contains, the types of bases, and the shapes of the molecules.

4-14   The Nature of Nucleic Acids

There are two kinds of **nucleic** (noo-*klay*-ik) **acids.** One is called **DNA**—from *deoxyribonucleic* (dee-*ahk*-see-ry-boh-noo-*klay*-ik) *acid.* (The other is called **RNA**—from *ribonucleic* (*ry*-boh-noo-*klay*-ik) *acid.* These substances were originally found in the part of the cell called the nucleus. This accounts for their general name. DNA is the hereditary material that is transmitted from one generation to the next during reproduction. Working together with RNA, it directs and controls the development and activities of all the cells of an organism. The way in which this is done is the subject of Chapter 27.

4-15   The Structure of DNA and RNA

The general structure of a nucleic acid molecule is that of a very long chain of repeating units. The backbone of the chain consists of two alternating chemical units. One unit is a 5-carbon sugar (deoxyribose in DNA, ribose in RNA). The other is the phosphate group, PO_4. In human cells, a single DNA molecule may have as many as 3 *billion* of these units!

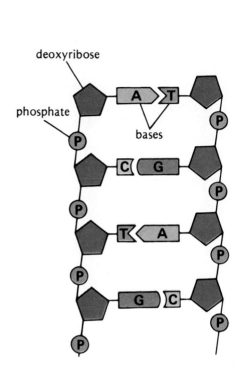

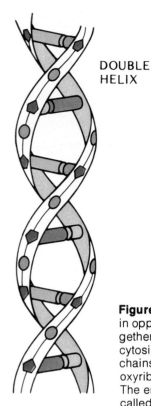

DOUBLE HELIX

Figure 4-11. DNA Molecule. The bases in opposite side chains of DNA bond together, adenine (A) with thymine (T) and cytosine (C) with guanine (G). The side chains are formed of alternating deoxyribose and phosphate groups (P). The entire molecule is coiled in a shape called a double helix.

Attached to the sugar groups along one side of the chain, there are chemical groups called bases. In DNA, there are only four different bases that may be attached to the chain. They are *adenine* (*ad*-uh-neen), *thymine* (*thy*-meen), *cytosine* (*syt*-uh-seen), and *guanine* (*gwah*-neen). Just as amino acids may be arranged in any sequence in a polypeptide chain, the four kinds of bases can be attached in any sequence along the length of the DNA molecule. As we will see in Chapter 27, the sequence of bases acts as a code that determines what proteins will be made in the cell. The proteins in turn determine the nature and activities of the cell.

A DNA molecule consists of two chains side by side, with the bases on opposite chains bonded together. In this bonding, an adenine is always bonded to a thymine. A cytosine is always bonded to a guanine (see Figure 4-11). The entire molecule is coiled into the form called a *double helix* (hee-liks). The double helix is coiled upon itself many times. A human DNA molecule would be about 4 centimeters long if it were stretched out in a straight line. By repeated coilings it is able to fit into tiny structures within the cell.

An RNA molecule is similar in chemical composition to DNA, but it has certain differences. The RNA molecule consists of only one chain, or strand, of bases. The sugar in RNA is ribose, not deoxyribose. And the base thymine is replaced by *uracil* (*yoor*-uh-sil). As we will see in Chapter 27, RNA is involved in protein synthesis.

Figure 1.

Figure 2.

Chemistry of Cooking

Nobody knows when people started to cook their foods. It happened long before the earliest written records, most likely soon after fire was brought under control. People discovered that food was easier to eat and tasted better when it was heated over a fire. However, it is only since scientists have acquired extensive knowledge about the chemistry of foods that they can explain the processes that go on when food is cooked.

Take, for example, the simple matter of boiling an egg. Egg white is largely water —about 88 percent. Nearly all the rest is protein, the chief protein in egg white being albumin (see Figure 1). Albumin, like all proteins, is made up of polypeptides—long chains of amino acids. At room temperature or below, each chain is tightly folded upon itself many times. Adjacent lengths of the chain are held together by a weak kind of chemical bond called a hydrogen bond.

Heating a protein changes the shape of its molecule, a process called *denaturation*. Boiling an egg causes denaturation of the albumin in the egg white. At the temperature of boiling water, the denaturation of albumin is quite drastic. All the hydrogen bonds are broken,

and the molecule untwists. The polypeptide chain becomes a long, floppy structure. In this extended form, the chains tend to become bonded to each other rather than to themselves, a process called *coagulation*. The final result is the semisolid, elastic material of cooked egg white (see Figure 2).

The egg's amino-acid chains do not attach to each other quickly, even after they have opened out, because the chains have electrical charges scattered along their length. These charge distributions are the same on all the chains. Since like charges repel each other, the charges tend to keep the chains apart and slow down the coagulation process.

The coagulation of denatured egg-white protein can be hastened by adding salt to the egg. Salt dissolved in water breaks down into sodium and chloride ions. These charged particles collect around the oppositely charged regions of the protein molecules and neutralize them. The force of repulsion between the molecules is reduced and they quickly coagulate.

Acids have a similar effect on the charge distribution on protein molecules. Lemon juice, which contains citric acid, and vinegar (acetic acid) can be used in place of salt to help coagulate egg white.

ENZYMES

Objectives:
1. Explain the functions of enzymes in living cells.
2. Describe the lock-and-key model of enzyme action.
3. Explain the effects on enzyme action of temperature, pH, and enzyme and substrate concentrations.
4. Define the term *coenzyme.*

4-16 Importance of Enzymes

Enzymes (*en*-zymz) are protein substances that make it possible for the chemical reactions of life to go on in living cells. There is a major difference between chemical reactions of inorganic substances and the reactions of organic compounds in living things. Consider, for example, the burning of gasoline in an automobile engine. The gasoline vapor is admitted to the engine cylinder, it is ignited by a spark, and the vapor completely burns in a fraction of a second. In fact, the burning is so rapid that it produces a small explosion, which helps to drive the engine.

The chemical reactions of life are different. We sometimes say that glucose is "burned" to release energy in the cell. But the "burning" occurs in dozens of small steps. In some of these steps, a small part of a molecule is removed. In others, a small group of atoms is added on. In still others, atoms are just rearranged within the molecule. These steps must occur with great precision and in the right order. They must also occur at ordinary temperatures inside the cell and must not give off large amounts of heat. Otherwise, the cell would be destroyed.

Enzymes make all of this possible in the living cell. For each step of a reaction, there is a particular enzyme that brings it about. Enzymes enter into a chemical reaction only temporarily—just long enough to cause it to happen. Enzymes are not changed by the reaction. They remain to be used again and again for the same chemical step with other molecules. A substance that affects a reaction without being changed itself is called a **catalyst** (*kat*-uh-list). Enzymes are organic catalysts.

The substance that an enzyme acts upon is called its **substrate** (*sub*-strayt). The names of enzymes usually end with the suffix *-ase*, and the name is often derived from the name of the substrate. For example, the enzyme that acts to split maltose into two glucose molecules is called *maltase.* Enzymes that break down proteins into shorter polypeptides or into separate amino acids are called *proteases* (*proh*-tee-ay-zez). Enzymes that break down lipids are called *lipases* (*ly*-pay-zez).

4-17 How Enzymes Work

Many experiments have shown that the ability of enzymes to act as catalysts depends on their shape. Somewhere on the

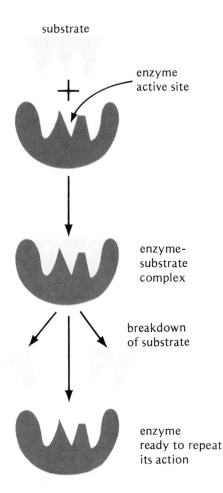

substrate

enzyme
active site

enzyme-
substrate
complex

breakdown
of substrate

enzyme
ready to repeat
its action

Figure 4-12. Lock-and-Key Model of Enzyme Action. In this theory of enzyme action, the substrate molecule fits into the active site on the enzyme, forming an enzyme-substrate complex. During this close association between enzyme and substrate the enzyme catalyzes a reaction in its substrate. When the reaction is finished, the enzyme and reaction product separate.

surface of each enzyme there is a region called the **active site.** The substrate molecules fit the shape of the active site (see Figure 4-12). When the substrate molecule comes in contact with the active site of the enzyme, it forms a temporary union with the enzyme. This is called an *enzyme-substrate complex.* During this time, the enzyme may break bonds within the substrate molecule and thus separate it into two smaller molecules.

An enzyme may also cause two molecules to join. In this case, there are two substrates. Each fits into the active site in such a way that they are brought into close contact. This enables bonds to form, joining the two substrate molecules.

The theory of enzyme action in which the enzyme and substrate fit together at an active site is called the *lock-and-key model.* The notched surface of a key can open only one lock. In a similar way, the shape of the active site of an enzyme fits the shape of only certain substrates. Thus, each enzyme can catalyze a reaction only of those substrates.

4-18 Characteristics of Enzyme Action

The following statements are generally true of enzyme action.

1. *Small amounts of an enzyme can cause the reaction of large quantities of substrate.* The time required for an enzyme-substrate complex to form and a reaction to occur is very short. A single enzyme molecule can catalyze thousands of substrate reactions each second. Thus, only small amounts of any enzyme need be present in a cell at any given time.

2. *Enzymes enable cell reactions to proceed at normal temperatures.* Many chemical reactions that occur very slowly at ordinary temperatures can be speeded up by raising the temperature. However, high temperatures would destroy living cells. Enzymes speed up reactions in the cell without requiring high temperatures.

3. *Enzymes work best at certain temperatures.* Enzyme action depends on the random motion of molecules, which brings the substrates into contact with the enzymes. This random motion increases as the temperature rises. If the temperature is low, the rate at which enzyme-substrate complexes form will be low (see Figure 4-13). The effect of the enzyme

Figure 4-13. The Effect of Temperature on the Rate of Enzyme Action.

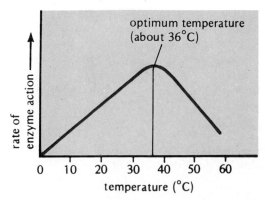

optimum temperature
(about 36°C)

rate of
enzyme action

temperature (°C)

0   10   20   30   40   50   60

will therefore be reduced. At somewhat higher temperatures, the enzyme becomes more effective, because complexes are forming at a faster rate. At still higher temperatures, however, the enzyme protein starts to break down, a process called *denaturation*. The shape of the enzyme molecule changes, its active site no longer fits the substrate molecule, and it loses its effectiveness. There is therefore a particular temperature—the *optimum temperature*—at which enzyme effectiveness is greatest. Optimum temperatures for enzymes in living cells are usually close to the normal cell temperature.

4. *Each enzyme works best at a certain pH*. The effectiveness of an enzyme depends on the pH of the surrounding medium (see Figure 4-14). The pH of the contents of the

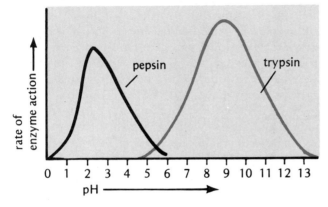

Figure 4-14. The Effect of pH on the Rate of Enzyme Action.

human stomach, for example, is slightly acid. The enzyme pepsin, which starts the digestion of proteins in the stomach, is most effective at this pH level. The pH in the intestine is slightly basic. Here the enzyme trypsin, which continues the digestion of proteins, works best.

5. *The rate of an enzyme-controlled reaction depends on the concentrations of enzyme and substrate*. If relatively little enzyme is present, the number of substrate molecules it can act on in a given time is limited. Increasing the amount of enzyme will increase the rate at which the reaction products are formed (see Figure 4-15). When, however, all the substrate molecules are being acted on, a further increase in enzyme concentration will have little or no effect on output. Likewise, when all the enzyme molecules and substrate molecules are

Figure 4-15. The Effects of Enzyme and Substrate Concentration on the Rate of Enzyme Action.

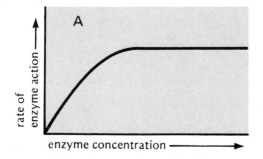

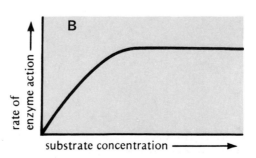

Figure 4-16. Digestion in a Fungus. *Rhizopus,* often called "bread mold" (left), will grow well on any starchy food source. *Rhizopus* secretes digestive enzymes through its filament-like hyphae that grow in masses (right). Digestion occurs outside the fungus, and the digested food products are then absorbed into the cells.

in the process of reaction, adding more substrate will have no effect on rate of output.

6. *Some enzymes need substances called coenzymes in order to function.* **Coenzymes** (koh-*en*-zymz), which are organic substances but are not proteins, enable enzymes to perform their catalytic function. Some coenzymes are built into the structure of an enzyme. Others are separate molecules. During the formation of the enzyme-substrate complex, the coenzyme is altered in a way that assists the reaction. After the reaction, the coenzyme is restored to its original form. It is now known that some vitamins are needed in the body because they are coenzymes or because coenzymes are made from them in the cell.

7. *Some enzymes function inside the cell, others act outside the cell.* All enzymes in a living organism are made by the cells of the organism. Most of these enzymes are used within the cell in which they are made. However, some enzymes are passed out of the cell to catalyze reactions outside the cell. All digestive enzymes produced in the human digestive tract are of this type. For example, pepsin is made inside the cells of glands in the stomach wall. It then leaves the cells and mixes with food in the stomach. Here, proteins in the food are broken down to simpler molecules, which can later be absorbed through cell membranes and enter the bloodstream. Another example of extracellular enzyme action is digestion in fungi (see Figure 4-16).

Chapter Review

SUMMARY

- Organic compounds often contain much larger and more complex molecules than do inorganic compounds because of the chemical nature of the carbon atom.

- Carbohydrates are organic compounds containing carbon, hydrogen, and oxygen. The simplest carbohydrates are the simple sugars, or monosaccharides. Two monosaccharides form a disaccharide. Long chains of repeating simple sugars form polysaccharides.

- Lipids include fats, oils, and waxes. Fats are formed from a combination of fatty acids and glycerol. Waxes are made up of fatty acids and alcohols other than glycerol. Lipids are important components of cells and cell products.

- Proteins serve many functions in living things. Proteins are made up of chains of amino acids. The sequence of the amino acids is characteristic of the particular protein.

- The nucleic acids are DNA and RNA. DNA contains hereditary information. DNA and RNA together control the synthesis of cell proteins.

- Enzymes enable biochemical reactions of the cell to occur. Substrate molecules react in the presence of enzymes. An enzyme may break bonds within a substrate molecule, or it may cause substrate molecules to join, thereby forming a larger molecule.

KNOW THE TERMS

active site	dehydration synthesis	hydrolysis	polypeptide
amino acid	dipeptide	inorganic compound	polysaccharide
amino group	disaccharide	lipid	protein
carbohydrate	DNA	monosaccharide	RNA
carboxyl group	enzyme	nucleic acid	saturated fat
catalyst	fatty acid	organic compound	starch
cholesterol	glycerol	peptide bond	substrate
coenzyme	glycogen	polymer	unsaturated fat

SECTION QUESTIONS

Organic Compounds

1. What element is always found in organic compounds?
2. What three elements are usually found in organic compounds?
3. How many covalent bonds can a carbon atom form?
4. Name four types of organic compounds.

Carbohydrates

5. Why are sugars biologically important?
6. How are two simple sugar molecules bonded together?
7. Define the term *polymer*.
8. How are complex sugar molecules broken apart?

Lipids

9. Name the common lipids.
10. What important group is found at the end of a fatty acid molecule?

Proteins

11. List the elements found in proteins.
12. What groups are found in each amino acid?

Nucleic Acids

13. Name two types of nucleic acids.
14. Which nucleic acid occurs as a double helix?

Enzymes

15. What are enzymes?
16. Name the theory of enzyme action.

KNOW THE FACTS

Copy the number of each sentence below on a sheet of paper. Beside each number, write the letter identifying the answer that correctly completes the sentence.

Base your answers to questions 1 and 2 on the diagram below.

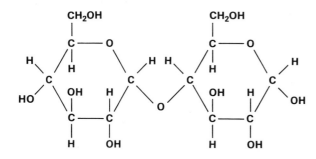

1. Which bond was formed within the maltose molecule shown above when the molecule was synthesized?
   a. C-H bond.   c. O-H bond.
   b. C-O bond.   d. O-O bond.
2. The building blocks of this compound can be used to synthesize
   a. starch.   c. a polypeptide.
   b. an enzyme.   d. a lipid.
3. A compound whose chemical composition is mostly closely related to maltose is
   a. starch.   c. protein.
   b. ATP.   d. RNA.
4. Fat and water react to produce a fatty acid, glycerol, and water. This is an example of
   a. hydrolysis.
   b. dehydration synthesis.
   c. neutralization.
   d. enzyme action.
5. Which group is formed in all fatty acids?
   a. PO_4.   c. SO_4.
   b. $-CH_3$.   d. -COOH.

6. Which process produces peptide bonds?
   a. digestion.   c. dehydration synthesis.
   b. hydrolysis.   d. enzyme deactivation.
7. The composition and structure of a protein are determined by
   a. the molecular weight of the protein.
   b. its amino acid sequence.
   c. the geometric arrangement of its saccharides.
   d. its fatty acid and monosaccharide content.
8. Examples of polymers that contain repeating units known as nucleotides are
   a. hemoglobin and maltase.
   b. starch and glycogen.
   c. fats and oils.
   d. DNA and RNA.
9. Which statement concerning enzymes is true?
   a. Their rate of action is influenced by pH.
   b. They can act on any substrate.
   c. They are not affected by temperature.
   d. They can only hydrolyze elements.
10. At 20° C the optimum reaction rate of a certain enzyme occurs at a pH of 7. A greater reaction rate could most probably be attained by increasing
    a. the temperature to 30° C and keeping the pH at 7.
    b. both the temperature and the pH.
    c. the pH and keeping the temperature at 20° C.
    d. the pH and decreasing the temperature.

UNDERSTAND THE CONCEPTS

11. What is the proportion of hydrogen to oxygen in carbohydrate molecules?
12. What is the empirical formula for monosaccharides?
13. Describe dehydration synthesis.
14. What type of compound is formed when two monosaccharides are joined by dehydration synthesis?
15. Explain the difference between a saturated and an unsaturated fatty acid.
16. List several functions of lipids in living organisms.
17. List several functions of proteins in living organisms.

18. Show the basic structure of an amino acid.
19. Describe the formation of a peptide bond.
20. What are the functions of the nucleic acids?
21. Describe the general structure of each type of nucleic acid.
22. How are most enzymes named?

23. Explain the lock-and-key model of enzyme action.
24. Describe how enzyme action is affected by the following: temperature, pH, enzyme concentration, and substrate concentration.
25. What is a coenzyme?

THINK CRITICALLY

26. The occurrence of living things comes from the ability of the carbon atom to form covalent bonds. Explain.
27. Compare and contrast the synthesis of starch with the hydrolysis of glycogen.
28. Excessive saturated fat consumption leads to the formation of cholesterol. What role might this play in increasing a person's chances for having a heart attack?

29. Proteins carry out many functions. Which of the functions listed in Section 4.10 would you rank as the most important? Why?
30. Many viruses are thought to enter the cell and destroy or change the normal DNA component of the cell. What does this behavior imply for the future functioning of the cell?
31. If enzymes did not act as catalysts, what consequences would this have for the cell?

THINK CREATIVELY

32. Life as we know it on this planet is based on carbon. What might life be like if it were based on another element?
33. The cell contains large numbers of molecules. Some of these molecules dissolve in water; others do not. What implications might the solubility of these molecules in water have on cell structure?

FOR FURTHER INVESTIGATION

1. An enzyme called protease breaks down protein into shorter polypeptides or into separate amino acids. You can demonstrate the action of this protein-digesting enzyme by dissolving 5 mL of unflavored gelatin in a teaspoon of hot water and then adding three-fourths of a cup of cold water. Pour the gelatin solution into each of two test tubes to solidify. To one test tube, add a few milliliters of juice from a fresh pineapple or commercially available protease; to the other test tube, add the same amount of water. Let the tubes sit overnight. What do you observe at the end of 24 hours? How do you explain any changes?

2. Prepare a report for the class on one of the career opportunities listed below. See suggested procedures, p. 9, "For Further Investigation" Activity 3.
   a. Crime laboratory technician
   b. Organic chemist
   c. Home economist
3. Write a brief report on the life and contributions of one of the following scientists:
   a. Marie Curie
   b. Ellen Swallow Richards
   c. Carl McClellan Hill
   d. Mildred Cohn

FOR FURTHER READING

Hopson, Janet, "Carbohydrates: A Key to Health and Performance," *Science Digest,* January, 1984.
Miller, J. A., "Beyond the Limits of Protein Building," *Science News,* June 8, 1985.

Raloff, J., "Oxidized Lipids: A Key to Heart Disease," *Science News,* May 4, 1985.
Silberner, J., "Cholesterol Confab: Advice and Dissent," *Science News,* December 22, 1984.

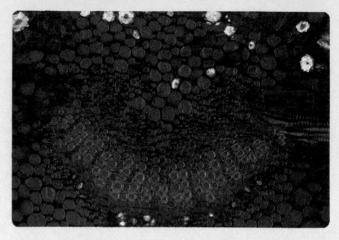

Chapter 5

THE CELL

Cellular organization is clearly evident in this microscopic view of leaf tissue.

THE CELL THEORY

Objectives:
1. Describe the contributions of the following scientists to the development of the cell theory: Robert Hooke, Anton van Leeuwenhoek, Robert Brown, Matthias Schleiden, Theodor Schwann, and Rudolf Virchow.
2. State the cell theory and explain its importance.

All living things are made up of small, individual units called **cells.** Some organisms consist of just one cell. Others contain billions of cells. In all cases, however, the life processes of the organism are actually carried on by its cells. To understand the workings of living things, we must first understand what goes on inside the cell.

5-1 Historical Development of the Cell Theory

The individual cells of most organisms cannot be seen with the naked eye. Not until the mid-1600s were microscopes used to study biological materials. Robert Hooke examined thin slices of cork and other plant tissues with a compound microscope and found that they were made up of boxlike structures, which he called *cells.* What Hooke saw were only the walls of dead cells. He never studied living materials in which the contents of cells could be seen. Hooke's findings were published in 1665 in his book *Micrographia.* Compound microscopes have become improved and refined over the centuries (see Figure 5-1) and remain the type in use today.

At the same time that Hooke was making and using compound microscopes, Anton van Leeuwenhoek (*lay*-ven-huk) was making single-lens microscopes of amazing power. Several of his microscopes still exist, and some have magnifying powers of more than 200×. Looking at drops of pond water with these microscopes, Leeuwenhoek saw living organisms that no one else had ever seen. We now know that many of them were one-celled organisms. Leeuwenhoek also observed and described human sperm cells and blood cells. In 1683 he described what must have been bacteria—the smallest kind of living cell. However, Leeuwenhoek did not know that he was seeing single cells, and he drew no conclusions about the cellular nature of organisms.

It was not until the early 1800s that the cellular nature of biological materials began to receive attention. In 1824, Henry Dutrochet (doo-troh-*shay*) proposed that all living things were composed of cells. However, the actual nature of living cells was still not known.

In 1831, Robert Brown noted that the small, dense, round body that had been observed in cells by other microscopists was a common feature of all plant cells. He called this structure the *nucleus.* However, the major role of the nucleus in cell function was not recognized at this time.

In 1838, Matthias Schleiden (*shly*-den) theorized that all plants were made up of cells. In the following year, Theodor Schwann (shvahn) proposed that all animals were also made up of cells. In the same year, Johannes Purkinje (per-*kin*-jee) used the term *protoplasm* to refer to the jellylike material that fills the cell. The last part of the cell theory was expressed by Rudolph Virchow (*vihr*-koh) in 1855, when he stated that all new cells arise only from existing cells.

In 1861, Max Schultze (shults) defined protoplasm as "the physical basis of life," and proposed that it was found in the cells of all types of organisms. At about the same time, Felix Dujardin (doo-zhar-*dahn*) recognized the existence of one-celled organisms. He also expressed the idea that protoplasm was associated with all forms of life. Justus von Liebig (*lee*-big) described protoplasm as consisting mainly of water, with the rest of the substance being proteins, fats, and carbohydrates.

By the end of the 1800s, biologists had discovered many of the structures found within the cell, including the chromosomes, which contain the hereditary information. They were also able to describe in detail the events of cell division, in which one cell divides, forming two cells.

Figure 5-1. A Nineteenth Century Compound Microscope.

5-2 Summary of the Cell Theory

The ideas that are generally called the **cell theory** are:
1. *All organisms are made up of one or more cells and the products of those cells.* An organism may be a single cell.

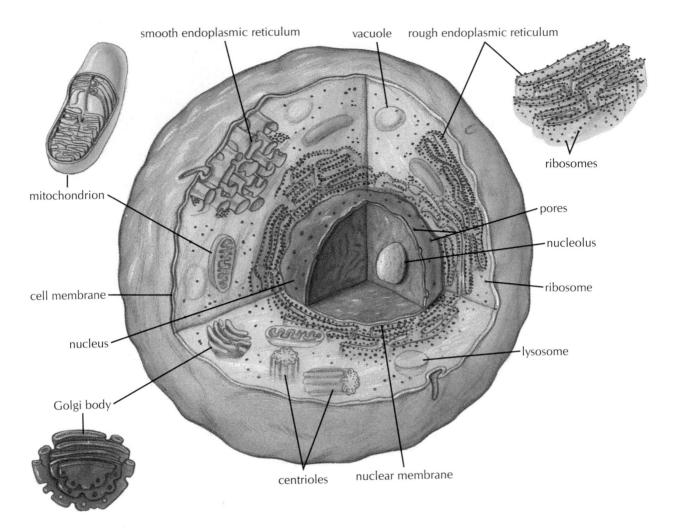

smooth endoplasmic reticulum

vacuole

rough endoplasmic reticulum

ribosomes

mitochondrion

pores

nucleolus

ribosome

cell membrane

nucleus

lysosome

Golgi body

centrioles

nuclear membrane

Figure 5-2. Generalized Structure of an Animal Cell.

Examples are the ameba, paramecium, and bacteria. In many-celled organisms there may be intercellular material made by the cells.

2. *All cells carry on their own life activities.* The life activities of a many-celled organism are the combined effect of the activities of its individual cells.

3. *New cells can arise only from other living cells by the process of cell division or reproduction.* Reproduction of a many-celled organism is brought about by reproduction of certain of its cells.

CELL STRUCTURE

Objectives:

1. Describe the structures and functions of the following cell parts: *cell wall, cell membrane, nucleus,* and *cytoplasm.*

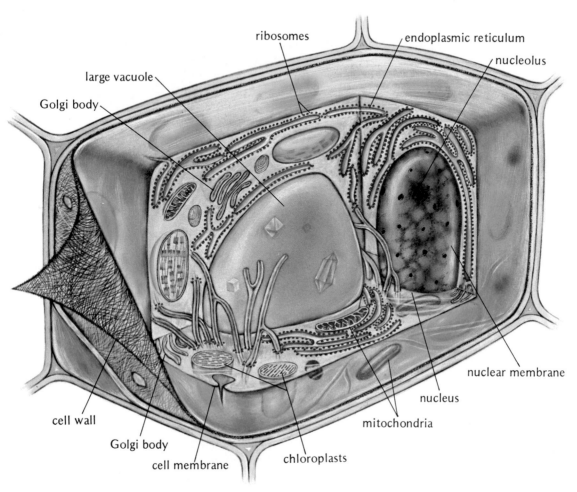

ribosomes
endoplasmic reticulum
nucleolus
large vacuole
Golgi body
nuclear membrane
cell wall
nucleus
Golgi body
mitochondria
cell membrane
chloroplasts

2. Describe the structures and functions of the following cell organelles: *endoplasmic reticulum, ribosomes, Golgi bodies, lysosomes; mitochondria, microtubules, microfilaments, centrioles, cilia, flagella, vacuoles,* and *plastids.*

3. Contrast and compare the general structures of an animal cell and a plant cell.

Figure 5-3. Generalized Structure of a Plant Cell.

5-3 General Characteristics of Cells

All processes necessary for life are carried on by cells. In addition, the cells of many-celled organisms are generally highly specialized to perform specific functions. There are nerve cells that can carry messages, muscle cells that can shorten, glandular cells that produce certain substances, and so on. Figure 5-2 shows the general structure of an animal cell and Figure 5-3 shows the general structure of a plant cell. However, actual animal and plant cells will show variations from these structures.

And, although most cells have diameters between 10 and 30 micrometers, variations in size and shape occur as well. For example, chicken egg cells may be 6 centimeters across while certain nerve cells extend more than 1 meter.

All cells are surrounded by a cell membrane that separates the cell contents from the environment. All cells, except those of *bacteria* and *blue-green algae*, contain a membrane-bounded nucleus. The fluid material that fills the space between the cell membrane and the nucleus is called the *cytoplasm*.

5-4   Cell Walls

The cells of plants and various microorganisms are enclosed by a rigid **cell wall,** which is outside the cell membrane. The cell wall gives the cell its shape and also provides mechanical protection (see Figure 5-4). In plants, this wall is composed largely of *cellulose* (*sel*-yuh-lohs). In other organisms it may contain other compounds. The cell wall has many small openings that allow the free passage of materials to and from the cell membrane. Thin strands of cytoplasm sometimes extend through the walls of adjacent cells, possibly allowing the direct passage of materials from one cell to another. Animal cells do not have a cell wall.

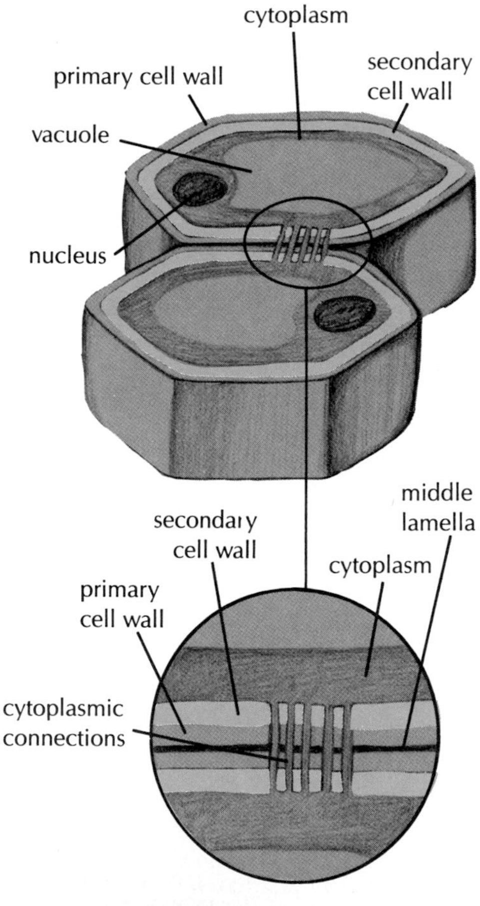

5-5   The Cell Membrane

The **cell,** or *plasma* (*plaz*-muh), **membrane** separates the cell from the surrounding environment. It controls the movement of materials into and out of the cell, thus making it possible for the cell contents to be chemically different from the environment. Its function is also to keep the internal conditions of the cell constant—to maintain homeostasis.

Permeability of the cell membrane. The cell membrane is **selectively permeable,** or *semipermeable* (sem-ee-*per*-mee-uh-bul). That is, some substances pass freely through it. Other substances can pass through only to some slight extent or only at certain times. And still other substances cannot pass through it at all. Through its selective permeability the cell membrane regulates the chemical composition of the cell. The semipermeable nature of the membrane results from the chemical and electrical properties of its molecules. The passage of materials through cell membranes is discussed in detail later in this chapter (page 79).

Structure of the cell membrane. The cell membrane is a two-layered structure composed of lipids, proteins and carbohydrates (see Figure 5-5). The two layers are lipids, and the proteins are embedded in them. Some of the proteins are on the outer surface of the double membrane, some are on the inner surface, and some are thought to extend through the membrane. Carbohydrates branch out from the external surface. In electron micrographs there appears to be a light middle layer. This middle layer consists of the "tail ends" of the lipid molecules.

Figure 5-4. Structure of the Plant Cell Wall. The primary cell wall, which is formed by the young plant cell, stretches as the cell grows. Full-grown cells produce a thick secondary cell wall inside the primary cell wall. The middle lamella is a layer that forms between adjacent cells and holds them together.

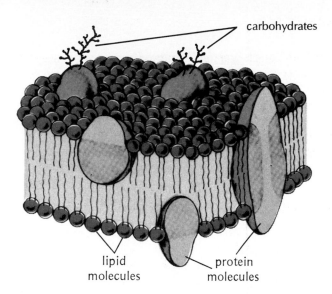

carbohydrates

lipid molecules

protein molecules

Figure 5-5. Structure of the Cell Membrane.

These ends are chemically different from the rest of the lipid molecule. They stain differently, thereby producing the appearance of a middle layer.

The proteins of the membrane are believed to be important in controlling the passage of substances through the membrane. In some cells the membrane proteins are thought to be involved in the pumping of various ions into and out of the cell. In nerve cells, they are involved in the transmission of messages, or impulses, along the cell membrane.

Pinocytosis and phagocytosis. Materials that cannot pass through the cell membrane may be taken into the cell by processes called pinocytosis and phagocytosis. In **pinocytosis** (pin-uh-sy-*toh*-sis), or "cell drinking," liquid from the surrounding medium or very small particles are taken into the cell. Where the substance is in contact with the surface of the cell membrane, the membrane forms an inpocketing or pouch (see Figure 5-6). The outer surface of the cell membrane closes over, and the pouch pinches off, forming a sac, or vacuole, within the cell. Inside the cell, the vacuole may open, releasing its contents.

In **phagocytosis** (fag-uh-sy-*toh*-sis), large particles or even small organisms are ingested into the cell. In this process, extensions of the cell called *pseudopods* (*sood*-uh-pahdz) flow around the particle to be taken in. When the particle has been surrounded, the membrane pinches off, forming a vacuole within the cell. Both phagocytosis and pinocytosis require the use of energy by the cell.

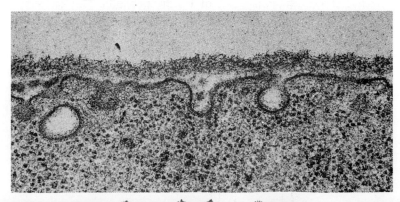

Figure 5-6. Pinocytosis. In pinocytosis, inpocketings of the cell membrane close over, forming vacuoles in the cytoplasm.

Figure 5-7. Electron Micrograph of the Cell Nucleus. The nuclear membrane and its pores are clearly visible. The round, dark structure within the nucleus is the nucleolus.

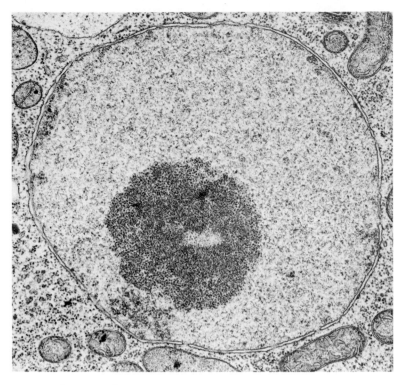

5-6 The Nucleus

The cell **nucleus** (*noo*-klee-us) (plural, **nuclei**) is a round, dense body surrounded by a double membrane (see Figure 5-7). The nucleus serves as the control center for cell metabolism and reproduction. If it is removed, the cell dies.

The nuclear membrane, like the cell membrane, is selectively permeable. Unlike the cell membrane, the nuclear membrane is a double membrane and has well-defined pores that can be seen in electron micrographs. The pores control the passage of certain substances into and out of the nucleus. The selective permeability of the nuclear membrane allows the contents of the nucleus, the *nucleoplasm*, to remain chemically different from the rest of the cell.

Within the nucleus are one or more **nucleoli** (noo-*klee*-uh-ly) (singular, **nucleolus**). These are dense, granular bodies that disappear at the beginning of cell division and reappear at the end. They are made up of DNA, RNA, and protein. Nucleoli are the sites of production of ribosomes (see below).

During the periods between cell divisions, much of the nucleoplasm consists of chromatin. *Chromatin (kroh*-muh-tin) is the material of the *chromosomes (kroh*-muh-sohmz) in the form of long, very thin threads. During cell division, the chromatin strands shorten by coiling and become thick enough to be clearly visible as separate chromosomes. The chromosomes contain the hereditary material of the cell. Nucleoli are often formed at a particular location on a specific chromosome. This area is called the *nucleolar organizer*.

5-7 The Cytoplasm

All the material within the cell between the cell membrane and the nucleus is the **cytoplasm** (*syt*-uh-plaz-um). The cytoplasm is a watery material in which are dissolved many of the substances involved in cell metabolism. Many of the chemical reactions of cell metabolism take place in the cytoplasm. Also found in the cytoplasm are a variety of specialized structures called **organelles** (or-guh-*nelz*). Each type of organelle carries out a specific function in cell metabolism. We will discuss the various organelles on the following pages.

5-8 Endoplasmic Reticulum and Ribosomes

The **endoplasmic reticulum** (en-duh-*plaz*-mik rih-*tik*-yuh-lum) consists of a system of fluid-filled canals or channels enclosed by membranes. These canals generally form a continuous network throughout the cytoplasm (see Figure 5-8). The canals of the endoplasmic reticulum serve as a path for transport of materials through the cell. In addition, the membranes of the network provide a large surface area on which many biochemical reactions are thought to occur. Also, the endoplasmic reticulum divides, or partitions, the cell into compartments, making it possible for a number of different reactions to be going on at the same time.

The membranes of the endoplasmic reticulum are similar in structure to the cell membrane and nuclear membrane. In places the membranes of the endoplasmic reticulum are observed to be continuous with the outer portion of the nuclear membrane. In electron micrographs endoplasmic reticulum has either a rough or smooth appearance. In rough endoplasmic reticulum, the outer surfaces of the membranes are lined with tiny particles called ribosomes. The ribosomes give the membrane a granular appearance. On smooth endoplasmic reticulum there are no ribosomes.

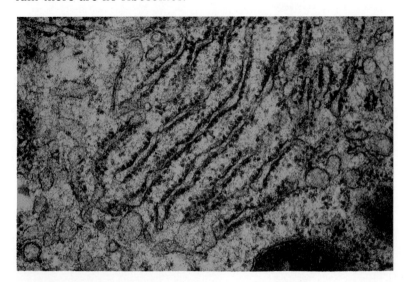

Figure 5-8. Rough Endoplasmic Reticulum. The membranes of the rough endoplasmic reticulum are lined with ribosomes.

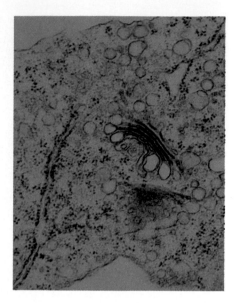

Figure 5-9. Golgi Bodies.

Ribosomes (*ry*-buh-sohmz) are the sites of protein synthesis in the cell. They are found both free in the cytoplasm and lining the membranes of the endoplasmic reticulum. In cells involved in the synthesis of proteins that are to be transported out of the cell, the ribosomes are mainly attached to the membranes of the endoplasmic reticulum. The proteins pass through these membranes into the canals, which carry them to the cell membrane and out of the cell. Where the products of protein synthesis are to be used within the cell, the ribosomes are generally free in the cytoplasm. Proteins synthesized on free ribosomes are usually enzymes that function in the cell cytoplasm.

5-9   Golgi Bodies

Golgi (*gohl*-jee) **bodies** consist of a stack of membranes forming flattened sacs and small spherical sacs, or vesicles (see Figure 5-9). Golgi bodies serve as processing, packaging, and storage centers for the secretory products of the cell. Animal cells generally have only one Golgi body, which is usually located near the nucleus. Plant cells may have up to several hundred Golgi bodies.

In some studies, connections between the Golgi body and the endoplasmic reticulum have been found. There is evidence that proteins synthesized on the ribosomes attached to the endoplasmic reticulum pass through the canals of the endoplasmic reticulum into the Golgi bodies. Here they are packaged in vesicles. The vesicles migrate to the cell surface, where their membranes fuse with the cell membrane. The materials in the vesicle are then released outside the cell. Cell secretory products other than proteins may also be packaged in the Golgi body. In plant cells, the Golgi bodies are thought to be involved in assembling materials for the cell wall.

5-10   Lysosomes

Lysosomes (*ly*-suh-sohmz) are small, saclike structures surrounded by a single membrane. These organelles contain strong digestive, or hydrolytic, enzymes. Lysosomes are thought to be produced by the Golgi bodies. They are found in most animal cells and in some plant cells. In one-celled organisms, lysosomes are involved in the digestion of food within the cell. In multicellular organisms, lysosomes serve several different functions. They break down worn-out cell organelles. In some animals they are part of the body's defense against disease. Lysosomes are present in white blood cells, which ingest disease-causing bacteria by phagocytosis. The lysosomes within the white cells break down the bacteria. Lysosomes are also involved in certain developmental processes. For example, as a frog develops from a tadpole to a mature frog, it loses its tail. Lysosomes are involved in the digestion and absorption of the tail.

5-11 Mitochondria

Mitochondria (myt-uh-*kahn*-dree-uh) (singular, **mitochondrion**) are round or slipper-shaped organelles surrounded by two membrane (see Figure 5-10). The inner membrane is highly folded, forming *cristae (kris*-tee) that extend into the mitochondrion itself. The cristae of the mitochondria provide a large surface area on which many biochemical reactions occur. Active cells, such as muscle cells, which use much energy, contain large numbers of mitochondria. Because most of the energy needed by cells is released in the mitochondria, this organelle is often called "the powerhouse of the cell." The process by which the energy of food is released in mitochondria and elsewhere in the cell is called *cellular respiration.* Typical cells contain from 300 to 800 mitochondria, depending on their activity. Within the cell, the mitochondria are usually in motion, moving individually or in groups. They may also be found at specific locations within the cell. For example, in muscle cells, the mitochondria are found along the fibers that cause the muscle cell to contract. Mitochondria contain their own DNA and are capable of duplicating themselves.

5-12 Microtubules

Microtubules (my-kroh-*toob*-yoolz) are long, hollow, cylindrical structures. They are found in the cell cytoplasm, where they serve as a sort of "skeleton" for the cell, giving it shape (see Figure 5-11). They are found in centrioles, cilia, and flagella, and may also be involved in movement of the chromosomes during cell division. Microtubules are composed of a protein called *tubulin (toob*-yuh-lin). The molecues of this protein consist of two subunits that stack alternately in a helix. This gives the microtubule its form.

5-13 Microfilaments

Microfilaments (my-kroh-*fil*-uh-ments) are long, solid, threadlike strands found in some types of cells. Most are composed of the protein *actin (ak*-tin) and are generally associated with cell movement. Microfilaments are thought to have the capacity to contract and to be involved in the movement of cytoplasm within the cell, a phenomenon known as *cyclosis*

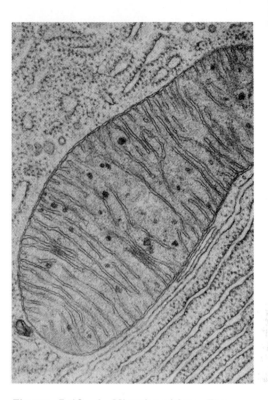

Figure 5-10. A Mitochondrion. The mitochondrion is surrounded by two membranes. The infoldings of the inner membrane are called cristae.

Figure 5-11. Microtubules. The system of microtubules present throughout the cytoplasm is evident in this photomicrograph of several cells.

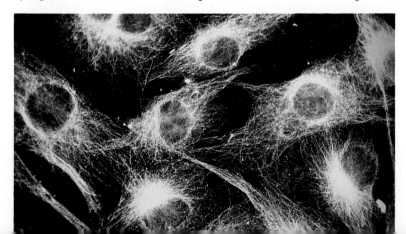

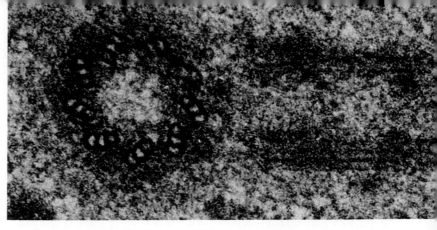

Figure 5-12. A Pair of Centrioles. A centriole consists of a ring of nine groups of three microtubules. In this electron micrograph, one centriole is seen in crossection (left); the other is seen in longitudinal view (right.)

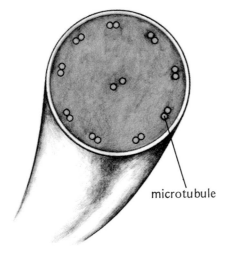

microtubule

Figure 5-13. Structure of Cilia. Cilia arise from organelles called basal bodies that are structurally similar to centrioles. Each cilium contains a ring of nine pairs of microtubules with one pair of microtubules in the center.

(sy-*kloh*-sis) or cell streaming. Actin microfilaments are also found in skeletal muscle cells and are involved in muscle contraction. Some microfilaments are not made of actin, and may serve as supporting structures for the cell.

5-14 Centrioles

Near the nucleus in animal cells there is a pair of cylindrical **centrioles** (*sen*-tree-ohlz) which lie at right angles to each other (see Figure 5-12). Each centriole consists of a ring of nine groups of three microtubules. Centrioles are involved in cell division in animal cells. They are also found in the motile cells of algae, fungi, and higher plants.

5-15 Cilia and Flagella

Cilia (*sil*-ee-uh) and **flagella** (fluh-*jel*-uh) are hairlike organelles with the capacity for movement (see Figure 5-13). They extend out from the surface of many different types of cells. Their structure is identical except that flagella are longer than cilia. There are usually only a few flagella on a cell, but cilia often cover the entire cell surface. In one-celled organisms, cilia and flagella are involved in cell movement. In larger, many-celled animals, ciliated cells serve to move substances over the surface of the cells.

Cilia and flagella arise from structures called *basal* (*bay*-sul) *bodies*. The structure of a basal body is similar to that of a centriole. The cilia and flagella are slightly different in structure from the basal body. They have a ring of nine pairs of microtubules, and in the center of the ring is another pair of microtubules.

5-16 Vacuoles

Vacuoles (*vak*-yuh-wohlz) are fluid-filled organelles enclosed by a membrane. Those found in plant cells are filled with a fluid called *cell sap*. In mature plant cells, there may be a single, very large vacuole that occupies most of the interior of the cell. In various microorganisms and simple animals, food is digested in special *food vacuoles* within the cells. Many of these organisms also have *contractile vacuoles* in which excess water from the cell collects. The water is periodically excreted from the cell directly into the environment. Vacuoles may also serve as storage sites for certain cell products.

5-17   Chloroplasts, Leucoplasts, and Chromoplasts

Chloroplasts, leucoplasts, and chromoplasts are all types of plastids. **Plastids** (*plas*-tidz) are membrane-enclosed organelles found in the cells of some single-celled organisms and almost all plants. They are not present in the cells of animals or fungi. Like mitochondria, plastids are bounded by two membranes and have systems of membranes within the organelle. There are three types of plastids. **Leucoplasts** (*loo*-kuh-plasts) are colorless plastids in which glucose is converted to starch, and in which starch and other plant nutrients are stored. **Chromoplasts** (*kroh*-muh-plasts) contain the pigments that give bright colors to fruits, flowers, and leaves. The pigments are synthesized within the chromoplasts. The most important type of plastids are **chloroplasts** (*klor*-uh-plasts), which contain the green pigment *chlorophyll (klor*-uh-fil). The chloroplasts are the site of *photosynthesis*, the food-making process of plants.

The inside of the chloroplast contains a system of double membranes called *lamellae* (luh-*mel*-ee) (see Figure 5-14). The lamellae are often arranged in the form of stacks called *grana* (*grah*-nuh). The pigments involved in photosynthesis are located in the lamellae. The protein-containing material that fills the rest of the chloroplast is called the *stroma (stroh*-muh). Chloroplasts, like mitochondria, contain their own DNA and have the ability to duplicate themselves.

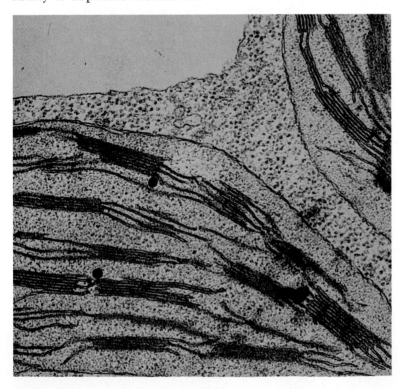

Figure 5-14. Electron Micrograph of Chloroplast. The lamellae contain photosynthetic pigments and are arranged in stacks called grana.

Frontier of Biology

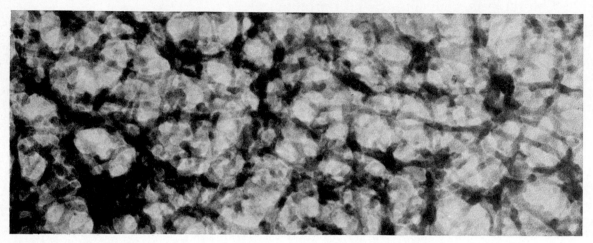

Electron micrograph showing the complex structure of the microtrabecular lattice.

The Microtrabecular Lattice

With the invention of the electron microscope in the 1940s, the study of the cell took a giant step forward. The electron microscope can produce magnifications hundreds of times greater than those produced by the light microscope. However, materials to be viewed in standard transmission electron microscopes must be sliced very thin (less than 0.2 micrometers). Thus, they reveal little about the three dimensional structure of the cell cytoplasm, the material surrounding the nucleus and organelles.

Standard electron microscope studies have revealed the presence in the cytoplasm of elements that could serve as an internal "skeleton" for cell structure. These elements included microtubules, microfilaments, and fine strands of protein material.

Special high-voltage electron microscopes are now allowing researchers to view much thicker sections of biological materials, and with this has come a new view of the internal structure of the cell. These instruments are huge, weighing over 20 tons and standing more than 10 meters high. They use electrons with energies of a million electron volts, which can pass through specimens several micrometers in thickness. They can produce images of the internal structures of cells in the same way as X-ray photographs show the internal structures of the body.

With the high-voltage electron microscope, researchers have observed interconnected thin strands forming a three-dimensional lattice throughout the cytoplasm. This structure, called the *microtrabecular lattice,* is composed of fine protein filaments that can assemble and disassemble as cell conditions vary. These strands are connected to microtubules and microfilaments in the cell. The cell organelles appear to be suspended in the lattice, and it is possible that enzyme systems may also be bound to the strands of the lattice. By organizing organelles and enzyme systems, the lattice would increase the efficiency of reactions occurring in the cell. It is thought that the lattice maintains the shape of the cell and plays a role in protein synthesis, cell differentiation, and the movement of materials within the cell.

The microtrabecular lattice and its functions is an emerging area of research. As high-voltage electron microscopy develops, we will learn more about this structural and organizational element.

PASSAGE OF MATERIALS THROUGH CELL MEMBRANES

Objectives:
1. Relate the structure of the cell membrane to the passage of various types of substances through the membrane.
2. Describe the roles of diffusion, facilitated diffusion, and osmosis in the passage of materials into and out of cells.
3. Explain what is meant by selectively permeable membrane, concentration gradient, turgor pressure, and plasmolysis.
4. Describe the effects of osmosis of cells placed in solutions containing different concentrations of water.
5. Compare passive transport with active transport.

5-18 Selective Permeability of the Cell Membrane

Certain types of substances pass through cell membranes more easily than others. For example, lipid molecules and molecules that dissolve in lipids, such as alcohol, ether, and chloroform, pass readily through cell membranes. Also, small molecules, such as water, glucose, amino acids, carbon dioxide, and oxygen, can pass freely through cell membranes. Large molecules, such as starch and proteins, cannot. Electrically neutral molecules enter and leave cells more easily than electrically charged ions. In addition, the permeability of cell membranes to certain substances varies from one type of cell to another. Even in the same cell, the permeability may vary from one moment to another. Thus, a given substance may pass freely through the cell membranes of one type of cell but not another, or it may pass through a cell membrane at one time, but be held back at another.

Some of the mechanisms by which substances move through cell membranes will be explained later in the chapter. Before considering these mechanisms, however, it is necessary to understand how molecules move from place to place and what determines the direction of their movement.

5-19 Diffusion

The molecules of gases and liquids are in constant motion. They move in all directions in straight lines until they collide with other molecules or the walls of their container. Collisions send them off in new directions so that their paths zigzag. As a result of this motion, the molecules of a substance tend to spread away from a region in which they are more concentrated to surrounding regions in which they are less concen-

Frontier of Biology

The Endosymbiotic Theory

The original theory of evolution stated that organisms compete for survival, and the most "fit" survive to reproduce. Lynn Margulis (shown above) has proposed a modification of this theory for the evolution of early cells. She hypothesizes that cells lacking membrane-bound organelles evolved into nucleated cells by means of symbiosis —living together for mutual benefit; that cooperation was as important as competition.

This theory, the endosymbiotic theory, proposes that the amount of atmospheric oxygen began to increase from the photosynthesis of early blue-green algae. This produced a crisis for organisms that had evolved in an oxygen-free environment.

Certain bacteria were able to metabolize oxygen, others were not. Some bacteria unable to use oxygen absorbed oxygen-users, creating hybrid cells. Eventually the internalized bacteria evolved into mitochondria, and from this association, true nucleated cells arose. Some hybrid cells also absorbed blue-green algae that evolved into chloroplasts, and nucleated plant cells arose. The fact that mitochondria and chloroplasts contain their own DNA, RNA, and ribosomes supports this theory.

trated (see Figure 5-15). For example, if some instant coffee is placed at the bottom of a glass of hot water, a concentrated solution of coffee will form first near the bottom. However, the coffee molecules will gradually spread upward through the liquid. Similarly, if a perfume bottle is opened in one corner of a room, molecules of perfume will evaporate into the air near the bottle. At first, the odor will be noticeable only in the vicinity of the bottle. Eventually, the odor will spread to all parts of the room. Both of these examples illustrate the process of diffusion. **Diffusion** (dih-*fyoo*-zhun) is the movement of molecules or particles from an area of greater concentration to an area of lesser concentration. Diffusion occurs simply because the molecules are in constant random motion.

The difference in concentration between a region of greater concentration and a region of lesser concentration is called the **concentration gradient** (kahn-sen-*tray*-shun *gray*-dee-ent). Diffusion occurs only if there is a concentration gradient. As a result of diffusion the molecules eventually become evenly distributed throughout the available space. At this point no further change in concentration occurs. The molecules are still in motion, but there are now as many molecules moving out of any given area as are moving into the area. Such a situation is called an *equilibrium* (ee-kwuh-*lib*-ree-um). In the example with instant coffee in hot water, equlibrium is reached when every drop of water in the glass contains the same amount of coffee.

Diffusion is important in the movement of molecules into and out of cells. Depending on the concentration gradient, certain materials will either enter or leave cells by diffusion. Let us consider the role of diffusion in a cell that is using oxygen and producing carbon dioxide during respiration.

Both oxygen and carbon dioxide will be in solution inside the cell and also in the liquid medium surrounding the cell membrane. As the cell uses the oxygen dissolved in its cytoplasm, the concentration of oxygen inside the cell will decrease. The concentration outside the cell will at first not be affected. Therefore a concentration gradient toward the inside of the cell will develop across the cell membrane. As a result, there will be a net diffusion of oxygen into the cell. The opposite situation will develop with respect to carbon dioxide. As the cell produces carbon dioxide, its concentration inside the cell increases, while its concentration outside remains the same. Therefore a concentration gradient for carbon dioxide develops across the cell membrane toward the outside of the cell. A net diffusion of carbon dioxide out of the cell occurs. If the concentration gradients of oxygen and carbon dioxide were reversed, then oxygen would leave the cell and carbon dioxide would enter. Thus, the process of diffusion plays an important role in the entry and exit of molecules in living cells. It should be noted that many different substances may be diffusing through the cell membrane at the same time.

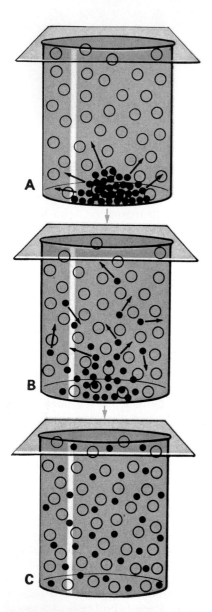

Figure 5-15. Diffusion. The substance indicated by black dots initially is present in high concentration only at the bottom of the beaker (top). With time the molecules of the substance diffuse into other regions of the beaker (middle). Eventually, the substance becomes evenly distributed throughout the available space (bottom).

5-20   Facilitated Diffusion

Some molecules diffuse through cell membranes at a faster rate than can be explained by diffusion alone. There is evidence that some of the proteins in the cell membrane have hollow centers that act as channels through the membrane. By twisting in one direction or the other, these protein channels may open wider or close down. When the channels are open, certain molecules are able to diffuse quickly through them. This process, which apparently involves temporary openings or pores in the cell membrane, is called **facilitated** (fuh-*sil*-uh-tay-ted) **diffusion.** Facilitated diffusion works only in the direction of the concentration gradient. It speeds up the normal movement of molecules from a region of higher concentration to one of lower concentration.

5-21   Osmosis

Up to this point we have been considering the diffusion of substances dissolved in water. A water solution is simply a mixture of water molecules and molecules of the dissolved substance, the solute. Water molecules are small. They can pass freely through a semipermeable membrane, just as other small molecules do. Therefore, water itself will diffuse through cell membranes. The direction of this diffusion will depend only on the difference in concentration of water on opposite sides of the membrane. The diffusion of water across a semipermeable membrane from a region of high concentration of water to a region of low concentration of water is called **osmosis** (os-*moh*-sis).

What do we mean by the "concentration" of water? The meaning is the same as for any other substance—it is the amount of water present in a given volume. Since two things cannot occupy the same space at the same time, the number of particles dissolved in a given amount of water determines the concentration of water molecules present. The concentration of water molecules is highest in pure water—water with nothing else in it. The more particles dissolved in a solution, the fewer the water molecules present in a given volume. For example, the concentration of water is higher in 100 ml of pure water than it is in 100 ml of a water and sugar solution.

Figure 5-16 shows an experiment that demonstrates osmosis. The glass bulb of a thistle tube is filled with a concentrated sugar solution. The bulb is then tightly covered with a semipermeable membrane of cellophane or sausage tubing, and placed in a jar of pure water. The membrane has pores through which the water molecules, but not the sugar molecules, can pass. The water concentration in the jar is 100 percent. The water concentration in the thistle tube is lower because the sugar solution contains fewer water molecules than the same volume of pure water. Since the water molecules can pass through the membrane, they move from

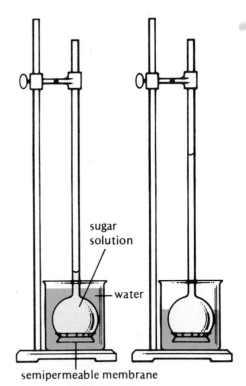

sugar solution

water

semipermeable membrane

Figure 5-16. Demonstration of Effects of Osmosis. A thistle tube containing a concentrated sugar solution and covered with a semipermeable membrane is put in a beaker of pure water (left). The sugar molecules cannot pass through the semipermeable membrane, but the water molecules can. Water enters the thistle tube by osmosis, and the solution rises in the tube (right).

the area of higher concentration (the jar of pure water) to the area of lower concentration (the sugar solution in the thistle tube). As osmosis occurs, the level of liquid in the thistle tube rises.

5-22   Osmotic Pressure

In the osmosis experiment in Figure 5-16, the water eventually stops rising in the thistle tube. The reason for this is that rates of diffusion depend on pressure as well as concentration. If the difference in pressure between the two sides of the membrane increases, the rate of diffusion of water from the high-pressure side to the low-pressure side increases. As the water-sugar solution rises in the thistle tube, its weight results in increased pressure on the inside of the membrane. This increasing pressure causes the water to diffuse back across the membrane at a faster rate. Finally, an equilibrium is reached. Water molecules are still passing into the thistle tube because of the concentration gradient across the membrane. But they are passing out at the same rate because of the pressure gradient in the opposite direction. Thus there is no net change in the amount of water inside the thistle tube, and the water level in the tube remains constant. There is, however, a steady excess of pressure inside the thistle tube. This increased pressure resulting from osmosis is called **osmotic** (os-*mah*-tik) **pressure.**

5-23   Effects of Osmosis

The cytoplasm of cells consists mainly of water containing a wide variety of dissolved substances. Water can pass freely through the cell membrane in both directions. Whether there is a net movement of water into or out of the cell depends on the concentration gradient—whether there is a higher concentration of water on one side of the cell membrane than the other. Let us consider what happens to cells placed in solutions containing different concentrations of water (see Figure 5-17).

An **isotonic** (i-suh-*tahn*-ik) **solution** is one that has the same concentration of dissolved substances as a living cell placed in it. The concentration of water molecules in the cell and in an isotonic solution is the same. Since the concentration gradient is zero, there is no net gain or loss of water by the cell.

A **hypotonic** (hy-puh-*tahn*-ik) **solution** contains a lower concentration of dissolved substances than the cell. The concentration of water molecules is therefore higher in the hypotonic solution than it is in the cell. Since the concentration of water is higher outside the cell than inside, there is a net movement of water into the cell by osmosis. Animal cells swell and burst when placed in a hypotonic solution because of the osmotic pressure produced by the water that enters. When a plant cell is placed in a hypotonic solution, the excess water collects in the large vacuole, which swells to fill most of the interior of

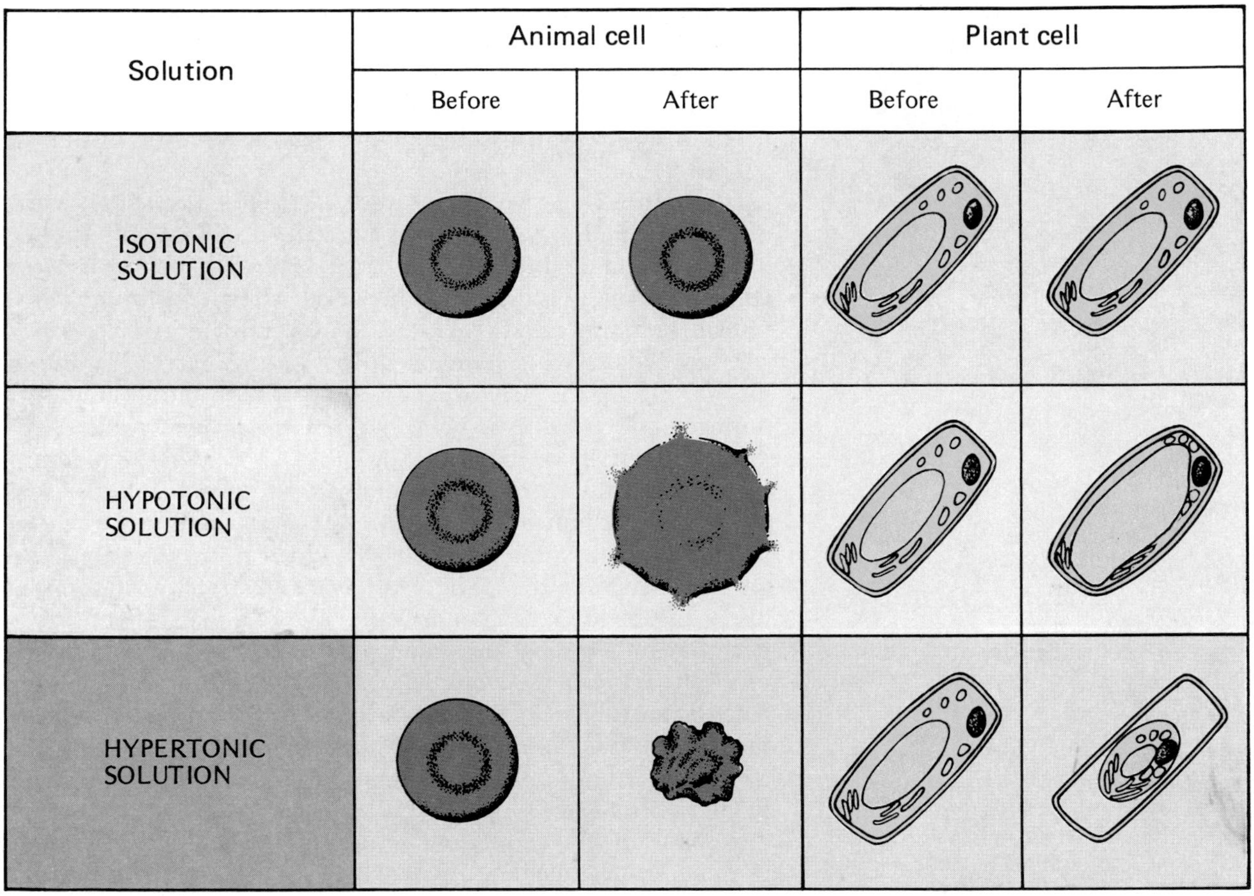

Solution	Animal cell		Plant cell	
	Before	After	Before	After
ISOTONIC SOLUTION				
HYPOTONIC SOLUTION				
HYPERTONIC SOLUTION				

the cell. The rest of the cell contents are pushed against the strong, but flexible cell wall. This pressure in a plant cell is called **turgor** (*ter*-ger) **pressure.**

A **hypertonic** (hy-per-*tahn*-ik) **solution** contains a higher concentration of dissolved substances than the cell. The concentration of water molecules in a hypertonic solution is therefore lower than that in the cell. The concentration gradient results in a net movement of water out of the cell. Animal cells shrink when placed in a hypertonic solution; in plant cells the vacuole collapses, causing the cytoplasm to shrink within the cell wall. The shrinking of cytoplasm by osmosis is called **plasmolysis** (plaz-*mah*-luh-sis).

5-24   Passive and Active Transport

In diffusion and osmosis, no cellular energy is used to move substances into or out of the cell. Because these processes move materials across cell membranes without the expenditure of cellular energy, they are called **passive transport.** Numerous substances move into and out of the cell by passive transport, with the direction of movement determined only by the concentration gradient.

Figure 5-17. Effects of Osmosis on Living Cells. Cells placed in an isotonic solution neither gain nor lose water. In a hypotonic solution animal cells swell and burst; the vacuoles of plant cells swell, pushing cell contents out against the cell wall. In a hypertonic solution, animal cells shrink; plant cell vacuoles collapse.

Figure 5-18. Concentration Gradients.
A bicycle can roll downhill by itself, without any outside source of energy. Particles moving down a concentration gradient also need no outside supply of energy. A bicycle cannot roll uphill by itself. Energy must be supplied by an outside source. The same is true for particles moving against a concentration gradient—energy must be supplied from an outside source.

When the movement of materials across a cell membrane requires the expenditure of cellular energy, the process is called **active transport**. Active transport usually involves the movement of materials against a concentration gradient, that is, from an area of lower concentration to an area of higher concentration.

In Figure 5-18, we have used a hill to represent a concentration gradient. The top of the hill represents the higher concentration, and the bottom of the hill represents the lower concentration. A bicycle moving downhill along the concentration gradient needs no outside source of energy to keep rolling. This is what happens in passive transport. To move the bicycle up the hill, or against the concentration gradient, requires energy. This is what happens in active transport.

Active transport makes it possible for cells to maintain internal conditions that are chemically different from the surrounding medium. For example, in a nerve cell, the concentration of potassium is higher inside the cell than in the medium outside the cell. The concentration of sodium is lower inside the cell than outside. The cell uses active transport to maintain these differences in concentration. As another example, certain seaweeds accumulate minerals, such as potassium and iodine, in their cells in concentrations that are a thousand times the concentrations in ocean water. In humans and many other animals, wastes are removed from the blood by active transport.

We do not yet know how active transport works. There is evidence that specific proteins in the cell membrane can transport certain molecules against a concentration gradient. This process, however, requires energy. It must therefore be coupled in some way to the production of energy in the cell.

ORGANIZATION OF CELLS IN LIVING THINGS

Objective:
>   Describe and compare the levels of organization and specialization in unicellular, colonial, and multicellular organisms.

5-25   Unicellular and Colonial Organisms

A cell, which is the smallest unit showing the characteristics of life, may exist alone, or it may be part of a larger organism made up of many cells. A cell that exists independently is regarded as a one-celled, or *unicellular, organism.* Many-celled, or *multicellular, organisms* may be made up of hundreds, thousands, millions, or billions of cells.

Unicellular organisms are able to carry on all the life processes. They synthesize and obtain nutrients, break them down for energy, synthesize new materials, reproduce, and so on. Unicellular organisms include bacteria, protozoa, many algae, and some fungi. These organisms vary widely in size and in complexity of structure.

The simplest level of multicellular organization occurs in *colonial organisms* which consist of from a few cells to thousands of cells attached together. In some colonies, the cells are all alike, and each cell carries on all its own processes. Such colonies are like a group of unicellular organisms that are stuck together. Any of the cells has the capacity to reproduce and form a new colony.

In some complex colonies, the cells show some specialization. That is, the cells forming the colony vary in their structure and function. For example, *Volvox*, an alga, forms spherical colonies that can include many thousands of cells (see Figure 5-19). However, only about twenty of these cells are capable of reproducing and forming new colonies. These are large cells found at the back of the colony. In the front of the colony are smaller cells containing large, light-sensitive organelles. These cells control the positioning and movement of the colony in the water. The cells of a *Volvox* colony are connected together by thin strands of cytoplasm that run between them.

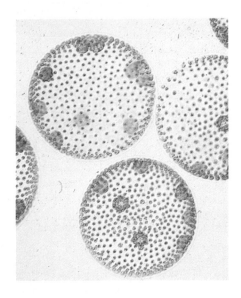

Figure 5-19. *Volvox* Colonies.

5-26. True Multicellular Organisms

Cells. True multicellular organisms can consist of from hundreds to billions of cells of many different types. Because these cells are specialized, they cannot function as independent, single-celled organisms, each performing all the possible life functions. Rather, they carry out only some of their own life processes, while accomplishing the specific whole-organism functions for which each cell is specialized. Therefore, cells of each type must depend on cells of all the other types, leading to many levels of multicellular organization and interaction.

Tissues. In multicellular organisms, a group of cells that are structurally similar and perform the same function forms a **tissue.** Each cell in a tissue carries on its own life processes, but it also carries on some special processes related to the function of the tissue. In plants there are tissues that transport water and nutrients throughout the plant, tissues that cover and protect the parts of the plant, tissues that contain chloroplasts and carry on photosynthesis, and so on. The structures and functions of plant tissues are discussed in Chapter 18 (page 298). Complex multicellular animals contain a greater variety of tissues than plants, and many of these tissues are more highly specialized than plant tissues.

Table 5-1 lists the main types of tissues found in animals. Most animal tissues are a form of either epithelial tissue or connective tissue. Muscle, nerve, and blood are highly specialized tissues that do not belong to either of these groups.

Epithelial tissues cover body surfaces and line body cavities and organs. They also form glands. They are generally in the form of sheets of closely packed cells (see Figure 5-20). The

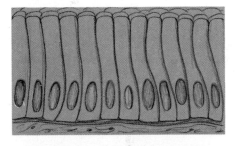

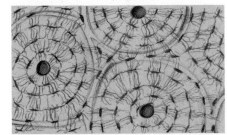

Figure 5-20. Animal Tissues. Shown above are examples of epithelial (top), bone (middle), and skeletal muscle (bottom) tissues.

Type of tissue	Structure	Functions	Location
Epithelium (epithelial tissue)	Cells arranged in sheets one or more cell layers in thickness	Protection (outer layer of skin) Absorption (inner lining of intestine) Secretion (glands)	Lines cavities Covers surfaces Forms glands
Connective tissue	Consists of cells and fibers embedded in a formless "ground sub-substance," or matrix	Support of other tissues, including epithelium, and of organs Connects or binds tissues and organs together	Throughout body
Adipose tissue	Specialized ovoid fat cells in connective tissue fibers	Adipose connective tissue stores fat	Throughout body; found in large numbers in some areas
Bone and cartilage	Consists of cells and fibers embedded in a formless "ground sub-substance," or matrix	Bone and cartilage are connective tissues that make up the skeleton. They support the body and give it form, and, with muscles, are responsible for movement.	Bone: found in skeleton Cartilage: found in skeleton, trachea, outer ear, nose
Blood	Specialized connective tissue—matrix is fluid	Transport of nutrients, wastes, oxygen, and carbon dioxide throughout body	Within vessels of the circulatory system
Nerve tissue	Consists of specialized cells, called neurons, which are bound together by connective tissue to form nerves	Conduction of impulses	Nerves and sense receptors throughout body
Muscle tissue	Individual cells or fused cells bound together by connective tissue to form bundles or sheets	Skeletal muscle: voluntary movement of body part	Skeletal muscles
		Smooth muscle: involuntary movement of internal organs	Internal organs
		Cardiac muscle: makes up heart and is responsible for beating of heart	Heart

Table 5-1. Types of Animal Tissues.

simplest epithelial tissues consist of sheets only one cell layer thick. More complex forms consist of several cell layers. Sheets of epithelial tissues generally rest on a network of fibers that form a *basement membrane*. The basement membrane supports the sheets of cells.

Connective tissues support other body tissues and bind tissues and organs together. They give the body form. In connective tissues, unlike epithelial tissues, the cells are widely separated. The space between them is filled with various types of substances. For example, in bone, the bone-producing cells secrete the hard, bony material, which fills the spaces between the cells. In tendons, which connect muscles to bones, there are dense bundles of tough elastic fibers.

Muscle tissues are specialized for contraction, or shortening. There are three types of muscle tissues. *Cardiac muscle* tissue is found only in the heart. *Skeletal muscle* tissue makes up the muscles that are attached to the bones of the skeleton. Movement of these muscles is under voluntary control by the animal. *Smooth muscle* tissue is found in various organs of the body, such as the stomach, intestine, and blood vessels. Contraction of smooth muscles is involuntary and automatic. (Skeletal and smooth muscle are discussed in Chapter 13.) The structure and function of blood is discussed in Chapter 10. The structure and function of nervous tissue is discussed in Chapter 14.

Organs and organ systems. A group of tissues that works together to perform a specific function forms an **organ.** The eye, which contains nerves, light-sensitive cells, muscles, and blood vessels, is an organ.

A group of organs that work together to perform a specific function forms an **organ system.** An example of an organ system is the digestive system, which includes the mouth, esophagus, stomach, intestines, pancreas, liver, etc.

Although the parts of a multicellular organism can be described in terms of separate cells, tissues, organs, and organ systems, all these parts must function together for the organism to carry on its life processes.

Chapter Review

SUMMARY

- Living things are composed of one or more cells. All cells are surrounded by a cell membrane that is selectively permeable. A rigid cell wall surrounds the cell membrane of the cells of plants and various micro-organisms. Except for bacteria and blue-green algae, all cells contain a distinct, membrane-bounded nucleus, which contains the hereditary material.

- Within the cytoplasm are specialized structures called organelles. These include the endoplasmic reticulum, ribosomes, Golgi bodies, lysosomes, mitochondria, microtubules, microfilaments, centrioles, cilia, flagella, vacuoles, and plastids.

- The movement of material through cell membranes takes place by diffusion and by processes involving active transport.

- Organisms are unicellular, colonial, or multicellular. In true multicellular organisms, cells are functionally and structurally specialized and are organized into tissues. Tissues are organized into organs. An organ system is a group of organs that work together for a specific function.

KNOW THE TERMS

active transport	cytoplasm	lysosome	osmotic pressure
cell	diffusion	microfilament	passive transport
cell membrane	endoplasmic reticulum	microtubule	phagocytosis
cell theory	epithelial tissue	mitochondrion	pinocytosis
cell wall	facilitated diffusion	muscle tissue	plasmolysis
centriole	flagellum	nucleolus	plastid
chloroplast	Golgi body	nucleus	ribosome
chromoplast	hypertonic solution	organ	selective permeability
cilium	hypotonic solution	organ system	tissue
concentration gradient	isotonic solution	organelle	turgor pressure
connective tissue	leucoplast	osmosis	vacuole

SECTION QUESTIONS

The Cell Theory

1. What instrument led to the discovery of cells?
2. How many cells make up an organism?
3. How do new cells arise?

Cell Structure

4. What structure separates the cell contents from the external environment?
5. What is one component of plant cell walls?
6. What is the function of the cell membrane?
7. How does the nuclear membrane differ from the cell membrane?
8. What structures within the nucleus contain the hereditary material of the cell?
9. Name the watery substance lying between the cell membrane and the nucleus.
10. Name the sites of protein synthesis in the cell?
11. Which organelle releases secretory products?
12. What is stored in lysosomes?
13. What is the organelle of cellular respiration?
14. What process are centrioles involved in?
15. List the structures involved with cell movement.
16. Name the three types of plastids.
17. What factors affect how easily a substance passes through a membrane?

Passage of Materials Through Cell Membranes

18. Define the term *diffusion.*
19. Define the term *osmosis.*
20. What term describes a solution in which cells lose water?
21. What process moves substances against a concentration gradient?

Organization of Cells in Living Things

22. What are colonial organisms?
23. List, from simple to complex, the levels of organization in multicellular organisms.

KNOW THE FACTS

Copy the numbers from Column 1 on a sheet of paper. Select the letter for the term or phrase from Column 2 that matches each numbered item, and write it beside the number.

Column 1

1. Schwann
2. Schleiden
3. cytoplasm
4. semipermeable
5. pinocytosis
6. nucleolus
7. endoplasmic reticulum
8. Golgi bodies
9. mitochondria
10. microtubules
11. microfilaments
12. vacuoles
13. isotonic
14. active transport
15. colonial organisms

Column 2

a. same concentration of substances as the cell
b. plants composed of cells
c. animals composed of cells
d. fluid-filled canals
e. folded membranes called cristae
f. fluid cell contents
g. produces ribosomes
h. cell skeleton of tubulin
i. selective
j. package cell products
k. taking in small particles
l. thread like organelles that contract
m. filled with cell sap
n. expends cellular energy
o. cells attached together
p. lower concentration of substances than cell

UNDERSTAND THE CONCEPTS

16. State the cell theory.
17. Explain the functions of the cell membrane.
18. Describe cell membrane structure.
19. Discuss nucleus structure and function.

20. Describe the structure and functions of smooth, and of rough, endoplasmic reticulum.
21. Explain how Golgi bodies are involved in secretory processes.
22. Describe how lysosomes are involved in preventing disease.
23. What is the significance of cristae in mitochondria?
24. Describe the structure and chemical make-up of microtubules.
25. Explain the functions of cilia and flagella.
26. What functions do vacuoles serve in plant cells, animal cells, and microorganisms?
27. Describe the internal structure of a chloroplast.
28. Explain how diffusion is dependent on a concentration gradient.
29. Explain the process of facilitated diffusion.
30. Explain how turgor pressure develops in a plant cell.
31. Explain why a cell placed in a highly concentrated solution will shrink.
32. Why is active transport important in maintaining a cell's chemical composition?

THINK CRITICALLY

33. Leeuwenhoek's microscopes were capable of magnifying objects nearly as well as many of today's microscopes on low power. If high school students can use these microscopes to identify cells as the smallest units of living things, why was Leeuwenhoek unable to identify cells in the same way?
34. What conditions are necessary to support the continuous passage of materials in and out of the cell by way of the cell membrane?
35. What important assumption is hidden in biologists' belief that living cells can only come from other living cells?
36. What factors might cause a change in cell permeability from time to time?
37. Compare and contrast the structure and function of mitochondria with the structure and function of chloroplasts.
38. The reproductive activity of a multicellular organism is restricted to only a small group of cells. How is this an advantage to the organism?

THINK CREATIVELY

39. Imagine that you have shrunk to the size of a large bacterium. Suggest a type of protective clothing to wear in order to enter a typical animal cell.
40. How might you go about entering the cell in question 39?

FOR FURTHER INVESTIGATION

1. Construct models that illustrate selective permeability, diffusion, and osmosis in cells. Use glass beakers, water, food coloring, starch, and small cellulose bags. Explain what you observe in terms of a molecular model.
2. Write a brief report on the life and scientific contributions of one of the following scientists:
   a. Libbie Hyman   c. Cornelia Clapp
   b. Ernest E. Just   d. Louis Pasteur
3. Prepare a report on one of the career opportunities listed below. See suggested procedures, p. 9, "For Further Investigation" Activity 3.
   a. Cytologist   c. Histologist
   b. Biology teacher

FOR FURTHER READING

Lake, J.A., "The Ribosome," *Scientific American,* August, 1981.
Nachmias, Vivianne T., "Microfilaments," (Carolina Biology Reader) Carolina Biological Supply, Burlington, NC, 1984.
Nomura, Masayasu, "The Control of Ribosome Synthesis," *Scientific American,* January, 1984.
Unwin, Nigel, and Henderson, Richard, "The Structure of Proteins in Biological Membranes," *Scientific American,* February, 1984.

Chapter 6

CLASSIFICATION OF LIVING THINGS

To classify organisms into a useful system, biologists must evaluate the importance of many similarities and differences.

CLASSIFICATION

Objectives:

1. Explain the function of classification systems.
2. Describe the history of taxonomy, including the works of Aristotle, Theophrastus, John Ray, and Carolus Linnaeus.
3. List in order from broadest to narrowest the classification categories used in modern biology.
4. Explain the system of nomenclature used in modern biology.
5. Describe how the theory of evolution and its supporting evidence have changed the science of taxonomy.
6. Explain how the modern view of a species differs from the earlier view.
7. Describe the types of evidence used by taxonomists to determine relationships between groups of organisms.

6-1 The Need for Classification

There are approximately 1.5 million different kinds of living organisms known today, and each year several thousand more are identified. Some experts believe that there may be as many as 10 million different kinds of organisms in existence. They vary in form from bacteria 5 micrometers in diameter to redwood trees over 100 meters tall.

To deal with this huge number of diverse organisms,

Figure 6-1. Organization in a Supermarket. Think of how long you could search for a single item if all the products in a supermarket were arranged randomly.

biologists identify and name them according to an established international system. This makes it much easier for scientists to communicate with one another about the types and characteristics of living things. The branch of biology that deals with the classification and naming of living things is **taxonomy** (tak-*sahn*-uh-mee).

6-2 Classification Systems

The function of any classification system is to allow you to find the object or information you are looking for without checking every item in a large group. In many situations that we deal with every day, objects or information is organized or classified into groups. To help you understand what is involved in classification, let us consider the arrangement of goods in a supermarket.

A large supermarket carries 7,000 to 10,000 items (see Figure 6-1). If these items were placed on the shelves at random, shopping for the week might take an entire day, or even longer. However, finding the items you need can be done in a relatively short time because related items are arranged together in groups. First, items are grouped into broad categories, such as frozen food, meat, produce, cleaning supplies, paper goods, and dairy products. Each of these departments is subdivided into a series of smaller related categories. For example, the frozen food department has separate sections for vegetables, juices, cakes, fish, TV dinners, and ice cream. Each of these sections is further subdivided. The ice cream section is divided into half-gallons, quarts, pints, and cups. Within each size range, the ice cream may be grouped by flavor.

Figure 6-2. An Early Classification System. Aristotle grouped organisms as air-dwellers, land-dwellers, and water-dwellers.

Once you are familiar with the organization of the supermarket, it is easy to locate a particular item. Or if the market manager gets a new kind of frozen cake, it is a simple matter to place it with the other frozen cakes. In a similar manner, the classification system used in modern biology enables biologists to identify an organism and place it in its proper group with related organisms.

6-3 Early Classification Schemes

In all early attempts at classification, living things were separated into two major groups—the plant kingdom and the animal kingdom. These two groups were then subdivided in various ways. In the Bible, for example, plants were divided into grasses, herbs, and trees, while animals were classified as fish, creeping creatures, fowl, beasts, and cattle.

In the 4th century B.C., the Greek philosopher Aristotle (*ar*-uh-stot-ul) made a study of animals; another philosopher, Theophrastus (thee-uh-*fras*-tus), studied plants. Aristotle grouped animals mainly according to the kind of environment in which they lived. Thus there were air-dwellers, land-dwellers, and water-dwellers (see Figure 6-2). Theophrastus grouped plants according to stem structure. Thus there were herbs with soft stems, shrubs with several woody stems, and trees with a single woody stem. Using these crude subdivisons of the plant and animal kingdoms, these two early scientists identified and classified more than 500 kinds of plants and 500 kinds of animals.

The classification systems of Aristotle and Theophrastus worked only for the relatively small number of organisms fa-

miliar to the people of Europe and the Mediterranean region. However, during the 1400s and 1500s, explorers from Europe returned home from their travels with many new types of organisms. The development of the microscope in the 1500s led to the discovery of many new organisms not visible to the unaided eye. As the number and kind of different known organisms increased, the need for a more effective classification system became clear.

The next major advance in classification was made in the mid-1600s by the English naturalist John Ray. In his travels through England and Europe, Ray identified and classified more than 18,000 different types of plants. He also classified the members of several different animal groups. Ray was the first to use the term **species** (*spee*-sheez) for each different kind of organism. Ray defined a species as a group of organisms that were structurally very similar and that passed these characteristics on to their offspring (see Figure 6-3). Closely related species were included together in a broader group called a **genus** (*jee*-nus) (plural, *genera*) (see Figure 6-4). Related genera were arranged, in turn, in still broader groups.

Figure 6-3. Varieties of Cats. The Persian cat (left), Siamese cat (center), and alley cat (right) all belong to the same species, *Felis domesticus.*

Figure 6-4. Closely Related Species of the Genus *Canis.* These animals belong to different, closely related species, but to the same genus. (A) The German shepherd dog is *Canis familiaris;* (B) the wolf is *Canis lupus;* (C) the coyote is *Canis latrans;* and (D) the dingo is *Canis dingo.*

A

B

C

D

Figure 6-5. Categories in the Modern Classification System.

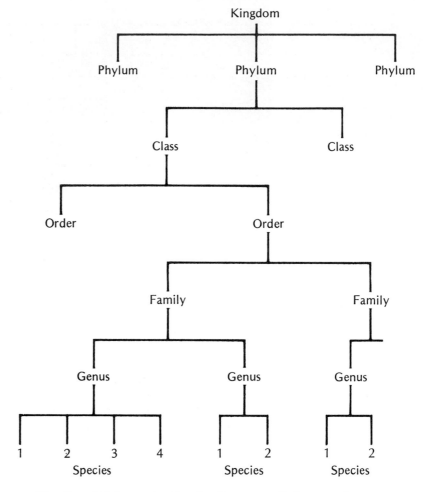

The Swedish botanist Carolus Linnaeus (luh-*nee*-us) is generally recognized as the founder of modern taxonomy. Linnaeus established methods for classifying and naming organisms that are still used. In his highly workable system, plants and animals were arranged in such a way that they could be identified easily. Like Ray, Linnaeus used structural similarities as a basis for his classification system.

6-4   Classification Categories

Between the time of Linnaeus and the present, taxonomists have added several categories to the classification system. The broadest and most inclusive category is the kingdom. The narrowest category is the species. In classifying living things, biologists generally use the following categories: **kingdom, phylum** (*fy*-lum) (plural, *phyla*), **class, order, family, genus,** and **species.**

As shown in Figure 6-5, related species are grouped in a genus; related genera are grouped in a family; related families are grouped in an order; related orders are grouped in a class; related classes are grouped in a phylum; and related phyla are grouped in a kingdom. Each species—that is, each type of

Category	Human	Chimpanzee	Dandelion	Housefly
KINGDOM	Animalia	Animalia	Plantae	Animalia
PHYLUM	Chordata	Chordata	Tracheophyta	Arthropoda
CLASS	Mammalia	Mammalia	Angiospermae	Insecta
ORDER	Primates	Primates	Asterales	Diptera
FAMILY	Hominidae	Pongidae	Compositae	Muscidae
GENUS	*Homo*	*Pan*	*Taraxacum*	*Musca*
SPECIES	*Homo sapiens*	*Pan troglodytes*	*Taraxacum officinale*	*Musca domestica*

organism—belongs to one kingdom, one phylum, one class, one order, one family, and one genus. Table 6-1 shows the complete classification for several different species.

Table 6-1. Classification of Some Familiar Organisms.

6-5 Nomenclature

The system for naming organisms is called **nomenclature** (*noh*-men-klay-chur). The modern system for naming organisms was devised by Linnaeus. Before Linnaeus, each species was identified by its genus name followed by a number of Latin words that described the species. In some cases a string of eight or ten words followed the genus name. In his books, Linnaeus identified each species by its genus name followed by only one descriptive word, both in Latin. Within each genus, no two species could be described by the same word. This is the system that is still in use.

This two-word system of identifying each kind of organism is known as **binomial** (by-*noh*-mee-ul) ("two names") **nomenclature.** It is equivalent to our system of using two names to identify a person—a family name and a given (or first) name. The genus name is like a person's family, or last, name, while the species name is like his or her first name.

In modern biology, each kind of organism has a two-word Latin name, which is its scientific name. The first word is its genus name, the second identifies the species within that genus. Most large plants and animals also have common names. However, for several reasons these names are not suitable for scientific use. For one thing, common names are often confusing and inexact. A starfish, for example, is not a fish. Also, one species may have several different common names. The blue jay *Cyanocitta christata* is also known as the blue coat, the corn thief, and the nest robber. In other cases, the same common name is used for two or more different species. More than a dozen different species of plants are commonly known as raspberries. Finally, common names vary from language to language. An English "dog" is a Spanish "perro" and a Japanese "inu." However, the scientific name *Canis familiaris* is understood by biologists everywhere.

Figure 6-6. Fossil and Modern Brittle Star. Fossilized animals and plants enable biologists to trace the changes in groups of organisms over long periods of time.

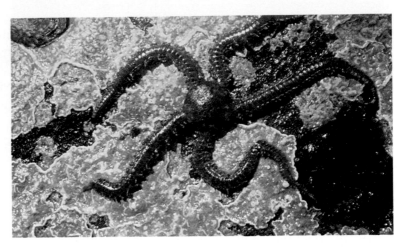

6-6 Modern Taxonomy

Until the mid-1800s, most scientists viewed each species as a constant and unchanging form. The description of a species was based on a single specimen, called a *type specimen*, that served as the standard for that species. Variations from the type specimen were considered to be of little significance. Today, variations in a species are known to be important for the species' survival.

This fact was recognized after the theory of **evolution** was proposed in 1859, then supported by a continually growing body of evidence. The theory states that over long periods of time, a species either changes in response to conditions in the environment or becomes extinct. (The mechanisms for these events are discussed in detail in Unit 6.)

Today, a species is defined as a natural group, or *population,* of similar organisms that interbreed in nature. If the members of a species become separated into groups that breed independently for long periods of time, each group will evolve differently, depending on the opportunities and demands of the particular environment. Eventually, the separated groups may become so different that they must be classified as different species.

The theory of evolution has greatly enriched the science of taxonomy. Today's taxonomists know that similar, related species share a common ancestor species at some point in their evolution. Related genera share a common ancestor much earlier in their evolution. Therefore, taxonomists base their classifications on more than structural similarity. They also consider biochemical similarities such as the amino acid sequence of certain proteins, patterns of embryonic development, behavior, and the study of fossils (see Figure 6-6).

Despite the progress that has been made in taxonomy, there are still challenging problems to be solved. Many of these involve the simplest living things, especially the microorganisms. These life forms often show such diversity that they cannot be categorized as easily as larger, complex forms. The next section of this chapter explains how taxonomists have coped with some major classification problems.

MAJOR TAXONOMIC GROUPS

Objectives:
1. Name the five kingdoms used in classification in this book, and give a brief description of each.
2. Explain the use of a taxonomic key.

6-7 Kingdoms of Organisms

In all early classification schemes, living things were divided into two major groups, or kingdoms—plants and animals. This system works well with large organisms. Trees, grass, flowers, and shrubs are obviously plants, while frogs, fish, insects, birds, and cats are obviously animals. However, some organisms show both plantlike and animal-like characteristics. The euglena, for example, is a unicellular organism that carries on photosynthesis like a plant, yet it is *motile*—it moves from place to place like an animal. The euglena presents a problem in classification.

To solve the problem of classifying organisms that are not distinctly animals or plants, taxonomists have added new kingdoms to the modern classification systems. However, there is not universal agreement about how many additional kingdoms are needed and which organisms should be placed in them. Each possible arrangement has some advantages and some disadvantages. There does not seem to be a completely satisfactory way to classify the simplest organisms.

Table 6-2. Organization of the Five-Kingdom Classification System.

CHARACTERISTICS OF THE FIVE KINGDOMS*					
Characteristics	Monera	Protista	Fungi	Plantae	Animalia
Cell wall	Present (peptidoglycan)	Present in some (substance varies)	Present (chitin)	Present (cellulose)	Absent
Nuclear membrane	Absent	Present	Present	Present	Present
Mitochondria	Absent	Present	Present	Present	Present
Ability to perform photosynthesis	Some do	Some do	No	Yes	No
Ability to move from place to place	Some motile, some not	Some motile, some not	No	No	Yes
Body form	Unicellular	Unicellular or multicellular	Unicellular or multicellular	Unicellular or multicellular	Multicellular
Reproductive structures	Unicellular	Unicellular	Multicellular	Multicellular	Multicellular
Nutrition	Absorption, photosynthesis, or chemosynthesis	Absorption, photosynthesis, or ingestion	Absorption	Photosynthesis	Ingestion
Nervous system	Absent	Absent	Absent	Absent	Present

*In the four-kingdom system, the fungi are classified as plants. In the three-kingdom system, some protists are classified as animals, while the rest of the protists and the fungi are classified as plants.

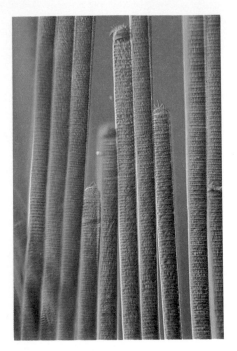

Figure 6-7. An Example from the Kingdom Monera. Blue-green algae of the genus *Oscillatoria* form chains of connected cells.

In this book we use a five-kingdom system of classification. The five kingdoms are Monera, Protista, Fungi, Plantae, and Animalia. This system emphasizes certain very basic differences among large groups of organisms. It also simplifies somewhat the classification within the kingdoms. The general characteristics of the five kingdoms are described briefly in the following sections (also see Table 6-2).

6-8   Kingdom Monera

Members of the kingdom **Monera** (muh-*ner*-uh) are mostly unicellular, although some types form chains, clusters, or colonies of connected cells. Moneran cells are radically different from all other cells. They do not have an organized nucleus with a nuclear membrane. They lack most organelles, such as mitochondria, lysosomes, and Golgi bodies, found in other cells. They have cell walls, but these are chemically different from the cell walls of plants.

The kingdom Monera includes only two phyla—bacteria and blue-green algae (*al*-jee). Most bacteria do not carry on photosynthesis and must absorb nutrients from the environment. Blue-green algae contain chlorophyll and carry on photosynthesis (see Figure 6-7). However, this chlorophyll is not contained in chloroplasts.

6-9   Kingdom Protista

Members of the kingdom **Protista** (proh-*tist*-uh) are either unicellular or very simple multicellular organisms (see Figure 6-8). Protist cells have a structure like the cells of more complex organisms. They contain a membrane-bound nucleus and different types of cell organelles. There are different types of protists. Some are *algae* that resemble plant cells with cell walls and chlorophyll in chloroplasts. Some are motile *protozoa* that resemble animals whose cells lack chlorophyll and cell walls. Some are like the fungi (described in paragraph 6-10). Some, like the euglena, contain chlorophyll and carry on photosynthesis, yet they move around like protozoa.

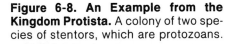

Figure 6-8. An Example from the Kingdom Protista. A colony of two species of stentors, which are protozoans.

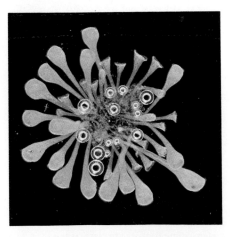

6-10   Kingdom Fungi

In the past, members of the kingdom **Fungi** (*fun*-jy) (singular, *fungus*) were placed in the plant kingdom because they resemble plants more than animals (see Figure 6-9). However, major differences between fungi and plants have led most biologists to place fungi in a separate kingdom. Fungi contain no chlorophyll and cannot synthesize food. Instead, they secrete enzymes that digest food particles outside the organism, then they *absorb* the nutrients. Some fungi are unicellular, while others have unusual multicellular forms. Fungi have cell organelles and distinct nuclei surrounded by nuclear membranes. When fungi have cell walls, they are chemically different from plant cell walls.

Figure 6-9. An Example from the Kingdom Fungi. Chicken-of-the-woods is a brightly colored fungus.

6-11 Kingdom Plantae

The plants, members of the kingdom **Plantae** (*plan*-tee), include the green, brown, and red algae, and the mosses, liverworts, and vascular plants (see Figure 6-10). Except for the algae, plants show a true tissue and organ level of organization. Plants cannot move around from place to place on their own. Nearly all plants carry on photosynthesis. The chlorophyll in plant cells is found in chloroplasts.

6-12 Kingdom Animalia

Animals, members of the kingdom **Animalia** (an-uh-*mal*-yuh), generally show an organ and organ system level of organization. During at least some part of their life cycle, most animals can move about from place to place on their own. Animals cannot carry on photosynthesis, so they must obtain

Figure 6-10. Examples from the Kingdoms Plantae and Animalia. The daisy is a plant, while the katydid is an insect, a member of the animal kingdom.

COMPARISON OF PLANTS AND ANIMALS.		
Characteristic	Plants	Animals
nutrition	Most are autotrophs—photosynthetic	Heterotrophs—nutrients from the environment
motility	Nonmotile	Usually motile during at least one stage of development
cell structure	Cell wall, chloroplasts, and large vacuoles present; centrioles lacking	Lack cell wall, chloroplasts, and large vacuoles; small vacuoles and centrioles present
body structure	Only a few types of organs present; no organ systems	Many types of organs present; organs organized into organ systems
growth pattern	Rate of growth and shape of organism depend on environmental conditions and vary within wide limits	Size and shape of adult closely regulated and vary within narrow limits
sensitivity	Lack nervous system or specialized sensory organs; responses to stimuli are slow and limited	Nervous system and sensory organs present; very responsive to stimuli

Table 6-3. Characteristics of Plants and Animals.

food from the environment. Most animals search actively for food. Their body plans support this activity, with the sense organs, brain, and mouth concentrated at one end of the body. Many types of animals have highly specialized sensory systems, well-developed brains, and nerve-muscle systems that permit complex types of behavior. Sexual reproduction is more common in animals than asexual reproduction. In some species, there is specialized courtship behavior, and there may be extensive parental care of the young.

The characteristics of plants and animals are shown in Table 6-3. A more complete list of all the taxonomic groups is found on page 725-728.

6-13   Taxonomic Keys

A **taxonomic key** is a tool used to identify and classify organisms. Most keys are *dichotomous*. They consist of a series of *paired* statements, each describing a certain characteristic. These characteristics are generally the presence or absence of certain structures that are easily seen or measured, like the presence or absence of bone, or the number of legs present. As an example of such characteristics, an animal may or may not have a spinal column. If it has a spinal column, it may or may not have fins or gills. If fins or gills are absent, its body may or may not be covered with scales, and so on. By choosing from such a series of paired characteristics, an unknown organism can be identified. Of course, it is necessary to arrange each set of choices in proper order so that each step produces smaller and smaller groupings. Table 6-4 is an example of a taxonomic key for identifying *vertebrates*, animals with backbones.

KEY FOR CLASSIFYING VERTEBRATE ANIMALS		
1	1A.	Spinal column present . . . go to 2.
	1B.	Spinal column absent . . . Invertebrate.
2	2A.	Fins and gills present . . . Fish.
	2B.	Fins and gills absent . . . go to 3.
3	3A.	Scales present . . . Reptile.
	3B.	Scales absent . . . go to 4.
4	4A.	Feathers present . . . Bird.
	4B.	Feathers absent . . . go to 5.
5	5A.	Hair or fur present . . . Mammal.
	4B.	Hair or fur absent . . . Amphibian.

Table 6-4. A Sample Taxonomic Key.

6-14 Representative Heterotrophic Organisms

As we saw in Chapter 1, all living things carry on the life processes of nutrition, respiration, transport, excretion, and regulation. Size greatly influences how an organism carries out these processes. The cells of single-celled and small multicellular organisms are in close contact with their environment. Because they are small, they can carry on their life processes in a simple fashion. However, as animals become larger, most of the cells are not in contact with the environment. In these animals, the life functions are carried out by groups of organs that are arranged in systems.

In Unit 2, you will study how certain *heterotrophs*, organisms that must obtain food from the environment, solve the problems of life. Since we cannot consider every organism, we will study six *representative organisms*. Two of these, the *ameba* and *paramecium*, are protozoa—unicellular protists that ingest their food as animals do (see Figure 6-11). The others are animals: the hydra, the earthworm, the grasshopper (see Figure 6-12), and the human.

The ameba and paramecium are common inhabitants of ponds and streams. They carry out their life processes within a single cell. They are very small but can be seen with the unaided eye. Under the microscope, the ameba appears as a transparent mass that constantly changes shape. It has cytoplasm with a cell membrane and a nucleus. In ameboid locomotion, a creeping movement is produced by the flowing of cytoplasm into temporary structures called pseudopods.

The paramecium is easily recognized because of its slipper-like shape. It contains two nuclei. The larger macronucleus controls the general cell activities. The smaller micronucleus is involved chiefly in reproduction. The paramecium is surrounded by a stiff cell membrane called the pellicle through which

A

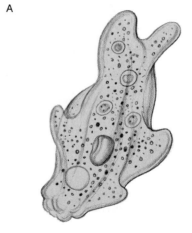

B

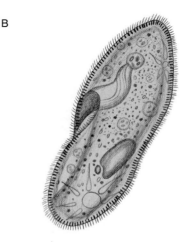

Figure 6-11. Representative Protozoa. The ameba (A) and paramecium (B) are protists that resemble animals.

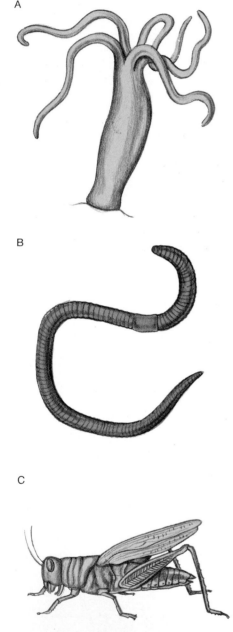

A

B

C

Figure 6-12. Representative Animals.
The hydra (A), the earthworm (B), and the grasshopper (C) show different levels of complexity in their body structures and processes.

numerous hairlike cilia project. The paramecium swims by means of its cilia. On one side of the paramecium is a depression, the oral groove, which terminates in a tubular gullet. Both these structures are involved in nutrition. Undigested material is discharged from the cell through the anal pore.

The *hydra* belongs to the phylum *Coelenterata.* It is about 5 mm long and lives in fresh water, usually attached to an underwater plant or some other solid object. The hydra has a tubelike body with only one opening, a mouth. The mouth is surrounded by tentacles which lead into the gastrovascular cavity. The body wall is composed of only two cell layers, an outer ectoderm and an inner endoderm. In its structure and function, the hydra is a relatively simple animal.

The *earthworm* belongs to the phylum *Annelida.* Its long, round body is separated into segments. The earthworm has a well-developed digestive system, circulatory system, excretory organs, and a well defined nervous system.

The grasshopper belongs to the class *Insecta* of the phylum *Anthropoda.* The grasshopper has a well-developed digestive system, an open circulatory system, respiratory system, excretory organs, and nervous system.

Human beings belong to the class *Mammalia* of the subphylum *Vertebrata* of the phylum *Chordata.* Mammals nourish their young with milk. Their bodies are covered with hair or fur. Many have well developed brains.

6-15   Other Useful Classification Schemes

For biologists, the five-kingdom system is the most basic, commonly used classification system. However, there are other ways of classifying organisms that are useful for specific purposes. For example, when we study interrelationships among organisms in a particular environment, we may group organisms as food producers, consumers, or decomposers. Consumers may be subdivided into omnivores, herbivores, and carnivores. Carnivores may be either predators or scavengers (see page 675).

For agricultural purposes, we may label organisms as beneficial organisms or pests, edible or inedible, domestic or wild. As we consider how animals respond to daily and seasonal temperature changes, we may contrast warm-blooded and cold-blooded animals (see page 600). When we are concerned with health and disease issues, we may group all disease-producing organisms together.

All these groupings are useful upon occasion, but none of them is as thorough and detailed as the five-kingdom system. More important, only the biologist's taxonomy arranges organisms into groups that reflect hereditary relationships and the evolutionary history of living organisms.

Chapter Review

SUMMARY

- All living things are named and placed in categories according to an established international classification system.

- The system of classification established by Linnaeus was based on structural similarities among related organisms. Linnaeus named each species with a genus name followed by a single descriptive species name. His system of binomial nomenclature is still in use.

- Each species belongs to one kingdom, one phylum, one class, one order, one family, and one genus. Related species are grouped in a genus; related genera in a family; related families in an order, and so forth.

- The theory of evolution has resulted in major changes in modern taxonomy. Species are now defined in terms of interbreeding populations rather than as type specimens. In addition to structural similarities, taxonomists now base their classifications on similarities in biochemistry, embryonic development, behavior, and fossils.

- The kingdoms of the five-kingdom system of classification are: Monera, which includes bacteria and blue-green algae; Protista, which includes the protozoa and some of the algae; Fungi; Plantae, which includes mosses, liverworts, vascular plants, and red, brown, and green algae; and Animalia.

KNOW THE TERMS

Animalia	Fungi	nomenclature	Protista
binomial nomenclature	genus	order	species
class	kingdom	phylum	taxonomic key
evolution	Monera	Plantae	taxonomy
family			

SECTION QUESTIONS

Classification

1. Name the branch of biology that deals with the classification and naming of organisms.
2. What is the function of a classification system?
3. Who was the founder of modern taxonomy?
4. List the modern classification categories from the narrowest to the broadest.
5. What is the name of the system used by Linnaeus for naming organisms?
6. What is the modern definition of a species?
7. When classifying organisms what factors must today's taxonomists consider and why?

Major Taxonomic Groups

8. Name the five kingdoms.
9. Name the phyla that make up Monera.
10. Name several types of Protista.
11. Name two characteristics of fungi that distinguish them from plants.
12. What level of organization is shown by plants? By animals?
13. What is a taxonomic key used for?

KNOW THE FACTS

Copy the number of each sentence below on a sheet of paper. Beside each number, write the term(s) that complete(s) the sentence correctly.

1. Members of the kingdom_____ carry out photosynthesis and usually are not motile.
2. A _____ is a group of related phyla.
3. A_____ is an organism that must obtain its food from the environment.
4. The branch of biology called_____ deals

with the classification and naming of organisms.

5. A _____ is a group of structurally similar organisms.

6. _____ is a two-word system of naming each type of organism.

7. A _____ is a group of closely related species.

8. A _____ is a tool used to identify organisms.

UNDERSTAND THE CONCEPTS

9. On what basis did Carolus Linnaeus classify organisms?
10. Explain binomial nomenclature.
11. List the types of evidence used by modern taxonomists in determining relationships among different types of organisms.
12. Why have modern taxonomists added new kingdoms in their classification schemes?
13. What are the distinguishing characteristics of members of the kingdom Monera?
14. Describe the basic characteristics of the kingdom Protista.
15. Describe the basic characteristics of plants.
16. Describe the basic characteristics of animals.

THINK CRITICALLY

17. Of what value is it for a biologist to be able to place a previously unidentified organism in its proper group with related organisms?
18. How has the theory of evolution changed John Ray's definition of a species?
19. Under what circumstances might a biologist decide to use a three-kingdom rather than a five-kingdom system?
20. How has the adoption of modern classification systems changed Linnaeus's two-word system of identifying organisms?
21. Why has it been so difficult for biologists to decide on the correct number of kingdoms?
22. Why is it possible that biologists might adopt another classification scheme that included a greater number of kingdoms?

THINK CREATIVELY

23. Design an exhibit of live organisms that would teach the classification system to young students. The exhibit must fit into your school gym.
24. Classification schemes are important for all scientists. Propose some possible classification schemes that chemists might use to communicate among themselves.

FOR FURTHER INVESTIGATION

1. Collect a variety of specimens of leaves or insects. Bring them to the classroom and use a local field guide to help identify them. See whether you can determine the kingdom, phylum, class, order, family, genus, and species for each specimen.
2. Use a field guide and a microscope to identify protists found in a pond or fish tank.
3. Find out how scientists use similarities in protein structure to determine relationships between groups of organisms.
4. Prepare a report on one of the career opportunities listed below. See suggestions, p. 9, "For Further Investigation," Activity 3.
   a. Librarian   c. Taxidermist
   b. Taxonomist
5. Report on the life and contributions of one of the following scientists:
   a. Carolus Linnaeus   c. John Ray
   b. Lynn Margulis   d. R. H. Whittaker

FOR FURTHER READING

Margulis, Lynn, and Schwartz, Karlene, *Five Kingdoms*, W. H. Freeman & Co., New York, 1982.

Mayr, E., "Biological Classification: Towards a Synthesis of Opposing Methodologies," *Science*, October 30, 1981.

Issues in Biology

Health Risk Analysis

When you drink diet soda, you consume a sweetening additive that went through extensive risk-benefit analysis before being approved for human consumption. Risk analysis is a way of estimating the safety of a substance, process, or piece of equipment that has possible disadvantages as well as benefits. Risk analysis is particularly important in matters relating to health and safety.

To evaluate the safety of a potential food additive, researchers collect information about the substance and its effects. Since it is unethical to feed untested substances to humans, scientists usually experiment on rats or mice. They feed the animals large amounts of the additive and evaluate the substance's effects on the animals. Scientists then predict the effects that the additive would have on humans if specified small amounts were ingested.

Usually some information needed for complete risk analysis is not available. Analysts make assumptions to compensate for the missing information. This adds an element of uncertainty to the assessment process.

For example, analysts agree that there are many problems in using data from animal studies to predict the effects of a substance on humans. What can we conclude if large doses of an additive cause cancer in laboratory animals? Will low doses also cause cancer in humans?

In matters relating to health, we often do not have absolute safety. Some analysts say that if there is a risk that one person might be harmed, a food additive should be banned. Others argue that the acceptable exposure level should be determined, and the additive should be allowed below that level. But defining acceptable exposure levels is not easy. Sometimes analysts find that a small percent of people are at risk from an otherwise beneficial additive. In these cases, there is often controversy about whether the additive should be banned.

Once the health risks of a substance have been determined, those risks must be weighed against the corresponding benefits. In some cases, even though a substance poses some health risks,

Some people believe organic foods, those grown without artificial chemicals, and natural foods, those processed without additives, enhance their health.

analysts may judge that its benefits outweigh those risks.

Risk-benefit analysis is a complex process involving Congress, the law, and the courts as well as health professionals, researchers, business, and the general public. It will continue to be an important part of the decision-making process on many issues related to health.

---

1. Explain the process of risk analysis. Give three different examples where risk analysis could be particularly useful.

2. What role does science play in risk-benefit analysis?

3. People involved in risk analysis often have to make decisions based on incomplete information. When you have to make important decisions, do you always have all the relevant information? How much information do you require before you are willing to make your decision?

UNIT 2

ANIMAL MAINTENANCE

The long, cold winter in this forest in Ontario does not deter the Canadian lynx from its search for food. Indeed, as the forest changes with the seasons, the animal's survival depends on its ability to adjust to new conditions. Its body systems must maintain a stable internal state while external conditions vary widely. In this Unit, you will see how the highly regulated systems of animals and animal-like protists carry out the activities essential to life.

Chapter 7

CELLULAR RESPIRATION

Muscular activity, like all life activities, requires energy supplied through the process of cellular respiration.

ENERGY FOR LIFE

Objectives:
1. Define the term *cellular respiration*.
2. Explain the importance of energy for living things.

7-1 The Uses of Energy

Energy is defined as the ability to do work. All living things need a continuous supply of energy to carry on their life activities and thus stay alive. Some of this energy is needed for physical or mechanical work. A flying bird needs energy just as an airplane does. A beaver building a dam, or a worm burrowing in the soil, needs energy just as construction or earth-moving equipment does. Even tree frogs singing on a spring evening need energy just as a radio does. Most movements of living things require energy. Energy is also needed for less obvious purposes. The synthesis of complex compounds from simpler ones, and, in many cases, the transfer of materials across cell membranes, require energy (see Chapter 5).

In recent years we have all become conscious of the importance, and the cost, of energy for doing the work of our industrial civilization. Although some of this energy is obtained from falling water (hydroelectric power plants), some from nuclear energy, and some directly from solar radiation, most of it comes from the burning of fuels, such as oil, gas, and coal. Burning a fuel releases energy in the form of heat and light. The heat can then be used to run engines and electric generators, turning the heat energy into other forms of energy. The burning of fuel is a chemical process in which carbon and hydrogen in the fuel combine with oxygen from the air, forming carbon dioxide and water. The fuels contain stored chemical energy, which is released mostly as heat during the chemical changes of burning.

7-2 Energy from Food

Living things rely upon chemical energy stored in their food. Carbohydrates are the foods most commonly broken down for energy. This energy is released, in most cases, by chemical changes that resemble burning. However, when organisms break down food, only part of the energy is released as heat —this is the source of heat that maintains your body temperature. The rest of the energy is preserved in chemical form. Organisms can use only chemical energy to carry out their life functions. Living things cannot use heat energy to do work. It is not surprising, therefore, that the breakdown of food, with the consequent release of energy, occurs without the direct reaction between carbohydrate and oxygen. Rather, food breakdown occurs in many small chemical steps that are linked to the formation of new high-energy compounds.

The release of energy stored in food is accomplished inside the individual cells of every organism. The entire process is called **cellular respiration.** In this chapter we will examine the process by which the cell releases energy from food and makes it available for the life functions of the cell itself and for the organism as a whole.

STORAGE AND TRANSFER OF ENERGY

Objectives:
1. Describe the role of *ATP* in energy transfer and storage in the cell.
2. Explain what is the source of energy for ATP production in the cell.
3. Explain what happens in an *oxidation-reduction reaction.*
4. Explain the function of hydrogen acceptors in cellular respiration.

7-3 ATP and ADP

Energy released during cellular respiration is not used directly. It is first "packaged" in molecules of a compound called *adenosine triphosphate* (uh-*den*-uh-seen try-*fahs*-fayt), abbreviated **ATP.** Figure 7-1 shows the structure of the ATP molecule. The main part of the molecule is composed of a molecule of adenine joined to a molecule of ribose. Adenine is one of the nitrogen bases found in DNA and RNA. Ribose is the 5-carbon sugar found in RNA. The combination of the two

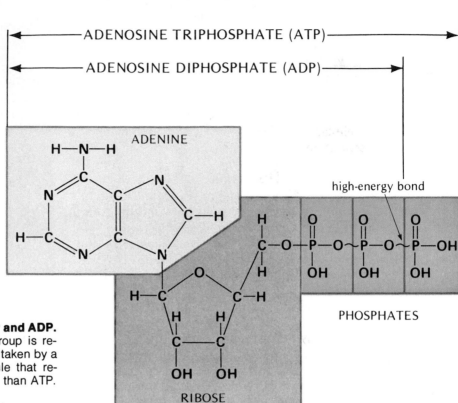

ADENOSINE TRIPHOSPHATE (ATP)

ADENOSINE DIPHOSPHATE (ADP)

ADENINE

high-energy bond

PHOSPHATES

RIBOSE

Figure 7-1. Structure of ATP and ADP. When the third phosphate group is removed from ATP, its place is taken by a hydrogen atom. The molecule that remains, ADP, has less energy than ATP.

is called *adenosine*. There are three phosphate groups bonded end-to-end to the adenosine in ATP. You will recall that phosphate groups are also part of the structure of DNA and RNA. It is interesting that the cell uses these same molecular units for different purposes. There are many examples of such multiple uses of chemical groups in the chemistry of life.

The important part of the ATP molecule as far as energy storage is concerned is the bond linking the last phosphate group to the molecule. This bond is shown as a wavy line. This symbol means that the bond contains a relatively large amount of energy. It is called a *high-energy bond*. When the third phosphate is detached from ATP and bonded to another compound, it transfers energy to the other compound. This transfer is called *phosphorylation* (fahs-for-uh-*lay*-shun). Phosphorylation is a common way for chemical energy to be transferred in biochemical reactions (see Figure 7-2).

When one phosphate is removed from ATP, the remaining molecule is called *adenosine diphosphate*, or **ADP**. ADP is a compound in a lower energy state than ATP. Its second phosphate is attached through a high-energy bond, but this bond is used less often in the cell as a source of energy.

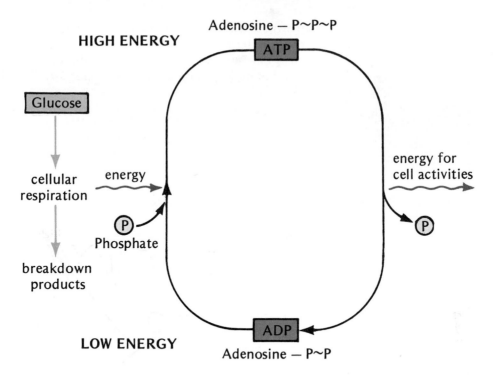

Adenosine — P~P~P

HIGH ENERGY

ATP

Glucose

cellular
respiration

energy

P

Phosphate

energy for
cell activities

P

breakdown
products

LOW ENERGY

ADP

Adenosine — P~P

7-4 Source of Energy for ATP

During cellular respiration, energy released by the gradual breakdown of food molecules is used to attach a third phosphate to ADP, thus returning it to its high-energy state as a molecule of ATP. The ATP can then be used in any part of the cell where its energy is needed for some chemical process.

The most common food substance from which cells obtain energy is the sugar glucose. Glucose is usually the starting point for cellular respiration. From the energy in a single molecule of glucose, a cell can produce up to 36 molecules of ATP from ADP. That is, the total energy that can be obtained by breaking down a molecule of glucose is actually divided into as many as 36 small units. If all this energy were released in a single burst, it would be too much for the cell to handle. There is no way the cell can use that much energy all at once. However, the amount of energy in a single molecule of ATP is just about right for the average reaction in the cell that requires energy. Thus the packaging of energy in these small units is convenient and efficient for the needs of the cell.

7-5 Oxidation-Reduction Reactions

It is interesting to follow the main steps by which the energy in glucose is used to generate ATP. The idea of chemical oxidation and reduction can help you understand these steps. The term **oxidation** (ok-suh-*day*-shun) originally referred to combination with oxygen. Chemists later broadened the meaning of the term to include reactions that were like combination with oxygen as far as shifts of electrons were

Figure 7-2. The Energy Cycle in the Cell. Energy obtained from the breakdown of glucose is used to attach a third phosphate to ADP, forming ATP and storing energy in it. When the third phosphate is detached from ATP, the stored energy can be used for cell activities. The low-energy ADP is returned for reuse. The energy from a single glucose molecule can form 36 molecules of ATP.

concerned. This broadened meaning of oxidation refers to any chemical change in which an atom or a molecule loses electrons. For example, when sodium combines with chlorine, the sodium atom loses an electron (see page 34). This is an example of oxidation. We say that the sodium atom is oxidized.

At the same time, the chlorine atom acquires an electron. Gaining electrons is called **reduction.** We say that the chlorine atom is reduced. Oxidation and reduction always occur as pairs of reactions. When one substance is oxidized, another must be reduced. That is, the electrons given up by the substance being oxidized are taken up by another substance being reduced. The pair of reactions is called an **oxidation-reduction reaction.**

In some oxidation-reduction reactions, an electron is transferred as part of a hydrogen atom. That is, one compound may transfer hydrogen atoms to another. The loss of hydrogen atoms is a form of oxidation. Gaining hydrogen atoms is a form of reduction.

Oxidation-reduction reactions involve a transfer of energy. The substance that is oxidized (loses electrons or hydrogen) usually loses energy. The energy is carried by the electrons or the hydrogen atoms to the substance that is reduced. This substance thus gains energy. In cellular respiration, almost all the energy released by the breakdown of glucose is at first carried off by hydrogen atoms. The oxidation of glucose in the cell is actually a loss of hydrogen atoms, not a reaction with oxygen.

7-6 Hydrogen Acceptors

The breakdown of glucose in cellular respiration occurs as a series of numerous chemical steps. A sequence of chemical reactions that leads to a particular result in the living cell is called a *biochemical pathway.* At several points in the pathway of cellular respiration, one of the compounds involved is oxidized by giving up hydrogen atoms. For this oxidation to occur, some other compound must accept the hydrogen and thus be reduced. Each of these oxidation-reduction steps requires the action of a specific enzyme. Each enzyme, in turn, requires a coenzyme (see page 62) to act as the *hydrogen acceptor* in the reaction that the enzyme catalyzes.

One of the coenzymes that act as hydrogen acceptors in cellular respiration is represented as *NAD* (from its full name nicotinamide adenine dinucleotide). Another is *FAD* (flavin adenine dinucleotide). Each of these molecules can accept two hydrogen atoms, thus undergoing reduction:

$$NAD + 2H \longrightarrow NADH_2\text{*}$$
$$FAD + 2H \longrightarrow FADH_2$$

*This is a simplified way of showing the reduction of NAD. The oxidized form of NAD actually carries a positive charge. A more accurate equation for its reduction is:

$$NAD^+ + 2H \longrightarrow NADH + H^+$$

As the hydrogen atoms are transferred to the coenzymes, the coenzyme molecules also gain energy. The reduced coenzymes are thus carrying hydrogen and added energy. This is a temporary state of affairs. In another series of reactions, the coenzymes give up the hydrogen and return to their oxidized form. At the same time, the extra energy the coenzymes were carrying is used to form ATP from ADP. Oxygen acts as the final acceptor of the hydrogen, producing water. In the following sections we will examine some of the details of this process.

ANAEROBIC RESPIRATION

Objectives:
1. Explain the difference between *aerobic respiration* and *anaerobic respiration.*
2. Describe the overall scheme of *glycolysis.*
3. Describe the process of *fermentation.*

7-7 Types of Respiration

In the process of cellular respiration, glucose is broken down to simpler compounds. Energy stored in the chemical bonds of the glucose molecule is extracted and used to form ATP from ADP and phosphate.

In most organisms, respiration is carried on in the presence of free oxygen. Oxygen is obtained from the air or from water, in which it is dissolved. This type of respiration is called **aerobic** (uh-*roh*-bik) **respiration.** In aerobic respiration, glucose is completely oxidized to carbon dioxide and water, and the maximum amount of energy is extracted from it.

A number of one-celled organisms, including yeast and many forms of bacteria, can carry on cellular respiration in the absence of oxygen. This is called **anaerobic** (an-uh-*roh*-bik) **respiration.** In anaerobic respiration, only a partial breakdown of the glucose molecule occurs. Relatively little of the chemical energy in the glucose is extracted and stored as ATP.

The initial steps of both aerobic and anaerobic respiration are the same. We will therefore examine first the chemical pathway that includes the steps common to both forms of respiration.

7-8 Splitting of Glucose (Glycolysis)

The first steps in respiration are phosphorylation reactions. In these reactions, two phosphate groups are attached to the glucose molecule. These steps *require* energy. The energy and the phosphate groups are obtained by the breakdown of two ATP molecules to ADP. The energized glucose molecule then goes through a series of chemical reactions that split it into two molecules of a 3-carbon compound called phosphoglyceraldehyde (PGAL). PGAL is then oxidized by the loss of

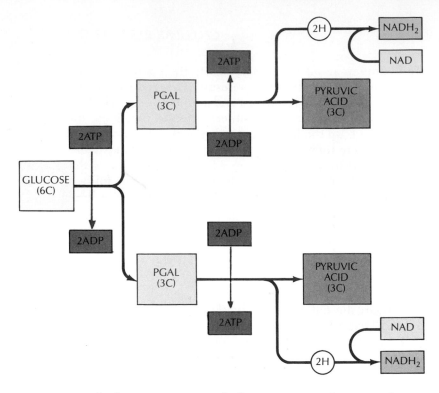

Figure 7-3. Glycolysis. In glycolysis the 6-carbon molecule (6C), glucose, is split into two 3-carbon molecules (3C) of pyruvic acid. These reactions produce 4 ATP and 2 NADH₂. Since 2 ATP are used to energize glucose at the beginning of glycolysis, the pathway produces a net gain of 2 ATP.

two hydrogen atoms and changes to another 3-carbon compound call pyruvic (py-*roo*-vik) acid. The oxidation of PGAL releases energy. Some of this energy is used directly to form two ATP. At the same time the hydrogen removed from PGAL is accepted by NAD, forming NADH₂. The NADH₂ also carries some energy that may be used to form ATP at a later stage. The process of breaking down the glucose molecule into two 3-carbon pyruvic acid molecules is called **glycolysis** (gly-*kahl*-uh-sis) (see Figure 7-3).

For each pyruvic acid molecule produced by glycolysis, two ATP are formed. Since the splitting of one glucose molecule produces two pyruvic acid molecules, a total of four ATP are formed per glucose molecule. However, two ATP are used to energize the glucose molecule. So the net energy output of glycolysis is two ATP for each molecule of glucose.

7-9 Fermentation

In anaerobic organisms, energy is obtained by the process of glycolysis. In this process, glucose is converted to pyruvic acid, and NAD is reduced to NADH₂. Several different chemical changes may follow, depending on the metabolism of the particular organism. In all cases the pyruvic acid accepts the hydrogens from NADH₂, oxidizing it to NAD so that it can be used again. However, no additional ATP is produced. At the same time the pyruvic acid is changed to other compounds. In yeast cells, the pyruvic acid is converted to ethyl alcohol and carbon dioxide (see Figure 7-4). In certain bacteria, such as those found in milk, the end product is lactic acid.

Glycolysis followed by the conversion of pyruvic acid to some other end product with no further release of energy is

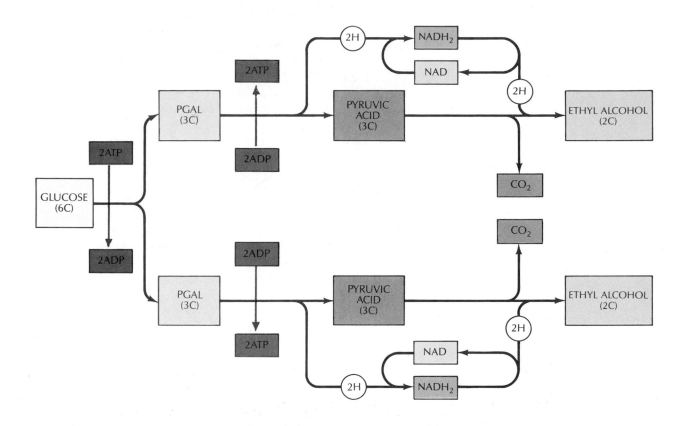

Figure 7-4. Fermentation. In the absence of oxygen, pyruvic acid (3C) produced by glycolysis gives up CO_2 and accepts 2H from $NADH_2$, forming ethyl alcohol (2C). The result of this type of fermentation is the production of two ATP (net), two molecules of CO_2, and two molecules of ethyl alcohol per molecule of glucose.

Figure 7-5. Industrial Fermentation. In bread dough (left), yeast cells break down carbohydrates to carbon dioxide and alcohol. The carbon dioxide forms gas bubbles in the dough, causing it to "rise." The alcohol evaporates during baking. Yeasts are used to make beer, wine, and other alcoholic beverages (right). In this case, the alcohol produced by fermentation is the desired product. Some of the carbon dioxide may or may not be retained in the beverage, depending on the particular processing used.

called **fermentation** (fer-men-*tay*-shun). Several industrial processes make use of natural fermentation (see Figure 7-5). Yeast fermentation is used in making bread; the carbon dioxide causes the bread to "rise." The manufacture of ethyl alcohol for beverages and other purposes is another well-known example.

AEROBIC RESPIRATION

Objectives:
1. Describe the function of the Krebs cycle.
2. Explain where and how the electron transport chain operates.
3. Compare the efficiency of aerobic and anaerobic respiration.
4. Explain how oxygen debt occurs in muscle cells.

7-10 The Importance of Oxygen

In anaerobic respiration, or fermentation, the only energy-yielding process is the formation of pyruvic acid from the splitting of glucose. The hydrogen accepted by NAD during this process is transferred to the pyruvic acid, producing an end product such as ethyl alcohol. The end products of fermentation have almost as much energy as the glucose from which they are made.

A cell that can use oxygen from the environment for its respiration can extract the energy remaining in these end products. It can do this because oxygen will accept the hydrogen removed during the oxidation of these compounds.

7-11 The Krebs Cycle

Aerobic respiration begins with glycolysis—the splitting of a molecule of glucose into two molecules of pyruvic acid, the reduction of two molecules of NAD to two molecules of $NADH_2$, and the net output of two molecules of ATP. These steps are the same in both aerobic and anaerobic respiration. In anaerobic respiration, the pyruvic acid accepts the hydrogen from $NADH_2$, ending the respiratory pathway. In aerobic respiration, the pyruvic acid undergoes further breakdown and energy release. Some energy is also obtained from the $NADH_2$ formed during glycolysis.

The remaining steps of aerobic respiration take place inside the mitochondria of the cell. The pyruvic acid produced by glycolysis enters the mitochondrion, where it reacts to form carbon dioxide, $NADH_2$, and a 2-carbon compound. The 2-carbon compound undergoes the first in a series of reactions that result in its complete breakdown to carbon dioxide and hydrogen. The carbon dioxide is given off as a waste product. The hydrogen is accepted by the coenzymes NAD or FAD.

A mitochondrion has a double membrane (see page 75). The inner membrane is deeply folded and has a very large surface area. Research indicates that most of the enzymes, coenzymes, and other special molecules needed for aerobic respiration are located on this membrane surface. It is the presence of these molecules in an organized pattern on the membrane that makes the entire process possible.

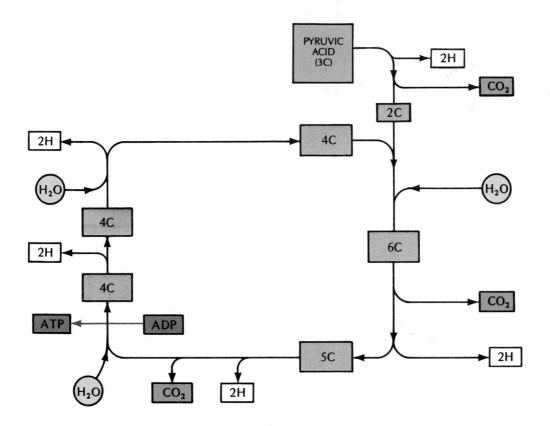

The series of chemical reactions that begin with the 2-carbon (2C) compound formed from pyruvic acid is called the **Krebs cycle** (see Figure 7-6). Its details were discovered by Sir Hans Krebs of Oxford University in England. He received a Nobel Prize in 1953 for this accomplishment. Krebs found that the series of reactions has the form of a repeating cycle. Certain organic acid molecules that are part of the cycle are used over and over again. They are changed to other compounds during the cycle but are then changed back to their original form.

Each "turn" of the cycle requires the 2-carbon compound derived from one pyruvic acid molecule and yields two molecules of carbon dioxide and four pairs of hydrogen atoms. In addition, one carbon dioxide molecule and one pair of hydrogen atoms are removed from the pyruvic acid molecule before the cycle. The hydrogen atoms are picked up by NAD, forming $NADH_2$. Almost all the chemical energy extracted from the pyruvic acid is carried by the hydrogen and temporarily transferred to the reduced coenzymes. Only one ATP is produced directly by each turn of the Krebs cycle.

Figure 7-6. The Krebs Cycle. For each turn of the cycle, two molecules of CO_2 and 4 pairs of hydrogen atoms are produced from one 2-carbon molecule (2C). Hydrogen is removed by coenzymes. Note that three water molecules are used during the Krebs cycle.

7-12 The Electron Transport Chain

We have seen so far that in aerobic respiration, two ATP are produced by the splitting of glucose into two molecules of pyruvic acid, and one ATP is produced by each turn of the Krebs cycle (two ATP for each glucose molecule). This is a

Figure 7-7. The Electron Transport Chain. Reduced coenzymes deliver hydrogen to the electron transport chain. The hydrogen is split into hydrogen ions (H$^+$) and electrons (e$^-$). The electrons participate in a series of oxidation-reduction reactions by passing through a specific sequence of electron carrier molecules (C$_1$-C$_6$). Some of the energy released by the electrons during these oxidation-reduction reactions is used to drive the synthesis of ATP. At the end, the electrons, hydrogen ions, and free oxygen combine to form water molecules.

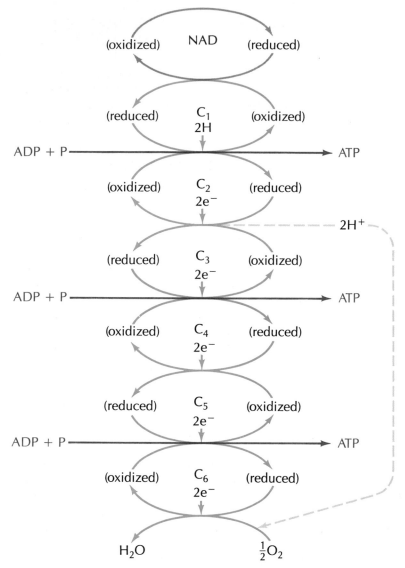

total of four ATP per glucose molecule. All the remaining energy released by the breakdown of glucose is carried by the hydrogen in NADH$_2$ and FADH$_2$. This energy is used to form ATP by a highly organized system of enzymes and coenzymes called the **electron transport chain.**

In the electron transport chain, a series of oxidation-reduction reactions take place. Hydrogen atoms are carried into the chain by NADH$_2$ and FADH$_2$. The electrons from the hydrogen atoms are then passed along from one compound to another (see Figure 7-7). At three places along the chain, the electrons give up some energy, and molecules of ATP are formed. Altogether, in most cells 32 ATP are produced by the electron transport chain for each molecule of glucose. Since 2 ATP come directly from glycolysis and 2 ATP from the Krebs cycle, aerobic respiration can produce a total of 36 ATP from each molecule of glucose.

The final step in this process involves free oxygen. Oxygen becomes the final hydrogen acceptor, combining with hydrogen to form water.

Water produced by cellular respiration is called the *water of metabolism*. It may be used by the cell or it may be excreted as a waste product. For desert animals, such as the kangaroo rat, the water of metabolism is an essential source of water for survival.

7-13 Net Reactions of Aerobic Respiration

The net result of all the steps of aerobic respiration is usually summarized in the following chemical equation:

$$C_6H_{12}O_6 + 6\ O_2 \rightarrow 6\ CO_2 + 6\ H_2O + \text{Energy (36 ATP)}$$

This equation is somewhat oversimplified. Water is needed as a raw material for the Krebs cycle. In Figure 7-6 you can see three places where a molecule of water enters the cycle. Since the Krebs cycle runs twice for each glucose molecule, six molecules of water are needed for each glucose molecule that is broken down. This water should be shown as a raw material in the equation. The equation should therefore be written as follows:

$$C_6H_{12}O_6 + 6\ H_2O + 6\ O_2 \rightarrow 6\ CO_2 + 12\ H_2O + \text{Energy (36 ATP)}$$

7-14 Efficiency of Cellular Respiration

The oxidation of glucose is usually used as a measure of the energy output of cellular respiration. In anaerobic respiration, the glycolysis pathway produces a net yield of two ATP per molecule of glucose. This type of respiration is relatively inefficient, leaving most of the potential energy of the glucose in the end products of fermentation. The method is, however, adequate for the energy needs of many simple organisms, such as yeast and bacteria.

Aerobic respiration yields almost 20 times as much energy per molecule of glucose as fermentation does. It is, moreover, a very efficient process. About 45 percent of the total energy that could theoretically be obtained from the oxidation of glucose is stored as ATP after aerobic respiration. In comparison, an automobile engine converts only about 25 percent of the chemical energy of its fuel to useful work.

7-15 Muscle Fatigue and Oxygen Debt

Some organisms that have the capacity for aerobic respiration can function by anaerobic respiration alone when free oxygen is not available. Yeast cells, for example, employ aerobic respiration when the supply of oxygen is ample, but they can live and grow by anaerobic respiration in the absence of oxygen. Muscle cells in humans and other animals normally

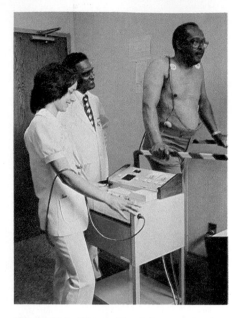

Figure 7-8. Stress Test. In an exercise stress test, a person's capacity to supply oxygen to the muscles is measured. Such tests provide information about the condition of the circulatory system.

rely on aerobic respiration for their energy needs. They can, however, function for a short time without oxygen, making do with the energy obtained from glycolysis alone.

During periods of intense or prolonged physical activity, the muscle cells may use oxygen faster than it can be supplied by the respiratory and circulatory systems (see Figure 7-8). When the oxygen supply gets too low, the electron transport chain cannot function. This means that $NADH_2$ and $FADH_2$ accumulate in the mitochondria and are not recycled. This forces the Krebs cycle to stop working.

Under these circumstances, the muscle cells continue to release energy by glycolysis, but the pyruvic acid becomes the acceptor for hydrogen and is converted to lactic acid. The accumulation of lactic acid in the muscle cells produces the sensation of fatigue and gradually reduces the ability of the cells to do their normal work.

The cells require a period of rest or reduced activity to recover to a normal condition. During this time, fresh supplies of oxygen allow the lactic acid to be oxidized back to pyruvic acid, and the accumulated hydrogen is passed down through the electron transport chain. The amount of oxygen needed to dispose of the lactic acid is called **oxygen debt.** You know that during periods of strenuous activity, the breathing and heart rates increase in order to deliver greater supplies of oxygen to the muscles. When the intense activity stops, the breathing and heart rates remain high for a time. During this time, extra supplies of oxygen are being delivered to pay back the oxygen debt of the previous period of exertion.

CATABOLISM AND ANABOLISM

Objective:
   Explain the terms *catabolism* and *anabolism*.

7-16   Breakdown and Synthesis in the Cell

The discussion of aerobic respiration has focused on the breakdown of glucose to furnish energy for the cell. The food of most organisms does not contain glucose in its simple form. The glucose is obtained by the breakdown, or digestion, of more complex carbohydrates. Cells that carry on aerobic respiration can also extract energy from other types of food substances, such as fats and proteins. These substances are broken down and converted into compounds that can enter the respiratory pathway at some intermediate point. Therefore, pyruvic acid, produced through glycolysis, is not the only source of compounds that can enter the Krebs cycle.

The proteins and fats in the food supply of an organism are broken down by digestion for use within the body. However, even the proteins and fats that are part of the tissues of the organism are constantly being broken down and then formed again. In the cells of the human body, about half the body proteins are broken down and reformed every 80 days. Some proteins are replaced every 10 days. Some liver enzymes are destroyed and remade in periods as short as 2 hours.

As explained earlier (page 7) all the chemical reactions occuring within the cell or cells of an organism constitute its metabolism. The phase of metabolism consisting only of breakdown reactions is called catabolism. These reactions generally yield energy. The processes of catabolism are balanced by the complementary phase of metabolism called anabolism. Anabolism involves reactions that result in the buildup or synthesis of materials needed for the continued functioning of the cell. An input of energy is required for these reactions. Obviously, in cells, energy-yielding and energy-requiring reactions occur simultaneously and are interdependent.

Chapter Review

SUMMARY

- All living things require chemical energy to carry on their life processes. The chemical energy is obtained from the breakdown of food through the process of cellular respiration. Cellular respiration involves a series of oxidation-reduction reactions in which energy is transferred from one substance to another. The food substance most commonly broken down in cellular respiration is the sugar glucose. Energy released by the breakdown of glucose is packaged in molecules of ATP, which in turn can be broken down to provide energy for other processes.

- The pathways of both aerobic and anaerobic respiration begin with glycolysis—the breakdown of a glucose molecule to two molecules of pyruvic acid. In anaerobic respiration (fermentation), pyruvic acid is converted to ethyl alcohol or lactic acid, and no further release of energy occurs. In aerobic respiration, pyruvic acid is broken down completely to carbon dioxide and to hydrogen atoms. Most of this breakdown occurs in the reactions of the Krebs cycle, which is present in mitochondria. In a series of reactions involving the electron transport chain, the energy of the hydrogen atoms is used to form additional molecules of ATP. The final reaction of this series involves hydrogen atoms combining with oxygen to form water. Aerobic cellular respiration yields almost 20 times as much ATP as does anaerobic respiration.

- During prolonged, strenuous physical activity, muscle cells undergo a kind of anaerobic respiration that produces lactic acid. As oxygen becomes available, lactic acid is oxidized back to pyruvic acid, which is then completely broken down by aerobic respiration.

- Catabolism consists of the breakdown, energy-yielding reactions of metabolism; anabolism consists of the synthetic, energy-requiring reactions of metabolism.

KNOW THE TERMS

ADP	cellular respiration	Krebs cycle	oxygen debt
aerobic respiration	electron transport chain	oxidation	reduction
anaerobic respiration	fermentation	oxidation-reduction reaction	
ATP	glycolysis		

SECTION QUESTIONS

Energy for Life

1. What are the end products of burning?
2. What is the source of the energy that is released during cellular respiration?
3. Name the only form of energy that all organisms use for their life functions.

Storage and Transfer of Energy

4. How many phosphate groups are there in a molecule of ATP?
5. What is the most common food substance for cellular respiration?
6. Name the type of reaction in which a molecule gains one or more electrons.
7. What is the function of the coenzyme NAD?

Anaerobic Respiration

8. What does aerobic respiration require that is not required by anaerobic respiration?
9. How many ATP molecules must be used to activate glucose for glycolysis?

10. Name the product of fermentation that is important in bread-making.

Aerobic Respiration

11. What is the function of oxygen in aerobic respiration?
12. Where in the cell do the reactions of the Krebs cycle occur?
13. Which system of enzymes and coenzymes uses the energy from $NADH_2$ to form ATP?
14. What are the three end-products of aerobic respiration?
15. During strenuous physical activity, what substance becomes an end-product of respiration in muscle cells?

Catabolism and Anabolism

16. What phase of metabolism is involved in breakdown reactions?

KNOW THE FACTS

Copy the number of each sentence below on a sheet of paper. Beside each number, write the term(s) that complete(s) the sentence correctly.

1. In cellular respiration, food is chemically broken down to release _____.
2. The chemical energy of ATP is stored in its _____.
3. The process of atoms or molecules losing electrons is called _____.
4. Two coenzymes that act as hydrogen acceptors are _____ and _____.
5. The biochemical pathway that is common to both aerobic and anaerobic respiration is _____.
6. In _____ the final products are carbon dioxide and ethyl alcohol.
7. Two molecules of _____ and four pairs of atoms of _____ are formed by each "turn"

of the Krebs cycle.
8. The energy of electrons from $NADH_2$ is used to form three molecules of _____ in the electron transport chain.
9. Water and _____ are the two chemical end-products of aerobic respiration.
10. Aerobic respiration yields _____ ATP per molecule of glucose.
11. Glucose, oxygen and _____ are the three reactants in aerobic respiration.
12. The amount of oxygen needed to oxidize lactic acid back to pyruvic acid is called the _____.
13. The body synthesizes needed materials by the process of _____.

UNDERSTAND THE CONCEPTS

14. Explain the function of cellular respiration.
15. What happens in order for ATP to become ADP?
16. Explain what a phosphorylation reaction is.
17. What is the significance of cellular respira-

tion occurring in small chemical steps?
18. Explain what happens during an oxidation-reduction reaction.
19. Describe the role of coenzymes in oxidation-reduction reactions.

20. Explain why there is a net gain of only two ATP molecules for each glucose molecule that goes through glycolysis.
21. Explain the relationship between NADH$_2$ and the synthesis of ATP.
22. What is the mechanism by which lactic acid forms in muscles?
23. How can foods other than carbohydrates be used for respiration?

THINK CRITICALLY

24. How many molecules of ATP can be formed from the complete breakdown of three molecules of glucose during cellular respiration?
25. If the energy released during cellular respiration were suddenly packaged only in molecular ADP, would this have any effect on cellular respiration? Explain.
26. Why are oxidation-reduction reactions important to the cell?
27. How is the production of lactic acid in certain bacteria similar to the production of water in the kangaroo rat? How are the two processes different?
28. What are the advantages of aerobic respiration over alcoholic fermentation?
29. Carbon monoxide prevents one of the enzymes of the electron transport chain from operating. What effects would you expect this to have on aerobic respiration?

THINK CREATIVELY

30. Two ATP molecules are formed by the electron transport chain when FADH donates its electrons to the chain. However, three ATP molecules are formed when NADH donates its electrons to the chain. Suggest some possible explanations to account for this.
31. Victims of a heart attack often have small amounts of lactic acid present in the blood that leaves the heart muscle. Use this observation to explain the nature of a heart attack.

FOR FURTHER INVESTIGATION

1. Investigate various types of bacteria, such as those that cause botulism and tetanus, that produce substances dangerous to humans. Discuss the methods of respiration of these bacteria and how they are affected by the presence of free oxygen.
2. Prepare a report on one of the career opportunities listed here. See suggested procedures, p. 9, "For Further Investigation" Activity 3.

   a. Biochemist
   b. Nuclear medicine technician
   c. Pharmaceutical chemist
3. Prepare a brief report on the life and scientific contributions of one of the following scientists:
   a. Gerty T. Cori
   b. Paul Erlich
   c. Hans Krebs
   d. Birget Vennesland

FOR FURTHER READING

Baggett, James D., "Bioluminescence: Nature's Living Lights," *Scholastic Science World*, May 11, 1984.
Chappell, J. B., *The Energetics of Mitochondria*, 2nd ed. (Carolina Biological Reader), Carolina Biological Supply Co., Burlington, NC, 1972.
Monmany, Terence, "Yeast at Work," *Science 85*, July/August, 1985.
Sheeler, Phillip, and Bianchi, Do[...] *Biology: Structure, Biochemistr[...]* John Wiley and Sons, New Y[...]
Yudkin, Michael, and Offo[...] *Guidebook to Biochemi[...]* bridge University Pre[...]

Chapter 8

NUTRITION

Giant pandas feed primarily on bamboo.

THE NUTRITIVE PROCESS

Objectives:
1. Describe the functions of the six basic types of nutrients found in foods.
2. Define the terms *calorie* and *kilocalorie* and explain how the energy content of food is measured.
3. Contrast autotrophic nutrition and heterotrophic nutrition.
4. Distinguish between mechanical breakdown and chemical digestion of food.

8-1 Nutrients

All living organisms need food. It is from food that they obtain energy and materials for growth and repair. **Nutrition** is the process by which organisms obtain food, use it to carry on their life activities, and transform it into their own proteins, fats, polysaccharides, and nucleic acids.

All foods contain **nutrients,** which are substances that can be used in metabolism. Some nutrients are simple, inorganic compounds, while others are more complex organic compounds. Some can be synthesized within the organism, and some must be taken in from the environment. Nutrients required by living organisms include proteins, carbohydrates, fats, vitamins, minerals, and water. Sources and functions of these nutrients are given in Table 8-1.

In addition to nutrients, many foods contain bulky, indigestible materials called **roughage** (*ruhf*-idj). The main kind of roughage in human foods is cellulose. Cellulose is an indigestible material found in the cell walls of fruits, vegetables, and grains. Roughage stimulates the muscles of the digestive tube and thus keeps food moving through it.

8-2 Energy Content of Food

Living organisms need energy to carry on their life processes. This energy is provided in most cases by the chemical breakdown of carbohydrates, fats, and proteins obtained from food. As explained in the discussion of cellular respiration in Chapter 7, the energy is released in a series of small steps and stored in molecules of ATP for later use.

The total amount of energy released by the gradual breakdown of a given quantity of food by cellular respiration is the same as would be released by burning, which is a rapid process. The energy content of a food sample is the amount of energy given off by the complete breakdown of that sample. It

Table 8-1. Nutrients Important for Human Metabolism.

Nutrient	Functions	Sources
Carbohydrates (sugar and starch)	Supply energy for body functions	*Sugar:* fruit, table sugar, sweets, syrups, jelly *Starch:* bread, cereals, potatoes, rice, corn, beans, spaghetti
Fats & Oils	Supply energy; storage form of fuel in the body	Margarine, butter, bacon, cooking oils, fat in meat, nuts
Proteins	Growth and repair of body tissue; can supply energy	Meat, milk, fish, eggs, beans, peas
Water	Solvent in which chemical reactions take place; transport of materials	Drinking water and other beverages; most foods; product of metabolism
Minerals	Body building; regulation of metabolism	Meats, milk, vegetables, fruits
Calcium	Makes up bones and teeth; needed for normal muscle activity and blood clotting	Milk and dairy products, leafy vegetables, fruits
Phosphorus	Part of ATP, ADP, etc.; makes up bones	Milk and dairy products, leafy vegetables, fruits
Iron	Part of hemoglobin	Liver, red meat, eggs, green leafy vegetables
Iodine	Part of thyroid hormone	Sea food, iodized table salt
Vitamins	Many serve as coenzymes in metabolic reactions. Prevent deficiency diseases.	Varied diet
A	Growth, night vision	Vegetables, fruit
D	Needed for good teeth and bones. Prevents rickets.	Eggs, meat, milk
C	Keeps body tissues healthy. Prevents scurvy.	Citrus fruits, tomatoes
B (complex)	Coenzymes in cellular metabolism.	Liver, eggs, milk, enriched bread, cereals

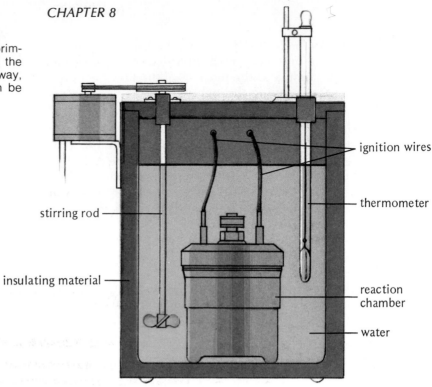

ignition wires

thermometer

stirring rod

insulating material

reaction chamber

water

is determined by completely burning a sample of the food and measuring the amount of heat given off. The instrument used to measure the energy content of a food sample is a *calorimeter* (kal-uh-*rim*-uh-ter) (see Figure 8-1).

A unit used in measuring the energy content of food is the **calorie** (*kal*-uh-ree). This is the amount of heat needed to raise the temperature of 1 g of water 1°C. The calorie is a very small unit that is not convenient for expressing the energy content of food. The preferred unit used in measuring the energy content of food is the **kilocalorie** (*kil*-uh-kal-uh-ree). A kilocalorie is one thousand calories and is the amount of heat needed to raise the temperature of 1 kg of water 1°C. In tables giving the "Calorie" content of foods, the unit is actually a kilocalorie.

With the use of a calorimeter, it has been determined that the amount of heat liberated by 1 gram of carbohydrate or 1 gram of protein is about 4 kilocalories. One gram of fat, on the other hand, releases 9 kilocalories. Fat contains more than twice as many calories as an equal weight of carbohydrate or protein. Now you can see why most weight-reducing diets restrict fat intake. The energy contents of some common foods are shown in Table 8-2.

Individuals vary in their daily calorie requirements. In general, younger people need more calories than older people, males need more calories than females, and active people need more calories than inactive people. A person whose diet contains more calories than are needed gains weight. A person whose diet includes fewer calories than are needed loses weight.

8-3   Types of Nutrition

There are two basic ways that organisms obtain the organic nutrients they need. Some organisms are capable of making, or synthesizing, these nutrients from simple inorganic substances. Such organisms are **autotrophs** (*awt*-uh-trohfs). Green plants and algae and various other types of microorganisms are autotrophs. Most autotrophs are photosynthetic—that is, they use energy from sunlight, and carbon dioxide and water from the environment to make their own organic nutrients. These organisms are called *phototrophs*. However, certain types of bacteria that are autotrophs do not use light as a source of energy. They are chemosynthetic, i.e., they obtain energy from special types of chemical reactions. Such organisms are called *chemotrophs* (*kee*-muh-trohfs). (See a discussion of photosynthesis and chemosynthesis in Chapter 17.)

Heterotrophs (*het*-uh-ruh-trohfs) are organisms that cannot synthesize their own organic nutrients. All animals and cer-

Table 8-2. Energy Content of Some Common Foods.

Food	Portion	Calories
apple	1 medium (150g)	70
bacon	2 slices (16g)	100
banana	1 (150g)	85
bread, white	1 slice (23 g)	70
candy, bar	1 plain (57g)	300
carrot	1 cup (145g)	45
cheese, American	1 oz. (28g)	105
corn	1 cup (256g)	170
cupcake	1 (50g)	185
egg	1 large (50g)	80
frankfurter	1 (51g)	155
ham	3 oz. (85g)	245
hamburger	3 oz. (85g)	245
ice cream	½ cup	225
milk	1 cup (244g)	150
orange	1 (180g)	60
peas	1 cup (160g)	115
pork roast	3 oz. (85g)	310
potato	1 medium (130g)	105
tomato	1 medium (150g)	35

Career

Clinical Dietitian

Clinical dietitians are concerned with the nutritional needs of patients in health care facilities such as hospitals, nursing homes, and clinics. They develop and carry out nutrition care plans for patients, often consulting with doctors and other members of the health care team. They also instruct patients and their families on dietary matters, and suggest ways to maintain proper diets after patients leave the hospital.

Clinical dietitians often set up and supervise food service systems for institutions. They also promote sound eating habits through educational activities and research. The clinical dietitian interacts with patients, doctors and other health care professionals, hospital administrators, and food service workers.

A college degree with a major in foods and nutrition is a basic requirement for clinical dietitians. In addition, an approved internship is often a prerequisite for employment. Advancement to higher-level positions usually requires academic training beyond the bachelor's degree.

tain types of microorganisms are heterotrophs. Such organisms must take in, or ingest, food containing "ready-made" nutrients from other plants or animals.

8-4   Digestion

For a nutrient to be used by the cells of an organism, it must pass through the cell membranes. In general, the nutrient molecules in food are too large to pass through cell membranes. Thus, to be used by the cells, most food molecules must be broken down into smaller, simpler forms. The process by which food molecules are broken down is called **digestion** (dy-*jes*-chun).

The term *digestion* usually refers to the chemical breakdown of food substances into simpler compounds. In many organisms, pieces of food are first cut, crushed, or broken into smaller particles without being changed chemically. This treatment results in the mechanical breakdown of the food. Mechanical breakdown increases the surface area of the food particles. Chemical digestion is carried out by digestive enzymes, which act only on the surface of food particles. Thus, mechanical breakdown prepares the food for more rapid chemical digestion by exposing more food surface to the action of the digestive enzymes. Chemical digestion, like mechanical breakdown, takes place in stages. Large molecules are broken down into smaller molecules, and these in turn are broken down into still simpler forms. The usable, simplest products of digestion are the end products of digestion.

ADAPTATIONS FOR NUTRITION

Objectives:
1. Contrast intracellular digestion and extracellular digestion.
2. Compare digestive processes in protozoa, hydra, the earthworm, and the grasshopper.

8-5   Nutrition in Protozoa

Among the protozoa, digestion is *intracellular* (in-truh-*sel*-yuh-ler)—that is, it occurs within the cell. However, members of this group show a variety of adaptations for food-getting. The ameba and paramecium are one-celled protozoans that live in water and feed on small organisms. Both have the ability to move, and they appear to be attracted to food by chemical stimuli.

Amebas crawl along solid surfaces by a flowing of cytoplasm into projections of the cell called *pseudopods*, or "false feet." When an ameba comes in contact with a food particle, pseudopods surround the particle (see Figure 8-2). The cell

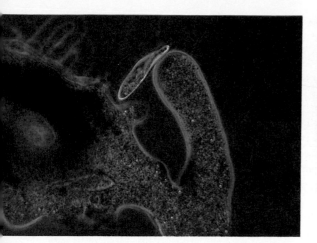
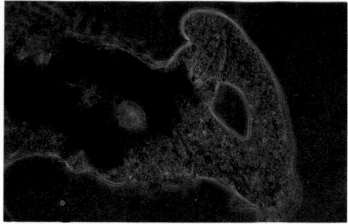

membranes of the pseudopods then join so that the particle is incorporated into the cell but is enclosed within a membrane. Although the food is within the cell, it is separated from the other cell contents by a membrane. It now is in a food vacuole that moves about within the cell cytoplasm. The food vacuole fuses with a lysosome, and digestive enzymes from the lysosome break down the food in the vacuole into forms usable by the cell. These products of digestion diffuse across the vacuole membrane into the cytoplasm. Indigestible materials remain in the food vacuole. The food vacuole eventually fuses with the cell membrane, and its contents are expelled from the cell.

The paramecium moves by the beating of hairlike cilia that cover the outside of the organism. The movement of the cilia also sweeps food particles down the **oral groove** into the **gullet** (*gul*-et) (see Figure 8-3). As food collects at the end of the gullet, the cell membrane bulges inward and pinches off, forming a food vacuole. The food vacuole travels through the cytoplasm. As in the ameba, the food vacuole fuses with a lysosome, which contains digestive enzymes. Digestion occurs within the vacuole, and the usable products diffuse into the cytoplasm. Indigestible material is discharged from the cell at the **anal** (*ayn*-ul) **pore.**

Figure 8-2. Food-Getting in Ameba. As the ameba senses its food, a paramecium, its pseudopods reach out to surround it (left). The engulfed paramecium is enclosed in a food vacuole inside the ameba (right). Note that the ameba had already captured another paramecium.

Figure 8-3. Food-Getting in Paramecium. Food particles are swept down the oral groove into the gullet by the beating of the cilia.

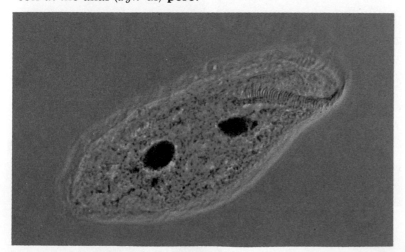

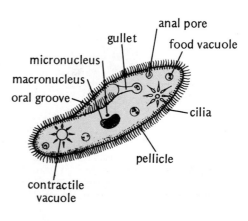

anal pore
gullet
food vacuole
micronucleus
macronucleus
oral groove
cilia
pellicle
contractile vacuole

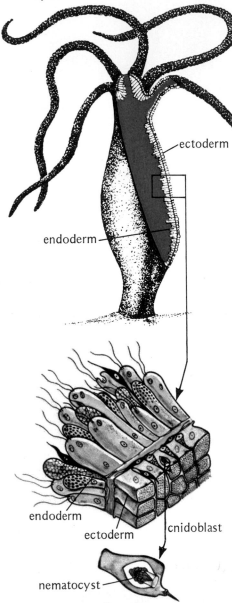

Figure 8-4. Structure of Hydra. The hydra body has two cell layers, the ectoderm and endoderm. Tentacles surround the mouth. The stinging cells of the tentacles each contain a nematocyst.

8-6 Nutrition in Hydra

The hydra is a relatively simple multicellular animal about 5 millimeters long from the tip of its tentacles to its base. The body of the hydra is a hollow cylinder made up of two layers of cells (see Figure 8-4). The outer layer is the *ectoderm* (*ek*-tuh-derm), and the inner layer is the *endoderm* (*en*-duh-derm). The tentacles, which surround the mouth, contain stinging cells called *cnidoblasts* (*nyd*-uh-blasts). Within each cnidoblast is a capsule called a *nematocyst* (neh-*mat*-uh-sist), which contains a coiled, hollow thread.

The hydra captures its food with its tentacles. When a water flea or some other small animal comes in contact with a tentacle, the nematocysts discharge their long threads. Some of the threads wind around the prey, while others inject a poison that paralyzes the animal. By movements of the tentacles, the food is stuffed through the mouth and into the **gastrovascular cavity**, where digestion begins (see Figure 8-5).

Digestion in hydra is both intracellular and extracellular. *Extracellular digestion* takes place outside the cells. Nutrients are then absorbed into the cells. Specialized cells in the endoderm secrete digestive enzymes into the gastrovascular cavity. These enzymes partially break down the food. Other endoderm cells have flagella, and the waving of these organelles

Figure 8-5. Food-Getting in Hydra. The hydra uses its tentacles to capture a water flea (daphnia) and stuff it into its gastrovascular cavity, where digestion will occur.

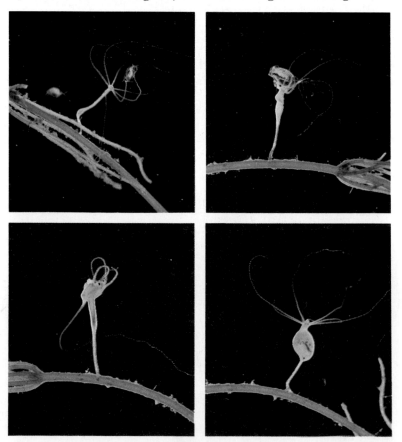

circulates the food particles through the gastrovascular cavity. Some endoderm cells form pseudopods and engulf, or *phagocytize*, the small food particles, thus forming food vacuoles. Digestion is completed by enzymes secreted into the food vacuoles. Since the hydra is only two cell layers thick, the end products of digestion pass easily from the cells of the endoderm into the cells of the ectoderm by diffusion. Wastes from the ectoderm cells diffuse directly into the surrounding water. Wastes from the endoderm diffuse back into the gastrovascular cavity and are carried out through the mouth by water currents.

8-7 Nutrition in the Earthworm

The earthworm is a complex multicellular animal with a "tube-within-a-tube" body plan. The inner tube is the digestive system, while the outer tube is the body wall (see Figure 8-6). The digestive tube, or **alimentary** (al-uh-*ment*-uh-ree) **canal,** has two openings—the mouth, through which food enters the body, and the **anus** (*ayn*-us) through which waste matter leaves. Food travels through the digestive system in one direction—from the mouth to the anus. The food is broken down both mechanically and chemically in the digestive tract. Usable nutrients are then absorbed into the body cells.

As earthworms burrow through the ground, they ingest large quantities of soil. They also come to the surface to eat leaf litter and other decaying plant matter. Food is pulled into the mouth by the sucking action of the muscular **pharynx** (*fa*-rinks). The food is then pushed through the digestive tube by waves of muscular contraction. From the pharynx, food passes through the **esophagus** (eh-*sahf*-uh-gus) into a round, thin-walled organ called the **crop.** The crop, which functions as a storage chamber, gradually releases food into the **gizzard** (*giz*-urd). The gizzard is a thick-walled grinding organ that

Figure 8-6. Digestive System of the Earthworm.

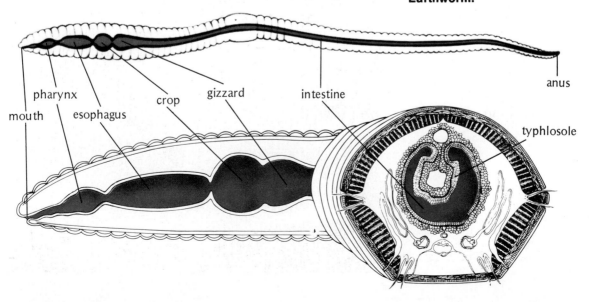

crushes the food. Mechanical breakdown is accomplished by the muscular movements of the gizzard, which grind the organic material against the sand grains from the soil. From the gizzard, the pastelike food mass passes into the long **intestine.**

Chemical digestion and absorption take place in the intestine. The surface area of the intestine is increased by a fold in the wall called the **typhlosole** (*tif*-luh-sohl). Cells lining the intestine secrete enzymes that break down large food molecules into smaller molecules. The products of digestion are absorbed by cells of the intestine and are picked up by the blood. The food molecules are transported in the blood to all parts of the body. Undigested materials and soil from which the food has been removed pass out of the worm through the anus.

8-8   Nutrition in the Grasshopper

The grasshopper, like the earthworm, has a tubular digestive system (see Figure 8-7). Food is broken down mechanically by the mouthparts, which are well-adapted for chewing leafy vegetation. In the mouth the food is mixed with **saliva** (suh-*ly*-vuh) secreted by the **salivary** (*sal*-uh-ver-ee) **glands.** The food then passes through the esophagus into the crop, where it is stored temporarily. From the crop the food passes into the muscular gizzard, where it is ground into smaller particles by the action of teethlike plates made of *chitin* (*kyt*-un). From the gizzard, food passes into the **stomach,** where chemical digestion takes place. Digestive enzymes produced by glands just outside the stomach pass into the stomach, where they act on food particles. The products of digestion are absorbed into the bloodstream through the stomach walls and are transported to all the cells of the body. Undigested material passes through the intestine and is stored temporarily in the **rectum** where water absorption occurs. The dried wastes are eliminated through the anus.

Figure 8-7. Digestive System of the Grasshopper.

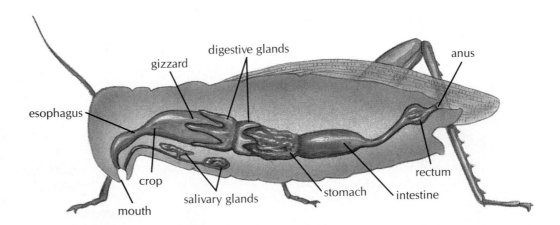

Vitamins and Health

Vitamins are necessary for good health. They are coenzymes or are converted into coenzymes, and they function with certain enzymes to catalyze metabolic reactions in the cells. A lack of a particular vitamin leads to the development of a particular deficiency disease.

Although it has been established that vitamins are needed in certain minimum amounts, a controversy has arisen over the theory that higher daily doses of vitamins can be even more beneficial to health. The U.S. Food and Drug Administration (the FDA) has established a "recommended daily allowance," or RDA, for each vitamin. These are the amounts that the FDA has found are needed by the average person to prevent vitamin deficiency diseases.

However, some nutritional researchers feel that the FDA's allowances are much too low. They argue that much higher levels of vitamins are not only safe, but beneficial. They feel that it is not just a question of preventing deficiencies, but of giving large enough doses for individuals to reach optimal health. Some believe that vitamin therapy—very large doses (megadoses) of one or more vitamins—provides a wide variety of benefits for the body.

However, it does not necessarily follow that if small doses of vitamins are good for you, then large doses will be even better. Some vitamins (the B vitamins and vitamin C) are water-soluble. When these vitamins are taken in high doses, the excess is excreted from the body by the kidneys. Vitamin therapists argue that the water-soluble vitamins are safe in any amount since the body can get rid of the excess. This seems to be true of the B vitamins, but there is mounting evidence that large doses of vitamin C produce some ill effects before the body can excrete the excess.

Vitamins A, D, E, and K are fat-soluble. Excess fat-soluble vitamins are not simply ex-

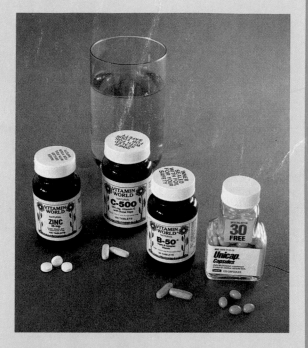

creted from the body. Instead they are stored in fatty tissues, and can accumulate to toxic levels. An excess of vitamin A can cause headaches, nausea, diarrhea, and fatigue. Still higher doses can cause increased pressure in the cerebrospinal fluid and brain damage. Vitamin D overdose can cause growth retardation and calcium deposits in children and serious kidney damage in adults. Some researchers now think that megadoses of vitamin E, which was once considered harmless in any amount, also can have toxic effects, including interfering with blood clotting.

Should you take large doses of vitamins to stay healthy? Most physicians and nutritionists feel that a good, balanced diet provides all the vitamins you need. If you don't eat a balanced diet, they may recommend a daily vitamin supplement containing RDA levels of the vitamins. Although some other experts believe that large doses of certain vitamins can be beneficial, even to people who eat well and are in good health, the evidence for this is disputed. Such large doses of vitamins, even those that are water-soluble, may be harmful.

THE HUMAN DIGESTIVE SYSTEM

Objectives:

1. Describe the functions of the various parts of the human digestive system—the mouth, esophagus, stomach, small intestine, liver, gallbladder, pancreas, large intestine, rectum, and anus.
2. List the principle digestive enzymes, where they are produced, the type of food they act upon, and the end products of enzymatic breakdown.

Figure 8-8. Human Digestive System. Accessory digestive glands are also a part of the digestive system.

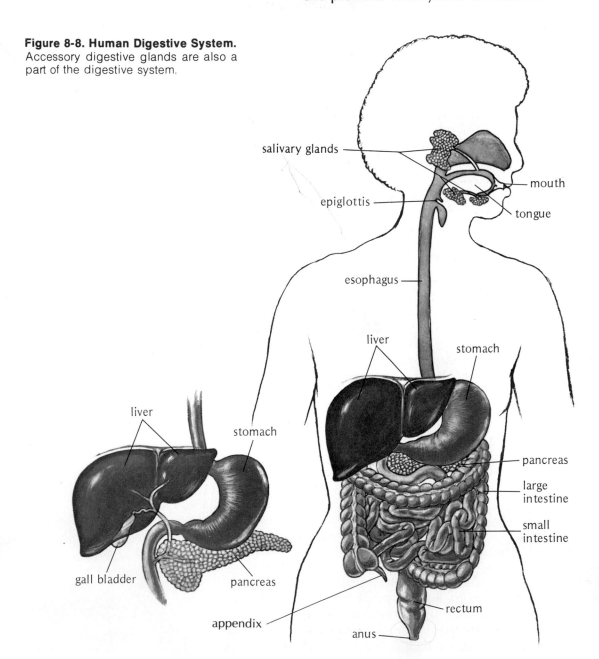

salivary glands

mouth

epiglottis

tongue

esophagus

liver

stomach

liver

stomach

pancreas

large intestine

small intestine

gall bladder

pancreas

appendix

rectum

anus

8-9   Parts of the Human Digestive System

The structure and function of the human digestive system is basically similar to that of the earthworm and the grasshopper. The digestive tube consists of a series of specialized organs, with different phases of digestion occurring in each organ. Food passes through the digestive tube in the following order: oral cavity (mouth), pharynx (throat), esophagus (gullet), stomach, small intestine, large intestine, rectum, and anus (see Figure 8-8). Several glands secrete digestive enzymes and juices into the digestive tube, where extracellular digestion occurs.

The *digestive glands* are groups of specialized secretory cells that are found in the lining of the alimentary canal or in separate accessory organs. The accessory glands lie outside the digestive tract. Their secretions pass into the digestive tract by way of a tube or duct. Food is never found within the accessory glands, only within the alimentary canal itself. The accessory glands include the salivary glands, the **liver,** and the **pancreas** (*pan*-kree-us).

Cells in the lining of the walls of the alimentary canal also secrete a slimy *mucus* (*myoo*-kus), which acts as lubricant for the food mass. It also provides a coating that protects the delicate cells of the digestive tube from the action of acid, digestive enzymes, and abrasive substances in the food.

8-10   The Mouth and Pharynx

Food enters the body through the mouth, where both mechanical breakdown and chemical digestion occur. Chunks of food are bitten off with the teeth and ground into pieces small enough to swallow. The tongue moves and shapes the food mass in the mouth.

As food is chewed, it is mixed with saliva, which is secreted into the mouth by three pairs of salivary glands. There are actually two types of saliva produced. One is a thin, watery secretion that wets the food. The other is a thicker, mucus secretion that acts as a lubricant and causes the food particles to stick together to form a food mass, or *bolus* (*boh*-lus). Saliva also contains a digestive enzyme called *ptyalin* (*ty*-uh-lin), or **salivary amylase** (*am*-uh-layz). This enzyme breaks down starch, which is a polysaccharide, into maltose, which is a disaccharide.

When the food has been chewed sufficiently, it is pushed by the tongue to the back of the throat, or pharynx (see Figure 8-9). This initiates the automatic swallowing reflex, which forces food into the esophagus, the tube leading to the stomach. However, air as well as food passes through the pharynx. The air must pass through the voice box, or *larynx* (*la*-rinks), and down the *trachea* (*tray*-kee-uh) to the lungs. To prevent food and liquids from entering the larynx, it is automatically closed off during swallowing by a flap of tissue

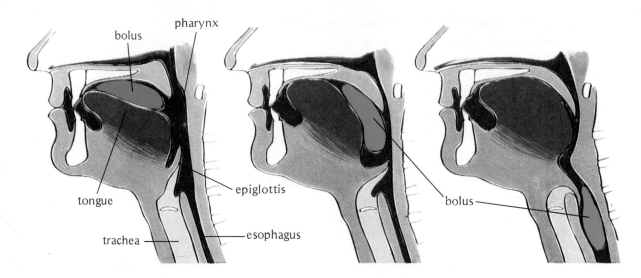

bolus

pharynx

tongue

epiglottis

trachea

esophagus

bolus

Figure 8-9. Swallowing. The epiglottis prevents food or liquid from entering the air passages during swallowing.

called the **epiglottis** (ep-uh-*glaht*-is). At the same time, breathing stops momentarily, and the passageways to the nose, ears, and mouth are blocked. When a person "swallows the wrong way" and food enters the trachea, it is brought back up into the throat by violent coughing.

8-11   The Esophagus

The esophagus is a tube through which food passes from the pharynx to the stomach. Beginning in the esophagus, the movement of food down the digestive tube is aided by alternate waves of relaxation and contraction in the muscular walls of the alimentary canal. This is called **peristalsis** (pehr-uh-*stahl*-sis). The muscles in front of the food mass relax, while those behind the food mass contract, pushing the food forward.

Aided by peristaltic contractions, food passes quickly down the esophagus. Where the esophagus opens into the stomach, there is a ring of muscle called a **sphincter** (*sfink*-ter). The sphincter acts as a valve and controls the passage of food from the esophagus into the stomach. When the wave of peristalsis reaches the sphincter, it relaxes and opens, and the food enters the stomach. The sphincter between the esophagus and the stomach is called the *cardiac sphincter*. During vomiting, a wave of peristalsis passes upward—reverse peristalsis—causing the cardiac sphincter to open, and the contents of the stomach to be "thrown up."

8-12   The Stomach

The stomach is a thick-walled, muscular sac that can expand to hold more than 2 liters of food or liquid. Food is stored temporarily in the stomach, and mechanical breakdown and chemical digestion occur there. Food is broken down mechanically into smaller particles by the contractions of the muscular stomach walls. The food mass is churned and mixed with gastric juice secreted by glands in the stomach walls.

The lining of the stomach contains two types of glands. *Pyloric* (py-*lor*-ik) *glands* secrete mucus, which covers the stomach lining and protects it from being digested. *Gastric* (*gas*-trik) *glands* secrete very acidic **gastric juice,** which has a pH of 1.5 to 2.5. This juice contains *hydrochloric* (hy-druh-*klor*-ik) *acid* (HCl) and the digestive enzyme **pepsin** (*pep*-sin). Pepsin is secreted in an inactive form called *pepsinogen* (pep-*sin*-uh-jen), which is activated after it is mixed with the hydrochloric acid. Pepsin breaks down large protein molecules into shorter chains of amino acids called *polypeptides* (pol-ee-*pep*-tydz).

Pepsin also curdles milk proteins—that is, it causes them to solidify. The liquid portion of milk passes quickly into the small intestine. The curdled proteins, however, remain in the stomach for a longer time, allowing digestion to occur. Without curdling, the milk proteins would pass through the stomach before any digestion had occurred.

The breakdown of starch by ptyalin, which begins in the mouth, continues for some time after the food mass reaches the stomach. Gradually, however, the low pH of the acid in the stomach inactivates this enzyme, and starch breakdown stops.

When no food is in the stomach, only small amounts of gastric juice are present. When food is taken in, the flow of gastric juice increases. There are three mechanisms involved in stimulating the flow of gastric juice.

1. The thought, sight, smell, or taste of food stimulates the brain to send messages to the gastric glands, causing them to secrete moderate amounts of gastric juice.

2. Food touching the lining of the stomach stimulates the secretion of moderate amounts of gastric juice.

3. When a food mass enters the stomach, it stretches the stomach walls. This stretching, as well as the presence of proteins, caffeine, alcohol, and certain other substances, stimulates the lining of the stomach to secrete a hormone called *gastrin* (*gas*-trin) directly into the blood. (A *hormone* is a substance that is secreted directly into the bloodstream and that produces a specific effect on a particular tissue.) Gastrin stimulates the gastric glands to produce large amounts of gastric juice.

Liquids pass through the stomach in 20 minutes or less. Solids, on the other hand, must first be reduced to a thin, soupy liquid called **chyme** (kyme). The chyme passes in small amounts at a time through the *pyloric sphincter,* the muscle that controls the passage of food from the stomach into the small intestine. The stomach empties from 2 to 6 hours after a meal. Hunger is felt when an empty stomach is churning.

If the thick mucus layer that protects the stomach wall breaks down, a part of the stomach wall may be digested, and a painful ulcer develops. It is thought that some ulcers are caused by the oversecretion of gastric juice brought on by nervousness or stress. Ulcers are treated by diet, medication, or, in severe cases, by surgery.

8-13 The Small Intestine

The **small intestine** is a coiled tube about 6.5 meters long and about 2.5 centimeters in diameter. Most chemical digestion and almost all absorption occur here. Unlike the stomach with its acid secretions, fluids in the small intestine are generally alkaline.

In the small intestine, chyme is mixed with **bile** from the liver, **pancreatic** (pan-kree-*at*-ik) **juice** from the pancreas, and **intestinal juice** from glands in the wall of the intestine. These three secretions contain the enzymes and other substances necessary to complete digestion.

Peristalsis of the small intestine. When food is present, the small intestine is in constant motion. These peristaltic movements have four main effects: (1) they squeeze chyme through the intestine; (2) they mix the chyme with digestive enzymes; (3) they break down food particles mechanically; and (4) they speed up absorption of digestive end products by bringing the intestinal contents into contact with the intestinal wall.

Pancreatic juice. When the acid chyme from the stomach enters the small intestine, it stimulates cells in the intestinal lining to secrete two hormones into the blood. These hormones are *secretin* (sih-*kreet*-in) and *cholecystokinin* (koh-luh-sis-tuh-*ky*-nin). These hormones stimulate the pancreas to secrete pancreatic juice and pancreatic enzymes, which pass through the *pancreatic duct* into the upper part of the small intestine. Pancreatic juice contains sodium bicarbonate, which neutralizes the acid in the chyme and makes the pH of the contents of the small intestine slightly alkaline (pH 8). The enzymes secreted by the pancreas act on every major component of food—proteins, carbohydrates, fats, and nucleic acids.

The pancreatic enzymes include *amylase*, which hydrolyzes any remaining starch to maltose; *proteases* (*pro*-tee-ay-zez) (protein-splitting enzymes), including *trypsin* (*trip*-sin) and *chymotrypsin* (ky-muh-*trip*-sin), which continue the breakdown of large protein molecules begun in the stomach; and *lipase*, which breaks down fats.

Bile. The cells of the liver produce bile, which passes through ducts into the **gallbladder,** where it is stored. Bile passes from the gallbladder to the upper part of the small intestine through the *bile duct.* The release of bile from the gallbladder is stimulated by the hormone cholecystokinin, which also acts on the pancreas. Bile contains no enzymes, but it aids in the digestion of fats and oils by breaking them up into tiny droplets. This process, called *emulsification* (ih-mul-suh-fuh-*kay*-shun), increases the surface area for enzyme action. Since bile is alkaline, it aids in neutralizing the acid chyme from the stomach.

Intestinal juice. The walls of the small intestine contain millions of intestinal glands, which secrete intestinal juice. Intestinal juice contains enzymes that complete the digestion of carbohydrates, fats, and proteins.

In the small intestine, molecules of proteins, carbohydrates, and fats are broken down into the end products of digestion. Proteins are broken down into amino acids, carbohydrates into simple sugars, and fats into fatty acids and glycerol. A summary of the secretions of the human digestive system and their functions is given in Table 8-3 (page 140).

Absorption. The small intestine is the site of **absorption.** Simple sugars, amino acids, vitamins, minerals, and other substances are absorbed through the wall of the small intestine into the blood vessels of the circulatory system. Fatty acids and glycerol are absorbed into tiny vessels of the lymphatic system called **lacteals** (*lak*-tee-uls) (see page 157).

The small intestine has a number of structural features that increase its surface area and make it ideally suited for absorption (see Figure 8-10). (1) The small intestine is very long. (2) Its lining has many folds. (3) The lining is covered with millions of fingerlike projections called **villi** (*vil*-ly). (4) The epithelial cells that make up the intestinal lining have *brush borders.* In the brush borders, the ends of the cells that face into the intestinal opening have tiny projections called *microvilli* that further increase the surface area.

Within each villus there is a network of blood capillaries, and in the center is a lacteal. The outer covering of each villus is a layer of epithelial cells with microvilli. During absorption, digested nutrients pass through the epithelial cells and enter either the capillaries or the lacteal. Absorption involves both diffusion and active transport.

8-14 The Large Intestine

Undigested and unabsorbed materials pass from the small intestine through a sphincter into the **large intestine.** The large intestine is about 1.5 meters long and 6 centimeters in diameter. No digestion occurs in this portion of the digestive system.

On the lower right side of the abdomen, where the small intestine joins the large intestine, is a small pouch, the **appendix** (uh-*pen*-diks). The appendix plays no part in the functioning of the human digestive system. Occasionally, however, the appendix becomes infected, a condition known as **appendicitis** (uh-pen-duh-*sy*-tus). If the condition is not treated, the appendix may burst, spreading the infection.

One of the principal functions of the large intestine is the reabsorption of water from the food mass. During digestion, water is mixed with the food as it moves through the digestive system. Under normal conditions, about three-fourths of the water is reabsorbed. This reabsorption into the capillaries of

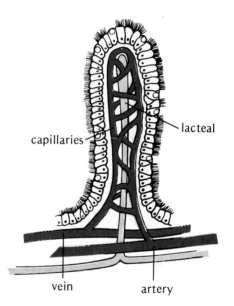

capillaries — lacteal

vein   artery

Figure 8-10. Longitudinal Section of a Villus.

Organ	Secretions and enzymes	Function
Salivary glands	Saliva: amylase	Enzyme that breaks down starch into maltose.
Esophagus	Mucus	Aids passage of food down esophagus to stomach.
Stomach (gastric glands)	Gastric juice:	
	pepsin	Enzyme that breaks down proteins into smaller molecules (peptones and proteoses).
	hydrochloric acid	Necessary for effective action of pepsin on proteins.
Liver	Bile	Breaks down fat mechanically into small droplets (emulsification).
Pancreas	Pancreatic juice:	
	amylase	Enzyme that continues digestion of starch to disaccharides.
	trypsin	Enzyme that digests peptones and proteoses into peptides.
	lipase	Enzyme that digests fat droplets into fatty acids and glycerol.
Small intestine (intestinal glands)	Intestinal juice:	
	peptidases	Enzymes that break down peptides into amino acids.
	maltase	Enzyme that breaks down maltose (a disaccharide) into glucose (a monosaccharide).
Large intestine	———————	Absorbs water from undigested materials. Forms feces.

Table 8-3. Secretions and Digestive Functions of the Human Digestive System.

the large intestine helps the body conserve water. If too little water is absorbed, diarrhea results; if too much water is absorbed, constipation results.

A second function of the large intestine is the absorption of vitamins produced by bacteria that normally live in the large intestine. The vitamins are absorbed with the water. Intestinal bacteria live on undigested food material. They produce vitamin K, which is essential for blood clotting, and some of the B vitamins. When large doses of antibiotics destroy the intestinal bacteria, a vitamin K deficiency may result.

The third function of the large intestine is the elimination of undigested and indigestible material from the digestive tract.

This material consists of cellulose from plant cell walls, large quantities of bacteria, bile, and mucus, and worn-out cells from the digestive tract. As this material travels through the large intestine, it becomes **feces** (*fee*-seez). Fecal matter is stored in the last part of the large intestine, the **rectum,** and periodically eliminated, or defecated, through the anus.

Chapter Review

SUMMARY

• The process by which organisms obtain food and use it to carry on their life activities is nutrition. The nutrients required by living organisms include proteins, carbohydrates, fats, vitamins, minerals, and water. Energy to carry on life processes comes from the breakdown of fats, carbohydrates, and proteins. The unit usually used in measuring the energy content of food is the kilocalorie or Calorie. Organisms are autotrophs or heterotrophs.

• Only nutrients that can pass through cell membranes can be used by an organism. Nutrients that are too large must first be broken down by digestion.

• In protozoa, digestion is intracellular. Food particles are ingested and enclosed within food vacuoles. The food is digested in the vacuoles, and the usable products of digestion diffuse into the cytoplasm. Digestion in hydra is both extracellular and intracellular.

• In all but the simplest animals, digestion is extracellular. Food enters the digestive tube, or alimentary canal, and enzymes are secreted into the tube. As food travels in one direction from the mouth to the anus, it is digested and absorbed. During absorption, usable nutrients pass from the digestive tube into the blood.

• Humans, like earthworms and grasshoppers, have a tube-within-a-tube body plan, in which the inner tube is the digestive tract. The human digestive tract includes the mouth, esophagus, stomach, small intestine, large intestine, rectum, and anus. The salivary glands, liver, and pancreas secrete their products into the digestive tube.

KNOW THE TERMS

absorption	epiglottis	kilocalorie	pharynx
alimentary canal	esophagus	lacteal	rectum
anal pore	feces	large intestine	roughage
anus	gallbladder	liver	saliva
appendicitis	gastric juice	nutrient	salivary amylase
appendix	gastrovascular cavity	nutrition	salivary gland
autotroph	gizzard	oral groove	small intestine
bile	gullet	pancreas	sphincter
calorie	heterotroph	pancreatic juice	stomach
chyme	intestinal juice	pepsin	typhlosole
crop	intestine	peristalsis	villi
digestion			

SECTION QUESTIONS

The Nutritive Process

1. What is nutrition?
2. Name six types of necessary nutrients.

3. Identify the instrument used to measure the energy content of food.
4. What are heterotrophs?
5. Define *digestion*.

Adaptations for Nutrition	The Human Digestive System
6. Where does digestion occur in the ameba and paramecium?	10. List the parts of the human digestive system, including the accessory glands.
7. Name an organism that utilizes both intracellular and extracellular digestion.	11. What are the functions of saliva and its enzyme, salivary amylase?
8. In the earthworm, what is the function of the typhlosole?	12. Name the process that causes food to move through the digestive tube.
9. List the parts of the digestive system of the grasshopper in order, beginning with the mouth.	13. Name the two types of glands in the stomach lining and their secretions.
	14. What three fluids mix with food in the small intestine?
	15. Name the end products of digestion.

KNOW THE FACTS

Copy the number of each sentence below on a sheet of paper. Beside each number, write the term(s) that complete(s) the sentence correctly.

1. Food substances that can be used in metabolism are called _____.
2. The main kind of roughage in our food is _____.
3. A _____ is the amount of heat required to raise the temperature of 1 g of water 1°C.
4. Organisms capable of synthesizing organic nutrients from simple inorganic substances are called _____.
5. Mechanical breakdown increases the _____ of the food particles.
6. Because digestion in the protozoa occurs within the cell, it is called _____ digestion.
7. Hydra captures food with its _____.
8. Complex multicellular animals such as the earthworm have a _____ body plan.
9. In a grasshopper, the _____ is the organ that grinds food into smaller particles.
10. _____ acts as a lubricant for food so that it slides through the human digestive tube.
11. During swallowing, the _____ blocks the opening of the human voice box.
12. The structure that connects the mouth to the stomach is called the _____.
13. In the stomach, solid food is reduced to a thin, soupy liquid called _____.
14. The process by which fats and oils are broken up into tiny droplets is called _____.
15. The secretion of the liver that aids in the breakdown of fats is _____.
16. The material that is periodically eliminated through the anus is called _____.

UNDERSTAND THE CONCEPTS

17. Why is roughage important in your diet?
18. Which nutrients supply energy?
19. How is the energy content of food determined?
20. How does an autotroph obtain organic nutrients?
21. Why does food have to be digested?
22. How is food digested in the protozoa?
23. Describe digestion in the hydra.
24. Trace the path of food through the alimentary canal of the earthworm, explaining what happens in each part of the digestive tube.
25. Describe the process of swallowing in human digestion, and explain why food and air are not usually mixed during swallowing.
26. What mechanisms stimulate the flow of gastric juice?
27. Describe the functions of hydrochloric acid and pepsin in the stomach.
28. What are the effects of peristalsis in the small intestine?
29. What structural features of the small intestine increase its surface area for absorption?
30. Which of the end products of digestion are absorbed into capillaries, and which enter the lacteals of the villi?
31. Describe the three major functions of the large intestine.

THINK CRITICALLY

32. Compare the energy content of a 3-oz. hamburger with that of a 3-oz. serving of American cheese.
33. Starchy foods taste sweet. Explain.
34. Compare and contrast the digestion of food in hydra and the grasshopper.
35. What prevents self-digestion by protozoa?
36. In what ways are the tubular digestive system of the earthworm and that of the human alike? In what ways are they different?
37. Why are the salivary glands, the liver, and the pancreas considered to be part of the human digestive system, even though food does not pass through them?
38. Food takes longer to digest when it has not been properly chewed. Explain.

THINK CREATIVELY

39. Diets that contain an excess of fat and red meat have recently been linked to colon cancer and heart disease. Develop an explanation to support the correlation between this kind of diet and each disease.
40. Why would an adolescent and an adult performing the same task have different energy needs?

FOR FURTHER INVESTIGATION

1. Do the following experiment to demonstrate how saliva digests starch. Fill a small test tube one-quarter full of saliva. Fill a second small test tube halfway with water, add a pinch of starch, and shake well. Add a drop of iodine to the starch suspension. Interpret what happens. Add all the saliva to the starch and shake well. Observe any color changes. Holding the tube in your hand will speed up the reaction. Why? What is happening to the starch? Using Benedict's solution, Testape, or Clinitest tablets, test the contents of the tube for simple sugars. Write up the experiment.
2. Prepare a report on one of the career opportunities listed below. See suggested procedures, p. 9, "For Further Investigation" Activity 3.
   a. Food technologist   c. Dentist
   b. Cook or chef
3. Prepare a brief report on the life and contributions of one of the following scientists.
   a. Christian Eijkman
   b. Lloyd Hall
   c. Johnnie H. Watts Prothro
4. Do library research on weight-reducing diets. Discuss the advantages and disadvantages of current fad diets, as well as the requirements for a safe weight-reducing diet. Write up your findings in the form of a feature article for a magazine or newspaper.
5. Find out why some people cannot digest milk. Suggest several milk substitutes they can use in order to meet calcium requirements.
6. Report on the experiments Dr. William Beaumont carried out on Alexis St. Martin.
7. Hold a class debate. Decide in advance whether you are going to argue for or against the following practices:
   a. The use of additives in foods.
   b. A vegetarian diet.
   c. The use of vitamin and mineral pills to supplement the diet.

FOR FURTHER READING

Cohen, I. Bernard, ed., *The Career of William Beaumont and the Reception of His Discovery.* Ayer Co., New York, 1980.

Editors of Time-Life Books, *Wholesome Diet,* Time-Life Books, Alexandria, VA, 1981.

Goldberg, Myron D., and Rubin, Julie, *The Inside Tract: The Complete Guide to Digestive Disorders,* Beaufort Books, New York, 1983.

Moog, Florence, "The Lining of the Small Intestine," *Scientific American,* November, 1981.

Peavy, Linda, and Smith, Ursula, *Food, Nutrition, and You,* Scribner's, New York, 1982.

Ward, Brian, *Food and Digestion,* Franklin Watts, New York, 1982.

A scanning electron micrograph of heart muscle tissue.

Chapter 9
TRANSPORT

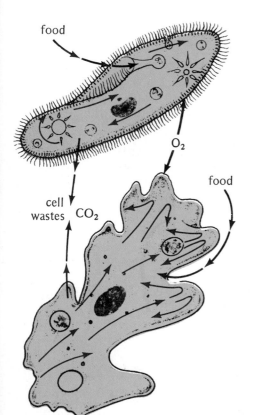
Figure 9-1. Transport in Ameba and Paramecium. In the paramecium (top) and ameba (bottom), the exchange of materials between the cells and the environment occurs by diffusion through the cell membrane.

food

O_2

cell wastes

CO_2

food

THE TRANSPORT PROCESS

Objective:
Describe the transport process and explain its importance to the organism.

9-1 Absorption and Circulation

Every cell needs substances from the environment to carry on its life processes. To enter the cell, these substances must move across cell membranes in a process called *absorption.* Once in the cell, substances must be moved to where they are to be used or stored. In multicellular organisms, materials must also be moved from one part of the organism to another. The movement of materials within a cell or between parts of an organism is called **circulation** (ser-kyoo-*lay*-shun). The term **transport** refers to circulation and all other processes by which substances pass into or out of cells and move within the organism.

In simple organisms, the processes of diffusion, active transport, and cytoplasmic streaming are adequate for circulating materials within cells and between cells. However, in large or complex organisms, many cells are far from the external environment. Such organisms need a special circulatory system to move materials to all parts of the organism. The circulatory system links the cells of the organism to its environment.

A circulatory system has three components: (1) a fluid in which transported materials are dissolved; (2) a network of tubes or body spaces through which the fluid flows; and (3) a means of driving the fluid through the tubes or spaces. In animals, the circulatory fluid is usually called *blood.* The organ that pumps blood through the system is called the *heart.*

ADAPTATIONS FOR CIRCULATION

Objectives:
1. Describe the process of transport in the ameba, paramecium, and hydra.
2. Compare the circulatory system of the earthworm with that of the grasshopper.

9-2   Transport in Protists

Protists have no circulatory system. Most are one-celled, and even in the colonial forms, most of the cells are in direct contact with the environment. Diffusion and active transport are adequate to transport materials between the organism and the external environment. Within the cell, the distribution of material is aided by *cyclosis*, which is the streaming of the cytoplasm.

In the ameba and paramecium, food vacuoles circulate through the cytoplasm by cyclosis (see Figure 9-1). As the food is digested, absorption takes place by diffusion or active transport across the food vacuole membrane.

9-3   Transport in Hydra

Simple multicellular animals, such as the hydra, can also get along without a circulatory system. The hydra lives in fresh water. Its body form is like a hollow sac (see Figure 9-2). The body wall of the hydra is composed of two layers of cells. The outer layer, the ectoderm, is in direct contact with the aquatic environment. The inner layer, the endoderm, lines the gastrovascular cavity. The endoderm is also in contact with water because water freely enters and leaves the gastrovascular cavity through the mouth. Therefore, both cell layers can exchange dissolved oxygen, carbon dioxide, and wastes directly with their watery environment by diffusion.

Nutrients from the gastrovascular cavity pass into the cells of the endoderm by active transport and diffusion. The outer layer of ectodermal cells absorbs nutrients from adjoining endoderm cells by diffusion. Within all cells, nutrients and other substances are circulated by cyclosis.

The muscular movements of the hydra as it stretches and contracts help to distribute materials within the gastrovascular cavity. This movement brings needed materials to all cells of the endoderm. It also prevents wastes from collecting near the surface of the endoderm. The flagella of endoderm cells also help move materials. Thus the gastrovascular cavity serves both a circulatory function and a digestive function in hydra.

9-4   Transport in the Earthworm

The earthworm is structurally much more complex than the hydra. It contains true organs and organ systems. Most of its cells are not in direct contact with the external environment.

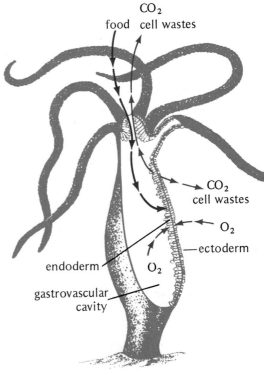

Figure 9-2. Transport in Hydra. In hydras, the cells of both layers of the body wall are in direct contact with the environment. The exchange of materials between the cells and the environment takes place by diffusion through the cell membranes.

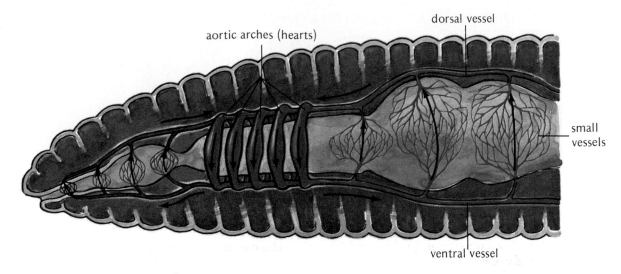

Figure 9-3. Circulatory System of the Earthworm. In the closed circulatory system of the earthworm, the blood is pumped through a system of vessels by the contractions of five pairs of "hearts."

The circulatory system of the earthworm makes possible the exchange of materials between the external environment and body cells.

The main features of the circulatory system of the earthworm are shown in Figure 9-3. The blood carries dissolved nutrients, gases, wastes, water, and other substances. It is red because it contains the red pigment **hemoglobin** (*hee*-muh-gloh-bin). Hemoglobin increases the oxygen-carrying capacity of the blood. The circulatory system of the earthworm is an example of a **closed circulatory system,** one in which the blood is always confined in vessels.

There are two major blood vessels in the earthworm—the *dorsal* (*dor*-sul) *vessel*, which runs along the top of the digestive tract, and the *ventral* (*ven*-trul) *vessel*, which runs below the digestive tract. These two vessels are connected near the anterior, or head, end of the worm by five pairs of blood vessels known as **aortic** (ay-*ort*-ik) **arches,** or "hearts." The pulsations of these heartlike blood vessels pump the blood from the dorsal vessel to the ventral vessel.

The ventral vessel divides into many smaller vessels that go to all parts of the body. These small blood vessels branch into still smaller and smaller vessels. The smallest blood vessels are the microscopic **capillaries** (*kap*-uh-ler-eez), which are so numerous that every cell in the body is near one. The exchange of materials between the blood and the body cells takes place through the walls of the capillaries. Dissolved materials diffuse across the thin walls of capillaries quite rapidly. The capillaries join to form larger vessels that carry the blood back to the dorsal vessel. The dorsal blood vessel contracts rhythmically, forcing the blood back into the aortic arches.

9-5   Transport in the Grasshopper

The grasshopper has an **open circulatory system.** In an open circulatory system, the blood is not always enclosed in blood

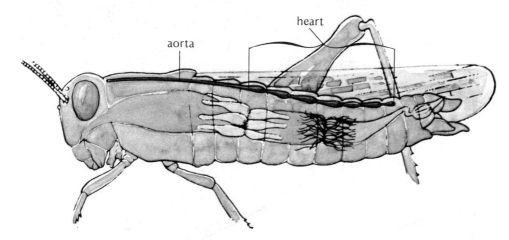

Figure 9-4. Circulatory System of the Grasshopper. In the open circulatory system of the grasshopper, blood pumped by the tubular heart passes through the aorta and into the body spaces, where it bathes the body tissues.

vessels, but flows into open spaces where it bathes the tissues of the body directly.

The blood of the grasshopper does not contain hemoglobin and is colorless. It serves mainly to transport food and nitrogen-containing wastes. It does not transport oxygen or carbon dioxide. Instead, these respiratory gases are transported in a series of tubes that are separate from the circulatory system.

The open circulatory system of the grasshopper is quite different from the closed system of the earthworm (see Figure 9-4). Along the upper, or dorsal, surface, above the digestive and reproductive systems, is a single vessel, the **aorta** (ay-*ort*-uh), and a tubular heart. Contraction of the heart, which is near the posterior, or rear, end of the animal, forces the blood forward through the aorta toward the head. In the head, the blood flows out of the aorta and trickles through the body spaces, or *sinuses* (*sy*-nuh-sez), and over the body tissues. The exchange of materials between the blood and the body cells takes place while the blood is in the sinuses. Blood is kept moving through the sinuses by breathing movements and other body movements. Eventually, the blood passes back into the heart through valvelike openings in the heart wall.

A basic characteristic of an open circulatory system is that the blood moves more slowly than in a closed circulatory system, where it is under pressure. However, open circulatory systems are efficient enough to meet the needs of insects and several other groups of animals.

THE HUMAN CIRCULATORY SYSTEM

Objectives:
1. Describe and compare the structures of an artery, a vein, and a capillary.
2. Identify the structures of the heart and describe their functions.
3. Trace the path of the blood through the heart.

4. Describe the heartbeat cycle and the mechanisms that control the rate and strength of the heartbeat.
5. State the factors that cause variations in blood pressure.

Humans, like other vertebrates, have a closed circulatory system. It is similar to that of the earthworm, but more complex. The system includes a single heart, which pumps the blood, and a network of blood vessels, which carries the blood to and from all the cells of the body. There are three kinds of blood vessels—arteries, veins, and capillaries.

9-6   Blood Vessels

Arteries. The blood vessels that carry blood away from the heart to the organs and tissues of the body are the **arteries** (*ar*-tuh-reez). The walls of arteries are thick and elastic. They contain layers of connective tissue, muscle tissue, and epithelial tissue (see Figure 9-5). As an artery enters a tissue or organ, it divides and subdivides many times to form smaller and smaller arteries. The smallest arteries are called *arterioles* (ar-*teer*-ee-olz).

Veins. The blood vessels that return blood from the body tissues to the heart are the **veins** *(vaynz)*. The smallest veins are called *venules* (*veen*-yoolz.) The venules join together to form veins, which also merge, forming larger and larger veins. The walls of veins are thin and only slightly elastic. Inside the veins are flaplike **valves** that allow the blood to flow in only

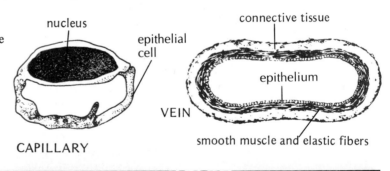
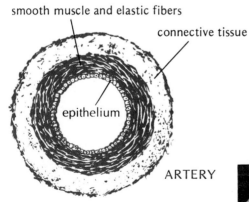

ARTERY   CAPILLARY   VEIN

Figure 9-5. Structure of Blood Vessels. The diagram above shows the structure of an artery (left), a capillary (middle), and a vein (right). Because the walls of veins contain less muscle tissue than the walls of arteries, they are often partially collapsed. In the scanning electron micrograph (right), which vessel is an artery and which is a vein?

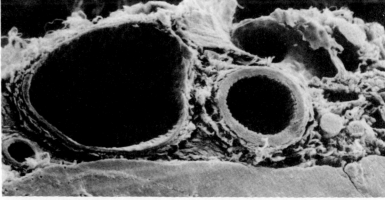

one direction—toward the heart (see Figure 9-6). When the valves do not function properly, blood tends to accumulate within the vein. The walls of the vein become stretched and lose their elasticity. This condition is called *varicose* (*var*-uh-kohs) *veins.*

Capillaries. Arterioles and venules are connected by networks of microscopic capillaries. The walls of the capillaries consist of a single layer of epithelial cells. These vessels are so narrow that red blood cells pass through them in single file. Dissolved nutrients, wastes, oxygen, and other substances are exchanged between the blood and the body cells while blood flows through the capillaries.

9-7   The Heart

The heart is a pump whose rhythmic contractions force the blood through the vessels. This muscular organ is somewhat larger than your fist and is located slightly to the left of the middle of the chest cavity. It is composed mostly of cardiac muscle. Microscope studies show that this tissue consists of individual cells, each with a single nucleus (see Figure 9-7). The cardiac muscle cells form a branching, interlocking network, which enables them to contract with great force.

The outside of the heart is surrounded by a tough protective membrane, the **pericardium** (per-uh-*kard*-ee-um). Internally, the heart is divided into four chambers (see Figure 9-8). The two upper, thin-walled chambers are the **atria** (*ay*-tree-uh), or *auricles* (*or*-ih-kulz). The two lower, thick-walled chambers are the **ventricles** (*ven*-trih-kulz). The right and left sides of the heart are separated by a partition called the *septum* (*sep*-tum).

The flow of blood through the heart is controlled by four flaplike valves that allow the blood to flow in only one direction. Two of these valves, called the *atrioventricular* (ay-tree-oh-ven-*trik*-yoo-ler), or *A-V, valves,* allow blood to flow from the atria into the ventricles. They prevent the flow of blood from the ventricles into the atria. In the right side of the heart, the A-V valve is called the *tricuspid* (try-*kus*-pid) valve because it has three flaps. In the left side, it is called the *bicuspid* (by-*kus*-pid), or *mitral* (*my*-trul) *valve.* The other two valves, called the *semilunar* (sem-ee-*loon*-er) *valves,* allow blood to move from the ventricles into the pulmonary artery and the aorta. They prevent backflow from these arteries into the ventricles.

Actually, the heart is a double pump. The right side of the heart sends oxygen-poor blood to the lungs, while the left side sends oxygen-rich blood to the rest of the body.

The heartbeat cycle. The pumping action of the heart involves two main periods. During one of these periods, the heart muscle is relaxed. This period of relaxation is called **diastole** (dy-*as*-tuh-lee). During the other period, the heart muscle is contracting. The period of contraction is called **systole** (*sis*-tuh-lee).

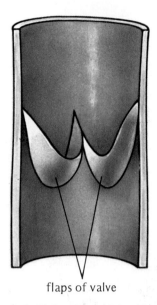

flaps of valve

Figure 9-6. Valve in a Vein. This longitudinal section of a vein shows the cuplike valve that prevents the backflow of blood.

Figure 9-7. Structure of Cardiac Muscle.

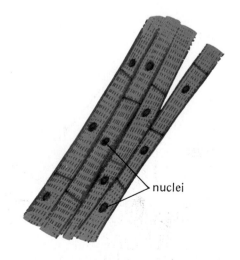

nuclei

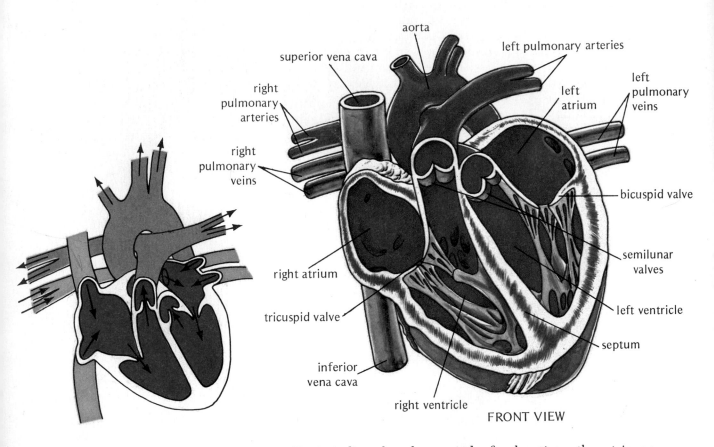

aorta

superior vena cava

left pulmonary arteries

right pulmonary arteries

left atrium

left pulmonary veins

right pulmonary veins

bicuspid valve

right atrium

semilunar valves

tricuspid valve

left ventricle

septum

inferior vena cava

right ventricle

FRONT VIEW

Figure 9-8. Structure of the Human Heart. The cross section of the heart (right) shows the four chambers, the valves, and the blood vessels that connect with the heart chambers. The small drawing above shows the path of the blood through the heart.

During diastole—the period of relaxation—the atrioventricular (A-V) valves are open. Blood flows from the atria into the ventricles. By the end of diastole, the ventricles are about 70 percent filled. Systole—the period of contraction—begins with contraction of the atria. The contraction of the atria forces more blood into the ventricles, filling them. The ventricles then contract. The pressure of this contraction closes the A-V valves and opens the semilunar valves. Blood flows out of the right ventricle into the pulmonary artery, which divides into two pulmonary arteries that lead to the lungs. Blood flows out of the left ventricle into the aorta, the largest artery of the body. The aorta branches and divides into many smaller arteries, which carry blood to all the body tissues.

While the ventricles are contracting, the atria relax. This permits blood to flow into the atria from the veins. Blood returning from the body tissues enters the right atrium. Blood returning from the lungs enters the left atrium. When the ventricles relax, a new period of diastole begins, and the cycle repeats.

As the heart valves open and close, they make a "lub-dup" sound that may be heard clearly through a stethoscope. The "lub" sound is produced by the closing of the tricuspid and bicuspid (A-V) valves. The "dup" sound is made by the closing of the semilunar valves. If any of the heart valves are damaged, there will be a leakage, or backflow, of blood at certain times during the heartbeat cycle. This produces abnormal heart sounds, commonly known as "heart murmurs."

Control of the heartbeat. The cardiac muscle that makes up the heart is different from the other muscle tissues of the body. Unlike other types of muscles, cardiac muscle fibers form a network, or lattice. The arrangement of muscle fibers is such that the atria are one functional unit and the ventricles are another.

The contraction of other types of muscle is controlled by the nervous system. Cardiac muscle, however, has a built-in, or innate, ability to contract. Even when it is removed from the body, the heart will keep beating for a while if kept in a special solution. Each heart-muscle fiber has its own innate rate of contraction. However, the heart must function as a unit. This is made possible by a structure in the heart called the *sinoatrial* (sy-no-*ay*-tree-ul) *node*, also called the **pacemaker**. The pacemaker is a specialized group of muscle cells in the wall of the right atrium. Contraction of the heart is initiated by electrical impulses from the pacemaker. A specialized system of fibers carries the impulses to all parts of the heart, causing the atria to contract first, and then the ventricles.

The minute electrical current produced each time the heart contracts can be recorded on a machine that produces an *electrocardiogram* (eh-lek-troh-*kard*-ee-o-gram), or *EKG* (see Figure 9-9). Physicians use electrocardiograms to check the health of the heart.

The rate of the heartbeat is regulated by certain nerves that enter the pacemaker. Impulses from the *vagus* (*vay*-gus) *nerves* slow down the pacemaker, while impulses from the *cardioaccelerator* (*kard*-ee-oh-ak-*sel*-uh-ray-tur) *nerves* speed up the pacemaker. The built-in rhythm of the heart is also affected by changes in body temperature and by certain chemicals circulating in the blood.

When the natural pacemaker of the heart does not function properly, the wires from a battery-powered electronic pacemaker can be attached surgically to the heart to regulate the heartbeat.

Frontier of Biology

The Artificial Heart

In recent years, several patients with severe heart disease and near death have received an artificial heart. One type of heart implant, the so-called Jarvik-7, is shown above. To implant it, the surgeon removes the diseased heart's ventricles and connects the mechanical heart to the remaining chambers, the left and right atria. The mechanical heart is powered by air pumped from an external source.

Results to date with the artificial heart suggest that efforts to perfect it should continue. There are unanswered questions, however. Who will pay the enormous operative and care costs? Should research dollars be spent on the artificial heart or on upgrading the health of natural hearts? These and other important questions as yet unknown will be debated at length in the future.

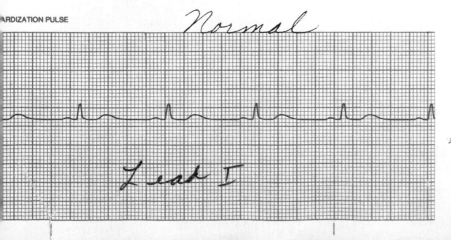

Figure 9-9. Electrocardiogram. The electrocardiogram records the changing electrical currents produced by the contractions of the heart. This electrocardiogram is from a normal heart.

9-8 Blood Pressure and the Flow of Blood

The thick, muscular walls of the arteries are elastic. When the ventricles contract, blood is forced out under great pressure into the arteries. Because of their elasticity, arteries can expand and absorb this great pressure. As the ventricles relax, the pressure decreases. However, the elasticity of the artery walls helps to maintain the pressure between heartbeats. In this way, blood is kept flowing continuously. The **pulse** is the alternate expansion (high pressure) and relaxation (lower pressure) that can be felt in an artery each time the left ventricle contracts and relaxes. Both the rate and the force of the heartbeat are reflected in the pulse.

The blood in the arteries is under pressure. Physicians measure arterial blood pressure with an instrument called a *sphygmomanometer* (sfig-moh-muh-*nahm*-uh-ter). Pressure is measured in terms of the height of a column of mercury in a tube in this instrument. During systole in an average adult at rest, the pressure is enough to support a column of mercury about 120 millimeters high. During diastole, the pressure drops, and the maximum height of the mercury is only about 80 millimeters. Blood pressure is commonly stated in the form of systolic pressure/diastolic pressure. Thus the normal blood pressure in a resting adult is 120/80. During exercise and time of stress, blood pressure increases.

High blood pressure, or *hypertension* (*hy*-per-ten-shun), is a condition in which the blood pressure remains much above normal throughout the heartbeat cycle. It is a serious and fairly common health problem. One frequent cause of high blood pressure is *atherosclerosis* (ath-uh-roh-skluh-*roh*-sis), a disease commonly called "hardening of the arteries." In this disease, deposits of cholesterol and other fatty materials collect on the inner walls of the arteries (see Figure 9-10). The

Figure 9-10. Atherosclerosis. The large deposit of fatty material in this artery has greatly narrowed the space through which blood can flow.

fatty deposit

reduced opening for blood flow

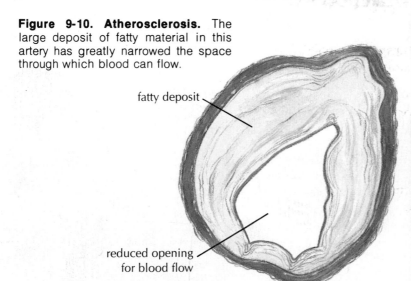
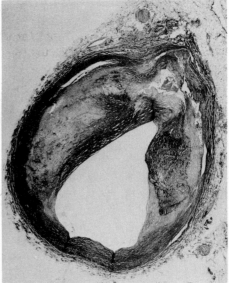

arteries become narrower and the walls inelastic, causing the blood pressure to increase. The condition puts a strain on both the heart and the blood vessels. If untreated, it can lead to heart attacks and strokes. Many studies indicate that the chance of developing atherosclerosis increases with the amount of cholesterol in the blood. This, in turn, seems to be related to the amount of fat, particularly animal fat, in the diet. Many physicians recommend that the amount of fat in the diet be kept low for this reason.

As the blood flows through the arteries, there is relatively little drop in pressure. However, there is a large drop when it reaches the arterioles. At the capillary ends of the arterioles there are rings of muscle, the *precapillary sphincters*, that control the blood flow through the capillaries. The capillaries are the most numerous blood vessels in the body. If all the capillaries were open at the same time, there would not be enough blood to fill them. The opening and closing of the precapillary sphincters directs the flow of blood to the parts of the body where it is needed. For example, when you run, the flow of blood into the capillaries of the skeletal muscles is increased, while the supply of blood to the capillaries of the digestive tract is decreased.

By the time blood reaches the veins, pressure is low. It is too low to return the blood to the heart, especially from the lower parts of the body. Blood flow in the veins is assisted by the squeezing action of the skeletal muscles as the body moves. As a contracting muscle presses against a vein, the blood in the vein is forced to move. The blood moves toward the heart, since the valves in the veins prevent flow in the opposite direction.

PATHWAYS OF HUMAN CIRCULATION

Objectives:
1. Trace the path of the blood through the pulmonary circulation and discuss the exchange of gases that occurs in the lungs.
2. Trace the path of the blood through the systemic circulation, including the coronary, hepatic-portal, and renal circulations.

In the second century A.D., a Greek physician proposed that blood flowed back and forth from the heart to the rest of the body through the veins. It was not until 1628 that the English physician William Harvey proposed the correct pathway for blood circulation. Harvey demonstrated that the heart pumps blood to the organs through arteries and that veins carry blood back to the heart. He thought that connections between the ends of tiny arteries and the ends of tiny veins must exist, but he could not find these connecting vessels. In 1660, an Italian

■ **Career** ■

Emergency Medical Technician

Emergency medical technicians, or EMTs, are popularly known as "paramedics." They generally drive ambulances and provide emergency treatment to victims of accidents, heart attacks, drowning, and other life-threatening events. They must determine the type of injury or illness and give appropriate emergency treatment when needed. Their job may include the control of bleeding, immobilization of fractures, administration of cardiopulmonary resuscitation, restoration of breathing, and treatment of shock. EMTs transport the patient to the hospital and provide the doctor with a full report on the treatment given and background of the case.

Emergency medical technicians work for police and fire departments, for private ambulance companies, and for hospitals. An EMT must pass a standard 81-hour course designed by the U.S. Department of Transportation. Such courses are given by police and fire departments as well as hospitals and colleges.

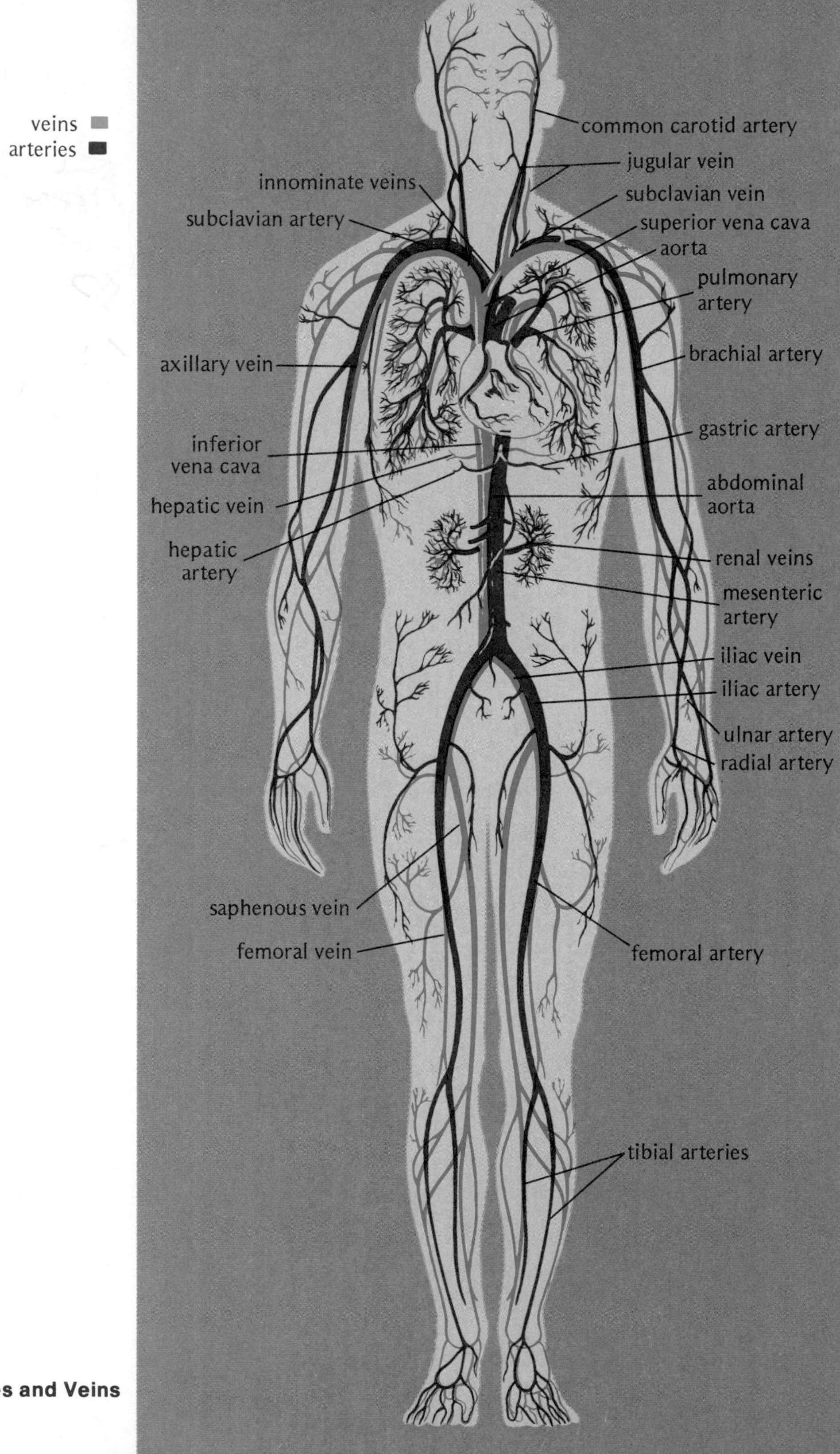

veins ▪
arteries ▪

common carotid artery
jugular vein
innominate veins
subclavian vein
subclavian artery
superior vena cava
aorta
pulmonary artery
axillary vein
brachial artery
gastric artery
inferior vena cava
abdominal aorta
hepatic vein
renal veins
hepatic artery
mesenteric artery
iliac vein
iliac artery
ulnar artery
radial artery
saphenous vein
femoral vein
femoral artery
tibial arteries

Figure 9-11. Major Arteries and Veins of the Human Body.

anatomist demonstrated that capillaries connect arteries to veins. Thus, Harvey's theory of the circulation of the blood was proved correct.

The major arteries and veins of the human circulatory system are shown in Figure 9-11.

As shown in Figure 9-12, the two major pathways of the blood are the **pulmonary** (*pul*-muh-ner-ee) **circulation** and the **systemic** (sis-*tem*-ik) **circulation.** The pulmonary circulation carries blood between the heart and the lungs. The systemic circulation carries blood between the heart and the rest of the body.

9-9 Pulmonary Circulation

Blood returning to the heart from the body tissues is low in oxygen and high in carbon dioxide. This blood enters the right atrium and flows into the right ventricle. The right ventricle pumps it through the pulmonary arteries to the lungs. The pulmonary arteries are the only arteries that carry oxygen-poor blood. All other arteries carry oxygen-rich blood. As the blood travels through the capillaries in the lungs, it gains oxygen and gets rid of carbon dioxide. The pulmonary capillaries merge into pulmonary veins, which carry the oxygen-rich blood to the left atrium of the heart. The pulmonary veins are the only veins that carry oxygen-rich blood. All other veins carry oxygen-poor blood.

9-10   Systemic Circulation

From the left atrium the blood enters the left ventricle. The systemic circulation begins in the left ventricle of the heart. The powerful left ventricle has thicker walls than the other chambers of the heart because it pumps blood throughout the body. From the left ventricle, the blood is pumped out into the aorta. The aorta branches, forming arteries that serve all parts of the body. The arteries divide and subdivide, forming smaller and smaller vessels, and finally forming capillaries. Every cell in the body is near a capillary. The exchange of materials between the blood and the body tissues takes place through the walls of the capillaries. Capillaries merge to form veins, which ultimately return the blood to the heart. The largest veins of the body, the **superior vena cava** (*vee*-nuh *kay*-vuh) and the **inferior vena cava,** empty into the right atrium of the heart. The superior vena cava returns blood from the head, arms, and chest; the inferior vena cava returns blood from the lower body regions.

The systemic circulation includes three subdivisions of special importance—the **coronary** (*kar*-uh-ner-ee) **circulation,** the **hepatic-portal** (heh-*pat*-ik *port*-ul) **circulation,** and the **renal** (*reen*-ul) **circulation.**

Coronary circulation. The coronary circulation supplies blood to the muscle of the heart. The right and left coronary arteries branch off the aorta just after the aorta leaves the

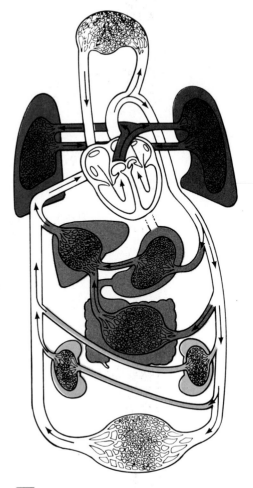

■ PULMONARY CIRCULATION
■ HEPATIC-PORTAL CIRCULATION
■ RENAL CIRCULATION

9-12. Pulmonary and Systemic Circulations. The pulmonary circulation includes the flow of blood between the heart and the lungs. The rest of the pathways, including the hepatic-portal and renal circulations, make up the systemic circulation.

heart. The coronary arteries run down either side of the heart, with branches entering the heart muscle. Within the heart, the arteries divide, eventually forming capillaries. The veins that drain the heart muscle empty directly into the chambers of the heart, mostly the right atrium. The cells of the heart require a constant supply of nutrients and oxygen. When a coronary artery is blocked by a blood clot or fat deposit, a heart attack can occur.

Hepatic-portal circulation. Generally, blood travels through only one set of capillaries before it returns to the heart. An exception is the hepatic-portal circulation, which transports blood from the digestive tract to the liver. Blood passing through the capillaries of the digestive tract picks up nutrients. Veins draining these capillaries do not lead directly back to the heart. Instead, they form the *portal vein*, which goes to the liver. Within the liver, the vein divides into smaller veins and then into vessels similar to capillaries—the *hepatic sinuses.* Fluids, nutrients, and even blood proteins diffuse easily out of the blood and into intercellular spaces in the liver. Blood in the sinuses of the liver is collected by a number of hepatic veins, which empty into the inferior vena cava.

The hepatic-portal circulation serves a vital homeostatic function. As blood passes through the liver, excess glucose is absorbed by the liver cells and converted to glycogen, which is then stored. If no food has been eaten for a time, the blood reaching the liver from the digestive tract will be low in glucose. The liver then converts some of its stored glycogen to glucose, which diffuses out of the liver cells and into the blood. Thus, the liver helps to maintain the blood glucose concentration at a constant level.

Renal circulation. One of the functions of the blood is to carry off the wastes of the body tissues. These wastes must be disposed of, or excreted. The gaseous waste product carbon dioxide is carried by the pulmonary circulation to the lungs and is excreted there. Other wastes are removed from the blood and excreted by the kidneys. The renal circulation is the special branch of the systemic circulation that carries blood to and from the kidneys.

THE HUMAN LYMPHATIC SYSTEM

Objectives:
1. Describe the formation, composition, and function of intercellular fluid.
2. Identify the structures of the lymphatic system and explain their functions.

9-11 Intercellular Fluid

All the cells of the body are bathed in a colorless, watery

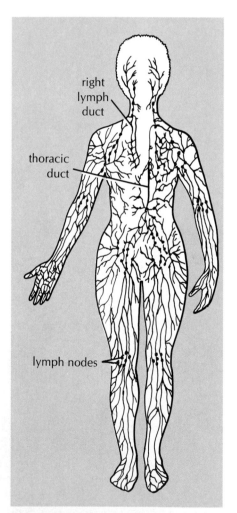

Figure 9-13. Human Lymphatic System. All tissues of the body are drained by vessels of the lymphatic system.

fluid called the **intercellular** (in-ter-*sel*-yoo-ler), or *interstitial* (in-ter-*stish*-ul), **fluid.** This fluid serves as a medium for the exchange of materials between the capillaries and the body cells. All substances exchanged between the blood and the body cells must diffuse through the intercellular fluid.

The intercellular fluid is formed from the liquid part of the blood (plasma) that diffuses out of the capillaries. It consists mostly of water and salts, but also contains proteins and nutrients. Diffusion of intercellular fluid into the body tissues occurs at the arteriolar end of the capillaries. At the venous end of the capillaries, most of the intercellular fluid and some of the substances it contains diffuse back into the capillaries. However, some of the fluid and all of the proteins remain outside the capillaries.

9-12   Structure and Function of the Lymphatic System

Excess fluid and proteins from the intercellular spaces are returned to the blood by a system of vessels called the **lymphatic** (lim-*fat*-ik) **system** (see Figure 9-13). Without the lymphatic system, the constant loss of fluid from the blood would drain the circulatory system, and the body tissues would be flooded. The lymphatic system begins in the body tissues with *lymph capillaries*, microscopic tubes that are closed at one end. The walls of these tubes are only one cell layer thick. Openings between the cells allow intercellular fluid and proteins to pass readily into the lymphatic vessels. The fluid inside the vessels is called **lymph.** Like veins, lymphatic vessels have flaplike valves that allow the lymph to flow only in one direction. Muscular activity squeezes the lymph vessels and pushes the lymph along.

The lymphatic capillaries merge to form larger and larger vessels. Eventually, all the lymph from the lower part of the body, the left side of the head and chest, and the left arm flows into the *thoracic* (thuh-*ras*-ik) *duct*, the largest lymphatic vessel in the body. Lymph from the thoracic duct is emptied into a large vein at the left side of the neck. All lymph from the right side of the head, the right arm, and the right side of the chest enters the *right lymph duct*, which drains into a large vein on the right side of the neck. In this way, fluid and proteins lost from the blood in the capillaries is returned to the circulation.

The lymph vessels in the villi of the small intestine are called *lacteals.* The products of fat digestion enter the lacteals and eventually enter the circulating blood with the lymph.

At various places along the lymphatic vessels there are **lymph nodes,** or *lymph glands*, which play an important role in the body's defense against disease (see Figure 9-14). They filter foreign matter from the lymph, preventing cancer cells, bacteria, and other disease-causing organisms from entering the bloodstream. They also produce some types of white

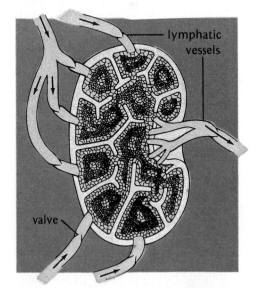

Figure 9-14. Structure of a Lymph Node. Foreign matter, including disease-causing organisms, are filtered out of the lymph in the lymph nodes.

blood cells (lymphocytes) whose products can destroy bacteria and other foreign substances. In the area of an infection, the lymph node may become enlarged and sore. These "swollen glands" indicate that the body is fighting an infection.

Lymphoid tissue like that found in lymph nodes is also found in the *spleen*, an organ located near the stomach. In the spleen, the lymphoid tissues filter out bacteria and worn-out red cells from the blood.

Chapter Review

SUMMARY

- Transport enables cells to exchange substances with their environment. The transport of materials into, out of, and within a cell takes place by diffusion and active transport, as well as by streaming of the cytoplasm. In one-celled and simple multicellular organisms, these processes are adequate for circulation. Larger, more complex organisms have specialized circulatory systems.

- The earthworm has a closed circulatory system, while insects have open circulatory systems. All vertebrates have closed circulatory systems.

- Humans have a closed circulatory system consisting of a heart and a complex network of blood vessels. The three kinds of blood vessels are arteries, capillaries, and veins.

- The muscular, four-chambered heart pumps blood rhythmically by means of alternating contractions of the atria and ventricles. Valves in the heart keep the blood flowing in only one direction. The heart is a double pump—the right side pumps blood to the lungs while the left side pumps blood to the rest of the body except the lungs. The basic heartbeat rate is determined by the pacemaker. Blood pressure is affected by the action of the heartbeat and by changes in the diameter of the arteries.

- The two major pathways of blood in the body are the pulmonary circulation and the systemic circulation. The systemic circulation includes the coronary, hepatic-portal, and renal circulations.

- The intercellular fluid bathes all the cells of the body. The lymphatic system returns intercellular fluid to the circulatory system and is part of the body's defense system against disease.

KNOW THE TERMS

aorta	diastole	open circulatory system	systole
aortic arches	hemoglobin	pacemaker	transport
artery	hepatic-portal circulation	pericardium	valve
atrium	inferior vena cava	pulmonary circulation	vein
capillary	intercellualar fluid	pulse	ventricle
circulation	lymph	renal circulation	
closed circulatory system	lymphatic system	superior vena cava	
coronary circulation	lymph node	systematic circulation	

SECTION QUESTIONS

The Transport Process

1. What is the function of a circulatory system?
2. What are the basic parts of a circulatory system?

Adaptations For Circulation

3. What processes are involved in the transport of materials in the protists?
4. What is a closed circulatory system?
5. What does the blood of the grasshopper transport?

The Human Circulatory System

6. Name the three kinds of blood vessels.
7. Name the four chambers of the heart.
8. Name the valves of the human heart.
9. What structure makes the heart-muscle fibers function as a unit?
10. What is the pulse?

Pathways of Human Circulation

11. Which arteries carry oxygen-poor blood?
12. What parts of the body are served by the systemic circulation?
13. What are the three major subdivisions of the systemic circulation?

Human Lymphatic System

14. What is the intercellular fluid?
15. What substances are contained in intercellular fluid?
16. What is the lymphatic system?
17. Name the fluid in the lymphatic system.

KNOW THE FACTS

Copy the number of each statement below on a piece of paper. Beside each number, write whether the statement is true or false. If the statement is false, replace the italicized word(s) with a term(s) that will make the statement true.

1. *Circulation* refers to all the processes by which substances pass into or out of cells and move within the organism.
2. *Cyclosis* is the streaming of the cytoplasm in a cell.
3. *Hemoglobin* is a red pigment that increases the oxygen-carrying capacity of the blood.
4. In a *closed* circulatory system, the blood is not always enclosed in blood vessels but flows into open spaces.
5. *Arteries* are blood vessels that carry blood toward the heart.
6. Substances are exchanged between the blood and the body cells while blood flows through *capillaries.*
7. The *pericardium* is a partition that separates the right and left sides of the heart.
8. The *ventricles* are the thin-walled upper chambers of the heart.
9. The heart is a *double* pump.
10. The period during the heartbeat cycle when the heart relaxes is called *systole.*
11. The *aorta* is the largest artery of the body.
12. Only *heart muscle* has a built-in, or innate, ability to contract.
13. An *electrocardiogram* is a recording of the electric current of the heart.
14. *Hypertension* is commonly called "hardening of the arteries."
15. Blood pressure is the *highest* in the veins.
16. The *pulmonary veins* are the only veins that carry oxygen-rich blood.
17. The largest veins of the body are the *jugular veins.*
18. The *coronary circulation* supplies blood to the muscle of the heart.

UNDERSTAND THE CONCEPTS

19. How do the cells of the hydra obtain nutrients and oxygen, and get rid of wastes?
20. Describe the circulation of blood in the earthworm.
21. Describe the circulation of blood in the grasshopper.
22. What is the function of valves in a circulatory system?
23. Trace the path of blood through the human heart.
24. How is the rate of the heartbeat controlled?
25. What forces the blood through the arteries?
26. What happens when the walls of the arteries lose their elasticity?
27. What controls the flow of blood through the capillaries?
28. How is the blood moved through the veins of the body?

29. Describe the pathway of the pulmonary circulation.
30. Explain the function of the pulmonary circulation.
31. How is the function of the superior vena cava different from that of the inferior vena cava?
32. Explain the function of the hepatic-portal circulation.
33. What is the function of the renal circulation?
34. What is the function of intercellular fluid?
35. Trace lymph from a lymph capillary until it is returned to the blood.
36. What are the functions of the lymphatic system?
37. Why is the swelling of the lymph nodes a cause of concern?

THINK CRITICALLY

38. Explain why large animals require a pump as part of their circulatory system.
39. A circulatory system is an advantage for the earthworm. Explain whether it would be an advantage for the hydra.
40. In more complex animals such as mammals, why is a closed circulatory system a more efficient mechanism than is an open circulatory system?

41. In what ways does an organism with a separate pulmonary circulation benefit?
42. Compare and contrast the open circulatory system of the grasshopper with the closed circulatory system of the earthworm.
43. In what ways is the circulatory system dependent on the lymphatic system?

THINK CREATIVELY

44. Would you expect the heart of an athlete to be larger than the heart of an inactive individual of similar age and weight? Why or why not?
45. Propose an explanation for the tendency of muscles used in swimming to tire more

easily if a person goes swimming immediately after eating.
46. If you were a scientist trying to find a way to produce artificial arteries for use in surgery, what qualities in the material used to construct the arteries would you look for?

FOR FURTHER INVESTIGATION

1. Obtain a beef, sheep, or hog heart from a butcher. Make a drawing of its external structure, adding a written description of its major features. Dissect the heart and describe its internal structure.
2. After holding one arm high in the air and letting the other hang at your side for two

minutes, compare the veins and color of each hand. Explain why there are differences.
3. Using reference materials, find out about the experiments of William Harvey. Then prepare a television script in which you show how he demonstrated the correct pathway for circulation.

4. Take a short course to learn how to do cardiopulmonary resuscitation (CPR). (The American Red Cross offers reputable courses.) Demonstrate the procedure for your class.
5. Prepare a report on one of the career opportunities listed below. See suggested procedures, p. 9, "For Further Investigation" Activity 3.
   a. Electrocardiograph technician
   b. Intensive-care nurse
   c. Cardiologist
6. Prepare a brief report on the life and contributions of one of the following scientists:
   a. Daniel Williams   c. Florence Sabin
   b. Edward Hawthorne   d. Helen Taussig
7. With your teacher's or school nurse's supervision, learn how to measure blood pressure with a sphygmomanometer. Then design an experiment to demonstrate that well-conditioned athletes have lower blood pressure and pulse rates than nonathletes. Be sure to control variables such as body weight, sex, and fatigue. Write up your findings in the form of an article that could be published in a science magazine.
8. Do library research on the advantages and disadvantages of coronary-bypass surgery. Write up your findings in the form of a feature article for a magazine or newspaper.
9. One of the leading causes of death in the United States is cardiovascular disease. Do library research on the risk factors involved in cardiovascular disease. What is the role of stress? Present your findings to the class.

FOR FURTHER READING

Comroe, J., "Doctor, You Have Six Minutes," *Science 84*, January/February, 1984.

Jarvik, R. K., "The Total Artificial Heart," *Scientific American*, January, 1981.

Johansen, K., "Aneurysms," *Scientific American*, June, 1982.

Silberner, J., "Anatomy of Atherosclerosis," *Science News*, March 16, 1985.

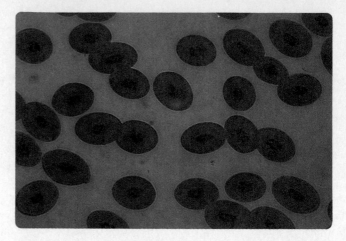

Chapter **10**

THE BLOOD

Red blood cells in frog's blood.

COMPOSITION OF BLOOD

Objective:
Describe the different parts of the blood and explain the functions of each.

10-1 Functions and Components of Blood

Blood is the liquid tissue of transport in humans and other vertebrates. Because it is a liquid, blood can transport dissolved and suspended materials. It carries respiratory gases, nutrients, cellular wastes, and regulatory substances, such as enzymes and hormones.

Blood contributes to the regulation of all bodily functions. It maintains and regulates the chemical state, pH, and water content of cells and body fluids. Blood is also involved in the regulation of body temperature.

Blood protects the body. The white blood cells and certain substances found in the blood protect the body from disease-causing microorganisms. The ability of the blood to clot protects the circulatory system from collapse that could be caused by loss of fluid from a wound.

The average human body contains about 5.5 liters of blood. Blood is a unique tissue in that it is made up of cells suspended in a liquid, the **plasma** (*plaz*-muh). Plasma accounts for about 55 percent of the total volume of the blood, while the cells, or *formed elements*, make up about 45 percent. The formed elements include red blood cells, white blood cells, and platelets. Red blood cells account for most of the volume of the formed elements.

10-2   Plasma

Plasma is a clear, straw-colored liquid (see Figure 10-1). It consists mainly of water (over 90 percent) and dissolved proteins (7 percent). It also contains salts, glucose, amino acids, fatty acids, vitamins, hormones, and cellular wastes.

The three types of protein found in blood plasma are *albumin* (al-*byoo*-min), *globulins* (*glahb*-yoo-linz), and *fibrinogen* (fy-*brin*-uh-jen). Albumin, which is the most abundant of the plasma proteins, causes an osmotic gradient that regulates the diffusion of plasma out of the capillaries into the intercellular spaces. The globulins serve a number of different functions. Some globulins are involved in the transport of proteins and other substances from one part of the body to another. Other globulins, particularly the gamma globulins, play a major role in the body's defense against infection. Fibrinogen is important in the clotting of blood.

10-3   Red Blood Cells

Red blood cells, or **erythrocytes** (eh-*rith*-ruh-syts), are by far the most numerous of the cells in the blood (about 5 million per cubic millimeter of blood). Their major function is to transport oxygen from the lungs to the body tissues and carbon dioxide from the body tissues to the lungs. Red blood cells are disk-shaped cells that are thinner in the center than around the rim (see Figure 10-2). However, they easily change shape. They are filled with the iron-containing pigment *hemoglobin*, which gives blood its characteristic red color. Hemoglobin functions in the transport of oxygen and carbon dioxide. (This is discussed in detail in Chapter 11.)

During the development of the human embryo, red blood cells are produced by various organs, including the liver, spleen, and lymph nodes. After birth, however, they are normally produced only by the bone marrow. Mature red blood

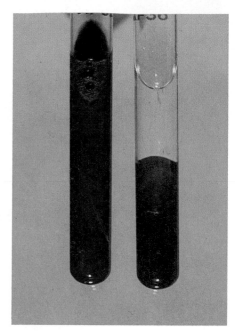

Figure 10-1. Plasma. When whole blood (left) is centrifuged, the cells collect at the bottom of the test tube, leaving the clear, straw-colored plasma at the top (right).

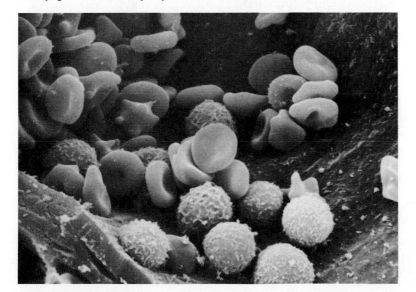

Figure 10-2. Scanning Electron Micrograph of Red Blood Cells and White Blood Cells. The red cells are mostly disk-shaped and thinner in the center than around the outside. The white cells are larger and spherical.

cells contain no nucleus. They live for about 120 days. Worn-out red cells are removed from the circulation by the liver and spleen and broken down. The iron from the hemoglobin molecule is reused by the body.

Anemia (uh-*nee*-mee-uh) is a condition in which a person has too few red blood cells or insufficient hemoglobin. In anemia, the cells of the body do not receive an adequate supply of oxygen. Some forms of anemia can be treated by injections of vitamin B_{12} or by eating iron-rich foods.

10-4   White Blood Cells

The *white blood cells,* or **leukocytes** (*loo*-kuh-syts), protect the body against infection by bacteria and other microorganisms. White cells are larger than red cells, and unlike red cells, they contain one or more nuclei (see Figure 10-2). Leukocytes are produced by the bone marrow and by lymphatic tissues. The mature leukocytes enter the bloodstream. They can squeeze between the cells of capillary walls and move through the body tissues. When there is an infection at a particular site in the body, the leukocytes collect there.

Structurally, there are several different kinds of white blood cells. However, in terms of function, leukocytes fall into two groups. One type acts as *phagocytes* (*fag*-uh-syts), engulfing microorganisms and other matter (see Figure 10-3). The second type is involved in the production of *antibodies* (*ant*-ih-bod-eez), which are protein molecules that attack foreign substances or microorganisms that enter the body.

Normally, there are only 6,000 to 8,000 white blood cells per cubic millimeter of blood. However, when there is an infection in the body, the number may increase to 30,000 per cubic millimeter. Among the phagocytic leukocytes, most can ingest from 5 to 25 bacteria before they die. The pus that forms at the site of an infected wound consists mainly of white blood cells that have died after ingesting bacteria.

Leukemia (loo-*kee*-mee-uh) is a form of blood cancer in which there is an uncontrolled increase in the number of white blood cells. Some forms of leukemia can now be controlled or even cured by drugs.

Figure 10-3. White Blood Cell Engulfing a Chain of Bacteria.

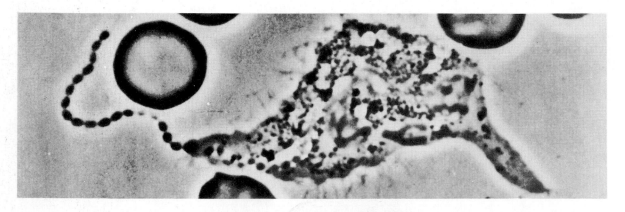

Figure 10-4. Scanning Electron Micrograph of Blood Platelets.

10-5   Platelets

Platelets (*playt*-lets) are small, round or oval fragments of a type of blood cell formed in the bone marrow. A platelet, which has no nucleus, consists of a bit of cytoplasm surrounded by a cell membrane (see Figure 10-4). There are generally from 200,000 to 400,000 platelets per cubic millimeter of blood. Platelets trigger the blood clotting process.

BLOOD CLOTTING

Objective:

Describe the process of blood clotting.

10-6   The Clotting Process

When a blood vessel is broken, the escape of blood is stopped by the formation of a solid mass that plugs up the hole, a *blood clot.* The solidification of blood is called **clotting.** Clotting is carried out primarily by the platelets and the plasma protein fibrinogen. The overall process of blood clotting may be summarized as follows:

1. Clotting is started by the release of a substance called *thromboplastin* (throm-boh-*plas*-tun) from the wall of the injured blood vessel.

2. As soon as the vessel is injured, platelets begin to stick to the broken vessel wall and to release thromboplastin as well.

3. The presence of thromboplastin and of several other factors at the site of the injury causes a complex series of enzyme-controlled reactions to occur that eventually converts the plasma protein *prothrombin* (proh-*throm*-bin) to *thrombin.*

4. Thrombin, which is an enzyme, converts another plasma protein, fibrinogen, into insoluble strands of *fibrin* (*fy*-brin) (see Figure 10-5). Thrombin also makes platelets sticky so that the hole in the vessel wall becomes filled with a mass of platelets and fibrin strands.

5. Red blood cells become trapped in the mass of fibrin strands and platelets and fill in the wound. As water evaporates from the clot, it hardens into a scab.

Figure 10-5. Fibrin Strands and Trapped Red Blood Cells.

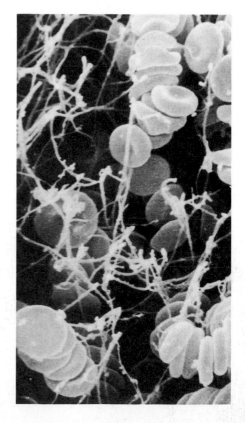

6. The wound is repaired by the growth of cells called *fibroblasts* (*fy*-broh-blasts) and by an outer layer of epithelial cells.

Clotting must be prevented if blood is to be used for transfusions. Calcium ions are necessary for many of the clotting reactions and are present in plasma. If sodium citrate is added to blood, calcium ions bind to the citrate and clotting cannot occur. Citrated blood is used for most blood transfusions.

10-7   Clotting Problems

There are various conditions in which the blood does not clot normally. This can lead to excessive bleeding, or *hemorrhaging* (*hem*-uh-rij-ing), from minor injuries. A tendency to bleed excessively may be caused by a deficiency of platelets in the blood, by a vitamin K deficiency (vitamin K is needed for the synthesis of prothrombin), or by a hereditary disease called **hemophilia** (hee-muh-*fil*-ee-uh) in which one of the clotting factors is missing from the blood.

While clotting is a major defense against loss of blood, it must occur only where and when it is needed. Two factors prevent clots from forming in the blood as it circulates through the blood vessels. First, the structure of the inner wall of the blood vessels prevents activation of the clotting reaction. Second, there are chemicals in the blood that act as *anticoagulants* (ant-ih-koh-*ag*-yuh-lunts) and prevent clot formation. Heparin is a powerful anticoagulant that may be used as a drug after surgery to prevent the formation of blood clots. It is normally present in the blood in low concentrations. It is produced by a number of different types of cells in the body, particularly in the tissues that surround the capillaries of the lungs and the liver.

Sometimes a clot does form within a blood vessel. When such a clot is attached to the vessel wall, it is called a *thrombus*. If a thrombus forms in an artery, the supply of blood to the organ fed by that artery could be cut off or reduced, with possibly disastrous effects. If a thrombus breaks loose, it forms an *embolus* (*em*-buh-lus), a clot that travels through the bloodstream. An embolus is very dangerous. It may eventually clog an artery to a vital organ, particularly the heart, lungs, or brain. A clogged coronary artery can cause a heart attack; a clogged artery to the brain can cause a stroke.

IMMUNITY

Objectives:
1. Explain how immunity works.
2. Compare inborn immunity with acquired immunity and active immunity with passive immunity.
3. Discuss the involvement of the immune system in autoimmune diseases, allergies, and transplant rejection.

10-8 Defenses Against Disease

The body has a number of general defenses against disease-causing organisms. The unbroken skin protects against the invasion of microorganisms. The acid of the stomach kills many microorganisms in food. Many microorganisms that do succeed in entering the body tissues are engulfed and destroyed by phagocytes. However, **immunity** (ih-*myoo*-nuh-tee), which is resistance to infection by a particular microorganism, is the strongest of the body's defenses. Immunity is defined as the ability of the body to resist a particular disease.

Although it is only recently that the actual mechanisms of immunity have been discovered, it has been known for hundreds of years that people who recover from certain diseases are unlikely to get them again—they are immune to those diseases. Smallpox was such a disease. (It has been wiped out in this century.) However, since it was often fatal, contracting smallpox was not a desirable way to acquire immunity to it.

In the 18th century, milkmaids often contracted a mild disease called cowpox, which was like smallpox in some ways. Many people believed that anyone who had had cowpox could not get smallpox. In 1796, Edward Jenner, an English physician, decided to test this theory. He took some fluid from a milkmaid's cowpox sores and injected it into a small cut that he made in the skin of a young boy. The boy developed the usual mild case of cowpox. After the boy recovered, Jenner treated his skin in the same way with material from the sores of a smallpox victim. The boy remained healthy. He had apparently become immune to smallpox. From this experiment Jenner developed the method of *vaccination* to give people immunity to smallpox. The method was later extended to the prevention of many other diseases.

Cowpox and smallpox are caused by closely related viruses so that immunity to cowpox also produces immunity to smallpox. However, this "cross immunity" between cowpox and smallpox is unusual. In general, immunity to one disease has no effect on immunity to any other disease.

10-9 How Immunity Works

The basis of immunity lies in the body's ability to distinguish between "self" (its own cells and molecules) and "nonself" (foreign cells and molecules). This recognition is based on differences in certain large molecules between one organism and another. When foreign cells or molecules enter the body, they are recognized as "nonself" by the *immune system*, which attempts to destroy or neutralize them. The immune system includes white blood cells called **lymphocytes** (*lim*-fuh-syts) and various tissues of the lymphatic system (*lymphoid tissues*). The reaction of the immune system to the presence of foreign cells or molecules is called the **immune response**.

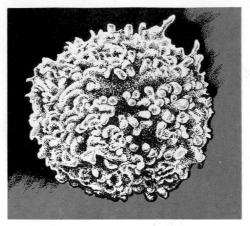 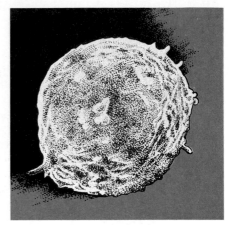

Figure 10-6. B and T Lymphocytes.   B lymphocyte   T lymphocyte

Antigens. Any substance that can cause an immune response is called an **antigen** (*ant*-ih-jun). Most antigens are proteins, but carbohydrates and nucleic acids may also be antigens. Most microorganisms and most *toxins* (poisonous substances produced by bacteria) contain substances that are antigens. Each human body contains a unique combination of proteins that no other human has. As a result, tissue from one person transplanted into another will contain "foreign" proteins that act as antigens. The presence of antigens in the body brings about an immune response that acts to destroy the antigens or the foreign tissue carrying them.

Lymphocytes and antibodies. The recognition and destruction of foreign antigens present in the body tissues is carried out by the lymphocytes. Lymphocytes are produced originally in the bone marrow of developing embryos. They enter the bloodstream, pass into the body tissues, and finally collect in the lymphoid tissues. There are two types of lymphocytes—*B lymphocytes* and *T lymphocytes* (see Figure 10-6).

Before becoming established in the lymphoid tissue, both B and T lymphocytes undergo "processing" at special sites in the lymphatic system. Without this processing, they cannot recognize antigens. It is estimated that there are between 10,000 and 100,000 different kinds of antigen receptors on human lymphocytes. However, each individual lymphocyte has receptors for only one kind of antigen. When an antigen enters the body, only those lymphocytes with receptors that recognize that particular antigen become activated. Depending on the antigen, B lymphocytes, T lymphocytes, or both may be stimulated.

When B lymphocytes are activated by antigens, they enlarge and undergo repeated cell divisions, forming two different types of cells—*plasma cells* and *memory cells.* Plasma cells secrete **antibodies,** which are proteins that react specifically with antigens and inactivate them (see Figure 10-7). Antibodies have active sites that fit a particular site on a par-

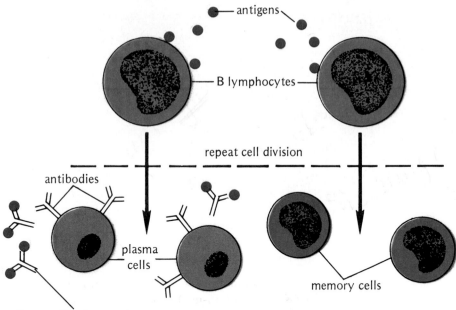

antigens

B lymphocytes

repeat cell division

antibodies

plasma cells

memory cells

antigen-antibody complex

ticular antigen. There are several different classes of antibodies, and they inactivate antigens in different ways (see Table 10-1).

The memory cells produced by the activated B lymphocytes remain in the lymphoid tissue. If the same antigen enters the body again, the memory cells immediately begin to produce antibodies against it, thereby providing immunity to that disease.

When a T lymphocyte is stimulated by the presence of an antigen, it also undergoes rapid cell division, forming more lymphocytes sensitive to that antigen. Some of these newly formed T lymphocytes remain in the lymphoid tissue and serve as memory cells. The rest pass from the lymphoid tissue into the circulatory system and body tissues. When they come in contact with the antigens to which they are sensitive, they combine with them and destroy them.

Figure 10-7. Antibody Formation by B Lymphocytes. B lymphocytes stimulated by the presence of a particular antigen in the blood undergo various cellular changes followed by repeated cell divisions. Some of the stimulated B lymphocytes form antibody-producing plasma cells; others form memory cells.

Table 10-1. Types of Antigen-Antibody Reactions.

Agglutination	Antigens are bound together into clumps by antibodies and thereby inactivated.
Precipitation	Antibodies combine with antigens, and the resulting complex settles out of solution.
Neutralization	Antibodies combine with antigens, inactivating the toxic site of the antigen molecule.
Lysis	Antibodies cause the cell membranes of antigenic microorganisms to burst.
Complement system	The complement system is a group of enzymes present in the plasma in inactive form. The presence of the antigen-antibody complex activates these enzymes, which attack the antigenic material.

10-10 Types of Immunity

There are two basic types of immunity—**inborn immunity** and **acquired immunity.**

Inborn, or innate, immunity to some diseases is present at birth. There are several types of chemicals in the blood that destroy certain types of microorganisms, and there are also specific antibodies that are present in the blood at birth that attack particular disease-causing organisms. Humans have inborn immunity to many microorganisms that cause diseases in other types of animals.

Acquired immunity is immunity that develops during an individual's lifetime. There are two types of acquired immunity—active and passive. In *active immunity* the body produces its own antibodies or sensitized lymphocytes to attack a particular type of antigen. In *passive immunity* a person is given antibodies obtained from the blood of either another person or an animal. Passive immunity is "borrowed" immunity.

Active acquired immunity may develop as the result of having a disease. For example, a person who has had chicken pox rarely gets the disease a second time. Memory cells remaining in the body tissues quickly produce antibodies or lymphocytes if the chicken pox virus invades the body again.

Active immunity may also develop through the use of a **vaccine** (vak-*seen*). A vaccine consists of dead or weakened bacteria or viruses or modified bacterial toxins. In each case, the organism or toxin can still stimulate the immune system, but it can no longer cause disease. Thus, when the vaccine is injected into the body, the immune system responds to the presence of the antigens and produces antibodies or activated lymphocytes against them. In this way a person develops an immunity to a disease without actually suffering through it. As a rule, active acquired immunity develops slowly, but lasts for years. With some vaccines, it is necessary to give periodic "booster shots" to keep the antibody level high.

Passive immunity is only temporary, and generally does not last for more than a month because the body destroys the borrowed antibodies. However, it is fast-acting, and it is used to help people who have been exposed to a serious disease or who have come down with such a disease.

Maternal immunity is a form of passive immunity. Antibodies from the mother enter the baby's blood before birth and provide immunity. They are also present in the mother's milk. Maternal immunity protects a child against most infectious diseases for the first few months of its life.

Interferon is a protein manufactured by body cells when they are attacked by viruses. This substance is carried in the bloodstream and blocks the production of viral DNA in the uninfected cells of the body. In this way it protects the uninfected cells from infection by the invading virus. Much research on the possible use of interferon in the prevention and cure of disease is being conducted. Unfortunately, interferon from other animals is not effective in humans. Scientists are trying to find ways to stimulate the body's own production of interferon.

10-11   Disorders of the Immune System

Disorders of the immune system appear to be involved in allergies, arthritis, cancer, and various other human diseases. The immune system may also be involved in the aging process.

A basic property of the immune system is that the cells of an individual's immune system do not react with the other cells of the body and destroy them. This property is called *tolerance.* It is thought that tolerance develops in the processing of the lymphocytes during embryonic development and just after birth. During processing, all lymphocytes sensitive to the antigens of the body's own cells are destroyed by constant exposure to these antigens.

There are various diseases in which the tolerance of a person's immune system breaks down, and antibodies and sensitized lymphocytes develop against the body's own antigens. Such diseases are called **autoimmune** (aw-toh-im-*yoon*) **diseases.** In rheumatic fever, for example, an immune response against the tissues of the heart and joints develops after exposure to a particular type of streptococcus bacteria. Another type of streptococcus causes an immune response to develop against kidney tissue.

Many people suffer from **allergies** (*al*-ur-jeez), such as hay fever and asthma. Allergies are caused by the production of antibodies against antigens that are not in themselves dangerous and do not bother most people. Such antigens include dust, penicillin, various foods, pollen, bee stings, and animal fur. Typical symptoms of allergy include a runny nose, swollen eyes, sneezing, coughing, and rashes (hives). These symptoms are generally caused by the release of a substance called *histamine* (*his*-tuh-meen) by the body cells following an antigen-antibody reaction. *Antihistamines* are drugs that are used to counteract the effects of histamine.

Experiments have shown that T lymphocytes attack cancer cells because the surfaces of these cells contain abnormal proteins that are recognized as antigens. This suggests that the body is normally protected from cancer by the immune response. There is evidence that some cancers develop when there is a deficiency in the immune response.

10-12   Transplants

When an organ or tissue, such as a heart, kidney, or skin, is transplanted from one person (the *donor*) to another (the *recipient*), the transplant is soon recognized by the recipient's immune system as "nonself," or foreign. This activates the immune response, and the organ or tissue is destroyed, a re-

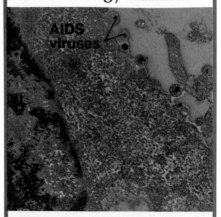

Frontier of Biology

AIDS viruses

AIDS

AIDS (*A*quired *I*mmune *D*eficiency *S*yndrome) is a disease caused by a virus. This disease, now at epidemic proportions in the West, is thought to have originated in Africa. The AIDS virus (see photo), which has just recently been identified, attacks and destroys certain white blood cells called T lymphocytes. These are the immunity-producing white blood cells that ward off infection. Without T lymphocytes, the body's immune system is crippled, unable to prevent infection by microorganisms that it would normally render harmless. Victims of AIDS usually die of either a particularly deadly form of pneumonia, a skin cancer called Kaposi's sarcoma, or some other system-wide infection.

Currently there is no cure for AIDS, although now that the virus has been identified, work is under way to produce a vaccine. In addition, clinical tests of several promising anti-AIDS drugs are in progress. Despite these small steps forward, it is thought that many years will pass before an effective vaccine or treatment is available. In the meantime, the disease continues to spread.

sponse called *rejection*. Rejection appears to take place in two steps. First, the transplanted tissue is invaded by T lymphocytes; then antibodies produced by B lymphocytes cause the disintegration of the tissue. In transplants between identical twins there is generally no rejection because their tissue proteins are identical.

The immune response to a transplant can be lessened by matching the tissue proteins of the donor as closely as possible to those of the recipient. In addition, the immune response may be controlled by the use of drugs that knock out the immune system. However, this leaves the patient highly susceptible to infection.

HUMAN BLOOD GROUPS

Objectives:
  1. Describe the biochemical basis of human blood groups.
  2. Discuss the significance of the ABO blood group and Rh factors in transfusions and in pregnancy.

10-13   ABO Blood Group

Before the discovery of blood groups, transfusions of blood from one person to another were occasionally attempted. The results were sometimes helpful, but at other times fatal. In the early 1900s the Austrian physician Karl Landsteiner succeeded in showing that there are four major types of human blood. If the wrong types are mixed in a transfusion, the red blood cells from the donor may clump together, a process called **agglutination** (uh-gloot-un-*ay*-shun). This clogs the blood vessels and causes kidney failure. The agglutination of the red cells is the result of an antigen-antibody reaction.

The blood types first discovered by Landsteiner are those of the ABO system. Since that time, more than 100 other blood groups have been discovered. The **ABO blood group** involves the presence of certain antigens on the surface of the red blood cells. There are two antigens involved, called A and B. In any individual's blood, the red cells may have only A antigens (type A blood); only B antigens (type B blood); both A and B antigens (type AB blood); or neither A nor B antigens (type O blood). In addition, the blood plasma contains antibodies that react with the antigens the blood does *not* have. In other words, it has antibodies that will detect the presence of "foreign" red cells. Thus type A blood contains anti-B antibodies. Type B blood contains anti-A antibodies. Type AB blood does not have either of these antibodies. Type O blood has both. These facts are summarized in Table 10-2.

The A and B antigens are called *agglutinogens* (uh-*gloot*-in-uh-jenz). The antibodies that react to them are called *agglutinins* (uh-*gloot*-in-inz). If blood containing red cells with

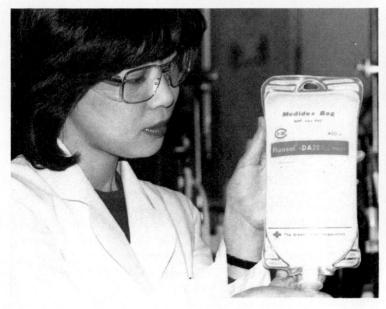

Photographs courtesy of the Green Cross Corporation.

Substitute Blood

In recent years medical scientists have developed a substance that can be used in place of real blood in transfusions. This substitute blood, called Fluosol, is chemically similar to Teflon. Its usefulness in transfusions derives from its capacity to carry oxygen and to replace blood volume. The oxygen-carrying capacity of Fluosol is 20 times greater than that of real plasma. In fact, a mouse can live completely submerged in Fluosol that is well-aerated (see photo). The mouse does not die from lack of oxygen as it would if submerged in water, in which the solubility of oxygen is very low.

Although Fluosol lacks clotting factors, platelets, immunoglobins, antibodies, and other blood-borne components, and thus cannot carry out all the complex functions of whole blood, it does have some advantages over real blood. Fluosol is superior to blood in being able to pass through blocked capillaries and service oxygen-starved tissues. Unlike red blood cells, which can be stored for only three weeks, Fluosol can be stored for three years. It contains no antigens, so there is no problem with matching blood types. Also, it contains none of the disease-causing organisms that might be present in real blood. One problem with Fluosol is that it remains in the circulation for only about 11 hours. By the end of that time, it has been broken down into waste gases and exhaled through the lungs. Thus, repeated injections must be administered if it is needed for longer periods of time. Another problem is that the patient must breathe supplemental oxygen to utilize the oxygen-carrying effectiveness of Fluosol.

Fluosol has been tested on animals, but its use in humans is still highly experimental. Mostly it has been used in surgery patients who, for religious reasons, refuse to receive transfusions of real blood, and in certain stroke victims where oxygen supply to the brain is critical.

Fluosol promises to gain wider use. For example, unlike real blood, Fluosol's ability to carry oxygen increases as temperature decreases. Thus it may be the fluid of choice in open-heart surgery, where cold temperatures are used to slow the heartbeat.

Table 10-2. Antigens and Antibodies of the ABO System.

Blood type	Antigens	Antibodies
O	none	Anti-A and Anti-B
A	A	Anti-B
B	B	Anti-A
AB	A and B	none

one of these antigens is mixed with blood containing the corresponding antibody, the antibody will react with the antigen and cause the red cells to clump together, or agglutinate (see Figure 10-8).

10-14 Transfusions

For a blood transfusion to be safe, the recipient's blood must not contain antibodies that will react with antigens of the ABO system in the donor blood. Knowing this, it is a simple matter to decide which types of blood can be safely given to each type of recipient. The results are shown in Table 10-3. Note particularly that a person with type AB blood can receive a transfusion of any type, since type AB blood contains no antibodies. People with AB blood are therefore called *universal recipients.* Type O blood, on the other hand, can be given to any recipient because type O blood has no antigens. People with type O blood are called *universal donors.*

In emergency situations, plasma is used for transfusions instead of whole blood. The plasma restores blood volume and maintains blood pressure. The advantages of plasma are that no blood typing is necessary, and the plasma can be frozen and stored for long periods of time.

10-15 Rh Factors

The **Rh factors** are another group of antigens found on the surface of red blood cells. These antigens were discovered by Karl Landsteiner in 1940. They were called Rh factors because they were first found in rhesus monkeys. Unlike the ABO system, which includes only two different antigens, the

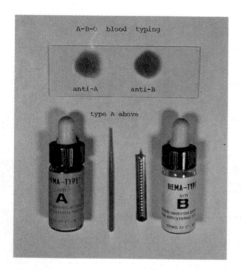

Figure 10-8. Blood Typing. When type A blood is mixed with anti-A antiserum, clumping of the red cells occurs. No clumping occurs when type A blood is mixed with anti-B antiserum.

Table 10-3. Matching Blood Types for Transfusions.

Recipient		Donor
Type O	Can safely receive	Type O
Type A	Can safely receive	Type A or O
Type B	Can safely receive	Type B or O
Type AB	Can safely receive	Type A, B, AB, or O

Rh system includes eight possible antigens. Some of these can cause severe agglutination reactions in transfusions, while the others cause little or no reaction. A person whose red blood cells contain one or more of the Rh factors that do cause transfusion reactions is said to be Rh-positive, or Rh+. A person whose red blood cells do not contain Rh factors that cause transfusion reactions is said to be Rh-negative, or Rh−. In the United States, about 85 percent of the population is Rh+, while 15 percent is Rh−.

In the ABO system, antibodies against nonself blood types develop spontaneously shortly after birth. However, anti-Rh antibodies do not develop spontaneously, but only after exposure to the Rh antigens. An Rh+ individual can receive both Rh+ and Rh− blood. The first time an Rh− person receives Rh+ blood, there are no ill effects. However, this transfusion stimulates the formation of anti-Rh antibodies. If a second transfusion of Rh+ blood is given, a serious antigen-antibody reaction may occur. In matching blood types for transfusions, the Rh factor must be taken into account as well as the ABO system.

The Rh factor may present a special problem during pregnancy when the mother is Rh− but the child has inherited Rh+ blood from its father. During birth there may be some leakage between the child's circulatory system and the mother's circulatory system. Some Rh antigens enter the mother's blood, which then begins to form anti-Rh antibodies. In later pregnancies, antibodies from the mother's blood enter the baby's blood. If the child is Rh+, the antibodies destroy the baby's red blood cells. In recent years a treatment has been developed that can eliminate the Rh problem in pregnancies. Within 72 hours after the birth of an Rh+ child, the Rh− mother is given an injection of anti-Rh antibodies. These antibodies destroy any Rh antigens that have entered the mother's blood from the baby's blood. In this way the mother's body is not stimulated to produce its own anti-Rh antibodies, and consequently there is no problem with the next Rh+ baby.

Chapter Review

SUMMARY

Blood carries materials to and from the cells of the body. The liquid portion, the plasma, carries suspended red blood cells, white blood cells, and platelets, and contains many dissolved substances. Red blood cells, or erythrocytes, transport oxygen and carbon dioxide. White blood cells, or leukocytes, protect the body from infection by microorganisms. Platelets are involved in blood clotting.

● The immune system destroys foreign substances and microorganisms. This system includes white blood cells called lymphocytes and certain lymphoid tissues. Lymphocytes respond to the presence of antigens either by attacking them directly or by producing antibodies. The antibodies react specifically with the antigens and destroy them. Immunity is either inborn or acquired.

- Failures of the immune system to function normally are involved in many diseases, including autoimmune diseases, allergies, and possibly cancer. The immune system also causes rejection of transplanted organs.

- The blood types of humans depend on the presence of particular antigens on the surface of red blood cells. When transfusions are given, the blood types of recipient and donor must be matched for both **ABO** and Rh antigens in order to prevent agglutination.

KNOW THE TERMS

ABO blood group	antigen	immune response	lymphocyte
acquired immunity	autoimmune disease	immunity	plasma
agglutination	clotting	inborn immunity	platelet
anemia	erythrocyte	interferon	Rh factors
antibody	hemophilia	leukocyte	vaccine

SECTION QUESTIONS

Composition of Blood

1. Name the cells or formed elements of blood.
2. Which blood cell is most abundant?
3. What is the type of leukocyte that engulfs microorganisms?
4. What is the function of platelets?

Blood Clotting

5. What is the insoluble protein that traps blood cells to form a clot?
6. List three conditions that cause blood not to clot normally.
7. What prevents blood from clotting within the blood vessels?

Immunity

8. What is immunity?
9. What is the immune response?
10. What are antibodies?
11. What are autoimmune diseases?

Human Blood Groups

12. Antibodies to both **A** and **B** antigens are found in individuals with what blood types.
13. For each of the four ABO blood types, list the types of blood that can be received safely in transfusions.
14. What is meant by an Rh+ blood type?

KNOW THE FACTS

Copy the number of each sentence below on a sheet of paper. Beside each number, write the term(s) that complete(s) the sentence correctly.

1. The liquid part of blood is called _____.
2. _____ is a plasma protein important in the clotting of blood.
3. _____ are disk-shaped blood cells that are thinner in the center than the rim and do not contain a nucleus when mature.
4. The condition in which a person has too few red blood cells or insufficient hemoglobin is called _____.
5. _____ are large blood cells that contain one or more nuclei.
6. _____ are small, round, or oval fragments of a type of blood cell.
7. The immune system includes white blood cells called _____ and _____ tissues.
8. A substance that causes the immune response is called a(n) _____.
9. Active immunity may develop through the use of a _____ consisting of dead or weakened bacteria or viruses.
10. The production of antibodies against antigens that are not in themselves dangerous and do not bother most people is called _____.
11. The process whereby red blood cells clump together is called _____.

UNDERSTAND THE CONCEPTS

12. Describe the functions of the blood.
13. How is the composition of red blood cells related to their function?
14. Explain how white blood cells protect the body from infection.
15. Explain the process of blood clotting.
16. Describe three of the body's defenses against disease.
17. What is the basis of immunity?
18. In what two ways do lymphocytes destroy antigens and provide immunity?
19. Describe how passive acquired immunity develops.
20. Explain what happens when body cells are attacked by viruses.
21. What causes the rejection of organs transplanted from one person to another?
22. Under what circumstances is the Rh factor a problem during pregnancy?

THINK CRITICALLY

23. How do erythrocytes benefit from the ability to change shape easily?
24. How do you think the structure of the inner wall of a blood vessel prevents a triggering of the clotting process?
25. Compare and contrast the action of phagocytes responding to a bacterial infection with the action of T lymphocytes in the presence of an antigen.
26. Why is it that in blood transfusions the agglutination of the recipient's own erythrocytes by the antibodies in the donor blood is not of concern?
27. Drugs are given to the recipient of an organ transplant to lessen the immune system response. What implications does this have for the way the recipient lives?

THINK CREATIVELY

28. Person A donated blood to be used for a friend, Person B, who was undergoing surgery. A year later Person A needed a transfusion, but the doctor would not allow Person B's blood to be used in the transfusion. What are several possible explanations for this?
29. Why do you think a single vaccine has not been developed to protect people against catching the common cold?
30. Suggest some reasons why a deficiency of the immune response might develop in some individuals.

FOR FURTHER INVESTIGATION

1. Learn how to make a blood smear. Describe and draw the white blood cells you see.
2. Write a report on one of the following topics in the form of a feature article for a magazine:
   a. Autoimmune diseases   c. Allergies
   b. Organ transplants   d. Interferon
3. Prepare a brief report on the life and contributions of one of the following scientists:
   a. Charles Drew   c. Albert Sabin
   b. Jonas Salk   d. Dorothy Hodgkin
4. Write a report describing how donated blood is stored, how it can be divided into its components, and how these components are used. Discuss the report with your class.
5. Prepare a report on one of the following career opportunities listed below. See suggested procedures, p. 9, "For Further Investigation" Activity 3.
   a. Registered nurse   c. Pathologist
   b. Blood bank technologist

FOR FURTHER READING

Collier, R. J., and Kaplan, D., "Immunotoxins," *Scientific American*, July, 1984.

Miller, Julie Ann, "A Vaccine for All Seasons," *Science News*, June 15, 1985.

Nourse, Alan, *Your Immune System* (a First Book), Franklin Watts, New York, 1982.

Silberner, J., "A New Look At Arthritis Origins," *Science News*, June 8, 1985.

Ward, Brian, *The Heart and Blood* (The Human Body Series), Franklin Watts, New York, 1982.

Chapter 11
RESPIRATION

Divers must carry an air supply so they can breathe while underwater.

THE RESPIRATORY PROCESS

Objectives:
1. Define the term *respiration*.
2. Distinguish respiration from cellular respiration.
3. Explain what is meant by a respiratory surface, and list the characteristics of such a surface.

11-1 Respiration vs. Cellular Respiration

In the process of *cellular respiration* nutrients are broken down and energy is released (see Chapter 7). In all but some microorganisms, cellular respiration is aerobic—it requires oxygen. The end products of aerobic cellular respiration are carbon dioxide and water. Thus, all organisms that carry on aerobic cellular respiration have the problem of obtaining oxygen from the environment and getting rid of carbon dioxide. The process by which a living organism exchanges oxygen and carbon dioxide with its environment is called **respiration.**

11-2 The Respiratory Surface

The exchange of oxygen and carbon dioxide between an organism and its environment involves the passage of these gases through a boundary surface. The surface through which gas exchange takes place is called the **respiratory surface.** A respiratory surface must have the following characteristics: (1) It must be thin-walled so that diffusion across it occurs rapidly (2) It must be moist because the oxygen and carbon dioxide must be in solution. (3) It must be in contact with an environmental source of oxygen. (4) In most multicellular organisms, it must be in close contact with the system that transports dissolved materials to and from the cells of the organism.

Gas exchange through the respiratory surface takes place by diffusion. The direction of the gas exchange is determined by the concentration gradients of the gases on each side of the respiratory surface. As oxygen is used up inside the organism's tissues, more oxygen diffuses in. When the carbon dioxide concentration builds up within the tissues, this gas diffuses out. The larger the area of the respiratory surface, the greater the amount of gas exchange that can occur over a given period of time.

In protists and very small multicellular animals, the diffusion of respiratory gases can take place directly between the cells and the environment. In larger animals however, most of the body cells are not in contact with the outside environment, and, therefore, direct diffusion cannot serve as the mechanism of gas exchange. In addition, larger animals often have an outer protective layer, such as scales, feathers, or skin, that prevents any significant gas exchange. Therefore, large multicellular animals have their respiratory surfaces in specialized organs or systems.

ADAPTATIONS FOR RESPIRATION

Objectives:
1. Describe the respiratory surfaces of protozoa and hydra and the processes by which respiratory gases are exchanged in these organisms.
2. Explain why specialized respiratory systems are necessary in large multicellular animals.
3. Describe the function of respiratory pigments.
4. Describe and contrast the respiratory processes in earthworms, grasshoppers, and animals with gills.

The major differences in overall respiratory activity among various types of animals is the method by which they exchange oxygen and carbon dioxide with their environments. Protists and animals show a variety of adaptations for the exchange of respiratory gases with their environment.

11-3   Respiration in Protozoa

Respiration is relatively simple in protozoa. The exchange of gases with the environment takes place directly through the body surface—the cell membrane. In the ameba and paramecium, oxygen dissolved in the surrounding water passes through the cell membrane into the cytoplasm by diffusion (see Figure 11-1). The carbon dioxide formed by cellular respiration diffuses out of the cytoplasm into the surrounding water.

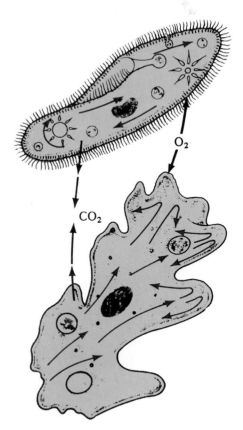

Figure 11-1. Respiration in Ameba and Paramecium. The exchange of respiratory gases in the ameba and paramecium takes place directly through the cell membrane.

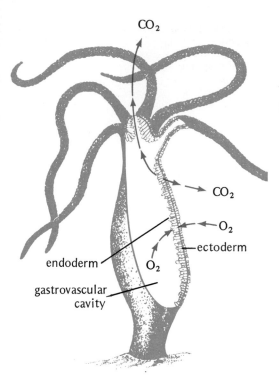

Figure 11-2. Respiration in Hydra. The exchange of respiratory gases in the hydra takes place by direct diffusion between the body cells and the environment.

11-4   Respiration in Hydra

The cells of the two layers that make up the body of the hydra are in direct contact with water (see Figure 11-2). Because of the small size and simple structure of the hydra, the exchange of respiratory gases can take place by direct diffusion between the body cells and the environment. There are no special structures for gas exchange in the hydra.

11-5   Respiration in Large Multicellular Animals

A large multicellular animal must exchange relatively large quantities of gases across a respiratory surface. Animals that live submerged in water have different respiratory problems from animals that breathe air. First, the concentration of dissolved oxygen in water is seldom higher than 0.5 percent, whereas the oxygen concentration in air is about 21 percent. (The oxygen that is chemically part of the water molecules is, of course, not available for respiration. Only the free dissolved oxygen can be used.) Second, diffusion of oxygen occurs much more slowly in water than in air. Consequently, to obtain adequate oxygen, an animal living underwater must continuously move a large volume of water over its respiratory surface.

Gases must be in solution before they can diffuse across living membranes. Therefore, air-breathing animals are faced with the problem of keeping their respiratory surfaces moist. Most air-breathing animals have respiratory systems that extend inward into the interior of the organism. This protects the respiratory surface and minimizes the rate of water loss by evaporation from the respiratory surface.

11-6   Respiratory Pigments

Many multicellular animals have protein pigments in the blood that carry oxygen and carbon dioxide between the respiratory surface and the body cells. These pigments enable the blood to carry more oxygen and carbon dioxide than plain water can. For example, 100 milliliters of water can carry about 0.2 milliliters of oxygen and 0.3 milliliters of carbon dioxide. Hemoglobin, the most common respiratory pigment, is an efficient carrier of respiratory gases. It enables 100 milliliters of human blood to carry about 20 milliliters of oxygen and 30 to 60 milliliters of carbon dioxide. (These are not the volumes of the gases when in solution, but their equivalent volumes as gases in the air.)

11-7   Respiration in the Earthworm

In earthworms, which live in moist soil, the skin is the respiratory surface (see Figure 11-3). It is thin and is kept moist by mucus secreted by special cells. It is supplied with an abundance of capillaries. Oxygen diffuses from the air in the soil through the moist skin into the capillaries. Blood in the

Figure 11-3. Respiration in the Earthworm. The moist skin of the earthworm is its respiratory surface. Gases are exchanged with the environment through the skin and are carried to and from the body cells by the blood.

capillaries picks up the oxygen and transports it to the cells of the body. The blood plasma contains the red pigment hemoglobin, which aids in the transport of oxygen. At the body cells, the blood releases oxygen and picks up carbon dioxide and carries it to the capillaries in the skin. The carbon dioxide diffuses through the skin into the air.

Damp soil keeps the earthworm's skin moist and helps its respiratory system to work efficiently. If earthworms are exposed to air, their skin soon dries out and they suffocate. When the weather is dry, they burrow deeper until they reach moist soil. Rain, however, is a problem for earthworms because their burrows become flooded, and they cannot obtain adequate oxygen from water. They have to leave their flooded burrows to avoid drowning.

11-8   Respiration in the Grasshopper

The respiratory system in grasshoppers does not depend on the circulatory system. *Blood* is not used for the transport of oxygen or carbon dioxide. Instead, air is carried directly to all the cells of the body through a system of branching air tubes called *tracheae* (*tray*-kee-ee), or **tracheal tubes.** Air enters and leaves the grasshopper's body through ten pairs of openings called **spiracles** (*speer*-uh-kulz) (see Figure 11-4). From each spiracle, the tracheal tubes branch repeatedly into smaller and smaller tubes. The fluid-filled ends of these microscopic air tubes are in direct contact with the body cells and are the actual respiratory surface. Here oxygen in the air diffuses from the tracheal tubes to the body cells, and carbon dioxide diffuses from the body cells into the tracheal tubes.

Figure 11-4. Respiratory System of the Grasshopper. In the grasshopper, air enters and leaves the animal through the spiracles. A branching system of tracheal tubes carries the air to and from the body tissues.

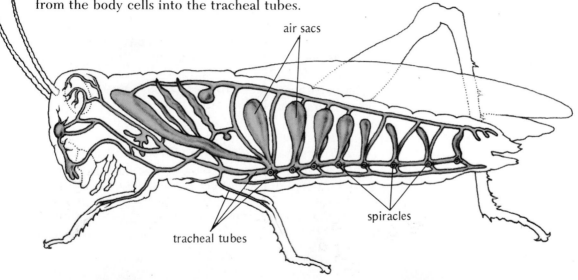

air sacs

spiracles

tracheal tubes

Figure 11-5. Gills of a Fish. The thin filaments of a gill are richly supplied with blood vessels and provide a large surface area for the exchange of respiratory gases.

Air is pumped into and out of the tracheal system by contraction of the grasshopper's muscles. During inhalation, the abdomen expands, and air is sucked into the tracheal tubes through the first four pairs of anterior spiracles. Several large air sacs connected to these tubes aid in this pumping action. During exhalation, the abdomen contracts, the four pairs of anterior spiracles close, and air is squeezed out of the tracheal tubes through the six posterior pairs of spiracles.

The system of tracheal tubes is relatively efficient for respiration in small animals. However, in a large animal it would not be possible to move the necessary volume of gases through such a system. Grasshoppers and other insects are all small, and the system of air tubes is adequate for their needs. Giant insects are found only in science fiction.

11-9   Gill Respiration

Gills are the respiratory organs of many aquatic animals, including fish, clams, oysters, and lobsters (see Figure 11-5). Gills are thin filaments of skin that generally grow out of the body. They are covered with a thin layer of cells and are richly supplied with blood vessels. They provide a large surface area for gas exchange. As water passes over the gills, dissolved oxygen diffuses from the water across the thin membrane and into the blood, which transports it to all parts of the body. Carbon dioxide from the blood diffuses out of the gills and into the water. There must be a continuous flow of water over the gills. If the water flow is stopped, the animal will die from lack of oxygen. Out of water the gills dry and stick to each other, preventing gas exchange.

THE HUMAN RESPIRATORY SYSTEM

Objectives:
   1. Identify the structures of the human respiratory system and state their functions.
   2. Describe the four phases of respiration: breathing, external respiration, circulation, and internal respiration.
   3. Describe how oxygen and carbon dioxide are transported in the blood.

The human respiratory system consists of the lungs and the system of air tubes that carry air to and from the lungs. **Lungs** are the most advanced organ for gas exchange in air-breathing animals. They consist of many small chambers, or air sacs, each surrounded by capillaries. These air sacs provide a huge respiratory surface for the diffusion of oxygen and carbon dioxide into and out of the blood.

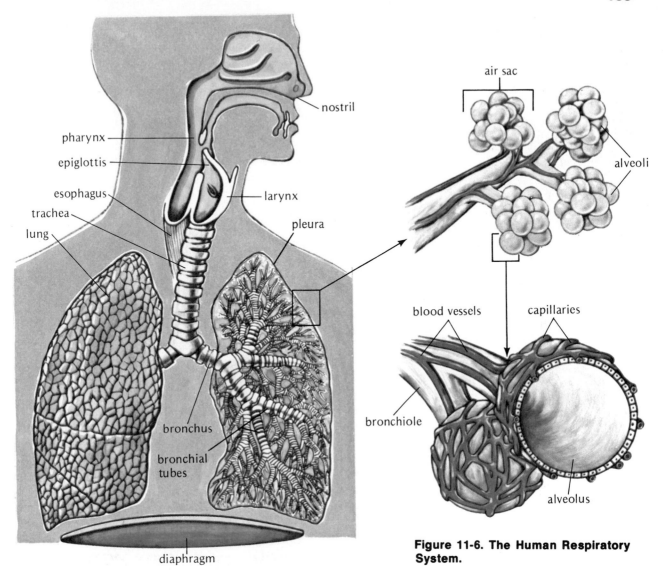

nostril

pharynx

epiglottis

esophagus

trachea

lung

larynx

pleura

bronchus

bronchial
tubes

diaphragm

air sac

alveoli

blood vessels

capillaries

bronchiole

alveolus

Figure 11-6. The Human Respiratory System.

11-10   Structure of the Human Respiratory System

The human respiratory system consists of the lungs and all the air passages that lead to them (see Figure 11-6). The lungs occupy a large portion of the chest cavity. They are separated from the abdominal cavity by the **diaphragm** (*dy*-uh-fram), a muscle that forms the floor of the chest cavity. Each lung is completely enclosed by a two-layered membrane called the **pleura** (*plur*-uh). One layer of the pleural membrane closely covers each lung, while the other layer is in contact with the diaphragm and other organs of the chest cavity. A lubricating fluid between the layers allows the lungs to move freely in the chest during breathing.

The air passages conduct air from the environment to the respiratory surface in the lungs. These passages include the nose, pharynx, trachea, bronchi, bronchial tubes, bronchioles, and alveoli.

The nose. Air normally enters the respiratory system through the *nostrils,* which lead into hollow spaces in the nose called the **nasal** (*nay*-zul) **passages.** Long hairs at the openings of the nostrils prevent the entrance of large foreign particles. The walls of the nasal passages, like the rest of the air passageways in the respiratory system, are lined with a mucous membrane made up mainly of ciliated epithelial cells. Other cells secrete mucus, a sticky fluid that traps bacteria, dust, and other particles in the air. The mucus also moistens the air. Just below the mucous membrane is a rich supply of capillaries. As air passes through the nose, it is warmed by the blood in these capillaries. Thus, the nasal passages serve to filter, moisten, and warm inhaled air before it reaches the delicate lining of the lungs. Although you can breathe through your mouth, you lose these advantages if you do not regularly breathe through your nose.

Pharynx. From the nasal passages, air passes into the **pharynx,** or throat, which is located behind the mouth cavity. The *adenoids* (*ad*-uh-noydz) and *tonsils* (*tahn*-sulz) are lymphoid tissues found in the throat. They are part of the body's defense system against infection.

Larynx. From the pharynx, air passes into the **larynx** (*lar*-inks), or voice box, which is made up largely of cartilage. The larynx is located at the upper end of the trachea, which is the air tube leading to the lungs. The **vocal cords** are two pairs of membranes that are stretched across the interior of the larynx. As air is exhaled, vibrations of the vocal cords can be controlled to make sounds. During swallowing, food and liquids are blocked from entering the opening of the larynx by the *epiglottis.*

Trachea. The larynx is continuous with the **trachea** (*tray*-kee-uh), or windpipe. The trachea is a tube about 12 centimeters long and 2.5 centimeters wide. The trachea is kept open by horseshoe-shaped rings of cartilage embedded in its walls. Like the nasal passages, the trachea is also lined with a ciliated mucous membrane (see Figure 11-7). Normally, the

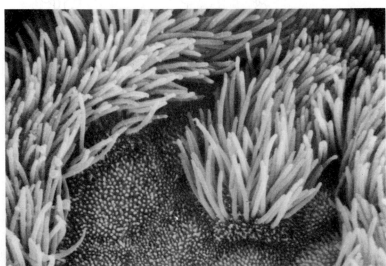

Figure 11-7. The Lining of the Trachea. The cilia of the cells lining the trachea beat rhythmically, moving mucus and foreign particles toward the pharynx.

cilia move mucus and trapped foreign matter to the pharynx, where they are expelled from the air passageways and usually swallowed.

As many people have discovered, the respiratory system is not designed to handle tobacco smoke. Smoking paralyzes the cilia. Just one cigarette stops the movement of the cilia for about 20 minutes. Furthermore, tobacco smoke increases the production of mucus in the air passages. A smoker's cough is the body's attempt to remove the excess mucus.

Bronchi. In the middle of the chest, the trachea divides into two cartilage-ringed tubes called **bronchi** (*brahn*-kee). The bronchi enter the lungs and branch in treelike fashion into smaller tubes called **bronchial** (*brahn*-kee-ul) **tubes** (see Figure 11-6).

Bronchioles. As the bronchial tubes divide and subdivide, their walls become thinner, and they gradually lose their cartilage. Finally, they become a network of microscopic tubes called **bronchioles** (*brahn*-kee-ohlz).

Air sacs and alveoli. Each bronchiole ends in a space called an **air sac.** An air sac resembles a cluster of grapes (see Figure 11-6). Each air sac contains several cup-shaped cavities called **alveoli** (al-*vee*-uh-ly) The walls of the alveoli, which are only one cell thick, are the respiratory surface. They are thin and moist and are surrounded by a rich network of capillaries. It is through these walls that the exchange of oxygen and carbon dioxide between blood and air occurs. It has been estimated that the lungs contain about 300 million alveoli, with a total surface area of about 70 square meters. This would be 40 times the surface area of the skin.

Besides irritating the trachea and bronchi, smoking interferes with the uptake of oxygen in the air sacs. When cigarette smoke is inhaled, about one-third of the particles·remain in the alveoli. Phagocytic cells called *macrophages* (*mak*-ruh-fay-jez) can slowly remove many of the particles (see Figure 11-8). However, an excess of particles from smoking or from

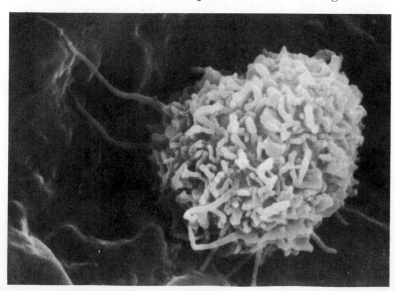

Figure 11-8. Lung Macrophage. The phagocytic macrophages ingest foreign particles. However, when an excess of particles accumulate, the macrophages become overwhelmed and can no longer prevent damage to the lungs.

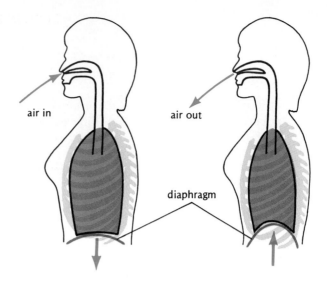

Figure 11-9. Breathing. During inhalation (left), the ribs are pulled up and out, the diaphragm is pulled down, and the chest cavity is enlarged. Because the pressure in the chest is reduced, air is forced into the lungs. During exhalation (right), the diaphragm and chest muscles relax, and the size of the chest cavity is decreased. This increases the pressure in the chest, and air is squeezed out of the lungs.

other sources of air pollution breaks down the walls of the air sacs and causes the formation of inelastic, scarlike tissue. This greatly reduces the functional area of the respiratory surface and may lead to a disease called emphysema.

11-11 Phases of Human Respiration

In humans, respiration can be divided into four distinct phases.

1. *Breathing* is the movement of air into and out of the lungs.

2. *External respiration* is the exchange of oxygen and carbon dioxide between the air and the blood in the lungs.

3. *Circulation* is the carrying of dissolved gases by the blood to and from the body cells.

4. *Internal respiration* is the exchange of oxygen and carbon dioxide between the blood and the body cells.

Note that these stages of respiration are *physical* processes. They should not be confused with *cellular* respiration, the chemical processes within the cells by which nutrients are broken down and energy is released.

Breathing. Breathing moves air into and out of the lungs. The two phases of breathing are **inhalation** (in-huh-*lay*-shun), which draws air into the lungs, and **exhalation** (eks-huh-*lay*-shun), which expels air from the lungs. Since the lungs contain no muscle tissue, they are not capable of independent movement. However, they are elastic, and during breathing they are forced to expand or contract as a result of pressure changes caused by the movement of the diaphragm, ribs, and rib muscles, and by the force of air pressure.

Inhalation is the active phase of breathing. As the ribs are pulled up and out and the diaphragm is pulled downward, the chest cavity is enlarged (see Figure 11-9). As a result, the pressure within the chest cavity is reduced. External air (at atmospheric pressure) rushes down the air passageways into the air sacs, forcing the lungs to expand.

Exhalation is the passive phase of breathing. The diaphragm relaxes and moves upward, and the rib muscles relax, causing the ribs to drop. This decreases the size of the chest cavity and increases the pressure on the lungs. Thus, air is squeezed out of the lungs.

Normal rates of breathing vary from about 12 to 25 times per minute. One of the effects of smoking is to increase the breathing rate.

Although breathing can be controlled voluntarily to some extent, it is basically an involuntary process. It is controlled by the *respiratory center* in the brain. There are also special structures in the aorta and several other large arteries that are sensitive to the concentrations of oxygen and carbon dioxide in the blood. These *chemoreceptors* send messages to the respiratory center. When the carbon dioxide concentration in the blood increases, the respiratory center of the brain is stimulated. Nerves from the respiratory center carry impulses to the diaphragm and chest muscles that increase the rate and depth of breathing. This lowers the carbon dioxide concentration and increases the oxygen concentration of the blood.

During heavy muscular exertion, lactic acid is produced as well as carbon dioxide. This increases the acidity of the blood. The increased acidity also stimulates the respiratory center of the brain and increases the rate of breathing.

External and internal respiration. External respiration is the exchange of oxygen and carbon dioxide between the air and the blood in the lungs (see Figure 11-10). After inhalation, the concentration of oxygen in the alveoli is higher than the concentration of oxygen in the blood. Oxygen dissolves into the moist lining of the alveoli and diffuses from the region of higher concentration (the alveoli) to the region of lower concentration (the blood). Independently, carbon dioxide diffuses in the opposite direction—out of the blood and into the alveoli.

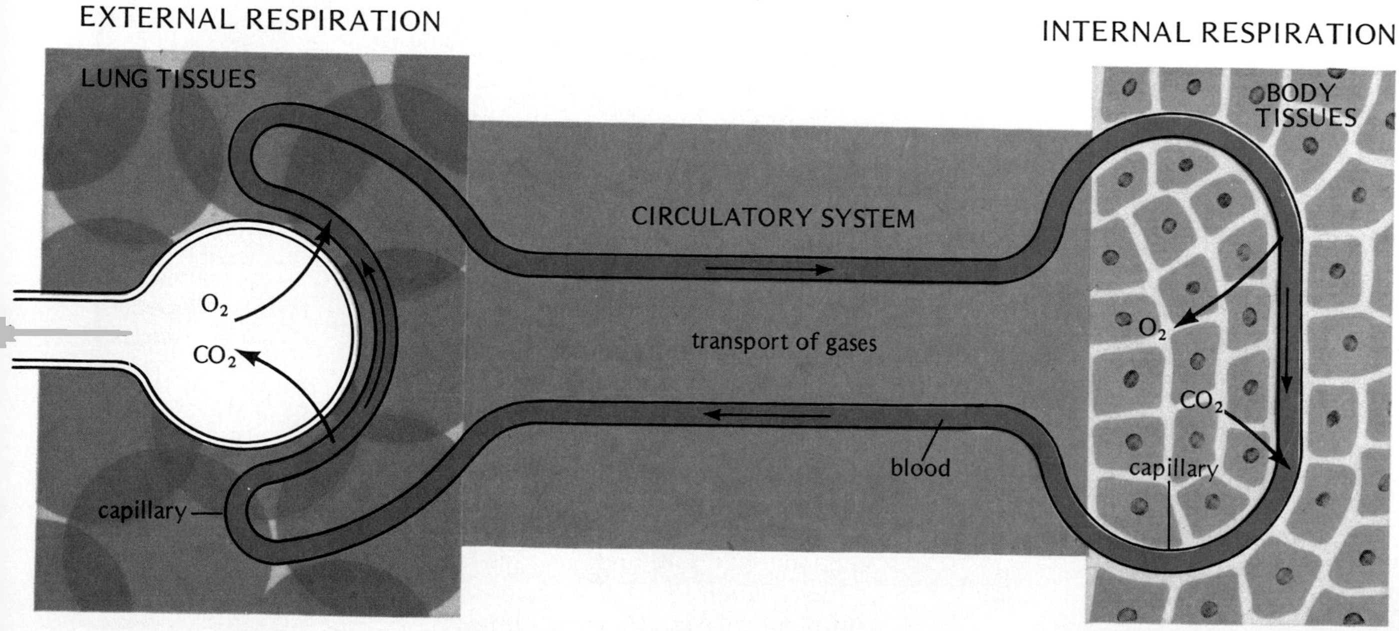

Figure 11-10. External and Internal Respiration. In human body tissues, all cells exchange gases with the internal environment by diffusion across the moist cell membranes. The gases are transported to and from the lungs by the blood and the circulatory system. Exchange with the external environment occurs by diffusion across moist cell membranes in the alveoli of the lungs.

EXTERNAL RESPIRATION

LUNG TISSUES

O_2

CO_2

capillary

CIRCULATORY SYSTEM

transport of gases

blood

INTERNAL RESPIRATION

BODY TISSUES

O_2

CO_2

capillary

Diving Mammals

Marine mammals, including whales, dolphins, porpoises, seals, and sea lions, must breathe air, but they dive hundreds of meters below the ocean's surface in search of food. Seals have been observed to dive as deep as 600 meters and to stay submerged for 70 minutes. Whales have been found at depths of over 1,000 meters, and they have been observed to stay submerged for as long as 75 minutes.

Marine animals are well adapted to their environment in terms of body form. Their bodies are sleek and streamlined. Movement of the strong tail propels them through the water. The modified forelimbs, the flippers, aid in balancing and steering the animal. The respiratory and circulatory systems show adaptations for life in the sea. In seals and sea lions, which spend time on shore or on ice floes, the head resembles that of a dog, and the nasal openings are in the front of the head. In whales, dolphins, and porpoises, which spend their lives completely in water, the nasal opening is called the blowhole, and it is located on the top of the head. The blowhole must be out of the water when the animal breathes. The location of the blowhole at the top of the head means that the animal does not have to lift much of its body above the surface to take a breath. When the animal exhales, a spout of air and liquid shoot out of the blowhole. The nasal passages of marine mammals are much more complicated than those of land mammals. They contain various adaptations that keep water away from the respiratory surface—the alveoli of the lungs.

Research has shown that the lungs of marine mammals are relatively the same size as those of land-dwelling mammals, and that the air needed for a long, deep dive is not stored in the lungs. In fact, in many diving mammals, the animal exhales before or shortly after diving. In some, the lungs become almost completely collapsed during a dive.

The circulatory system shows a number of

A beluga whale.

adaptations for diving. The heart of diving mammals is relatively the same size as in land-dwelling mammals, but the size and pattern of arteries and veins is different. The increased size of veins, in particular, results in an increased volume of blood in the body. In addition, the number of red blood cells per milliliter of blood is much higher in marine mammals than in land-dwelling mammals, and the concentration of hemoglobin in the red cells is also much greater. These adaptations greatly increase the oxygen-carrying capacity of the blood. Marine mammals also have a "diving response," which alters the pattern of blood flow in the body. In the diving response, the blood flow is directed to the heart and brain and away from the less sensitive tissues of the body. The rate of the heartbeat is greatly slowed during the dive, and other metabolic processes also slow down. These adaptations allow the animal to stay underwater for long periods of time.

As the blood is pumped through the vessels of the body by the beating of the heart, oxygen-rich blood from the lungs is carried to the body tissues and oxygen-poor blood from the tissues is returned to the lungs.

Internal respiration is the exchange of oxygen and carbon dioxide between the blood and the body cells. In the capillaries of the body tissues, oxygen diffuses from the blood through the intercellular fluid to the body cells; carbon dioxide diffuses from the cells through the intercellular fluid into the blood. Each gas diffuses down a concentration gradient, i.e., from a region of higher concentration to a region of lower concentration.

Oxygen transport. Most oxygen is transported from the lungs to the body tissues by the hemoglobin in the red blood cells. It is not dissolved in the plasma to any great extent. Hemoglobin is a unique iron-containing protein. Its most important characteristic is that it combines readily with oxygen. However, the oxygen is loosely held, and the reaction is reversible, depending on the oxygen concentration. In the lungs, where the oxygen concentration is high, hemoglobin (Hb) combines with oxygen (O_2) to form *oxyhemoglobin* (HbO_2). When the blood reaches the capillaries of the body tissues, where the oxygen concentration of the surrounding tissues is low, the oxyhemoglobin breaks down into oxygen and hemoglobin. The oxygen diffuses from the blood into the body cells, where it is used in cellular respiration.

Blood low in oxygen is a dark red or dull purple color because of the hemoglobin. Blood rich in oxygen is a bright red color because of the oxyhemoglobin.

Carbon dioxide transport. Cellular respiration produces carbon dioxide. Thus the concentration of carbon dioxide is greater in the body cells than in the capillary blood. Therefore, the carbon dioxide diffuses out of the cells and into the blood. Carbon dioxide is transported by the blood to the lungs in several ways .

When carbon dioxide diffuses into the blood, it combines with water, forming carbonic acid.

$$CO_2 + H_2O \longrightarrow H_2CO_3$$

The H_2CO_3 quickly breaks down (ionizes), forming hydrogen ions and bicarbonate ions.

$$H_2CO_3 \longrightarrow H^+ + HCO_3^-$$

These reactions are speeded up by the presence of an enzyme in the red blood cells. Most of the carbon dioxide (about 70 percent) is carried in the plasma in the form of bicarbonate ions.

Some of the carbon dioxide (about 20 percent) is carried in the red blood cells as carboxyhemoglobin.

$$CO_2 + Hb \longrightarrow HbCO_2$$

Sidelight

The Bends

As a human diver descends beneath the surface of the water, the pressure increases enormously. To be able to breathe, the diver must inhale air that is under pressure.

When a diver breathes pressurized air for long periods of time, the nitrogen in the air becomes dissolved in the body fluids and tissues. If the diver suddenly returns to the surface, where the pressure is much less, the nitrogen comes out of solution, forming bubbles in the body fluids and tissues. This condition, called the "bends," or decompression sickness, is very painful and can be fatal.

The bends can be avoided if decompression is gradual. Divers returning to the surface from depths of more than about 12 meters must do so gradually, with stops of varying lengths at certain depths. These stops give the body a chance to get rid of the excess nitrogen.

Diving mammals do not develop the bends when they surface quickly from a deep dive. This is largely because they do not inhale gases at high pressure underwater. Their bodies contain only the air left in their lungs when they dived.

A small amount of carbon dioxide (about 10 percent) is carried in solution in the plasma.

All these reactions are reversible, and in the lungs carbon dioxide is released.

11-12   Diseases of the Respiratory System

The following list includes some of the common disorders of the respiratory system.

1. *Asthma* (*az*-muh) is a severe allergic reaction in which contraction of the bronchioles makes breathing difficult.

2. *Bronchitis* is an inflammation of the linings of the bronchial tubes. The passageways to the alveoli become swollen and clogged with mucus. The condition is generally marked by severe coughing and by difficulty in breathing.

3. *Emphysema* (em-fuh-*zee*-muh) is a condition in which the lungs lose their elasticity. The walls of the air sacs break down, reducing the respiratory surface. Emphysema is marked by shortness of breath.

4. *Pneumonia* (noo-*moh*-nyuh) is a condition in which the alveoli become filled with fluid, preventing the exchange of gases in the lungs.

5. *Lung cancer* is a disease in which tumors (masses of tissue) form in the lungs as a result of irregular and uncontrolled cell growth. Numerous studies have demonstrated a definite relationship between lung cancer and smoking.

Smokers also run a greater risk of developing bronchitis and emphysema than nonsmokers.

Chapter Review

SUMMARY

- Respiration takes place by diffusion of gases across an organism's respiratory surface, which is thin and moist. In very simple organisms, cells exchange gases directly with the environment through the cell membrane. In complex multicellular animals, where most cells lie at great distance from the environment, complex respiratory and transport systems provide for gas exchange. In many animals, including humans, a pigment in the blood increases its capacity to carry respiratory gases.

- In earthworms, respiration takes place through the moist skin, which is well supplied with capillaries. The blood contains the pigment hemoglobin.

- In grasshoppers, the circulatory system is not involved in carrying respiratory gases. Instead there is a system of tracheal tubes that carry air to and from the body cells.

- In fish and many other aquatic animals, the respiratory organs are gills. Respiratory gases are exchanged as water flows over the gills.

- In humans, the respiratory system consists of lungs and a system of tubes that carry air to and from the lungs. Within the lungs are millions of tiny thin-walled alveoli, each surrounded by capillaries. The exchange of respiratory gases between the air and the blood takes place through the walls of the alveoli and capillaries. Respiration in humans occurs in four phases: breathing, external respiration, circulation, and internal respiration.

KNOW THE TERMS

air sac	diaphragm	lung	respiratory surface
alveolus	exhalation	nasal passage	spiracle
bronchial tube	gill	pharynx	trachea
bronchiole	inhalation	pleura	tracheal tubes
bronchus	larynx	respiration	vocal cords

SECTION QUESTIONS

The Respiratory Process

1. What is respiration?
2. What is a respiratory surface?

Adaptations For Respiration

3. What is the respiratory surface in the protozoa?
4. What is the respiratory surface of the earthworm?
5. Name the openings through which air enters and leaves the grasshopper.
6. Name the respiratory organs of such aquatic animals as fish, clams, and lobsters.

The Human Respiratory System

7. What is the diaphragm?
8. Name the structures found in the throat that fight infection.
9. What is the larynx?
10. How is the trachea kept open?
11. What is the respiratory surface in humans?
12. Name the four phases of respiration in humans.
13. What is accomplished by breathing?
14. Where is the control for breathing?
15. What is internal respiration?
16. Name five respiratory diseases.

KNOW THE FACTS

Copy the number of each sentence below on a sheet of paper. Beside each number, write the letter identifying the answer that most correctly completes the sentence.

1. In all animals, the exchange of oxygen and carbon dioxide is accomplished by
   a. the action of the alveoli of the lungs.
   b. the activity of the trachea and bronchi.
   c. diffusion across moist cell membranes.
   d. contraction of the diaphragm and rib muscles.
2. Protozoa obtain oxygen from the environment through the
   a. spiracles. c. vacuoles.
   b. cell membranes. d. mitochondria.
3. Gas exchange in protozoa and hydra occurs
   a. in gills.
   b. with the aid of respiratory pigments.
   c. through osmosis.
   d. by direct diffusion between the cells and the environment.
4. An animal that has most of its body cells in direct contact with its oxygen supply is the
   a. hydra. c. grasshopper.
   b. earthworm. d. human.

5. In most air-breathing animals the respiratory surface is kept moist by
   a. using internal gills.
   b. perspiration.
   c. being inside the organism.
   d. the blood in the capillaries.
6. Oxygen from the air enters the earthworm's body through the
   a. spiracles.
   b. mouth.
   c. skin.
   d. dorsal and ventral vessels.
7. Two organisms that have blood transport systems containing hemoglobin, which aids in the transport of oxygen, are the
   a. paramecium and ameba.
   b. hydra and earthworm.
   c. earthworm and human.
   d. grasshopper and human.
8. The structures involved in the distribution of

the respiratory gases in the grasshopper are the

a. blood vessels.   c. lungs.
b. alveoli.   d. tracheal tubes.

9. The pleura
   a. is a membrane that surrounds the lungs.
   b. is the respiratory surface of humans.
   c. is one of the air passages to the lungs.
   d. is a membrane lining the air passages.

10. The structure that closes the larynx during swallowing is the
   a. pharynx.   c. trachea.
   b. vocal cord.   d. epiglottis

11. The exchange of oxygen and carbon dioxide between the air and the blood occurs in
   a. the pharynx.   c. bronchioles.
   b. alveoli.   d. bronchi.

12. The smallest of the respiratory air passageways are the
   a. bronchioles.   c. bronchi.
   b. tracheae.   d. bronchial tubes.

13. A structure that contributes to pressure changes in the chest cavity is the
   a. pharynx.   c. alveolus.
   b. diaphragm.   d. epiglottis.

14. During breathing, the lungs
   a. are stimulated by pulmonary nerves.
   b. are forced to contract and expand by air pressure changes in the chest cavity.
   c. move independently.
   d. are filled with fluid.

15. After running, a person's breathing rate increases because of
   a. a decrease in the movement of the diaphragm.
   b. a demand by the body for more red blood cells.
   c. the action of the heart in response to an accumulation of lactic acid.
   d. an increased concentration of carbon dioxide in the blood.

16. Oxygen molecules move from the capillaries to the cells by the process of
   a. cyclosis.   c. pinocytosis.
   b. osmosis.   d. diffusion.

17. Oxygen in the blood is carried primarily
   a. as oxyhemoglobin.
   b. in solution in the plasma.
   c. as carboxyhemoglobin.
   d. as carbonic acid.

18. Most carbon dioxide is carried in the plasma in the form of
   a. hydrogen ions.   c. lactic acid.
   b. bicarbonate ions.   d. oxyhemoglobin.

19. A disease involving breakdown of the air sacs in lungs is
   a. bronchitis.   c. pneumonia.
   b. asthma.   d. emphysema.

20. The condition in which the alveoli become filled with fluid is called
   a. pneumonia.   c. bronchitis.
   b. emphysema.   d. asthma.

UNDERSTAND THE CONCEPTS

21. Why can't aerobic cellular respiration occur without the process of respiration?
22. What are the characteristics of a respiratory surface?
23. How is the direction of diffusion across a respiratory surface determined?
24. In the protozoa, how is gas exchange with the environment accomplished?
25. How do the cells of hydra obtain oxygen and get rid of carbon dioxide?
26. Why must aquatic animals move large volumes of water over their respiratory surfaces?
27. Why are respiratory pigments, such as hemoglobin, so important to respiration?
28. Describe respiration in the earthworm.
29. Explain how the respiratory system of the grasshopper functions.
30. How do gills function in the process of respiration?
31. What functions do the nasal passages serve in the human respiratory system?
32. Explain the function of the ciliated mucous membrane lining of the air passageways.
33. Trace the path of the air from the nasal passages to the alveoli.
34. How does tobacco smoke damage the respiratory system?
35. Describe the transport of oxygen in the blood from the lungs to the body cells.
36. Describe the transport of carbon dioxide in the blood from the body cells to the lungs.

THINK CRITICALLY

37. List five similarities between protist respiration and human respiration.
38. Blood has more functions in fish and in humans than in insects. Support this statement with evidence.
39. Describe how respiratory processes changed as animals evolved to live on land.
40. The exchange of oxygen and carbon dioxide between land animals and their environment has remained basically aquatic. Do you believe this statement to be true or false? Support your answer with evidence.
41. Some scientists compare cellular respiration to burning fuel. Explain why each of these processes requires oxygen.

THINK CREATIVELY

42. The same level of activity at sea level and at 10,000 feet above sea level results in different breathing rates and different degrees of stress or fatigue. Suggest some possible factors that could cause these differences. How do these factors affect the respiratory process?
43. What happens to the process of respiration when a person breathes into and out of a paper bag to treat hyperventilation?

FOR FURTHER INVESTIGATION

1. Build a balloon-lung model of the respiratory system. The following materials should be used: gallon-size plastic mayonnaise or pickle jar, one-hole rubber stopper, Y tube, two balloons, thin rubber sheeting, and string. Demonstrate how the model works.
2. Design and perform an experiment to test the effect of various types of exercise on the rate of respiration.
3. Write to the local chapter of the American Lung Association for information about the effects of smoking and chewing tobacco on health. Be sure to ask for information on respiratory diseases, various types of cancer, and damage to fetuses. Why does the use of tobacco affect other parts of the body besides the lungs? Prepare a bulletin board display showing the results of your study.
4. Prepare a report on one of the career opportunities listed below. See suggested procedures, p. 9, "For Further Investigation" Activity 3.
   a. Respiratory therapist
   b. Speech pathologist
   c. Otolaryngologist
5. Prepare a brief report on the life and contributions of one of the following scientists:
   a. Helen Ranney
   b. Mary Avery
   c. Garrett Morgan

FOR FURTHER READING

Bruun, Ruth Dowling, and Bruun, Bertel, *The Human Body*, Random House, New York, 1982. (Excellent chapter on respiratory system.)

Franklin, Deborah, "From Bust to Dust: Protective Masks on Trial," *Science News*, June 23, 1984.

Hughes, G. M., *The Vertebrate Lung* (Carolina Biology Reader), Carolina Biological Supply Co., Burlington, NC, 1979.

Silberner, J., "More Nails in Smoking's Coffin," *Science News*, June 1, 1985.

Ward, Brian, *The Lungs and Breathing* (The Human Body Series), Franklin Watts, New York, 1982.

Wolfe, M., "Hemosponge: A Breath of Fresh Air," *Science News*, December 24 and 31, 1983.

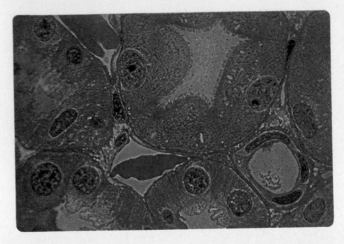

Chapter 12

EXCRETION

Cross-section of kidney tubules seen through a microscope.

THE EXCRETORY PROCESS

Objectives:
1. Define the term *excretion,* and describe how this process helps maintain homeostasis.
2. List the major metabolic wastes and name the processes by which they are formed.
3. Explain the difference between the process of excretion and that of defecation.

12-1 Importance of Excretion

Organisms can carry out their life processes only if the chemical environment of their internal fluids is kept constant within certain limits. However, as the cells carry on their life processes, wastes are produced. These wastes are the end products of metabolism. For example, in cellular respiration nutrients are oxidized, and the energy released is stored in the form of ATP. However, carbon dioxide and water are also produced, and these end products are wastes that must be removed from the organism. **Excretion** (ek-*skree*-shun) is the process by which the wastes of cellular metabolism are removed from the organism.

The excretory organs regulate the chemical makeup of the blood and other body fluids by removing metabolic wastes and excess materials. They also help to maintain a constant body temperature by removing excess heat. The excretory organs function together with the circulatory, nervous, and endocrine systems in maintaining a constant internal environment—they maintain homeostasis.

12-2 Major Metabolic Wastes

The most important of the cellular wastes are carbon dioxide, water, nitrogenous wastes, and mineral salts. Carbon dioxide and water are formed during cellular respiration. Water is also produced by dehydration synthesis (see page 50). Nitrogenous wastes in the form of ammonia, urea, or uric acid are produced by the breakdown of amino acids. Mineral salts, such as sodium chloride and potassium sulfate, accumulate during metabolism. All these wastes are poisons in high concentrations.

In addition to the wastes of metabolism, the excretory system must also remove any excess water, salts, or other substances that accumulate within the organism.

Many people confuse excretion with elimination. Elimination, or *defecation* (def-uh-*kay*-shun), is the removal from the digestive tract of unabsorbed and undigested food in the form of *feces*. Since these materials never enter the body cells, they are not metabolic wastes.

ADAPTATIONS FOR EXCRETION

Objectives:

1. List the metabolic wastes of protozoa and hydra and explain how each type of waste is removed from the cell.
2. Explain the function of the contractile vacuole in freshwater protozoa.
3. Describe and compare the excretory structures and products of the earthworm and the grasshopper.

12-3 Excretion in Protozoa

Excretion in protozoa is a relatively simple process. Wastes diffuse through the cell membrane into the surrounding watery environment. Metabolic wastes include carbon dioxide, mineral salts, and ammonia. Ammonia (NH_3) is the chief nitrogenous waste of microorganisms and many aquatic multicellular animals. Although ammonia is highly toxic to cells, it is very soluble in water. Thus, ammonia can easily be excreted as a waste product if plenty of water is available to wash it away.

Water continuously enters the cells of freshwater protozoans, such as ameba and paramecium, by osmosis. Some water is also produced as a by-product of cellular respiration. Excess water must be "pumped out" of the cell against a concentration gradient. The excess water collects in contractile vacuoles, which periodically burst at the cell membrane, ejecting the excess water from the cell (see Figure 12-1). This action, which involves active transport, maintains the normal water balance in the cell.

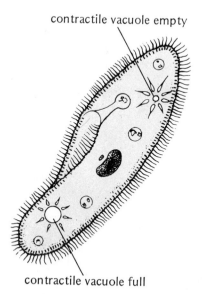

contractile vacuole empty

contractile vacuole full

Figure 12-1. Water Balance in the Paramecium. Water continuously enters the paramecium and other freshwater protozoa by osmosis. Water balance is maintained by means of contractile vacuoles. Excess water collects in the vacuoles and is periodically ejected from the organism.

12-4   Excretion in Hydra

The hydra is a very small animal, and its structure is such that most of its cells are in contact with the water of its environment. Hence, the metabolic wastes, including carbon dioxide, ammonia, and mineral salts, diffuse directly through the cell membrane of each cell into the surrounding water.

Hydras are freshwater organisms, and water tends to enter their cells by osmosis. However, no contractile vacuole has been observed in the cells of the hydra. Excess water may be pumped out through the cell membrane by active transport.

12-5   Excretion in the Earthworm

When most of the cells of an animal are not in contact with the external environment, the removal of metabolic wastes requires special excretory organs. The excretory organs of the earthworm are the **nephridia** (nih-*frid*-ee-uh). These structures are found in pairs, one on each side, in most of the segments of the earthworm's body (see Figure 12-2). Each nephridium occupies parts of two adjacent segments.

Some of the cellular wastes diffuse directly into the fluid in the body cavity of the earthworm. This fluid, which contains useful substances in addition to wastes, enters the funnel-like opening of the nephridium and is moved through it by the beating of cilia. The fluid travels through a tubule to the major part of the nephridium in the next segment. This part consists of several coiled loops and a large bladder with an opening to the outside of the body, the *nephridiopore* (nih-*frid*-ee-oh-por). The coiled loops of the nephridium are surrounded by a network of capillaries. Wastes from the bloodstream pass out of the capillaries and into the nephridium. Useful substances from the body fluid, such as glucose and water, are reabsorbed

Figure 12-2. Excretory System of the Earthworm. A pair of nephridia surrounded by capillaries is found in almost every segment of the earthworm. Fluid from the body cavity enters the nephridium and useful substances are reabsorbed into the bloodstream. Wastes in the form of urine pass through the bladder and are discharged from the body through the nephridiopore.

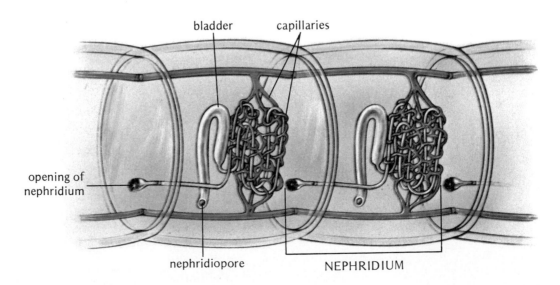

bladder   capillaries

opening of
nephridium

nephridiopore   NEPHRIDIUM

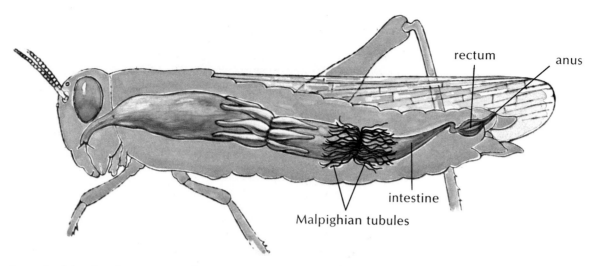

rectum

anus

intestine

Malpighian tubules

into the blood. The wastes in the nephridium are discharged through the nephridiopore as a dilute solution called **urine** (*yur*-en).

The wastes excreted by the nephridia include water, mineral salts, ammonia, and **urea** (yuh-*ree*-uh), which is formed from ammonia and carbon dioxide. Like ammonia, urea is very soluble in water. However, it is less toxic to cells than ammonia.

In the earthworm, carbon dioxide is excreted through the moist skin (see page 180).

12-6　Excretion in the Grasshopper

The excretory organs of grasshoppers and other insects are the **Malpighian** (mal-*pig*-ee-en) **tubules** (see Figure 12-3). Insects have open circulatory systems. Thus, the slender excretory tubules are bathed directly by the blood, which circulates freely within the body spaces. Wastes and other substances from the blood enter the tubules by diffusion and active transport. From the tubules they pass into the intestine. Water, nutrients, and other useful substances are reabsorbed both in the tubules and in the digestive tract, and are returned to the body fluids. The dry nitrogenous waste product, **uric** (*yur*-ik) **acid,** is eliminated from the body through the anus along with the feces.

Of all the nitrogenous wastes, uric acid is the least toxic. In fact, because it is insoluble in water, it is almost completely harmless. It is excreted as a solid or semisolid by birds and reptiles, as well as insects. Because its removal from the body of an organism requires almost no water, the excretion of uric acid helps to conserve water in land animals whose water supply is limited.

Carbon dioxide diffuses from the body tissues into the tracheal tubes and then out of the grasshopper through the spiracles (see page 181).

Figure 12-3. Excretory System of the Grasshopper. The Malpighian tubules of the grasshopper remove wastes from the blood by diffusion and active transport. A dry nitrogenous waste product, uric acid, is eliminated with the feces through the anus.

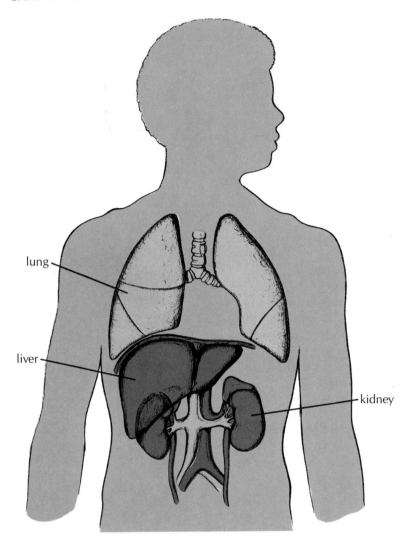

Figure 12-4. Organs of the Human Excretory System. The organs of excretion in humans include the liver, kidneys, lungs, and skin.

THE HUMAN EXCRETORY SYSTEM

Objectives:
1. Identify the principal metabolic wastes of the human body.
2. Describe the excretory functions of the liver.
3. Draw and label the parts of the human urinary system, including a nephron, and explain the function of each.
4. Describe the process of urine formation.
5. Explain the excretory functions of the lungs.
6. Describe the structure and functions of the skin.

The complex and highly developed excretory system of humans plays a major role in the maintenance of homeostasis. The principal metabolic wastes of humans are carbon dioxide, urea, water, and mineral salts. The organs of excretion are the liver, kidneys, lungs, and skin (see Figure 12-4).

12-7   Role of the Liver in Excretion

The role of the liver in digestion was discussed in Chapter 8. As an excretory organ the liver performs a number of functions that regulate the composition of body fluids.

Detoxification. A major function of the liver is the removal of harmful, or toxic, substances from the blood. Within the liver these substances are converted into inactive or less toxic forms. Thus the liver purifies, or *detoxifies,* the blood. The inactive substances formed in the liver are then released back into the bloodstream and are eventually excreted from the body by the kidneys.

Excretion of bile. Bile is synthesized by the cells of the liver. It consists of bile salts, cholesterol, and part of the hemoglobin molecule from worn-out red blood cells. Since some of the constituents of bile are metabolic wastes, bile is considered an excretory product. Bile collects in the gall bladder and passes through the bile duct to the small intestine, where it functions in the digestion and absorption of fats. In the last part of the small intestine, almost all the bile salts are reabsorbed into the blood and returned to the liver. From the liver, they again pass to the small intestine. Thus, bile salts are reused. The rest of the bile passes into the large intestine and is eliminated from the body in the feces.

Urea formation. Amino acids are both the building blocks and breakdown products of proteins. However, excess amino acids cannot be stored in the body. Instead, in the liver the amino group (NH_2) is removed, a process called *deamination* (dee-am-uh-*nay*-shun). The amino group is converted to ammonia (NH_3), while the remainder of the amino acid molecule is either converted to pyruvic acid and used as an energy source in cellular respiration or converted to glycogen or fat for storage (see Figure 12-5).

Ammonia is a highly toxic substance, and it is rapidly converted to the less toxic substance urea by a series of enzyme-

Figure 12-5. Fate of Excess Amino Acids in the Body. Excess amino acids undergo deamination, in which the amino group is removed and converted to ammonia. The ammonia is quickly converted to urea, which is excreted from the body. The carbon skeleton of the amino acid can be converted to pyruvic acid and used in cellular respiration or it can be converted to glycogen or fat and stored.

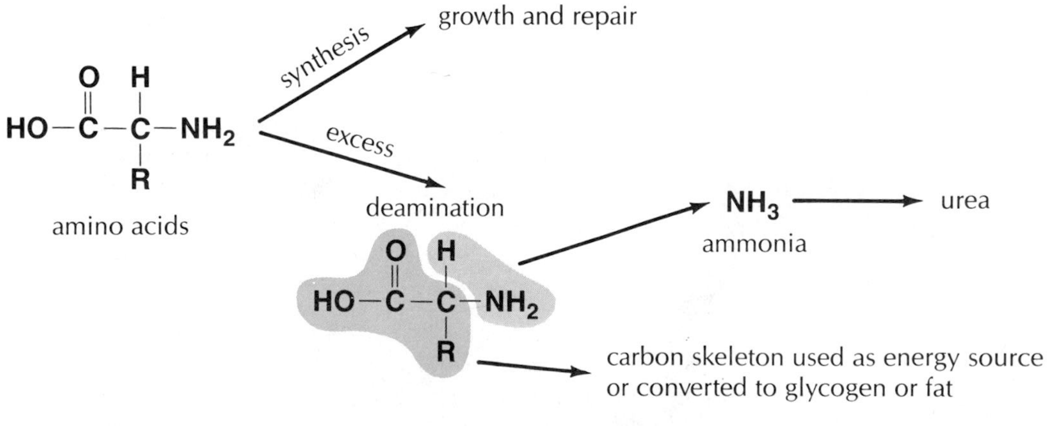

catalyzed reactions. The urea diffuses from the liver into the bloodstream, which transports it to the kidneys. The kidneys filter the urea from the blood, and it is then excreted from the body in the urine.

12-8   The Urinary System

The **urinary** (*yur*-uh-ner-ee) **system** includes the kidneys, bladder, and associated tubes (see Figure 12-6). The **kidneys** are bean-shaped organs about 10 cm long. They lie against the muscles of the back in the abdomen just below the diaphragm. The kidneys serve two major functions. First, they remove the wastes of cellular metabolism from the blood. Second, they control the concentrations of the various substances found in the body fluids. In these ways, the kidneys are vital in maintaining homeostasis. The kidneys filter metabolic wastes and various other substances from the blood, producing urine. Two tubes, the **ureters** (*yur*-et-urz), carry the urine to the **urinary bladder,** where it is stored temporarily. Another tube, the **urethra** (yuh-*ree*-thruh), carries the urine from the bladder to the outside of the body.

Structure of the kidneys. A lengthwise section of the kidney reveals that it is divided into three distinct regions. The

Figure 12-6. The Human Urinary System. The urinary system consists of the kidneys, ureters, bladder, urethra, and associated blood vessels. The adrenal glands rest on the kidneys, but are not part of the excretory system. The cross section of the kidney shows three distinct regions. Blood is filtered in the outermost region, the cortex. The filtrate passes through the tubes in the middle region, the medulla, and drains into the ureter from the innermost region, the pelvis.

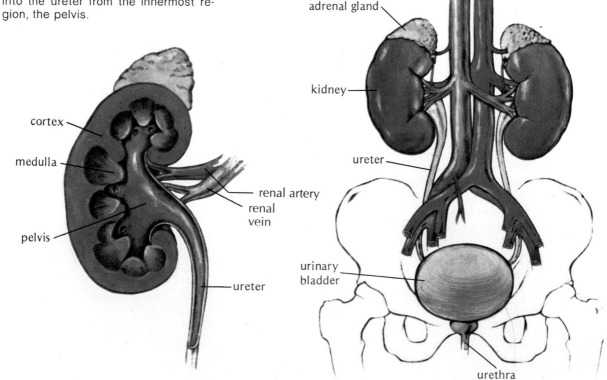

outermost region is the *cortex* (*kor*-teks), the middle region is the *medulla* (meh-*duhl*-uh), and the inner region is the *pelvis* (*pel*-vis). The filtering of the blood occurs in the cortex; the medulla consists of collecting ducts that carry the urine; and the pelvis is a cavity connected to the ureter, into which the urine drains.

The functional units of the kidneys are the **nephrons** (*nef-rahnz*). Each kidney contains about 1.25 million nephrons (see Figure 12-7). The nephron begins with a cluster of capillaries, the **glomerulus** (glah-*mer*-yuh-lus), which is surrounded by a double-walled, cup-shaped structure called **Bowman's capsule**. Coming from Bowman's capsule is a long tubule that winds and twists and then forms a long loop called the *loop of Henle* (*hen*-lee). From the loop, the tubule winds and twists again before emptying into a collecting duct. The collecting duct receives liquid waste from many nephrons.

Blood enters the kidneys through the **renal arteries.** It passes through two sets of capillaries before leaving the kidneys through the **renal veins.** The arteriole carrying blood to a nephron enters Bowman's capsule and subdivides into a capillary network, which is the glomerulus. Blood leaving the glomerulus flows into a second arteriole, which subdivides to form another capillary network that surrounds the tubules of the nephron. These capillaries merge to form a venule.

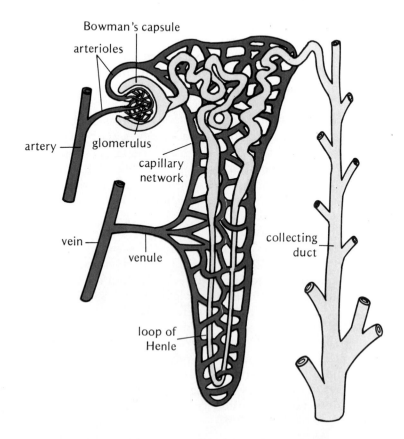

Figure 12-7. The Nephron. The nephron is the functional unit of the kidney. As blood flows through the glomerulus, water and other small molecules diffuse into the surrounding Bowman's capsule. The filtrate then passes through the tubules, where useful substances are reabsorbed into the blood. The collecting duct receives urine from many nephrons and passes it into the renal pelvis, from which it flows into the ureter.

Career

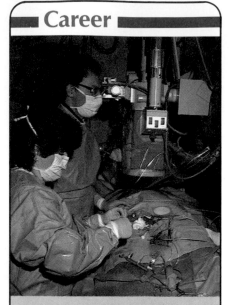

Some physician assistants work in specialty areas, such as surgery.

Physician Assistant

Physician assistants relieve medical doctors of many essential but time-consuming tasks. Working under the direct supervision of a doctor, they interview patients, take medical histories, perform physical examinations, order laboratory tests, make tentative diagnoses, prescribe some treatments, and administer certain medications. Studies show that physician assistants can provide adequate care for about eight of every ten patients who visit a family doctor's office. Physician assistants work in hospitals, clinics, health maintenance organizations, and doctors' offices, i.e., wherever doctors work.

Completion of an approved program of academic studies and clinical training is usually required for employment as a physician assistant. Admission requirements vary, but two years of college-level work in the sciences or a health profession is usually the minimum. Most applicants in fact, hold college degrees.

Urine formation. The formation of urine by the nephrons takes place in two stages—filtration and reabsorption. In *filtration,* substances pass from the blood into the nephron. In *reabsorption,* substances pass out of the nephron and back into the blood.

Filtration occurs while the blood is flowing through the glomerulus within Bowman's capsule. Blood entering the glomerulus is under pressure. The pressure forces water and many small molecules, such as salts, urea, glucose, and amino acids, out through the thin walls of the glomerulus, into the surrounding capsule. Blood cells and blood proteins are too large to pass through the walls of the glomerulus, and remain in the blood. The fluid in Bowman's capsule is called the *filtrate.* It is basically the same as plasma except for the absence of proteins. From Bowman's capsule, the filtrate passes into the tubule of the nephron.

About 180 liters of filtrate are formed by the kidneys during the course of 24 hours. If all the filtrate were excreted, the body would continually lose nutrients, salts, and large amounts of water. However the kidneys produce only about 1 to 1.5 liters of urine in 24 hours. The process that reduces the volume of filtrate and returns important substances to the blood is reabsorption. Normally, as the filtrate passes through the tubules of the nephrons, about 99 percent of the water, all the glucose and amino acids, and many of the salt ions are reabsorbed. These substances are returned to the blood in the capillary network that surrounds the tubules. The reabsorption of water in the tubules is an important means of water conservation in mammals. Since most of the water is reabsorbed, the substances left in the filtrate become highly concentrated.

While water is reabsorbed passively by osmosis, reabsorption of glucose, amino acids, and salt ions involves active transport. Energy for active transport, in the form of ATP, is supplied by the numerous mitochondria found in the cells of the tubules. The cells lining the tubules have microvilli that greatly increase the surface area, allowing reabsorption of huge amounts of water and other substances.

Most substances have what is called a *kidney threshold level.* If the concentration of the substance in the blood exceeds a certain level, the excess is not reabsorbed. It remains in the urine and is excreted from the body. In a person suffering from diabetes, the blood sugar level is so high that not all the glucose in the filtrate can be returned to the blood. Consequently, glucose appears in the urine.

After reabsorption, the fluid remaining in the nephrons consists mostly of water, urea, and various salts, and is known as *urine.* Urine flows from the tubules into the collecting ducts. It passes out of the kidneys through the ureters to the bladder and is periodically discharged from the bladder through the urethra.

12-9   The Lungs

Lungs are excretory organs in that they rid the body of carbon dioxide and water (in the form of water vapor). Both of
these substances are end products of aerobic cellular respiration. The functioning of the lungs is discussed in Chapter 11.

12-10   The Skin

The skin is the part of the body that is in contact with the
external environment. It consists of many different tissues and
performs a variety of functions, including the excretion of
wastes.

Structure of the skin. As shown in Figure 12-8, the skin
consists of two layers, an outer epidermis and an inner dermis.

The **epidermis** (ep-uh-*der*-mis) is composed of layers of
tightly packed epithelial cells. The lowermost portion of the
epidermis is made up of rapidly dividing cells. As these cells
are pushed farther and farther away from the dermis, they
receive less nourishment and die. However, before dying,
they produce large amounts of a tough, waterproofing protein
called *keratin* (*ker*-uh-tin). The outer part of the epidermis
consists of these hardened dead cells. It is continually wear-
ing away and being replaced by new cells from the dividing
layer. The function of the tough, waterproof epidermis is to
protect the dermis.

The **dermis** lies below the epidermis and is made up of
elastic connective tissue. It is a thick layer that supports the

Figure 12-8. Structure of the Skin. The
epidermis protects the dermis, which
contains blood and lymph vessels,
glands, nerves, sense receptors, and
hair follicles. Adipose tissue beneath
the dermis is not shown in this drawing.

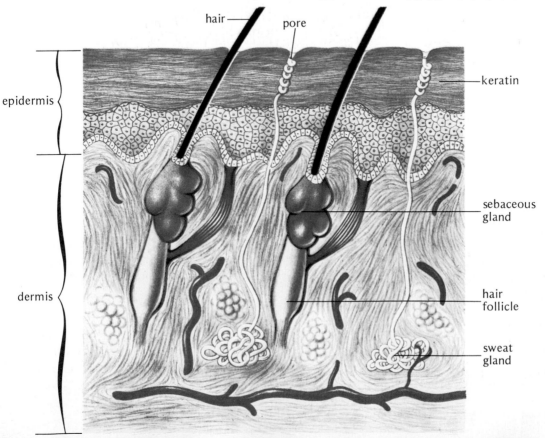

Frontier of Biology

Artificial Skin

Every year, some 130,000 Americans are burned severely enough to require hospitalization. Of these, about 10,000 die from fluid loss and infections. Until recently, doctors had only surgical dressings and other temporary coverings for severe burns. Now, however, there is a new type of artificial skin that is not rejected by the burn victim's immune system.

The new artificial skin, developed at Massachusetts Institute of Technology, has two layers, just as real skin does. The inner layer is *collagen*—a type of connective tissue—obtained from cowhide. The outer layer is a protective silicone rubber sheet that eventually is peeled away. When a sheet of artificial skin (see photo) is in contact with tissues exposed by severe burns, nerve fibers, blood vessels, and connective tissue grow up into it, forming a new, living layer of skin. After the outer sheet is peeled away, it is replaced by a thin graft of real skin obtained elsewhere on the patient's body.

A more advanced type of artificial skin eliminates the need for the second stage skin graft. Clinical trials of this substance are currently underway.

skin and binds it to the underlying muscle and bone. Within the dermis are blood vessels, lymph vessels, nerves, sense receptors, sebaceous glands, sweat glands, and hair follicles. Beneath the dermis is a layer of fat, or *adipose*, tissue. Thin people have little fat in this layer, whereas in obese people this layer is very thick.

The **sebaceous** (sih-*bay*-shus) **glands** produce oily secretions that keep the skin and hair soft and pliable and provide a protective coating. **Sweat glands** consist of tiny coiled tubes that open to the surface of the skin through holes called *pores.* The perspiration, or sweat, excreted by these glands consists mainly of water (99 percent) with some salts, such as NaC1, and a trace of urea.

Functions of the skin. The skin performs several important functions.

1. The skin protects the internal tissues of the body from injury and blocks the entrance of microorganisms and other foreign materials. It also protects the body from drying out.

2. The skin excretes a small amount of urea and salt in perspiration. However, the excretory function of the skin is actually a minor one.

3. Nerve endings in the skin detect pain, touch, pressure, heat, and cold.

4. The skin is involved in the regulation of body temperature. When the body becomes too warm, the excess heat is lost in two ways. Blood vessels in the skin become dilated, the supply of blood to the capillaries in the skin increases (causing a flushed appearance), and heat is radiated to the air. There is also increased sweating. Energy for the evaporation of sweat comes from body heat. Thus, when the sweat evaporates, it cools the body.

When the body is too cool, the reverse happens. Blood vessels in the skin constrict, the supply of blood to the skin capillaries decreases, perspiration is reduced, and less heat is lost from the body. In cold weather, shivering and muscle tension increase heat production by the muscles, and the body is warmed. The mechanisms by which the body maintains a constant temperature are a good example of homeostatic control.

Chapter Review

SUMMARY

- Organisms must maintain homeostasis—a constant internal chemical environment. However, the metabolic processes of cells produce wastes, which include carbon dioxide, water, nitrogenous wastes, and mineral salts. These cellular wastes are removed from the organism by the process of excretion.

- In simple organisms, wastes diffuse directly from the cells into the environment. In complex multicellular animals, excretion is accomplished by specialized excretory organs and organ systems. Earthworms have excretory organs called nephridia that excrete urine. Grasshoppers and other insects have excretory organs called Malpighian tubules that excrete the waste product uric acid.

- In humans, excretion is a complex process that involves the liver, kidneys, lungs, and skin. The activities of these organs regulate the chemical makeup of the blood and other body fluids.

- The liver performs several excretory functions. It detoxifies the blood. It manufactures and excretes bile, which contains the breakdown products of hemoglobin from worn-out red blood cells. Also it is the site of deamination and urea formation. The urea is filtered from the blood and excreted by the kidneys.

- The urinary system includes the kidneys, ureters, urinary bladder, and urethra. Each of the two kidneys consists of more than a million nephrons. The nephrons produce urine by filtration and reabsorption. The urine passes out of the kidneys and through the ureters to the bladder, and leaves the bladder through the urethra.

- During respiration, the lungs rid the body of carbon dioxide and water. The skin protects the internal tissues of the body and excretes small amounts of urea and salt in perspiration. The skin also helps maintain a constant body temperature.

KNOW THE TERMS

Bowman's capsule	kidney	renal vein	urethra
dermis	Malpighian tubule	sebaceous gland	uric acid
epidermis	nephridium	sweat gland	urinary bladder
excretion	nephron	urea	urinary system
glomerulus	renal artery	ureter	urine

SECTION QUESTIONS

The Excretory Process

1. What is excretion?
2. List the major metabolic wastes.

Adaptations for Excretion

3. What are the metabolic wastes of protozoa?
4. Name the earthworm's excretory organs.
5. Name the wastes found in the urine of earthworms.
6. What are the excretory organs of the grasshopper?
7. What animals excrete uric acid?

The Human Excretory System

8. Name the organs of excretion in humans.
9. List the excretory functions of the liver.
10. Name the parts of the urinary system.
11. Identify the three regions of the kidney.
12. What are the functional units of the kidneys?
13. Name the two stages involved in the formation of urine by the nephron.
14. What is the fluid in Bowman's capsule called?
15. What does urine contain?
16. Name the two layers of the skin.

KNOW THE FACTS

Copy the numbers from Column 1 on a sheet of paper. Select the letter
for the term or phrase from Column 2 that matches each numbered
item, and write it beside the number.

Column 1

1. feces
2. ammonia
3. freshwater protozoa
4. urea
5. uric acid
6. deamination
7. urethra
8. ureter
9. cortex
10. filtration
11. reabsorption
12. urine
13. dermis
14. epidermis
15. sebaceous glands
16. sweat glands

Column 2

a. filtering of blood occurs in this region of the kidney
b. the removal of an amino group
c. substances pass out of the nephron and back into the blood
d. produces oily secretions
e. the outer layer of skin
f. water continuously enters cells by osmosis
g. substances pass from the blood into the nephron
h. the thick inner layer of skin
i. carries urine to the urinary bladder
j. carries urine from the urinary bladder
k. not a metabolic waste
l. helps to lower the body temperature
m. the fluid that remains in the kidney tubules after reabsorption
n. glucose appears in urine
o. least toxic nitrogenous waste; insoluble in water
p. moderately toxic nitrogenous waste; soluble in water
q. highly toxic nitrogenous waste; very soluble in water

UNDERSTAND THE CONCEPTS

17. Describe the functions of excretory organs.
18. How are the major metabolic wastes formed?
19. Why must metabolic wastes be removed from an organism?
20. How do protozoa excrete wastes?
21. Explain how water balance is maintained in freshwater protozoa.
22. How is excretion accomplished in hydra?
23. Describe the structure of the earthworm's nephridium.
24. Explain how the nephridia of the earthworm function.
25. How do the Malpighian tubules of the grasshopper function?
26. How does the grasshopper excrete CO_2?
27. How does the human liver regulate the composition of body fluids?
28. What happens to excess amino acids?
29. What are the kidneys' two main functions?
30. Describe the structure of a nephron.
31. What occurs during the process of filtration in the kidney?
32. What occurs during the process of reabsorption in the kidney?
33. Describe the path of the urine after it leaves the kidneys.
34. In what ways are the lungs excretory organs?
35. Describe the structure of the skin.
36. Describe the four functions of the skin.
37. How does the human body get rid of excess heat?
38. How does the body conserve heat?

THINK CRITICALLY

39. Birds, like airplanes, need to have minimal weight in order to fly efficiently. Yet they still have to excrete metabolic wastes, even while flying. What advantage, then, is there for birds to excrete uric acid "paste" rather than ammonia or urea?

40. Rats and mice are often used in the laboratory to screen new chemical compounds for possible harmful effects in humans.
    a. What animal functions would a scientist monitor in order to detect a toxic reaction to a chemical?

b. What animal structures would most likely be damaged from a truly toxic chemical?

c. What assumptions are made in using laboratory animals to screen for human health effects?

41. What symptom would result if the walls of the glomerulus were damaged or broken?

42. In a person crossing a blazing hot desert on foot, how do the kidneys maintain the quality and quantity of body fluids?

43. How would the kidneys maintain homeostasis in a person who eats mostly potato chips, pretzels, and French fries?

44. If your appetite decreases when you are sick, why is it important to drink lots of water during this time?

45. Even before they hatch, reptilian and bird embryos are actively metabolizing and thus producing many wastes. Why do reptilian and bird embryos convert their nitrogenous wastes into uric acid? Would fish embryos produce uric acid? Would frog embryos?

THINK CREATIVELY

46. An organism with an increased metabolic rate could swim faster, obtain more food, and defend its territory more vigorously. Suggest some possible reasons why the organism's excretory requirements would limit how high its metabolic rate could increase.

47. Suggest a list of foods that a person hiking through the desert might pack in order to minimize the kidney's job of maintaining homeostasis.

FOR FURTHER INVESTIGATION

1. Make a model to show the structure of a nephron with capillaries. Hint: To construct the model try using a short glass thistle tube, plastic tubing, colored threads, string, and clay.

2. To find out the effect of exercise on body temperature, do the following experiment. While resting, take your temperature for one minute and record it. This is your normal resting body temperature. Then exercise vigorously for five minutes. Immediately take your temperature for one minute and record it. Next, take your temperature at three-minute intervals until your normal resting body temperature returns. Record and graph your results. How long did this process take? How did the heat-regulating mechanism of your body restore your temperature to its normal level?

3. People with diseased kidneys must frequently have waste products removed from their blood by a procedure called dialysis. Research this topic by using library resources. You might also want to interview a dialysis patient or a hospital dialysis technician.

4. When a person has a physical examination, the physician usually has a sample of the patient's urine analyzed. Prepare a report explaining what information about the patient's condition can be obtained from urinalysis.

5. Prepare a report on one of the career opportunities listed below. See suggested procedures, p. 9, "For Further Investigation" Activity 3.
   a. Urologist   c. Dermatologist
   b. Dialysis technician

6. Prepare a brief report on the life and scientific contributions of one of the following scientists:
   a. Theodore Lawless
   b. Vivian Pinn
   c. Joyce Kaufman
   d. Bodi Schmidt-Nielsen

FOR FURTHER READING

Cameron, Stewart, *Kidney Disease: The Facts,* Oxford University Press, New York, 1981.

Edelson, R., and Fink, J., "The Immunologic Functions of Skin," *Scientific American,* June, 1985.

Franklin, D., "Skin by the Yard Covers Massive Burns," *Science News,* August 18, 1984.

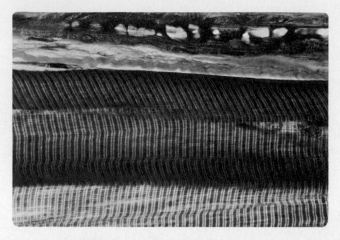
Striated, or skeletal, muscle seen through a microscope.

Chapter 13
SUPPORT AND LOCOMOTION

THE PROCESS OF LOCOMOTION

Objectives:
1. List the advantages of locomotion.
2. Name the two types of skeletons, and describe the advantages and disadvantages of each.

13-1 Advantages of Locomotion

Many types of living things have the capacity to move on their own from one place to another. Such self-generated movement is called *locomotion*. Organisms capable of locomotion are said to be *motile* (*moh*-til). A basic characteristic of most animals and many protists is that they are motile. A basic characteristic of plants, on the other hand, is that they are not motile. Not all animals are motile either. Some aquatic animals, such as corals, barnacles, and sponges, cannot move from place to place on their own. They live attached to the ocean floor or some object. These animals are stationary, or *sessile* (*ses*-il). However, by movement of various parts of their bodies they create water currents that enable them to obtain food and oxygen and carry out their life processes.

The capacity to move from place to place offers a number of advantages for an organism.

1. Locomotion increases the opportunities for organisms to obtain food. (A cougar may hunt for food over a territory of more than 160 square kilometers.)

2. Locomotion enables organisms to find suitable places to live and to move away from harmful conditions in the environment. (Fish tend to swim away from warm, oxygen-poor

Figure 13-1. Exoskeleton of a Mollusk. The exoskeleton of the flame scallop is a hard double shell composed of calcium compounds.

water to find cooler, oxygen-rich water.)

3. Locomotion enables organisms to escape from their enemies or to seek shelter. (Rabbits and deer survive because of their ability to move quickly.)

4. Locomotion enables organisms to find mates and reproduce. (Male and female salmon swim thousands of kilometers to reach their nesting grounds.)

13-2 Muscles and Skeletons

In all but the most simple animals, locomotion involves both muscles and a skeleton to which the muscles are attached. Muscles can exert force when they *contract*, or shorten. When muscles contract, they move the parts to which they are attached.

Most skeletons are composed of hard materials. If the skeleton is outside the body, enclosing the soft parts, it is called an **exoskeleton** (eks-oh-*skel*-uh-tun). Some protozoans and many invertebrates have exoskeletons—hard, outer coverings. Clams, oysters, and other mollusks have hard shells composed of calcium compounds (see Figure 13-1). The animal lives within the shell, and its movement is very limited. Crabs, spiders, insects, and other arthropods have exoskeletons composed of **chitin** (*kyt*-in), which is a tough material that is much lighter than the shells of mollusks. Exoskeletons serve as the site of attachment for muscles. In arthropods the exoskeleton is jointed, which makes it flexible and allows various kinds of movement (see Figure 13-2). Exoskeletons provide good protection for the soft parts of the body. However, since they are not composed of living cells, they cannot grow. Among the arthropods, the exoskeletons are periodically shed,

Figure 13-2. Exoskeleton of an Arthropod. The exoskeleton of the lobster is composed of tough, light-weight chitin. It protects the soft body parts and is jointed to allow movement.

or *molted,* and replaced by a new, larger covering. During the time between molting and growth of the new skeleton, the animal is in a very vulnerable, or unprotected, condition.

In vertebrates, the skeleton is composed of bone and cartilage and is located within the body walls. This type of skeleton, which is inside the body, is called an **endoskeleton** (en-doh-*skel*-uh-tun). An endoskeleton does not protect the entire animal as well as an exoskeleton. However, because bones and cartilage contain living cells and can grow, the skeleton can increase in size along with the rest of the animal. The bones of the endoskeleton serve as sites of attachment for skeletal muscles, making possible the movement of body parts. Endoskeletons are found in fish, amphibians, reptiles, birds, and mammals.

ADAPTATIONS FOR LOCOMOTION

Objective:

Describe locomotion in the ameba, paramecium, hydra, earthworm, and grasshopper.

Living things show a wide variety of adaptations for locomotion. In single-celled organisms, such as protozoa, locomotion may involve pseudopods or various cell structures. In multicellular animals, locomotion always involves specialized muscle tissue. Whatever the method of locomotion, the basis for nearly all protozoan and animal movement is *contractile proteins*—proteins that have the capacity to change in length.

13-3   Locomotion in Protists

Among the protists, some forms lack any means of locomotion, while others are highly motile. Among the motile forms, locomotion is generally carried out by pseudopods, cilia, or flagella.

Pseudopods. **Pseudopods** are temporary projections of the cell surfaces. The organism moves by a flowing of the cytoplasm into the projections. This type of locomotion is best known in amebas, but it is also found in slime molds and other organisms, as well as in white blood cells. Locomotion by means of pseudopods is also known as *ameboid movement.*

Studies of the ameba show that the cytoplasm within the organism is in two states. In the central portion of the cell the cytoplasm is more fluid and is said to be a *sol* (as in *sol*ution). As the ameba moves, this sol portion of the cytoplasm flows forward through the center of the pseudopod (see Figure 13-3). At the tip, it spreads out in all directions and changes into a firmer, less fluid state. In this state the cytoplasm is said to be a *gel* (jel) (as in *gel*atin). This gel travels backward along the sides of the cell, and near the "back" end, the gel is changed back into a sol and joins the forward-flowing stream.

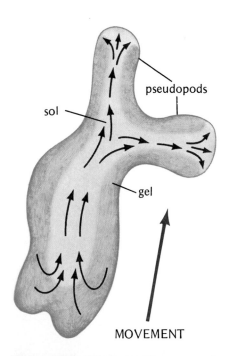

Figure 13-3. Ameboid Movement. In ameboid movement, the cell cytoplasm changes back and forth between a more fluid sol state and a less fluid gel state. Cytoplasm in the sol state flows forward into newly forming pseudopods and then changes to the gel state. At the rear of the cell, cytoplasm in the gel state changes to the sol state and flows forward. In this way the cell contents move in the direction of the new pseudopods.

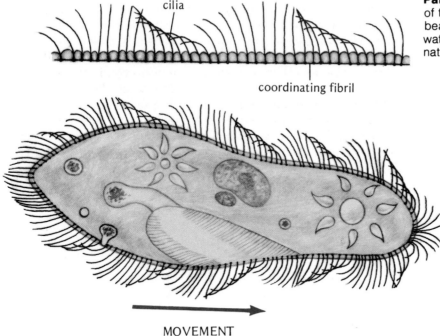

cilia

coordinating fibril

MOVEMENT

Figure 13-4. Locomotion in the Paramecium. The entire outer surface of the organism is covered by cilia that beat rhythmically to propel it through the water. The beating of the cilia is coordinated by a network of fibrils.

Energy for ameboid movement comes from the breakdown of ATP to ADP.

Cilia and flagella. Ciliated protists, such as the paramecium, move very quickly compared to the ameba. The paramecium is covered by thousands of short, hairlike **cilia**, whose rhythmic, oarlike beating propels the organism through the water (see Figure 13-4). The beating of the cilia is coordinated by a system of fibrils that connect the cilia at their bases.

Flagella (singular, flagellum) are similar to cilia except that they are longer and there are usually only one or two per cell. Euglena is a protist that moves by means of its long, thin flagellum (see Figure 13-5). The whiplike movements of the flagellum pull the euglena through the water.

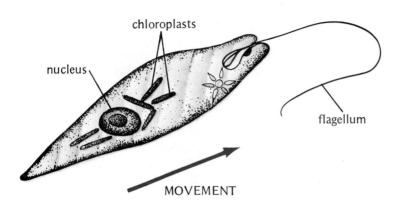

chloroplasts

nucleus

flagellum

MOVEMENT

Figure 13-5. Locomotion in the Euglena. Movement of the long, whiplike flagellum pulls the organism through the water.

13-4   Locomotion in Hydra

The hydra, like all multicellular animals other than sponges, has cells specialized for contraction. Although the hydra tends to be sessile (remain in one place), primitive muscle fibers enable it to contract various parts of its body and move about in several ways. The presence of mucus-secreting cells and ameboid cells enables it to "glide" along on its base. It can move rapidly by somersaulting its base completely over its tentacles. It can also inch along by bending over and attaching its tentacles to an object and then pulling its base closer. The hydra can produce an air bubble on its base and float in the water.

13-5   Locomotion in the Earthworm

The earthworm uses muscles to burrow through the soil. Within its body wall are two layers of muscles (see Figure 13-6). An outer layer of circular muscles goes around the worm, and an inner layer of longitudinal muscles extends the full length of the body. When the circular muscles contract, the worm lengthens and becomes thinner. When the longitudinal muscles contract, the body becomes shorter and thicker. Within the earthworm, the body cavity is filled with fluid. This fluid acts as a skeleton because it cannot be compressed. When the surrounding muscle layers contract, the fluid "skeleton" stiffens the body of the worm and allows it to push through the soil.

On almost all body segments are four pairs of tiny bristles called **setae** (*see*-tee) (see Figure 13-7). In locomotion, the setae (singular, seta) in the rear of the earthworm hook

Figure 13-6. Locomotion in the Earthworm. The earthworm has both circular and longitudinal muscle layers. When the outer layer of circular muscles contracts, the worm lengthens and becomes thinner. When the inner layer of longitudinal muscles contracts, the worm becomes shorter and thicker.

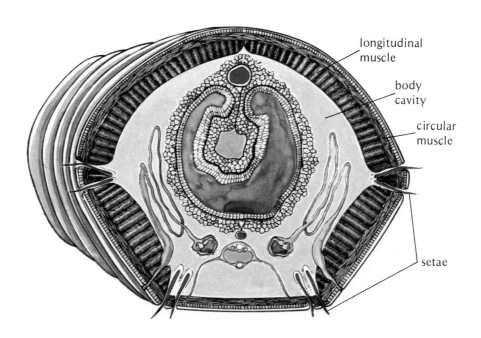

longitudinal
muscle

body
cavity

circular
muscle

setae

into the ground while the circular muscles contract. This lengthens the body and pushes the worm forward. Then the setae near the front of the worm anchor into the ground, and the setae in the rear relax. The longitudinal muscles contract, shortening the body and pulling forward the hind end of the worm. The earthworm moves by repeating these coordinated movements over and over again.

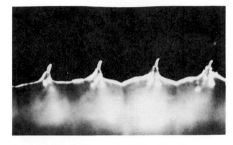

Figure 13-7. Setae of the Earthworm.

13-6   Locomotion in the Grasshopper

The body of the grasshopper is covered by an exoskeleton of chitin. The exoskeleton is divided into plates separated from each other by flexible joints. This arrangement allows the grasshopper to move freely (see Figure 13-8). Grasshoppers can walk, jump, and fly.

Like other insects, the body of the grasshopper has three major divisions—the *head, thorax* (*thor*-aks), and *abdomen* (*ab*-duh-men). Attached to the thorax are three pairs of jointed legs. The first two pairs are used for walking, while the powerful hind pair is used for jumping. A grasshopper can jump more than twenty times its body length. Also attached to the thorax are two pairs of wings. The outer pair is hard and protects the delicate inner pair, which is used in flying. The powerful vertical and longitudinal muscles involved in flight are attached to the exoskeleton of the thorax. They have no direct connection with the wings, but move the wings by changing the shape of the body wall of the thorax.

The muscles of a grasshopper work in pairs. When one muscle of a pair contracts and bends a joint, the other muscle relaxes. When the second muscle contracts, extending the joint, the first muscle relaxes.

Figure 13-8. Locomotion in the Grasshopper. The first two pairs of legs of the grasshopper are used for walking, while the powerful hind legs are used in jumping. The tough outer wings protect the delicate inner wings that are used for flying.

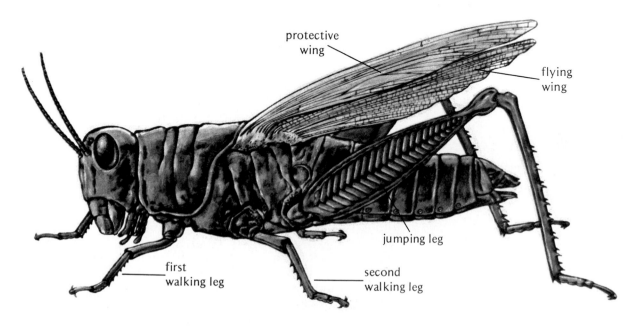

protective wing

flying wing

jumping leg

first walking leg

second walking leg

Career

Physical Therapist

Physical therapists carry out treatment programs to restore use of arms, legs, or other body parts that have been damaged by injury or disease. Treatment may involve exercise, massage, whirlpool baths, and application of heat. Physical therapists work with disabled people, teaching them how to overcome their handicaps. They also teach patients how to use artificial limbs, braces, and other supportive devices.

Physical therapists are state-licensed professionals with a bachelor's or master's degree from an accredited program.

THE HUMAN MUSCULOSKELETAL SYSTEM

Objectives:
1. Describe the functions of bones.
2. Explain how bone tissue forms.
3. Make a drawing showing the internal structure of a bone, and label its parts.
4. Define the following terms: *periosteum, marrow, cartilage,* and *ossification.*
5. Name the major parts of the human skeleton.
6. describe the various types of joints found in the human skeleton and give an example of each.
7. Describe the structure of skeletal muscle, and explain how contraction is accomplished.
8. Explain how locomotion is accomplished in humans.

13-7 Bones and Cartilage

The bones of the skeletal system serve a number of different functions.

1. They serve as sites of attachment for skeletal muscles, and they serve as levers that produce movement of body parts when these muscles contract.

2. They give the body its general shape and support body structures.

3. They protect delicate structures, such as the brain, spinal cord, heart, and lungs.

4. They serve as a storage site for minerals, such as calcium and phosphorus.

Bone is made up of living bone cells, connective tissue fibers, and inorganic compounds. It is a very active tissue, and there is a constant absorption of old tissue and laying down of new tissue. A basic part of the structure is **collagen** (*kahl*-uh-jen), a type of connective tissue. In bone formation, living bone cells called *osteoblasts* (*ahs*-tee-uh-blasts) secrete collagen molecules and certain polysaccharides. The collagen molecules form fibers that are then bound together by the polysaccharides, which act as cement. Bone is formed when calcium and phosphate ions from the body fluids combine, forming calcium phosphate, and precipitate as crystals within the mass of collagen fibers and cement. The hardness and heaviness of bone is due to the presence of the calcium phosphate. The osteoblasts are entrapped in small cavities within the bone substance to form cells called **osteocytes** (*ahs*-tee-uh-syts) (see Figure 13-9).

In the bone, the osteocytes are arranged in concentric circles (see Figure 13-10). In the center of each series of circles is a cavity called the **Haversian** (huh-*ver*-zhun) **canal,** which contains blood vessels and nerves. Tiny canals connect the osteocytes to each other and to the Haversian canal. The blood

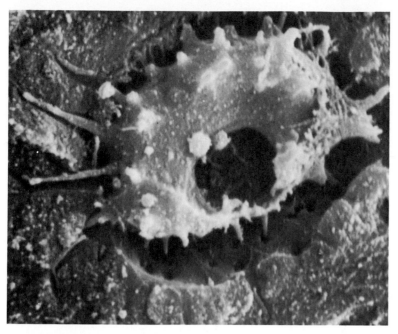

Figure 13-9. Scanning Electron Micrograph of an Osteocyte. Osteocytes are surrounded by bone. However, long, thin cytoplasmic processes extend through small canals in the bone, making contact with processes from adjacent cells.

vessels within the Haversian canals carry oxygen and nutrients to the bone cells and remove wastes. If a bone is broken, the osteocytes become active, producing new bone tissue to heal the wound.

The outside of a bone, except at its ends where it connects to other bones, is covered by a tough membrane called the **periosteum** (pehr-ee-*ahs*-tee-um). The chief function of the

Figure 13-10. Internal Structure of Bone. In the photo below, the dark spaces arranged in concentric circles around the central Haversian canal are the cavities in which osteocytes are found in living bone. The tiny canals extending from each cavity allow the osteocytes to exchange materials with each other and with the Haversian canal. The drawing at left shows the structure of a long bone.

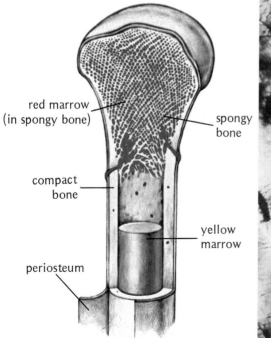

red marrow (in spongy bone)

spongy bone

compact bone

yellow marrow

periosteum

periosteum is the production of new bone for growth and repair. The periosteum also serves as the point of attachment for muscles to bones. This membrane contains blood vessels and nerves that enter the bone.

There are two types of bony tissue—*compact bone* and *spongy bone.* Their composition is the same, but compact bone is very dense and strong, while spongy bone is comparatively porous. Most bones contain both compact and spongy bone tissue.

Some of the bones of the body are hollow, and there is also much space in spongy bone. These spaces are filled with a soft tissue called **marrow** (*mar*-oh). There are two types of marrow—*red marrow* and *yellow marrow.* Red marrow produces red blood cells, platelets, and some types of white blood cells. In adults, red marrow is found in the spongy bone of the vertebrae, ribs, breastbone, cranium, and long bones. Yellow marrow consists of fat cells. In adults it is found in the hollow central region of long bones.

Cartilage (*kart*-il-idj), like bone, is a type of connective tissue. While bone is rigid, cartilage is flexible. In the embryo, most of the skeleton is cartilage. As the embryo develops, minerals are deposited, and the cartilage is gradually changed into bone. This process, called **ossification** (ahs-ih-fih-*kay*-shun), continues into adulthood. The bones of small children contain more cartilage than the bones of adults and are therefore more elastic and not as easily broken. In adults cartilage is found at the ends of ribs, at joints, and in the nose and outer ear. Cartilage provides support, while still permitting some bending or motion. It provides flexibility at joints and cushions against impact or pressure.

13-8 The Human Skeleton

Parts of the skeleton. The human skeleton contains 206 bones (see Figure 13-11). The skeleton has two main divisions: the **axial** (*ak*-see-ul) **skeleton** and the **appendicular** (ap-en-*dik*-yuh-ler) **skeleton.**

The axial skeleton includes the skull, vertebrae, ribs, and breastbone. The upper part of the skull, the **cranium** (*kray*-nee-um), houses and protects the brain. The rest of the skull includes the facial and jaw bones. The **spinal column,** or *backbone,* consists of 33 bones called **vertebrae** (*vert*-uh-bree). The vertebrae are separated from each other by disks of cartilage. The disks act as shock absorbers and give the spine flexibility. The ribs are attached at the back to the upper vertebrae and at the front to the breastbone, or *sternum.* The area enclosed by the sternum, ribs, and backbone is the *chest cavity.* Within the chest cavity, the heart and lungs are supported and protected by the ribs and sternum.

The appendicular skeleton includes the arms and legs and two ringlike sets of bones called the *pectoral* (*pek*-tuh-rul) *girdle* and the *pelvic girdle.* The pectoral girdle consists of the

Figure 13-11. The Human Skeleton.

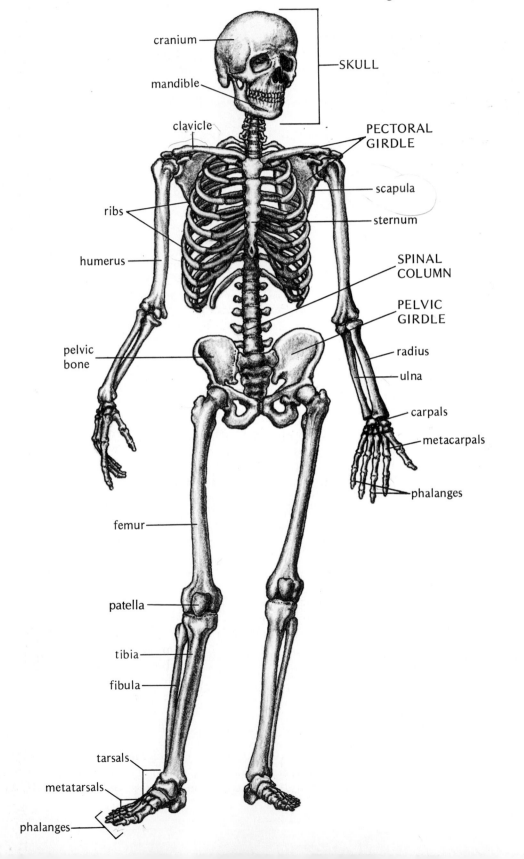

cranium

SKULL

mandible

clavicle

PECTORAL
GIRDLE

scapula

ribs

sternum

humerus

SPINAL
COLUMN

PELVIC
GIRDLE

pelvic
bone

radius

ulna

carpals

metacarpals

phalanges

femur

patella

tibia

fibula

tarsals

metatarsals

phalanges

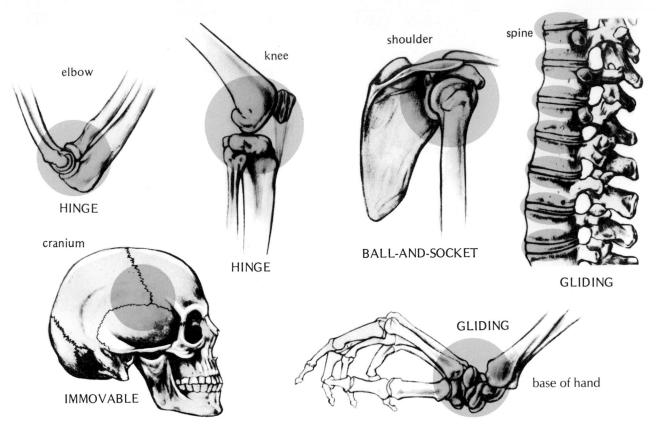

elbow

knee

shoulder

spine

HINGE

HINGE

cranium

BALL-AND-SOCKET

GLIDING

IMMOVABLE

GLIDING

base of hand

Figure 13-12. Types of Joints. Hinge joints at the knee and elbow permit back-and-forth motion. The ball-and-socket joint permits the wide range of movement of the arm at the shoulder. Gliding joints provide limited flexibility in all directions in the hand and between the vertebrae. The bones of the cranium are joined by immovable joints in which the bones are fitted tightly together.

shoulder blades and collar bones. It connects the arms to the spine. The pelvic girdle is made up of the hip bones, or pelvic bones. It connects the legs to the spine.

Joints. A point in the skeleton where bones meet is called a **joint.** As shown in Figure 13-12, there are several different types of joints in the body. Joints in which bones are tightly fitted together, as in the cranium, are **immovable joints.** However, most joints are movable. **Hinge joints,** such as those at the elbow and knee, permit back-and-forth motion. **Ball-and-socket joints,** such as those at the shoulder and hip, offer the widest range of movement—they allow movement in all directions. In this type of joint, the ball-shaped end of one bone fits into the cuplike hollow, or socket, of another bone. A **pivot** (*piv*-it) **joint,** such as that which permits the rotation of the skull, permits rotation from side to side as well as up and down movement. **Gliding joints,** such as those between the vertebrae, provide limited flexibility in all directions.

At movable joints, bones are held together by tough, fibrous bands of connective tissue called **ligaments** (*lig*-uh-ments). A fluid, called *synovial* (sih-*noh*-vee-ul) *fluid,* is secreted into movable joints by surrounding membranes. This fluid acts as a lubricant and reduces friction at the joint.

13-9　Skeletal Muscle

Striated (*stry*-ay-ted), or *skeletal,* **muscles** are involved in locomotion and all other voluntary movement. They are attached to the bones of the skeleton. Skeletal muscle tissue is not made up of clearly defined and separate cells. Instead, during development, cells fuse together, forming individual *muscle fibers.* A skeletal muscle consists of bundles of muscle fibers bound together by connective tissue.

Under a light microscope, the muscle fibers appear striped, or striated—that is, they show alternating bands of light and dark (see Figure 13-13). Electron microscope studies have shown that each fiber is actually a bundle of smaller fibers, and each of those is made up of still finer protein filaments, one thick and one thin. The thick filaments are myosin; the thin ones are actin. The two types of filaments are arranged in an overlapping pattern that gives the whole muscle fiber its striped appearance.

According to the *sliding filament theory* of muscle contraction, the muscle fibers shorten when the two types of filaments they contain slide over one another. The sliding increases the amount of overlap between the two types of filaments, and thereby shortens the fiber (see Figure 13-14). Cross bridges between the two types of filaments allow the fibers to exert a pull. Energy for the sliding of the filaments is supplied by ATP, which is produced in the numerous mitochondria of muscle fibers.

13-10   Voluntary Movement

All voluntary movement is originated and coordinated by impulses from the brain and spinal cord.

Skeletal muscles are attached to bones by strong fibers of connective tissue called **tendons.** Muscles can pull when they contract, but they cannot push when they relax. Thus, they must always work in *antagonistic* pairs. The bending and extending of the arm at the elbow illustrates how muscles and bones work together to produce movement (see Figure 13-15). When the *biceps* (*by*-seps) muscle on the front of the upper

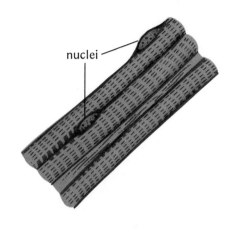

Figure 13-13. Striated Muscle. The overlapping arrangement of actin and myosin filaments gives striated muscle its striped appearance.

nuclei

Figure 13-14. Contraction of Striated Muscle. According to the sliding filament theory of muscle contraction, the muscle fibers shorten when the actin and myosin filaments slide over one another, increasing the amount of overlap.

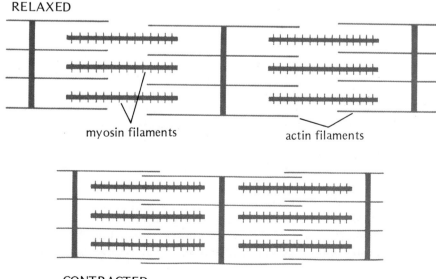

RELAXED

myosin filaments   actin filaments

CONTRACTED

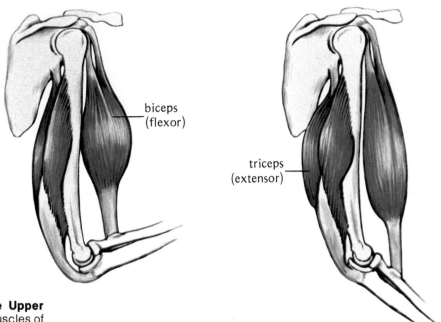

Figure 13-15. Muscles of the Upper Arm. The biceps and triceps muscles of the upper arm work as an antagonistic pair. When the biceps muscle, which is in the front of the arm, contracts, the triceps muscle in the back relaxes and the arm bends. The biceps is a flexor. When the triceps muscle contracts, the biceps muscle relaxes and the arm is straightened. The triceps is an extensor.

arm contracts, the arm bends. Because the biceps muscle bends, or flexes, the joint, it is called a **flexor** (*flek*-ser). Whenever the biceps contracts, the *triceps* (*try*-seps) muscle in the back of the arm relaxes, making it possible for the arm to bend. When the triceps muscle contracts, the biceps muscle relaxes, and the arm is extended, or straightened. Because the triceps muscle extends the joint, it is called an **extensor** (ek-*sten*-ser). Throughout the body, antagonistic pairs of muscles interact with the bones of the skeleton to produce movement.

As long as you are conscious, your skeletal muscles are never completely relaxed. Instead, all muscles are kept by the brain in a state of partial contraction called **muscle tone.** Muscle tone keeps the muscles ready for the powerful contractions of movement, and it maintains posture by keeping the muscles of the back and neck partially contracted.

13-11   Smooth Muscle

In addition to skeletal muscle, which is under conscious control, the body also contains muscle that operates without conscious control. Muscle tissue of this type is called **smooth muscle.** It is found in the walls of the digestive organs, in the walls of arteries and veins, in the diaphragm, and in various other internal organs. The cells of smooth muscle are distinct. They are somewhat elongated, and they overlap to form sheets of muscle rather than bundles of fibers. Smooth muscle does not appear striated (see Figure 13-16).

Cardiac muscle is a type of muscle that is found only in the heart. Cardiac muscle is discussed in Chapter 9 (page 149).

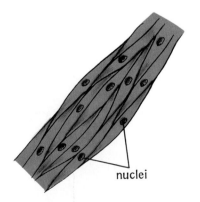

Figure 13-16. Structure of Smooth Muscle.

Chapter Review

SUMMARY

- Locomotion is a basic characteristic of some microorganisms and most animals. In all but the simplest animals, locomotion involves muscles and a skeleton to which the muscles are attached. The two types of skeletons are the exoskeleton and the endoskeleton. Exoskeletons are found in some protozoans and many invertebrates; endoskeletons are found in all vertebrates.

- Among the protists, locomotion is generally carried out by pseudopods, cilia, or flagella. The hydra, though often sessile, has specialized contractile cells that make movement possible. The earthworm uses its longitudinal and circular muscles, its fluid "skeleton," and its setae for locomotion. Grasshoppers have a flexible, jointed exoskeleton that enables them to walk, jump, and fly.

- The human skeleton is made up of bones and cartilage. Skeletal muscles attach to the bones, which serve as levers, allowing parts of the body to move. The bones also give the body shape and support, and protect various structures. The two divisions of the human skeleton are the axial skeleton and the appendicular skeleton. A few joints are immovable, but most joints are movable to some degree.

- Skeletal muscle is made up of muscle fibers that appear striped under a light microscope. Muscle contraction occurs when the muscle fibers shorten. When skeletal muscles contract, they pull on bones. Muscles act in antagonistic pairs, with one muscle bending the joint and the other straightening the joint.

- Smooth muscle, which is not under conscious control, is found in the walls of arteries and veins, as well as in the walls of various internal organs.

KNOW THE TERMS

appendicular skeleton	exoskeleton	ligament	skeletal muscle
axial skeleton	extensor	marrow	smooth muscle
ball-and-socket joint	flagellum	muscle tone	spinal column
cartilage	flexor	ossification	striated muscle
chitin	gliding joint	osteocyte	tendon
cilia	Haversian canal	periosteum	vertebra
collagen	hinge joint	pivot joint	
cranium	immovable joint	pseudopod	
endoskeleton	joint	setae	

SECTION QUESTIONS

The Process of Locomotion

1. What is locomotion?
2. What is an exoskeleton?
3. What is an endoskeleton?

Adaptations For Locomotion

4. What type of substance is the basis for most protozoan and animal movement?
5. Name the types of structures used by protists for locomotion.

6. Name the two layers of muscles involved in locomotion in the earthworm.
7. Name three ways by which grasshoppers can move.

The Human Musculoskeletal System

8. What are osteocytes?
9. What is the periosteum?
10. List the functions of the red marrow.
11. Name the two main divisions of the skeleton.

12. What is a joint?

13. Which type of muscle is under conscious control?

14. By what means are skeletal muscles attached to bones?

15. Name the three types of muscles.

KNOW THE FACTS

Copy the number of each statement below on a sheet of paper. Beside each number, write whether the statement is true or false. If the statement is false, replace the italicized word(s) with a term that will make the statement true.

1. Organisms capable of locomotion are said to be *sessile.*

2. Crabs, spiders, and insects have exoskeletons composed of *chitin.*

3. Among the arthropods, the exoskeleton periodically *grows.*

4. Locomotion by means of pseudopods is called *cyclosis.*

5. The hydra has *primitive muscle fibers* that enable it to contract parts of its body.

6. In the earthworm, the body segments have four pair of bristles called *setae.*

7. The hardness and heaviness of bone is due to the presence of an inorganic compound called *calcium phosphate.*

8. The cavity in bone surrounded by concentric circles of bone cells and containing the blood vessels and nerves that serve the bone cells is called the *periosteum.*

9. The soft tissue that fills the hollow spaces in bone is called *collagen.*

10. The process by which cartilage is converted to bone by the gradual deposition of minerals is called *ossification.*

11. Bones are held together at movable joints by *tendons.*

12. *Smooth* muscle is involved in locomotion and all other voluntary movements.

13. The source of energy for muscle contraction is *ATP.*

14. A muscle that bends a joint is called an *extensor.*

15. All muscles are kept in a state of partial contraction called *muscle tone.*

UNDERSTAND THE CONCEPTS

16. Describe the advantages that the capacity for locomotion gives an organism.

17. How does the amoeba move?

18. Describe locomotion in ciliated protists such as the paramecium.

19. How does the euglena move?

20. Briefly describe the three methods by which the hydra moves.

21. Explain how locomotion is carried out in the earthworm.

22. Identify which structures of the grasshopper are involved in locomotion, and give the function of each.

23. What are the functions of bones?

24. Describe the function of osteoblasts in human bone formation.

25. How do broken bones heal?

26. What are the functions of the periosteum?

27. Describe the human axial and appendicular skeletons.

28. What produces the striped appearance of striated muscle?

29. Explain what happens to actin and myosin filaments during muscle contraction.

30. How are skeletal muscles connected to bones?

31. Why must muscles work in antagonistic pairs?

32. Which parts of the human body are formed of smooth muscle?

THINK CRITICALLY

33. What are some advantages and disadvantages of exoskeletons? Of endoskeletons?

34. Relate the microscopic structure of muscle tissue to the visible act of contraction.

35. If the bicep muscle were paralyzed, what arm motion would be impossible? Why?
36. In humans, the ossification process takes place gradually, beginning in the embryo and continuing through adulthood. What advantages and disadvantages are associated with this gradual nature of ossification?
37. Does the earthworm have a true skeleton? Explain why or why not.
38. Arthropods are motile organisms, even though they have exoskeletons. List some explanations for why this is true.

THINK CREATIVELY

39. It is known that the total amount of phosphate in the adult rat skeleton is constant. However, it is believed that one-third of the phosphate in the skeleton is replaced every 20 days. Design an experiment to prove this hypothesis.
40. Aquatic animals need less skeletal support than animals of similar size that live on land. Propose an explanation for this fact.

FOR FURTHER INVESTIGATION

1. To help you study bone in detail, ask a butcher to saw a long bone down the middle from end to end. Record your observations as you examine the cartilage at the ends of the bone, the periosteum, the marrow inside the bone, the spongy bone, and the compact bone.
2. Sports injuries of famous athletes often appear in the news. Do library research and report to the class about the causes, prevention, and treatment of injuries involving the bones, joints, and muscles of famous athletes.
3. Do library research on scoliosis or hip replacement surgery. Write up your findings in the form of a feature article for a magazine or newspaper.
4. Prepare a brief report on the life and contributions of one of the following scientists:
   a. Luigi Galvani
   b. Albert Szent-Gyorgi
   c. Arda Green
5. Prepare a report for the class on one of the career opportunities listed below. See the suggested procedures, p. 9, "For Further Investigation" Activity 3.
   a. Orthopedic surgeon
   b. Chiropractor
   c. Occupational therapist
6. Write a short comical sketch for use on television to explain how broken bones are treated.
7. Electricity can be used to speed up the healing of broken bones. Do library research on this topic and write up your findings in the form of a newspaper article.
8. Design and conduct an experiment that will show the role of calcium phosphate in determining the hardness of bone. Hint: Calcium salts can be dissolved in dilute acids. Use a chicken leg and acetic acid (vinegar) or dilute hydrochloric acid. Demonstrate the results of your experiment to the class.

FOR FURTHER READING

Allen, Oliver E., and the Editors of Time-Life Books, *Building Sound Bones and Muscles,* Time-Life Books, Alexandria, VA, 1981.

Angier, Natalie, "How Fast? How High? How Far?" *Discover,* November, 1981.

Arehart-Treichel, Joan, "Boning Up on Osteoporosis," *Science News,* August 27, 1983.

Harrington, W. F., *Muscle Contraction* (Carolina Biology Reader), Carolina Biological Supply Co., Burlington, NC, 1981.

Keim, Hugo, *How to Care for Your Back,* Prentice-Hall, Englewood Cliffs, NJ, 1981.

Oster, G., "Muscle Sounds," *Scientific American,* March, 1984.

Chapter 14

NERVOUS REGULATION

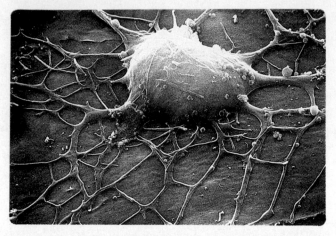

A single nerve cell as seen with a scanning electron microscope.

THE REGULATORY PROCESS

Objectives:
1. Explain the functions of a nervous system.
2. Describe the roles of receptors, nerve cells, and effectors in nerve pathways.
3. Name several different types of receptors.
4. Name the two types of structures that are effectors.
5. Define the term *stimulus*.

14-1 Functions of Regulation

The environment of an organism is always changing. Some of these changes take place in the external environment—that is, outside the body. Examples of such external changes are a change in temperature; the appearance of food; the appearance of a natural enemy. Changes also occur within the organism. For example, the concentration of a waste product may increase; a disease-causing organism may enter the body; the supply of a necessary substance may decrease.

To stay alive, an organism must respond to these external and internal changes. The organism must maintain homeostasis. It must keep all the factors of its internal environment within certain limits.

Responses are seldom single, independent events. An organism is continuously responding to the wide variety of changes occurring both inside and outside its body. In fact, the various life activities of an organism are in themselves examples of complex responses. These responses must be *regulated*—that is, controlled in amount and directed to the right place. They must also be *coordinated*—that is, made to occur in the right order or relationship.

In one-celled and some simple multicellular organisms, the regulation and coordination of responses is a function of each cell as a whole, including the special activities of its organelles. This capacity of a cell to respond is often called **irritability.** In more complex multicellular animals, the regulation and coordination of responses are controlled by a *nervous system* and an *endocrine system.* In this chapter and Chapter 15 we will examine the operation of nervous systems. In Chapter 16 we will discuss the human endocrine system.

14-2   Mechanisms of Nervous Regulation

The functioning of a true nervous system involves three basic types of structures—receptors, nerve cells, and effectors. **Receptors,** or *sense organs,* are specialized structures that are sensitive to certain changes, physical forces, or chemicals in the internal and external environments. Stimulation of a receptor causes "messages," or **impulses,** to be transmitted over a pathway of nerve cells. These impulses eventually reach an **effector,** which is either a gland or a muscle. If the effector is a gland, it will respond to the impulse by either decreasing or increasing its activity, depending on the nerve pathways involved. However, if the effector is a muscle, a nerve impulse can only cause it to contract.

Any factor that causes a receptor to trigger, or initiate, impulses in a nerve pathway is called a **stimulus** (*stim*-yuh-lus). The stimulus causes electrical and chemical changes in the receptor, and these, in turn, trigger the nerve impulses. Thus, the basic sequence of events in regulation by the nervous system involves (1) a stimulus that activates a receptor, (2) the triggering of impulses in associated nerve pathways, and finally, (3) a response by an effector (see Figure 14-1).

It should not be thought that a nerve pathway is a simple connection from a particular receptor to a particular effector. In most animals, each nerve pathway crosses and interconnects with many other pathways. Impulses arising from a single receptor are usually transmitted to a number of different nerve pathways. Impulses reaching an effector are the result of the combination and interaction of numerous impulses from many different pathways.

Multicellular animals possess several different types of receptors, each sensitive to a different type of stimulus. Among the sense organs found in animals are those sensitive to heat, cold, light, sound, pressure, and chemicals.

All but the simplest animals have a **brain,** a specialized group of nerve cells that controls and coordinates the activities of the nervous system. The more complex the organism, the more complex the structure and function of the brain.

Figure 14-1. Nervous Regulation. Eating a piece of pizza involves complex pathways in the nervous system. The pizza itself is a stimulus that starts impulses in sense receptors (the eyes and nose). Muscles of the hands and arms are effectors, allowing the pizza to be brought to the mouth.

NEURONS AND NERVES

Objectives:
1. Describe the structure of a neuron and give the function of each of its parts.
2. Describe the functions of sensory neurons, motor neurons, and interneurons.
3. Explain the difference between a neuron and a nerve, and name the different types of nerves.

14-3 Structure of Neurons

In the nervous systems of all multicellular animals, the basic unit of structure and function is the *nerve cell*, or **neuron** (*noo*-rahn). Neurons are specialized for the rapid conduction of impulses, which are both electrical and chemical (electrochemical) in nature. The capacity to conduct impulses is a property of the nerve-cell membrane. The changes associated with the impulses do not enter or pass through the cytoplasm of the cell; they are transmitted only along the cell membrane.

A nerve cell usually consists of three basic parts—a cell body, dendrites, and an axon (see Figure 14-2). The **cell body**, or *cyton* (*sy*-tahn), contains the nucleus and the cell organelles. The metabolic activities common to all cells are carried out in the cell body, which also controls the growth of the nerve cell. Materials necessary for the maintenance of the nerve cell are generally synthesized in the cell body and then moved to other parts of the cell where they are needed.

The **dendrites** (*den*-dryts) are short, highly branched fibers that are specialized for receiving impulses. Dendrites generally conduct impulses toward the cell body. In some neurons, the branching of the dendrites around the cell body gives the cell a bushy appearance.

The **axon** (*ak*-sahn) is usually a long, thin fiber that extends from the cell body. Axons carry impulses away from the cell body and transmit them either to other neurons or to effectors. Axons range in length from a fraction of a centimeter to more than a meter. *Nerve fibers* may be made up of either the axons or dendrites of neurons.

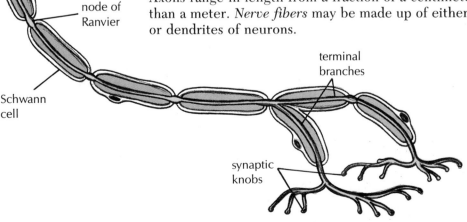

Figure 14-2. Structure of a Neuron.

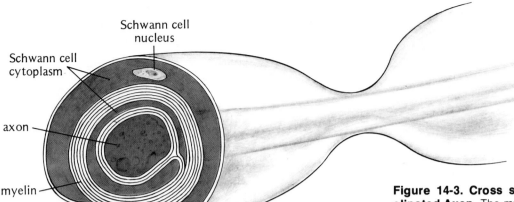

Schwann cell
nucleus

Schwann cell
cytoplasm

axon

myelin

Figure 14-3. Cross section of a Myelinated Axon. The myelin, which insulates the axon, is produced by Schwann cells.

All axons are surrounded by cells called **Schwann** (shwahn) **cells.** On some axons, the Schwann cells produce layers of a white fatty substance called **myelin** (*my*-uh-lin) (see Figure 14-3). The myelin forms a sheath around the axon, and axons having such a sheath are said to be *myelinated.* The myelin insulates the axon. At intervals along the myelinated axon, there are gaps in the myelin where the axon membrane is exposed to the surrounding medium. These gaps, which occur between adjacent Schwann cells, are called the *nodes of Ranvier* (*rahn*-vee-ay).

The nerve cells of mature animals cannot divide, so there is no periodic replacement of neurons as there is with other cells in the body. However, if the cell body is unhurt, axons and dendrites outside the brain and spinal cord can regenerate, or grow back, if they are damaged.

14-4 The Synapse

The axon of a neuron usually has no branches along its length, but it may have a great many branches at its end. Each of these *terminal branches* makes contact with another cell. The junction between the terminal branch of a neuron and the membrane of another cell is called a **synapse** (*sin*-aps). The synapse includes a microscopic gap between the end of the terminal branch and the adjoining cell. Impulses are transmitted from the axon to the adjoining cell across this gap. The structure of a synapse and the way in which impulses are transmitted across it are described in Section 14-8 (page 232). Each axon may have synapses with as many as 1,000 other neurons, and it may form many synapses with each of these other cells. Axons from other neurons may also make contact with the same cells. Thus the interconnections and impulse pathways of a typical nervous system are enormously complex.

14-5 Types of Neurons and Nerves

Neurons are generally grouped according to their function. **Sensory neurons** carry impulses from receptors toward the

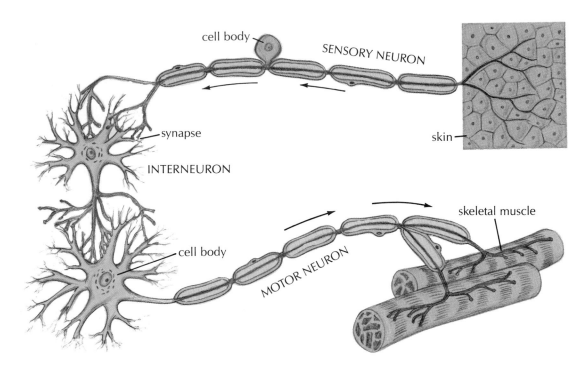

Figure 14-4. Pathway of Nerve Impulses. Sensory neurons receive stimuli and trigger impulses in other neurons. Motor neurons carry impulses toward effectors, such as skeletal muscle. Interneurons, which are found in the brain and spinal cord, relay impulses from one neuron to another.

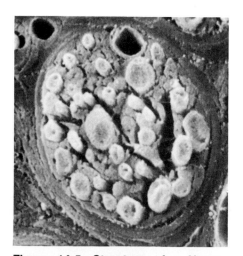

Figure 14-5. Structure of a Nerve. Nerves are made up of bundles of neurons bound together by connective tissue. Note the blood vessels that provide nutrients for the nerve fibers.

spinal cord and brain (see Figure 14-4). **Motor neurons** carry impulses from the brain and spinal cord toward effectors, usually muscles. **Interneurons,** or *associative* (uh-*soh*-shee-ay-tiv) *neurons,* relay impulses from one neuron to another in the brain and spinal cord. The great majority of neurons in the human nervous system are interneurons.

Nerves are bundles of axons or dendrites that are bound together by connective tissue (see Figure 14-5). Nerves are called *sensory nerves* if they conduct impulses from receptors toward the spinal cord and brain; *motor nerves* if they conduct impulses from the brain and spinal cord toward effectors; and *mixed nerves* if they are composed of both sensory and motor fibers.

THE NERVE-CELL MEMBRANE AND IMPULSES

Objectives:
1. Describe the electrical state of the resting neuron.
2. Describe the function of the sodium-potassium pump.
3. Describe the sequence of changes associated with the passage of an impulse along an axon.
4. Name two factors that affect the rate at which impulses are transmitted along an axon.
5. Explain what is meant by the refractory period and by the nerve threshold.

6. Explain how the nervous system distinguishes between different types of stimuli.
7. Explain how the nervous system distinguishes between stimuli of the same type but different strengths.

14-6   The Resting Neuron

The transmission of a nerve impulse is made possible by a difference in electrical charge between the outer and inner surfaces of the nerve-cell membrane. When the neuron is resting (not transmitting an impulse), the outside of the membrane has a net positive charge, and the inside has a net negative charge (see Figure 14-6). The cell membrane is said to be

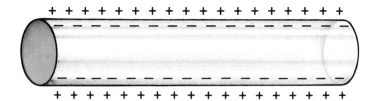

Figure 14-6. Electrical State of a Resting Neuron. As a result of the action of the sodium pump, the outside of the membrane of a resting neuron has a net positive charge and the inside of the membrane has a net negative charge.

electrically *polarized* because there is a difference in electrical charge between its outer and inner surfaces. This polarization is caused by different concentrations of certain ions in the mediums outside and inside the cell. The concentration differences result partly from the selective permeability of the membrane, but mainly from the active transport of these ions across the membrane. The ions involved in the polarization of the nerve-cell membrane are mainly sodium ions and potassium ions, both of which have a positive electrical charge.

The nerve-cell membrane has an active transport mechanism that pumps sodium ions out of the cell and pumps potassium ions in. This mechanism is called the **sodium-potassium pump**, or more simply, the *sodium pump*. In its resting state, the nerve-cell membrane is freely permeable to potassium ions, but not to sodium ions. As a result, the potassium ions pumped into the cell tend to diffuse back out. However, the sodium ions pumped out of the cell cannot diffuse freely through the membrane, and they accumulate outside the cell. The result is that an excess of positive charge (due to sodium ions) builds up outside the membrane. An excess of negative charge is left behind inside the membrane.

14-7   The Nerve Impulse

Membrane changes in the area of the impulse. A nerve impulse is initiated in the membrane of a neuron by the arrival of an impulse from another neuron or by a stimulus from a receptor. At the location on a neuron where the impulse is initiated, the first thing that happens is that the permeability of the membrane to sodium ions suddenly increases. Recall that there is a high concentration of sodium ions outside the membrane. Under the influence of this concentration gradient, sodium ions diffuse rapidly from the outside to the inside of the membrane. This flow of positive sodium ions reverses the polarization of the membrane. In the area of the impulse, the inside of the nerve cell membrane becomes positively charged; the outside becomes negatively charged (see Figure 14-7).

Figure 14-7. A Nerve Impulse. In the area of an impulse, the nerve cell membrane becomes permeable to sodium ions, which enter the cell. This causes a reversal of the polarity of the membrane. The area of reversed polarity is the nerve impulse, and it travels quickly down the axon membrane.

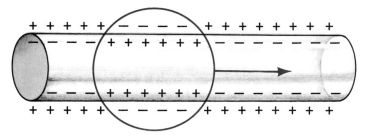

This reversal of polarity occurs in a small area of the membrane. However, it results in a flow of electrical current that affects the permeability of adjacent areas of the membrane. Sodium ions now rush through these new regions of increased permeability, causing the polarization there to become reversed. In this way the reversal of polarization travels over the entire length of the axon. The reversal of polarization is the nerve impulse. The passage of the impulse along an axon is like the burning of a firecracker fuse. The region of burning travels along the fuse by igniting the portion ahead. The big difference is that a fuse cannot be used again, while a neuron can transmit one impulse after another.

In the area of the nerve impulse, the high permeability of the cell membrane to sodium ions lasts for only a brief fraction of a second. It then returns to normal, preventing the further diffusion of sodium ions across the membrane. However, the diffusion of potassium to the outside of the membrane, together with the action of the sodium pump, soon restores the normal distribution of ions. The polarity of the membrane is thus returned to normal, with a positive charge outside and a negative charge inside.

Following the passage of an impulse, there is a brief recovery period during which the nerve cell membrane cannot be stimulated to carry impulses. This time, which lasts only a few thousandths of a second, is called the **refractory period.** When it is over, the membrane is again ready to transmit another impulse.

Rate of impulse conduction. The rate at which impulses travel depends on the size of the nerve fiber and on whether or not it is myelinated. In small unmyelinated fibers, the nerve impulse travels at a relatively slow 2 meters/second. In large myelinated fibers it may travel at over 100 meters/second.

The reason that conduction is so much faster in myelinated fibers is that the impulse travels in "jumps" from one node of Ranvier, where the axon is bare, to the next. This type of conduction is called *saltatory* (*sal*-tuh-tor-ee) *conduction*. The myelin insulates the nerve. Ions cannot flow through this substance. However, in these nerve fibers, the membrane at the nodes is highly sensitive. Saltatory conduction is not only faster than nonsaltatory conduction, but it also uses less energy because depolarization occurs only at the nodes. Thus less active transport is necessary for restoring the normal distribution of ions after the impulse has passed.

Nerve cell thresholds. For an impulse to be initiated in a given nerve cell, the stimulus must have at least a certain minimum strength. Each nerve cell has a minimum level of sensitivity, or **threshold.** A stimulus whose strength is below that threshold cannot initiate impulses in the neuron. However, any stimulus above the threshold level will trigger impulses in the neuron. The impulses transmitted by a given neuron are all alike—they are all the same "size," and they pass along the neuron at the same rate. Thus, a neuron operates on an "all-or-none" basis. That is, either an impulse is triggered or it is not triggered, depending only on whether the stimulus is above or below the threshold level. The situation is much like the firing of a gun. If enough force is exerted on the trigger, the gun fires. But the size of the explosion and speed of the bullet are always the same. Squeezing the trigger harder has no effect.

Distinguishing strength and type of stimulus. If all nerve impulses are basically alike, how does an organism know what type of stimulus caused the impulses or how strong the stimulus was? For example, why does touching a hot stove feel different from touching a merely warm surface? How do you distinguish a bright light from a loud sound?

The strength of a stimulus is measured by two effects. First of all, a stronger stimulus causes more impulses to be transmitted each second (see Figure 14-8). That is, the impulses follow each other more closely. Secondly, different neurons have dif-

Figure 14-8. Strength of a Stimulus. A strong stimulus (hot object, bottom) triggers more impulses in more neurons than a weak stimulus (warm object, top). These differences enable the brain to determine the strength of the stimulus.

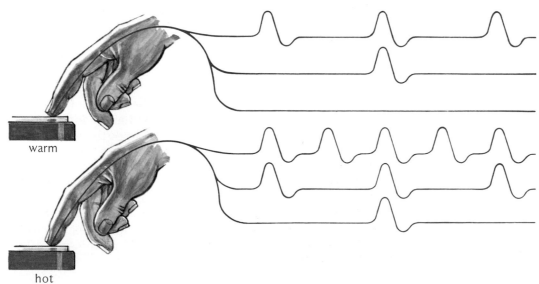

warm

hot

ferent thresholds. Some require a stronger stimulus than others to transmit an impulse. Therefore, a larger number of neurons will fire when a stimulus is stronger.

Recognition of the *type* of stimulus is determined by the particular pathways that carry the nerve impulses. Each type of receptor is sensitive to a particular type of stimulus. For example, light-sensitive receptors in the retina of the eye transmit nerve impulses only when light strikes them. Impulses from the retina travel along the optic nerve to a part of the brain that interprets them as sight. Artificial stimulation of the optic nerve causes a person to "see" flashes of light. Sound waves, on the other hand, have no effect on the eye. They trigger impulses in the auditory nerve of the ear. When these impulses reach the brain, they are interpreted as sound.

SYNAPSES

Objectives:
1. Identify the structures associated with the synapse.
2. Describe the transmission of an impulse across a synapse.
3. Name several neurotransmitters.
4. Describe the transmission of an impulse at a neuromuscular junction.

14-8   Transmission at the Synapse

The structure of a synapse is shown in Figure 14-9. At the synapse, the axon ends in a *synaptic knob.* The cell membrane at the knob is called the *presynaptic membrane.* The cell membrane of the adjacent cell is called the *postsynaptic membrane.* Between the pre- and postsynaptic membranes is a very narrow space called the *synaptic cleft.* When an impulse arrives at the synaptic knob, it must be transmitted from the presynaptic membrane, across the synaptic cleft, to the postsynaptic membrane of the adjoining cell.

The transmission of the impulse across the synaptic cleft is a chemical process. Within the synaptic knob are many small sacs called *synaptic vesicles.* The vesicles contain substances called **neurotransmitters,** or *neurohumors* (noor-oh-*hyoo*-merz). Among the most common of these chemical transmitters are *acetylcholine* (uh-seet-ul-*koh*-leen) and *norepinephrine* (*nor*-ep-uh-*nef*-rin). When an impulse reaches the synaptic knob, some of the synaptic vesicles fuse with the membrane of the synaptic knob and release their contents into the synaptic cleft. The neurotransmitter diffuses across the synaptic cleft and initiates impulses in the adjacent nerve cell by changing the permeability of its membrane. There are special receptor proteins embedded in the membrane of the dendrites, and it is at these receptors that the neurotransmitters produce their effects.

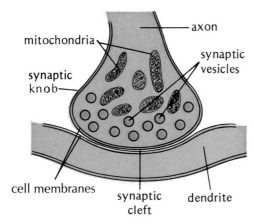

Figure 14-9. Structure of the Synapse. When a nerve impulse reaches the synaptic knob, some synaptic vesicles release their contents, which are neurotransmitters, into the synaptic cleft. The neurotransmitters diffuse across the synaptic cleft and initiate nerve impulses in the adjacent neuron.

NERVOUS REGULATION **233**

Note that it is not the nerve impulse that crosses the synaptic cleft from one neuron to the next. Instead, it is a chemical compound—the neurotransmitter—that is sent across the gap. Each impulse that reaches a synapse causes the release of a certain amount of neurotransmitter. When the impulses are arriving at a faster rate (representing a stronger initial stimulus), more neurotransmitter is released into the synaptic cleft. This greater quantity of neurotransmitter acts as a stronger stimulus on the adjacent neuron, and the neuron then transmits more impulses per second. In this way, information about the strength of the original stimulus is passed across the synapse and down the nerve pathway. As soon as the neurotransmitter has done its work, it must be removed from the synaptic cleft to clear the way for new signals. This is generally accomplished by enzymes present in the synaptic cleft. These enzymes quickly break down the molecules of neurotransmitter after the neuron has responded to them.

Because neurotransmitters are released only by the ends of axons and because they exert their effects only at specialized receptor sites, impulses can travel in only one direction across synapses—from axons to dendrites or cell bodies. Thus, synapses control the direction of flow of information over nerve pathways.

Different types of neurons release different neurotransmitters. Some neurons release *excitatory neurotransmitters*. These chemicals initiate impulses in adjacent neurons. Acetylcholine, norepinephrine, and the amino acids histamine and glutamic acid are excitatory neurotransmitters. Still other neurons release neurotransmitters that do not initiate impulses in adjacent neurons. Instead, they have the opposite effect—they *inhibit* the firing of impulses. *Inhibitory neurotransmitters* include serotonin, epinephrine, and the amino acid glycine. Thus, while some synapses trasmit impulses from one neuron to the next, other synapses block the transmission of impulses.

Our discussion of the basic mechanisms of nervous regulation has been in terms of one neuron synapsing with another neuron and stimulating or inhibiting impulses in that neuron. However, this is an oversimplification of the actual arrangement. As previously mentioned, the axon of a single neuron may form a thousand or more synapses. These may include many synapses on the same neuron. The dendrites of one neuron may also have synaptic connections with a thousand or more other neurons. Thus, the dendrites of a single neuron receive impulses from many neurons. Some of these impulses may be excitatory, while others may be inhibitory. What happens is that the cell body, in effect, totals or averages these impulses. If the overall results are excitatory, impulses are transmitted down the axon to the next set of synapses. If the results are inhibitory, no impulses are transmitted. Thus, in a nerve pathway, stimulation of certain neurons results in the

Career

Biomedical Engineer

Biomedical engineers use mathematical, scientific, and medical facts and principles to devise solutions to problems faced by handicapped people. The activities of biomedical engineers include the development of artificial hearts, pacemakers to regulate the heart's beat, kidney dialysis machines, hearing aids, and artificial joints and limbs, as well as research aimed at relieving other handicaps. In addition, many biomedical engineers are involved in the testing and manufacture of devices. This profession, actually a combination of medicine and engineering, is changing so quickly that it is difficult to predict just what the career opportunities will be in the future.

Training in biomedical engineering is available at numerous universities. Many professionals in the field hold graduate degrees, and all have strong backgrounds in the biological and physical sciences, mathematics, and medical subjects.

inhibition of other neurons. Much of the complex behavior of an organism results from the great number and variety of synaptic circuits formed when neurons are "switched" on and off.

14-9 Neuromuscular Junctions

The passage of impulses from motor neurons to muscles occurs at special points of contact called **neuromuscular** (noor-oh-*mus*-kyoo-ler) **junctions** (see Figure 14-10). The axons of motor neurons end in structures called *motor end plates.* Like synaptic knobs, motor end plates contain synaptic vesicles. When impulses reach the motor end plates, they cause the release of the chemical transmitter acetylcholine. The acetylcholine diffuses across the gap between the end of the axon and the muscle cell and combines with receptor molecules on the muscle cell membrane. The effect of the acetylcholine is to increase the permeability of the muscle cell membrane to sodium, causing impulses to travel along the muscle cell membrane. These impulses cause the muscle cell to contract. As in the synapses between neurons, the acetylcholine at the neuromuscular junction is quickly destroyed by enzyme action.

14-10 Drugs and the Synapse

Many poisons and drugs affect the activity of chemical transmitters at synapses. Nerve gas, *curare* (kyoo-*rah*-ree), *botulin* (*bahch*-uh-lin) *toxin* (a bacterial poison), and some insecticides are poisons that interfere with the functioning of acetylcholine at neuromuscular junctions and cause muscle paralysis. If the muscles of the respiratory system become paralyzed, death follows.

Figure 14-10. Structure of the Neuromuscular Junction. When a nerve impulse reaches the motor end plates of a motor neuron, acetylcholine is released from the synaptic vesicles. The acetylcholine diffuses across the synaptic cleft to the muscle cell membrane and initiates impulses that cause the muscle cell to contract.

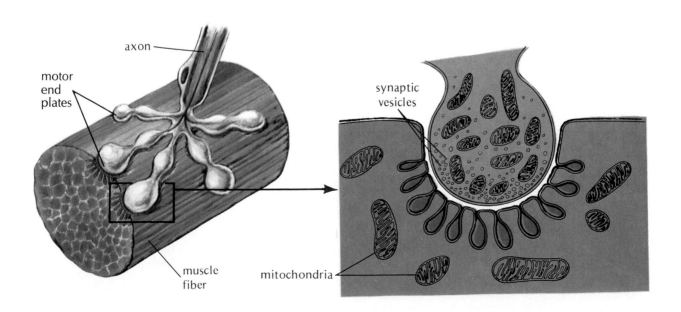

■ Frontier of Biology ■

Treating Damaged Brain Cells

To people who suffer from spinal cord injuries or damage to brain cells, medical science has not been able to offer any hope for recovery. Damage to the central nervous system (the brain and spinal cord) is permanent because these tissues cannot regenerate—or so it was thought.

It is known that some nerves of the peripheral nervous system—those of the muscles and skin—are able to regenerate and regain function after injury. Also, scientists have shown that in certain animals, brain cells are able to repair themselves. How do these nerve cells and those of the human central nervous system differ? Neurobiologists are slowly getting closer to the answer.

The first clue came from studying the cells *surrounding* the neurons, rather than the neurons themselves. The cells that surround the neurons of the peripheral nervous system secrete a certain protein during nerve-cell growth. This protein, which is not produced by the cells surrounding the neurons of the central nervous system, perhaps functions as a signal, switching on the growth of nerve cells. Researchers are now attempting to isolate this protein for further study. If it does function as a switch, scientists may succeed in turning on growth of the cells of the central nervous system by exposing them to this chemical.

In other experiments, neurobiologists are using transplanted brain cells. Tissue from the brains of normal rat embryos was implanted into the brains of brain-damaged rats. These treated rats were then made to master a maze. It took the treated rats 8½ days to learn the maze. Untreated brain-injured rats needed 18 days. The scientists concluded that some degree of functional recovery resulted from the brain cell transplant.

Other brain-cell transplant experiments have been done on rats with symptoms resembling Parkinson's disease in humans. After fetal-rat brain cells capable of secreting dopa-

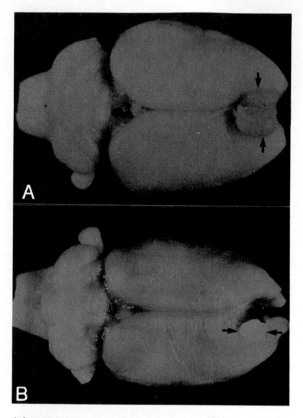

A fetal brain tissue transplant (A, arrows) and a frontal cortex lesion (B, arrows) in two adult rat brains.

mine were implanted into the brains of diseased rats, the symptoms were relieved. Dopamine is a brain chemical lacking in people with Parkinson's disease. Scientists predict that this technique has the potential to lead to a cure for Parkinson's. They also believe that it may be possible to regenerate parts of the damaged brains of patients with multiple sclerosis and Alzheimer's disease, and even to repair spinal cord injuries.

Neurobiologists are also attempting to stimulate nerve-cell growth with electrical energy and radio waves. Experiments with hormones, implanted plastic channels to guide the growth of neurons, and various other procedures are also under way. All these techniques show some promise.

Drugs that affect the mind and the emotions or that alter the activity of body systems also act on synapses. *Stimulants* are drugs that produce a feeling of well-being, alertness, and excitement. Among the stimulants, *amphetamines* (am-*fet*-uh-meenz) ("uppers") produce their effects by binding to certain receptors, thereby mimicking norepinephrine. *Caffeine* (kah-*feen*), which is found in coffee, tea, and cola drinks, aids synaptic transmission.

Depressants are drugs that slow down body activities. *Barbiturates* (bar-*bich*-uh-ritz) ("downers") produce a depressant effect by blocking the formation of norepinephrine.

Some of the mind-altering or hallucinatory drugs, such as *LSD* ("acid") and *mescaline* (*mes*-kuh-lin), interfere with the effect of the inhibitory transmitter serotonin.

ADAPTATIONS FOR NERVOUS REGULATION

Objectives:
1. Describe the responses of protozoans to various stimuli.
2. Compare and contrast the nervous systems of the hydra, earthworm, and grasshopper.

In the animal kingdom, all groups of organisms, from the coelentrates (jellyfish, hydra) on up, have some type of nervous system. As animals become more complex, their nervous systems also become more complex and increasingly specialized. The more highly specialized nervous systems allow animals to respond to their environments with more varied behavior.

14-11   Regulation in Protozoa

Protozoans do not have true nervous systems. However, they are able to respond to certain stimuli in a coordinated way. Amebas have no specialized sense receptors, but they can distinguish between food and nonfood and move away from such things as strong light and irritating chemicals. The mechanisms of these responses are not yet understood.

Some protozoa have specialized filaments that function in a manner similar to the neurons of more complex animals. In the paramecium, the beating of the cilia is controlled by an interconnected system of fibers found at the base of the cilia. The paramecium can respond to various stimuli—it can move toward food or away from strong acids and can change direction to avoid solid matter in its path. Some protozoa have organelles that are sensitive to certain stimuli and initiate responses in the organism.

14-12   Regulation in Hydra

The nervous system of the hydra is in the form of a **nerve net** (see Figure 14-11). In this system, the nerve cells form an

Figure 14-11. Nervous System of the Hydra. The nerve net of the hydra allows the muscles of the organism to react to stimuli in a coordinated manner. The system contains special receptor cells, but no brain or nerve cord.

irregular network between the two layers of the body wall. This network connects special receptor cells in the body wall with muscle and gland cells. There is no organized center, such as a brain or nerve cord, to control and coordinate the nerve impulses. Instead, when a stimulus is received by any part of the body, impulses spread slowly from the stimulated area in all directions through the nerve net. Thus all the muscle fibers in the organism respond, but the response shows coordination. For example, when a tentacle comes in contact with food, such as a daphnia, the impulses travel slowly through the entire organism. In response, the animal stretches toward the food, and the tentacles work together in a coordinated manner to capture the food and stuff it into the mouth.

14-13   Regulation in the Earthworm

The nervous system of the earthworm includes a **central nervous system** and a **peripheral nervous system** (see Figure 14-12). The central nervous system consists of a "brain" connected to a pair of solid, ventral nerve cords. The nerve cords enlarge into *ganglia* (*gang*-lee-uh) in each segment. **A ganglion** (*gang*-lee-un) is a group of cell bodies and interneurons that switch, relay, and coordinate nerve impulses. The so-called "brain" is actually a pair of fused ganglia that is only the beginning of a brain.

The peripheral nervous system includes the nerves branching from the central nervous system and passing to all parts of the body. These nerves contain sensory neurons, which carry impulses from receptors in the skin to the nerve cords, and motor neurons, which carry impulses from the nerve cords to muscles and glands (effectors). The specialized receptors in the skin are sensitive to light, vibrations, chemicals, and heat.

In the earthworm, the nerves of the peripheral nervous system connect receptors and effectors to the central nervous system. Impulses travel over definite pathways in only one direction. The nervous systems of the more complex animals are similar to the nervous system of the earthworm.

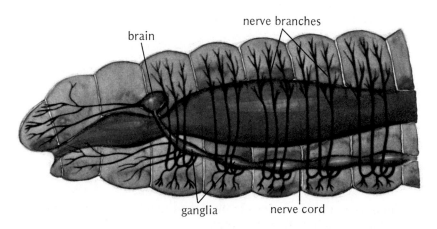

Figure 14-12. Nervous System of the Earthworm. The central nervous system of the earthworm consists of a brain connected to a pair of ventral nerve cords. The sensory and motor nerves that branch from the nerve cords make up the peripheral nervous system.

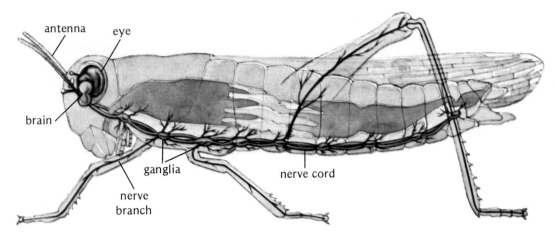

Figure 14-13. Nervous System of the Grasshopper. The nervous system of the grasshopper consists of a brain, a pair of ventral nerve cords, and branching nerves. In addition, the grasshopper has well-developed sense organs, including antennae, eyes, and taste organs.

14-14   Regulation in the Grasshopper

The nervous system of the grasshopper is basically similar to that of the earthworm (see Figure 14-13). It consists of a brain in the head region; a pair of solid, ventral nerve cords that run the length of the body; and ganglia. Nerves branch out from the ganglia to all parts of the body. The sense organs of the grasshopper are more highly developed than those of the earthworm. The grasshopper has eyes, *antennae* (an-*ten*-ee) or "feelers," and taste organs that respond to a variety of stimuli. Grasshoppers are also sensitive to sound. Because the grasshopper has a more highly developed nervous system than the earthworm, it is capable of more complex behavior.

Chapter Review

SUMMARY

- A nervous system regulates and coordinates responses to external and internal change. The functioning of a true nervous system involves receptors, nerve cells, and effectors. Various physical forces and chemical substances stimulate the receptors, which in turn trigger impulses in nerve-cell pathways. These impulses eventually cause effectors to respond.

- Neurons are specialized for the rapid conduction of impulses. A neuron generally consists of dendrites, a cell body, and an axon. Impulses usually travel along a neuron in one direction—from dendrites to axon. The three basic types of neurons are sensory neurons, interneurons, and motor neurons. Bundles of axons or dendrites that are bound together by connective tissue form nerves.

- In a resting neuron, the outside of the cell membrane is electrically positive while the inside is negative. The membrane is polarized because of an unequal distribution of certain ions inside and outside the membrane.

- An impulse is produced when the polarization of the nerve-cell membrane becomes reversed. In the area of the impulse, the inside of the membrane is electrically positive, and the outside is negative. An electrical current flows from the area of the impulse to the adjacent area of the membrane, causing a reversal of polarization there. In this way, the impulse travels along the nerve-cell membrane.

- The junction between the terminal branch of a neuron and the membrane of another cell is called a synapse. When impulses reach the synaptic knob at the end of the axon, neurotransmitters are released into the synaptic cleft. These chemical compounds stimulate or inhibit the firing of impulses in the adjacent neuron. At neuromuscular junctions, the motor end plates of axons release chemical transmitters that stimulate contraction of adjacent muscle fibers.

- While protozoans do not have true nervous systems, they can respond to certain stimuli. In the hydra, there is a nerve net that transmits impulses throughout the organism, producing coordinated responses. The earthworm has a primitive "brain" and two ventral nerve cords that enlarge into ganglia in each segment. Sensory and motor nerves branch from the "brain" and nerve cords. The nervous system of the grasshopper is similar to that of the earthworm, but the sense organs are more highly developed in the grasshopper.

KNOW THE TERMS

axon	impulse	neuromuscular junction	sensory neuron
brain	interneuron	neuron	sodium-potassium pump
cell body	irritability	neurotransmitter	stimulus
central nervous system	motor neuron	peripheral nervous system	synapse
dendrite	myelin	receptor	threshold
effector	nerve	refractory period	
ganglion	nerve net	Schwann cell	

SECTION QUESTIONS

The Regulatory Process

1. Name the two systems involved in the regulation and coordination of responses.
2. What are the three basic types of structures found in a true nervous system?
3. What happens when a receptor is stimulated?
4. Name the two types of effectors.

Neurons and Nerves

5. List the three basic parts of a nerve cell.
6. What is a synapse?
7. What is a sensory neuron?
8. What is a nerve?

The Nerve-cell Membrane and Impulses

9. What do we call a neuron that is not transmitting a nerve impulse?

10. What is the sodium-potassium pump?
11. What is a nerve cell threshold?

Synapses

12. What crosses the synapse during the transmission of a nerve impulse?
13. Name two neurotransmitters.
14. What are neuromuscular junctions?

Adaptations for Nervous Regulation

15. Name the types of stimuli to which protozoans respond.
16. What type of nervous system does the hydra have?
17. Name the two parts of the nervous system of the earthworm.
18. What specialized sense organs does the grasshopper possess?

KNOW THE FACTS

Copy the numbers from Column 1 on a sheet of paper. Select the letter
for the term or phrase from Column 2 that matches each numbered
item, and write it beside the number.

Column 1

1. irritability
2. receptors
3. stimulus
4. brain
5. myelin
6. motor neurons
7. interneurons
8. refractory period
9. neurotransmitter
10. synapse
11. depressants
12. protozoans
13. ganglion

Column 2

a. a specialized group of nerve cells that controls and coordinates the activities of the nervous system
b. relay(s) impulses from one neuron to another in the brain or spinal cord
c. the brief period of time during which the nerve cell membrane cannot be stimulated to carry impulses
d. drugs that slow down body activities
e. the capacity of a cell to repond to change
f. a group of cell bodies and interneurons that switch, relay, and coordinate nerve impulses
g. sense organs, such as eyes, ears, taste buds, and skin
h. a substance released from the synaptic knob that diffuses across the synaptic cleft and initiates impulses in adjacent neurons
i. carry impulses from the brain and spinal cord toward effectors, usually muscles
j. any factor that causes a receptor to initiate impulses in a nerve pathway
k. produce(s) a feeling of well being
l. microscopic space between nerve cells
m. a white fatty substance, produced by Schwann cells, that surrounds the axon and insulates it
n. have no true nervous systems

UNDERSTAND THE CONCEPTS

14. What happens when a receptor or a sense organ is stimulated?
15. How do effectors respond to nervous stimulation?
16. Explain the basic sequence of events in regulation by the nervous system.
17. Describe the structure and function of the three basic parts of a neuron.
18. Describe the electrical state of the membrane of a resting neuron.
19. Explain how the difference in electrical charge across the nerve-cell membrane is maintained.
20. Describe the electrical state of the nerve-cell membrane in the area of an impulse.
21. What changes in ion distribution are found in the area of an impulse?
22. Describe the process by which an impulse travels along a nerve-cell membrane.

23. In what way does a neuron fire on an all-or-none basis?
24. Describe the structure of a synapse.
25. Explain how nerve impulses cross the synaptic cleft.
26. Describe the structure of the neuromuscular junction.
27. How do impulses pass from a motor neuron to a muscle cell?
28. Describe three ways in which drugs can affect the transmission of impulses across the synapse.
29. What kinds of responses to stimuli do protozoans show?
30. How does the hydra respond when a part of its body receives a stimulus?
31. Describe the structures of the central and peripheral nervous systems in the earthworm.

THINK CRITICALLY

32. Explain the relationship between a nerve and a neuron.
33. Explain how nervous regulation helps an animal to maintain homeostasis.
34. Imagine that the nerve fibers from pain receptors in your thumb could be exchanged with nerve fibers from pain receptors in your index finger. You then prick your thumb with a needle. Predict your response.
35. You are walking barefooted along a beach. Suddenly you step on a hard, sharp object. What will happen in your nervous system when you experience the sharpness?
36. The hydra's nervous system is more like that of the earthworm than that of the paramecium. Defend or refute this statement.
37. In the laboratory an isolated neuron is stimulated in the middle of the neuron. An impulse travels in both directions. Why is it impossible for this to happen inside an animal?

THINK CREATIVELY

38. Suggest an explanation for how the dentist's injection of procaine (often called by the trade name Novocain) produces its effect.
39. Sometimes people who have had an arm or a leg amputated feel pain at the site of the removed limb. Develop a hypothesis to explain this phenomenon.

FOR FURTHER INVESTIGATION

1. Design and conduct an experiment to find out how paramecia, hydras, earthworms, or fruit flies respond to various stimuli, such as light and darkness, acidic and basic solutions, or warmth and cold. Be sure to include controls in your design.
2. Do library research on the effects of various drugs on the synapse. Write up your findings in the form of a feature article for a magazine or newspaper.
3. Prepare a report for the class on one of the career opportunities listed below. See suggested procedures, p. 9, "For Further Investigation" Activity 3.
   a. Electroencephalographic technologist
   b. Neurologist
   c. Psychiatric social worker
4. Prepare a brief report on the life and contributions of one of the following scientists:
   a. Ottow Loewi
   b. Rita Levi-Montalcini
   c. Rita Guttman

FOR FURTHER READING

Adrian, R. H., *The Nerve Impulse,* (Carolina Biology Reader), Carolina Biological Supply Co., Burlington, NC, 1980.

Bloom, F. E., "Neuropeptides," *Scientific American,* October, 1981.

Calvin, William, and Ojemann, George A., *Inside the Brain: Mapping the Cortex, Exploring the Neuron,* New American Library, New York, 1980.

Dunant, Y., and Israel, M., "The Release of Acetylcholine," *Scientific American,* April, 1985.

Miller, J. A., "Dissection of the Inebriated Brain," *Science News,* June 8, 1985.

Morrell, P., and Nortin, W. T., "Myelin," *Scientific American,* May, 1980.

Rodgers, Joann, "Brain Triggers: Biochemistry and Behavior," *Science Digest,* January, 1983.

Chapter 15

THE HUMAN NERVOUS SYSTEM

Surfing requires careful control and coordination of thousands of muscular responses.

THE CENTRAL NERVOUS SYSTEM

Objectives:
1. Describe the functions of the skull, spinal column, meninges, and cerebrospinal fluid.
2. Name the major parts of the brain and describe the structure and function of each.
3. Describe the structure and functions of the spinal cord.

The human nervous system, like that of other vertebrates, can be divided into two main subdivisions. One of these is the *central nervous system*, which consists of the brain and the spinal cord. Included in the central nervous system are the cell bodies of most motor neurons and interneurons. The other is the *peripheral nervous system*, which is a vast network of nerves that conduct impulses between the central nervous system and the receptors and effectors of the body. This system consists of sensory neurons, including their cell bodies, and the axons of motor neurons.

Most of the activities of the body are controlled by the central nervous system—the brain and the spinal cord. Impulses from sense receptors throughout the body bring a constant flow of information about the internal state of tissues and organs and about the external environment. In the brain and the spinal cord the information is interpreted, and impulses are sent out to muscles and glands, causing appropriate responses.

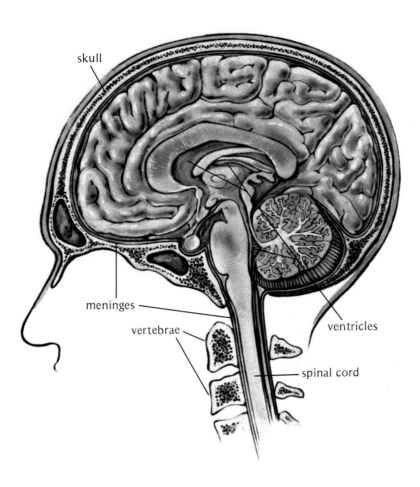

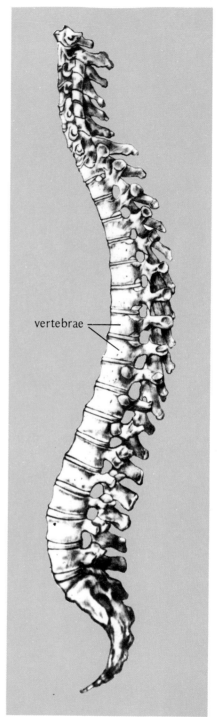

15-1 The Skull and Spinal Column

The brain and the spinal cord are protected by bone (see Figure 15-1). The brain is enclosed by the skull, while the spinal cord is surrounded by the vertebrae of the spinal column, or backbone. The brain and the spinal cord are also covered and protected by three tough membranes known as the *meninges* (muh-*nin*-jeez). A liquid, the *cerebrospinal* (suh-ree-broh-*spyn*-ul) *fluid,* cushions the delicate nervous tissues against shock. Within the brain are four spaces, or *ventricles,* that are filled with cerebrospinal fluid. These spaces connect with a space between the meninges and with the central canal of the spinal cord, which are also filled with fluid.

15-2 The Brain

The brain is one of the most active organs in the body. It receives 20 percent of the blood pumped from the heart, it replaces most of its protein every three weeks, and it is the major user of glucose in the body. Unlike the cells of other tissues the cells of the brain generally metabolize only glu-

Figure 15-1. The Skull and Spinal Column. The brain is protected by the skull, and the spinal cord is protected by the vertebrae of the spinal column. Added protection is provided by the meninges and by the cerebrospinal fluid, which cushions the tissues against shock.

Figure 15-2. Structure of the Brain. The major regions of the brain can be seen in this lengthwise view.

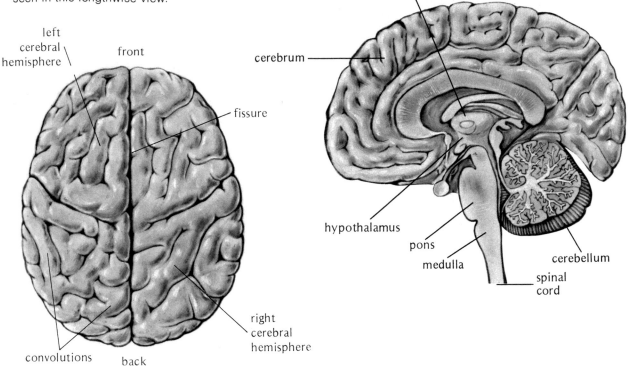

left cerebral hemisphere

front

fissure

convolutions   back

right cerebral hemisphere

thalamus

cerebrum

hypothalamus

pons

medulla

cerebellum

spinal cord

Figure 15-3. External View of the Cerebrum. The longitudinal fissure divides the cerebrum into right and left hemispheres. The convolutions greatly increase the surface area of the cortex, which is made up primarily of unmyelinated fibers and vast numbers of interneurons.

cose for the release of energy. The major parts of the brain are the cerebrum, cerebellum, and medulla (see Figure 15-2).

Other parts of the brain are the thalamus, hypothalamus, and pons. The **thalamus** serves as a relay center between various parts of the brain and the spinal cord; it also receives and modifies all sensory impulses except those involved in smell before they travel to the cerebral cortex; and it may be involved in pain perception and maintenance of consciousness. The **hypothalamus** is involved in control of body temperature, blood pressure, sleep, and emotions; it is also involved in the functioning of the endocrine system (see page 271). The **pons** serves as a relay system linking the spinal cord, medulla, cerebellum, and cerebrum.

The cerebrum. The **cerebrum** (suh-*ree*-brum) is the largest part of the human brain, making up about two-thirds of the entire organ. The greatest difference between the human brain and the brains of other vertebrates is in the larger size and greater development of the human cerebrum. The cerebrum is divided in half from front to back by a deep groove, or fissure, which separates it into the right and left **cerebral hemispheres** (see Figure 15-3). Nerve fibers from each hemisphere pass to the other hemisphere and to other parts of the nervous system.

The outermost layer of the cerebrum is the **cerebral cortex**, or *gray matter*, which is made up of the cell bodies of motor

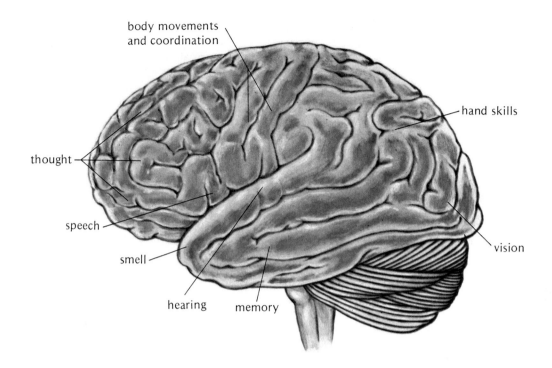

body movements
and coordination

hand skills

thought

speech

smell

vision

hearing   memory

neurons and a huge number of interneurons, interconnected by
unmyelinated fibers. The outer surface of the cortex is highly
folded. These ridges, or *convolutions* (kahn-vuh-*loo*-shunz),
greatly increase the surface area of the gray matter.

The cerebral cortex performs three major types of
functions—sensory, motor, and associative functions. Each
part of the cortex is specialized to carry out a particular function. However, some functions may involve two or more areas
of the cortex as well as other parts of the brain. The functions
of the various parts of the cortex are shown in Figure 15-4.

The sensory areas of the cortex receive and interpret impulses from the sense receptors, including the eyes, ears, taste
buds, and nose, as well as the touch, pain, pressure, heat, and
cold receptors in the skin and other organs. The motor areas of
the cortex initiate impulses that are responsible for all voluntary movement and for the position of the movable parts of the
body. Impulses from the motor cortex may be modified by
other parts of the brain. The associative areas of the brain are
responsible for memory, learning, and thought.

Recent research indicates that the two cerebral hemispheres do not perform identical functions. Instead, some
functions are performed by the left hemisphere and others by
the right hemisphere.

Beneath the gray matter of the cerebrum is an inner area
called the *white matter*. This area consists of myelinated
nerve fibers. One of the bundles, or tracts, of fibers in the
white matter connects the right and left hemispheres, so that

**Figure 15-4. Functions of Various
Areas of the Cerebral Cortex.**

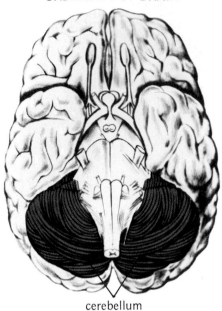

cerebellum

Figure 15-5. The Cerebellum. The cerebellum coordinates and controls all voluntary movements and some involuntary movements. It is also involved in the maintenance of muscle tone.

UNDERSIDE OF BRAIN

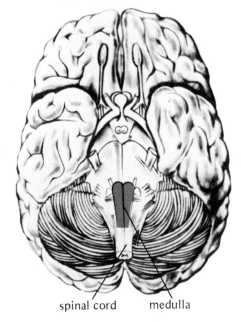

spinal cord   medulla

Figure 15-6. The Medulla. The medulla controls many involuntary activities, such as breathing, heartbeat, and blood pressure.

there is an exchange of information between the two halves of the cerebrum. Other tracts from the white matter connect the cortex with other parts of the nervous system.

Nerve fibers leaving the cerebral hemispheres pass down through the brain and spinal cord. At some point along their pathway, these fibers cross over to the opposite side of the brain or spinal cord and then continue to various parts of the body. Thus the left cerebral hemisphere controls the right side of the body, and the right hemisphere controls the left side of the body. Therefore, an injury to one side of the cerebrum will affect the opposite side of the body.

The cerebellum. The **cerebellum** (sehr-uh-*bel*-um) is located below the rear part of the cerebrum (see Figure 15-5). The cerebellum, like the cerebral cortex, is divided into two hemispheres. The highly folded outer layer of the cerebellum consists of gray matter, while the inner portion is white matter.

The cerebellum coordinates and controls all voluntary movements and some involuntary movements. Motor impulses from the cerebral cortex are carried by nerve pathways that send some branches directly to the muscles involved and some branches to the cerebellum. The muscles also send impulses over sensory nerve pathways to the cerebellum, providing information about their position, rate of contraction, and so on. The cerebellum then sends impulses to the cerebral cortex to correct and coordinate the movement of the muscles. Thus, the cerebral cortex and the cerebellum function together to produce smooth and orderly voluntary movement. With certain involuntary movements, the cerebellum functions in the same manner, but in cooperation with other parts of the brain. The cerebellum, using information from receptors in the inner ear, maintains balance, or *equilibrium.* It is also involved in the maintenance of *muscle tone* (keeping the muscles slightly tensed). Damage to the cerebellum results in jerky movements, tremor, or loss of equilibrium. Staggering and other signs of coordination loss seen with alcohol intoxication reflect a temporary loss of cerebellar function.

The medulla. Beneath the cerebellum and continuous with the spinal cord is the **medulla** (muh-*duhl*-uh) (see Figure 15-6). In this lowest part of the brain, the white matter makes up the outer layer, while the gray matter is the inner layer. The medulla consists mainly of nerve fibers connecting the spinal cord to the various other parts of the brain. Nerve centers in the medulla control many involuntary activities, including breathing, heartbeat, blood pressure, and coughing.

15-3 The Spinal Cord

The **spinal cord**, which is about 45 centimeters long, extends from the base of the brain down through the vertebrae of the spinal column. A cross section of the spinal cord shows an

Figure 15-7. Structure of the Spinal Cord. Note that the spinal cord is completely surrounded by the bone tissue of the vertebrae.

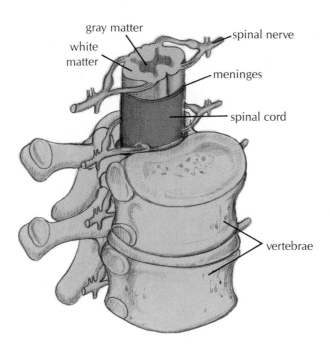

gray matter
white matter
spinal nerve
meninges
spinal cord
vertebrae

inner H-shaped region of gray matter surrounded by an outer layer of white matter (see Figure 15-7). The gray matter contains many interneurons, as well as the cell bodies of motor neurons. The white matter contains myelinated fibers that carry impulses between all parts of the body and the spinal cord and brain. In the center of the cord is the *spinal canal*, which is filled with cerebrospinal fluid.

The spinal cord performs two main functions. First, it connects the nerves of the peripheral nervous system with the brain. Impulses reaching the spinal cord from sensory neurons travel up the cord through interneurons to the brain. Impulses from the brain are transmitted down the spinal cord by interneurons to motor neurons. These impulses travel through peripheral nerves to muscles and glands. Second, the spinal cord controls certain reflexes, which are automatic responses not involving the brain (see page 259).

THE PERIPHERAL NERVOUS SYSTEM

Objectives:
1. Identify the nerves that make up the peripheral nervous system.
2. Compare and contrast the structures and functions of the somatic and autonomic nervous systems.
3. Identify the two divisions of the autonomic nervous system and compare and contrast their functions.

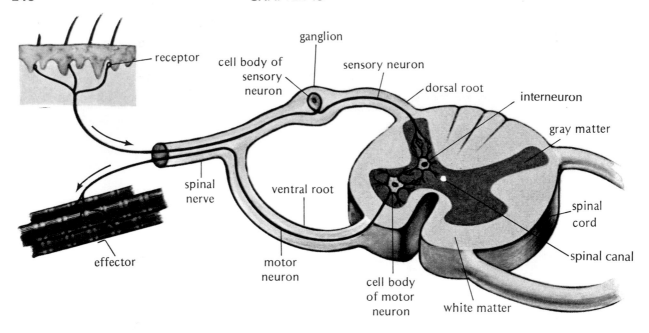

Figure 15-8. Structure of a Spinal Nerve. A spinal nerve contains both motor and sensory fibers. Sensory fibers transmit impulses into the dorsal root of the spinal cord, and motor fibers transmit impulses from the ventral root to effectors. Note that the cell bodies of sensory neurons are outside the spinal cord.

15-4 Structure of the Peripheral Nervous System

The peripheral nervous system includes all the neurons and nerve fibers outside the brain and spinal cord. The neurons of the peripheral nervous system are connected to either the brain or the spinal cord. The neurons are in bundles, forming nerves. The nerves connected to the spinal cord are called the **spinal nerves,** while those connected to the brain are called the **cranial** (*kray*-nee-ul) **nerves.**

There are thirty-one pairs of spinal nerves, each serving a particular part of the body . Each nerve contains both sensory and motor fibers (see Figure 15-8). The cell bodies of the motor fibers are found in the gray matter of the spinal cord. The cell bodies of the sensory fibers are found in ganglia outside the spinal cord. Just outside the spinal cord, the sensory and motor fibers separate. The sensory fibers enter the *dorsal root* (toward the back) of the spinal cord, while the motor fibers leave through the *ventral root* (toward the front) of the cord.

There are twelve pairs of cranial nerves. Those serving the eyes, ears, and nose are made up mostly of sensory fibers. The other cranial nerves contain more equal numbers of sensory and motor fibers. Most of the cranial nerves serve the sense organs and other structures of the head.

On the basis of function, the peripheral nervous system is divided into the somatic nervous system and the autonomic nervous system.

15-5 The Somatic Nervous System

The **somatic** (soh-*mat*-ik) **nervous system** contains both sensory and motor neurons that connect the central nervous sys-

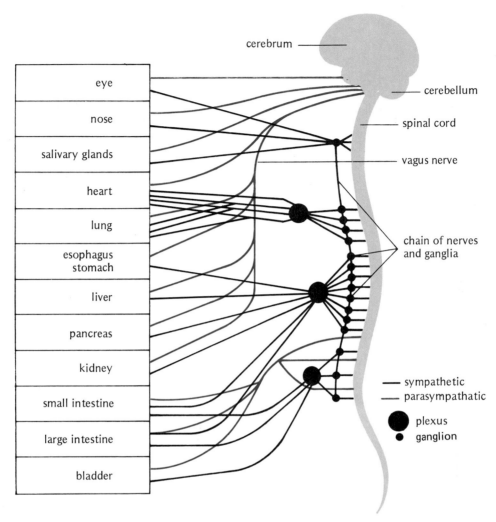

Figure 15-9. Nerve Pathways of the Sympathetic and Parasympathetic Nervous Systems.

tem to skeletal muscles, the skin, and the sense organs. This system is responsible for body movements over which there is some conscious awareness or voluntary control.

15-6   The Autonomic Nervous System

The **autonomic** (awt-uh-*nahm*-ik) **nervous system** consists of certain motor fibers from the brain and spinal cord that serve the internal organs of the body. There is no voluntary control over the activities of the autonomic system. The autonomic system controls many vital functions of the body, including the rate of heartbeat, the diameter of arteries, breathing movements, movements of the digestive system, and secretions of certain glands, such as sweat glands.

The autonomic system consists entirely of motor neurons. Sensory information for this system is provided by the same sensory nerves that serve the somatic system. Impulses in the autonomic system start in motor neurons in the brain or spinal cord. However, the axons of these neurons do not extend to the organ involved. Instead, each axon synapses with a second motor neuron, which then carries the impulses to the muscle or gland. Some of the cell bodies of these second neurons are located in ganglia just outside the brain and spinal cord. The ganglia, which are interconnected by nerves, form two chains alongside the spinal column. Other ganglia are located elsewhere in the body. Some of them form large clusters called *plexuses (plek-*sus-sez).

The autonomic nervous system consists of two divisions, the **parasympathetic** (par-uh-sim-puh-*thet*-ik) **nervous system** and the **sympathetic nervous system** (see Figure 15-9). Organs served by the autonomic nervous system generally contain nerve endings from both the sympathetic and parasympathetic divisions. The effects of these two types of nerve endings are antagonistic, or opposite, because they release different neurotransmitters at their synapses. Nerves of the sympathetic system release norepinephrine, while those of the parasympathetic system release acetylcholine. Where one system accelerates an activity, the other retards the same activity. For example, the beating of the heart is slowed down by the vagus nerves of the parasympathetic system and speeded up by the accelerator nerves of the sympathetic system. This antagonistic relationship between the two divisions of the autonomic nervous system allows more precise and sensitive control over the organs. In this way the autonomic nervous system helps maintain the homeostatic balance of the body.

The actions of the two divisions of the autonomic nervous system on various structures are listed in Table 15-1. Generally, the sympathetic system helps the body deal with emergency situations by accelerating some body activities, whereas the parasympathetic system promotes normal, relaxed body functioning.

Table 15-1. Functions of the Autonomic Nervous System.

Effects of the Autonomic Nervous System		
Organ	Sympathetic division	Parasympathetic division
Heart	speeds up and strengthens beat (stimulates)	slows and weakens beat (inhibits)
Digestive tract	slows peristalsis, slows activity (inhibits)	speeds peristalsis, increases activity (stimulates)
Blood vessels	mostly constricts	mostly dilates
Bladder	relaxes	constricts
Bronchi	dilates	constricts
Iris of eye	dilates pupil	constricts pupil

Sidelight

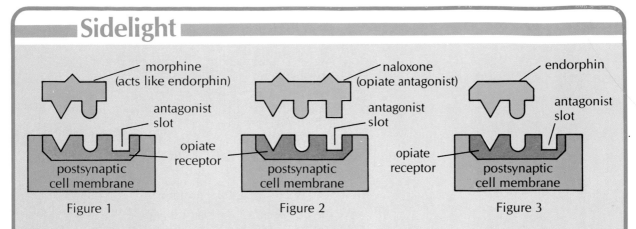

Figure 1   Figure 2   Figure 3

Endorphins

Opiates are plant-derived compounds, such as opium and related substances, e.g., morphine, codeine. They bind to specific receptor sites on certain brain cells (see Figure 1), resulting in pain relief and a feeling of pleasure. These "opiate receptors" have been studied using naloxone, a chemical antagonistic to the actions of morphine. Scientists labeled naloxone with a radioisotope and followed its path in the brain. Naloxone, they learned, binds to the opiate receptors even more strongly than morphine. (see Figure 2).

The presence of opiate receptors on brain cells suggests that the brain might secrete its own pain-relieving chemicals similar to opiates. In 1975, scientists discovered the brain's natural pain-reliever. Using the brains of more than 2,000 pigs, they isolated a small amount of a substance with the same painkilling effects as morphine. They named the substance *enkephalin,* meaning "in the head." Since then, other brain substances with similar properties have been found. This group of compounds is called *endorphins (endogenous morphines).*

Further study showed that endorphins are peptides, or short chains of amino acids. Endorphin molecules have an active region that fits the brain cells' opiate receptors (see Figure 3). This relationship is similar to the lock-and-key fit between enzymes and their substrates. Purely through evolutionary chance, a region of the plant-derived morphine molecule is identical to the endorphin's active group. Thus the brain's "opiate receptors" should really be called endorphin receptors.

Since the action of endorphins appears identical to that of morphine, it would seem that they should be ideal painkillers. Unfortunately, research shows they are just as addictive as morphine and heroin. Also, endorphins are destroyed by enzymes just seconds after their release, so they cannot build up in the brain. Research is currently underway to synthesize endorphin derivatives that are both pain-relieving and enzyme-resistant.

New findings suggest endorphin production is a complex process. In a recent experiment two comparable groups of dental patients were given either a painkiller or a placebo (an inert substance the patients *believed to be* a painkiller). Both groups reported a decrease in pain. Then naloxone—which blocks the action of painkillers, including endorphins—was given to both groups. As expected, those who received painkillers reported an increase in pain, but so did those who received the placebo. The second result was not expected because the placebo was not a painkiller, nor could it stimulate endorphin production. Scientists thus inferred that endorphins were produced as a result of the patients' *belief* that they had received a painkiller. Thus endorphins seem to be involved in complex intellectual, emotional, and behavioral matters.

SENSE RECEPTORS

Objectives:
1. Draw and label the parts of the eye.
2. Explain how vision works.
3. Draw and label the parts of the ear.
4. Explain how the ear functions in hearing and balance.
5. Identify the sense receptors of the skin.
6. Describe the structures and functions of taste buds and olfactory cells.

In animals, sense receptors provide information about both the external and internal environments. The receptors of the human nervous system range from those in the skin, which are relatively simple structures, to the eye and ear, which are highly complex organs.

15-7 The Eye

Sight is the dominant sense in humans. It provides more than 80 percent of the information received about the external environment.

Structure of the eye. The walls of the human eye are composed of three basic layers (see Figure 15-10). The outer layer of the eye is the **sclera** (*sklehr*-uh), or the "white" of the eye. It is tough and fibrous and maintains the shape and protects the inner structures of the eye. In the front, it bulges and becomes the transparent **cornea** (*kor*-nee-uh). Light enters the eye through the cornea.

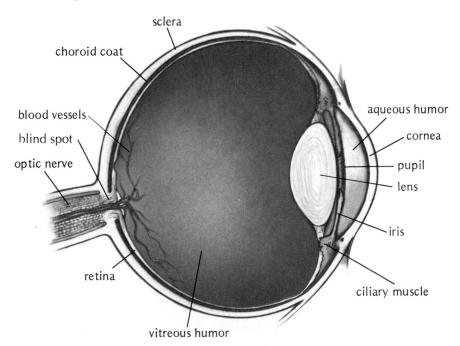

Figure 15-10. Structure of the Eye.

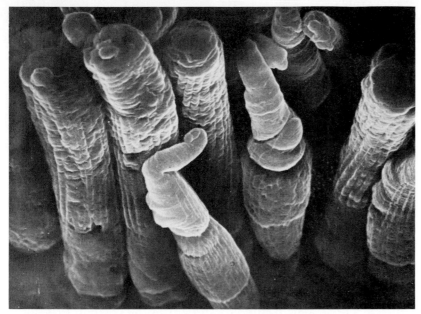

Just inside the sclera is the darkly pigmented middle layer, the **choroid** (*kor*-oyd) **coat.** This layer prevents the reflection of light within the eye and also contains many blood vessels. At the front of the eye the choroid layer forms the **iris** (*i*-ris), which is the colored part of the eye. In the center of the iris is an opening called the **pupil.** The iris functions like the diaphragm of a camera. It has muscles that regulate the size of the pupil. In dim light the pupil becomes larger, or dilates, allowing more light to enter the eye. In bright light the pupil becomes smaller, or constricts, reducing the amount of light that enters the eye. The size of the pupil is controlled automatically by the central nervous system.

Behind the iris is the **lens.** It focuses the light on the **retina** (*ret*-in-uh) in the rear of the eye, producing an image like that on the film in a camera. *Ciliary* (*sil*-ee-ehr-ee) *muscles* attached to the choroid layer hold the lens in place. These muscles also change the shape of the lens, which allows the eye to focus on objects whether close or far away.

The innermost layer of the eye, the retina, contains the light receptors. At the rear of the eye the retina is attached to the **optic** (*op*-tik) **nerve,** which carries impulses from the light-sensitive cells to the brain.

The eyeball is a hollow sphere that is divided into two cavities. The cavity between the cornea and the lens is filled with a transparent watery fluid called the *aqueous* (*ahk*-wee-us) *humor.* The large cavity behind the lens is filled with a colorless, jellylike liquid called the *vitreous* (*vih*-tree-us) *humor.*

Vision. Light entering the eye passes through the cornea, aqueous humor, pupil, lens, and vitreous humor, and forms an image on the retina. The retina is made up of several different layers of cells. The innermost layer contains the light-sensitive cells—the **rods** and the **cones** (see Figure 15-11). Rods are

Optometrist and Optician

Optometrists and dispensing opticians provide vision care for people who wear glasses or contact lenses. Optometrists examine people's eyes to diagnose vision problems and to detect disease. They prescribe corrective lenses and carry out some treatments. Dispensing opticians fit and adjust eyeglasses, following prescriptions written by optometrists or ophthalmologists.

Optometrists must obtain a Doctor of Optometry degree before they can be licensed. This degree requires six or seven years of higher education.

Most dispensing opticians learn their skills on the job. Others have had formal training at community colleges, vocational-technical institutes, trade schools, and manufacturers of optical goods.

Both optometrists and opticians should have good backgrounds in physics, algebra, and geometry. Skill in mechanical drawing also is helpful.

sensitive to weak light, but not to color. They are responsible for vision in dim light, which is black-and-white vision. Cones are sensitive to color, but require bright light to function. There are three different types of cones in the retina—one type is sensitive to red light, one to green light, and one to blue light. The retina contains about 125 million rods and 6.5 million cones.

Both black-and-white and color vision involve the light-sensitive pigment *retinal* (ret-in-al), which is synthesized from vitamin A. Retinal combines with proteins within the rods and cones. The proteins in the rods and in the three types of cones are all different, and each binds with retinal differently. It is the effect of each type of protein on the retinal that allows this pigment to respond to different colors and intensities of light.

When light strikes a rod or cone, it breaks the chemical bond between the retinal and the protein with which it was combined. This results in the initiation of impulses from that rod or cone. Nerve fibers from the rods and cones join to form the optic nerve, which carries the impulses to the brain. The brain interprets them as vision. The point where the optic nerve leaves the eye contains no rods or cones and is called the *blind spot*.

A severe deficiency of vitamin A leads to a condition called *night blindness*, which is an inability to see in dim light. In this condition the amount of retinal in both the rods and cones is decreased, and both become less sensitive to light. Thus, vision in dim light is greatly affected. However, there is enough pigment left for vision in bright light. *Color blindness*, which is an inability to see certain colors, is a hereditary condition in which the proteins of one or more of the three types of cones do not function properly.

15-8   The Ear

The human ear has two sensory functions. One of course, is hearing. The other is maintaining balance, or equilibrium.

Structure of the ear. The three parts of the ear are the *outer ear*, the *middle ear*, and the *inner ear*. (see Figure 15-12). The outer ear is the visible part of the ear. It consists of the *pinna* (*pin*-uh), a flap of skin supported by cartilage, and a short **auditory** (*aw*-dih-tor-ee) **canal.** Stretched across the inner end of the auditory canal is the delicate **tympanic** (tim-*pan*-ik) **membrane,** or *eardrum.*

The middle ear is an air-filled chamber that begins at the eardrum. It contains three tiny bones—the *hammer, anvil,* and *stirrup.* These bones form a chain across the middle ear linking the eardrum to another membrane, the **oval window.** The hammer is attached to the eardrum, the anvil connects the hammer to the stirrup, and the stirrup is connected to the oval window. Extending between the middle ear and the throat is

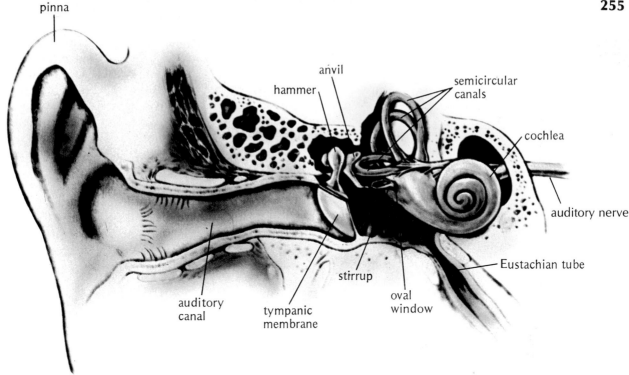

the **Eustachian** (yoo-*stay*-shun) **tube.** Its function is to equalize the pressure in the middle ear with that of the atmosphere outside.

The inner ear consists of the **cochlea** (*kahk*-lee-uh) and the **semicircular canals.** The cochlea is the organ of hearing. It consists of coiled, liquid-filled tubes that are separated from one another by membranes. Lining one of the membranes are specialized hair cells that are sensitive to vibration.

The semicircular canals enable the body to maintain balance. They consist of three interconnected loop-shaped tubes at right angles to one another. These canals contain fluid and hairlike projections that detect changes in body position.

Hearing. Sound waves are vibrations in air or some other medium, such as water. Hearing takes place when these vibrations are transmitted to the inner ear, where they initiate impulses that are carried to the brain by the **auditory nerve.**

Sound waves collected by the outer ear pass down the auditory canal to the eardrum. They cause the eardrum to vibrate, and the vibrations are transmitted across the middle ear by the hammer, anvil, and stirrup. Vibrations of the stirrup cause vibrations in the oval window, which in turn cause the fluid within the cochlea to vibrate. The movement of the fluid causes vibrations in specialized hair cells lining one of the membranes within the cochlea. This initiates impulses in nerve endings around the hair cells. These impulses are carried to the cerebral cortex, where their meaning is interpreted.

Balance. Balance, or equilibrium, is a function both of the inner ear and the cerebellum. In the inner ear, the fluid-filled

Figure 15-12. Structure of the Ear.

semicircular canals lie at right angles to one another in the three different planes of the body. As the head changes position, the fluid in the canals also changes position, which causes movement of hairlike projections. This in turn stimulates nerve endings, which initiate impulses that travel through a branch of the auditory nerve to the cerebellum. The cerebellum interprets the direction of movement, and sends impulses to the cerebrum. Impulses initiated by the cerebrum correct the position of the body.

If you spin around for a time, the fluid in the semicircular canals also moves. When you stop suddenly, you feel as though you are still moving and are dizzy because the fluid in the canals continues to move and stimulate the nerve endings. In some people, the rhythmic motions of a ship, plane, or car may overstimulate the semicircular canals, resulting in motion sickness.

Also in the inner ear are two sacs containing crystals, or stones, that rest on sensory hairs. The pressure of the stones on the sensory hairs provides information on the body's position in relation to gravity.

15-9 Receptors of the Skin

Located in the skin are sense receptors for touch, pressure, heat, cold, and pain (see Figure 15-13). Each type of receptor differs in structure from the others and is sensitive to only one kind of stimulus. When a receptor is stimulated, it produces impulses that travel over sensory nerve pathways to the brain, where they are interpreted.

Although all types of receptors are present all over the body, the different types are not uniformly distributed. For example, receptors sensitive to touch are farthest apart on the back, much closer together on the fingertips, and closest together on the tip of the tongue. The ability to judge the size of an object you feel is partly determined by the number of touch receptors stimulated.

Figure 15-13. Sense Receptors of the Skin.

Pressure receptors lie deep in the skin. They are stimulated only when firm pressure is applied to the skin. Heat receptors

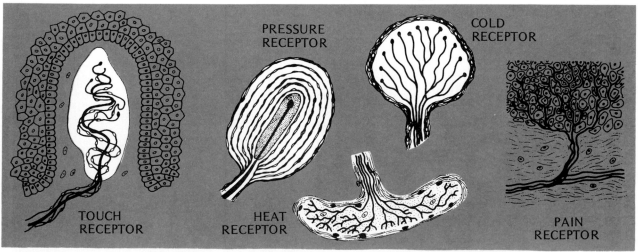

PRESSURE RECEPTOR

COLD RECEPTOR

TOUCH RECEPTOR

HEAT RECEPTOR

PAIN RECEPTOR

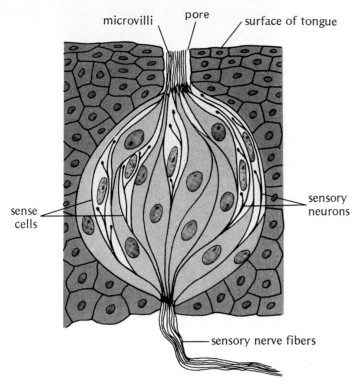

microvilli pore surface of tongue

sense cells

sensory neurons

sensory nerve fibers

Figure 15-14. Structure of a Taste Bud.

and cold receptors respond to the direction of heat flow. The sensation of warmth is the result of heat flowing into the skin and stimulating the heat receptors. The sensation of coolness is the result of heat flowing out of the skin and stimulating the cold receptors. Pain receptors warn against injury. They respond to all types of massive stimulation. The sensation of pain is the same regardless of the stimulus.

15-10 Taste

The surface of the tongue is covered with small projections called *papillae* (puh-*pil*-ee). Within the papillae are the taste receptors, or **taste buds.** Each taste bud consists of a number of sense cells and opens to the surface of the tongue through a pore (see Figure 15-14). Microvilli from the sense cells extend through the pore. Nerve fibers branch among the cells of the taste bud, and each cell is in contact with one or more neurons.

Only substances that are in solution can stimulate the taste buds. Many substances dissolve in the saliva in the mouth. Taste buds are sensitive to only four basic tastes—sweet, sour, salt, and bitter. Each taste bud is particularly sensitive to one of these tastes, responding only slightly to the others. The taste buds for each taste tend to be localized on specific areas of the tongue: taste buds for sourness are found along the sides of the tongue, taste buds for bitterness at the back of the tongue, and taste buds for sweetness and saltiness on the tip of the tongue.

When taste buds are stimulated, impulses are initiated by the sensory cells of the structure and carried by sensory pathways to the brain, where they are interpreted. Actually, most of the flavor of food comes from its smell. This is why most food seems tasteless to a person with a stuffy nose.

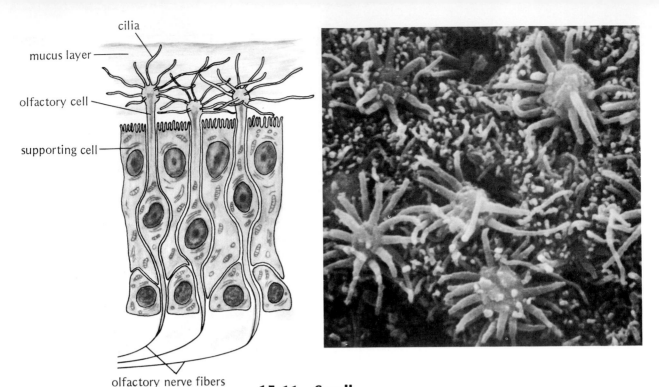

cilia

mucus layer

olfactory cell

supporting cell

olfactory nerve fibers

Figure 15-15. Structure of Olfactory Receptors.

15-11 Smell

The receptors for smell, the **olfactory** (ol-*fak*-tuh-ree) **cells,** are located in the mucous membrane lining the upper nasal cavity. Odor is detected when molecules of a gaseous substance enter the nose, dissolve in the mucus, and stimulate the olfactory receptors. The olfactory cells are specialized nerve cells (see Figure 15-15). When they are stimulated, impulses are carried by the *olfactory nerves* to the brain, where they are interpreted.

Unlike taste buds, which respond to only four basic tastes, olfactory cells appear to respond to more than fifty different basic odors. Like the taste buds, each olfactory cell appears to be more sensitive to one basic odor than to all the others. Continuous exposure to a specific odor quickly leads to an inability to detect that odor, but does not interfere with the detection of other odors. This is called *adaptation,* and is thought to be partly a response of the central nervous system.

Both taste and smell result from the chemical stimulation of receptors. However, olfactory receptors are much more sensitive than the cells of the taste buds. They are stimulated by much lower concentrations of chemicals and they are sensitive to a much greater variety of chemicals.

REFLEXES, VOLUNTARY BEHAVIOR, AND MEMORY

Objectives:

1. Define the term *reflex,* and name several body functions that are controlled by reflexes.
2. Describe the operation of a reflex arc.

3. Give examples of voluntary behavior.
4. Describe the three types of memory.

15-12   Reflexes

A **reflex** is an involuntary, automatic response to a given stimulus. It involves a relatively simple pathway between a receptor, the spinal cord or brain, and an effector. Many normal body functions are controlled by reflexes. These include blinking, sneezing, coughing, breathing movements, heartbeat, and peristalsis. The knee-jerk reflex and the reflex constriction and dilation of the pupil of the eye in response to light are used by doctors to check the condition of the nervous system. The absense of a reflex response, or excessive slowness in a reflex response, may indicate a nervous system disorder.

Reflex arcs. The pathway over which the nerve impulses travel in a reflex is called a **reflex arc.** The simplest reflex arcs involve only two neurons—one sensory and one motor. The pathway of the knee-jerk reflex is of this type. Most reflexes, however, involve three or more neurons. Withdrawal reflexes, for example, involve a three-neuron reflex arc (see Figure 15-16).

When your hand touches a hot stove, it is pulled back before you feel the sensation of heat or pain. This removal of your hand is accomplished by a withdrawal reflex. The parts of this reflex arc are as follows:

1. A receptor in the skin is stimulated by the heat.
2. The receptor initiates impulses in a sensory neuron, which carries impulses to the spinal cord.
3. Within the spinal cord, the sensory neuron synapses with an interneuron, which synapses with a motor neuron. Impulses

Figure 15-16. A Reflex Arc. The withdrawal reflex involves a sensory neuron, an interneuron, and a motor neuron.

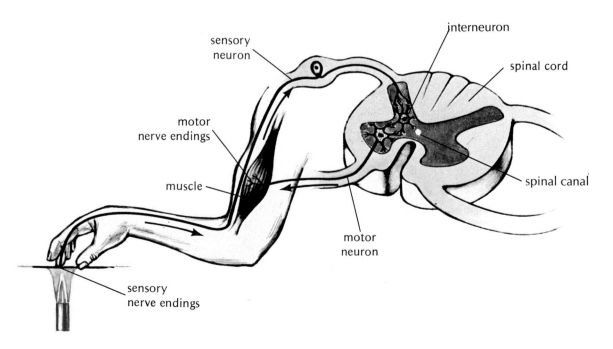

are also carried to the brain, but this is not part of the reflex arc.

4. The motor neuron transmits impulses to the effector. In this example impulses are carried to certain muscles of the arm.

5. The muscles receiving impulses from the motor neuron contract, moving the hand and arm.

The withdrawal reflex is accomplished without the involvement of the brain. However, shortly after the hand is withdrawn from the hot object, there may be sensations of heat and pain. These result from impulses passing up the spinal cord to the brain.

15-13   Voluntary Behavior

Unlike reflexes, voluntary behavior is purposeful and under a person's conscious control. It includes all the physical and mental activities that an individual wants to do, such as writing a story, memorizing a song, or cooking. All voluntary behavior is controlled by the cerebrum and involves a combination of memory of past experiences, associations, reasoning, and judgments. This most complex type of behavior is more developed in humans than in other animals.

15-14   Memory

Most learning depends on the ability to store and recall memories of past experiences. Memory is thought to be a function of the cerebral cortex. Although there are several theories on how memory is stored, there is relatively little that is actually known about the process. However, scientists now recognize the existence of three kinds of memory—momentary, short-term, and long-term memory.

Momentary memory is memory that is retained for a few minutes at most. Looking up a phone number and remembering it only long enough to dial it is memory of this type. *Short-term memory* can be recalled for up to several hours. Memory lasting weeks or years is *long-term memory.* By some process as yet unknown, short-term memory is converted into long-term memory. A person can lose momentary and short-term memories and still retain long-term memory. This is sometimes found in older people, who may be unable to remember recent events but can recall in detail events that took place decades earlier.

At this time no one knows how memories are stored, transferred, or recalled in the human brain. There is some evidence that short-term memory is associated with patterns of impulses circulating repeatedly through particular pathways of neurons. Long-term memory may be the result of permanent changes in particular synapses, or changes within certain neurons. Memory is a field of research that is wide open for new hypotheses, experiments, and theories.

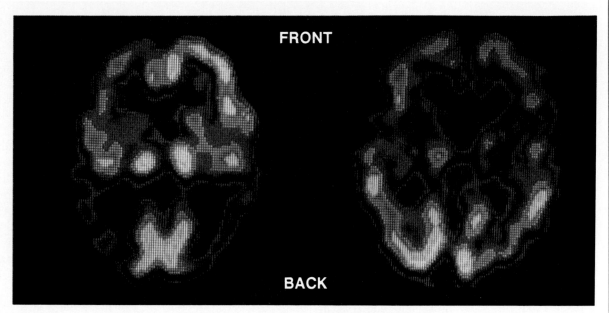

FRONT

BACK

Cross sectional views of normal (left) and diseased (right) brains at eye level. Dark areas at back of diseased brain show regions of decreased blood flow.

Alzheimer's Disease

Alzheimer's disease, a debilitating illness that affects the brain, currently afflicts some 1.5 to 2 million people in North America. By the year 2000, it is estimated that 3 to 4 million North Americans will be victims. Although most Alzheimer's patients are elderly, a significant number of those affected are in their 40's and 50's. The cause of the disease is unknown, its diagnosis difficult, and there is as yet no cure.

The autopsied brain tissues of Alzheimer's victims show characteristic changes. There is a reduction in neurons, especially in parts of the brain that control memory, learning, and thought processes. Twisted filaments and other abnormal structures are present within neurons. Shapeless masses of protein occur around and within blood vessels, decreasing the blood flow (see computer-generated images), and there are scattered clumps of cellular debris in the brain tissue.

Medical researchers have followed the course of symptoms in more than a thousand victims and have identified seven stages of the disease, which parallel, in reverse, the stages of skill development in children. Thus, an early symptom of the disease is the inability to hold a job; working regularly is one of the last stages of development in young people. As the disease progresses, the victim of Alzheimer's disease cannot use the toilet without help; children at about four years of age acquire this skill. In very late Alzheimer's disease, victims cannot walk, sit up, or smile; babies learn to do these things between two months and one year of age.

At the present time, several hypothetical models for the cause of Alzheimer's disease are being tested. One model attempts to explain the loss of neurons that release the neurotransmitter, acetylcholine. Various other models propose that the loss of neurons has a genetic basis; that it occurs because of an abnormal accumulation of protein; that it results from an infectious agent such as a virus or a prion (a protein particle with no DNA or RNA); or that it is caused by some toxic substance in the environment.

Chapter Review

SUMMARY

- The human nervous system consists of the brain and spinal cord of the central nervous system and the nerve network of the peripheral nervous system.

- The major parts of the brain are the cerebrum, cerebellum, and medulla. The largest part of the brain is the cerebrum, which consists of an outer layer of gray matter, called the cerebral cortex, and an inner layer of white matter. The cerebral cortex performs sensory, motor, and associative functions. The white matter includes bundles of nerve fibers connecting the cerebral cortex with various parts of the nervous system.

- The cerebellum coordinates and controls all voluntary movements. It is also responsible, using input from the inner ear, for maintenance of physical balance. The medulla connects the spinal cord with the other parts of the brain. It controls many involuntary activities of the body. The spinal cord connects the nerve network of the peripheral nervous system with the brain and controls certain reflexes that do not involve the brain.

- The peripheral nervous system consists of all neurons and nerve fibers outside the brain and spinal cord. These include the spinal nerves and the cranial nerves. On the basis of function, the peripheral nervous system is divided into the somatic nervous system and the autonomic nervous system.

- The somatic nervous system is responsible for all body movements over which there is some conscious awareness or voluntary control. The autonomic nervous system controls many important functions over which there is no conscious control. The autonomic nervous system is divided into two systems whose effects are antagonistic—the sympathetic and parasympathetic nervous systems.

- The sense receptors of the human nervous system include the eyes, ears, taste buds of the tongue, olfactory cells of the nose, and the receptors for touch, pressure, pain, heat, and cold in the skin.

- A reflex is an involuntary, automatic response to a stimulus. The nerve pathway followed by impulses in a reflex is called a reflex arc. Unlike reflexes, voluntary behavior is purposeful and under conscious control, requiring the participation of the brain. Memory is the ability to store and recall past experiences. It is the basis of most learning.

KNOW THE TERMS

auditory canal	cone	oval window	semicircular canals
auditory nerve	cornea	parasympathetic nervous	somatic nervous system
autonomic nervous	cranial nerve	system	spinal cord
system	Eustachian tube	pons	spinal nerve
cerebellum	hypothalamus	pupil	sympathetic nervous system
cerebral cortex	iris	reflex	taste bud
cerebral hemisphere	lens	reflex arc	thalamus
cerebrum	medulla	retina	tympanic membrane
choroid coat	olfactory cell	rod	
cochlea	optic nerve	sclera	

SECTION QUESTIONS

The Central Nervous System

1. Name the two main subdivisions of the human nervous system.
2. Name the three major parts of the brain.
3. Name the two layers of the cerebrum and cerebellum.
4. Where is the cerebellum located?
5. What structure connects the peripheral nervous system to the brain?

The Peripheral Nervous System

6. What are the names of the nerves of the peripheral nervous system that are connected to the spinal cord and to the brain?
7. Name the two divisions of the peripheral nervous system.
8. Name the two divisions of the autonomic nervous system.

Sense Receptors

9. Which part of the eye regulates the amount of light entering the eye?
10. Name the two kinds of light-sensitive cells found in the retina.
11. Name the three parts of the ear.
12. Name the part of the ear which is involved in balance or equilibrium.
13. Name the sense receptors in the skin.
14. Name the four basic tastes.

Reflexes, Voluntary Behavior, and Memory

15. Give four examples of reflexes.
16. What part of the brain controls voluntary behavior?
17. Name the three kinds of memory.

KNOW THE FACTS

Copy the number of each sentence below on a sheet of paper. Beside each number, write the term(s) that complete(s) the sentence correctly.

1. The central nervous system consists of the _____ and the _____.
2. As an active organ, the brain replaces most of its _____ every three weeks and uses _____ as its major source of energy.
3. The _____ is involved in controlling body temperature, blood pressure, sleep, and emotions.
4. The relay system that links the various parts of the brain and the spinal cord and that modifies sensory impulses is called the _____.
5. The ridges of the surface of the cerebrum are called _____.
6. Damage to the _____ results in jerky movements, tremor, or loss of equilibrium.
7. Beneath the cerebellum and continuous with the spinal cord is the _____.
8. Reflexes not involving the brain are controlled by the _____.
9. The peripheral nervous system includes all the neurons and nerve fibers that are located outside the _____ and _____.
10. The somatic nervous system is responsible for body movements over which there is some _____.
11. There is no _____ over the activities of the autonomic nervous system.
12. The protective, outer, white layer of the eye is called the _____.
13. In the eye, the _____ focuses light on the light receptors of the _____.
14. _____ is the light-sensitive pigment involved in vision and synthesized from _____.
15. The _____ nerve carries impulses from the eye to the brain and the _____ nerve carries impulses from the ear.
16. The taste receptors in the tongue are called _____.
17. The receptors for smell are the _____ located in the upper nasal cavity.
18. A _____ is an involuntary, automatic response to a given stimulus.

UNDERSTAND THE CONCEPTS

19. What is the function of the central nervous system?
20. How is the central nervous system protected?
21. Describe the structure of the cerebrum.
22. Describe the structure of the gray matter, or cerebral cortex, of the cerebrum.
23. Describe the three types of functions performed by the cerebral cortex.
24. Describe the structure of the white matter of the cerebrum.
25. What is the function of the white matter of the cerebrum?
26. Describe the structure of the cerebellum.
27. What are the functions of the cerebellum?
28. What are the functions of the medulla?
29. Describe the structure of the spinal cord.
30. What body functions does the autonomic nervous system control?
31. Trace the path of light through the eye.
32. What are the functions of the rods and cones and under what conditions do they function?
33. Explain how sound waves travel through the ear.
34. Briefly explain how hearing occurs.
35. How is the ear involved in the maintenance of equilibrium?
36. Explain the operation of a reflex arc when a hot object is touched.

THINK CRITICALLY

37. Construct a diagram that shows the relationships among the central nervous system, the peripheral nervous system, the somatic nervous system, the autonomic nervous system, the sympathetic nervous system, and the parasympathetic nervous system.
38. There are about 50 known kinds of neurotransmitters in the central nervous system. Only a few neurotransmitters have been discovered in the peripheral nervous system. Why might this be the case?
39. Explain the significance of the arrangement of the semicircular canals.
40. A doctor observes that the pupils in a patient's eyes are unable to change sizes. What is the consequence of such a disability?
41. Many animals behave instinctively. A newborn herring gull automatically pecks at the red spot on the mother's beak. When the mother receives this stimulus, she feeds the newborn regurgitated food. Relate the newborn's behavior to its central and peripheral nervous systems.
42. One sees with the brain rather than the eyes. Do you agree or disagree? Explain.

THINK CREATIVELY

43. Suggest some possible adaptive values of reflex arcs.
44. Describe a method to demonstrate that the left hemisphere of the brain contains speech centers.
45. Only substances that are in solution (on the moist surface of the tongue) can stimulate taste. Develop a hypothesis to explain why this is true.

FOR FURTHER INVESTIGATION

1. Obtain a calf or sheep brain from a butcher. Examine it and dissect it. Describe its internal and external anatomy.
2. Make a drawing relating a simple camera to the human eye. Write a short report in which you compare the structure and functioning of the camera and the eye.
3. Design an experiment to demonstrate that it is easier to remember words that make sense than to remember nonsense words. Be sure to include a control. Try the experiment with several of your classmates.

4. Do library research on one of the following topics. Then write a report in the form of a feature magazine or newspaper article.
   a. the use of biofeedback in medicine
   b. extrasensory perception (ESP)
   c. optical illusions
   d. headaches
5. Design an experiment to demonstrate the effects of silence and of loud noise on memorizing two poetry stanzas of equal difficulty.
6. Prepare a report on one of the career opportunities listed below. See suggested procedures, p. 9, "For Further Investigation" Activity 3.
   a. Psychologist   c. Hearing therapist
   b. Neurosurgeon
7. Write a brief report on the life and contributions of one of the following scientists:
   a. Louis Tompkins Wright
   b. Humberto Fernandez-Moran
   c. Margaret Floy Washburn
   d. Ivan Pavlov

FOR FURTHER READING

"All about Memory: A Special Section," *Science Digest,* November, 1983.

"The Brain," a special issue of *Scientific American* devoted to the neuron and the nervous system, September, 1979.

Facklam, Margery, and Facklam, Howard, *The Brain: Magnificent Mind Machine,* Harcourt Brace Jovanovich, New York, 1982.

Franklin, D., "Crafting Sound from Silence," *Science News,* October 20, 1984.

Gilling, Dick, and Brightwell, Robin, *The Human Brain.* Facts on File, Inc., New York, 1982.

Loeb, G., "The Functional Replacement of the Ear," *Scientific American,* February, 1985.

Maranto, G., "Einstein's Brain," *Discover,* May, 1985.

Miller, J. A., "Wiretap on the Nervous System," *Science News,* February 26, 1983.

Morrison, A. R., "A Window on the Sleeping Brain," *Scientific American,* April, 1983.

Rahn, Joan Elma, *Eying and Seeing,* Atheneum, New York, 1981.

Ward, Brian, *The Brain and Nervous System,* Franklin Watts, New York, 1981.

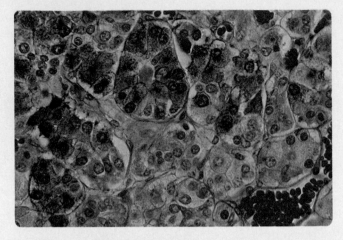

Chapter **16**

CHEMICAL REGULATION

A section of an adrenal gland seen through a microscope.

GLANDS AND HORMONES

Objectives:

1. Compare the operations of the nervous system and the endocrine system.
2. Define the following terms: *exocrine gland, endocrine gland, hormone.*
3. List the bodily processes regulated by hormones.
4. Explain the regulation of hormone secretion by negative feedback.
5. Describe the mechanisms of hormone action according to the one-messenger and two-messenger models.

16-1 Chemical vs. Nervous Regulation

The systems of the body are never at rest. They are continually making adjustments to changing conditions both outside and inside the body in order to maintain homeostasis. We have already seen how the nervous system takes part in this process. The body has another system, called the *endocrine system*, that also helps to regulate and coordinate its functions.

The nervous system operates by means of electrical impulses in nerve fibers and neurotransmitters that cross the tiny gaps that separate adjacent neurons. This system acts quickly and directs its messages to specific parts of the body. The endocrine system, on the other hand, operates by means of chemicals released into the bloodstream, which then carries them to all tissues of the body. It takes time for these substances to reach their target organs and produce an effect. The endocrine system is therefore slower in its action than the nervous system. Its effects also tend to last longer. Generally speaking, the nervous system enables the body to make rapid responses of short duration. The endocrine system produces effects that last for hours, days, or even years. However, the endocrine and nervous systems work together. When you run from danger, for example, nerves control your muscle activity, while the endocrine system controls the blood sugar level and respiration rate.

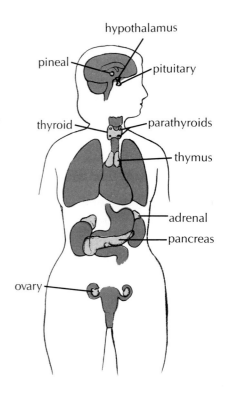

16-2   Glands

Glands are organs made up of epithelial cells specialized for secretion of substances needed by the organism. Some glands, such as the digestive glands, discharge their secretions into ducts, which carry the secretions to where they are used. Such glands are called **exocrine** (*ek*-suh-krin) **glands.** Other glands release their secretions directly into the bloodstream. These glands are called **endocrine glands,** and they make up the endocrine system. (Figure 16-1 shows the glands of the human endocrine system.) Endocrine glands are also called *ductless glands*, or glands of internal secretion. The secretions of the endocrine glands are called **hormones.**

16-3   Hormones

Hormones are released into the bloodstream by cells in one part of the body, but they exert their effect somewhere else in the body. Because of this, hormones are sometimes called "chemical messengers."

Hormones are usually present in the bloodstream in very low concentrations. Each type of hormone is recognized only by specific tissues. The tissues regulated by a given hormone are called the *target tissues* of that hormone. The hormone may stimulate the target tissue and increase its activities, or it may inhibit the target tissue and decrease its activities.

Hormones affect the functioning of target tissues by changing the rates of certain biochemical reactions in those tissues. A hormone may cause a reaction to start, to speed up, to slow down, or to stop. However, hormones do not produce their effects by acting directly on the reacting substances, as enzymes do. They appear to act always through some intermediate cellular process. The processes in the body that are chiefly regulated by hormones include: (1) overall metabolism; (2) maintenance of homeostasis; (3) growth; and (4) reproduction.

In terms of their chemical makeup, most hormones fall into two classes. *Protein-type hormones* consist of chains of amino acids or related compounds. Insulin, oxytocin, and ACTH are examples of this type of hormone. *Steroid* (stihr-oyd) *hormones* are lipidlike, carbon-ring compounds that are chemi-

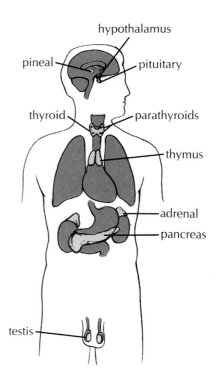

Figure 16-1. Glands of the Human Endocrine System.

cally similar to cholesterol and bile. Cortisone, testosterone, and estrogen are examples of steroid hormones.

16-4   Regulation of Hormone Secretion

As a general rule, endocrine glands do not secrete their hormones at a constant rate. The rate varies with the needs of the body. The signals or messages that cause a gland to speed up, slow down, or stop its production of a hormone may be nerve impulses. However, in most cases they are chemical stimuli, including other hormones.

The mechanism that alters the activity of a gland is usually an example of **negative feedback.** Negative feedback has the effect of returning a condition toward its normal value. If the condition decreases below its normal level, negative feedback acts to increase it. If the condition rises above normal, negative feedback acts to decrease it.

A common example of a negative feedback mechanism is the thermostat that keeps an oven at a constant temperature. When the temperature rises above the set value, the thermostat turns the oven off, allowing it to cool down. When the temperature drops below the set value, the thermostat turns the oven on again. A driver who maintains a speed of 55 miles per hour by adjusting pressure on the gas pedal is also using negative feedback.

To understand negative feedback in terms of metabolic processes, consider a situation in which factor A affects factor B (see Figure 16-2). Any change in A will produce a change in B. If a change in B then produces a change in A, we say that there is *feedback* from B to A. If the effect of the feedback on A is to oppose its original change, the feedback is *negative*, and it prevents any great variation in A. If the feedback were positive, the change in A caused by B would be in the same direction as the original change in A.

In negative feedback in the endocrine system, the secretion of a hormone is controlled by the concentration of another substance in the blood, often another hormone. For example,

Figure 16-2. Negative Feedback. A and B represent two related metabolic processes. In this example an increase in A causes an increase in B. However, the change in B also causes a change in A. This is called feedback. If the change caused by B is opposite to the original change in A, the feedback is negative. Negative feedback prevents A from changing very much in either direction. It is an important factor in maintaining homeostasis.

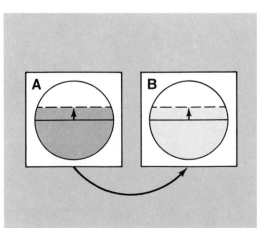

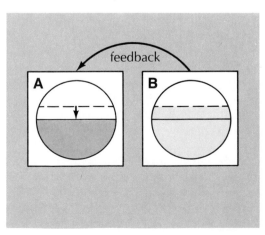

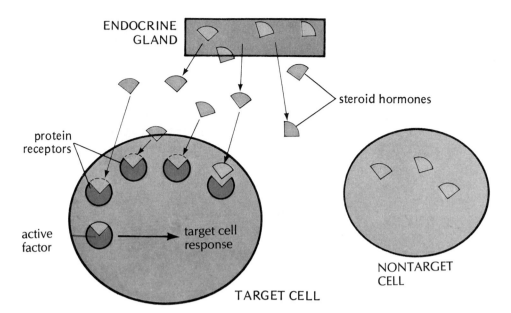

ENDOCRINE GLAND

steroid hormones

protein receptors

active factor

target cell response

TARGET CELL

NONTARGET CELL

the secretion of the hormone thyroxine by the thyroid gland is regulated by thyroid-stimulating hormone, or TSH, which is secreted by the pituitary gland. When the thyroxine level is low, the pituitary is stimulated to secrete TSH, which in turn stimulates the thyroid to produce thyroxine. When the thyroxine level reaches a certain point, the secretion of TSH by the pituitary is inhibited. The pituitary stops secreting TSH, and the thyroid stops secreting thyroxine. Some endocrine organs are controlled by the blood levels of simple substances, such as calcium and glucose.

Figure 16-3. One-Messenger Model of Hormone Action. Steroid hormones produced by endrocrine glands pass through the cell membranes of target cells and combine with special receptors. The resulting active factors trigger the response of the target cell. Nontarget cells do not have the protein receptors and are not affected by the hormones.

16-5 Mechanisms of Hormone Action

Each hormone controls the activity of a particular target tissue. Since hormones are carried in the bloodstream and therefore reach all body tissues, each target tissue must have a way of recognizing the particular hormone intended for it. There must also be a mechanism by which the hormone produces its effect within the target cells.

Recent research indicates that there are two basic mechanisms of hormone action. One of these, called the *one-messenger model,* applies mainly to steroid hormones. The other, called the *two-messenger model,* applies to protein hormones.

One-messenger model. Steroid hormones are small molecules that are able to pass through cell membranes. These hormones therefore enter most of the cells of the body. However, it is only in the target cells that the hormones produce any effect. In these cells there are receptor proteins that recognize a particular steroid hormone and combine with it, forming an active factor (see Figure 16-3). The active factor alters the rate of some chemical reaction in the cell, thereby producing the hormonal effect. There is evidence that the ac-

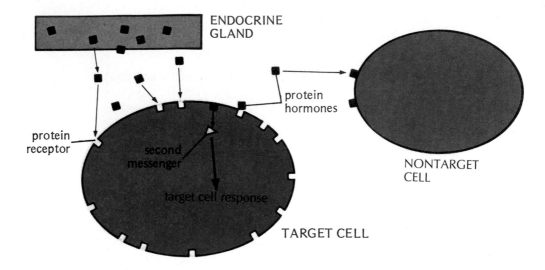

Figure 16-4. Two-Messenger Model of Hormone Action. Protein hormones produced by endocrine glands cannot pass through cell membranes. Instead, they react with receptors on target cell membranes, which then produce a second messenger. The second messenger enters the cell and produces the hormonal effect.

tive factors produce their effect by entering the cell nucleus and acting on the genetic material (DNA) that controls the cell's activities.

Two-messenger model. Protein hormones are generally not able to pass through cell membranes. They are, however, recognized by specific receptors on the outer surface of target cell membranes (see Figure 16-4). When the hormone combines with the receptor on the membrane surface, the combination causes enzymes in the membrane to produce a compound that acts as the second messenger. The second messenger diffuses throughout the cell interior and produces the hormonal effect. The hormone does not enter the cell in this model. Instead, a second messenger does its work.

Although the same second messenger may be produced in different types of target cells, it produces different effects in different cells. For example, it causes thyroid cells to produce thyroxine, adrenal cortex cells to produce cortisol, and kidney tubule cells to reabsorb more water.

THE HUMAN ENDOCRINE SYSTEM

Objective:

Name the major endocrine glands of the human body, list the hormones secreted by each, and briefly describe the action of each hormone in the body.

16-6   Functioning of Endocrine Glands

The human endocrine system consists of a number of endocrine glands that regulate a wide range of activities. In addition, there are a few tissues that are not organized as separate glands, but which do secrete hormones. For example, certain cells in the lining of the stomach and small intestine function in this way. The improper functioning of an endocrine gland may result in a disease or disorder of the body. An excess, or **hypersecretion** (hy-per-suh-*kree*-shun), of a hormone may cause one type of disorder, while a deficiency, or **hyposecretion** (hy-poh-suh-*kree*-shun), of a hormone may cause another disorder. In the following sections we will describe the structure and function of the human endocrine glands.

16-7 Pituitary Gland

The **pituitary** (pih-*too*-uh-tehr-ee) is a small gland about 1 centimeter in diameter. It consists of an anterior, or front, lobe and a posterior, or back, lobe (see Figure 16-5). Between these two lobes there is a very small intermediate zone that is not functional in humans, but which is larger and functional in other animals. The pituitary is often called the "master gland" of the body because it controls the activity of a number of other endocrine glands.

The pituitary is connected by means of a stalk to a part of the brain called the *hypothalamus* (hy-poh-*thal*-uh-mus). The hypothalamus controls the release of hormones by the pituitary and serves as a major link between the nervous system and the endocrine system. The hypothalamus receives information from many different parts of the nervous system. This information is a major factor in determining when the hypothalamus stimulates the pituitary to release its hormones. Another factor is the concentration of various hormones in the blood.

Anterior pituitary. The anterior lobe of the pituitary secretes several different hormones, many of them very important in controlling metabolic functions. The release of hormones from the anterior pituitary is controlled by hormones produced by the hypothalamus. The hormones from the hypothalamus are called *releasing hormones,* or **releasing factors.** The release of each type of hormone from the anterior pituitary is controlled by a specific releasing factor. The releasing factors are produced by the endings of specific neurons within the hypothalamus. When they are released by the neurons, the factors are absorbed directly into capillaries that carry them to the anterior pituitary.

It is thought that each different hormone of the anterior pituitary is produced by a different type of cell. The major hormones of the anterior pituitary and their functions are as follows:

1. *Thyroid-stimulating hormone,* or TSH, stimulates the production and release of thyroid hormone by the thyroid gland.

2. *Adrenocorticotropic* (uh-*dree*-noh-kort-ih-koh-troh-pik) *hormone,* or ACTH, stimulates the production and release of hormones from the cortex layer of the adrenal glands. ACTH is used in the treatment of arthritis, asthma, and allergies.

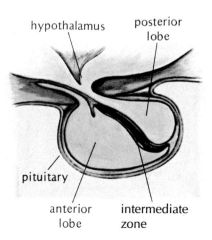

Figure 16-5. Structure of the Pituitary Gland. The pituitary gland, shown in longitudinal section, is connected by a stalk to the hypothalamus, which regulates the release of pituitary hormones.

GLANDULAR DISORDERS			
Gland	Hormone	Effect of oversecretion (hypersecretion)	Effect of undersecretion (hyposecretion)
Anterior pituitary	growth hormone	*in childhood:* Oversecretion causes giantism. Individual grows very tall, but is normally proportioned. Mental development is not affected. *in adulthood:* Oversecretion causes acromegaly. Individual has abnormally large hands and feet, and enlarged facial structures. Does not affect mental processes.	*in childhood:* Undersecretion results in dwarfism. Individual is very small, but is normally proportioned. Adult sexual development often does not occur.
Adrenal cortex	aldosterone, cortisol	Oversecretion results in Cushing's disease. Individual has excess fat deposits in the upper body, a puffy face, excess growth of facial hair, and a high blood glucose level. Decreased immunity to disease also occurs.	Undersecretion results in Addison's disease. Normal blood glucose level cannot be maintained. Individual becomes sluggish, weak, loses weight, and develops increased skin pigmentation. Tolerance to stress is reduced. Without medication, the disease causes death.
Thyroid	thyroxine	Oversecretion results in hyperthyroidism. Individual is nervous, irritable, loses weight, and cannot sleep. Often eyes protrude, a condition called exophthalmos. Hyperthyroidism is often accompanied by a goiter, or enlarged thyroid.	*in infancy:* Undersecretion results in cretinism. Individual is a dwarf whose body parts are out of proportion. Mental retardation occurs. *in adulthood:* Undersecretion results in myxedema. Individual gains weight and skin becomes puffy. A slowdown of mental activity also occurs.
Pancreas (β cells, islets of Langerhans)	insulin	Oversecretion results in diabetic shock. The blood glucose level falls, and convulsions, unconsciousness, and death may occur if untreated.	Undersecretion results in diabetes. Individual has an abnormally high blood glucose level, becomes dehydrated, loses weight, and cannot resist infections. If untreated, can cause death.
Pancreas (α cells, islets of Langerhans)	glucagon	Oversecretion results in an abnormally high blood glucose level. Similar to diabetes.	Undersecretion results in an abnormally low blood glucose level.

Table 16-1. Effects of Oversecretion and Undersecretion of Hormones.

3. *Growth hormone,* or GH, controls growth of the body. It affects the growth of bone and cartilage. This is accomplished indirectly by its control of the production of another factor that acts directly on these tissues. Growth hormone directly affects protein, carbohydrate, and fat metabolism at a cellular level. (See Table 16-1 for the effects of over- and undersecretion of GH.)

4. *Follicle-stimulating hormone,* or FSH, stimulates the development of egg cells in the ovaries in females. In males, it controls the production of sperm cells in the testes.

5. *Luteinizing* (*loot*-ee-in-iz-ing) *hormone,* or LH, causes the release of egg cells from the ovaries in females, and it

controls the production of sex hormones in both males and females.

6. *Prolactin* (*proh*-lak-tin) stimulates the secretion of milk by the mammary glands of the female after she gives birth. Otherwise, it is secreted only in very small amounts. It is thought that the production of prolactin is normally inhibited by a factor secreted by the hypothalamus. Following childbirth, the secretion of this inhibitory factor is blocked, and prolactin is produced.

Posterior pituitary. The posterior lobe of the pituitary is directly connected to the hypothalamus. Two tracts of nerve fibers originating in the hypothalamus have their endings in the posterior pituitary. Two hormones, *oxytocin* (ahk-sih-*toh*-sin) and *vasopressin* (vay-zoh-*pres*-in), are produced by these nerve cells in the hypothalamus. The hormones then pass down the axons to the posterior lobe of the pituitary for storage and eventual release.

Oxytocin stimulates contraction of the smooth muscles of the uterus during childbirth. Vasopressin, which is also known as *antidiuretic* (ant-ih-dy-uh-*ret*-ik) *hormone* or ADH, controls the reabsorption of water by the nephrons of the kidneys. ADH increases the permeability of the tubules to water, so that water is reabsorbed by osmosis.

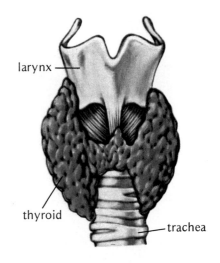

Figure 16-6. The Thyroid Gland. The hormones of the thyroid regulate the rate of metabolism in the body and the blood calcium level.

16-8   Thyroid Gland

The **thyroid** (*thy*-royd) **gland** is located in the neck just below the larynx and in front of the trachea (see Figure 16-6). This gland secretes the iodine-containing hormone **thyroxine** (thy-*rahk*-sin). Thyroxine regulates the rate of metabolism in the body. It increases the rate of protein, carbohydrate, and fat metabolism and the rate of cellular respiration. This hormone is essential for normal mental and physical development. The thyroid secretes another hormone, *calcitonin* (kal-suh-*toh*-nin), which is involved in the regulation of the blood calcium level.

The secretion of thyroxine is regulated by the interaction of several hormones (see Figure 16-7). If the concentration of

Figure 16-7. Regulation of Thyroxine Secretion.

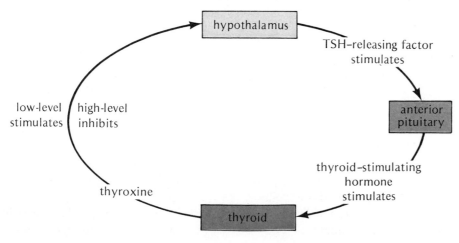

VIEW FROM BEHIND

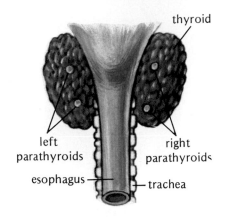

Figure 16-8. The Parathyroid Glands.
The four small parathyroid glands embedded in the back of the thyroid produce hormones that regulate calcium and phosphate metabolism in the body.

thyroxine in the blood falls below a certain level, the hypothalamus is stimulated to produce TSH-releasing factor. The releasing factor stimulates the anterior pituitary to secrete thyroid-stimulating hormone (TSH). The TSH, in turn, stimulates the release of thyroxine by the thyroid. Increasing levels of thyroxine in the blood inhibit the production of releasing factor by the hypothalamus. This inhibits the production of TSH, and thereby decreases the stimulation of the thyroid. Thus, by negative feedback the concentration of thyroxine in the blood controls the system by which it is produced. (See Table 16-1 for the effects of over- and undersecretion of thyroxine.)

16-9   Parathyroid Glands

Four tiny, oval glands called the **parathyroids** (par-uh-*thy*-royds) are embedded in the back of the thyroid (see Figure 16-8). They secrete parathyroid hormone, or *parathormone* (par-uh-*thor*-mohn). This hormone regulates calcium and phosphate metabolism.

Calcium is necessary for proper growth, the health of bones and teeth, blood clotting, nerve function, and muscle contraction. Phosphate is found in bone and in many important compounds in the body, including ATP, DNA, and RNA.

The concentration of calcium ions in the blood must be kept within relatively narrow limits for the normal functioning of nerves and muscles. Calcium is stored to some extent within cells, but it is stored mainly in bones in the form of calcium phosphate compounds. When the blood calcium level drops even slightly, the parathyroids are stimulated to secrete parathormone. This hormone causes the release of calcium from bone into the plasma. When the blood calcium concentration rises above a certain level, calcium is stored in bone. Excess calcium can also be excreted by the kidneys and intestines.

A deficiency of parathormone results in low blood calcium levels. If the level is low enough, the skeletal muscles become hypersensitive and contract violently, a condition called *tetany* (*tet*-uh-nee). Oversecretion of parathormone results in the removal of calcium from bones to the point where they become brittle and break easily.

16-10   Adrenal Glands

Capping the two kidneys are the **adrenal** (uh-*dreen*-ul) **glands** (see Figure 16-9). Each gland consists of an inner layer called the *medulla* and an outer layer called the *cortex*. The hormones of the adrenal gland help the body to deal with stress. The hormones of the medulla are released to handle sudden stress, while hormones of the cortex help the body deal with long-term stress.

Adrenal medulla. The tissue of the adrenal medulla is related to nerve tissue. The two hormones secreted by the adrenal medulla are **epinephrine,** or *adrenalin* (uh-*dren*-uh-lin), and **norepinephrine,** or *noradrenalin* (nor-uh-*dren*-uh-lin). About 80 percent of the secretion is epinephrine, and 20 percent norepinephrine. Secretion of these hormones by the adrenal medulla is regulated directly by nerves of the sympathetic nervous system. In general, the effects of these hormones are the same as those produced by stimulation of the sympathetic nervous system, except that the effects of the hormones are much longer lasting.

Epinephrine and norepinephrine produce what is called the "emergency response," or "fight-or-flight" reaction. They are secreted in response to sudden stresses, such as fear, anger, pain, or physical exertion. Both hormones constrict the blood vessels of the body. Epinephrine increases the rate of metabolism. It increases the release of glucose by the liver. It increases the rate and strength of the heartbeat, blood pressure, breathing rate, blood clotting rate, and sweating.

Adrenal cortex. The hormones of the adrenal cortex are compounds called **corticosteroids** (kort-ih-koh-*stihr*-oyds). They are all synthesized from cholesterol. The major hormones of the adrenal cortex are cortisol and aldosterone, but more than thirty others also are known.

Cortisol (kort-uh-sahl), or *hydrocortisone* (hy-druh-*kort*-uh-sohn), affects the metabolism of carbohydrates, proteins, and fats. Its major action involves the synthesis of glucose in the liver and other tissues. It is important in regulating the glucose level in the blood.

Cortisone is a compound that is closely related to cortisol. Cortisone is produced synthetically and used as a drug for the treatment of arthritis and for counteracting the symptoms of allergies.

Aldosterone and related hormones maintain the normal mineral balance in the blood. Aldosterone increases both the reabsorption of sodium by the kidney tubules and the excretion of potassium by the kidney tubules. By controlling the concentrations of these ions, aldosterone also controls the volume of the intercellular fluid and the blood.

The adrenal cortex also secretes both male and female sex hormones, although the amount of female hormones produced is very slight. The male sex hormones may play some role in regulating sexual development in males. (See Table 16-1 for the effects of over- and undersecretion of the hormones of the adrenal cortex.)

16-11 Pancreas—Islets of Langerhans

The pancreas is both an exocrine gland and an endocrine gland. The exocrine portion secretes digestive juices into the pancreatic duct (see page 138). The endocrine portion consists of small clusters, or islands, of hormone-secreting cells—the **islets of Langerhans** (*lahng*-er-hahnz). These are scattered

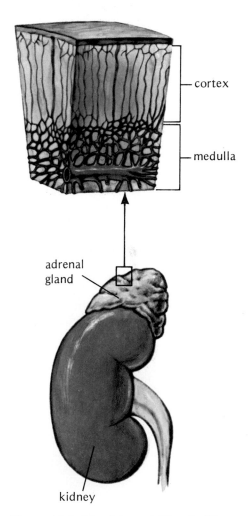

Figure 16-9. The Adrenal Glands. The adrenal glands are located on top of the kidneys. Hormones of the adrenal medulla deal with sudden stress, while hormones of the adrenal cortex deal with long-term stress.

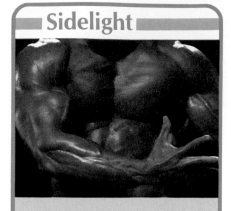
throughout the pancreas. There are two types of cells in the islets—*alpha* (α) *cells*, which secrete the hormone glucagon, and *beta* (β) *cells*, which secrete the hormone insulin. Both of these hormones function in the control of carbohydrate metabolism.

Insulin. **Insulin** (*in*-suh-lin) affects glucose metabolism in several ways. It increases the rate of transport of glucose through cell membranes in most of the tissues of the body. When the level of glucose in the blood is high, the beta cells of the pancreas are stimulated to secrete insulin. The insulin promotes the passage of the glucose into the body cells, thereby lowering the blood glucose level. Within the cells of the liver and skeletal muscle, insulin promotes the conversion of glucose to glycogen, and in fatty tissues, it promotes the conversion of glucose to fat. It also increases the rate of oxidation of glucose within cells.

Glucagon. The effects of **glucagon** (*gloo*-kuh-gahn) on glucose metabolism are generally opposite, or antagonistic, to those of insulin. While insulin lowers the blood glucose level, glucagon raises it. When the glucose concentration in the blood falls below a certain level, the alpha cells of the pancreas are stimulated to secrete glucagon. Glucagon promotes the conversion of glycogen to glucose in the liver. This glucose quickly diffuses out of the liver into the bloodstream.

When the supply of liver glycogen is exhausted, glucagon causes the conversion of amino acids and fatty acids to glucose. Thus, when adequate carbohydrates are not available, body fat and proteins are broken down to provide glucose to meet energy requirements.

Diabetes. When the islets of Langerhans fail to produce enough insulin, the amount of glucose that can enter the body cells is greatly decreased. Instead, the concentration of glucose in the blood increases, and the excess sugar is excreted in the urine. This condition is called **diabetes** (dy-uh-*beet*-eez). Symptoms of diabetes include loss of weight despite increased appetite, thirst, and general weakness. If untreated, diabetes causes death. Proper diet and daily injections of insulin can control the disease. (See Table 16-1 for the effects of over- and undersecretion of the hormones of the islets of Langerhans.)

16-12   Gonads

The *gonads*, or sex glands, are the ovaries of the female and the testes of the male. The ovaries produce egg cells and the testes produce sperm cells. The gonads also secrete *sex hormones*, which control all aspects of sexual development and reproduction. The role of sex hormones in reproduction is discussed in Chapter 23.

The ovaries. The **ovaries** (ohv-uh-reez) produce two hormones, **estrogen** (*es*-truh-jen) and **progesterone** (proh-*jes*-tuh-rohn). During development, estrogen stimulates the development of the female reproductive system. Estrogen also promotes the development of the female secondary sex characteristics, such as broadening of the hips and development of breasts. Estrogen acts with progesterone to regulate the menstrual cycle .

The testes. The **testes** (*tes*-teez) secrete male sex hormones called *androgens.* The most important androgen is **testosterone** (tes-*tahs*-tuh-rohn). During fetal development, testosterone stimulates development of the male reproductive system. This hormone also promotes development of male secondary sex characteristics, such as a deep voice, beard, body hair, and the male body form.

16-13　Stomach and Small Intestine

Special cells in the lining of the stomach secrete the hormone *gastrin,* which stimulates the flow of gastric juice (see page 137). In the lining of the small intestine there are cells that secrete the hormone *secretin* (see page 138), which stimulates the flow of pancreatic juice. Secretin was the first hormone to be discovered.

16-14　Thymus

The **thymus** (*thy*-mus) is a gland located in the upper chest cavity near the heart. It is large in infants and children, but shrinks after the start of adolescence. Early in life, the thymus is involved in the processing of lymphocytes, which are part of the body's defense against infection (see page 168). Current research indicates that through childhood the thymus produces a hormone called *thymosin* (*thy*-muh-sin). Thymosin is thought to stimulate development of T lymphocytes, which are important in immunity. The thymus appears to serve no function in adults.

16-15　Pineal Gland

The **pineal** (*pin*-ee-uhl) **gland** is a pea-sized structure attached to the base of the brain. It produces a hormone called *melatonin* (mel-uh-*toh*-nin). In frogs, this hormone acts on the pigment cells, while in rats it inhibits the functioning of the ovaries and testes. Some recent research indicates that melatonin may inhibit sexual development in human males. At puberty, when sexual development begins, the secretion of melatonin decreases. Melatonin may also inhibit sexual development in human females.

16-16　Prostaglandins

Prostaglandins (prahs-tuh-*glan*-dinz) are "local hormones" that produce their effects on the cells in which they are synthesized without ever entering the bloodstream. They may act by modifying the effects of other hormones. They are thought to influence a wide variety of metabolic activities, including

heartbeat, blood pressure, excretion of urine, and contraction of the uterus at childbirth. Prostaglandins are being studied for possible use in the treatment of such diverse diseases as high blood pressure, stroke, asthma, and ulcers.

Chapter Review

SUMMARY

• The endocrine system consists of specialized glands and tissues that secrete hormones. The hormones, which act as chemical messengers, are released directly into the bloodstream and carried throughout the body. Each hormone exerts its effects on its target tissue alone.

• The rate at which a hormone is secreted varies with the needs of the body. The activity of most endocrine glands is controlled by a negative feedback mechanism in which the concentration of a certain substance in the blood stimulates or inhibits gland function. A hormone produces its effect within target cells by one of two basic mechanisms—the one-messenger model or the two-messenger model.

• The glands of the human endocrine system and their major hormones are listed below.

–pituitary gland: TSH, ACTH, GH, FSH, LH, prolactin, oxytocin, vasopressin
–thyroid gland: thyroxine, calcitonin
–parathyroid glands: parathormone
–adrenal glands: epinephrine, norepinephrine, cortisol, aldosterone
–islets of Langerhans (pancreas): insulin, glucagon
–ovaries: estrogen, progesterone
–testes: testosterone
–stomach lining: gastrin
–intestinal lining: secretin
–thymus: thymosin
–pineal gland: melatonin
–"local hormones" called prostaglandins

KNOW THE TERMS

adrenal gland	glucagon	norepinephrine	releasing factor
corticosteroid	hormone	ovary	testis
diabetes	hypersecretion	parathyroid gland	testosterone
endocrine gland	hyposecretion	pineal gland	thymus gland
epinephrine	insulin	pituitary gland	thyroid gland
estrogen	islets of Langerhans	progesterone	thyroxine
exocrine gland	negative feedback	prostaglandin	

SECTION QUESTIONS

1. What two systems regulate and coordinate body functions?

Glands and Hormones

2. Name the two types of glands found in the human body.

3. What are hormones?

4. What are target tissues?

5. Name the mechanism that alters the activity of an endocrine gland.

6. Give an example of a negative feedback mechanism.
7. Name the two basic mechanisms of hormone action.

The Human Endocrine System

8. Define the terms *hypersecretion* and *hyposecretion.*
9. List the hormones of the anterior pituitary.
10. Where are the hormones of the posterior pituitary produced?

11. What two hormones are secreted by the thyroid?
12. Where are the adrenal glands located?
13. Name the hormones produced by the islets of Langerhans.
14. Name the hormones secreted by the ovaries and the testes.
15. Name the hormones secreted by the stomach and the small intestine.
16. What are prostaglandins?

KNOW THE FACTS

Copy the number of each statement below on a sheet of paper. Beside each number, write whether the statement is true or false. If the statement is false, replace the italicized word(s) with a term that will make the statement true.

1. The endocrine system is *faster* in its action than is the nervous system.
2. *Glands* are organs made up of epithelial cells specialized for secretion.
3. Endocrine glands are called *duct* glands or glands of internal secretions.
4. Hormones are sometimes called *neurotransmitters.*
5. The one-messenger model applies to *protein* hormones.
6. The parathyroid glands are embedded in the back of the *thyroid gland.*
7. Parathormone regulates *iron* and *nitrogen* metabolism.

8. *Epinephrine* and *norepinephrine* are secreted by the adrenal medulla.
9. The *somatic nervous system* controls the secretion activity of the adrenal medulla.
10. The *adrenal cortex* secretes cortisol and aldosterone.
11. *Cortisone* is used to treat arthritis and is related to cortisol.
12. The *motor end plates* are located in the pancreas.
13. *Oversecretion* of insulin results in diabetes.
14. *Estrogen* is important in the development of male secondary sex characteristics.
15. The *pineal gland* secretes melatonin.

UNDERSTAND THE CONCEPTS

16. How do hormones affect the metabolism of target tissues?
17. Which body processes are regulated chiefly by hormones?
18. Describe the chemical makeup of hormones.
19. Why is the pituitary called the master gland?
20. How is the secretion of hormones by the anterior pituitary controlled?
21. Describe the functions of the hormones of the anterior pituitary.
22. What are the functions of the posterior pituitary hormones?
23. What are the functions of the hormones secreted by the thyroid gland?

24. Why must blood calcium levels be kept fairly constant?
25. Explain the function of the hormones secreted by the adrenal medulla?
26. What are the functions of cortisol and aldosterone?
27. What is the function of insulin?
28. What is the function of glucagon?
29. What are the symptoms of diabetes?
30. How is diabetes treated?
31. What is the function of the thymus in children and adults?
32. Describe how prostaglandins may work in the body.

THINK CRITICALLY

33. Compare and contrast the operation of hormones with that of enzymes.
34. Explain why table salt is enriched with iodine.
35. Acromegaly is the sudden growth of certain body parts, such as the face and hands, after normal body growth has been completed.

Explain how this condition could occur.
36. Predict the effect of removing the pancreas from a person's body.
37. Describe the events that would occur after a person is injected with insulin.
38. Explain how negative feedback helps maintain homeostasis in the body.

THINK CREATIVELY

39. Some hormones prescribed for medical purposes are taken orally while others are injected directly into the body. Suggest a possible explanation for these different methods of administering hormones.

40. A patient who had a thyroid removed and a patient with an excessively large thyroid showed the same symptoms of hypothyroidism. Propose possible explanations for the fact that symptoms of hypothyroidism arose from apparently opposite conditions.

FOR FURTHER INVESTIGATION

1. Imagine that you are writing a computer program to show the stages in the human body's response to a sudden threat. Construct a computer flowchart for this program. Be sure to include all chemical pathways, all involved organs and systems, and the resulting behaviors.
2. The discovery of secretin by Bayliss and Starling is an intriguing story of biological detective work and careful experimentation. Do library research on their work and write up your findings in the form of a television script.
3. Do library research on one of the topics listed below. Write up your findings in the form of a feature article for a magazine or newspaper.

a. the discovery of insulin
b. prostaglandins
c. diabetes
d. Hans Selye's stress theory
4. Prepare a report on one of the career opportunities listed below. See suggested procedures, p. 9, "For Further Investigation" Activity 3.
a. Licensed practical nurse
b. Internist
c. Endocrinologist
5. Prepare a brief report on the life and contributions of one of the following scientists:
a. Rosalyn S. Yalow
b. Percy L. Julian
c. Choh Hao Li

FOR FURTHER READING

Blake, C., *The Pituitary Gland* (Carolina Biology Reader), Carolina Biological Supply Co., Burlington, NC, 1984.

Bliss, Michael, *The Discovery of Insulin*, University of Chicago Press, Chicago, 1982.

Franklin, D., "Steroids Heft Heart Risks in Iron Pumpers," *Science News*, July 21, 1984.

Morse, G., "Insulin Independence for Some Diabetics," *Science News*, June 16, 1984.

Randle, P. J., and Denton, R. M., *Hormones and Cell Metabolism*, 2nd ed. (Carolina Biology Reader), Carolina Biological Supply Co., Burlington, NC, 1982.

Silverstein, A., and Silverstein, V., *Runaway Sugar: All About Diabetes*, Lippincott, New York, 1981.

Ward, Brian R., *Body Maintenance* (The Human Body Series), Franklin Watts, New York, 1983.

Issues in Biology

Physical Fitness Choices

Physicians and other health professionals agree that good nutrition and regular physical exercise improve the chances of having a long and healthy life. Good nutrition means eating a variety of foods from the four basic food groups. It also involves eating the right amount of food, avoiding foods with too much fat, sugar, and salt, and eating foods that provide adequate amounts of fiber and complex carbohydrates. Physical exercise at work or in recreational activities such as walking, swimming, running, and bicycling help keep the body in good condition.

Maintaining the proper weight is an important aspect of health that relates to nutrition and exercise. Physicians have found that people who are overweight and/or who do not get much exercise are more likely to suffer from life-threatening conditions such as heart disease and high blood pressure than people who are physically fit. Sensible eating habits and regular exercise are critical factors that affect how individuals manage their weight.

Yet, while health professionals attempt to educate the public about healthful lifestyles, people receive contradictory messages daily. Advertisements and commercials from magazines, billboards, radio, and television encourage us to buy snack foods, which often tend to be disproportionately high in calories and/or salt. Peer pressure may influence a person to make poor food choices. Stereotyped images of slim, attractive women may influence a young woman to eat so little that she becomes malnourished.

Various studies have shown that many Americans do not eat what is considered to be a healthy diet. For example, nutritionists say that a healthy diet contains about 30 percent fat. In 1910, the average American diet contained about 32 percent fat. Today, Americans consume foods containing, on the average, about 40 percent fat. Also, Americans take in, on the average, about 10 percent more salt than that which their bodies require.

In addition, many people's lifestyles do not include much physical activity. For convenience, most people regularly travel by car or by public

Bicycling is a form of recreation that is both enjoyable and healthful.

transportation instead of walking or bicycling. Many people work at jobs that do not require significant physical activity. In addition some people spend many hours playing video games and watching TV or VCR movies. One study published in 1985 indicated that the number of hours spent by teenagers watching TV was directly related to the frequency of obesity. For example, only 10 percent of the teenagers who watched one hour of TV a day were overweight, compared to 20 percent for those who watched more than five hours a day.

People who live in developed countries such as the United States can obtain both the information and the means to be physically fit. But certain pressures, whether they be cultural or otherwise, often run counter to the most healthful lifestyles. Ultimately the choice of how to live must be up to each individual.

---

1. Why do health professionals constantly emphasize the importance of exercise and good nutrition?

2. What are some pressures that affect your own eating and exercise habits? Which of these pressures are positive and which are negative? How could you avoid or re-direct any negative pressures?

3. Besides exercising and eating well, what other choices or precautions can help people live longer, healthier lives?

UNIT 3

PLANT MAINTENANCE

17 **Plant Nutrition**
18 **Plant Structure**
19 **Plant Maintenance**

It is easy to overlook the small plants that cover the ground of this Pennsylvania forest. But, on close inspection, the diversity of plant species is striking—mosses, spring beauties, skunk cabbage, and rue anemones all thrive on the forest floor. What should not be overlooked, though, is how important these and other plants are to the perpetuation of all life. Plant leaves are centers of activity. They capture energy from the sun and use it to make the high-energy organic compounds essential for life. In this Unit, you will examine how different plants are adapted to perform the energy conversion process known as photosynthesis. You will also learn how plants use the energy they produce to carry out their own life processes.

283

Chapter 17

PLANT NUTRITION

Chloroplasts are the sites of photosynthesis in the cells of green plants.

PHOTOSYNTHESIS

Objectives:
1. Describe the early experiments that provided the basic facts about the process of photosynthesis.
2. Explain the nature of light.
3. Describe what happens when light is absorbed by a pigment.
4. Describe some of the characteristics of chlorophyll —which colors of light it absorbs, which colors it reflects, where it is found in the plant, and what happens when light strikes chlorophyll.
5. Write the general equation for photosynthesis.
6. Explain what happens in the light reactions.
7. Explain what happens in the dark reactions.
8. List the environmental factors that affect the rate of photosynthesis, and describe the effects of each.

Green plants are **autotrophs**—they can synthesize all the organic nutrients that they require from inorganic sources. These nutrients can then be broken down by cellular respiration for the release of energy, or they can be incorporated into the structure of the plant (see Figure 17-1). The process by which organic nutrients are synthesized from inorganic sources using the energy of light is **photosynthesis.** Organisms that carry out photosynthesis are called **phototrophs.**

Photosynthesis requires the presence of special pigments that can absorb the energy of light. A few types of plants do not contain such pigments and obtain their nutrition by heterotrophic means.

17-1 Historical Background

"Tall oaks from little acorns grow." That simple statement contains what was once a most puzzling scientific mystery. It is easy to see that animals live and grow by eating food. But where does the material come from that enables a tiny seed to develop into a plant millions of times as large and as heavy?

One of the earliest known scientific attempts to solve this mystery was made by the Flemish physician Jan van Helmont in the early 1600s. He planted a small willow tree in a pot of soil after first weighing each the tree and the soil. The soil was watered regularly, and the tree thrived and grew. At the end of 5 years, the tree and soil were weighed again. The tree had gained 75 kilograms. There was no significant change in the weight of the soil. As far as van Helmont could see, water had been the only substance supplied to the tree. He concluded that new plant material came entirely from water.

Van Helmont was partly right. Water is one of the substances from which new plant tissues are formed. It did not occur to him that the air could have contributed anything to the growth of the plant. In fact, no one was aware that air was even necessary to the life of a plant. It was known that animals need a supply of fresh air, and that an animal placed in a closed container eventually died. Another well-known fact was that a burning candle placed in a closed container soon went out. Something happened to the air in the container so that nothing could burn in it. It was also known that animals could not live in air that had lost its ability to support burning.

In the 1770s the English chemist Joseph Priestley was investigating these phenomena. He decided to see what would happen to a plant placed in air that had been "damaged" by a burning candle. He found that the plant survived very well. In fact, he discovered that the plant actually restored the ability of the air to support a flame and to support the life of an animal. This was the first real evidence that plants interact with air in some way.

Within a few years, the French chemist Antoine Lavoisier showed that the gas oxygen was removed from the air during burning. (Priestley had discovered oxygen, but had not recognized its true nature.) It could now be seen that animals need oxygen from the air to survive, just as a flame does. Air loses the capacity to support animal life or a flame when its oxygen has been used up. On the other hand, plants can restore this capacity to air by giving off oxygen to it.

Additional discoveries followed fairly quickly. In 1779 the Dutch physician Jan Ingenhousz found that plants can restore the air only in sunlight; in the dark, they actually "damage" it just as animals do. A Swiss pastor, Jean Senebier, found that plants take in carbon dioxide (called "fixed air" at that time) during growth in sunlight. Thus, by the beginning of the 19th century, scientists could state the basic facts of plant growth and photosynthesis: In sunlight, green plants use carbon

Figure 17-1. Photosynthetic Organisms. Green plants, like these irises, synthesize all their constituent molecules, using initially only the energy of light and the simple inorganic compounds CO_2 and H_2O.

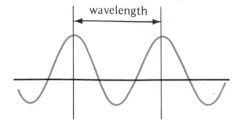

Figure 17-2. The Meaning of Wavelength. The various colors of light differ from one another in wavelength. Violet light has the shortest wavelength, red light has the longest, and green and yellow light are in between.

dioxide and water for the synthesis of organic material and release oxygen in the process.

The concept of energy was not developed until later in the century. In 1842, after the idea of energy had been clearly formulated, the German surgeon Julius Robert Mayer stated that during photosynthesis, plants convert light energy into chemical energy.

17-2   Light

Light is the original source of energy for almost all living things. Light is a form of radiation. It travels through space in waves. The distance between the crest of one wave and the crest of the next wave is the *wavelength* of the light (see Figure 17-2). The various colors of light differ from one another in wavelength. Visible light has wavelengths between 3,600 Å (violet light) and 7,600 Å (red light). (The Angstrom unit, Å, is defined on page 13.)

Sunlight is a mixture of all visible wavelengths. When all wavelengths of light are reflected equally by an object, the object appears white to the human eye. Sunlight is therefore called "white light." When white light is passed through a prism, the rays of different wavelengths are bent by different amounts, and the beam is spread out, forming a *spectrum* (*spek*-trum) (see Figure 17-3). In a spectrum, which is like a rainbow, the different colors of light appear in order of wavelength, from violet (shortest wavelength) to red (longest wavelength).

Although light travels through space in waves, it also acts as though it is made of particles. These particles are called **photons** (*foh*-tahnz). Each photon carries a definite amount of energy that depends on its wavelength.

When light falls on a material, some of the atoms may absorb energy from the light. Atoms absorb energy from light when the energy of a single photon is transferred to one of the electrons in the atom, thus raising the electron to a

Figure 17-3. Spectrum of White Light. When white light (light consisting of all visible wavelengths) is passed through a prism, the light rays of different wavelengths spread out to form a spectrum. The colors in the spectrum are arranged in order of wavelength.

higher energy level. In most cases the absorbed energy is changed to heat, which is then radiated away as radiation of a longer wavelength. However, green plants and other photosynthetic organisms are able to store some of this energy in chemical form in high-energy compounds.

17-3 Photosynthetic Pigments

A **pigment** is a substance that absorbs light of particular wavelengths. Wavelengths that are not absorbed are *transmitted* (pass through the material) or *reflected* (bounce back off the material). Thus, the material in which the pigment is found appears to have the color of the wavelengths that are not absorbed. For example, a ball that appears red reflects red light and absorbs other wavelengths.

Photosynthetic pigments are pigments that absorb light energy and make it available for conversion to chemical energy. Like other pigments, the atoms of photosynthetic pigments capture photons, whose energy raises certain electrons to higher energy levels. In the reactions of photosynthesis, some of the energy of these electrons is used, in a stepwise fashion, to form new chemical bonds.

The most important photosynthetic pigments are the **chlorophylls** (*klor*-uh-filz). If white light is passed through a solution of chlorophyll and then through a prism, the resulting spectrum shows mainly green and yellow. Most of the violet and blue and much of the red and orange wavelengths are absorbed by the solution. A more precise measurement of which wavelengths are absorbed by a solution can be obtained with an instrument called a *spectrophotometer* (spek-(troh-fuh-*tahm*-uh-ter). A beam of light of different wavelengths is passed through the solution, and the amount of light at each wavelength that is absorbed is measured by the instrument. The results are called an *absorption spectrum.* Figure 17-4 shows the absorption spectrum for chlorophyll. It is the

Figure 17-4. Absorption Spectrum for Chlorophyll. The peaks on this graph represent wavelengths of high absorption, i.e. little reflection. Very little energy in the green-yellow range is absorbed. Most of the light of these wavelengths is reflected. This accounts for the characteristic color of plant leaves and other structures containing chlorophyll.

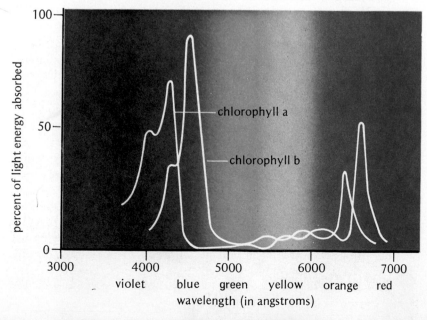

Figure 17-5. Summer and Autumn Leaf Colors in the Sugar Maple.

reflection of green and yellow wavelengths that gives plants their characteristic color.

There are two major types of chlorophyll, *a* and *b*, which differ very slightly in their chemical makeup. Except for photosynthetic bacteria, all photosynthetic organisms contain chlorophyll *a*. Green plants contain both *a* and *b*. Bacteria contain a special form of chlorophyll called *bacteriochlorophyll* (bak-tihr-ee-oh-*klor*-uh-fil). In addition to chlorophyll, the leaves of many plants contain one or more other pigments, including *carotenes* (*kar*-uh-teenz) which are orange, and *xanthophylls* (*zan*-thuh-filz), which are yellow. These other pigments absorb light of wavelengths not absorbed by chlorophyll. The energy they absorb is then transferred to the chlorophyll. In this way more of the incoming light energy can be used by the plant. In many plants the presence of these other pigments is masked by the chlorophyll. In the fall, however, when chlorophyll production decreases and chlorophyll breakdown continues, the other pigments show up, giving leaves their bright autumn colors (see Figure 17-5).

17-4   Photosynthetic Membranes

Chlorophyll molecules cannot by themselves cause photosynthesis to occur. If chlorophyll is extracted from plant cells and exposed to light, it does momentarily absorb light energy. However, this energy is almost immediately reradiated as light, usually of a different wavelength. For the energy absorbed by chlorophyll to be used for photosynthesis, the chlorophyll must be embedded in special cell membranes—the photosynthetic membranes. These membranes contain electron acceptors and other molecules that are needed for the conversion of the absorbed light energy to chemical-bond energy.

In chloroplasts the photosynthetic membranes are folded and stacked to form the grana. In the cells of photosynthetic bacteria and blue-green algae, which do not have chloroplasts, the photosynthetic membranes are distributed through the cytoplasm or associated with the cell membrane. Photosynthetic membranes are remarkably rapid and efficient in converting light energy to chemical energy, but very little is known about their chemical structure and organization. Scientists who would like to trap the energy of sunlight for their own purposes would very much like to know how these membranes are put together and how they work. This is an active area of current research (see the *Frontier* on this page).

17-5 Chemistry of Photosynthesis

Photosynthesis is, in effect, the reverse of cellular respiration. In respiration, glucose and oxygen are used to produce carbon dioxide, water, and energy (see page 119). In photosynthesis, carbon dioxide and water and the energy of light are used to produce glucose and oxygen. In simplest terms, these processes can be represented by the following chemical equations:

respiration: $C_6H_{12}O_6 + 6O_2 \rightarrow 6CO_2 + 6H_2O + \text{Energy}$

photosynthesis: $6CO_2 + 6H_2O + \text{Energy} \rightarrow C_6H_{12}O_6 + 6O_2$

Although these equations describe the net chemical changes involved in photosynthesis and respiration, they do not accurately reflect the actual complexities of the overall reactions. For example, in the photosynthesis equation, it would appear that the 12 atoms (6 molecules) of free oxygen are derived from the 12 oxygen atoms present in the 6 molecules of carbon dioxide. In fact, at one time it was thought that carbon dioxide was the source of the oxygen released during photosynthesis. However, scientists have shown that in photosynthesis, free oxygen is derived solely from water.

It is apparent, then, that 12 molecules of water, rather than 6, are required to provide the 12 atoms of oxygen. Moreover, half the hydrogen atoms from water are recombined with half the oxygen atoms from CO_2 to form water. Thus, in photosynthesis, as in respiration, water is both a reactant and a product. The complete equation for photosynthesis, then, is as follows:

$$6\,CO_2 + 12\,H_2O + \text{Energy} \rightarrow C_6H_{12}O_6 + 6H_2O + 6O_2$$

(The reverse of this equation is the complete equation for the respiration. See page 119). Note that there are now enough oxygen atoms in the water on the left to provide the free oxygen produced on the right.

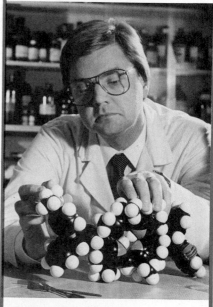

Frontier of Biology

Dr. Michael Wasielewski with model of molecule that traps light energy.

Artificial Photosynthesis

The dream of creating an artificial photosynthetic system appears to be getting close to reality. Dr. Michael Wasielewski has synthesized a light-absorbing molecule that undergoes changes in the light similar to those believed to occur in photosynthetic membranes. When this large molecule absorbs light, electrons are shifted, resulting in a molecule with one negative end and one positive end. Thus the energy of light is trapped in the form of an electrical charge separation. This energized state lasts only 2.4 millionths of a second before the excited electron returns to its normal state, releasing the energy.

This research gives an insight into how photosynthesis occurs. It also suggests that sunlight could be used to synthesize fuels and other useful chemicals.

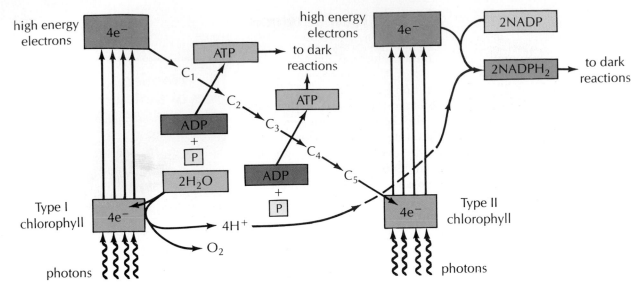

Figure 17-6. The Light Reactions.
Light absorption by Type I chlorophyll causes electron excitation and the oxidation of water with the release of oxygen. As the excited electrons pass through a series of electron carrier molecules (C_1–C_5), some of the energy of the electrons is used to generate ATP. Electrons are passed to Type II chlorophyll, where electron excitation by light absorption causes the reduction of NADP to form $NADPH_2$.

Photosynthesis occurs in two stages. The first set of reactions of photosynthesis, which are called the **light reactions,** require light energy. The end products of the light reactions are the energy carrier ATP and the hydrogen carrier $NADPH_2$. The second set of reactions, the **dark reactions,** can take place without light. However, they cannot proceed without the ATP and $NADPH_2$ produced by the light reactions. The end products of the dark reactions are carbohydrates.

17-6   The Light Reactions

The light reactions of photosynthesis begin when light is absorbed by chlorophyll. The absorbed light energy drives three types of reactions: the oxidation of water, the formation of ATP, and the reduction of *NADP*, a hydrogen carrier coenzyme similar to NAD (see Figure 17-6).

Two systems of chlorophyll participate in the light reactions. When Type I absorbs a photon and loses an excited electron, it replaces the electron by oxidizing a nearby water molecule. When four chlorophylls each absorb a photon and lose an electron, two molecules of water are oxidized, releasing four electrons, four protons, and one molecule of oxygen (see Figure 17-6). As the excited electrons pass along a system of electron carrier molecules, some of their energy drives the synthesis of ATP.

Eventually the electrons are donated to the chlorophylls of the second system, Type II. Light absorption by these chlorophylls causes transfer of the excited electrons to NADP, which also acquires protons released earlier from the oxidation of water. Thus the light reactions generate oxygen and make ATP and $NADPH_2$ through the linked activities of two chlorophyll systems.

17-7   The Dark Reactions

In the dark reactions, carbon dioxide is converted to carbohydrates, a process called **carbon fixation.** These reactions

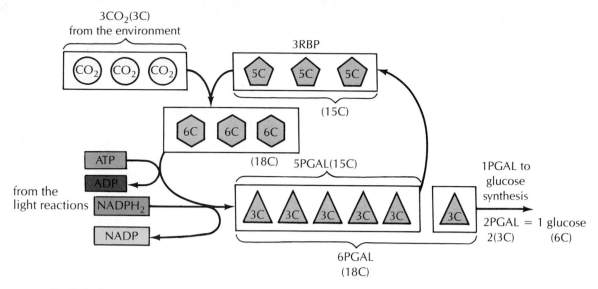

Figure 17-7. The Dark Reactions (Calvin Cycle). In the Calvin cycle, carbon dioxide from the environment is reacted with ATP and NADPH$_2$ from the light reactions to produce the 3-carbon compound PGAL. Glucose, as well as other nutrients, can be synthesized by plant cells from PGAL.

are called dark reactions because, unlike the light reactions, they do not require light. They can proceed with or without light, but they do need the ATP and NADPH$_2$ produced by the light reactions.

In 1961, Dr. Melvin Calvin of the University of California received the Nobel Prize for his research on the sequence of events in the dark reactions of photosynthesis. These reactions are now also known as the *Calvin cycle*. In their research, Calvin and his associates used the radioactive isotope carbon-14 to "label" carbon dioxide. This labeled carbon dioxide was then taken up by green algae during photosynthesis. By stopping the dark reactions after varying periods of time, the researchers could isolate and identify the labeled compounds—those containing carbon-14. In this way, the path of the carbon from carbon dioxide to carbohydrate was traced.

The reactions of the Calvin cycle are shown in Figure 17-7. The cycle involves two compounds that are used over and over—the 5-carbon sugar ribulose and the 3-carbon compound glyceraldehyde. Both of these compounds are present in their phosphorylated forms—ribulose bisphosphate (RBP) and phosphoglyceraldehyde (PGAL).

The cycle begins with the combination of a molecule of carbon dioxide (CO_2) with the 5-carbon RBP, forming a 6-carbon molecule. In a series of reactions involving NADPH$_2$ and ATP from the light reactions, this molecule is changed to two molecules of the 3-carbon PGAL. These reactions repeated three times produce six molecules of PGAL from 3 RBP and 3CO_2.

Out of every six molecules of PGAL formed, only one is released as a product. The other five remain in the cycle. Five PGALs contain fifteen carbons. By a complex series of reactions, the five PGALs are converted to three RBP (which also contain fifteen carbons). These three RBPs are available to pick up three more CO_2 molecules, produce six more PGALs, and repeat the cycle. Glucose is synthesized by combining two molecules of PGAL. The Calvin cycle must operate twice to produce enough PGAL for one glucose molecule.

17-8   The Importance of PGAL

Glucose, a 6-carbon sugar, is formed in plant cells by combining two molecules of the 3-carbon compound PGAL. Glucose may then be stored as the polysaccharide starch. You will recall from Chapter 7 (page 113) that PGAL is an intermediate product of glycolysis, the breakdown of glucose that occurs at the beginning of respiration. In photosynthesis, the process is reversed. Glucose is formed by combining two molecules of PGAL, and it occurs at the end of the process, rather than at the beginning. This is just one example of the many ways in which aerobic respiration and photosynthesis are similar chemical processes running in opposite directions.

From the point of view of heterotrophs, the sugars and other carbohydrates that plants make and store are the products of photosynthesis. From the point of view of the plant, however, PGAL may be considered the true product. Plant cells use PGAL for the synthesis of fats and amino acids as well as glucose. They also use PGAL as the source of energy for cellular respiration. It is only the excess PGAL, produced during active photosynthesis, that is converted to glucose and stored as starch.

17-9   Factors Affecting the Rate of Photosynthesis

Several environmental factors influence the rate of photosynthesis. Often, it is the rate of enzyme action that is affected.

Temperature. Up to a certain point, the rate of photosynthesis increases as the temperature of the environment increases (see Figure 17-8). Photosynthesis in some plants occurs most rapidly at 35°C. As the temperature increases above this point, the rate of photosynthesis declines steeply, possibly due to the inactivation or destruction of enzymes.

Light Intensity. As the strength, or intensity, of light increases up to approximately one-third the strength of summer sunlight, the rate of photosynthesis in an individual leaf increases (see Figure 17-9). Beyond this point, the rate declines because the stomates close to cut water loss or because the pigments begin to oxidize. (Stomates are small openings in the leaves through which gases enter and leave the plant.) However, the most favorable light intensity for a whole plant is much higher than for an individual leaf because most of the leaves are at least partly shaded. Thus, with increased light intensity, the rate of photosynthesis continues to increase in the many shaded leaves.

The intensity of sunlight varies with time of day, season, and position on the earth's surface. Water vapor, clouds, dust, and air pollutants reduce light intensity.

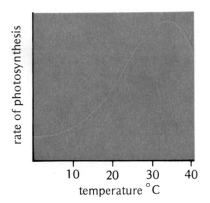

Figure 17-8. Effect of Temperature on Photosynthesis. The rate of photosynthesis is most rapid at 35°C. Above this temperature, the rate decreases sharply.

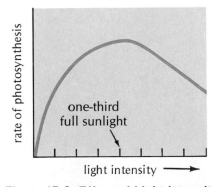

Figure 17-9. Effect of Light Intensity on Photosynthesis. The rate of photosynthesis in a single leaf is greatest with a light intensity of approximately one-third that of summer sunlight.

Barley, a plant with relatively low productivity.

Sugar cane, a plant with high productivity.

Plant Productivity

Today the productivity of plants is of great concern. As the human population increases and the available cropland decreases, plant productivity is becoming ever more important a factor in determining the adequacy of the world's food supply.

In the past, plant productivity has been improved significantly. This was accomplished by using fertilizers and through the careful selection or breeding of plant varieties with favorable qualities such as higher yields and resistance to disease. However, a recently discovered aspect of plant metabolism presents new possibilities in the quest to improve crop productivity.

Research on flowering plants shows that, under certain circumstances, different kinds of plants photosynthesize at very different rates. This is important because the rate at which a plant photosynthesizes is a measure of its productivity.

Plants like corn, sugar cane, and sorghum photosynthesize rapidly. Beans, potatoes, barley, and wheat are examples of plants with relatively low net rates of photosynthesis. The differences result from variations in the kinds of metabolic reactions that occur in the leaf cells during photosynthesis.

In the process of photosynthesis, plants take up CO_2 and give off O_2. At the same time, most plants also carry out a process called *photorespiration*. This is not to be confused with the respiration that occurs in mitochondria at all times and that generates ATP. During photorespiration, CO_2 is given off and O_2 is taken up. No ATP is generated. This obviously reduces a plant's productivity, for it counteracts the effects of photosynthesis. No one is certain why this process occurs. Plants, such as corn, sugar cane, and sorghum, show rapid rates of photosynthesis because they have evolved a metabolic way of inhibiting photorespiration. Scientists are now working on methods of artificially inhibiting photorespiration in those plants that normally photorespire. If this is successful, it may be possible to greatly improve the yields of many important crop plants.

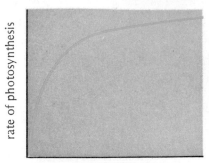

Figure 17-10. Effect of Carbon Dioxide Concentration on Photosynthesis.

Figure 17-11. Indian Pipe.

Carbon dioxide level. The concentration of carbon dioxide in the atmosphere is only about 0.03 percent. It has been found under experimental conditions that, up to a certain point, increasing carbon dioxide concentration can increase the rate of photosynthesis (see Figure 17-10).

Water. Only a small amount of the water taken in by a plant is used in photosynthesis. However, a shortage of water does cause a decrease in the rate of photosynthesis. This is largely because when water is in short supply, the stomates close, preventing an exchange of gases between the leaf and the atmosphere. This slows or stops photosynthesis.

Minerals. Certain minerals play a role in photosynthesis. Magnesium and nitrogen are important in the formation of chlorophyll. Zinc, manganese, iron, and copper are involved in various metabolic reactions. If any of these minerals is in short supply, the whole metabolic process is affected.

HETEROTROPHIC NUTRITION IN PLANTS

Objective:

Describe the two types of heterotrophic nutrition found in plants and give examples of each.

17-10   Parasitic Plants

Some plants have developed heterotrophic methods of nutrition in addition to or instead of photosynthesis. The Indian pipe, for example, completely lacks chlorophyll (see Figure 17-11). Instead, its roots contain innumerable filaments of a fungus, forming a combination of root and fungus. The fungus in the roots obtains nutrients from decaying matter in the soil. The Indian pipe is completely dependent on the fungus for nutrients and water. Dodder is a parasitic plant, which appears as a leafless, coffee-colored vine wrapped around other plants. The roots of the dodder are modified to enter the tissues of its host, from which it draws nutrients and water.

17-11   Insect-eating Plants

Some plants that are capable of photosynthesis supplement their nutrition by trapping and digesting insects. Extracellular digestion is carried out by enzymes, and nutrients are absorbed into the cells of the plant. Insect-eating plants most commonly grow in bogs or marshes where the acidic water tends to reduce the rate of decay of dead organisms. The slow rate of decay limits the amount of nitrogen available for plants to use in synthesizing proteins. Insect-eating plants capture insects to acquire needed nitrogen-containing compounds.

The pitcher plant has green, pitcher-shaped leaves lined with downward-pointing hairlike bristles that prevent escape of the prey. At the base of the leaf is a pool of water that contains digestive enzymes. Eventually, the insect falls into the pool and is digested. Venus's-flytrap has hinged leaves (see Figure 17-12). Along the leaf margins are "trigger hairs." When several trigger hairs are stimulated by an insect, the leaf snaps shut, trapping the insect. Digestion occurs within the closed leaf.

AUTOTROPHIC NUTRITION IN BACTERIA

Objective:
   Describe the processes of bacterial photosynthesis and chemosynthesis.

17-12   Bacterial Photosynthesis

   Photosynthesis in bacteria is similar to photosynthesis in green plants. In these organisms the photosynthetic pigment is *bacteriochlorophyll*, which is similar to chlorophyll *a*. With this pigment, light energy is converted to chemical energy. The chemical energy is used in carbon fixation.

   A major difference between photosynthesis in bacteria and photosynthesis in plants is that in bacteria, water is not the source of hydrogen for the dark reactions. Instead, hydrogen sulfide (H_2S), gaseous hydrogen (H_2), or various organic compounds serve as hydrogen donors. Since water is not split in bacterial photosynthesis, no oxygen is released by the process. In purple and in green sulfur bacteria, for example, H_2S is the hydrogen source. When this compound is broken down and hydrogen atoms and electrons removed, free sulfur is left. Thus, these bacteria accumulate sulfur crystals in their cytoplasm or expel sulfur from their cells.

$$6CO_2 + 12H_2S \rightarrow C_6H_{12}O_6 + 6H_2O + 12S$$
$$\text{(sulfur)}$$

Figure 17-12. Venus's-Flytrap.

17-13   Chemosynthesis

   Chemosynthesis is a form of autotrophic nutrition carried on only by a few types of bacteria called **chemotrophs.** In this process, as in photosynthesis, carbon dioxide is fixed into carbohydrate via the Calvin cycle, using ATP and $NADPH_2$. However in chemosynthesis, the energy to make ATP and $NADPH_2$ does not come from the absorption of light energy, but from the oxidation of inorganic substances. For example, sulfur bacteria oxidize sulfur to sulfate.

$$2S + 3O_2 + 2H_2O \longrightarrow 2SO_4^{-2} + 4H^+ + \text{Energy}$$

The sulfur bacteria and many other chemosynthetic bacteria play an important role in the recycling of materials in the environment.

Chapter Review

SUMMARY

- By the middle of the nineteenth century, scientists knew that photosynthesis in green plants was the process whereby water, carbon dioxide, and light energy are used to synthesize organic compounds and release oxygen.

- Pigments are substances that absorb light energy. The most important photosynthetic pigments are the chlorophylls, which give plants their characteristic green color.

- The rate of photosynthesis depends on a num-
ber of environmental factors, including temperature, light intensity, carbon dioxide level, and the availability of water and minerals.

- Some species of plants have lost the ability to photosynthesize. Instead, they are parasitic.

- Chemosynthesis is a form of autotrophic nutrition found in only a few types of bacteria. In this process the oxidation of inorganic compounds, rather than the absorption of light, provides the energy for carbon fixation.

KNOW THE TERMS

autotroph	chemotroph	light reactions	phototroph
carbon fixation	chlorophyll	photon	pigment
chemosynthesis	dark reactions	photosynthesis	

SECTION QUESTIONS

Photosynthesis

1. Name the process used by plants to synthesize organic nutrients.
2. What substance is restored to air by plants?
3. Name the two types of energy involved in photosynthesis.
4. What is the result of passing sunlight through a prism?
5. What instrument measures wavelength?
6. Name the various pigments involved in photosynthesis.
7. Name the two phases of photosynthesis.
8. What is another name for the dark reactions?

Heterotrophic Nutrition in Plants

9. Name two parasitic plants.
10. Where are insect-eating plants commonly found?

Autotrophic Nutrition in Bacteria

11. What substance is used in place of water by photosynthetic bacteria?
12. Name the autotrophic process that does not use light energy.

KNOW THE FACTS

Copy the numbers from Column 1 on a sheet of paper. Select the letter for the term or phrase from Column 2 that matches each numbered item, and write it beside the number.

Column 1

1. autotroph
2. light reactions
3. parasite
4. glucose
5. NADP

Column 2

a. formed from two molecules of PGAL
b. produce two $NADPH_2$ and ATP
c. produces food
d. lives and feeds on an organism
e. a coenzyme

UNDERSTAND THE CONCEPTS

6. Briefly describe the series of experimental findings that provided the basic facts about the process of photosynthesis.
7. Explain what happens when light is absorbed by a material.
8. What function is served by the photosynthetic pigments other than chlorophyll?
9. What role do photosynthetic membranes play in photosynthesis?
10. Write a balanced equation showing the overall reaction of photosynthesis.
11. Describe the light reactions of photosynthesis, including the essential materials and end products.
12. Describe the dark reactions of photosynthesis, including the essential materials and end products.
13. Discuss the role of PGAL in the metabolism of plant cells.
14. Explain how temperature, light intensity, carbon dioxide level, and the supplies of water and minerals affect the rate of photosynthesis.
15. Explain why photosynthesis in purple sulfur bacteria does not result in the release of oxygen.
16. What is chemosynthesis?

THINK CRITICALLY

17. A plant sealed in an air-tight jar will die in about a week. An animal placed in a similar air-tight jar will die in a matter of hours. (a.) What is the cause of the plant's death? The animal's death? (b.) Would the survival times for these organisms change if they were placed in the same sealed jar?
18. In a dense forest, why would the Indian pipe plant have a distinct competitive edge over other ground-dwelling plants?
19. Would the Indian pipe be a good competitor in a bog full of pitcher plants or other insect-eating plants?
20. As part of their work, ecologists measure the average daily amount of photosynthetic activity in ecosystems. Why would making this determination for a dense forest be more difficult than for a grassland meadow?

THINK CREATIVELY

21. Suggest some experimental conditions that would maximize the likelihood that plants and one animal could keep each other alive in a sealed container.
22. Suggest some physical characteristics of an ecosystem where chemosynthetic bacteria would thrive, but photosynthetic bacteria would not.

FOR FURTHER INVESTIGATION

1. Grow a number of seedlings of the same type of plant. Put each one under a tent made of a different color of cellophane; keep all other growing conditions the same. Which colors of light produce the best growth? How can you explain your results?
2. Write a brief report on the life and scientific contributions of one of the following scientists:
   a. Melvin Calvin
   b. Robert Emerson
   c. Margaret Clay Ferguson
   d. Robin Hill
3. Prepare a report for the class on one of the career opportunities listed below. See suggested procedures, p. 9, "For Further Investigation" Activity 3.
   a. Plant physiologist
   b. Forest ranger
   c. Plant pathologist

FOR FURTHER READING

Heslop-Harrison, Yolande, "Carnivorous Plants," *Scientific American,* February, 1978.

Miller, Kenneth R., "The Photosynthetic Membrane," *Scientific American,* October, 1979.

Chapter **18**

PLANT STRUCTURE

Flowers, like all plant structures, are composed of various cell types organized into tissues.

PLANT TISSUES

Objectives:
1. Name the organs of a plant and describe their functions.
2. Explain the functions of meristematic, protective, vascular, and fundamental tissues.
3. Describe in detail the structure and function of xylem and phloem.
4. Name and describe the three types of cells that comprise the fundamental tissues.

18-1 Organization Of Tissues

Plants, like animals, are made up of various types of tissues that form organs. The organs of a plant are its roots, stems, leaves, and reproductive structures (see Figure 18-1). Unlike animals, however, plants contain no organ systems.

Roots anchor a plant in the soil and absorb water and minerals from the soil. **Stems** hold the leaves and expose them to the sun. They also display flowers and hold fruits and seeds. **Leaves** are the sites of photosynthesis, the process by which plants synthesize food. *Flowers* and *cones* are reproductive organs. (Plant reproduction is discussed in Chapter 24.)

Plants have many fewer types of tissues than animals. Some plant tissues consist of only one type of cell. Others are made up of two or more different types of cells functioning together. Some tissues are found throughout the plant, while others are found only in specific structures. The basic types of plant

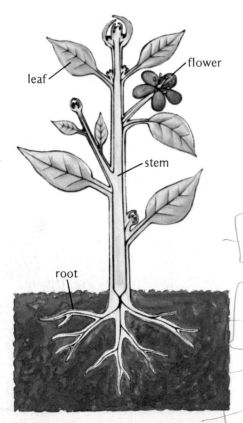

leaf

flower

stem

root

Figure 18-1. Organs of a Plant.

tissues are meristematic, protective, vascular, and fundamental tissues.

18-2 Meristematic Tissues

During growth and development in most animals, cell division occurs uniformly throughout the animal's body. In plants, however, cell division is generally confined to highly localized regions called **meristems** (mur-ah-stehms). **Meristematic** (mur-ah-stuh-mat-ik) **tissues** are composed of thin-walled cells that lack vacuoles. The cells are usually much smaller in size than mature plant cells, and undergo frequent cell division. Meristems are present in the growing tips of stems and roots (see Figures 18-2 and 18-9). These areas are called apical meristems because they are located at the apex of the root or the stem. The cells produced by apical meristems become the mature tissues of the plant body and account for the growth in length of roots and stems. In plants which also grow in width, as in woody plants, a special layer of cells called the **vascular cambium** is the meristem involved.

18-3 Protective Tissues

The **epidermis** is the **protective tissue** that forms the outer layer on leaves, green stems, and roots. The epidermal layer is generally one cell thick. The cells of the epidermis fit tightly together. In the epidermis of plant parts that are aboveground, the cell walls contain a waxy substance called *cutin (kyoot*-in). Cutin forms a continuous layer over the surface of the epidermis. This layer, the **cuticle** (*kyoot*-ih-kul), reduces water loss and protects against infection by microorganisms.

Cork is a protective tissue that covers the surface of woody stems and roots (see Figure 18-3). It protects the more delicate inner tissues from mechanical injury. It also waterproofs the outer surface and prevents infection. Cork is formed by a special layer of meristematic cells called the **cork cambium.** The cork cells live only a short time. At maturity cork cells are dead, and they contain no living cytoplasm. It is these dead cells with their waxy cell walls that provide protection for the underlying living tissues.

18-4 Vascular Tissues

Xylem (*zy*-lum) and **phloem** (*floh*-em) are the **vascular,** or conducting, **tissues** of the plant. Xylem conducts water and minerals from the roots upward through the stems and into the leaves of the plant. It also plays an important part in supporting the plant and holding it erect. Phloem conducts food and other dissolved materials in both directions along the length of the plant.

Most of the cells that form mature xylem are dead—they contain no cytoplasm. They form continuous tubes from the roots up through the stems and leaves. Xylem is composed

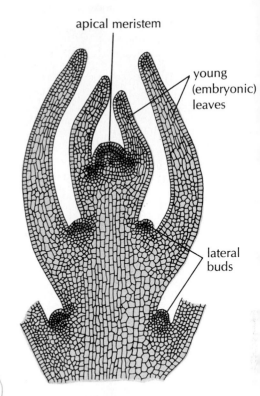

apical meristem

young (embryonic) leaves

lateral buds

Figure 18-2. Longitudinal Section Through a Stem Tip. The cells of the stem apical meristem undergo rapid cell division, producing the cells that form new leaves and new stem tissue. The cells of the lateral buds are inactive, but at some future time may start to divide and become the apical meristems of branches.

Figure 18-3. Cork. The nonliving cork cells protect the internal tissues of woody stems and roots.

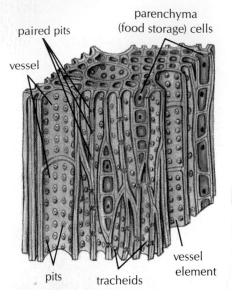

parenchyma (food storage) cells
paired pits
vessel
vessel element
pits
tracheids

Figure 18-4. Structure of Xylem. Water passes from tracheid to tracheid through their cell walls, especially in the pit areas. Vessel elements, whose end walls are absent at maturity, form long vessels through which water passes without crossing cells walls.

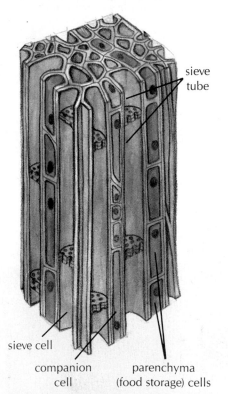

sieve tube
sieve cell
companion cell
parenchyma (food storage) cells

Figure 18-5. Structure of Phloem. The companion cells of phloem are thought to control the food transport activities of the sieve cells. The cells of phloem are alive and contain cytoplasm.

mainly of two types of cells—*tracheids* (tray-kee-idz) and *vessel elements* (see Figure 18-4). Tracheids contain pits, or depressions, in the cell wall. The pits of adjacent tracheids are aligned, permitting the passage of water and minerals. Vessel elements are cells that form conducting tubes. These cells, which lack end walls, are positioned end-to-end, forming long, tiny tubes called *vessels.* Xylem also contains some living cells that serve as storage cells. What we know as wood is the xylem.

Unlike the tracheids and vessel elements of xylem, phloem cells are alive and contain cytoplasm. The substances transported by phloem are mainly organic compounds dissolved in water. These compounds include amino acids and sugars and other carbohydrates. Food synthesized in the leaves is transported through the phloem to other parts of the plant. Surplus food is often transported to the roots for storage. In the spring, sap containing dissolved materials is transported upward through the phloem.

Phloem is composed mainly of two types of cells, *sieve cells* and *companion cells* (see Figure 18-5). Sieve cells contain cytoplasm, but do not have a nucleus at maturity. The end walls of sieve cells have many small openings. Thin strands of cytoplasm extend through the openings connecting adjacent cells. The *sieve tubes* formed by the sieve cells are the pathways through which dissolved nutrients are transported. Companion cells, which contain both a nucleus and cytoplasm, are thought to control the transport activities of sieve cells.

18-5 Fundamental Tissues

Fundamental tissues are involved in the production and storage of food and in the support of the plant. The three types of fundamental tissues are parenchyma, collenchyma, and sclerenchyma.

Parenchyma (puh-*ren*-kuh-muh) is a tissue made up of unspecialized cells with thin cell walls. These cells are found in roots, stems, leaves, and fruits. Parenchyma cells in leaves and young stems have chloroplasts and produce food by photosynthesis. In roots, fruits, and portions of stems, parenchyma cells are used for food storage.

Collenchyma (kuh-*len*-kuh-muh) cells are similar to parenchyma, but are elongated and have thickened cell walls. They strengthen and support stems and leaves and other parts of the plant. Collenchyma cells may also contain chloroplasts.

Sclerenchyma (skluh-*ren*-kuh-muh) tissue consists of thick-walled cells that are found where support is needed. When mature, the cells usually contain no cytoplasm. Occasionally, the cell walls are so thick that the internal space of the cell is almost completely filled. *Fibers* are a type of sclerenchyma cell. They are long cells with tapered ends, and are strong and flexible. They are often found in xylem and phloem. Fibers are used to make twine, rope, and linen.

THE ROOT

Objectives:
1. Explain the functions of the root.
2. Describe each of the following: primary root, secondary roots, taproots, fibrous roots, and adventitious roots.
3. Name the different zones of the root tip, beginning with the root cap, and describe what happens to the cells in each zone.
4. Name and describe the tissues of the root, and explain their arrangmement and functions.

18-6   Types of Roots

The roots of a plant are generally found underground. Roots serve several functions. They anchor the plant in the soil and absorb water and minerals from the soil. They transport water and minerals upward to the stem and dissolved food downward from the stem. In addition, the roots of some plants are specialized for the storage of food. The root system underground is generally as large as the system of stems and branches aboveground. The roots spread out, covering a large area. They usually grow no deeper than 1 meter into the soil.

The first structure to emerge from a sprouting seed is the **primary root** (see Figure 18-6). As the plant grows and matures, new roots develop from within the tissues of the primary root. These new branches of the primary root are called **secondary roots.** As roots grow, their direction of growth is influenced by obstructions, such as rocks or other roots, in the soil. Other factors, such as moisture and chemical composition of the soil, also influence growth. These factors cause the root to grow in an irregular fashion, with frequent bends and kinks.

There are two common types of root systems—taproots and fibrous roots (see Figure 18-7). A *taproot* system develops when the primary root grows most rapidly and remains the largest

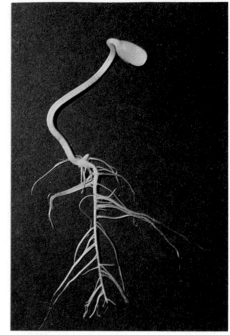

Figure 18-6. Primary and Secondary Roots. Secondary roots branch from the tissues of the primary root.

Figure 18-7. Types of Root Systems. The taproot of the dandelion (left) grows rapidly and deeply into the soil. In the fibrous root system of the African violet (center), the numerous roots are all about the same size. The taproot of the beet (right) is modified for food storage.

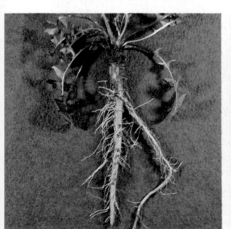

Figure 18-8. Adventitious Roots. The climbing roots of ivy (left) grow from the stem and attach the plant to a solid support. The prop roots of corn (right) help to brace the plant.

root of the root system. Taproots grow deep into the soil and become thick and fleshy. Oak trees and dandelions have taproots. A *fibrous root* system is made up of numerous roots, many of which are nearly equal in size. This type of system develops when branching secondary roots are as large as or larger than the primary root. Corn and grasses have fibrous root systems. In some plants, taproots and fibrous roots are modified for food storage. The carrot, radish, and beet are storage taproots, while the sweet potato and tapioca are fibrous storage roots.

Adventitious (ad-ven-*tish*-us) *roots* do not originate from the primary root or one of its branches. Instead, they grow from stems or leaves (see Figure 18-8). The *climbing roots* of ivy are adventitious roots that grow out from the stem and attach the plant to a solid support. The *prop roots* of corn grow from the stem down into the soil and help to brace the plant. Spanish moss, a plant that lives attached to trees, develops *aerial roots.* These roots absorb moisture from the air.

18-7 Root Tip Zones

The branches of a root system may extend for many meters. However, roots grow in length only in a small region at their tips. There may be thousands of such root tips gradually extending themselves into the soil. Other parts of the roots may be increasing in thickness, but they are not increasing in length. A mark made on the surface of a root will be found in the same location year after year.

Examination of a root tip shows that it is divided into a number of different zones, each zone containing cells at different stages of development (see Figure 18-9).

Root cap. The **root cap** is a thimble-shaped group of cells that form a protective covering for the delicate meristematic tissues of the root tip behind it. As the root tip is pushed through the soil by the addition of cells behind it, the outer cells of the root cap are crushed. The crushed cells release a lubricating fluid that aids the passage of the root tip through the soil. New root cap cells are continuously formed by the meristematic tissue.

Meristematic zone. The **meristematic zone** is a region of actively dividing cells just behind the root cap. The cells of this region are small and thin-walled. All the other cells of the root are formed from these cells.

Elongation zone. Behind the meristematic zone is the **elongation zone.** In this zone, the cells, which were produced in the meristematic zone, enlarge, pushing the root tip forward.

Maturation zone. In the **maturation zone,** which is behind the elongation zone, the cells differentiate. **Differentiation** (dif-uh-rhen-she-*a*-shen) is the process whereby unspecialized cells develop into specialized cell types. In the root, as in the stem, cells develop into mature, functioning cells of various types such as xylem, phloem, and parenchyma.

18-8 Root Structure and Function

In a cross section through the maturation zone, the root can be seen to consist of several distinct tissue layers (see Figure 18-10). The outermost layer, the epidermis, is only one cell layer thick. Absorption of water and minerals from the soil is the major function of the epidermis. Many epidermal cells have hairlike extensions called **root hairs,** which greatly increase the surface area for absorption. The delicate root hairs are short-lived. As the root tip grows, new root hairs are formed, and older ones farther back die and fall off. Note that root hairs are present only in the small zone of maturation behind the growing root tips. It is in this region at the ends of the root branches that practically all water absorption takes place.

Just beneath the epidermis is the **cortex.** The parenchyma cells of the cortex store food, mainly starch. They also transport water absorbed by the root hairs to the conducting tissues

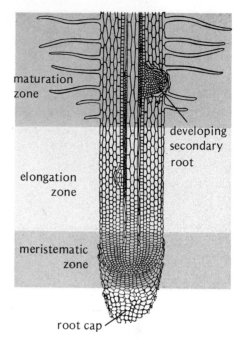

Figure 18-9. Zones of the Root Tip. The meristematic zone consists of rapidly dividing, undifferentiated cells. In the elongation zone, the newly formed cells grow in length, forcing the root tip through the soil. In the maturation zone, the cells develop into specialized tissues.

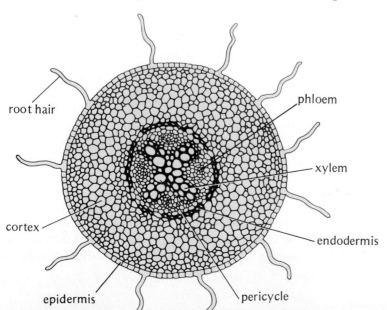

Figure 18-10. Cross Section of Root Tip. The mature tissues of a root are seen in a cross section through the root hair, or maturation, zone.

in the center of the root. Beneath the cortex is the **endodermis** (en-duh-*der*-mis). The cells of this layer control the movement of water into the central cylinder.

The *central,* or **vascular, cylinder** is the central core of the root. It is surrounded by a ring of parenchyma cells called the *pericycle (per*-uh-sy-kul) which is just inside the endodermis. The pericycle is the layer from which all secondary roots originate. These roots push their way through the cortex and epidermis into the soil (see Figure 18-9).

At the center of the vascular cylinder are the conducting tissues, the xylem and phloem. The xylem carries water and minerals up the root to the stem and leaves. The phloem carries dissolved food manufactured in the leaves throughout the plant. In some older roots a vascular cambium develops between the xylem and phloem. The cambium produces new xylem on the inside and new phloem on the outside.

THE STEM

Objectives:
1. Describe the two types of stems.
2. Compare and contrast the internal structures of the stems of herbaceous dicots, woody dicots, herbaceous monocots, and woody monocots.
3. Describe the external structure of a woody dicot stem.

18-9   Woody and Herbaceous Stems

Stems serve to hold leaves and reproductive structures in the air. Some underground stems are specialized for food storage.

There are two types of plant stems—woody and herbaceous. **Woody stems** contain thick, tough tissue—wood. Trees, such as oaks and maples, and shrubs, such as lilac and forsythia, have woody stems. Plants with woody stems normally live for more than 2 years. **Herbaceous** (her-*bay*-shus) **stems** are soft, green, and juicy. Corn and tomatoes are plants with herbaceous stems. Plants with herbaceous stems usually live either 1 or 2 years.

18-10   Monocots and Dicots

Flowering plants are divided into two major groups, depending on whether their seeds have one or two *cotyledons* (kaht-uh-*leed*-uns), or seed leaves. (The structure and functions of cotyledons are discussed in detail on page 401). Plants whose seeds have one cotyledon are called **monocots** (*mahn*-uh-kahts). Plants whose seeds have two cotyledons are called **dicots** (*dy*-kahts). There are a number of structural differences between the stems and leaves of monocot and dicot plants. In

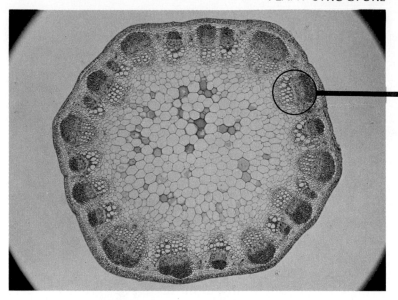

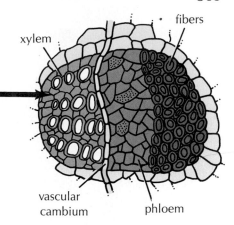

Figure 18-11. Cross Section of a Herbaceous Dicot Stem. The vascular bundles of a herbaceous dicot stem are arranged in a ring inside the cortex. Pith cells fill the center of the stem. The drawing above is an enlarged view of a single vascular bundle.

both groups, some plants have herbaceous stems and some have woody stems.

18-11 Dicot Stems

Herbaceous dicot stems. Herbaceous dicot stems are generally soft and green, such as those of the sunflower, geranium, buttercup, or alfalfa. Figure 18-11 shows a cross section of a herbaceous dicot stem. The stem is enclosed by a protective layer of epidermis. Inside the epidermis is the cortex, which is made up of collenchyma and parenchyma. These tissues provide support for the stem and serve for food storage. Inside the cortex is a ring of **vascular bundles.** Each bundle is made up of an outer group of phloem cells, an inner group of xylem cells, and the vasacular cambium, which is between the xylem and the phloem. The cambium undergoes a finite period of cell division, producing a small amount of new xylem to its inside and a small amount of additional phloem to its outside. The central region of the stem is called the **pith.** Pith consists of parenchyma cells that store food.

Woody dicot stems—external structure. Woody dicot stems are very hard but flexible. Figure 18-12 shows the external features of a dormant twig, one that has lost its leaves for the winter. At the tip of the twig is the **terminal bud.** The main function of the bud begins with the growing season. The protective *bud scales* drop off. The apical meristem in the bud begins active cell division, forming cells that develop into new stem tissues and leaves. At the place on the twig where the bud scales drop off, scars remain called *bud scale scars.* These scars mark the point at which the season's growth began. The length of stem between two sets of bud scale scars represents 1 year's growth.

Another feature of the dormant twig are the *leaf scars.* The leaf scars mark the points of attachment of leaves from previ-

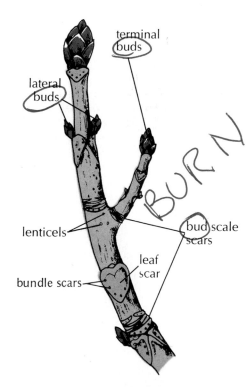

Figure 18-12. External Structure of Dormant Woody Dicot Stem.

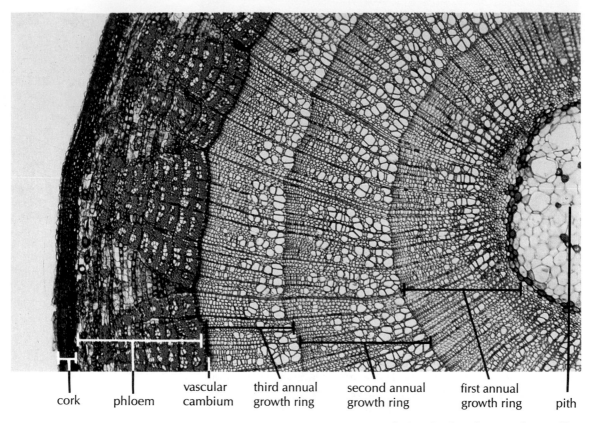

cork   phloem   vascular   third annual   second annual   first annual   pith
cambium   growth ring   growth ring   growth ring

Figure 18-13. Cross Section of a Woody Dicot Stem. The cell division activity of the vascular cambium produces xylem to its inside and phloem to its outside. The xylem accumulates as annual growth rings. The phloem, and the cork that develops within it, is continuously being sloughed off.

ous growing seasons. Scars are formed when leaves drop off in the autumn. A layer of protective tissue is produced at the scar to protect the internal tissues of the stem. Within the leaf scars are small dots called *bundle scars.* These are the points at which vascular bundles containing xylem and phloem are passed from the stem into the leaf.

Above the leaf scar is a **lateral,** or *axillary,* **bud.** Lateral buds are found just above the point where a leaf is or was attached to the stem. During any growing season, a lateral bud can begin to form a new twig, becoming the terminal bud of that twig. However, most lateral buds remain dormant for several years after they form. The points along the stem where leaves and lateral buds form are called *nodes.* The space between two nodes is called an *internode.* Along the surface of the twig there are small raised openings called lenticels. **Lenticels** *(lent*-uh-sels) are holes that pass through the cork tissue. They allow the exchange of oxygen and carbon dioxide between the atmosphere and the internal tissues.

Woody dicot stems—internal structure. A woody dicot is woody because there is long-term cell division activity in its vascular cambium, producing large amounts of new xylem and phloem. The xylem accumulates on the inside of the cambium as continuous, concentric layers of wood that increase the girth of the stem (see Figure 18-13). The new phloem, also produced in continuous layers but on the outside of the cambium, does not accumulate. Rather, its older, outer layers are sloughed off as new phloem is produced underneath.

The production of new xylem during each growing season results in the formation of *annual rings* (see Figure 18-14). The age of a woody dicot stem may be determined by counting these rings. Each annual ring represents 1 year's growth. In some woody dicot stems, the cells of the xylem formed in the spring *(spring wood)* are larger and lighter in color than those formed in the summer *(summer wood)*.

In young woody dicots,the center of the stem is filled with pith, and there is a cortex layer inside the epidermis. In older woody stems,the cortex and pith are lost. The cells of the pith eventually die. The older, inner, dark-colored region of xylem is called *heartwood,* and it increases in size every year. The xylem of the heartwood does not conduct water. It does serve to strengthen the stem. The functional xylem cells, which conduct water, lie next to the cambium. This functional light-colored xylem is called *sapwood.* The thickness of the sapwood remains more or less constant from year to year.

The outermost layer of a woody stem is the **bark,** a protective tissue. On young stems the bark may be relatively thin, but older stems and trunks have bark of considerable thickness. Bark consists of phloem, cork cambium, and cork cells. The cork cells are produced by the cork cambium. The inner, younger portion of the bark is alive, while the outer, older portion is dead tissue. Bark is continually produced as the stem grows in diameter. As the stem size increases, the older outer bark cracks and peels off and is replaced by new bark.

18-12   Monocot Stems

Herbaceous monocot stems. Most monocots have herbaceous stems. Corn is a typical herbaceous monocot. Enclosing the soft, green stem is a protective epidermis (see Figure 18-15).

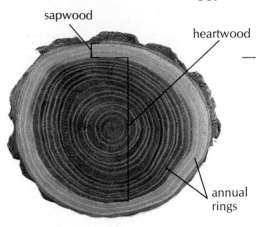

Figure 18-14. Annual Rings. Each year's growth is visible as an annual ring in the cross section because of differences in spring and summer wood.

Figure 18-15. Cross Section of a Herbaceous Monocot Stem. In corn, a herbaceous monocot, the vascular bundles are scattered throughout the tissues of the stem. Because no cambium is present, there is little growth in stem diameter.

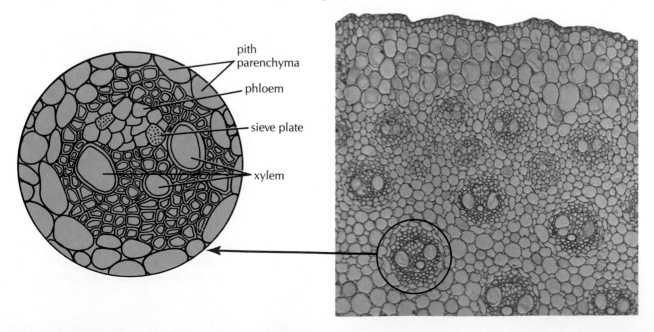

pith
parenchyma

phloem

sieve plate

xylem

The epidermis is dotted with small openings, the stomates, that allow an exchange of gases between the internal tissues of the stem and the atmosphere.

Under the epidermis is a layer of chloroplast-containing cells. This layer of photosynthetic cells is interrupted by fiber cells that stiffen and support the stem. The interior of the corn stem is made up of parenchyma cells throughout which vascular bundles are scattered. Each bundle contains xylem and phloem enclosed by supporting thick-walled cells. Unlike most herbaceous dicots, the stems of herbaceous monocots have no cambium. Thus, they show very little growth in diameter.

Woody monocot stems. The stems of woody monocots are similar in structure to those of herbaceous monocots. Vascular bundles are scattered throughout the stem parenchyma, and there is no vascular cambium. The stems become woody by the thickening of the walls of the parenchyma cells. Woody monocots with thick stems, such as palm trees, have a special thickening meristem located just below the apical meristem. Cells produced by this meristem determine how thick the stem forms. Once established, the stem diameter at any given point along the stem does not change. As in other plants, the apical meristem causes the increase in length of the stem and adds new leaves.

THE LEAF

Objectives:
1. Make a drawing showing the external structure of a leaf, and label the blade, petiole, and veins.
2. Draw and label a cross section of a leaf.
3. Relate the structure of a leaf to its function.

18-13   External Structure of the Leaf

A typical leaf consists of a thin, flat **blade,** and a *stalk,* or **petiole** (*pet*-ee-ohl). The petiole attaches the leaf to the stem (see Figure 18-16). The leaves of some plants, such as corn, lilies, and irises, do not have petioles. Instead, the leaf blades are attached directly to the stem. Visible on the surface of the leaf is a network of **veins.** The veins contain the vascular tissues of the leaf. The shape of the blade and the pattern of the veins vary from one type of plant to another and are characteristic of each species. Leaves are generally arranged around the stem in a way that maximizes exposure to sunlight.

18-14   Internal Structure of the Leaf

Cuticle and epidermis. Figure 18-17 shows a cross section of a leaf. The outermost layer of both the upper and lower leaf surfaces is the clear, waxy cuticle. This layer protects the inner tissues and slows down water loss from the leaf. Beneath the cuticle is the epidermis, which also protects the inner

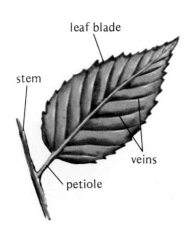

Figure 18-16. External Structure of a Leaf.

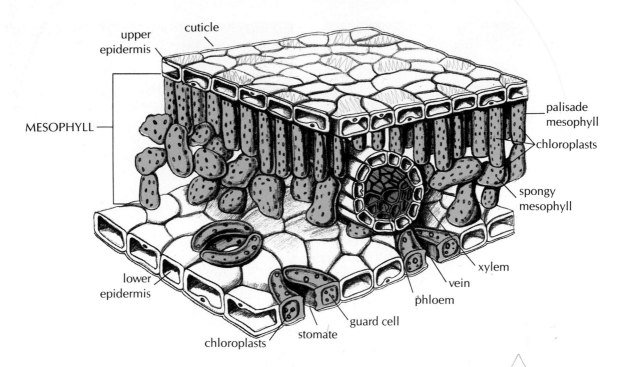

upper epidermis
cuticle
MESOPHYLL
palisade mesophyll
chloroplasts
spongy mesophyll
xylem
vein
phloem
lower epidermis
guard cell
stomate
chloroplasts

Figure 18-17. Cross Section of a Leaf.

tissues. The epidermal layer is only one cell thick. The cells are flattened and fit together like the pieces of a jigsaw puzzle. Most cells of the epidermis are clear, containing little or no pigment. This allows light to reach the photosynthetic tissues below.

Scattered through the epidermis are small openings called **stomates** (*stoh*-mayts). There are generally many more stomates on the lower surface of the leaf than on the upper surface. The stomates allow the exchange of carbon dioxide and oxygen between the internal tissues of the leaf and the environment. Water vapor also passes out of the leaf through the stomates. The stomates are not open continuously. Instead, they open and close according to the needs of the leaf. Each stomate is surrounded by a pair of specialized epidermal cells called **guard cells**. The kidney-shaped guard cells regulate the opening and closing of the stomates. The mechanisms by which this is accomplished are described in Chapter 19 (page 316).

Mesophyll. Between the upper and lower layers of epidermis is a layer of photosynthetic tissue called **mesophyll** (*mez*-uh-fil). In some species the mesophyll contains two types of thin-walled cells. The upper portion of the mesophyll is called **palisade** (pal-uh-*sayd*) **mesophyll.** It is one or two cells in thickness. This layer consists of tall, tightly packed cells filled with chloroplasts. Below the palisade layer is the **spongy mesophyll.** This layer consists of irregularly shaped cells separated by large air spaces. The stomate openings of the lower epidermis are continuous with the intercellular air spaces of the spongy mesophyll. The cells of the spongy mesophyll contain fewer chloroplasts than the cells of the palisade layer.

 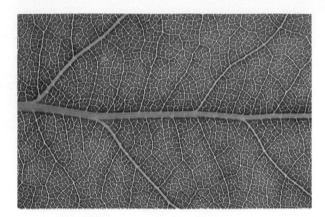

Figure 18-18. Vein Patterns in Leaves. A monocot leaf (left) typically has parallel veins. A dicot leaf (right) has a network arrangement of veins.

Veins. Within the mesophyll layer is a network of veins. The veins contain the vascular tissues. The vein network is so fine that no mesophyll cell is far from a vein. The xylem and phloem of the leaf veins are continuous with the xylem and phloem of the stem and roots. There are distinct differences between the vein patterns of monocot and dicot leaves. In the leaves of monocots, the main veins usually run parallel to one another along the length of the leaf. In dicots, the veins form a network of branches.

Chapter Review

SUMMARY

- Plants are made up of various types of tissues that form organs. Mature plants are composed of meristematic tissues, protective tissues, vascular tissues, and fundamental tissues.

- Roots anchor the plant in the soil and absorb water and minerals from the soil. Plants develop two types of roots: primary roots and secondary roots. Most plants form either a taproot system or a fibrous root system.

- The root tip is divided into zones along its length: the root cap, the meristematic zone, the elongation zone, and the maturation zone.

- The cells of the root epidermis have hairlike projections that increase the surface area for absorbing water and minerals. The root cortex serves as the site of food storage.

- Herbaceous dicot stems are soft and green. Their vascular bundles are arranged in a circle around the pith. In woody dicot stems, the xylem and phloem are arranged in concentric rings with cambium between them. Externally, a dormant twig of a woody dicot has a terminal bud at its end, and lateral buds above the point of attachment of leaves.

- In herbaceous and woody monocots, the vascular bundles are scattered throughout. Neither type of monocot stem contains cambium.

- Leaves are the major sites of photosynthesis in the plant. They usually consist of vascular tissues and a thin, clear epidermis that is covered by a waxy cuticle. Between the top and bottom epidermis are the mesophyll layers. Stomates allow the exchange of gases between the leaf tissues and the atmosphere.

KNOW THE TERMS

bark	fundamental tissue	monocot	spongy mesophyll
blade	guard cell	palisade mesophyll	stem
cork	herbaceous stem	petiole	stomate
cork cambium	lateral bud	phloem	terminal bud
cortex	leaf	pith	vascular bundle
cuticle	lenticel	primary root	vascular cambium
dicot	maturation zone	protective tissue	vascular cylinder
differentiation	meristem	root	vascular tissue
elongation zone	meristematic tissue	root cap	vein
endodermis	meristematic zone	root hair	woody stem
epidermis	mesophyll	secondary root	xylem

SECTION QUESTIONS

Plant Tissues

1. Name the organs of a plant.
2. What type of tissue produces new plant cells?
3. Name two kinds of protective tissue.
4. What two conductive tissues are found in plants?
5. List the fundamental tissues found in plants.

The Root

6. What types of root systems are found in plants?
7. What happens in the maturation zone?
8. Which root cells greatly increase absorption?

The Stem

9. Name two types of stems.
10. What is a dicot?
11. Where does active cell division occur in the woody dicot stem?
12. What stem tissue produces growth in diameter?

The Leaf

13. List the visible parts of a leaf.
14. What layer slows down water loss from a leaf?
15. Where does photosynthesis occur in the leaf?

KNOW THE FACTS

Copy the number of each statement below on a sheet of paper. Beside each number, write whether the statement is true or false. If the statement is false, replace the italicized word(s) with a term that will make the statement true.

1. The protective tissue cork is formed by cork *cambium.*

2. *Phloem* conducts water and minerals from the roots upward through the stem.

3. Parenchyma is a tissue composed of *unspecialized* cells with thin cell walls.
4. The first structure to emerge from a sprouting seed is the *primary root.*
5. In a *fibrous* root system, the primary root grows the most rapidly and remains the largest root.
6. Each year, the *entire root* of a tree grows in length.
7. The *elongation zone* covers the root tip.
8. The *cortex* of the root stores food, mainly starch.
9. Plants with *herbaceous* stems usually live for many years.
10. Flowering plants are divided into two major groups, depending on whether their seeds have one or two *cotyledons.*
11. During the growing season, *lateral buds* may form a new twig.
12. The *heartwood* conducts water up the stem.
13. Most monocots have *woody stems.*
14. *Guard cells* regulate the opening and closing of the stomates.
15. The veins of a leaf contain *xylem* and *phloem.*

UNDERSTAND THE CONCEPTS

16. Identify the function of each kind of plant organ.
17. What is the role of apical meristems?
18. Describe the epidermis and explain how it performs its function.
19. What are the functions of the root?
20. List in order, beginning with the root cap, the different zones of cellular activity in the root tip. Describe the cellular activities within each zone.
21. What occurs when root cells differentiate?
22. The root is a specialized organ for anchoring the plant and absorbing water and minerals. Describe the characteristics of the root that enable it to perform its functions.
23. What are lenticels? What is their function?
24. How does growth occur in the woody dicot stem?
25. What are annual rings, and how are they produced?
26. Draw a dormant twig of a woody dicot and label its main structures.
27. What makes a woody monocot stem woody?
28. Where does growth occur in woody monocot stems? Does the stem increase in diameter?
29. Describe the structure of a leaf in cross section.
30. Explain how vascular plants obtain oxygen from the environment and get rid of carbon dioxide and water vapor.

THINK CRITICALLY

31. How would each of the following characteristics of meristematic cells be advantageous in rapid cell division: (a) thin walls; (b) no vacuoles; (c) much smaller size than mature cells?
32. Why would the functional efficiency of xylem cells increase after they were dead?
33. When a sugar maple tree is tapped in the late winter, from which vascular tissue is the sweet liquid withdrawn? Why must this process be carefully monitored?
34. When exposed to air and moisture, the outer layer of mortar that holds adjacent bricks together in a wall gradually softens to a crumbly consistency. What effect might an ivy plant, growing up the side of a building, have on this crumbling process?
35. What evolutionary advantage do plants with woody stems have?
36. Compare and contrast herbaceous dicot and woody dicot stems in the following categories: (a) means of support, (b) external appearance, (c) arrangement of vascular tissue, (d) consistency of central region.

THINK CREATIVELY

37. Design an experiment that would show where root growth occurs.
38. Root cells absorb water by osmosis. What would happen to water absorption in the roots if a large amount of salt were dumped on the soil around the plant?

FOR FURTHER INVESTIGATION

1. Make a collection of different types of leaves. Examine them individually, then compare and contrast them with one another. Without consulting a reference book, try to classify them as monocots or dicots. Consult a reference to determine how accurate your classification was.
2. Start bean plants from seed. From some seedlings, remove both cotyledons; from others, remove one cotyledon. Leave some intact. Compare the growth over a period of time.
3. Obtain a herbaceous land plant and a large aquatic plant such as a water lily. Compare the roots, stems, and leaves of the two types of plant, and analyze how each is adapted to its environment.
4. Prepare a report on one of the career opportunities listed below. See suggested procedures, p. 9, "For Further Investigation" Activity 3.
   a. Botanist
   b. Florist
   c. Tree surgeon
6. Prepare a brief report on the life and scientific contributions of one of the following scientists:
   a. Sophia H. Eckerson
   b. Matthias Schleiden
   c. Frits W. Went
   d. Lorna Maneum Shields

FOR FURTHER READING

Baggett, James, "The Science of Tree Rings," *Scholastic Science World*, April 12, 1985.

Laetsch, Watson M., *Plants: Basic Concepts in Botany*, Little, Brown and Co., Boston, 1979.

Nadkarni, Nalini M., "Roots That Go Out on a Limb," *Natural History*, February, 1985.

Sandued, Kjell, "The Plant World's Leafy Spectacle," *Smithsonian*, April, 1985.

Thomas, Barry, *The Evolution of Plants and Flowers*, St. Martin's Press, New York, 1981.

Trefil, James, "Concentric Clues from Growth Rings Unlock the Past," *Smithsonian*, July, 1985.

Chapter 19

PLANT MAINTENANCE

The efficient functioning of a leaf depends upon the system of veins that carry materials to and from the leaf tissue.

TRANSPORT

Objectives:
1. Describe the process of transpiration and the factors that affect it.
2. Explain the mechanism of transport of fluid in the xylem of plants, describing each of the factors involved.
3. Describe the transport of nutrients in plants.

Plants, like animals, must carry out the basic life processes to remain alive. These processes include transport, nutrition, excretion, cellular respiration, synthesis, and reproduction. In terms of the life processes, the major difference between plants and animals is the capacity of green plants to synthesize the organic nutrients they need by the process of photosynthesis. Because the plant synthesizes its nutrients, it does not need the kinds of complex organ systems for locomotion, ingestion, digestion, circulation, or excretion that animals possess. The necessary functions are carried out by specialized tissues.

In this chapter we will discuss all the life processes of plants except photosynthesis and reproduction, which are discussed in separate chapters.

19-1   Transpiration

Transpiration (tranz-puh-*ray*-shun) is the loss from a plant of water in the form of water vapor. Most transpiration takes place by evaporation through the stomates of the leaves, but

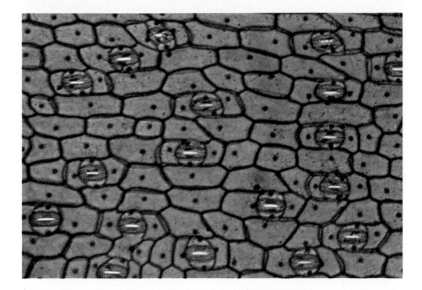

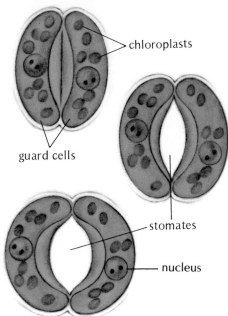

Figure 19-1. Stomates and Guard Cells. A light microscopic view of a leaf surface reveals many stomates in the open position. The drawing shows how a stomate opens when the walls of the guard cells buckle outward.

some also occurs through the cuticle and through the lenticels of the stem. Transpiration is closely related to the plant's need to exchange carbon dioxide and oxygen with the atmosphere. For these gases to diffuse through the plant cell membranes, the cell surfaces must be moist. The internal surfaces of leaf cells are kept moist by water drawn up from the roots. This water continuously evaporates into the intercellular spaces of the leaf and passes out through the stomates. Large quantities of water are removed from the soil and released into the atmosphere as the result of transpiration. During the summer, one large tree can give off as much as 250 liters of water each day. The evaporation of water from the leaves removes heat. Thus transpiration also has a cooling effect on the plant.

The rate of transpiration is regulated by the opening and closing of the stomates of the leaves. The stomates are generally closed when there is a shortage of water in the leaves, when the temperature is low, or when there is little light. They are open only when there is adequate water and when an exchange of gases with the environment is necessary, as during photosynthesis.

The opening and closing of each stomate is controlled by the pair of guard cells that surrounds it. The guard cells are sausage-shaped, and their inner walls are thicker than their outer walls (see Figure 19-1). When the guard cells become *turgid* (*ter*-jid) (filled with water and swollen), the uneven thicknesses of their walls causes them to buckle outward. The opening left between the two cells is the stomate. When the guard cells lose water and become less turgid, they resume their original shape, and the stomate closes.

The mechanism by which guard cells reversibly gain and lose water, and thus open or close stomates, is an osmotic process. The guard cells take up water by accumulating a higher concentration of solutes than that present in the surrounding water.

Consequently water from the surrounding tissue diffuses into the guard cells causing the stomates to open. When guard cells release the solutes, water diffuses back into the adjacent tissues, and the stomates close.

Research has established that the major solute involved in guard cell function is the potassium ion. The concentration of potassium ions in the guard cells of open stomates is many times higher than in the guard cells of closed stomates. In guard cell membranes ATP is used to power an active transport system that pumps potassium ions into the cells. At least part of the ATP needed for this process is supplied during photosynthesis by the chloroplasts of the guard cells. Guard cells usually are the only epidermal cells that contain chloroplasts. No ATP is needed for stomates to close. The active transport system simply stops, allowing potassium and other solutes to freely diffuse from the guard cells.

Although light is an important factor affecting stomate opening, carbon dioxide concentration *in the leaf* appears to be more critical. A low concentration causes stomates to open, even in complete darkness. A high concentration causes stomates to close, even in light. However, scientists do not know how these environmental factors act to turn on or off the active transport system that controls guard cell solute concentrations.

19-2   Transport in the Xylem

Water and dissolved minerals absorbed by the roots from the soil travel upward through the xylem of the roots, stems, and leaves of the plant. In tall trees, such as redwoods and Douglas firs, water is raised to heights of more than 125 meters. The mechanism by which this is accomplished has long puzzled botanists. It cannot be a matter of active transport within the xylem, because xylem does not contain living cells. Two processes that can be easily observed are part of the answer. These are capillary action and root pressure. However, their effects are not strong enough to be the whole answer. In recent years a process called transpiration pull has been proposed to complete the picture.

Capillary action. Capillary action, or *capillarity* (kap-uh-*lar*-uh-tee), is the upward movement of a liquid in a tube of narrow diameter. As you can see in Figure 19-2, the water in the tubes has risen above the surface of the water in the container. How far the water rises depends on the diameter of the tube—the narrower the tube, the higher the water rises.

There are two factors involved in capillary action—adhesion and cohesion. *Adhesion* (ad-*hee*-zhun) is an attractive force between unlike molecules. Thus, there is an attractive force between the water molecules and the glass sides of the tube. Because of adhesion, water creeps up the sides of the tube. *Cohesion* (koh-*hee*-zhun) is an attractive force between identical or similar molecules. Thus, there is an attractive force between the water molecules in the tube. Water moving up the

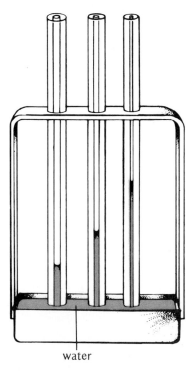

water

Figure 19-2. Capillary Action. The upward movement of water in tubes of small diameter involves the forces of adhesion and cohesion. The water rises highest in the narrowest tube.

sides of the tube pulls other water molecules up with it because of cohesion.

Xylem is similar to a narrow tube. Water will rise in it as the result of capillary action. However, the most that capillary action can do is to raise water several centimeters.

Root pressure. When the stem of a well-watered plant is cut off close to the soil, sap flows from the stump. If a glass tube is attached to the cut end of the stump, sap rises in the tube to a height of 1 meter or so (see Figure 19-3). The pressure that holds up the column of water is **root pressure,** an osmotic pressure in the root cells. The situation is very much like the demonstration of osmosis in Figure 5-16 (page 81). The cytoplasm of the root cells has a higher concentration of dissolved materials than the water in the soil. Therefore, water diffuses into the cells by osmosis and produces an osmotic pressure. This pressure drives the water into and up the xylem of the central cylinder. There is also evidence that active transport plays a part in generating root pressure. Some plant physiologists believe that the cells of the endodermis, which surround the vascular cylinder of the root, act as an active transport membrane, pumping solute into the xylem. In any event, root pressure cannot account for more than about a meter of the rise of the sap in stems.

Transpiration pull. In the latest theory of upward movement of water, the sap in the xylem of a tall plant is viewed as a continuous column of liquid. This column extends from the roots, through the stem, and into the leaves (see Figure 19-4). It is held together by the cohesive forces of the water molecules. As a result of transpiration from the leaves, molecules evaporate from the upper end of the column of water. As this occurs, other molecules are drawn into the leaf tissues to replace them. These molecules, through cohesion, exert a pull, or tension, on the ones below them. In this way, the entire column of water is slowly pulled up. At the base of the column (the roots), water molecules constantly move into the xylem to keep the column intact. According to this theory, water is not pushed up, but *pulled* up, through the xylem as transpiration occurs. Experiments have shown that this process, called **transpiration pull,** can account for the movement of water to the tops of the tallest trees.

19-3   Translocation

The movement of dissolved inorganic and organic materials through a plant is called **translocation** (tranz-loh-*kay*-shun). Minerals and other inorganic substances absorbed from the soil are transported upward through the plant in the xylem. Some of these substances are absorbed and used as needed by individual cells. Others are circulated from place to place within the plant, depending on where they are needed at a particular time. Circulation of these substances takes place in the phloem.

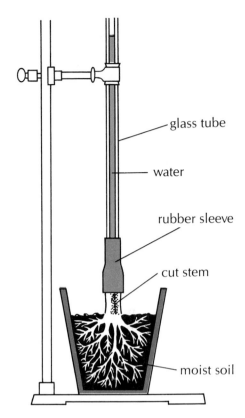

glass tube

water

rubber sleeve

cut stem

moist soil

Figure 19-3. Root Pressure. Root pressure, an osmotic pressure in the root cells, can hold up a column of water about 1 meter high.

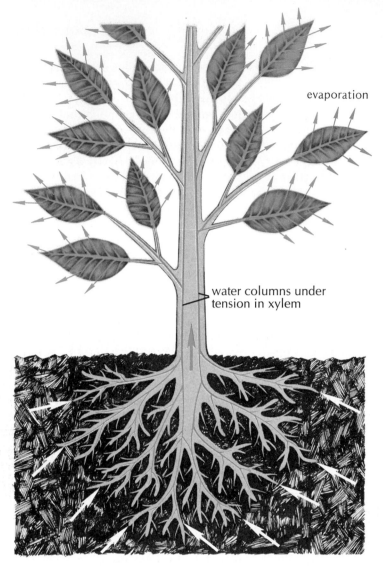

evaporation

water columns under
tension in xylem

Figure 19-4. Transpiration Pull. As water molecules evaporate from the stomates of the leaves, other water molecules are drawn up the column to replace them. Transpiration pull can account for the movement of water through xylem.

Sugars and other nutrients are produced by photosynthesis in the leaves of plants. These nutrients are transported as needed to all other parts of the plant. The translocation of these dissolved organic compounds occurs through the sieve tubes of the phloem. The movement of substances in the phloem can be either upward or downward. Furthermore, different substances in adjacent sieve cells can move in opposite directions, and the direction of movement can change very quickly. Although movement of materials in the phloem generally occurs in the direction of the concentration gradient, it can also occur against the concentration gradient, a process requiring active transport.

The movement of water and minerals in the xylem is a passive, mechanical process because the cells of the xylem are dead. The cells of the phloem, however, are alive. If they are killed, the movement of materials in the phloem stops. The movement of materials through the phloem is very rapid, much more rapid than can be explained by simple diffusion. Several theories have been developed to explain this rapid movement. However, none is completely satisfactory. The most widely accepted theory at this time is the *pressure flow theory*. According to this theory, the rapid movement of soluble materials occurs because of differences in osmotic pressure in different parts of the column of sieve cells. Where cells have a high concentration of dissolved substances, as in the leaves, water enters by osmosis. This produces an osmotic pressure that forces the dissolved substances into adjacent cells. The concentration of the dissolved substances therefore increases in these cells. Water now enters these cells, and the process is repeated from cell to cell. Where cells have a low concentration of dissolved substances because sugars are being used up, water will leave by osmosis. The osmotic pressure inside the cells will therefore drop, and materials will be forced in from adjacent cells.

EXCRETION

Objectives:
1. Describe the exchange of respiratory gases between green plants and the environment, and also the use of carbon dioxide and oxygen produced by cellular respiration and photosynthesis.
2. Describe how nitrogenous wastes and other wastes are treated in plants.

19-4 Gas Exchange

In green plants, not all metabolic wastes are excreted; some are used by the plant. This is true to some extent for oxygen and carbon dioxide. Plants carry on cellular respiration both day and night. Oxygen, which is needed for cellular respiration, is a by-product of photosynthesis. During the day, when photosynthesis is occurring, some of the oxygen produced is used for cellular respiration. The rest diffuses out of the plant through the stomates of the leaves. Carbon dioxide, which is an end product of cellular respiration, is used in photosynthesis. Thus, during the day, the carbon dioxide produced by cellular respiration is used in photosynthesis. At night, when there is no photosynthesis going on, carbon dioxide is excreted through the stomates and lenticels.

19-5 Nitrogenous and Other Wastes

Nitrogenous, or nitrogen-containing, wastes are normally excreted by animals, but may be used by plants. When, for example, there are excess amino acids, the amino group (NH_2) is removed, and the nitrogen is used in the synthesis of other compounds required by the plant.

Other wastes may be stored within vacuoles in certain cells, either in solution or as crystals. Spinach, for example, stores

Sidelight

Poisonous Plants

Many plant tissues are poisonous. Despite their beauty, some lovely flowers, green leaves, and bright berries and pods can be extremely dangerous. Each year, several thousand people are treated after ingesting poisonous plant tissues. With regard to children, plants are among the top ten causes of poisoning. Since they are particularly attracted to colorful beans, berries, and pods, young children especially should be cautioned about placing plant tissues in their mouths.

Plants from gardens, fields, forest and marsh, house plants, and parts of some vegetables can be toxic. Castor beans, wisteria seed pods, yew berries and leaves, poinsettia (shown above), and the tissues of azaleas, laurel, and rhododendron are a few common ornamental plants that pose a threat.

Even some crop plants may have poisonous parts. The leaves of potato and rhubarb are poisonous, as are the pits of peaches, cherries, and apricots. Furthermore, not all poisonous plants need to be ingested to cause harm. Some, like poison ivy and poison sumac, irritate the skin and eyes. If handled properly, however, some plant poisons, like aconite and strychnine, can be used as medicines.

oxalic acid crystals in the vacuoles of its leaf cells.

Actively dividing meristematic cells grow away from their waste materials. The wastes are simply left behind in the cells produced by these tissues.

NUTRITION AND SYNTHESIS

Objectives:
1. Name the various types of nutrients required by plants.
2. List the basic types of nutrients that can be synthesized by plants.

19-6   Plant Nutrients

Plants are able to synthesize the carbohydrates, proteins, and other organic compounds they need. However, to do so, they need inorganic raw materials. For making carbohydrates, they need water and carbon dioxide, which provide hydrogen, oxygen, and carbon. For amino acids and proteins, they need a source of nitrogen. Some plants are supplied with usable nitrogen compounds by bacteria that live in their roots. Most, however, must obtain nitrogen compounds from the soil. Plants must also obtain various inorganic substances, called minerals, from the soil. Minerals required by plants include compounds of magnesium, iron, phosphorus, calcium, and sulfur. Magnesium and iron are needed for the synthesis of chlorophyll. Copper, zinc, and a few other mineral elements are needed in very small, or trace, amounts. A deficiency of any of these elements can have serious effects on plant growth (see Figure 19-5).

19-7   Plant Synthesis

Plants have the capacity to synthesize a wide variety of complex organic substances. They are able to synthesize amino acids, proteins, carbohydrates, lipids, nucleic acids, and vitamins. Certain plants also synthesize unusual organic compounds that humans have found useful. For example, digitalis, morphine, and quinine are plant products that are used as drugs. Other plants produce substances that are used in making beverages—for example, cocoa beans, coffee beans, tea leaves, ginger root, and cola nuts.

Figure 19-5. Plant Nutrients. The healthy plant (left) was grown with an adequate supply of minerals, such as magnesium, copper, and iron. The smaller, less healthy plant (right) was grown in a mineral-deficient medium.

HORMONES AND GROWTH RESPONSES

Objectives:
1. Describe the effects of auxins on different parts of the plant.
2. Define the term *tropism.*
3. Describe positive phototropism in a stem.

4. Describe the various effects of gibberellins on plant growth.
5. Explain how plant growth is coordinated by the interaction of various hormones.
6. Define the term *photoperiodism*.

19-8   Plant Hormones

Hormones play an important role in the regulation of plant functions. Like animal hormones, plant hormones are complex organic compounds that act as chemical messengers. They affect cell metabolism, cell division, and plant growth in general. Most hormones are synthesized by actively dividing meristematic tissues at the tips of roots and stems.

There are a number of different types of hormones in plants, but the three most important kinds are auxins, gibberellins, and cytokinins. These hormones affect the growth of various plant tissues.

Auxins. Auxins (*awk*-sinz) are hormones that affect the growth of all types of plant tissues. Whether growth is stimulated or inhibited by auxins depends on the type of tissue and the concentration of the hormone. The most common auxin in nature is IAA, indoleacetic acid.

In the growing tips of roots and stems, auxins stimulate the differentiation of cells in the maturation zones. These new cells are initially unspecialized and nonfunctional. Under the influence of specific concentrations of auxins, they develop the characteristics of the various types of mature cells they will become.

Auxins produced by the terminal bud of a stem stimulate stem growth, but inhibit the growth of lateral buds for some distance along that stem. When a terminal bud has grown a sufficient distance away from a lateral bud, the lateral bud will begin to grow. It will become the terminal bud of a new stem. Snipping off the terminal buds of house plants will result in the development of lateral stems and produce a bushier plant.

High auxin concentrations that stimulate the growth of stems inhibit the growth of roots. However, low auxin levels stimulate growth in the roots. The development of fruits is stimulated by auxins.

Leaves, flowers, and fruits drop off the plant when a special layer of cells, called the *abscission* (ab-*sizh*-un) *layer*, forms at the point of attachment to the stem. Auxins inhibit the formation of the abscission layer and thus prevent the dropping of the structures until the proper time. Another hormone, ethylene (see page 322), stimulates production of this layer when the auxin level drops. For example, leaves fall when the production of auxins by the blade decreases.

Auxins and tropisms. A tropism (*troh*-piz-um) is a growth response of a plant to a stimulus, in which the direction of growth is related to the direction from which the stimulus is received. An easily observed tropism is *phototropism* (*foh*-toh-

Career

Plant Pathologist

Plant pathologists are doctors of plant disease. Plant diseases, caused by bacteria, fungi, and viruses, result in billions of dollars in losses annually of many different crop plants. Plant pathologists provide knowledge that helps control some of the 50,000 or so destructive plant diseases that threaten food crops, ornamental plants, and our forests. Without their work, for example, it would not be possible to grow large crops of wheat and corn in North America, sugar cane in the South, potatoes in Maine and Idaho, and sugar beets in Utah—all major crops in the North American farm economy.

Jobs for plant pathologists range from positions with agricultural chemical manufacturers, food processors, schools, and state and Federal agencies at the bachelor's degree level, to research and high-level decision-making positions at the doctoral level. Plant pathology is growing in importance as the need for higher yields of quality plant products increases.

Figure 19-6. Phototropism. The bending of the plant toward the light is positive phototropism.

troh-piz-um), the bending of a plant stem toward, or away from, a light source (see Figure 19-6). Growth of a plant toward the light is an example of a *positive tropism*—the plant grows toward the stimulus. In a *negative tropism*, the plant grows away from the direction of the stimulus. Roots, unlike stems, generally show negative phototropism—they grow away from the light source.

Another type of tropism is *geotropism (jee*-oh-*troh*-piz-um), the response of the plant to the force of gravity. Roots generally show a positive geotropism—they grow down into the earth in the direction of the force of gravity. Stems, on the other hand, generally show a negative geotropism—they grow up against the force of gravity. Other tropisms include *chemotropism,* which is a response to various chemicals; *hydrotropism,* which is a response to water; and *thigmotropism,* which is a response to touch.

The growth responses seen in tropisms result from an uneven distribution of auxins in the growing tips of roots and stems. In phototropism, for example, the concentration of auxins is higher on the shaded side of the stem than on the lighted side. The stem cells are stimulated by auxins, so those with the higher auxin concentrations (the shady side) grow faster than those with the lower concentration (the lighted side). Thus, through uneven growth, the stem bends toward the light. It is not known how the auxins become unevenly distributed in the plant tissues.

Gibberellins. **Gibberellins** (jib-uh-*rel*-inz) are hormones that affect plant growth as well as the development of fruits and seeds. Unlike auxins, gibberellins are evenly distributed throughout the plant tissues. Thus they are not involved in the uneven growth responses of tropisms. Under the influence of gibberellins, plant stems begin to grow early in the spring when temperatures are still low. In dwarf plants and plants whose stems normally show little growth (for example, cabbage), the application of gibberellins stimulates rapid stem growth. In plants with normally tall stems, gibberellins have much less effect. Gibberellins have also been found to cause seeds to sprout, to increase the size of fruits, and to cause flowering in some plants.

Other hormones. **Cytokinins** (syt-uh-*ky*-ninz) are a group of plant hormones that stimulate cell division and growth. They are thought to function together with auxins in stimulating the differentiation of different plant tissues. **Ethylene** (*eth*-uh-leen), a relatively simple organic compound, stimulates flowering in some groups of plants and hastens the ripening of fruit. **Abscisic** (ab-*siz*-ik) **acid** influences the shedding of leaves and the seasonal slowing down of plant activities.

Interaction of plant hormones. In the early phases of a plant's life, gibberellins play an important role. During seed germination these hormones promote the synthesis of enzymes that digest stored food material so that it can be used by the developing embryo. After germination, cytokinins stimulate cell division in the embryo and may influence tissue and organ formation. Auxins generally influence the growth of plants after the early stages of development.

19-9 Photoperiodism

Although light is important to plants, because it is required in photosynthesis, light also affects many aspects of plant growth and development in ways that are unrelated to its role in photosynthesis. For example, a number of plant phenomena, such as flowering, and leaf fall in autumn, are in response to changes in day length that occur over the course of the year. This response of a plant to changes in the duration of light (and of dark) is called **photoperiodism** (fo-toe-*pir*-e-uh-diz-em).

In many types of plants, flowering is dependent on the length of light and darkness in the daily cycle. At one time it was thought that the length of the light period was what induced flowering. Plants could be classified as *short-day plants*, or *long-day plants*, depending on the length of the light period required for flowering. Plants whose flowering was unaffected by the lengths of light and dark were called *day-neutral* plants.

Subsequent studies revealed that the length of uninterrupted darkness, rather than of light, was the critical factor determining flower induction. However, the names of the categories were never changed. Consequently, short-day plants are still called short-day plants, even though they are actually "long-night plants." Similarly, the term long-day plant is still used for plants that are actually "short-night plants."

Short-day plants include forsythia, tulip, chrysanthemum, aster, goldenrod, and many other plants. These plants flower in the early spring, late summer, or fall when the days are short, i.e., the nights are long. Clover, potato, corn, beet, and gladiolus are examples of long-day plants, producing flowers in summer when days are long, i.e., nights are short.

The effects of photoperiod on flowering and on other processes are the result of changes that occur in a pigment called phytochrome (*fy*-ta-krom). This pigment, which occurs in very low concentration in plant cells, has a profound influence on plant growth and development. Although the details are not yet known, changes occurring in the phytochrome molecule during the dark period bring about metabolic changes in certain plant tissues. These changes in turn may influence the production or release of certain hormones or may affect plant cells at other levels of metabolism.

Figure 19-7. Short-Day and Long-Day Plants. The morning glory (top) is a short-day plant. The poppy (bottom) is a long-day plant.

Chapter Review

SUMMARY

- In green plants, water is lost by evaporation through the stomates and cuticle of the leaves and through the lenticels of the stem. A complex physiological system controls stomatal opening by osmotically regulating the turgor pressure inside the guard cells. The upward movement of water and dissolved minerals from the roots through the stem to the leaves takes place in the xylem. It is accomplished by a combination of capillary action, root pressure, and transpiration pull. The movement through the plant of dissolved organic and inorganic materials takes place in the phloem which, unlike the xylem, operates under positive pressure and requires the expenditure of energy.

- Not all wastes are excreted by plants. Some of the oxygen produced by photosynthesis may be used in cellular respiration, while some of the carbon dioxide produced by cellular respiration may be used in photosynthesis. Nitrogenous wastes may be broken down and the nitrogen reused. Many wastes are stored in vacuoles.

- All the complex organic substances that make up the plant body are synthesized by the plants themselves. To do this they need not only the raw materials for photosynthesis (carbon dioxide and water) but also numerous minerals that exist in the soil. Deficiencies of any of these minerals seriously retard plant development.

- Plant hormones are generally produced by meristematic tissues. The three most important types of plant hormones are auxins, gibberellins, and cytokinins. All stages of plant growth and development, as well as all tropisms, are controlled by the interplay of hormones on plant tissues. Even the effects of photoperiodism on phenomena such as flowering, seed germination, dormancy, and leaf fall are thought to be influenced by hormones.

KNOW THE TERMS

abscisic acid	cytokinin	photoperiodism	transpiration
auxin	ethylene	root pressure	transpiration pull
capillary action	gibberellin	translocation	tropism

SECTION QUESTIONS

Transport

1. List the life processes carried on by plants.
2. What is transpiration?
3. Why is it impossible for xylem cells to carry on active transport?
4. What is root pressure?
5. How are dissolved organic and inorganic materials moved through a plant?

Excretion

6. When do plants carry on cellular respiration?
7. How does carbon dioxide leave the leaf?
8. What happens to nitrogen-containing wastes in plants?

Nutrition and Synthesis

9. Which organic substances are plants able to synthesize?
10. Name three plant products that are used as medicinal drugs.

Hormones and Growth Responses in Plants

11. Define the term *hormone.*
12. List several plant hormones.
13. What factors affect the growth of plants?

KNOW THE FACTS

Copy the number of each sentence below on a sheet of paper. Beside each number, write the letter identifying the answer that correctly completes the sentence.

1. Most transpiration takes place by evaporation through
   a. root hairs.
   b. stomates.
   c. turgid palisade cells.
   d. meristematic tissue.

2. The attraction of water molecules to the cell wall of a xylem vessel is known as
   a. cohesion.
   b. translocation.
   c. adhesion.
   d. diffusion.

3. Water moves from the roots of a plant to its leaves by
   a. root and osmotic pressure.
   b. adhesion and capillary action.
   c. active transport.
   d. transpiration pull.

4. Sugars and other nutrients are transported as needed through the
   a. sieve cells of phloem.
   b. vessels of xylem.
   c. companion cells of phloem.
   d. tracheids of xylem.

5. Auxins produced in the stem
   a. stimulate lateral bud growth.
   b. stimulate root growth.
   c. stimulate stem growth.
   d. inhibit differentiation of stem cells.

6. High auxin concentration
   a. inhibits stem growth.
   b. inhibits root growth.
   c. stimulates the abscission layer.
   d. increases secondary roots.

7. The bending of a stem towards a light source is a growth response called
   a. phototropism.
   b. thigmotropism.
   c. chemotropism.
   d. geotropism.

8. In plant tissues, auxins are distributed
   a. evenly.
   b. unevenly.
   c. in a diffusion gradient.
   d. periodically.

9. Under the influence of gibberellins, plant stems
   a. grow early in the spring.
   b. show little growth.
   c. grow early in summer.
   d. grow at the same rate as roots.

10. After a seed sprouts, cytokinin
    a. weakens the seed coat.
    b. influences later stages of development.
    c. inhibits tissue and organ formation.
    d. stimulates cell division.

UNDERSTAND THE CONCEPTS

11. How do guard cells control the opening and closing of the stomates?
12. Describe the processes that explain how water and dissolved minerals travel upward from a plant's roots to its leaves.
13. Define the terms *adhesion* and *cohesion*, and explain how these processes are involved in capillary action.
14. Describe transpiration pull.
15. What evidence is there that transport of material in phloem involves active transport?
16. Describe how nitrogenous wastes are handled by plants.
17. How do auxins affect the growth in various types of plant tissues?
18. What is meant by phototropism?
19. Explain how plant hormones interact within a plant.
20. What is photoperiodism?

THINK CRITICALLY

21. Plants cannot survive without transpiration, but this very process is one of the most serious causes of dehydration for the plant. Nowhere is this problem more severe than in desert ecosystems. How would each of the following desert plant adaptations help prevent water loss: (a) very small leaves (less than 1 cm each, as in mesquite, ironwood, or paloverde); (b) thick, leathery leaves (yucca, jojoba, or aloe); (c) leaves that drop off in dry weather (ocotillo, brittlebush); (d) leaves that have degenerated to nonphotosynthetic spines or thorns (cactus)?

22. The opening and closing of each stomate is controlled by an osmotic process within the guard cells that surround it. This osmotic process can be triggered by internal cues, such as the level of carbon dioxide, and external cues, such as light intensity. (a) How could each of these cues increase chances for survival? (b) Under what conditions would these cues trigger maximal opening of the stomates? Minimal opening?

23. A plant stem's terminal buds grow for some time before any lateral buds appear. How does this benefit the plant?

24. What possible evolutionary advantages would a plant gain by having auxins stimulate the growth of stems at the same time that they inhibit the growth of roots?

THINK CREATIVELY

25. Develop a list of problems that you think would arise if gardens were grown in large space stations orbiting the earth every 90 minutes.

26. Imagine that you are a commercial gardener who must produce fresh flowers in time for special holidays. How would you go about this task, when these holidays do not coincide with the natural flowering period of the plants in demand?

FOR FURTHER INVESTIGATION

1. Visit a garden center and interview a greenhouse worker. Ask about the methods used to cultivate house and garden plants. How are chemicals and hormones used? How are environmental factors manipulated to foster growth and induce flowering?

2. Write a letter to an industrial producer of plant hormones, such as auxins. Ask for materials describing how they produce the hormones. Prepare a short talk for the class.

3. Write to the United States Department of Agriculture in Washington, DC, to inquire about recent research projects in genetic engineering to improve food products.

4. Prepare a report on one of the career opportunities listed below. See suggested procedures, p. 9, "For Further Investigation" Activity 3.
   a. Farmer
   b. Agricultural engineer
   c. Plant breeder

5. Prepare a brief report on the life and contributions of one of the following scientists:
   a. H.A. Allard   c. Henrik Lundegardh
   b. Assa Gray   d. Marie Clark Taylor

FOR FURTHER READING

Baggett, James, "Hydroponics: The Science of Growing Plants Without Soil," *Scholastic Science World,* March 2, 1984.

Gwyne, P., and Carey, J., "Hormones for Profit," *Newsweek,* October 27, 1980.

Westenberg, Kerri, "Blooming Smart: How Do Plants Know When to Grow?" *Scholastic Science World,* May 10, 1985.

Zimmermann, Martin H., "Piping Water to the Tree Tops," *Natural History,* July, 1982.

Crop Pests

Today the United States enjoys an abundant food supply. However, this productivity can be maintained only through the control of destructive insects, weeds, and fungal infections. Maintaining an effective pest control program is not without problems. If adequate precautions are not taken, some control methods involve risks to the environment and to human health.

Two different approaches to pest control have been helpful. One has been the use of chemical pesticides. These are synthetic substances designed to control various crop pests. Insecticides are sprayed on plants to kill a broad spectrum of insect pests. Herbicides kill weeds. Fungicides prevent the growth of destructive fungi like rusts and smuts. Some pesticides work on the surface of plants. Others enter the tissues of the plant and work from within.

A second approach to the crop pest problem uses biological controls. This system avoids introducing synthetic chemicals into the environment. Instead, some natural event or process is exploited. For example, species that prey on insect pests can be used to control those pests. Bacteria that cause disease in specific insects can be introduced to an area. Traps containing artificial sex hormones can lure insects to their death. Also, selective breeding techniques can be used to develop crops naturally resistant to fungal infection.

The various effects of both types of pest control must be carefully considered. Chemical pesticides sometimes poison organisms other than the targeted pest. Also, many pesticides are not biodegradable. They persist in the environment in toxic form, enter the food chain, and pass harmful chemicals from organism to organism, and eventually to people.

Biological control techniques also have drawbacks. Natural controls, like chemical ones, may harm other than the targeted organisms. The introduction of a new predator may upset an area's ecological balance. Plants bred for fungal resistance sometimes produce less food per plant. The form of biological control appropriate for a specific crop may be far less effective than a pesticide. In addition, the effectiveness of both

Crop-duster planes carrying gallons of pesticide can treat huge areas in a short time.

chemical and natural pesticides may eventually be compromised if the pest species develops a resistance to the control.

Assuring an adequate food supply is a vital social concern. Many people of the world are currently undernourished, and the world's population continues to grow. Yet crop pests are still destroying about one-third of unharvested crops and about one-tenth of harvested crops. Researchers continue to face a major challenge— to find safe, effective ways to protect more of our harvests from the ravages of crop pests.

1. Compare and contrast the two major approaches to crop pest control. Discuss the advantages and disadvantages of each type.

2. Why is crop pest control such an important societal issue?

3. How might risk-benefit analysis (described on page 105) be applied to existing methods of crop pest control? How might risk assessment be used to evaluate new methods of pest control?

UNIT 4

REPRODUCTION AND DEVELOPMENT

The yucca moth and the yucca plant have a remarkable relationship. The female yucca moth deposits her eggs within the ovary of a yucca flower and then pollinates the flower. The seeds that develop serve as food for the moth larvae which, after hatching, eat some but not all of the seeds. Thus each species' reproduction is intimately tied to the other's. In this Unit, you will explore the process of reproduction in all its diversity. You will also examine different adaptations that can increase a species' reproductive efficiency.

329

Chapter 20

MITOSIS AND ASEXUAL REPRODUCTION

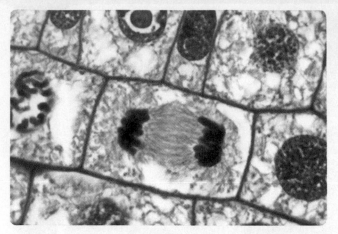

Stained onion root tip cells in various stages of cell division as seen with a light microscope.

TYPES OF REPRODUCTION

Objective:

Name and briefly describe the two basic types of reproduction.

20-1 Asexual and Sexual Reproduction

All cells arise from other cells. This occurs by the division of the original cell into two cells. In a unicellular organism, the result of the cell division is reproduction. In a multicellular organism, cell division usually results in growth in size of the organism or replacement of tissue. However, division of body cells may also be a method of reproduction in some multicellular organisms if the new cells separate from the parent and form a complete, independent individual.

There are two basic types of reproduction—asexual and sexual. In **asexual** (ay-*sek*-shuh-wul) **reproduction,** there is only one parent, and no special reproductive cells or organs are involved. The new individual is a separated part of the parent organism. **Sexual reproduction,** however, involves the union of two nuclei from special cells, which are usually produced by two separate parent organisms. Some organisms reproduce only asexually, others reproduce only sexually, and still others can reproduce by either method.

In this chapter we will discuss the process of cell division and its role in asexual reproduction. Sexual reproduction will be discussed in Chapter 21.

MITOSIS

Objectives:
1. Name and briefly describe the two basic processes involved in cell division.
2. Explain why each cell must contain a full set of chromosomes to function properly.
3. Explain what occurs during interphase.
4. List the stages of mitosis and briefly describe the events in each.
5. Explain how cytokinesis occurs in animal cells.
6. Explain how mitotic cell division differs in plant and animal cells.
7. Explain which types of cells divide frequently and which do not.
8. Discuss the mechanisms that are thought to control mitotic cell division in unicellular and in multicellular organisms.

20-2   Nuclear and Cytoplasmic Division

Cell division consists of two processes—the division of the nucleus and the division of the cytoplasm. The process by which the nucleus divides is called **mitosis** (my-*toh*-sis), and the division of the cytoplasm is called **cytokinesis** (sy-toh-kih-*nee*-sis). Prior to mitosis, a series of changes occurs in the nucleus that results in the duplication of the hereditary material. When the nucleus divides, each daughter nucleus receives a complete copy of this material. During cytokinesis, the cytoplasm of the cell is divided into two parts, each containing one of the newly formed nuclei and approximately half of the other contents of the parent cell. Cytokinesis may occur at the same time as mitosis or after mitosis is completed.

20-3   Nuclear Material

As you learned in Chapter 5, the nucleus is the control center of the cell. Without the nucleus and the hereditary material it contains, the rest of the cell quickly dies. The nucleus also plays a major role in cell division.

The hereditary material of the nucleus is DNA (deoxyribonucleic acid). The information necessary for the synthesis of all components of each cell is stored in the structure of the DNA. The DNA also includes information that determines the makeup and functions of the organism as a whole. This information must be passed on to all cells produced. In nondividing cells, DNA is found in the dark-staining nuclear material called **chromatin** (*kroh*-muh-tin), which consists of a network of long, thin, twisting threads. During cell division, the chromatin becomes organized into the rodlike structures called **chromosomes** (*kroh*-muh-sohmz) (see Figure 20-1).

Figure 20-1. Chromosome From Salivary Gland Cell of Fruit Fly.

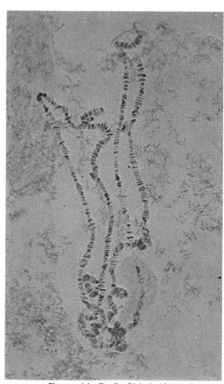

Photograph by Carolina Biological Supply Company

Figure 20-2. The Eight Chromosomes of the Fruit Fly. Note that the eight chromosomes consist of four pairs. The chromosomes in each pair are similar in size and shape.

Each type of organism has a specific and characteristic number of chromosomes in its body cells. For example, humans have 46 chromosomes, wheat has 42, fruit flies have 8, crayfish have 20, and potatoes have 48 (see Figure 20-2). The number of chromosomes in the body cells of an organism is constant. Since each chromosome contains only part of the total hereditary information, each cell must receive an entire set of chromosomes to function properly.

20-4   Interphase and Mitosis in Animal Cells

Once begun, mitosis is a continuous process. However, for convenience it is divided into stages, or phases. These stages are prophase, metaphase, anaphase, and telophase. There is no sharp distinction between these stages; each merges into the next. Figure 20-3 shows interphase and the major events of each stage of mitosis.

Interphase. When a cell is between mitotic cycles, it is in the **interphase** (*in*-ter-fayz) stage. Although interphase is also called the resting stage, the cell is never really at rest. Interphase lasts from the end of one cell division to the beginning of the next.

Figure 20-3. Interphase and Mitotic Cell Division in Animal Cells.

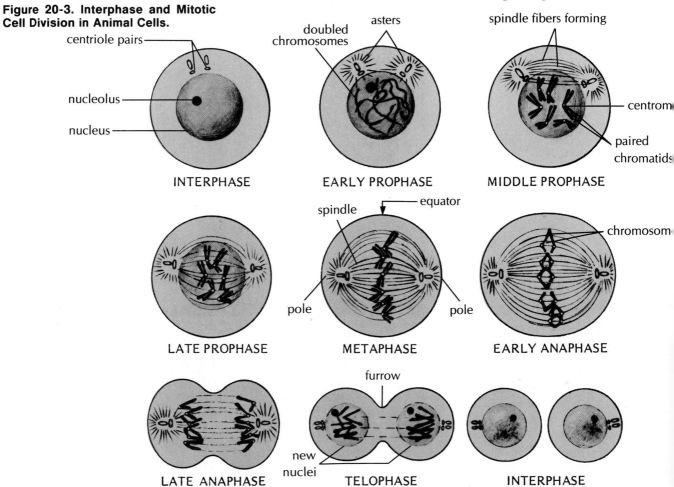

During interphase, the nucleus is synthesizing nucleic acids, the cytoplasm is synthesizing proteins, and the cell is growing. At some point before mitosis begins, each chromosome makes a copy of itself, or *replicates* (*rep*-luh-kayts), and is actually a double chromosome.

During interphase, the nucleus of the cell is bounded by the nuclear membrane, and one or more nucleoli are present (see Figure 20-4). The chromosomes are not distinguishable through the microscope at this time. Instead, the DNA appears as a tangled, threadlike mass of chromatin. Near the nucleus are the **centrioles**, two tiny, cylindrical bodies that lie at right angles to each other. The centrioles also replicate during interphase forming two pairs.

Prophase. During **prophase** (*proh*-fayz), the doubled chromosomes become visible as long threads that coil and contract into thick rods. The two halves of each double chromosome are called **chromatids** (*kroh*-muh-tidz). They are connected at a region called the **centromere** (*sen*-truh-meer) (see Figure 20-5).

At the beginning of prophase, the two pairs of centrioles move toward the opposite ends, or *poles*, of the cell. The centrioles appear to be involved in the formation of protein-containing structures that were in the past thought to be fibers. Although electron microscope studies have shown them to be microtubules, they are still referred to as fibers. Fibers extending outward from the centrioles form star-shaped structures called **asters.** Other threadlike fibers extend between the poles. These fibers form a football-shaped structure called the **spindle.** Some of the spindle fibers become attached to the centromeres of the chromosomes. As prophase progresses, the double chromosomes start moving toward the *equator*, which is the region midway between the poles (see Figure 20-6). At the end of prophase, the nuclear membrane and the nucleolus disappear.

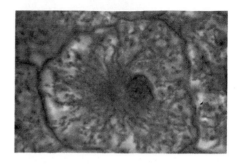

Figure 20-4. Interphase.

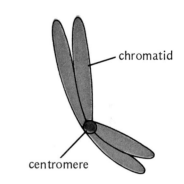

Figure 20-5. Chromatids. The two chromatids are connected at the centromere.

Figure 20-6. Prophase In early prophase (left), the double chromosomes become visible. In late prophase (right), the double chromosomes begin to move toward the cell equator, and the nuclear membrane has disappeared.

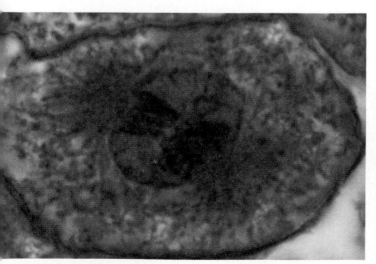

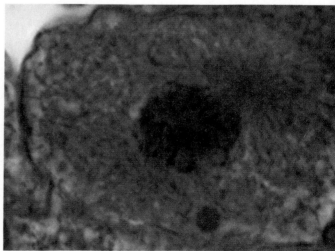

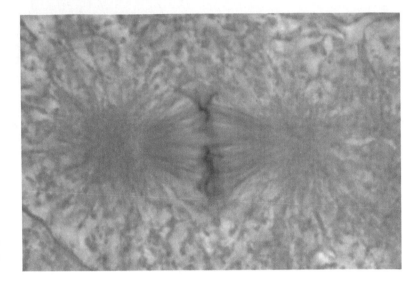

Figure 20-7. Metaphase. In metaphase, the double chromosomes are lined up at the cell equator.

Metaphase. During **metaphase** (*met*-uh-fayz), the centromeres of the double chromosomes are lined up on the equator (see Figure 20-7). At the end of metaphase, the centromeres divide, and the two chromatids of each doubled chromosome become separate, duplicate chromosomes. In other words, each double-stranded chromosome gives rise to two single-stranded, identical chromosomes.

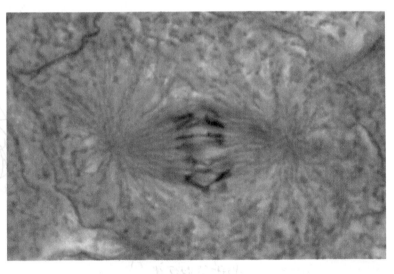

Figure 20-8. Anaphase. In anaphase, the duplicate chromosomes move to opposite poles of the cell.

Anaphase. In anaphase (*an*-uh-fayz), the duplicate chromosomes move apart to opposite poles (see Figure 20-8). The spindle fibers aid in this movement, which results in one complete set of chromosomes going to one pole while the other identical complete set goes to the other pole.

Telophase. Telophase (*tel*-uh-fayz) begins when the chromosomes reach the poles. The chromosomes elongate, uncoil, and gradually assume the threadlike appearance of chromatin (see Figure 20-9). The spindle and asters disappear. A nuclear

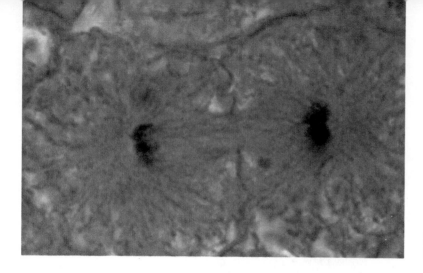

Figure 20-9. Telophase. In telophase, two daughter nuclei form.

membrane forms around each daughter nucleus, and the nucleoli reappear. This completes the nuclear division of an animal cell.

20-5   Cytokinesis in Animal Cells

Cytokinesis often begins during late anaphase and is completed during telophase. In animal cells, the division of the cytoplasm is accomplished by a pinching-in of the cell membrane. This furrow occurs in the middle of the cell and results in the formation of two daughter cells of about the same size (see Figure 20-10).

Figure 20-10. Cytokinesis. Division of the cytoplasm occurs by a pinching-in of the cell membrane, forming a furrow in the middle of the cell (left). The two daughter cells formed are approximately equal in size (right).

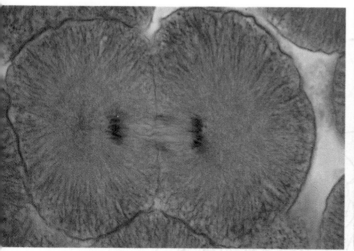
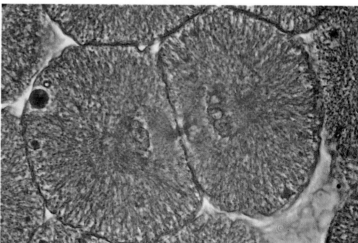

20-6   Mitosis and Cytokinesis in Plant Cells

Cell division in plants can be observed fairly easily in developing seeds and in the growing regions of roots and stems. The main events of nuclear division are the same in plants as in animals (see Figure 20-11). However, division in plant cells differs from that in animal cells in two ways. First, plant cells do not have centrioles. Thus, there is no formation of asters. But a spindle does form, and the movement of the chromosomes is the same as in animal cells. Second, the rigid cell wall of plant cells does not pinch in during telophase. Instead, a structure

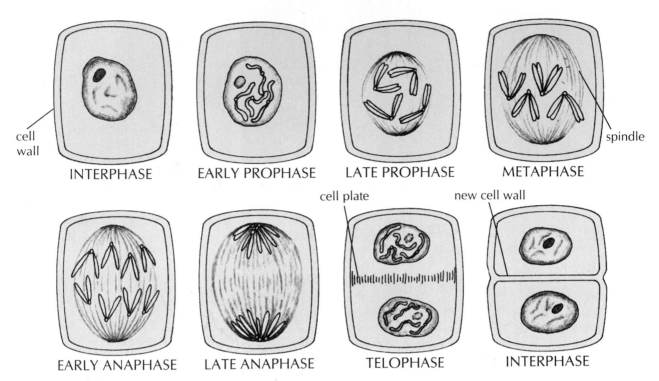

Figure 20-11. Interphase and Mitotic Cell Division in Plant Cells.

called the **cell plate** forms across the middle of the cell (see Figure 20-12). The cell plate grows outward and joins the old cell wall, thus dividing the cell in half. New cell wall material is secreted on each side of the cell plate.

20-7   Time Span of Mitotic Cell Division

The time required for a cell to pass through all the stages of mitosis varies from one type of organism to another and from one type of tissue to another. In general, the interphase period is long compared with the stages of mitotic cell division. For example, a human cell in tissue culture takes about 1 hour to divide and then remains in interphase for 16 to 20 hours.

Mitosis is most frequent in cells that are least specialized. Most cells in a developing embryo divide at a very rapid rate. However, as the embryo matures, cells become specialized, and the rate of mitosis decreases. In adults, frequent cell division is restricted to certain tissues. Some cells, such as cambium and root tips in plants and bone marrow and skin epithelial cells in animals, divide at a rapid rate. Specialized cells, such as xylem, nerve, and muscle cells, seldom or never divide once they are formed.

20-8   Control of Mitotic Cell Division

The mechanisms or factors that start and control mitotic cell division are not known. In unicellular organisms, it is thought that an increase in cell size triggers mitotic cell division. As a cell enlarges, its volume increases faster than its surface area

Figure 20-12. Cytokinesis in Plant Cells. In plant cells the cytoplasm is divided in half by formation of a cell plate.

Photograph by Carolina Biological Supply Company

—in this case, the area of the cell membrane. When cell size increases above a certain point, the surface area of the membrane becomes inadequate for the necessary exchange of materials between the cell interior and the environment. Thus, for a cell to function, there is an upper limit to its size. When a cell reaches the maximum size characteristic of its type, it either stops growing or it divides.

In complex multicellular organisms, some cells divide regularly, others divide very rarely or not at all once they are formed, and still others divide only under certain circumstances. Normally, cell division occurs only as needed for tissue repair or growth. It is possible that the cells themselves regulate their own division by secreting a control substance that acts through a negative feedback mechanism (see page 268). According to this hypothesis, when the number of cells is normal, the concentration of the control substance that they secrete is high enough to prevent cell division. If the number of cells decreases, the concentration of control substance also decreases, thus permitting cell division to occur until the normal cell population is restored.

Occasionally a group of cells begins to divide in an uncontrolled fashion, invading surrounding tissue and interfering with normal organ functions. Such uncontrolled cell division is called cancer. Understanding the factors that normally initiate and control cell division would be of great help in controlling cancer.

ASEXUAL REPRODUCTION

Objectives:
1. Describe the process of binary fission in bacteria, ameba, and paramecium.
2. Describe budding in yeast and hydra.
3. Describe spore formation in bread mold.
4. Explain regeneration, and name three types of animals in which regeneration can be a form of reproduction.
5. Briefly describe each of the various types of natural and artificial vegetative reproduction.
6. Explain why farmers or gardeners might prefer to use artificial vegetative reproduction of plants rather than growing plants from seed.

Unicellular organisms, many simple animals, and many plants reproduce asexually, at least during part of their life cycles. In asexual reproduction in multicellular organisms, the offspring develop from undifferentiated, unspecialized cells of the parent.

Because asexual reproduction involves only mitotic cell division, each offspring has exactly the same hereditary informa-

tion as its parent. The offspring show little variation—that is, they are all nearly identical to each other and to the parent. Thus asexual reproduction results in stable characteristics within a species from one generation to the next.

Asexual reproduction is efficient in that it is generally rapid and often results in the production of large numbers of offspring. There are several types of asexual reproduction, including binary fission, budding, spore formation, regeneration, and vegetative reproduction.

20-9 Binary Fission

In the simplest form of asexual reproduction, **binary fission** (*by*-nehr-ee *fish*-un), the parent organism divides into two approximately equal parts. Each of the daughter cells becomes a separate individual and grows to normal size. No parent is left by this method of reproduction because the parent has become two individuals. Binary fission is the usual method of reproduction among one-celled organisms, including bacteria, protozoa, and many algae. In binary fission in cells that contain a distinct nucleus, the nucleus divides by mitosis.

Fission in Bacteria. Bacteria lack an organized nucleus. The hereditary material is in the form of a single circular chromosome. Prior to cell division, the chromosome replicates. A cell wall forms near the center of the parent cell, dividing it into two daughter cells, each containing one of the replicated chromosomes (see Figure 20-13). Each daughter cell grows to normal size before it divides. Sometimes the daughter cells do not separate from each other, thereby forming chains of bacteria. Under favorable conditions some bacteria can divide every 20 minutes.

Fission in Protozoa. When an ameba reaches full size, it rounds up, and the nucleus undergoes mitosis. After nuclear division, the cytoplasm in the middle of the cell pinches in, or constricts, producing two daughter cells (see Figure 20-14). The two resulting cells are both smaller than the original parent cell, but they eventually grow to full size.

The paramecium has two nuclei, a *micronucleus* (my-kroh-*noo*-klee-us) and a *macronucleus* (mak-roh-*noo*-klee-us). The small micronucleus controls the reproductive functions of the

Figure 20-13. Binary Fission in Bacteria.

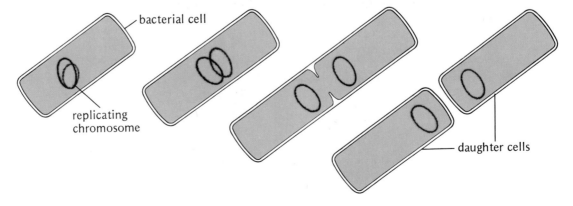

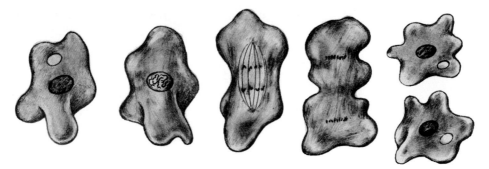

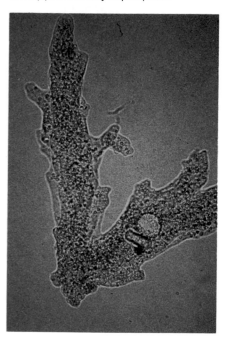

Figure 20-14. Binary Fission in the Ameba. In fission, the nucleus divides by mitosis and the cytoplasm divides into two approximately equal parts.

cell. During binary fission, the micronucleus divides by mitosis. The macronucleus divides by a modified mitosis. One of each kind of nucleus goes to each daughter cell. The oral groove and gullet also replicate, and two new contractile vacuoles appear. Thus, before separation occurs, the parts necessary for two complete organisms are present. Division of the cytoplasm occurs when the middle of the cell pinches in. The paramecium can also reproduce sexually.

20-10   Budding

Budding is a type of asexual reproduction in which the parent organism divides into two unequal parts. New individuals develop as small outgrowths, or buds, on the outer surface of the parent organism. The buds may break off and live independently or they may remain attached, forming a colony. Budding differs from binary fission in that the parent and offspring are not of equal size. Budding occurs in yeast and hydra, as well as in sponges and some worms.

Budding in yeast. When a yeast cell reaches a certain size, the nucleus moves toward the side of the cell. The cell wall there is softened by an enzyme so that it bulges outward, forming a small knoblike structure called a *bud* (see Figure 20-15). The nucleus then undergoes mitosis, producing two daughter nuclei. One daughter nucleus moves into the bud, while the other remains in the parent cell. A cell wall forms between the parent cell and the bud. The bud may remain attached to the parent cell or it can separate from it. In either case, the bud is an independent cell that can increase in size and eventually produce its own buds.

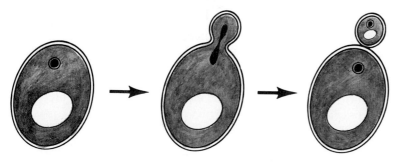

Figure 20-15. Budding in Yeast. Budding differs from binary fission in that the cytoplasm divides unequally.

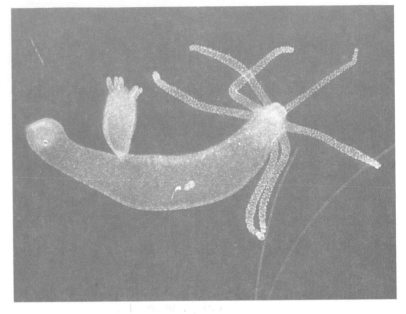

Figure 20-16. Budding in Hydra. The bud begins as a small mound of cells on the side of the parent. The cells divide, producing a complete hydra, which eventually separates from the parent.

Budding in hydra. Budding in hydra is quite different from budding in yeast. Hydras are composed of several kinds of cells. As budding begins, undifferentiated cells on the side of the parent hydra undergo repeated mitotic divisions, producing a small mound of cells. These cells continue to divide, and in a few days a small, complete hydra with a mouth and tentacles is formed (see Figure 20-16). The hydra bud eventually separates from the parent. Hydras can also reproduce sexually.

20-11   Spore Formation

Spores are single, specialized cells that are produced by certain organisms and that, when released, germinate and grow to form new individuals. The term spore, in fact, is applied to a staggering variety of different single-celled structures that differ greatly in appearance, structure, and origin, but which all function as single units of reproduction. Each spore contains the usual components of a cell and is often surrounded by a special thick, hard outer wall. Other spores lack such walls and may be flagellated.

Spores can be formed sexually or asexually. (Sexually formed spores are discussed in chapters 24 and 31). Asexually formed spores are the products of mitotic cell division, and are a common method of reproduction in many simple organisms, such as fungi, algae, and protozoa. Large numbers of these spores are generally produced. They are formed within, and released from, a single cell structure that is the remains of the original parent cell from which the spores are derived.

Spore formation in bread mold. Bread mold, which is a fungus, can often be seen growing as a dark, cottony mass on bread and other foods. The spores are produced by mitotic cell division in spore cases on specialized stalks that grow upward from the surface (see Figure 20-17). Thousands of black spores develop within each spore case. At maturity, the walls of the spore case break down, and the tiny, light spores are carried away by air currents. When a spore lands in an environment where there is warmth, food, and moisture, it germinates and grows to form a new mass of mold. Bread molds also reproduce sexually, as described in Chapter 31.

20-12 Regeneration

Regeneration (rih-jen-uh-*ray*-shun) is the ability of an organism to regrow lost body parts. Relatively simple animals, such as the hydra, planaria, starfish, and earthworm, have the ability to regenerate lost parts. If a hydra is cut in half, each half will regenerate into a new individual. Planaria can be cut into several pieces, each of which will grow into a complete worm.

Starfish feed on oysters. Oyster harvesters used to try to destroy the starfish they caught by chopping them into pieces and tossing the pieces back into the water. However, each part of a starfish can regenerate into a whole new organism as long as it contains a piece of the central disc. Thus the people were actually helping the starfish to multiply, rather than destroying them.

The power of regeneration decreases as animals become more complex. A crab can regrow a lost claw, but cannot regenerate a whole animal from small pieces. Mammals can repair damaged tissue, but cannot regenerate a leg or even a toe. Although simple organisms have great powers of regeneration, they do not usually reproduce in this manner under natural circumstances.

20-13 Vegetative Reproduction

Although most plants reproduce sexually by means of seeds, asexual reproduction involving roots, stems, and leaves is also quite common. Roots, stems, and leaves are called *vegetative* (*vej*-uh-tay-tiv) structures. They normally function in nutrition and growth of plants. When they give rise to a new plant, the process is called **vegetative reproduction,** or *vegetative propagation.*

In vegetative reproduction, undifferentiated cells, such as cambium and epidermal cells, divide mitotically and then differentiate to give rise to an independent plant. The new plant has the same hereditary characteristics as its parent. Vegetative reproduction occurs naturally, and it can also be brought about artificially.

Natural vegetative reproduction. Vegetative propagation occurs naturally in several different ways (see Figure 20-18).

1. A **bulb** is a short underground stem surrounded by thick, fleshy leaves that contain stored food. Tulips, onions, and lilies reproduce by bulbs. As the plant grows, small new bulbs

Figure 20-17. Spore Cases of Bread Mold.

A

C

E

D

B

Figure 20-18. Some Types of Natural Vegetative Propagation. Bulbs, corms, tubers, runners, and rhizomes are specialized structures from which complete plants can develop. (A) Bulb—onion. (B) Corm—crocus. (C) Tuber—potato. (D) Runner—strawberry plant. (E) Rhizome—iris.

sprout from the old one. Each of the new bulbs can give rise to a new plant.

2. **Corms** (kormz) resemble bulbs, but they do not contain fleshy leaves. Rather, corms are short, stout underground stems containing stored food. Gladioli, crocuses, and water chestnuts are plants that grow from corms.

3. A **tuber** (*too*-ber) is an enlarged portion of an underground stem that contains stored food. White potatoes are tubers. Along the surface of a tuber are indentations called "eyes." These eyes are actually tiny buds. When a farmer plants white potatoes, the tuber is cut into pieces, each piece having at least one "eye." Each eye develops into a shoot that grows upward through the soil surface and that also produces roots. The young shoot uses the stored food of the tuber until it develops sufficiently to carry on photosynthesis.

4. A **runner,** or *stolon* (*stoh*-lun), is a horizontal stem with buds. It grows along the surface of the ground. Where buds from a runner touch the soil, roots, stems, and leaves develop to form a new independent plant. Strawberry plants and many kinds of grasses reproduce quickly in this manner.

5. A **rhizome** (*ry*-zohm) is a stem that grows horizontally underground. It is usually thick and fleshy and contains stored food. Along the rhizome are enlarged portions called *nodes*. Buds produced at nodes on the upper surface of the rhizome give rise to leaf-bearing branches. The lower surface of the

A

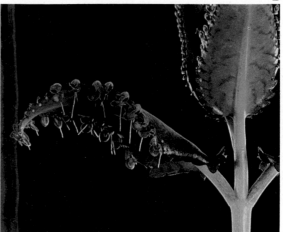

B

Figure 20-19. Some Types of Artificial Vegetative Propagation. (A) Stem cutting. (B) Kalanchoe leaves with plantlets. (C) Grafting—joining the stock and scion.

C

rhizome produces roots. Ferns, irises, cattails, and water lilies reproduce by rhizomes.

Artificial vegetative reproduction. Farmers and gardeners have developed several methods of artificial vegetative reproduction (see Figure 20-19). These techniques enable them to maintain plants with desirable traits.

1. A **cutting** is any vegetative part of a plant—stem, leaf, or root—used to produce a new individual. In a *stem cutting*, a branch, or slip, is cut from a plant and placed in water or moist sand. Usually the bottom of the cutting is dipped into hormones to stimulate root growth. When roots develop, the cutting becomes an independent plant and is transplanted to soil. Geraniums, roses, ivy, and grapevines are propagated in this manner.

In a *leaf cutting*, a leaf or part of a leaf is placed in water or moist soil. After a while, a new plant develops from certain cells in the leaf. African violets, snake plants, and begonias are regularly propagated by leaf cuttings.

Under natural conditions, the leaves of kalanchoe give rise to tiny plants along their edges. These plantlets have tiny leaves, stems, and sometimes roots. When they fall from the parent plant, they take root and continue to grow in the soil. They can be separated and used to produce new plants.

The sweet potato is an enlarged root containing stored food. Farmers place it in moist sand or soil until it sprouts several new plants. Then the sprouts are removed and planted.

2. In **layering,** a stem is bent over so that part of it is covered with soil. After the covered part forms roots, the new plant may be cut from the parent plant. Layering is used to reproduce such plants as raspberries, roses, and honeysuckle. It also occurs naturally.

3. In **grafting,** a stem or bud is removed from one plant and joined permanently to the stem of a closely related plant. The

part of this combination providing the roots is called the *stock;* the added piece is called the *scion* (*sy*-en). The cambium layers (growing regions) of the scion and stock must be in close contact. Usually they are held together by tape and coated with wax to protect the growing tissue from water loss and from disease. After a time the cambiums of the two pieces form new xylem and phloem, which grow together and connect the scion and stock. The stock supports and nourishes the scion. However, the scion retains its own characteristics. For example, although scions of McIntosh apples can be grafted onto stock of any kind of apple tree, the scions will produce only McIntosh apples. Grafting is used to propagate roses, peach trees, plum trees, grapevines, and various seedless fruits, including navel oranges, grapes, and grapefruits.

Advantages of artificial vegetative propagation. Among the advantages of vegetative propagation are:

1. Plants grown from seeds do not always show the same characteristics as the parent plant. Vegetative propagation ensures the production of new plants exactly like the parent. There is little variation because all offspring have the same hereditary makeup as the parent.

2. The development of a plant by vegetative propagation often takes less time than development from seed. In the development of an improved plant variety, stem cuttings or grafts made onto mature plants will produce fruit in much less time than it takes for small plants to bear fruit.

3. Plants bearing *seedless fruit* can be grown only by vegetative propagation (see Figure 20-20).

4. Grafting can be used to obtain higher yields of fruits or nuts.

Figure 20-20. Seedless Oranges.

Chapter Review

SUMMARY

- New cells arise from existing cells by the division of the original cell into two cells. Cell division is necessary for growth, cell replacement, and reproduction. Cell division consists of two processes—the division of the nucleus, which is called mitosis, and the division of the cytoplasm, or cytokinesis.

- The nucleus contains the hereditary material, which is found in the chromosomes. Each type of organism has a specific and characteristic number of chromosomes in its body cells. In mitotic cell division, the chromosomes must be duplicated, and each new cell must receive an entire set for it to function properly.

- Mitosis is divided into stages, or phases. The stage between the end of one cell division and the beginning of the next is interphase. During this stage the chromosomes, which are in the form of chromatin, double.

- The four stages of mitosis are prophase, metaphase, anaphase, and telophase. The same basic stages of mitosis are found in the cells of plants and animals. However, cytoplasmic division in animal cells differs from that in plant cells.

- Asexual reproduction involves mitotic cell division of only one parent. The simplest form of asexual reproduction is binary fission, in which the parent divides into two daughter cells of approximately equal size. In budding, the parent organism divides into two individuals of unequal size—the new individual is smaller than the parent and grows to full size after separation from the parent.

- Spores can be formed sexually or asexually. The asexual formation of spores involves mitotic cell division. Each spore contains a nucleus and a small amount of cytoplasm and is surrounded by a thick outer wall. Spores can withstand cold, heat, and dryness. When conditions become favorable, the spore develops into a new organism.

- Regeneration is the ability to regrow lost body parts. It is observed in relatively simple animals, such as the starfish and earthworm, and is not generally a method of reproduction under natural circumstances.

- In plants, asexual reproduction involves vegetative structures, including roots, stems, and leaves. In vegetative reproduction, undifferentiated cells undergo mitotic division, differentiate, and give rise to an independent plant. Vegetative reproduction occurs naturally with bulbs, corms, tubers, runners, and rhizomes. Vegetative reproduction can also be accomplished artificially with cuttings, layering, and grafting.

KNOW THE TERMS

anaphase	centromere	interphase	sexual reproduction
asexual reproduction	chromatid	layering	spindle
aster	chromatin	metaphase	spore
binary fission	chromosome	mitosis	telophase
budding	corm	prophase	tuber
bulb	cutting	regeneration	vegetative reproduction
cell plate	cytokinesis	rhizome	
centriole	grafting	runner	

SECTION QUESTIONS

Types of Reproduction

1. What is the result of cell division in a unicellular organism? In a multicellular organism?
2. Identify and describe the two basic types of reproduction.

Mitosis

3. Identify the two processes involved in cell division.
4. List the stages of mitosis.
5. In what two ways does division in plant cells differ from that in animal cells?
6. What is cancer?

Asexual Reproduction

7. Define the term *binary fission*.
8. What is budding?
9. What are spores?
10. What is regeneration?
11. Which animals have the greatest powers of regeneration?
12. What is vegetative reproduction?
13. List five ways plants can propagate by natural vegetative reproduction.
14. Name three methods of artificial vegetative reproduction.

KNOW THE FACTS

Copy the number of each sentence below on a sheet of paper. Beside each number, write the letter identifying the answer that correctly completes the sentence.

1. Sexual reproduction differs from asexual reproduction in that, in sexual reproduction **a.** no reproductive cells or organs are involved. **b.** there is one parent. **c.** large numbers of offspring are produced. **d.** there is a union of two sex cells.
2. In nondividing cells, the hereditary information is found in the **a.** chromosomes. **b.** chromatin. **c.** mitochondria. **d.** chromatids.
3. The two strands of a replicated double chromosome are called **a.** chromatids. **b.** centromeres. **c.** chromatin. **d.** spindle fibers.
4. A mitotic stage in which the nuclear membrane and nucleolus cannot be seen is **a.** interphase. **b.** prophase. **c.** anaphase. **d.** telophase.
5. Unlike animal cells, plant cells **a.** form asters. **b.** have no centrioles. **c.** form a spindle. **d.** form two daughter nuclei.
6. In plants, two areas of rapid mitotic division are the **a.** epidermis and xylem. **b.** xylem and phloem. **c.** root tip and cambium. **d.** cambium and phloem.
7. Mitosis occurs most frequently in **a.** cells with small surface areas. **b.** noncancerous cells. **c.** nerve and muscle cells. **d.** unspecialized cells.
8. The dark patches that give moldy bread its appearance consist mainly of **a.** hyphae. **b.** rhizoids. **c.** spores. **d.** stolons.
9. A horizontal stem with buds that grows along the surface of the ground is called a **a.** rhizome. **b.** runner. **c.** corm. **d.** tuber.
10. The white potato is an example of a **a.** rhizome. **b.** bulb. **c.** tuber. **d.** corm.

UNDERSTAND THE CONCEPTS

11. What is the hereditary material in the cell and where is it located?
12. Why is the nucleus so important in cell division?
13. What events occur during interphase before mitosis begins?
14. Briefly describe what occurs in each stage of mitosis in an animal cell.
15. Describe cytoplasmic division in animal cells.
16. How is mitotic division involved in cancer?
17. Describe binary fission in bacteria.
18. Describe bud formation in yeast.
19. Describe bud formation in hydra.
20. Describe spore formation in bread mold.
21. What is a tuber? Explain how vegetative reproduction occurs in a tuber.
22. Briefly describe three methods of artificial vegetative reproduction.
23. What are the advantages of vegetative reproduction over growing plants from seeds?

THINK CRITICALLY

24. Is mitosis occurring in your body right now? If so, where?
25. Nerve cells and muscle cells seldom divide after they are formed. How does this fact affect the human body?
26. How does fission in bacteria differ from fission in the ameba? How is it similar?
27. How does a yeast bud differ from its parent? How is it similar?
28. If only a limited supply of nutrients were available to a unicellular organism, how might this affect its growth? Its reproduction?
29. Prior to anaphase in animals, many cell parts divide. List them. Choose one cell part and explain how it might affect mitosis in the parent cell if it did not divide.
30. Compare and contrast asexual reproduction as it occurs in yeast and in hydra. Pay particular attention to the ways in which the specialized cells develop.

THINK CREATIVELY

31. Suppose that the substance that controls mitosis in humans were isolated and identified. Suggest possible ways that this substance might be used to combat cancer.
32. Propose an explanation for the fact that the ability to regenerate decreases as animals become more complex.

FOR FURTHER INVESTIGATION

1. Grow plants at home by means of vegetative reproduction. Begonias and African violets can be raised by planting stems with attached leaves in moist soil. Geraniums and coleuses can be grown from stem cuttings kept in water; when they have developed sturdy roots, plant them in soil. Experiment with other green plants, taking cuttings below stem nodes. Raise potato plants in soil, using pieces of potato that contain eyes. To grow flowering tulips, hyacinths, and narcissuses, plant the bulbs to half their depth in a bowl filled with pebbles; keep the pebbles moist.
2. Obtain some planaria from running streams under rocks or from a biological supply house. Keep them in spring water in a petri dish. Set up and conduct experiments to test their ability to regenerate. First, anesthetize the planaria with an ice cube. Then place them on a wood block and use a sharp scalpel or razor to make longitudinal, horizontal, or partial cuts. (Caution: Use the scalpel or razor carefully, to avoid cutting yourself.) What is the smallest piece of planarian that will regenerate itself? You may wish to test the effect of chemicals, variation in light intensity, pH, and temperature on the process of regeneration.
3. Prepare a report on one of the career opportunities listed below. See suggested procedures, p. 9, "For Further Investigation" Activity 3.
   a. Cooperative extension service worker
   b. Landscape gardener
   c. Oncologist
4. Prepare a report on the life and contributions of one of the following scientists:
   a. Jane C. Wright
   b. Alexis Carrel
   c. Charlotte Friend
   d. Mary Petermann

FOR FURTHER READING

Bienz, D. R., *The Why and How of Home Horticulture*, W. H. Freeman, New York, 1980.

Lewis, B. J., and Lewis, K. R., *Somatic Cell Division*, 2nd ed. (Carolina Biology Reader), Carolina Biological Supply Co., Burlington, NC, 1980.

Pardee, A., and Reddy, G., *Cancer: Fundamental Ideas* (Carolina Biology Reader), Carolina Biological Supply Co., Burlington, NC, 1982.

Sundberg, M., "Making the Most of Onion Root Tip Mitosis," *The American Biology Teacher*, October, 1981.

Chapter 21
MEIOSIS AND SEXUAL REPRODUCTION

This sea urchin egg contains half the hereditary information that the new organism will need.

SEXUAL REPRODUCTION

Objectives:
1. Compare and contrast asexual reproduction and sexual reproduction, and discuss the advantages and disadvantages of each.
2. Explain the terms *gamete, fertilization,* and *zygote.*

21-1   Advantages of Sexual Reproduction

All living things give rise to new members of their own kind by either asexual or sexual reproduction. In asexual reproduction, a single parent gives rise to new offspring by mitotic cell division. Each new individual receives a set of chromosomes identical to its parent's chromosomes. Therefore, in asexual reproduction, the hereditary information transmitted from generation to generation remains the same. Asexual reproduction does not produce differences, or variations, in the offspring. Sexual reproduction, on the other hand, does introduce hereditary variation.

In sexual reproduction there is always a fusion of nuclei from two cells. These two cells generally come from two separate parent organisms. The cells that provide the nuclear material for sexual reproduction are called **gametes** (*gam*-eets). In most species there are two physically distinct types of gametes, which are called male and female. The female gamete is generally larger and nonmotile, while the male gamete is generally smaller and motile. The fusion of the nuclei of two gametes is called **fertilization,** and the single cell formed from this fusion is called a **zygote** (*zy*-goht).

In sexual reproduction, the offspring produced are not identical to either parent. Instead, they show new combinations of characteristics. Thus, in any species in which sexual reproduction occurs, the members will show variations in structure and/or function. Increasing the amount of variation in members of a species increases the possibility that some individuals of that species will be better adapted than others to survive both short-term and long-term changes in the environment. The better-adapted individuals are more likely to survive environmental changes and to transmit the helpful variations to their offspring. Variations may also enable certain individuals in a population to move into new environments. By making a population more varied, sexual reproduction helps to ensure the survival of the species.

MEIOSIS

Objectives:
1. Explain the importance of meiosis in sexual reproduction.
2. Explain the terms *somatic cell, diploid chromosome number,* and *haploid chromosome number.*
3. Explain which cells have the diploid chromosome number and which have the haploid number.
4. Describe the end results of the first meiotic division and the second meiotic division.

21-2 Diploid and Haploid Chromosome Numbers

Somatic (soh-*mah*-tic) **cells,** or body cells, are all the cells of an organism except for certain specialized cells that are involved in sexual reproduction. The body cells of each species contain a characteristic number of chromosomes. For example, human body cells contain 46 chromosomes, bullfrog body cells contain 26 chromosomes, and fruit fly body cells contain 8 chromosomes. However, these chromosomes are present as pairs of similar, or **homologous** (hoh-*mahl*-uh-guhs), **chromosomes.** Except for the pair of chromosomes that determines sex, the chromosomes in each pair of homologous chromosomes are similar in size and shape, and they control the same hereditary characteristics, or traits. Thus, the 46 chromosomes in human body cells consist of 22 pairs of homologous chromosomes and one pair of sex chromosomes (see Figure 21-1). Cells that contain the full number of chromosomes characteristic of the species are called **diploid** (*dip*-loyd), or 2n, cells.

In animals, the gametes that fuse in sexual reproduction do *not* have the same number of chromosomes as the body cells. Gametes do not contain pairs of homologous chromosomes as

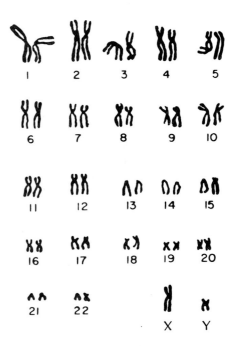

Figure 21-1. Human Chromosomes. The chromosomes of cells undergoing mitosis were stained and photographed. The photographs were then cut apart and assembled into pairs of homologous chromosomes. These chromosomes were from a male. The pair labeled X and Y are the sex chromosomes. In a human female cell, this pair consists of two X chromosomes.

diploid (2n) cell
(4 chromosome pairs)

haploid (n) cell
(4 chromosomes)

Figure 21-2. Diploid and Haploid Cells. The haploid cell contains only one chromosome from each pair of homologous chromosomes. The diploid cell contains both chromosomes of each pair of homologous chromosomes.

Figure 21-3A. Prophase of First Meiotic Division. (Left) Early prophase; (center) mid-prophase; (right) late prophase.

the diploid cells do. They contain only one of the chromosomes of each pair. As a result, they have only half the diploid number of chromosomes. For example, human gametes contain 23 chromosomes—one from each of the 23 pairs in body cells. Such cells are said to be **haploid** (*hap*-loyd), or *monoploid* (*mahn*-uh-ployd). Haploid cells contain *n* chromosomes, rather than 2*n* (see Figure 21-2).

If gametes were diploid cells, the chromosome number per cell would double with each generation. The doubling would occur when two gametes unite at fertilization. Because of the process of meiosis, the doubling of the chromosome number does not occur. **Meiosis** (my-*oh*-sis) is a type of cell division in which the daughter cells receive only half the number of chromosomes present in the parent cells. They receive only one member of each pair of homologous chromosomes. Meiosis produces gametes in animals and spores in plants.

21-3   Stages of Meiosis

Meiosis, which is also known as *reduction division,* occurs in special cells. At the start of meiosis, these cells have the diploid number of chromosomes. In meiosis, each cell divides twice. However, the chromosomes replicate only once. This replication occurs before the first meiotic division. In the second meiotic division, no replication of the chromosomes occurs. As a result of the two meiotic divisions, each original cell produces four daughter cells, each containing the haploid number of chromosomes.

Both the first and second meiotic divisions can be divided into stages similar to the stages of mitosis. Thus, both divisions show a prophase, metaphase, anaphase, and telophase. The events of the first and second meiotic divisions are shown in Figure 21-3A-H.

Prophase I. At the beginning of prophase of the first meiotic division, each chromosome has already replicated and consists of two chromatids, as in mitosis. However, the replicated chromosomes do not move independently to the equator. Instead, each chromosome lines up very exactly with its homologous chromosome, and they become attached at their centromeres. This pairing process is called *synapsis* (suh-*nap*-sis), and

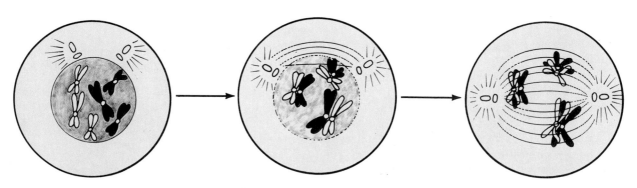

the chromosome pairs, each consisting of four chromatids, are called *tetrads*. The strands of the tetrad sometimes twist about each other, and at this time they may exchange segments. The exchange of segments between chromatids during synapsis is called *crossing-over*.

While these chromosomal changes are occurring, the nuclear membrane disappears and the spindle fibers form. As prophase I ends, the homologous chromosome pairs move toward the equator of the cell.

Metaphase I. In metaphase of the first meiotic division, the centromeres of the chromosome pairs (tetrads) line up on the equator. The chromosomes are attached to the spindle fibers at their centromeres.

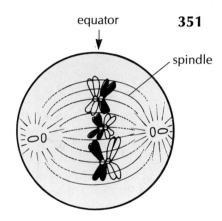

Figure 21-3B. Metaphase of First Meiotic Division.

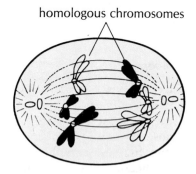

Figure 21-3C. Anaphase of First Meiotic Division.

Anaphase I. During anaphase of the first meiotic division, the homologous chromosomes of each tetrad separate from each other and move to opposite ends of the cell. This process of separation of the tetrad is called **disjunction** (dis-*junk*-shun). The cluster of chromosomes around each pole is haploid —there are half as many chromosomes as in the original cell. However, each chromosome is double-stranded.

Telophase I. Telophase marks the end of the first meiotic division. The cytoplasm divides, forming two daughter cells. Each of the newly formed daughter cells has half the number of chromosomes of the parent cell, but each chromosome is already in replicated form.

Sometimes at the end of telophase I, nuclear membranes form and a short interphase follows. However, in most cases, the cells immediately begin the second division. No further replication of the chromosomes occurs, but the remainder of the division is exactly like mitosis.

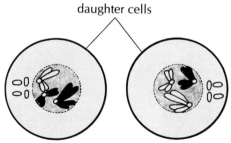

Figure 21-3D. Telophase of First Meiotic Division. The first meiotic division produces two daughter cells.

Prophase II. During prophase II, each of the daughter cells forms a spindle, and the double-stranded chromosomes move toward the middle of the spindle.

Figure 21-3E. Prophase of Second Meiotic Division.

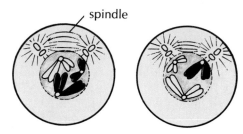

Metaphase II. During metaphase II, the chromosomes become attached to spindle fibers at their centromeres, and the centromeres of the chromosomes line up on the equator. Each chromosome still consists of two strands, or chromatids.

Figure 21-3F. Metaphase of Second Meiotic Division.

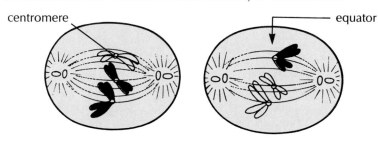

Anaphase II. During anaphase II, the centromeres divide, and the sister chromatids separate. The chromatids, which are now single-stranded chromosomes, move toward the opposite ends of the spindle.

Figure 21-3G. Anaphase of Second Meiotic Division.

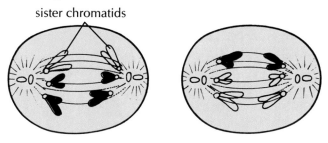

Telophase II. During telophase II, both daughter cells divide, forming four haploid cells. In each cell, chromosomes return to their interphase state, and the nuclear membrane reforms.

Figure 21-3H. Telophase of Second Meiotic Division. The second meiotic division produces four haploid cells.

Table 21-1 presents a comparison of the events of mitosis and meiosis.

MITOSIS	MEIOSIS
1. Occurs in growth and asexual reproduction.	1. Occurs in production of gametes in animals, and spores in plants and in some simple organisms.
2. Homologous chromosomes do not pair up during prophase. There is no exchange of parts between homologous chromosomes.	2. Homologous chromosomes pair up during prophase of first division. While paired, there may be an exchange of parts between homologous chromosomes.
3. Involves one cell division. In the course of division, the double-stranded chromosomes line up at cell equator, centromeres divide, and one chromatid of each chromosome goes to each daughter cell.	3. Involves two cell divisions. During first division, pairs of homologous two-stranded chromosomes line up at equator. The members of each pair separate, and one two-stranded chromosome of each pair of homologous chromosomes goes to each daughter cell. During second division, centromeres of two-stranded chromosomes divide, and chromatids separate, one going to each daughter cell.
4. As a result of mitosis, each daughter cell receives the same number of chromosomes as the original cell. Mitosis maintains the chromosome number.	4. As a result of meiosis, each daughter cell receives only one member of each pair of homologous chromosomes. It therefore has only one-half the number of chromosomes in the original cell. Meiosis reduces the chromosome number by one-half.

Table 21-1. Comparison of Mitosis and Meiosis.

SEXUAL REPRODUCTION IN SIMPLE ORGANISMS

Objectives:
1. Explain the importance of sexual reproduction in protists and simple plants.
2. Describe the basic events of conjugation.
3. Explain the importance of mating types.
4. Briefly describe conjugation in spirogyra and paramecium.

21-4   Conjugation and Mating Types

The simplest type of sexual reproduction occurs in protists and other simple organisms. Although these organisms usually reproduce asexually, some also reproduce sexually. In these organisms, sexual reproduction has the effect of restoring the organism's ability to grow and reproduce. If sexual reproduction is prevented in some species, they die. Sexual reproduction also permits a recombination of hereditary material, thereby introducing variation within the species.

Among simple organisms that reproduce sexually, there are no distinct sexes—that is, all members of a single species are almost identical in appearance. Although no male or female cells can be distinguished, there are usually two different *mating types*, or *strains*, which are commonly designated as plus

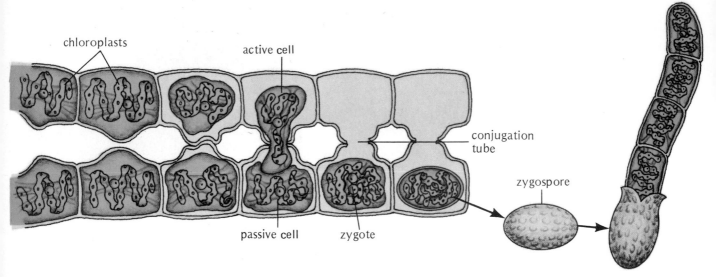

Figure 21-4. Conjugation in Spirogyra. The drawing above shows the conjugation tube, the flow of the cell contents from the active into the passive strand, and the formation of a zygospore. The zygospore undergoes meiotic division, forming a haploid cell that gives rise to a new filament by mitotic cell division. The photograph below shows the conjugation tubes and the zygospores.

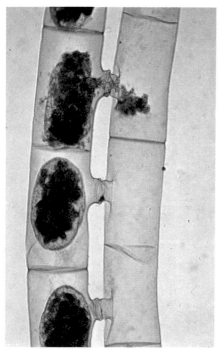

(+) and minus (−). Apparently there are biochemical and chromosomal differences between different mating types.

The type of sexual reproduction most commonly found among simple organisms is **conjugation** (kahn-juh-*gay*-shun). In conjugation, a cytoplasmic bridge forms between two cells, and an exchange or transfer of nuclear material occurs through the bridge. Conjugation occurs only between two cells of different mating types.

21-5   Conjugation in Spirogyra

Spirogyra is a type of filamentous green alga. The filaments consist of cells attached end to end. These organisms usually reproduce asexually by binary fission, but sometimes they reproduce sexually by conjugation.

During conjugation, two filaments of opposite mating types come to lie side by side. Projections develop on the sides of adjacent cells (see Figure 21-4). These projections meet, the walls where the projections meet break down, and a passageway called the *conjugation tube* opens between the cells of the two filaments. The two mating types of spirogyra are called *active* and *passive*. The contents of the active cells flow through the conjugation tube and fuse with the nucleus and cytoplasm of the adjacent passive cells, forming zygotes. The cells of the filaments are haploid, while the newly formed zygotes are diploid.

Each zygote secretes a thick wall that protects it during its dormant season. This new structure is called a **zygospore** (*zy*-guh-spor). The cell walls of the original filaments decay and release the zygospores. After a period of rest, and when favorable conditions return, each zygospore undergoes meiosis, forming four haploid cells. Only one cell survives, and it divides by mitosis, giving rise to a new haploid filament.

21-6   Conjugation in Paramecium

Paramecia usually reproduce asexually by binary fission. However, they periodically reproduce by conjugation. Conjugation takes place between two different mating types—plus and minus. In some species, the periodic exchange of hereditary material by conjugation is necessary for the cells to reproduce asexually. If it does not occur, the cell stops dividing and eventually dies.

During conjugation, two paramecia—one plus, the other minus—stick together at the region of their oral grooves (see Figure 21-5). A protoplasmic bridge forms between them. A complex series of nuclear changes then occurs in each. Paramecia and other ciliates have two types of nuclei— macronuclei and micronuclei. Each cell may contain more than one of each type of nucleus. During conjugation, the macronucleus disappears. The micronucleus divides by meiosis. One of the newly formed haploid micronuclei from each paramecium moves across the protoplasmic bridge into the opposite cell where it fuses with a micronucleus of that cell. Both cells now contain a diploid micronucleus. The conjugating paramecia now separate, and the new micronuclei undergo several mitotic divisions. These divisions result in the formation of new macronuclei and micronuclei. Both organisms then divide twice without nuclear division. Eight new organisms are produced.

Photograph by Carolina Biological Supply Company

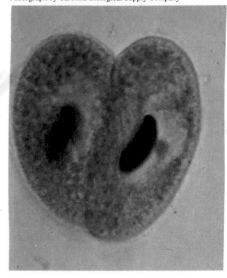

Figure 21-5. Conjugation in Paramecium.

SEXUAL REPRODUCTION IN ANIMALS

Objectives:
1. Define the following terms: *gonad, ovary, ovum, testis, sperm, hermaphrodite, gametogenesis.*
2. Briefly describe the processes of oogenesis and spermatogenesis.
3. Describe the structures of a sperm and an egg.
4. Explain what occurs in fertilization.
5. Contrast the processes of external fertilization and internal fertilization, and discuss the problems involved in each.
6. Define the term *parthenogenesis.*

21-7   Reproductive Systems

Sexual reproduction in animals involves two sexes—male and female. In many animals, the sex of the individual can be identified by physical appearance. Even in animals where there is little or no difference in external appearance between the sexes, there are internal differences. The gametes of animals develop in specialized organs called **gonads** (*goh*-nadz). The female gonads are called **ovaries** (*oh*-vuh-reez). The ovaries produce the female gametes, which are called *egg cells,*

Figure 21-6. Earthworms Mating.

or **ova** (*oh*-vuh) (singular, *ovum*). The male gonads are called **testes** (*tes*-teez). The testes (singular, *testis*) produce male gametes, which are called **sperm cells.** For convenience, egg cells are commonly referred to as eggs, and sperm cells are referred to as sperm (either singular or plural). In addition to the gonads, most animals also have other organs that perform functions necessary for reproduction. These organs together with the gonads form the reproductive system.

21-8   Separation of Sexes and Hermaphroditism

In most types of animals the sexes are separate—that is, each individual has either testes or ovaries and is either male or female. In some animals, however, each individual contains both testes and ovaries. Such organisms are called **hermaphrodites** (her-*maf*-ruh-dyts). *Hermaphroditism* (her-*maf*-ruh-dit-iz-um) is generally found among slow-moving or sessile animals such as earthworms, snails, and hydra.

Although hermaphroditic organisms can produce both eggs and sperm, self-fertilization is rare. Instead, these organisms exchange sperm with another individual of the same species. For example, during mating, two earthworms lie parallel to each other (see Figure 21-6). Each transfers sperm to the *sperm receptacle* of its partner. After they separate, each worm uses the stored sperm from the partner to fertilize its own eggs.

21-9   Gametogenesis: Meiosis in Females and Males

The process by which gametes develop in the gonads is called **gametogenesis** (guh-meet-uh-*jen*-uh-sis). More specifically, the formation of eggs in the ovaries is called **oogenesis** (oh-uh-*jen*-uh-sis), while the formation of sperm in the testes is called **spermatogenesis** (sper-mat-uh-*jen*-uh-sis). Although the same basic processes are involved in the production of both eggs and sperm, there are some differences.

Oogenesis. Oogenesis is the production of eggs in the ovary. The major steps in oogenesis are shown in Figure 21-7. Eggs develop in the ovary from immature cells called *oogonia* (oh-uh-*goh*-nee-uh) (singular, *oogonium*). In many animals the

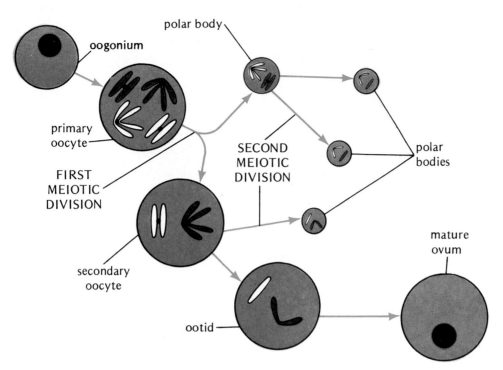

Figure 21-7. Oogenesis. A single functional egg cell is produced by meiotic division of a primary oocyte. The oocyte is diploid, the egg cell is haploid.

oogonium is surrounded by a *follicle*, a small spherical sac of cells within which the mature egg develops. Oogonia contain the diploid number of chromosomes. During early development of the female organism, the oogonia divide many times by mitosis to form a supply of oogonia. In human females, the production of oogonia stops at birth. Thus, each human female has a limited number of oogonia.

In the human female fetus, by the third month of development, oogonia within the ovary begin to develop into cells called *primary oocytes* (*oh*-uh-syts). By birth, the primary oocytes are in prophase of the first meiotic division. At this point, meiosis stops until the female reaches sexual maturity. Then periodically (about once a month in most women) one of these primary oocytes completes meiosis and develops into a functional egg.

When the first meiotic division occurs in the primary oocyte, the cytoplasm of the cell is divided unequally. One of the daughter cells, which is large and receives most of the cytoplasm, is called the *secondary oocyte*. The other daughter cell is very small and is called the first *polar body*. Each of these daughter cells contains the haploid number of chromosomes.

During the second meiotic division, the secondary oocyte divides unequally into a large cell called an **ootid** (*oh*-uh-tid) and another polar body. The first polar body may also divide into two polar bodies. The ootid grows into a mature egg, which has the haploid chromosome number. The polar bodies disintegrate and die.

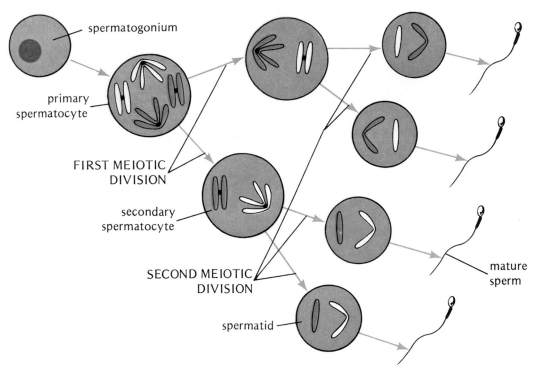

spermatogonium

primary
spermatocyte

FIRST MEIOTIC
DIVISION

secondary
spermatocyte

SECOND MEIOTIC
DIVISION

spermatid

mature
sperm

Figure 21-8. Spermatogenesis. Four functional sperm cells are produced by meiotic division of a primary spermatocyte.

Spermatogenesis. Spermatogenesis is the production of sperm in the testes. The major steps in spermatogenesis are shown in Figure 21-8.

Within the testes the sperm develop from immature sex cells called **spermatogonia** (sper-mat-uh-*goh*-nee-uh). Throughout childhood, these spermatogonia (singular, *spermatogonium*) divide mitotically many times to produce additional spermatogonia. The spermatogonia contain the diploid number of chromosomes. In humans, after a male matures sexually, there is a continual development of some spermatogonia into functional sperm. Other spermatogonia continue to divide mitotically, producing more spermatogonia. Thus, while the number of the eggs is limited, the number of sperm is not limited.

In the course of development, a spermatogonium increases in size to become a *primary spermatocyte* (sper-*mat*-uh-syt). The primary spermatocyte undergoes the first meiotic division, forming two cells of equal size. These are *secondary spermatocytes.* Each secondary spermatocyte then undergoes the second meiotic division, forming four *spermatids* (*sper*-muh-tids), all of equal size. The spermatids contain the haploid number of chromosomes. With no further division each spermatid develops into a mature sperm with a flagellum. Thus, each primary spermatocyte gives rise to four sperm.

21-10   Comparison of Egg and Sperm

The male and female gametes of a species differ in structure. Eggs are round in shape and nonmotile. They contain a nucleus and stored food in the form of **yolk** (yohk). The egg is always larger than the sperm of the same species. The size of the egg varies from one species to another and depends on the amount of yolk stored in it. Yolk is used as nourishment by the developing animal. The yellow center of a chicken egg is the egg cell. It contains a great deal of yolk because the developing chicken receives no other nourishment while in the egg. The eggs of humans and other mammals are usually microscopic and contain little yolk because the developing animal gets nourishment from the mother. The human egg is about 0.1 millimeter in diameter.

Most sperm cells are microscopic. A typical sperm is made up of a head, a middle piece, and a long, thin tail called a flagellum (see Figure 21-9). The head consists of the nucleus, which contains the chromosomes, and an *acrosome* (*ak*-ruh-sohm), which aids in the penetration of the egg. The middle piece is packed with mitochondria, which provide energy so the sperm can move. The long, whiplike flagellum enables the sperm to swim through liquids.

Figure 21-9. Structure of a Human Sperm Cell. The overall length of the sperm is about 0.05 millimeters, half the diameter of a human egg.

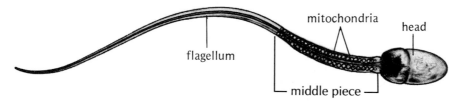

flagellum   mitochondria   head

middle piece

21-11   Fertilization and Zygote Formation

As previously mentioned, the union of an egg cell nucleus and a sperm cell nucleus is called fertilization, and the resulting cell is the zygote. The joining of the two haploid gametes produces a diploid zygote. Fertilization restores the species number of chromosomes.

Eggs are nonmotile—they have no power to move by themselves. Sperm, on the other hand, are streamlined cells specialized for fast movement. When sperm are released by the male, their flagella beat rapidly, pushing them along in all directions. As they approach an egg, they encounter a chemical called *fertilizin*, which is released by the egg. Fertilizin stimulates the sperm to move faster and aids in their attachment to the surface of the egg.

When a sperm comes in contact with an egg, the acrosome releases enzymes that dissolve an opening through the protective membranes of the egg. This allows the head of the sperm to enter the egg, while the tail remains outside. The sperm cell nucleus moves through the cytoplasm toward the egg cell nucleus. The n chromosomes of the sperm nucleus join with

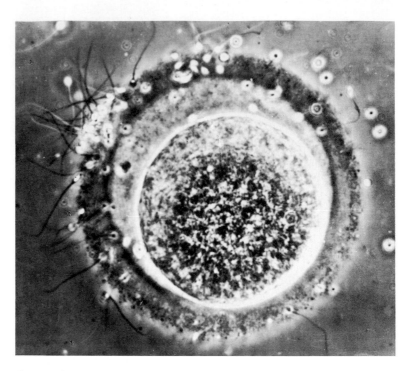

Figure 21-10. Human Egg Surrounded by Sperm.

the *n* chromosomes of the egg nucleus to form the zygote, which thus has 2*n* chromosomes.

A *fertilization membrane* is formed around the egg after a sperm penetrates it (see Figure 21-10). This membrane prevents additional sperm from entering the egg, and also serves as a protective covering.

For fertilization to occur, there must be a fluid medium so that the sperm can swim to the egg. Also, because sperm and eggs live for only a short period of time, the male and female gametes must be released together. There are two basic ways in which the gametes are brought together. One is external fertilization, in which the gametes fuse outside the body of the female. The other is internal fertilization, in which the gametes fuse inside the body of the female.

External Fertilization. In **external fertilization,** the eggs are fertilized in the environment outside the body of the female. This type of fertilization is limited to aquatic animals. In such animals, the only sex organs needed besides the gonads are the ducts that transport the gametes from the gonads to the water. Fertilization occurs directly in the water after each parent releases its gametes. The sperm swim through the water to the eggs. Although there is no problem about moist surroundings for fertilization, there are many hazards in the environment. The sperm and eggs may not meet, the eggs or developing offspring may be eaten by other animals, they may die because of variations in the temperature and/or oxygen concentration in the water, and so on. To overcome the hazards of external fertilization, large numbers of eggs and sperm are released. External fertilization occurs in almost all aquatic invertebrates, most fish (but not sharks), and many amphibians.

Figure 21-11. Amplexus. The male and female frogs release their gametes into the water at the same time, thereby ensuring fertilization of some of the eggs.

To improve the chances of eggs and sperm meeting, aquatic animals do not release their gametes at random. There are many hormonally controlled behavior patterns that ensure that sperm and eggs are released at approximately the same time and place. In some fish, the female deposits thousands of eggs, and the male swims over them releasing sperm. This process is known as *spawning.* Salmon hatch in freshwater streams. The young fish then travel downstream to the ocean where they mature. When the salmon are ready to spawn, they return to the freshwater stream where they were hatched. This adaptation ensures that the males and females are in the same place and in a proper environment for spawning.

In frogs, when a female is full of eggs and ready to mate, she approaches a male. The male embraces the female with his front legs in a process called *amplexus* (see Figure 21-11). This stimulates the female to release her eggs, and at the same time, the male releases his sperm. Because they are in close contact and the gametes are released at the same time, the sperm reach many of the eggs. Amplexus coordinates the proper release of the gametes.

Internal Fertilization. **Internal fertilization,** fertilization within the body of the female, is characteristic of animals that reproduce on land. It is also found in some aquatic animals, such as sharks and lobsters. Internal fertilization requires a specialized sex organ to transfer the sperm from the body of the male into the body of the female. After the sperm are placed within the female's body, they travel to the eggs and fertilize them. The moist tissues of the female provide the watery environment required for the sperm to swim to the egg. After fertilization, either the zygote is enclosed in a protective shell and released by the female, or it remains and develops within the female's body.

Internal fertilization avoids the scattering of gametes and the hazards of the outside environment. Fewer eggs are needed

Career

Veterinarian

Most veterinarians treat sick and injured animals. They prescribe and administer medicines and vaccines, and perform surgery. Some veterinarians work only with small animals, usually pets. Others work with farm animals such as horses, cattle, sheep, and poultry. Yet others treat zoo and game-farm animals. A small number inspect food, work in government laboratories, or teach.

For people who enjoy research, there are important veterinary functions such as investigating disease outbreaks among game or farm animals, and conducting campaigns to eradicate the disease. They may also conduct research to develop vaccines that will prevent future outbreaks.

Veterinarians may work in hospitals or clinics, out of mobile clinics when treating large farm animals, or in a laboratory setting. Some work outdoors in all kinds of weather, and most put in long working days.

In the U.S., veterinarians must have a state license. This requires a doctoral degree from a college of veterinary medicine. Entrants to such institutions usually have a bachelor's degree, with emphasis on the biological and physical sciences. Admission to veterinary college is highly competitive.

because they are well protected and the chances of fertilization are much greater than they are when the gametes are released externally into water. However, even with internal fertilization, large numbers (often in the millions) of sperm are released by the male into the body of the female. Even within the female's body, the sperm can fertilize the egg only for a brief period of time. Because the sperm store little food, they live only a short time. Also, the egg can be penetrated by the sperm only for a brief time. In humans, the egg can be fertilized for only about 24 hours.

In animals with internal fertilization, many of the specialized adaptations involved in reproduction are concerned with the timing of the release of sperm and eggs. Since the gametes generally live only for a short time, mating must occur within certain time periods for fertilization to occur. Many of the reproductive adaptations are controlled by hormones. Reproductive adaptations include such things as singing, the display of special feathers, color patches on the skin, and the release of chemicals called *pheromones* (*fer*-uh-mohnz), which have distinctive odors. These adaptations stimulate the mating response, and trigger the release of eggs and sperm.

In many insects and in bats the problem of timing is solved in an interesting way. After mating, the sperm are stored in specialized structures in the female and then used to fertilize the eggs at some later time. In the queen honeybee, for example, enough sperm are stored from one mating to fertilize the hundreds of thousands of eggs she lays during her lifetime. In bats, mating occurs in the fall, and the sperm are stored until the following spring, when fertilization occurs. It is not known how the sperm remain alive for such long periods.

21-12 Parthenogenesis

The development of an unfertilized egg into an adult animal without fusion with sperm is called **parthenogenesis** (par-thuh-noh-*jen*-uh-sis). In nature, it occurs in many insects, including bees, wasps, aphids (plant lice), certain ants, and in rotifers and other microscopic animals. For example, in bees, the queen bee mates only once. She can then produce either unfertilized eggs or fertilized eggs. The unfertilized eggs become male drones while the fertilized eggs become female workers or queens. Female aphids reproduce by parthenogenesis during the spring and summer. In the fall, the eggs produce both males and females. These insects mate, and the females produce fertilized eggs that hatch in the spring.

Chapter Review

SUMMARY

- Sexual reproduction involves hereditary material from two parents. Two specialized sex cells, or gametes, one from each parent, unite in a process called fertilization. Sexual reproduction produces offspring that are not identical to either parent, thereby introducing variation within the species.

- The body cells of each organism contain a constant number of chromosomes that is characteristic of its species. The sex cells of the organism contain half the number of chromosomes.

- The formation of gametes involves a type of cell division called meiosis. In meiosis, the chromosomes replicate once and the cell divides twice. Meiosis results in the formation of four haploid cells.

- The most common type of sexual reproduction found among protists is conjugation. In spirogyra and paramecium, conjugation serves to rejuvenate the nuclear material.

- In animals the development of gametes takes place in the ovaries of the female and in the testes of the male. The ovaries produce eggs and the testes produce sperm. The process of meiosis by which eggs develop is called oogenesis, while the development of sperm is called spermatogenesis.

- Fertilization restores the species number of chromosomes. Fertilization can be external—outside the body of the female, or internal—within the body of the female.

KNOW THE TERMS

conjugation	gonad	ootid	spermatogonium
diploid	haploid	ovary	testis
disjunction	hermaphrodite	ovum	yolk
external fertilization	homologous pair	parthenogenesis	zygospore
fertilization	internal fertilization	somatic cell	zygote
gamete	meiosis	sperm cell	
gametogenesis	oogenesis	spermatogenesis	

SECTION QUESTIONS

Sexual Reproduction

1. What is sexual reproduction?
2. What is fertilization?

Meiosis

3. Which cells of an animal are diploid and which are haploid?
4. What are pairs of homologous chromosomes?
5. What are the products of meiosis in animals? In plants?

Sexual Reproduction in Simple Organisms

6. What are mating types?

7. What type of sexual reproduction is found among protists?
8. What is a zygospore?

Sexual Reproduction in Animals

9. Where do the gametes of animals develop?
10. Name two hermaphroditic organisms.
11. What is gametogenesis?
12. How many mature sperm are produced from each primary spermatocyte?
13. In what type of animal does external fertilization occur?
14. In what types of animals does internal fertilization occur?
15. What is parthenogenesis?

KNOW THE FACTS

Copy the number of each sentence below on a sheet of paper. Beside each number, write the term(s) that complete(s) the sentence correctly.

1. Each new individual receives a set of chromosomes identical to its parent's chromosomes in _____ reproduction.
2. The type of reproduction that produces variations in the offspring is _____ reproduction.
3. The single cell formed from fertilization is called a(n) _____.
4. Cells that contain the full number of chromosomes characteristic of the species are called _____, or 2n, cells.
5. Spirogyra and paramecium reproduce sexually by _____.
6. In some types of animals, known as _____, individuals contain both testes and ovaries.
7. The formation of eggs in the ovaries is called _____.
8. The formation of sperm in the testes is called _____.
9. Eggs develop in the ovary from immature sex cells called _____.
10. Immature sex cells contain the _____ number of chromosomes.
11. Mature eggs and mature sperm contain the _____ number of chromosomes.
12. The stored food in the egg is called _____.
13. The external fertilization of fish eggs is called _____.
14. The embracing process in frogs, _____, coordinates the proper release of gametes.

UNDERSTAND THE CONCEPTS

15. Why is variation among members of a species advantageous?
16. What is accomplished by meiosis?
17. Describe the process of synapsis and disjunction.
18. What exchange may occur during synapsis?
19. How is the chromosome content of the cell changed by the first meiotic division?
20. How is the chromosome content of the cell changed by the second meiotic division?
21. Describe conjugation in the protists.
22. Describe conjugation in spirogyra.
23. What are the functions of ovaries and testes?
24. Describe mating and fertilization in the earthworm.
25. How many mature eggs and polar bodies are produced from each primary oocyte?
26. Describe the fertilization of an egg by a sperm.
27. What prevents additional sperm from entering an egg after a sperm penetrates it?
28. Why do organisms in which fertilization is external produce large numbers of gametes?
29. Why are relatively few eggs produced in animals in which fertilization is internal?
30. Describe parthenogenesis in bees.

THINK CRITICALLY

31. Compare and contrast meiosis I with mitosis; meiosis II with mitosis.
32. Explain why slow-moving animals, such as earthworms, snails, and hydras, are generally hermaphrodites.
33. In the world of living things, which process occurs more frequently, mitosis or meiosis? Explain why.
34. Why is it important to future generations that during anaphase I the distribution of members of a pair of homologous chromosomes is random?
35. Explain the ways in which the human sperm's shape and structures are suited to its functions.
36. The human organism has evolved many adaptive ways to aid the fertilization process. Discuss three of them. Put them in order

of importance to the survival of the species. Explain your order.
37. Many people enjoy eating chicken eggs. Are these eggs haploid or diploid? Which part of an egg is the more nutritious, the white or the yolk? Explain.

THINK CREATIVELY

38. Develop a hypothesis to explain why the meiotic divisions during oogenesis produce unequal-sized cells—the oocytes and the polar bodies.

39. Develop a hypothesis to explain how the sperm of a bat can remain alive in a female bat for six months.

FOR FURTHER INVESTIGATION

1. Observe pigeons, sea gulls, ducks, or other birds that live in your area. Record your observations, and note which behaviors may be related to reproduction. Do library research to confirm your hypothesis.
2. The aphid, an insect that damages crops and ornamental plants, has unusual reproductive abilities. Do library research on the aphid's life cycle and eating habits. Using a computer, calculate approximately how many aphids will be produced from two adults in one year. Write up your report in the form of a feature article for a magazine.
3. Prepare a report on one of the career opportunities listed below. See suggested procedures, p. 9, "For Further Investigation" Activity 3.
   a. Fish hatchery supervisor
   b. Museum technician
   c. Pharmaceutical sales representative
4. Prepare a report on the life and contributions of one of the following scientists:
   a. Elizabeth Blackwell
   b. Oskar Hertwig
   c. Jacques Loeb
   d. Alice Eastwood

FOR FURTHER READING

Clutton-Brock, T. H., "Reproductive Success in Red Deer," *Scientific American,* February, 1985.

John, B., and Lewis, K., *The Meiotic Mechanism,* 2nd ed. (Carolina Biology Reader), Carolina Biological Supply Co., Burlington, NC, 1984.

Miller, J., "Pass-Along Sperm: A Snail Sex Option," *Science News,* May 5, 1984.

Morse, G., "Why is Sex?" *Science News,* September 8, 1984.

Chapter 22
ANIMAL DEVELOPMENT

A salamander embryo developing within its transparent egg case.

EMBRYONIC DEVELOPMENT

Objectives:
1. Explain the terms *development* and *embryo*.
2. Describe in general terms the events of cleavage and embryonic development through the gastrula stage.
3. Name the three germ layers and list a few of the tissues and organs formed from each.
4. Explain the term *differentiation*.

22-1 Cleavage

Fertilization in animals, as in plants, is the start of a complex series of events that eventually give rise to an adult organism. These events are referred to as **development.** In the early stages of development, the organism is called an **embryo** (*em*-bree-oh). The study of embryonic development is called *embryology* (em-bree-*ahl*-uh-jee).

Although there are many different patterns of embryonic development, in animals the basic processes involved are always the same. These processes include cleavage, growth, and differentiation.

After fertilization, the zygote begins a series of cell divisions known as **cleavage** (*klee*-vidj). During cleavage, the fertilized egg divides by mitosis into two cells. Each of these cells divides again, producing four cells. These four produce eight, and so on (see Figure 22-1).

fertilized cell

first division
(2 cells)

second division
(4 cells)

third division
(8 cells)

Figure 22-1. Early stages of Cleavage. Although the number of cells doubles at each division during cleavage, no growth occurs.

During cleavage, the cells do not grow, so with each division, cell size decreases. The eggs of a species are generally many times larger than the average cell of the adult organism. Cleavage continues until the size of the cells of the developing embryo has been reduced to the size of the cells of the adult organism. Cleavage thereby converts a single, large fertilized egg into many small cells.

The early divisions of cleavage result in the formation of a solid ball of cells. At this stage the embryo is called a **morula** (*mor*-yuh-luh) (see Figure 22-2). As cleavage continues, the cells undergo a rearrangement, forming a hollow sphere. The layer of cells in the sphere is generally only one cell thick. The cavity of the sphere is filled with fluid. At this stage the embryo is called a **blastula** (*blas*-chuh-luh), and the fluid-filled cavity is called the **blastocoel** (*blas*-tuh-seel) (see Figure 22-3).

Although the events of cleavage are generally as described above, the arrangement of cells in the developing embryo depends on the amount and distribution of yolk in the egg. Some eggs, such as those of humans, have very little yolk. In such eggs, cleavage results in a blastula in which all the cells are nearly equal in size. However, other eggs, such as those of amphibians, bony fish, birds, and reptiles, have a large amount of yolk concentrated at one end of the egg cell. Since yolk tends to impede cell division in eggs with a large amount of yolk, cleavage occurs principally or exclusively at the non-yolk pole of the egg.

In frog eggs, the large amount of yolk found at one pole retards cleavage in that region. This results in a blastula with larger cells at the yolk-filled, or *vegetal*, pole and more numerous, smaller cells at the yolkless, or *animal*, pole (see Figure 22-4). The blastocoel is formed only within the region of the animal pole.

In the chicken egg, the nucleus and cytoplasm are concentrated in the *germinal disc*, a platelike area on the surface of the ball of yolk (see Figure 22-5). Cleavage occurs only in the cells of the germinal disc. The blastocoel is formed when these cells separate from the yolk, leaving a space between the yolk and the cells. The developing chick eventually uses the yolk for food and completely fills the space within the egg.

Figure 22-2. Morula. At this stage, the developing embryo is a solid ball of cells.

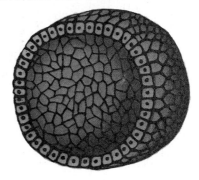

Figure 22-3. Blastula. At this stage, the developing embryo is a hollow sphere with a fluid-filled interior.

Figure 22-4. Blastula of Frog Egg.

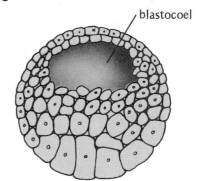

blastocoel

Figure 22-5. Blastocoel Formation in the Chicken Egg.

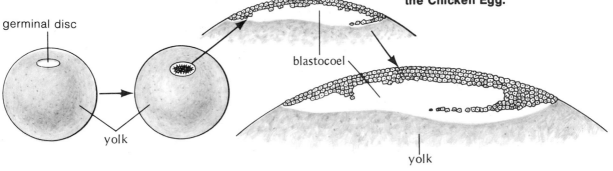

germinal disc

yolk

blastocoel

yolk

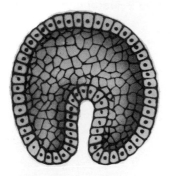

Figure 22-6. Gastrulation. In gastrulation a second cell layer is formed when the cells of one side of the embryo push inward, forming an indentation.

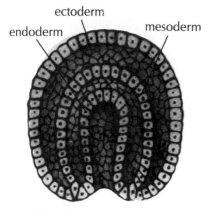

Figure 22-7. The Three Germ Layers of the Developing Embryo. The mesoderm forms between the outer layer, the ectoderm, and the inner layer, the endoderm.

22-2 Gastrulation

As development of the blastula continues, a point is reached when the cells begin to grow before dividing. Mitotic division continues, but it is now accompanied by growth. In addition, various movements of the cells occur that will establish the shape of the embryo.

When the blastula reaches several hundred cells, gastrulation occurs. In **gastrulation** (gas-truh-*lay*-shun), the cells on one side of the blastula move inward and form a two-layered embryo called the **gastrula** (*gas*-truh-luh) (see Figure 22-6). The opening created by the gastrulation process is called the **blastopore** (*blas*-tuh-por). It later becomes one of the openings to the digestive system in the adult organism.

The outer layer of cells in the gastrula is called the **ectoderm.** The inner layer is called the **endoderm.** The cavity within the gastrula is called the **primitive gut**, or *archenteron* (ar-*kent*-uh-rahn). It later becomes the digestive system. Eventually, the primitive gut cavity breaks through the end of the developing embryo opposite the blastopore, forming the second opening of the digestive system. After the endoderm and ectoderm are established, a third cell layer, the **mesoderm** (*mez*-uh-derm), forms between them (see Figure 22-7).

In the frog, the yolk-containing cells of the vegetal pole do not take part in gastrulation. The blastopore forms next to the mass of yolk cells (see Figure 22-8.) Cells from the animal pole migrate downward and move in through the blastopore at the edge of the yolk mass.

In the chicken, the cells of the blastula separate into an outer and an inner layer. The outer layer becomes the ectoderm, and the inner layer becomes the endoderm. The space between the two layers is the blastocoel. The cells of the outer layer roll inward to produce the third cell layer, the mesoderm. This inward movement of cells gives rise to a visible line, called the *primitive streak*, on the surface of the germinal disc. The primitive streak is really an elongated blastopore.

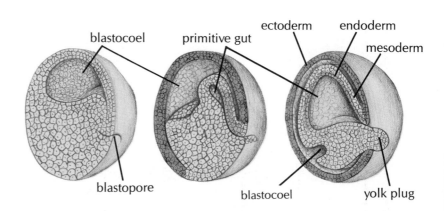

Figure 22-8. Gastrulation and Formation of Germ Layers in the Frog Egg.

Ectoderm	Mesoderm	Endoderm
Nervous system, including brain, spinal cord, nerves.	Bones and muscles.	Lining of digestive tract.
Lining of mouth, nostrils, and anus.	Blood and blood vessels.	Lining of trachea, bronchi, and lungs.
Epidermis of skin, sweat glands, hair, nails.	Reproductive and excretory systems.	Liver, pancreas.
	Inner layer (dermis) of skin.	Thyroid, parathyroid, thymus.
		Urinary bladder.

The three cell layers—ectoderm, mesoderm, and endoderm—are called the **germ layers,** because they give rise to all the tissues and organs of multicellular animals. Table 22-1 shows some of the organs and systems that arise from each layer.

Table 22-1. Development of Organs and Organ Systems from the Germ Layers.

22-3 Growth and Differentiation

As the development of the gastrula proceeds, the number of cells continues to increase. Since the cells are now growing before dividing, the embryo as a whole begins to increase in size. Cell growth alone would produce only a formless mass of cells. It is necessary for the cells of the embryo to be arranged into specific structures, and within these structures, the cells must be specialized to perform particular functions. Although the cells of the gastrula are organized into distinct layers, they are all very much alike in appearance. The series of changes that transforms the unspecialized embryonic cells into the specialized cells, tissues, and organs that make up the organism is called **differentiation.**

Early evidence of differentiation is found on the upper surface of the gastrula. Here the ectoderm cells divide, forming a *neural plate* with two raised edges, called *neural folds* (see Figure 22-9). The neural folds unite over the center of the neural plate, forming a *neural tube.* The neural tube later forms the brain and spinal cord.

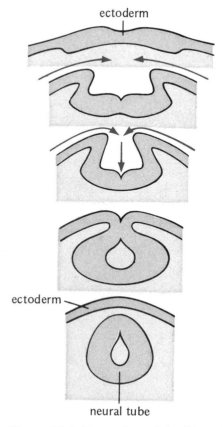

Figure 22-9. Formation of the Neural Tube.

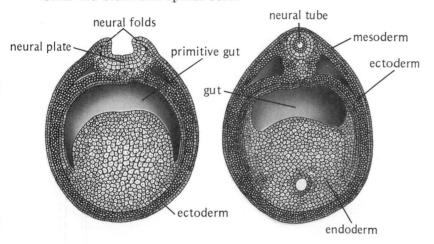

Frontier of Biology

Embryo Cloning

Up to three fourths of the cells of a seven- to ten-day old blastula can be removed or damaged, and the embryo will still develop into a normal organism. Knowing this, researchers at Colorado State University's Animal Reproduction Laboratory decided to use a new technique to split a horse blastula and produce twins.

To produce the horse twins, the researchers first flushed out the uterus of a pregnant mare to capture the dot-sized embryo. Then, using a micromanipulator, (see Figure 2-14), a technician carefully divided the blastula in two. Each half was then placed in the uterus of another mare where it became embedded in the mare's uterine wall. The twin horses produced are normal and healthy in every respect (see photo).

The use of the micromanipulator reduces the time of the twinning procedure to about two hours. Previous artificial twinning methods in domestic animals were more difficult and time consuming.

CONTROL OF DEVELOPMENT

Objectives:
1. Describe the roles of the nucleus and cytoplasm in controlling development.
2. Describe the process of embryonic induction and explain how this process controls development.

22-4   Role of the Nucleus and Cytoplasm in Development

Within the nucleus of the fertilized egg is the hereditary material, which contains all the information necessary for the development of the organism. The hereditary information is encoded within the chemical structure of DNA in the chromosomes. DNA controls the chemical processes of the cell and determines which proteins are synthesized by the cell. Because the cells of the embryo divide by mitosis, each cell contains the same chromosomes and DNA as the original fertilized egg cell.

If DNA controls cellular activities and all cells of an organism contain the same DNA, how are the many different kinds of cells in the organism produced? It has been found that different sections of the DNA of a cell can be turned off or on, and this results in the formation of different types of cells. Thus, in muscle cells, for example, the part of the DNA that controls the synthesis of muscle cell proteins is turned on, while the part of the DNA that controls the synthesis of nerve cell proteins is not turned on. In nerve cells, on the other hand, only the part of the DNA involved in the synthesis of nerve cell proteins is turned on. If this were not the case, differentiation would not occur and all the cells of an embryo would be the same. However, very little is known at this time about how the activity of DNA in different cells is controlled.

Experiments with frogs have demonstrated that a nucleus from a fully differentiated cell contains a complete copy of the hereditary information. In 1962, the English biologist J. G. Gurden surgically replaced the haploid nuclei of unfertilized frog's eggs with diploid nuclei from intestinal cells of tadpoles. Some of the eggs that received the intestinal nuclei developed into normal frogs. This would indicate that some of the DNA that was inactivated, or switched off, in the intestinal cell nucleus was activated when the nucleus was placed in the egg cell. From this and other research, it appears that the control of development involves an interaction between the DNA and certain cytoplasmatic constituents. As a result of the interaction, parts of the hereditary material are switched on and off, and this in turn determines the direction of cellular differentiation.

Other experimental evidence indicates that differentiation begins early in development. For example, if the cells of a four-celled frog embryo are carefully separated, each cell will develop into a normal tadpole. But if the cells of an older embryo are separated, the cells develop abnormally and die. In the older embryo, the cells have already begun to differentiate and can no longer produce a whole, normal organism.

22-5 Role of Neighboring Cells in Differentiation

As an embryo develops, there must be coordination and communication between its tissues. By the late blastula or early gastrula stage, the path of development of groups of cells is determined. Cells in specific regions are committed to specific lines of development. For example, there is a particular region in the frog gastrula that normally develops into an eye. If this tissue is removed from the embryo and placed in a special nutrient solution, it develops into an irregular mass of cells. On the other hand, if this tissue is transplanted into any other part of another frog embryo, it will develop into a recognizable eye, even though it is not a functioning eye. Some of the tissues in the extra, non-functioning eye did not develop from the transplanted tissue. Instead, the transplanted tissue caused some of the surrounding tissue, which would not ordinarily be part of the eye, to develop into eye structures. This experiment showed that a tissue can influence the differentiation of neighboring tissues (see Figure 22-10).

It has been found that certain parts of the developing embryo act as *organizers*, influencing the development of adjacent cells. The process by which the organizer induces another structure to differentiate is called **embryonic induction.** The mechanism by which induction is accomplished is not yet known. Some chemical substances have been shown to cause induction. Cell contact is probably also important. It may be that as development proceeds, organizers, in some way and at certain times, influence which parts of a cell's hereditary material become active, and, thus, determine the course of differentiation of those cells.

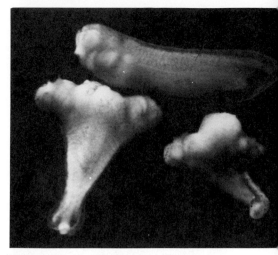

Figure 22-10. Embryonic Tissue Induction. The uppermost figure is a normal frog embryo. The lower frog embryos show the development of two heads, the result of induction by tissue transplanted from other embryos.

EXTERNAL AND INTERNAL DEVELOPMENT

Objectives:
1. Compare and contrast external development in water and internal development on land.
2. Describe the adaptations of reptiles, birds, non-placental mammals, and placental mammals for reproduction on land.

22-6 External Development in Water

Embryonic development may be either outside or inside the mother's body, depending on the type of organism. Regardless of where development occurs, the embryo has certain

Figure 22-11. (Top) Eggs of a Red-winged Blackbird. (Bottom) Eggs of a northern Black Racer Snake.

requirements. It needs nourishment, proper temperature, oxygen, protection, and a means of getting rid of wastes.

In most aquatic animals, fertilization and development occur externally in the water. Nourishment for these embryos is supplied by yolk stored in the egg. The developing young are usually assured proper environmental conditions because mating and fertilization occur at specific times of the year. Oxygen from the surrounding water diffuses into the embryo, and wastes diffuse from the embryo into the water.

In most aquatic animals, there is usually little or no care of the young by the parents. Some fish, however, do provide a certain amount of care for the developing young. For example, the male stickleback guards the nest and fans the embryos with water currents to provide oxygen. Some fish are "mouth-breeders"—that is, the fertilized eggs are held in one parent's mouth until they hatch. In general, survival of species that develop in water is dependent on the production and fertilization of large numbers of eggs. Many of the eggs are eaten or destroyed in other ways, and only a small percentage of the original number survive from each mating.

22-7   External Development on Land

Internal fertilization followed by external development occurs in birds and most reptiles, as well as in a few mammals. In these animals the fertilized egg, which contains a large amount of yolk, is enclosed in a protective shell. The shelled egg is moist inside, providing the embryo with a self-contained aquatic environment. The shell is practically waterproof, but it is porous enough to allow oxygen from the air to diffuse into the egg and carbon dioxide from the embryo to diffuse out. The percentage of embryos that survive to hatching is greater for animals whose eggs are shelled than for those whose eggs lack a shell. In fact, animals that lay shelled eggs produce fewer eggs than animals that lay eggs without a shell. Both the hard, calcium-containing shell of the bird egg and the tough, leathery shell of the reptile egg provide good protection for the embryo (see Figure 22-11). Reptiles lay considerably more eggs than birds. Reptile eggs are usually abandoned by the mother, whereas bird eggs and young birds are carefully tended by the parents. Thus, the percentage of reptile eggs that survive is less than the percentage of bird eggs that survive.

Internal structure of the chicken egg. As the chicken embryo develops, it forms four membranes that are outside the embryo itself but inside the shell. These are the **extraembryonic membranes** (see Figure 22-12). The extraembryonic membranes perform a number of important functions.

1. The **chorion** (*kor*-ee-ahn) is the outermost membrane. It lines the inside of the shell and surrounds the embryo and the other membranes. The chorion aids in gas exchange.

2. The **allantois** (uh-*lan*-tuh-wis) is a saclike structure that grows out of the digestive tract of the embryo. It is through the

blood vessels of the allantois that the exchange of oxygen and carbon dioxide occurs. The metabolic wastes of the embryo also collect in the allantois.

3. The **amnion** (*am*-nee-ahn) is a fluid-filled sac that surrounds the embryo. The amniotic fluid within the sac provides a watery environment for the embryo and acts as a cushion to protect it from shocks.

4. The **yolk sac** surrounds the yolk, the source of food for the embryo. Blood vessels in the yolk sac transport the food to the embryo.

The shelled egg with its extraembryonic membranes is an important adaptation that allows bird embryos to develop on land. When the young bird hatches, the extraembryonic membranes are discarded along with the shell. The eggs of reptiles have similar features. Figure 22-13 shows various stages of development in the chicken.

22-8 Internal Development

In some sharks and in some reptiles, such as garter snakes, fertilization and development are internal. However, in these animals, the young do not receive nourishment directly from

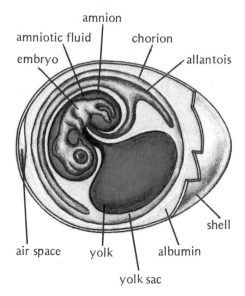

Figure 22-12. Internal Structure of the Chicken Egg.

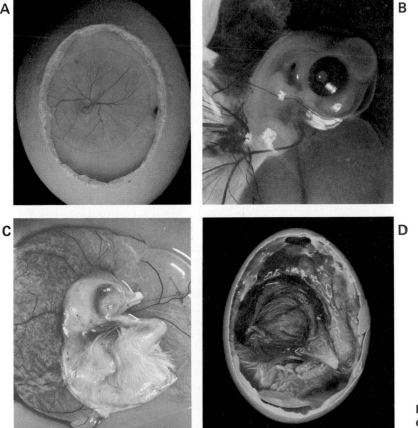

Figure 22-13. Stages of Development of Chicken. (A) 3 days (B) 7 days (C) 14 days (D) 19 days.

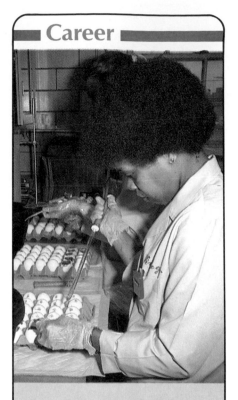

Career

Embryologist

Embryologists are biological scientists who study the development of living organisms from the fertilized egg stage through hatching or birth. In animals, an embryo is an organism in early stages of development that lacks a distinctly recognizable form. In plants, an embryo is the tiny rudimentary plant contained within a seed.

Embryology is a specialty within the field of biology. To do research in this field, a doctoral degree is usually required. A master's degree is adequate for some jobs in applied research, while a bachelor's degree may qualify a candidate for a beginning job. People preparing to be embryologists usually major in biology or zoology in college, with numerous courses in the physical sciences and mathematics as well, and then specialize in embryology in graduate school.

the mother. Instead, the source of their food is yolk stored in the egg. By the time the yolk is used up, the embryos have reached a stage of development at which they can maintain themselves, and they are born.

Among mammals, fertilization is internal, and the embryos typically develop internally within a structure called the *womb* (woom), or **uterus** (*yoo*-tuh-rus). They are born in relatively undeveloped condition and for a period feed on milk produced by the mother's mammary glands. The young are well-protected both during development and after birth, and a high percentage survive to adulthood. Thus, as might be expected, in animals in which the young develop internally, relatively few eggs are produced.

Placental mammals. Most mammals, including humans, are *placental* (pluh-*sent*-ul) *mammals*. In these mammals, blood vessels of the embryo's circulatory system are in close contact with the mother's circulatory system (see Figure 23-5). This contact occurs in a specialized structure called the **placenta** (pluh-*sent*-uh), which is in the wall of the uterus.

In the placenta, nutrients and oxygen diffuse from the mother's blood into the embryo's blood, and carbon dioxide and other wastes diffuse from the embryo's blood into the mother's blood. However, there is no direct connection between the two circulatory systems. The embryo is attached to the placenta by a structure called the **umbilical** (um-*bil*-ih-kul) **cord.** This structure contains blood vessels that connect the embryo's circulatory system to capillaries in the placenta.

Nonplacental mammals. There are two types of *nonplacental mammals*—mammals in which no placenta forms during development of the embryo. These are the *egg-laying mammals*, of which there are only two living species, and the *pouched mammals*.

The duckbill platypus is an example of an egg-laying mammal. The embryo of the platypus is encased in a leathery egg resembling that of a reptile. Unlike the eggs of other mammals, the eggs of the platypus contain a large amount of yolk. The female lays the eggs in a nest. When the young hatch out of the eggs, the female gathers them against her body. The young animals then feed on milk from the mother's mammary glands while completing their development.

In the pouched mammals, or *marsupials*, some internal development of the embryo occurs in the uterus, but no placenta is formed. The embryo obtains nourishment from the yolk of the egg. The young animal is born in a very immature condition. It crawls into a pouch on the outside of the mother's body and attaches itself to a mammary gland. Development is completed in the pouch. Most marsupials are found in Australia. The kangaroo is the most familiar example (see Figure 22-14). The opossum is a marsupial found in the Western Hemisphere.

Figure 22-14. Mother Kangaroo and Baby

Chapter Review

SUMMARY

- Development is the complex series of events by which a single cell becomes an adult multicellular organism. In animals, the development of the embryo includes cleavage, growth, and differentiation. Cleavage results in the formation of the blastula.

- At the end of the blastula stage, gastrulation occurs, leading to the formation of the three germ layers—ectoderm, endoderm, and mesoderm.

- Patterns of development are controlled by the DNA of the chromosomes. Interactions between neighboring cells greatly influence the course of development of cells.

- Development in animals may be external or internal. In most aquatic animals, eggs lack shells and development is external. Some land animals, such as birds, reptiles, and a few mammals, produce shelled eggs that develop externally. Stored yolk within the egg provides nourishment for the externally developing embryo.

- Among placental mammals, development is internal. A special structure, the placenta, provides for the exchange of substances between the mother and developing young. Pouched mammals, after a period of internal development, develop in an external pouch.

KNOW THE TERMS

allantois	cleavage	endoderm	morula
amnion	development	extraembryonic membrane	placenta
blastocoel	differentiation	gastrula	primitive gut
blastopore	ectoderm	gastrulation	umbilical cord
blastula	embryo	germ layers	uterus
chorion	embryonic induction	mesoderm	yolk sac

SECTION QUESTIONS

Embryonic Development

1. What is cleavage?
2. What is a blastula?
3. What substance in the egg affects cleavage?
4. Name the three germ layers in the gastrula.
5. Define the term differentiation.

Control of Development

6. Name the material that controls development in a fertilized egg.
7. What part of the cell turns portions of the DNA on and off?

8. What are organizers?

External and Internal Development

9. Where may embryonic development occur?
10. List the needs that must be met for an embryo to develop.
11. Name two groups of animals that have internal fertilization and external development.
12. Name the four extraembryonic membranes.
13. Name the two types of mammals.
14. Name the two types of nonplacental mammals and give an example of each.

KNOW THE FACTS

Copy the number of each statement below on a sheet of paper. Beside each number, write whether the statement is true or false. If the statement is false, replace the italicized word(s) with a term that will make the statement true.

1. The hollow-ball stage of development in an animal embryo is called a *blastula.*
2. The complex series of events by which a fertilized egg gives rise to an adult organism is called *development.*
3. When an animal embryo is a solid ball of cells, it is called the *morula.*
4. In the chicken egg, the nucleus and cytoplasm are concentrated at the *vegetal pole.*
5. The cavity within the gastrula is called the *primitive gut.*
6. The *digestive* tube is formed by the neural plate.
7. The hereditary material that controls development is found in the *cytoplasm.*
8. In most *aquatic* animals, fertilization and development are external.

9. Species that develop in *water* produce large numbers of eggs.
10. *Reptile* eggs are usually abandoned by the mother.
11. The *yolk sac* is the outermost extraembryonic membrane in a chicken.
12. The *allantois* is the fluid-filled sac that surrounds a chicken embryo and cushions it from shock.
13. The *placenta* is the organ in which the embryos of mammals develop.
14. The *umbilical cord* attaches the embryo to the placenta.
15. The *placenta* brings the blood of the mother into close contact with the blood of the embryo.

UNDERSTANDING THE CONCEPTS

16. Explain how cleavage reduces the size of the cells of the embryo.
17. Describe the process of gastrulation.
18. Where are the three germ layers located?
19. Give examples of structures formed by each germ layer.
20. How are the two openings of the digestive system formed?
21. Explain the role of embryonic induction in differentiation.
22. How do eggs that develop in water obtain nourishment and oxygen?
23. Briefly describe the structure of a bird's egg.
24. What are the advantages of a shelled egg for external development on land?
25. What are the functions of the four extraembryonic membranes of the bird's egg?
26. What are the functions of the placenta?

THINK CRITICALLY

27. Why do reptiles lay more eggs than do birds? Why are most mammalian eggs smaller than bird and reptile eggs?
28. What conclusion would J. G. Gurden have drawn if the frog eggs in his experiment had not developed into normal frogs but into intestinal cells?
29. *Ecto-* means external and *-derm* means skin. Explain why *ectoderm* is an appropriate term for the outer germ cell layer. Why is it odd that an organism's nervous system develops from the ectoderm? Explain the process by which the ectoderm differentiates into nervous system tissues.
30. Which germ cell layer do you think gives rise to the human heart? Explain your conclusion.
31. List the factors that affect differentiation. Which do you think has the greater impact on differentiation? Explain why.
32. Scientists have discovered that certain toxic substances in a mother's body—hallucinatory drugs, for example—can have dangerous effects on her developing fetus. Explain why.
33. Many marsupial species inhabit Australia. However, scientists fear that these mammals are doomed to extinction because they are unable to compete with placental mammals. Why might this be so?

THINK CREATIVELY

34. Design a simple experiment to locate an organizer for the neural tube of a developing frog embryo.
35. Imagine that you found two birds' nests—one on the ground with two large speckled eggs in it, and one in a tree with five small white eggs in it. What conclusions would you draw about the two bird species? Support your conclusions.

FOR FURTHER INVESTIGATION

1. Guppies are live-bearing fish; zebra fish are egg layers. In order to compare reproduction and development, set up separate fish tanks for breeding each type of fish. Record and date your observations carefully and write a report.
2. In the early spring, if it is legal in your area, collect some frog eggs or tadpoles. Place them in a large jar of pond water and watch them develop. Record your observations and write a report.
3. Study slides that show chick embryo or amphioxus development. Write an illustrated report.
4. Write a report on one of the career opportunities listed below. See suggested procedures, p. 9, "For Further Investigation" Activity 3.
   a. Naturalist
   b. Poultry scientist
   c. Tropical fish store manager
5. Prepare a report on the life and contributions of one of the following scientists:
   a. Mary Reddnick
   b. Frances Kelsey
   c. Granville Woods
   d. Marjorie Horning

FOR FURTHER READING

Beaconsfield, P., and others, "The Placenta," *Scientific American,* August, 1980.

Johnson, Sylvia A., *Inside an Egg,* Lerner Pub. Minneapolis, 1982.

Lauber, Patricia, *What's Hatching Out of That Egg?* Crown Pub., New York, 1979.

Monmaney, Terence, "Life Taking Shape: A Developing View," *Science 85,* September, 1985.

Restak, R., "Newborn Knowledge," *Science 82,* January/February, 1982.

Chapter 23

HUMAN REPRODUCTION

Several generations of a native American family are represented in this portrait.

HUMAN REPRODUCTIVE SYSTEMS

Objectives:
1. List the major structures of the male reproductive system and briefly describe the functions of each.
2. List the major structures of the female reproductive system and briefly describe the functions of each.
3. Describe the male and female secondary sex characteristics, and name the hormones involved in the development of these characteristics.

23-1 The Male Reproductive System

The male gonads are the testes. The testes produce sperm cells, which are the male gametes, and the male sex hormone, testosterone. Testosterone is responsible for the **secondary sex characteristics** such as the body hair, muscle development, and deep voice characteristic of males. These traits usually appear during adolescence.

The structure of the male reproductive system is shown in Figure 23-1. There are two testes, which are located in a sac of skin that is outside the body wall. This sac, which is called the **scrotum** (*skroht*-um), keeps the temperature of the testes slightly lower than that of the rest of the body. The lower temperature is best for the production and storage of sperm.

Each testis consists of small, coiled tubes called the *seminiferous* (sem-uh-*nif*-uh-rus) *tubules*. There are 300 to 600 tubules in each testis. Immature sperm are produced in

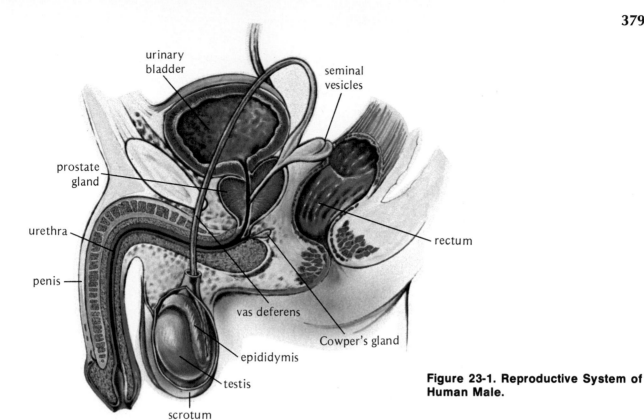

urinary bladder

seminal vesicles

prostate gland

urethra

penis

vas deferens

Cowper's gland

rectum

epididymis

testis

scrotum

Figure 23-1. Reproductive System of Human Male.

the seminiferous tubules. From there, the sperm pass to the **epididymis** (ep-uh-*did*-uh-mis), a storage area on the upper, rear part of the testis. The sperm remain in the epididymis until they are mature. They leave the epididymis through the **vas deferens** (*def*-uh-renz), a tube that leads upward from each testis into the lower part of the abdomen.

The two vas deferens join at the **urethra**, the passageway for the elimination of urine (see page 200). In the human male, the urethra passes through the penis to the outside of the body. It is also the passageway through which sperm leave the body. As sperm enter the urethra, the *seminal vesicles, Cowper's glands,* and the *prostate* (*prahs*-tayt) *gland* all secrete fluids into the urethra. The mixture of these fluids and the sperm is called **semen** (*see*-men). The passage of semen through the urethra occurs by a process called **ejaculation** (ih-jak-yuh-*lay*-shun). For a short time before, during, and after ejaculation, reflex actions keep the outlet of the urinary bladder closed, thereby preventing urine from entering the urethra.

23-2 The Female Reproductive System

The female gonads are the ovaries. The ovaries produce eggs, which are the female gametes, and also secrete the female sex hormone estrogen. Estrogen is responsible for the female secondary sex characteristics, such as development of the breasts, broadened pelvis, and pattern of fat distribution.

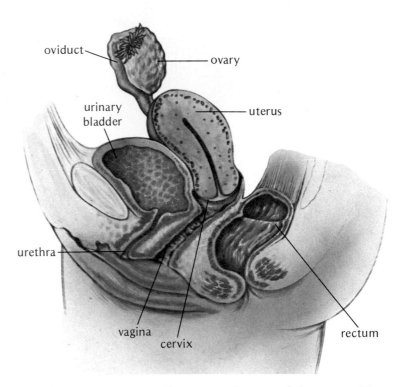

Figure 23-2. Reproductive System of Human Female.

These characteristics usually appear during adolescence. Estrogen also plays a large role in the menstrual cycle, which we will study in the next section.

The structure of the female reproductive system is shown in Figure 23-2. The female has two ovaries, located deep in the lower part of the abdomen. They are about 4 centimeters long and 2 centimeters wide. Each ovary contains about 200,000 tiny egg sacs called **follicles.** Each follicle contains an immature egg. These immature eggs are already present at the time of birth (see page 357). During the life of a female, no more than about 500 mature eggs are produced.

When an egg matures, the follicle surrounding it ruptures, or bursts, and the egg is released at the surface of the ovary (see Figure 23-3). This process is called **ovulation** (ahv-yuh-*lay*-shun). Ovulation first occurs at puberty, when the individual becomes sexually mature and capable of reproduction. Thereafter ovulation occurs about once a month.

Near each ovary, but not connected to it, is an **oviduct** (*oh*-vuh-duhkt), or *Fallopian* (fuh-*loh*-pee-un) *tube.* The oviduct is a tube with a funnel-like opening. Ciliated cells lining the oviduct create a current that draws the released egg into the tube. The egg passes through the oviduct to the **uterus** (*yoot*-uh-rus), a thick-walled, muscular, pear-shaped organ. If sperm are present in the oviduct, the egg may be fertilized. If the egg is fertilized, it completes its development in the uterus. The narrow neck of the uterus is called the **cervix** (*ser*-viks). The cervix opens into the **vagina** (vuh-*jy*-nuh), or *birth canal*, which

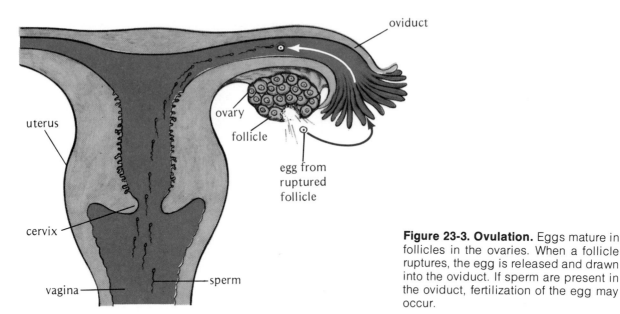

uterus

ovary

follicle

egg from
ruptured
follicle

cervix

vagina

sperm

oviduct

Figure 23-3. Ovulation. Eggs mature in
follicles in the ovaries. When a follicle
ruptures, the egg is released and drawn
into the oviduct. If sperm are present in
the oviduct, fertilization of the egg may
occur.

leads to the outside of the body. At birth, the child leaves the
mother's body through this passageway. In the human female,
the urethra has its own opening and is completely separate from
the reproductive system.

THE MENSTRUAL CYCLE

Objectives:
1. Describe the events of the menstrual cycle.
2. Name the hormones involved in the menstrual
   cycle, and describe the functions of each.

23-3   Characteristics of the Menstrual Cycle

In the human female, a mature egg develops and is released
from one of the ovaries approximately every 28 days. At this
time, the wall of the uterus has undergone a build-up and is
prepared to accept a fertilized egg for development. If the egg
is not fertilized, the newly built-up portion of the uterine wall
breaks down, and this material, along with the unfertilized
egg, is discharged from the body. The cycle then begins again
with the maturing of another egg and the build-up of the
uterine wall. This cycle is known as the **menstrual** (*men-
struhl*) **cycle.** The changes that take place during the cycle
involve the interaction of hormones produced by the
hypothalamus, pituitary gland, and ovary.

The menstrual cycle begins at puberty, which usually occurs in human females sometime between the ages of 10 and
14. The cycle ceases temporarily during pregnancy. It ceases
permanently sometime in middle age, usually between the

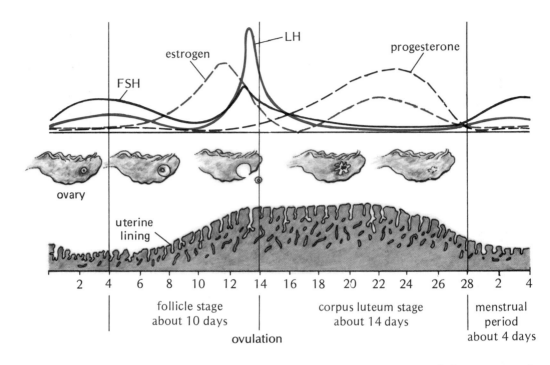

ovary

uterine
lining

| 2 | 4 | 6 | 8 | 10 | 12 | 14 | 16 | 18 | 20 | 22 | 24 | 26 | 28 | 2 | 4 |

follicle stage
about 10 days

ovulation

corpus luteum stage
about 14 days

menstrual
period
about 4 days

Figure 23-4. The Menstrual Cycle. This cycle of changes results in the release of an egg, the preparation of the uterine lining for a possible implantation and pregnancy, and the return to the initial state if no implantation occurs. The cycle is controlled by four interacting hormones and repeats about every 28 days.

ages of 45 and 50. The permanent cessation of the menstrual cycle is called *menopause* (*men*-uh-pawz).

23-4 Stages of the Menstrual Cycle

The menstrual cycle can be divided into four stages (see Figure 23-4).

Follicle stage. Follicle-stimulating hormone (FSH) is secreted by the pituitary gland (see page 272). FSH causes several follicles in the ovary to begin developing. Usually, only one matures. As the follicle develops, it secretes estrogen. The estrogen stimulates the uterine lining to thicken with mucus and a rich supply of blood vessels. These changes prepare the uterus for a possible pregnancy. This stage lasts 10 to 14 days.

Ovulation. A high level of estrogen in the blood causes the pituitary to decrease secretion of FSH and begin secretion of luteinizing hormone (LH). When the concentration of LH in the blood reaches a certain level, ovulation occurs—that is, the follicle ruptures, releasing a mature egg. Ovulation usually takes place in about the middle of the menstrual cycle.

Corpus luteum stage. After ovulation, LH causes the ruptured follicle to fill with cells, forming a yellow body called the **corpus luteum** (*kor*-pus *loot*-ee-um). The corpus luteum begins to secrete the hormone progesterone, which maintains the continued growth of the uterine lining. Because of its role in maintaining the uterine wall, progesterone is often called the hormone of pregnancy. It also prevents the development of new follicles in the ovary by inhibiting the release of FSH. The corpus luteum stage lasts 10 to 14 days.

Menstruation. If fertilization does not occur, secretion of LH decreases, and the corpus luteum breaks down. This results in a decrease in the level of progesterone. With a drop in the progesterone level, the thickened lining of the uterus can no longer be maintained, and it breaks down. The extra layers of the lining, the unfertilized egg, and a small amount of blood pass out of the body through the vagina. This is called **menstruation** (men-*stray*-shun). It lasts from about 3 to 5 days. While menstruation is occurring, the amount of estrogen in the blood is dropping. The pituitary increases its output of FSH, and a new follicle starts to mature.

FERTILIZATION, IMPLANTATION, AND DEVELOPMENT

Objectives:
1. Describe fertilization and implantation in humans.
2. Explain the role of the placenta and umbilical cord in pregnancy.
3. List the extraembryonic membranes of human pregnancy, and explain the functions of each.
4. Explain the following terms: *gestation period, labor, navel, afterbirth.*
5. Explain the difference between fraternal and identical twins.

23-5 Fertilization

In human mating, or sexual intercourse, hundreds of millions of sperm are ejaculated into the vagina. The sperm then travel through the cervix, across the uterus, and into the oviducts. If an egg is passing down one of the oviducts at this time, fertilization—the fusion of a sperm and an egg nucleus—may occur. The egg secretes a chemical that attracts the sperm. One of the sperm breaks through the membranes surrounding the egg, and the sperm cell nucleus enters the cytoplasm of the egg cell. When this happens, the membranes around the egg change, preventing penetration by any other sperm. The sperm nucleus fuses with the egg nucleus, resulting in the diploid cell called the zygote.

23-6 Implantation and Development

After fertilization, the zygote undergoes cleavage and develops into a blastula (see page 367) as it moves down the oviduct toward the uterus. About 5 to 10 days after fertilization, the embryo enters the uterus. Within the uterus, the outer layer of cells of the embryo secrete enzymes that digest part of the thick lining of the uterus, and the embryo attaches itself at this spot.

Sidelight

The Estrous Cycle

Humans and other primates (apes and monkeys) are the only mammals that have a menstrual cycle. Other mammals have an *estrous cycle*. This cycle is marked by periodic changes in the female's sex organs and in the urge to mate, but there is little or no bleeding at the end of the cycle.

During most of the cycle, the female is not fertile and will not mate. Mating occurs only during the short periods in the estrous cycle when the female is fertile—when the uterus and associated structures increase in size in preparation for pregnancy. Ovulation occurs spontaneously during the fertile period, or after mating, depending on the species. During fertile periods, the female is said to be "in heat." If fertilization does not occur, the sex organs regress to their normal state.

Mammals, such as foxes (see photo), coyotes, and wolves, have one estrous cycle a year while cats and dogs have two.

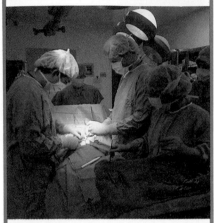

Fetal Surgery

In recent years surgeons have begun to perform corrective surgery on fetuses in the womb. This procedure is being used in cases where the condition of the fetus, if left untreated, would lead to abnormal development, or even death. Amoung the fetal conditions now being corrected by surgery are hydrocephalus—a build-up of excessive fluid in the brain, and hydronephrosis—a blockage in the urinary tract that causes a backup of urine in the fetus's abdomen. Both conditions cause severe developmental problems.

Fetal surgery is a highly specialized type of surgery. Although it is not as common as other forms of corrective surgery, it does constitute a significant advance in medical science. As the ability to detect fetal developmental problems improves, and as experience in fetal surgery continues, the range of disorders that can be corrected surgically will certainly expand.

The great appeal of fetal surgery is that it has the potential for correcting conditions that can cause a lifetime of physical suffering.

The attachment of the embryo to the wall of the uterus is called **implantation** (im-plan-*tay*-shun). Implantation marks the beginning of **pregnancy**, the period during which the developing baby is carried in the uterus.

After implantation, the embryo undergoes gastrulation. The three germ layers are formed, and all the tissues and organs of the body develop from these layers by growth and differentiation. The developing human is called an *embryo* from the time of fertilization up to about 8 weeks. After this time, it is usually called a **fetus** (*feet*-us).

During pregnancy, the menstrual cycle is suppressed by a hormone secreted by the chorion, one of the membranes that surround the embryo. This hormone prevents the breakdown of the corpus luteum. The corpus luteum continues to secrete high levels of progesterone, which in turn maintains the thickened wall of the uterus.

23-7 Nourishment of the Embryo

From the time of fertilization until implantation in the uterus, the embryo is nourished by food stored in the egg. After implantation, the embryo receives food and oxygen from the mother's body through a temporary organ, the **placenta**.

In humans, the outer cell layer of the blastula becomes the **chorion**—the membrane that surrounds the embryo. Small fingerlike projections called *chorionic* (kor-ee-*ahn*-ik) *villi* form on the outer surface of the chorion, and extend into the uterine lining. The chorionic villi and the uterine lining form the placenta, which provides for the exchange of nutrients and wastes between the embryo and the mother. It also secretes hormones necessary for the maintenance of pregnancy.

The blood of the fetus and the mother do not mix. Fetal blood carrying wastes flows to the placenta through arteries in the **umbilical cord**. These arteries branch repeatedly, finally forming capillaries in the chorionic villi (see Figure 23-5). The villi are bathed in maternal blood that has been forced by arteriole blood pressure out of maternal blood vessels into spaces around the villi. Nutrients and oxygen in the maternal blood diffuse into the fetus's blood, and wastes diffuse from it. Fetal veins in the umbilical cord then return blood rich in nutrients and oxygen to the fetus. The blood containing fetal wastes returns to the maternal circulation from which the wastes are excreted.

The placenta acts as a barrier that protects the fetus from some harmful substances in the mother's blood. However, many dangerous substances can pass through the placenta from the mother's blood to the fetus's blood. The German measles virus, as well as nicotine, alcohol, and many drugs, can pass through the placenta and harm the fetus.

23-8 Extraembryonic Membranes

The human embryo develops the same extraembryonic membranes as birds and reptiles (see page 372). However,

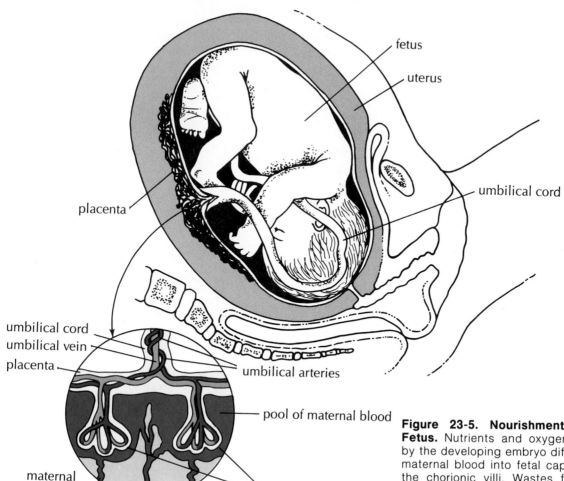

placenta

fetus
uterus

umbilical cord

umbilical cord
umbilical vein
placenta

umbilical arteries

pool of maternal blood

maternal
circulation

chorionic villi

Figure 23-5. Nourishment of the Fetus. Nutrients and oxygen needed by the developing embryo diffuse from maternal blood into fetal capillaries in the chorionic villi. Wastes from fetal blood diffuse into maternal blood. Materials are transported to and from the fetus through the fetal blood vessels in the umbilical cord. There is no direct connection between the circulatory systems of the fetus and the mother.

these membranes serve different functions in human development. The chorion is involved in implantation and the formation of the placenta. The amnion, which is filled with **amniotic fluid,** surrounds the fetus. The fluid protects the fetus, providing it with a stable environment and absorbing shocks. The allantois is a membrane that grows out of the fetal digestive tract. Along with the yolk sac it forms the umbilical cord.

23-9 Birth

The length of a pregnancy is called the **gestation** (jes-*tay*-shun) **period.** The human gestation period is a little over nine months. When the fetus is ready to be born, the uterine muscles begin slow, rhythmic contractions. This is called **labor.** At this time the opening of the cervix begins to enlarge. Its diameter must expand from 1 or 2 centimeters to 11 or 12 centimeters before the baby can pass out of the uterus and into the birth canal. When the cervix is expanded, the contractions force the baby, head first, from the uterus into the vagina and out of the mother's body. During labor, the amniotic membrane bursts, releasing the amniotic fluid. This fluid eases the passage of the baby through the birth canal.

Figure 23-6. Identical Twins. Identical twins develop from the same egg. They are always of the same sex and look very much alike.

When the baby is expelled from the mother's body, the umbilical cord is still attached to the placenta. The umbilical cord is then tied and cut, leaving a scar called the **navel.** Shortly after the birth of the baby, additional uterine contractions expel the placenta and amnion, which are known as the **afterbirth.**

During pregnancy, progesterone and estrogen prepare the breasts for nursing. After birth, the pituitary hormone prolactin causes the mammary glands in the breasts to secrete milk.

23-10 Multiple Births

Occasionally, two eggs mature at the same time and are released into the oviduct together. Each egg may then be fertilized by a different sperm. Both embryos may become implanted in the uterus and develop independently. Since the two embryos have received different hereditary material, they develop into individuals with different characteristics. Two individuals born from the same pregnancy are called *twins.* When they have developed from different eggs, they are called **fraternal twins.** Fraternal twins may be of opposite sex, and they are no more alike than any two children of the same parents.

Figure 23–7. Quadruplets. In this multiple birth, two individuals are female and two are male.

In other cases, a single fertilized egg divides into two embryos at a very early stage of development. The two individuals that then develop have the same hereditary makeup and are physically very much alike (see Figure 23-6). Two individuals that develop from the same egg are called **identical twins.** Identical twins are always of the same sex.

Twins are the most common type of multiple birth. However, in rare cases, three or more embryos may form during the same pregnancy. Such multiple births may be fraternal, identical, or a combination of both types. (see Figure 23-7)

Chapter Review

SUMMARY

- The male gonads, the testes, produce sperm and secrete testosterone. The mixture of sperm and the secretions of several glands is called semen.

- The female gonads, the ovaries, produce eggs and secrete estrogen. The ovaries are filled with follicles, each containing an immature egg. Once a month a follicle bursts, releasing a mature egg at the surface of the ovary. The release of the egg from the ovary is called ovulation. Once released, the egg enters an oviduct, which is connected to the uterus.

- Ovulation occurs about every 28 days. Prior to the release of the mature egg, the wall of the uterus becomes thickened in preparation for the receipt of a fertilized egg. If the egg is not fertilized, the newly built-up portion of the uterine wall breaks down, and the layers of tissue and the unfertilized egg pass out of the body, along with a small quantity of blood.

- Another egg then begins to mature, and the wall of the uterus again begins to thicken. This is the menstrual cycle. The menstrual cycle is regulated by estrogen and progesterone from the ovaries and FSH and LH from the pituitary.

- After an egg is fertilized, it undergoes cleavage as it passes down the oviduct into the uterus. The outer layer of the embryo secretes enzymes that prepare a part of the uterine wall for implantation of the embryo. Here, the development of the embryo continues. The human embryo develops four extraembryonic membranes. The fetus is attached to the placenta by the umbilical cord.

- The human gestation period is about nine months. At the end of pregnancy, rhythmic uterine contractions push the baby out of the uterus into the birth canal and then out of the mother's body.

KNOW THE TERMS

afterbirth	fetus	menstrual cycle	secondary sex characteristic
amniotic fluid	follicle	menstruation	semen
cervix	fraternal twins	navel	umbilical cord
chorion	gestation period	oviduct	urethra
corpus luteum	identical twins	ovulation	uterus
ejaculation	implantation	placenta	vagina
epididymis	labor	scrotum	vas deferens

SECTION QUESTIONS

Human Reproductive Systems

1. What are the male gonads?
2. Name the glands whose secretions are added to the sperm.
3. What is the passage of semen through the urethra called?
4. What are the female gonads?
5. What is ovulation?

The Menstrual Cycle

6. What is menopause?
7. Name the four stages of the menstrual cycle.

Fertilization, Implantation, and Development

8. In which part of the female reproductive system does fertilization generally occur?
9. What cell is formed by fertilization?
10. Define the term *pregnancy*.
11. What organ provides food and oxygen for the developing embryo?
12. Name the extraembryonic membranes of human development.
13. What kind of twins develop from a single fertilized egg?

KNOW THE FACTS

Copy the number of each sentence below on a sheet of paper. Beside each number, write the letter identifying the answer that correctly completes the sentence.

1. Semen consists of
   a. mature and immature sperm.
   b. mature sperm and secretions of the epididymis.
   c. sperm and secretions from the testes and epididymis.
   d. sperm and secretions from seminal vesicles, Cowper's glands, and prostate gland.
2. In the human female, the ovaries are located
   a. in the uterus.
   b. next to the vagina.
   c. near the Fallopian tubes.
   d. in the lower part of the stomach.
3. The follicle-stimulating hormone (FSH) is
   a. an ovarian hormone responsible for building up the uterine lining.
   b. a pituitary hormone that stimulates the growth of a follicle.
   c. a hormone stimulated by the follicle that is responsible for building up the uterine lining.
   d. an ovarian hormone that stimulates a follicle to produce an egg.
4. The correct order of events in the menstrual cycle of the human female is
   a. growth of follicle, rupture of follicle, and ovulation.
   b. growth of follicle, breakdown of corpus luteum, and ovulation.
   c. menstruation, ovulation, and rupture of follicle.
   d. rupture of follicle, menstruation, and ovulation.
5. Progesterone
   a. stimulates the development of follicles.
   b. maintains the growth of the uterine lining.
   c. stimulates development of the uterine lining.
   d. stimulates secretion of LH.
6. The lining of the uterus is shed during
   a. ovulation.
   b. the follicle stage.
   c. menstruation.
   d. the corpus luteum stage.

7. The correct pathway that sperm must travel to reach the egg is
   a. vagina, uterus, cervix, and oviduct.
   b. vagina, oviduct, cervix, and uterus.
   c. vagina, cervix, oviduct, and uterus.
   d. vagina, cervix, uterus, and oviduct.
8. A developing embryo is normally implanted in the lining of the
   a. oviduct.   c. cervix.
   b. vagina.   d. uterus.
9. Which statement about the placenta is *not* true?
   a. It is made up of chorionic villi and uterine lining.
   b. It secretes hormones necessary for pregnancy.
   c. The blood of the fetus and mother are mixed in it.
   d. Nutrients and wastes are exchanged across it.
10. The umbilical cord is formed from the
    a. allantois and yolk sac.
    b. amnion and chorion.
    c. allantois.
    d. amnion.
11. The rhythmic contractions that force a baby from its mother's body during birth are known as
    a. afterbirth.   c. puberty.
    b. gestation.   d. labor.
12. The navel is the
    a. scar where the umbilical cord was attached to the baby.
    b. scar where the placenta was attached to the baby.
    c. site of implantation of the embryo.
    d. extraembryonic membrane which forms the placenta.
13. Twins that are *not* identical result from the fertilization of
    a. one egg by one sperm, and the egg splits during cleavage.
    b. one egg by two sperm.
    c. two eggs by two sperm.
    d. two eggs by one sperm.

UNDERSTAND THE CONCEPTS

14. What are the functions of the testes?
15. What is the function of testosterone?
16. Why are the testes located in the scrotum?
17. What are the functions of the ovaries?
18. What are the functions of estrogen?
19. Trace the path of an unfertilized egg from the ovarian follicle until it leaves the body.
20. Describe briefly what happens during the menstrual cycle.
21. Describe what happens to the ovaries and uterus during each stage of the menstrual cycle.
22. Approximately how long is each stage of the menstrual cycle?
23. Describe the development of a zygote from fertilization through implantation.
24. How is the menstrual cycle suppressed during pregnancy?
25. What are the functions of the chorion?
26. How does the placenta perform its functions?
27. What are the amnion and amniotic fluid and what are their functions?
28. Describe what happens during the birth of a baby.
29. What is the afterbirth?

THINK CRITICALLY

30. Why is it that sperm can survive for only about 24 hours in the female body, whereas they survive much longer in the male testes?
31. What role do the fluids that make up semen play in fertilization? Why can amniotic fluid and semen be considered adaptations to life on land?
32. What could prevent the embryo from implanting in the uterus? Could it survive and develop anyway? Explain.
33. Describe the fertilization process that would give rise to this multiple birth: two identical females and two identical males.

THINK CREATIVELY

34. Suggest some possible ways in which the timing of the onset and cessation of the menstrual cycle is adaptive.
35. Some men and women are unable to have children. Suggest some possible explanations for their infertility.

FOR FURTHER INVESTIGATION

1. It is now generally accepted that breast feeding is better than bottle feeding. Interview one mother who has nursed her children and one who has used bottle feeding. Prepare a short written report on this topic.
2. Smoking, some drugs such as alcohol, and certain diseases such as German measles can cause abnormal development of a fetus. After doing library research, write up your findings in the form of a feature article for a magazine or newspaper.
3. Prepare a report on one of the career opportunities listed below. See suggested procedures, p. 9, "For Further Investigation" Activity 3.
   a. Gynecologist
   b. Nurse-midwife
   c. Pediatrician
4. Prepare a report on the life and contributions of one of the following scientists:
   a. Sara Josephine Baker
   b. William Hinton
   c. Alfred Kinsey
   d. Virginia Johnson

FOR FURTHER READING

Gold, M., "The Baby Makers," *Science 85*, April, 1985.

Johnson, Eric W., *Sex: Telling It Straight*, Lippincott Co., Philadelphia, PA, 1979.

Miller, J., "Window on the Womb," *Science News*, February 2, 1985.

Ward, Brian R., *Birth and Growth* (The Human Body Series), Franklin Watts, New York, 1983.

Chapter 24

SEXUAL REPRODUCTION IN PLANTS

The flower is the part of the plant containing structures involved in sexual reproduction.

THE GENERALIZED PLANT LIFE CYCLE

Objectives:
1. Name the major land plant groups.
2. Explain the concepts of *sporophyte, gametophyte,* and *alternation of generations.*
3. Explain the term *dominant generation.*

Sexual reproduction in plants, as in animals, involves two processes: meiosis, and fusion of gametes. Special structures in plants produce sperm cells and egg cells, and there are various adaptations in the different kinds of plants for bringing the sperm nucleus and the egg nucleus together.

The major land plant groups are the mosses, ferns, and seed plants. The seed plants, which evolved more recently than the mosses and ferns, include the **gymnosperms** (*jim*-nuh-spermz) and the **angiosperms** (*an*-jee-uh-spermz). Most gymnosperms are cone-bearing plants, such as the pines. Their seeds are borne in an exposed condition on cones. In contrast, the angiosperms, which are the flowering plants, produce their seeds within the protective tissue of a specialized flower structure that later forms the fruit.

In mosses and ferns sperm are motile, and water is required for the sperm to swim to the egg. In these plants moisture in the form of dew or rain is necessary for sexual reproduction to occur. Gymnosperms and angiosperms, on the other hand, have evolved special adaptations for transporting sperm to egg that do not require water. Thus seed plants can thrive and reproduce sexually on land in areas where the sexual reproduction of mosses and ferns is not possible, for lack of moisture.

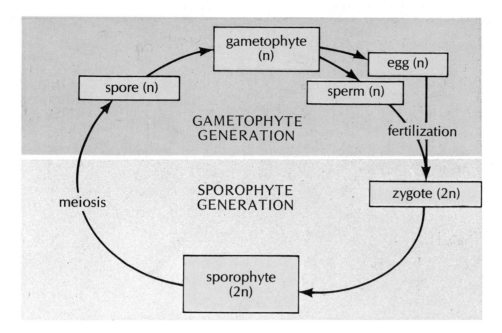

Figure 24-1. Alternation of Generations in Land Plants. In land-dwelling plants there is a haploid, gamete-producing generation, the gametophyte, and a diploid spore-producing generation, the sporophyte. The gametophyte and sporophyte are not two stages in the life of an individual plant, but rather two separate individual plants of the same species.

24-1 Alternation of Generations

The life cycles of land-dwelling plants show an alternation between two generations—a haploid, gamete-producing generation and a diploid, spore-producing generation. Each generation of the life cycle consists of a separate and different form of the plant. Organisms having these two different generations are said to show an **alternation of generations.**

In the gamete-producing, or **gametophyte** (guh-*meet*-uh-fyt), **generation,** all the cells of the plant—the gametophyte—are haploid (*n*) (see Figure 24-1). Gametes are produced by the plant through ordinary mitosis (*not meiosis*), followed by differentiation. When fertilization occurs, a male and a female gamete fuse to form a diploid (2*n*) zygote. The spore-producing, or **sporophyte** (*spor*-uh-fyt), **generation** develops from the zygote and is a diploid plant. In the sporophyte, certain cells undergo meiosis, or reduction division, resulting in the formation of spores. Spores, therefore, contain haploid nuclei. When the spores are released, they germinate, developing into haploid gametophytes.

Usually one generation is more conspicuous than the other. The more obvious generation is said to be the *dominant generation.* The plant of the dominant generation is larger and lives longer than the plant of the other generation.

LIFE CYCLES OF NON-SEED PLANTS

Objective:
1. Describe the life cycle of mosses.
2. Describe the life cycle of ferns.

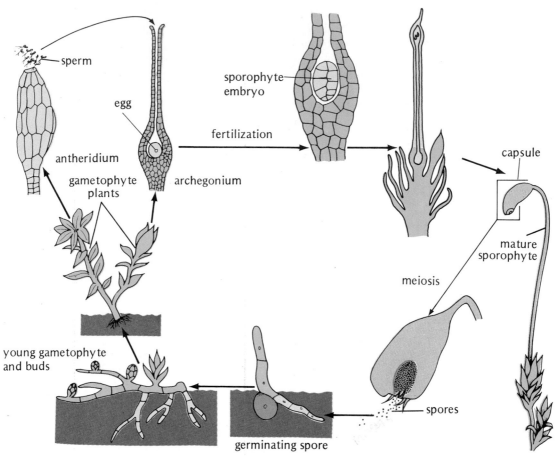

Figure 24-2. Life Cycle of Mosses. In mosses, the haploid, or gametophyte, generation is dominant.

24-2   Life Cycle of Mosses

The **mosses** are among the most primitive land plants. These plants have structures similar in function to the roots, stems, and leaves of higher plants, but they are simpler in organization. The stemlike structure is short, usually only several centimeters in height. It is surrounded by small leaflike structures only one cell thick. Anchoring the plant are hairlike rhizoids. which are composed of only one type of cell. Mosses lack the specialized conducting tissues of higher plants, so that transport of materials through the plant is relatively inefficient. Mosses, therefore, are small in size. They require a moist environment for growth and reproduction, and are found on the damp floor of the forest, on shaded rocks, and in swamps.

Mosses show an alternation of generations in which the gametophyte generation is dominant (see Figure 24-2). The gametophyte is much larger than the sporophyte. The haploid gametophyte generation is what we recognize as the moss plant. The sporophyte grows from the gametophyte and cannot live independently.

In some mosses, there are separate male and female gametophytes. The male reproductive organ is called the *antheridium* (an-thuh-*rid*-ee-um); the female reproductive organ is called the *archegonium* (ar-kuh-*goh*-nee-um). Each produces haploid gametes. Sperm released from the antheridium of a male plant swim through rain or dew to reach the egg in the archegonium of the female plant.

Fertilization of the egg produces a diploid zygote that grows directly into a sporophyte. The sporophyte grows out of the archegonium, becoming a single leafless stalk that is dependent on the leafy green gametophyte for nourishment. The sporophyte obtains its nourishment by means of a structure called a *foot*, which grows down into the gametophyte tissue. At the tip of the mature sporophyte, a cylindrical *capsule* develops. Within the capsule many haploid spores are produced by meiosis. These spores are released into the air. When they germinate, they form new haploid gametophytes, completing the life cycle.

24-3   Life Cycle of Ferns

In **ferns,** unlike mosses, the leafy green dominant generation is the sporophyte (see Figure 24-3). The diploid sporophyte consists of an underground stem called a rhizome,

Figure 24-3. Life Cycle of Ferns. In ferns, the diploid, or sporophyte, generation is dominant.

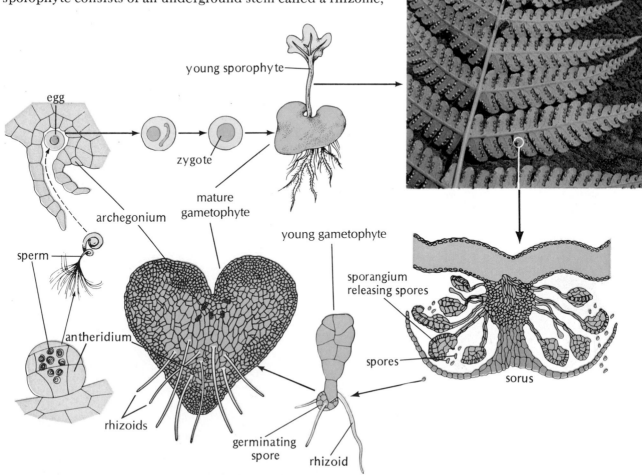

young sporophyte

egg

zygote

mature gametophyte

archegonium

young gametophyte

sperm

sporangium releasing spores

antheridium

spores

rhizoids

germinating spore

rhizoid

sorus

which grows just beneath the surface of the soil. From the lower surface of the rhizome, true roots develop, which anchor the plant and absorb water and minerals. From its upper surface the rhizome bears large leaves called *fronds*.

On the underside of some fronds are rows of small dots called *sori* (*sor*-ee). Within the sori, haploid spores are produced by meiosis. The spores are eventually released into the air and dispersed by the wind. Under favorable conditions of moisture, light, and temperature they germinate. The germinating spore forms a small, heart-shaped structure called a *prothallus* (proh-*thal*-us), which is the fern gametophyte. A prothallus bears both antheridia and archegonia in which gametes develop. The sperm released from the antheridia can fertilize an egg in an archegonium on the same gametophyte, or they can swim (in rain or dew) to a different gametophyte. The fertilized egg then grows into the mature sporophyte, the fern plant. The gametophyte withers and dies.

LIFE CYCLE OF GYMNOSPERMS

Objective:
    Describe the life cycle of a gymnosperm.

24-4   Development of Gametes

Seed plants are the most abundant land-dwelling plants. The seeds of the plant contain the plant embryo. Within the seed the embryo is protected from physical injury and from drying out. Gymnosperms include the cone-bearing seed plants, such as pines, spruces, and hemlocks (see Figure 24-4). Angiosperms are flowering seed plants.

In gymnosperms, the sporophyte generation is dominant. In many of these plants, the leaves are in the form of needles, and the reproductive organs are in the form of cones. Pine trees and other gymnosperms produce two types of cones (see Figure 24-5). The male cone is called the *pollen cone*; the larger female cone is called the *seed cone*. A single tree usually produces both pollen and seed cones. The spore-producing structures are found on the *scales* of the cones. The scales are actually modified leaves or branches.

In a pollen cone there are two spore cases, or *sporangia* (spaw-*ran*-jee-uh) on the underside of each scale. Many haploid spores are formed by meiosis in each sporangium. Within the confines of its spore wall, each haploid spore undergoes two rounds of mitosis. The resulting four-celled, thick-walled organism is an immature male gametophyte called a **pollen grain**. Two of its cells degenerate, leaving two cells—the *tube cell* and the *generative cell*.

In the seed cone, two sporangia are found on the upper surface of each scale. Meiosis within each sporangium produces

Figure 24-4. A Gymnosperm.

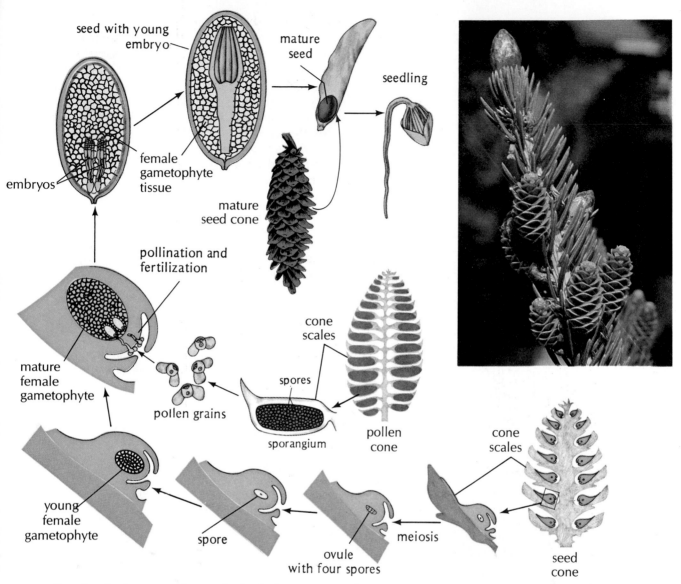

four haploid spores, three of which degenerate. The remaining spore divides by mitosis, forming the female gametophyte. The female gametophyte, sporangium, and associated structures form the **ovule** (*ohv*-yool). The female gametophyte forms two or three archegonia, and within each archegonium an egg cell develops.

24-5   Fertilization and Seed Development

When the pollen cones are mature, the sporangia burst, releasing millions of pollen grains. The pollen grains are carried by the wind. Some of the pollen grains land on a sticky material near a small opening on the ovule, the **micropyle** (*my*-kruh-pyl). A tube grows from a pollen grain through the micropyle and into the ovule and archegonium. This is the **pollen tube,** and it serves as a bridge between the pollen grain

Figure 24-5. Life Cycle of Gymnosperms. In most gymnosperms, the spore-bearing organs are in the form of cones and the leaves are in the form of needles. The photograph shows young seed cones near the end of a branch.

and the egg. The activities of the pollen tube are controlled by
the tube cell of the pollen grain. The generative cell of the
pollen grain forms two sperm cells. The two sperm pass through
the pollen tube into the ovule. One of the sperm fertilizes an
egg in the archegonium. The resulting zygote forms the plant
embryo. The ovule, which contains the plant embryo, develops
into a seed, which is eventually released from the cone. The
seeds are carried by the wind. Under favorable conditions, they
germinate, forming new sporophytes, such as pine trees.

   Note that in the life cycle of the gymnosperms, the small
gametophyte is totally dependent on the sporophyte. Also,
water is not necessary for fertilization because wind carries
the male gametophyte to the female gametophyte and the
sperm travels to the egg through the pollen tube.

LIFE CYCLE OF ANGIOSPERMS

Objectives:
   1. Draw a flower and label the following parts: pedicel;
      receptacle; sepals; petals; filament and anther of the
      stamen; and stigma, style, and ovary of the pistil.
   2. Describe the formation of male and female gametes
      in flowering plants.
   3. Describe pollination and fertilization in flowering
      plants.
   4. Describe the formation of fruits and seeds in flower-
      ing plants.
   5. Describe the structure of a seed, and explain the
      functions of the cotyledon, epicotyl, and hypocotyl.
   6. Describe several mechanisms for seed dispersal.

24-6   Structure of a Flower

   The angiosperms, the flowering plants, are the most successful and abundant land plants. The reproductive structures
of angiosperms are within the flowers. In these plants the
seeds are enclosed within a fruit. As in the gymnosperms,
the sporophyte generation is dominant and water is not required for fertilization.

   The flower develops from tissues that resemble those from
which stems and leaves grow. It is made up of rings of modified leaves on a specialized stem (see Figure 24-6). In the
center are the reproductive organs. The parts of the flower are
described below.

   1. The **pedicel** (*ped*-uh-sel) supports the flower and connects it to the stem of the plant.

   2. The **receptacle** (ruh-*sep*-tuh-kul) is the expanded end of
the pedicel to which the other flower parts are attached.

   3. The **sepals** (*seep*-ulz) are leaflike structures that form a
ring around the base of the flower. They enclose and protect
the flower bud before it blossoms. The sepals may be small

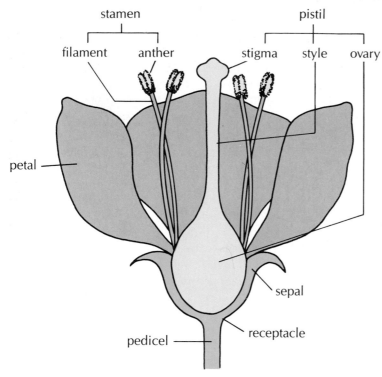

Figure 24-6. Structure of a Flower.

and green, or they may be large and brightly colored like the petals. The complete circle of sepals is called the **calyx** (*kay*-liks).

4. The **petals** are found within the sepals. In some flowers the petals are white, in others they are brightly colored. The complete circle of petals forms the **corolla** (kuh-*rohl*-uh). The petals surround the reproductive organs of the flower, the stamens and pistils.

5. The **stamens** (*stay*-menz) are generally called the male reproductive organs of the angiosperms. They are located inside the corolla. A stamen is often made up of two parts—a stalklike **filament** at the tip of which is a saclike structure called the **anther** (*an*-ther). Pollen grains are produced within the anthers. A flower may contain one to many stamens.

6. The **pistil** (*pis*-tul) is generally called the female reproductive organ of the angiosperms. It is located in the center of the flower. The pistil is made up of three parts. The top of the pistil is the **stigma** (*stig*-muh), which consists of an enlarged sticky knob that receives the pollen. Supporting the stigma is the **style**. At the base of the pistil is the expanded **ovary**, which contains the ovules. The ovary and other associated flower parts develop into the **fruit**, while the ovules develop into seeds. A flower may have one to many pistils.

Stamens and pistils are the *essential organs* of the flower. The corolla and calyx are *accessory organs*. Some flowers contain stamens, pistil, corolla, and calyx, while others are missing one or more of these structures. *Pistillate* (*pis*-tuh-layt) *flowers* contain pistils but no stamens, and *staminate* (*stam*-uh-nayt) *flowers* contain stamens but no pistils. Plants bearing only

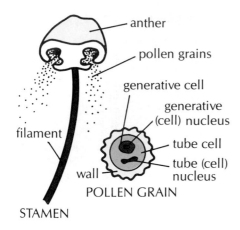

Figure 24-7. The Stamen. When the anther bursts, pollen grains are released.

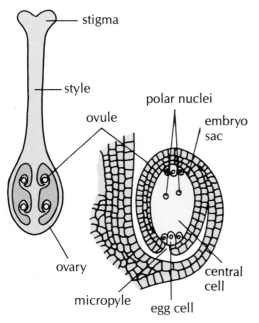

Figure 24-8. The Pistil. After fertilization, the ovary develops into a fruit and each ovule develops into a seed.

pistillate flowers are considered female plants, while those bearing only staminate flowers are considered male plants. Some plants contain both pistillate and staminate flowers.

24-7   Development of Gametes

Within the anthers of the stamens, haploid spores are produced by meiosis. The spores undergo one mitotic division, developing into pollen grains, which consist of a thick, protective wall that encloses two haploid cells—the tube cell and the generative cell (see Figure 24-7). The pollen grain is the male gametophyte generation of the angiosperm. The mature pollen grains are released when the anther bursts.

The ovary of the pistil contains one or more ovules (see Figure 24-8). The ovules are actually sporangia. Each ovule has a small opening called the micropyle and is attached to the wall of the ovary by a short stalk. Four haploid spores are produced by meiosis in each ovule. Three of the four spores degenerate, while the remaining spore undergoes mitosis three times. The resulting female gametophyte, called the **embryo sac,** has seven cells but eight haploid nuclei. Two of the nuclei, called the *polar nuclei*, reside within the large central cell. A cell near the micropyle becomes the egg cell.

24-8   Pollination

Pollination (pahl-uh-*nay*-shun) is the transfer of pollen from an anther to a stigma. In some plants, *self-pollination* occurs. In this case pollen grains either fall or are transferred from an anther to a stigma on the same plant. Where the pollen grains fall onto the stigma, the anthers are generally located above the stigmas. *Cross-pollination* occurs when pollen from an anther on one plant is transferred to a stigma on another plant. The transfer of pollen carried out by humans is called artificial pollination. This is done in plant breeding, where specific characteristics are desired.

Cross pollination is most commonly accomplished by wind, insects, or birds. Pollination is not generally a haphazard event. Flowers and flower parts are adapted for specific modes of pollination. Flowers pollinated by animals are usually showy and/or give off an aroma to attract pollinators. They often produce a sugary liquid, nectar, that pollinators use as food, and their heavy pollen sticks easily to the pollinators' bodies. Wind-pollinated flowers are not showy and produce no nectar or odor. They do produce large quantities of light, loose pollen that is easily carried off by the wind. Their stigmas are expanded and feathery to aid in catching the wind-borne pollen.

24-9   Fertilization

When a pollen grain reaches the stigma of a flower, it germinates (see Figure 24-9). Its protective coat breaks open. A pollen tube grows down through the stigma and style and into

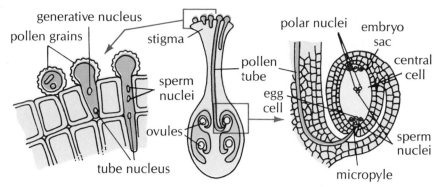

Figure 24-9. Fertilization in a Flower.
When a pollen grain lands on a stigma and germinates, a pollen tube grows from the pollen grain down through the style of the pistil to an ovule. The generative nucleus divides into two sperm nuclei. The tube nucleus directs the growth of the pollen tube. The sperm nuclei enter the ovule through the micropyle. One sperm nucleus fuses with the egg cell nucleus to form a diploid zygote. The other sperm nucleus fuses with the two polar nuclei, forming a triploid (3n) cell that develops into endosperm tissue.

the ovary. It then enters the ovule through the micropyle. The tube cell nucleus (which controls the activities of the pollen tube) and the generative cell nucleus pass from the pollen grain down the pollen tube. As the generative nucleus moves down the pollen tube, it divides to form two haploid sperm nuclei. The two sperm nuclei enter the embryo sac. One fertilizes the egg cell to form a diploid zygote that develops into the sporophyte embryo. The other fuses with the two polar nuclei of the central cell to form a triploid (3n) *endosperm nucleus.* The endosperm nucleus divides by mitosis to form the **endosperm,** the tissue which stores food for the developing plant embryo. This **double fertilization** of the egg and the two polar nuclei is a unique characteristic of flowering plants.

24-10 Fruits

After fertilization, each ovule develops into a seed, and the ovary develops into a fruit (see Figure 24-10). In angiosperms,

Figure 24-10. Stages in the Formation of a Peach Fruit.

A

C

D

E

B

the seeds are always enclosed within the fruit. Other tissues associated with the ovary may also form part of the fruit. A *simple* fruit develops from a single pistil, with or without associated tissues. When several pistils occur in a single flower, as in strawberry and raspberry, the resulting simple fruits of each flower collectively are called an *aggregate fruit*. In some plants, such as pineapple, the simple fruits of many separate flowers fuse together to form what is called a *multiple fruit*.

Shortly after fertilization, the parts of the flower not involved in the formation of the fruit wither and die. The ovary grows larger, and its wall thickens. The wall of the ripened ovary may be hard or soft, dry or fleshy, and it may consist of several distinct layers. Figure 24-11 shows the structures of various types of fruits. To a botanist, string beans, olives, and milkweed pods are as much fruits as apples and peaches. The term "vegetable" is not used by botanists. Tomatoes and cucumbers are actually fruits. On the other hand, radishes, beets, and carrots are roots, lettuce and spinach are leaves, and rhubarb and celery are petioles.

24-11 Structure of the Seed and Embryo

The seed, which is the ripened ovule, consists of the seed coat, the embryo, and endosperm. The tough, protective **seed coat** develops from the wall of the ovule. On the outside of the

Figure 24–11. Fruits. (A) Strawberry. (B) Milkweed. (C) Orange. (D) Green pea. (E) Walnut. (F) Tomato.

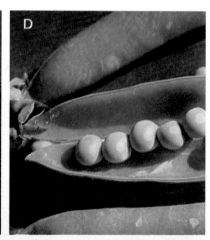

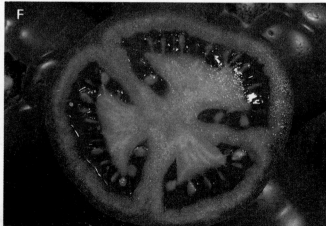

seed there is a scar called the *hilum* (*hy*-lum), which marks where the ovule was attached to the ovary. The embryo develops by mitosis from the fertilized egg. The endosperm, which is a food storage tissue, develops by mitosis from the endosperm nucleus. The nutrients stored in the endosperm cells are obtained from the parent plant.

The plant embryo consists of one or two cotyledons, and the epicotyl, the hypocotyl, and the radicle. **Cotyledons** (kaht-uh-*leed*-unz) are modified leaves. Plants with one cotyledon are called **monocots,** and those with two cotyledons are called **dicots.** In some plants, during seed development the endosperm is digested and its nutrients are incorporated into the cotyledons. In this case the mature seed lacks an endosperm; the cotyledons which contain food storage tissue, are greatly thickened and do not look like leaves. In other plants, where an endosperm is present in the mature seed, the cotyledons are thin and leaflike in appearance. Until it can synthesize its own nutrients, the developing seedling obtains nourishment from the stored food in the cotyledons or in the endosperm, as the case may be.

The part of the embryo above the point of attachment of the cotyledons is called the **epicotyl** (*ep*-uh-kaht-ul). It generally gives rise to the terminal bud, leaves, and the upper part of the stem of the young plant. The **hypocotyl** (*hy*-puh-kaht-ul) is the part of the embryo below the point of attachment of the cotyledons. The **radicle** (*rad*-uh-kul) is the lowermost part of the embryo. In some plants the hypocotyl gives rise to the lower part of the stem, while the radicle gives rise to the roots. In other plants, the stem forms entirely from the epicotyl, and the roots arise from both the hypocotyl and radicle.

Beans are dicots, and in the bean seed, the two large cotyledons enclose the rest of the embryo between them (see Figure 24-12). In the mature bean seed the endosperm is

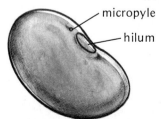

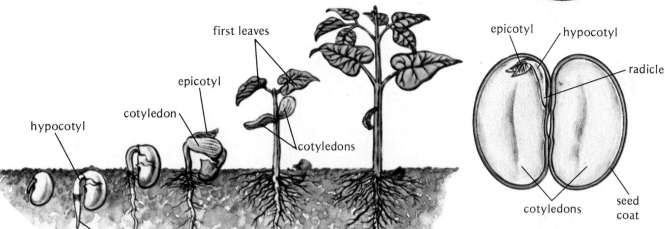

Figure 24-12. Development of a Bean Seedling.

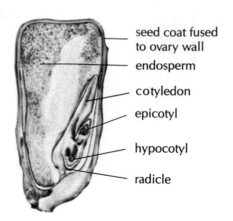

seed coat fused
to ovary wall

endosperm

cotyledon

epicotyl

hypocotyl

radicle

Figure 24-13. Development of a Corn Seedling.

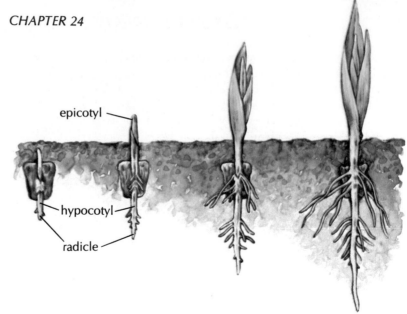

epicotyl

hypocotyl

radicle

absent, nutrients being stored only in the cotyledons. In the developing bean seedling, the epicotyl gives rise to the terminal bud, the leaves, and the upper part of the stem. The hypocotyl gives rise to the lower part of the stem, and the radicle gives rise to the roots.

Corn is a monocot. Each kernel of corn is a single-seeded fruit. The embryo is partially surrounded by endosperm. In the sweet corn that we eat, the endosperm contains sugar and starch as food storage products. The cotyledon also stores nutrients in the form of oils and proteins. In the developing corn seedling, the epicotyl gives rise to the stem and leaves, while the hypotoctyl and radicle give rise to the roots (see Figure 24-13).

24-12   Seed Dispersal

The scattering, or dispersal, of seeds away from the parent plant is of great importance in the survival of the species. Plants growing very close together must compete for water, minerals, and sunlight. Thus, many different adaptations have arisen for the dispersal of seeds (see Figure 24-14). In some plants, pressure develops within the drying fruit. When the fruit bursts, the seeds are released with enough force to scatter them over a large area. This type of dispersal occurs in snapdragons. Many seeds and single-seeded fruits such as those of milkweed, maple, and dandelion, are very light, and are carried great distances by the wind. Others, such as the coconut, float and are carried by water. Some seeds or fruits, such as those of sandbur and wild carrot, have burs or hooks. They become attached to the fur of animals and are dispersed in that way. Sweet, fleshy fruits are often eaten by birds and mammals. The seeds, which are usually indigestible, are later deposited elsewhere along with other digestive wastes.

24-13 Seed Dormancy and Germination

For a seed to begin to sprout, or germinate, it needs water and oxygen and the proper temperature. Some seeds also require light. Many seeds go through a dormant, or resting, period before they begin to grow. During the dormant phase, the seed will not sprout even if all necessary conditions are present. The length of the dormant period varies with the type of plant. Even within a single species individual seeds show different lengths of dormancy. Some seeds might begin to grow after 1 year, some after 2 years, some after 3 years, and so on. This characteristic is useful for the survival of the species, because not all seeds would be killed by unusually harsh conditions during a given year.

There are several ways in which **dormancy** (*dor*-mun-see) is brought about. In some species, dormancy occurs because the seed coat does not permit water and/or oxygen to reach the embryo. In others, the seed coat is so strong that the embryo cannot break through it. In still others, the embryo must undergo further development before growth can occur, or chemical inhibitors are present that prevent germination. Where dormancy is caused by the toughness of the seed coat, it lasts until the seed coat decays or is broken down sufficiently for germination to occur. With immature embryos and chemical inhibitors, a certain amount of time must pass either for the embryo to mature or for the chemicals to disappear.

In many species native to areas that have a cold winter, seed dormancy is broken by exposure to low temperatures and moisture (in combination) for a certain length of time. Such a system ensures that germination will occur only after the harsh conditions of winter have passed. Thus the seeds will germinate in the spring, and the seedlings will have the whole growing season in which to complete their development.

Figure 24-14. Some Adaptations for Seed Dispersal. The single-seeded fruits of dandelion (left) are dispersed by the wind. The burdock fruit (right) has hooks that cling to the fur of passing animals.

Chapter Review

SUMMARY

- The major land plant groups are the mosses, ferns, and seed plants (gymnosperms and angiosperms). The life cycles of terrestrial plants show an alternation of generations, with a haploid, gamete-producing generation, the gametophyte, and a diploid, spore-producing generation, the sporophyte.

- The mature sporophyte produces haploid spores by meiosis. By mitosis, these spores form the haploid gametophyte generation. In the gametophyte, male and female gametes are formed by mitosis. They fuse to form a diploid zygote, which is the beginning of the sporophyte generation.

- In mosses the gametophyte generation is dominant; in ferns the sporophyte generation is dominant. In both of these plants water is required for fertilization.

- In the seed plants—the gymnosperms and the angiosperms—the sporophyte generation is dominant, and water is not required for fertilization. Gymnosperms produce separate pollen and seed cones. The pollen cones produce pollen grains; the seed cones produce ovules. Pollination is followed by pollen tube growth through the ovule and fertilization of an egg by a sperm nucleus. The ovule then matures into a seed.

- In angiosperms the spore-producing organs —the stamens and the pistils—are in the flower. When a pollen grain lands on a stigma, it germinates, forming a pollen tube that grows down into an ovule. Two sperm nuclei enter the embryo sac, where one fuses with the egg, forming a zygote. The other fuses with the two polar nuclei, forming an endosperm nucleus. The fertilized egg develops into a sporophyte embryo, the ovule becomes a seed, and the overy develops into a fruit.

KNOW THE TERMS

alternation of generations	endosperm	moss	receptacle
angiosperm	epicotyl	ovary	seed
anther	fern	ovule	seed coat
calyx	filament	pedicel	sepal
corolla	fruit	petal	sporangium
cotyledon	gametophyte generation	pistil	sporophyte generation
dicot	gymnosperm	pollen grain	stamen
dormancy	hypocotyl	pollen tube	stigma
double fertilization	micropyle	pollination	style
embryo sac	monocot	radicle	

SECTION QUESTIONS

The Generalized Plant Life Cycle

1. Which of the alternate generations produces gametes?
2. Which generation consists of diploid organisms?

Life Cycles of Non-Seed Plants

3. Which is the dominant generation in mosses?
4. Name the male and female organs of a moss.

5. Which is the dominant generation in ferns?
6. Name the structure that produces spores on the fronds of ferns.
7. What is the gametophyte generation of a fern called?

Life Cycle of Gymnosperms

8. List three examples of gymnosperms.

9. Which is the dominant generation of gymnosperms?
10. Name the reproductive organs of gymnosperms.
11. What serves as a bridge between the pollen grain and the egg?

Life Cycle of Angiosperms

12. List the parts of a flower.
13. What structure in a flower ovary forms the female gametophyte?
14. Which part of the seed tissue stores food for the plant embryo?
15. List some methods of seed dispersal.

KNOW THE FACTS

Copy the number of each sentence below on a sheet of paper. Beside each number, write the term(s) that complete(s) the sentence correctly.

1. The spore-producing generation is termed the _____ generation.
2. At the tip of a mature moss sporophyte, a cylindrical _____ develops.
3. The sperm of mosses and ferns require _____ in order to reach the eggs.
4. Pollen grains carry the _____ gametes.
5. Seeds of gymnosperms are formed within seed _____.
6. A flower is made up of rings of modified _____.
7. The anther of a stamen produces _____ _____.
8. The ovary of a flower pistil contains _____.
9. A fruit develops from the _____.
10. After fertilization each ovule develops into a(n) _____.
11. Beans are dicots, which means that each bean seed has two _____.
12. In a developing seedling the radicle gives rise to the _____.
13. The terminal bud of a young plant arises from the part of the embryo called the _____.
14. Many seeds pass through a period of _____ before they begin to grow.

UNDERSTAND THE CONCEPTS

15. Explain alternation of generations.
16. Outline the life cycle of mosses.
17. Describe the structures of the fern sporophyte and gametophyte.
18. Trace the life cycle of a fern.
19. Describe the life cycle of a gymnosperm.
20. Briefly explain the function of each part of the flower.
21. Describe the development of the male and female gametes in flowers.
22. Explain what is meant by self-pollination and cross-pollination.
23. Explain how double fertilization occurs in flowering plants, beginning with the germination of the pollen grain.
24. Identify the basic parts of the seed and explain how they are formed.
25. Name the parts of the plant embryo, and state what part(s) of the plant each develops into.
26. Why is the dispersal of seeds important in plant reproduction?
27. What environmental factors affect seed germination?
28. What is seed dormancy, and what is the advantage of a dormant period?

THINK CRITICALLY

29. How are seeds and pollen adapted to life on land?
30. People generally refer to string beans, cucumbers, olives, and tomatoes as vegetables. Why, then, do botanists classify them as fruits?
31. Explain how angiosperms and gymnosperms are like hermaphrodites (organisms that contain both ovaries and testes).
32. List three ways in which gymnosperm and angiosperm fertilization and development differ.
33. What structure in a plant is functionally similar to the placenta (organ through which an embryo receives food and oxygen from the mother's body)?

THINK CREATIVELY

34. Cases of self-pollination are relatively rare. Propose some possible explanations for this.

35. Design a seed that could be dispersed via land and water.

FOR FURTHER INVESTIGATION

1. Compare the features of wind-pollinated flowers with those of insect-pollinated flowers. Gather, press, and dry several examples of each type of flower.
2. In the spring, gather pollen by placing glass slides coated lightly on one side with petroleum jelly in an open window. At the end of the day view the slides through a microscope. Do this for several days. Count the types of pollen found each day. Record your findings in a data table. Construct a line graph of your daily count.
3. Interview an orchard operator. How do they ensure pollination? How do they get the best fruits possible?
4. Write a report on one of the career opportunities listed below. See suggested procedures, p. 9, "For Further Investigation" Activity 3.
   a. Nursery operator
   b. Horticulturist
   c. Agricultural worker
5. Prepare a report on the life and contributions of one of the following scientists:
   a. Thomas Wyatt Turner
   b. Arman Takhtajan
   c. Estella Bergere Leopold
   d. Nathaniel L. Britton

FOR FURTHER READING

Batra, Suzanne, "Solitary Bees," *Scientific American*, February, 1984.

Dilcher, David, and Crane, Peter R., "In Pursuit of the First Flower," *Natural History*, March, 1984.

Meijer, Willem, "Saving the World's Largest Flower," *National Geographic*, July, 1985.

Newman, Cathy, "Pollen: Breath of Life and Sneezes," *National Geographic*, October, 1984.

Stiles, Edmund, "Fruit, for All Seasons," *Natural History*, August, 1984.

Wiens, Delbert, "Secrets of a Cryptic Flower," *Natural History*, May, 1985.

Issues in Biology

Nutrition and Human Development

The three critical periods of human development, when growth rates are the highest, are the fetal stage, the first year after birth, and adolescence. At these stages, lack of the basic nutrients can cause health problems that will follow a person through life.

Nutrition-related problems in a developing fetus are most often caused by nutritional deficiencies in the mother. A pregnant woman who is malnourished or gains too little weight during the course of the pregnancy is more likely to have a low birth weight baby than is a well-nourished mother.

A low birth weight baby weighs about five pounds or less. Some low birth weight babies are carried the full 37-week term of a normal pregnancy, while others are born prematurely. Survival during the first year of life is less frequent for low birth weight babies than for normal weight ones. Those infants who do survive the perilous first year often experience continuing health problems.

Because the prenatal and postnatal periods are so important to brain development, low birth weight babies and malnourished infants have an increased risk of developing learning difficulties later in life. They also have poor growth rates and experience a greater frequency of illness due to infections than do their normal birth weight counterparts.

Malnutrition during adolescence can produce health problems such as anemia, stunted bone growth, and poor muscle development. However, unlike the two earlier critical developmental periods this growth period in one in which at least some of the food choices may be made by the individual, rather than exclusively by a parent or some other adult.

The most basic factor leading to malnutrition is the availability of food. People who live in severe poverty have little opportunity to achieve a balanced diet. In cases where food is accessible, people's food choices are affected only partly by what they know about good nutrition. Food choices are also affected by cultural, social economic, and psychological factors. Family attitudes and habits, food industry advertising, and

People who know the rules of good nutrition can plan healthful, enjoyable meals and snacks.

the amount of time available to prepare food influence food selection to varying degrees. Children quickly develop positive or negative associations based on odor, appearance and taste. Later, they may be influenced by people they respect, such as peers or public figures.

Because an individual's whole life is so seriously affected by malnutrition during the three key periods of human development, concerned helath professionals argue continually for an improved food distribution network. In addition, they seek to provide effective nutrition education for pregnant women, for the parents of young children, and for adolescents who are assuming control of their own food selections.

---

1. Name the high-growth periods in humans. Who might be involved in planning proper nutrition for individuals at each growth stage?

2. Imagine that you are in charge of maintaining adequate nutrition for (a) your family, and (b) for an underdeveloped country. What food choices would you make? How would you ensure that everyone had enough food to be adequately nourished?

3. Devise a workable plan to provide essential nutrition information to individuals of various age groups.

4. Discuss how nutrition-related deaths and development problems could be reduced.

UNIT 5

GENETICS

Even at a quick glance, the resemblance between this opossum mother and her twelve-day-old offspring is striking. What produces this similarity? How are a parent's traits passed on to its young? Why does an organism always produce a member of its own species? The answers to these questions are found in a remarkable and complex molecule known as DNA. In this Unit, you will learn how DNA controls the transfer of hereditary information from parents to offspring. You will examine the structure and function of DNA, and see how it ensures that both individual and species characteristics are passed from one generation to the next. You will also learn how it has recently become possible to scientifically alter the DNA of some organisms, controlling the way these organisms function.

The pea plant was the experimental subject in the first scientific study of heredity.

Chapter 25

MENDELIAN GENETICS

Objectives:
1. Describe Mendel's experimental procedure.
2. State and give an example of Mendel's law of dominance.
3. State and give an example of Mendel's law of segregation.
4. Explain Mendel's law of segregation in terms of chromosomes and meiosis.

25-1 The Study of Heredity

In sexual reproduction, the new individual develops from a single cell—the zygote—that was formed by the union of two gametes, one from each parent. The chromosomes of each gamete bring hereditary material to the new cell. This material controls the development and characteristics of the embryo as well as the features of the adult organism. Since the hereditary material comes from two parents, the offspring resembles both parents in some ways, but it also differs from both parents in other ways. The offspring has all the characteristics of its species, but it also has its own individual characteristics that distinguish it from all other members of the species.

Genetics (juh-*net*-iks) is the branch of biology that is concerned with the ways in which hereditary information is transmitted from parents to offspring. Modern genetics started with the scientific work done in the nineteenth century by an Austrian monk.

25-2   Mendel's Experiments

The first scientific study of heredity was conducted by Gregor Mendel (*men*-dul), a monk who was interested in mathematics and science. Mendel lived at the Abbey of St. Thomas, a monastery in the town of Brünn in what is now Czechoslovakia. He also taught science at the local high school. For eight years—from 1857 to 1865—Mendel investigated the inheritance of certain traits in pea plants that he grew in the monastery garden. Through a series of experiments, Mendel arrived at the basic principles of heredity that scientists accept today.

Pea plants were an excellent choice for the investigations that Mendel wished to make. They are fairly easy to grow, and they mature quickly. Pea plants have several pairs of sharply contrasting traits, such as tallness or shortness, green or yellow pods, and smooth or wrinkled seeds, which are readily observable (see Figure 25-1). Furthermore, the structure of the pea flower and its natural method of pollination make it easy to use in controlled experiments. Pea flowers normally self-pollinate because the stigma and anthers are enclosed by the petals, as shown in the photograph on the facing page. This effectively prevents cross-pollination in nature. However, by removing the stamens from a flower before they ripened, Mendel could cross-pollinate the flower by dusting pollen from another plant onto the stigma. If he wanted certain plants to self-pollinate in the normal way, he left them alone.

Mendel kept careful records of his treatment of each generation of plants. He collected the seeds from each experimental cross and planted them in a definite place so he could observe the results. Mendel made a careful count of each type of offspring and analyzed his results mathematically. It was this use of mathematics that enabled him to draw the important conclusions that he did.

Mendel wrote a paper about his discoveries. It was published in the journal of his local scientific society and distributed to other scientific organizations and libraries. However, no other scientists seem to have noticed its importance at the time. Mendel died in 1882, never knowing the real significance of his work. In 1900, however, three European scientists, all working independently, reached the same conclusions about heredity that Mendel had. Before they published their works, they researched past scientific literature and found Mendel's papers. They gave him credit for his original discoveries. Mendel finally obtained the recognition he deserved.

25-3   The Law of Dominance

Mendel had observed that pea plants have certain traits that come in two forms. For example, plants are either tall or short; seeds are either yellow or green; and so on. In his experiments, Mendel studied seven such pairs of contrasting traits.

Figure 25-1. Pea Seeds. Mendel used the contrasting traits of wrinkled and smooth seeds in his experiments with peas.

Mendel discovered that some plants "bred true" for a particular trait. For example, when short plants were allowed to self-pollinate through several generations, the offspring were always short. Mendel considered these plants to be pure for shortness. In his experiments, Mendel always started with plants that he knew were pure for the particular trait he was interested in.

Mendel then proceeded to find out what would happen if he cross-pollinated pure plants that had contrasting traits. To do this, he removed the stamens from a plant that was pure for one trait, to prevent self-pollination. He then pollinated that plant with pollen from a plant that was pure for the contrasting trait. For example, he pollinated short plants with pollen from tall ones, and he pollinated tall plants with pollen from short ones. In these experiments, the pure plants made up the parent, or P, generation. Mendel collected the seeds produced by this cross-pollination, planted them, and allowed them to grow. Mendel found that all the offspring of this cross were tall (see Figure 25-2). The short trait disappeared in this *first filial*, or F_1, generation. Similar results were obtained for all seven of the pairs of contrasting traits that Mendel investigated. The offspring of crosses between pure parents showing contrasting traits are called **hybrids.** In Mendel's experiments, the hybrids showed only one of the contrasting traits and not the other.

Mendel was curious to find out whether the trait of shortness had been permanently lost as a result of the cross. To investigate this question, he allowed the hybrid plants of the F_1 generation to self-pollinate (see Figure 25-3). When their seeds were planted and grown, only three-fourths of the offspring were tall. One-fourth were short. These plants made up the F_2 generation. The presence of short plants in the F_2 generation demonstrated that the shortness trait had somehow still been present in the F_1 generation.

Mendel described the traits that were expressed in the

Figure 25-2. A Cross of Pure Tall and Pure Short Pea Plants. All offspring in the first filial (F_1) generation are tall.

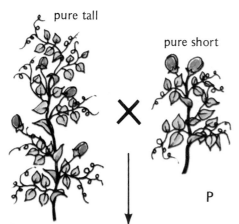

pure tall

pure short

P

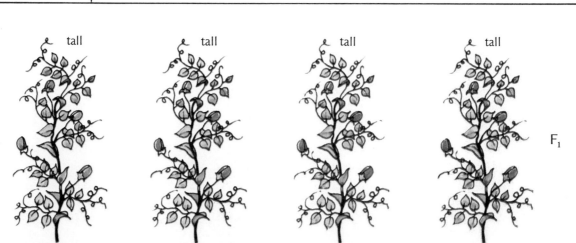

tall   tall   tall   tall

F_1

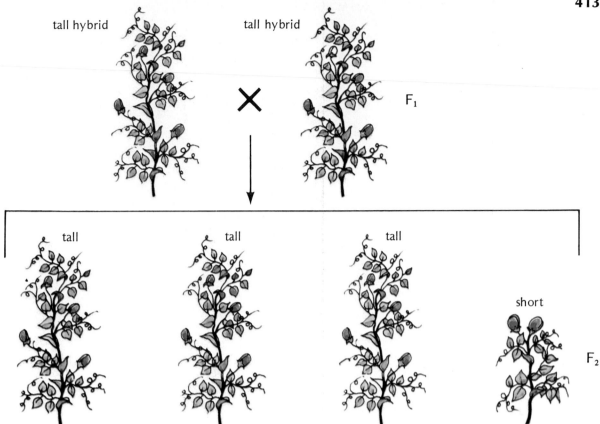

tall hybrid   tall hybrid F_1

tall   tall   tall   short F_2

F_1 generation as **dominant,** and the traits that were hidden in the F_1 as **recessive.** He concluded that *when an organism is hybrid for a pair of contrasting traits, it shows only the dominant trait.* This is called the **law of dominance.**

Figure 25-3. A Cross of the Hybrid Plants of the F_1 Generation. Only three-fourths of the offspring are tall. One-fourth are short.

25-4   The Law of Segregation

Mendel tried to explain the disappearance and reappearance of the recessive trait in successive generations. He formed the hypothesis that in an individual, each trait was controlled by a pair of factors. And a factor could be one of two kinds. There was, for example, a factor for tallness and another factor for shortness. The factors in a pair could be alike or different. In a cross, the offspring received one factor from each parent. Thus, in a cross between a tall plant and a short plant, the offspring received both kinds of factors. However, only the dominant factor was expressed. The recessive factor was suppressed or hidden.

Since the factor for shortness was still present in these tall plants, it was possible for this factor to show itself in the later generations. This would happen when fertilization brought two shortness factors together in the same seed. The idea that *factors that occur in pairs are separated from each other during gamete formation and recombined at fertilization is called Mendel's* **law of segregation.**

Normal pollen-producing, staminate ("male") flowers of corn (left) and pollen-free male-sterile flowers of corn (right).

Cytoplasmic Inheritance

The nuclei of cells do not hold a monopoly on heredity. Some genetic material resides outside the nucleus, in a cell's cytoplasm. This genetic material, which is passed to the offspring along with the cytoplasm, determines some inherited traits. Examples of this phenomenon, called cytoplasmic inheritance, are found in plants and microorganisms.

In plants, the egg is much larger than the sperm. This means that nearly all the cytoplasm of the zygote comes from the female parent. Therefore, any of the offspring's traits determined by cytoplasmic factors reflect those of the "mother" and not the "father."

The four-o'clock plant offers an example of cytoplasmic inheritance. The leaves of this plant are white, green or a mixture of both colors. The coloration depends on the types of chloroplasts within the leaves' cells. Since chloroplasts reside in the cytoplasm and possess their own DNA, their characteristics are passed to the offspring through the cytoplasm, not the nucleus. The coloration of a plant's leaves, then, is determined solely by the choloroplasts of the female parent.

Corn plants provide another example of cytoplasmic inheritance. Normal corn plants bear both "male", staminate flowers and "female", pistillate flowers. However, there are plants with a male sterility factor in their cytoplasm. These individuals lack staminate flowers (see photos). Able to produce eggs but no sperm means two things for these plants. First, *all* their offspring receive the male sterility factor and, second, they cannot self-pollinate. The second fact is exploited by geneticists who produce hybrid corn by artificially cross-pollinating the male sterile plants.

A third example of cytoplasmic inheritance occurs in microorganisms. Some strains of paramecium secrete a toxin that kills neighboring paramecium. The ability to secrete the toxin, called the killer trait, can be inherited cytoplasmically. Generally when a "killer" conjugates with a "non-killer", even though the two paramecium end up with identical nuclei (see pg. 335), nothing changes with respect to the killer trait. Since little cytoplasm is exchanged during conjugation, the killer factor typically has no chance to pass through to the "non-killer." In rare cases, though, enough cytoplasm *does* manage to pass from one paramecium to the other so that the "non-killer" gains the killer trait.

25-5   The Concept of the Gene

The importance of Mendel's work may have been overlooked in the mid-1800s because little was known about chromosomes, mitosis, and meiosis at that time. But when Mendel's research was rediscovered in 1900, chromosomes had been stained and observed in cells, and the processes of mitosis and meiosis had been described in detail. It soon became clear that Mendel's results could be explained by assuming that the chromosomes carry the hereditary factors. If so, the separation of homologous chromosome pairs during meiosis and their recombination during fertilization would account for the separation and recombination of the Mendelian factors. During the early 1900s, numerous experiments confirmed this hypothesis. At that time, the term **gene** was adopted to replace Mendel's "factor." Research provided evidence not only that chromosomes carry genes, but that the genes are arranged in a definite sequence along each chromosome. This work led to the establishment of the modern gene-chromosome theory of heredity, which is discussed in Chapter 26.

BASIC CONCEPTS IN GENETICS

Objectives:
1. Explain the terms *homozygous* and *heterozygous*.
2. Explain the relationship between genotype and phenotype.
3. State the basic law of probability, and explain how it applies to Mendel's experimental results.
4. Use Punnett squares to work out the possible results of various types of genetic crosses.
5. Explain Mendel's law of independent assortment in terms of genes and meiosis.
6. Describe the procedure for a test cross, and explain the significance of the results.
7. Explain and give examples of incomplete dominance, codominance, and multiple alleles.

25-6   Alleles

According to Mendelian principles, each body cell of an organism has two copies of the gene for each trait. For example, a pea plant has two copies of the gene for plant height. From modern genetics we know that one copy of the gene for height is found at the same position on each chromosome of a pair of homologous chromosomes. In an individual organism, the two copies of the gene for a particular trait may be alike, or may be different. For example, in a pea plant the two copies of the gene for height can both be tall, both be short, or be one of each. Different copies or forms of a gene controlling a particular trait are called **alleles** (uh-*leelz*). In pea plants, the gene controlling height exists as either an allele for tallness or an allele for shortness.

Figure 25-4. Guinea Pigs. The genetics of some single traits, such as hair color in guinea pigs, is more complicated than that of other traits, such as plant size in peas.

An organism in which the alleles for a certain trait are the same is said to be **homozygous** (hoh-muh-*zy*-gus) for that trait. If the alleles are different, the organism is said to be **heterozygous** (het-uh-roh-*zy*-gous). Homozygous and heterozygous mean *pure* and *hybrid*, respectively.

25-7   Genotypes and Phenotypes

By general agreement, the allele for a dominant trait is represented by a capital letter. For example, the allele for tallness is represented by the symbol T. It is customary to represent the contrasting recessive allele by the lowercase form of the letter used for the dominant allele. Therefore, the allele for shortness is represented by the symbol t.

A pure tall pea plant has two alleles for tallness. Its genetic makeup is represented as TT. The genetic makeup of a pure short plant is tt, while that of a hybrid is Tt. The genetic makeup of an organism is called its **genotype** (*jee*-nuh-typ). The physical trait that an organism develops as the result of its genotype is called its **phenotype** (*fee*-nuh-typ). Two different individuals may have the same phenotype but different genotypes. A pure tall plant and a hybrid tall plant have the same phenotype (both are tall), but they have different genotypes (TT for the pure plant and Tt for the hybrid) (see Figure 25-4).

25-8   The Law of Probability

To explain the *numerical* results of Mendel's experiments, we must apply the laws of chance, or probability, to the separation and recombination of alleles. If you toss a coin, you know that the chance of its turning up heads is 1 out of 2, or ½. If you toss the coin 100 times, you expect to get about 50 heads and 50 tails; that is, you expect the ratio of heads to tails to be about 1:1. In any actual trial, the ratio of heads to tails is seldom exactly 1:1. In a short trial, say, 4 tosses, you might even get a run of 4 heads or 4 tails. However, if you made a large number of tosses, say, 1000, you would expect the ratio of heads to tails to be quite close to 1:1. Experiments have shown that the larger the number of trials, the closer the ratio comes to the expected value. This assumes, of course, that there is nothing special about the coin or the way it is tossed to make one side *more likely* to turn up than the other.

Consider another example—the rolling of a die. A die is a cube with six faces numbered from 1 to 6. When the die is rolled, each face is as likely as any other to turn up. If you roll the die 600 times, you would expect to get about 100 of each face: 100 1's, 100 2's, 100 3's, and so on.

These examples illustrate the basic law of chance, or probability: If there are several possible events that might occur, and no one of them is more likely to occur than any other, then they will all occur in equal numbers over a large number of trials. This law enables us to predict the results of breeding

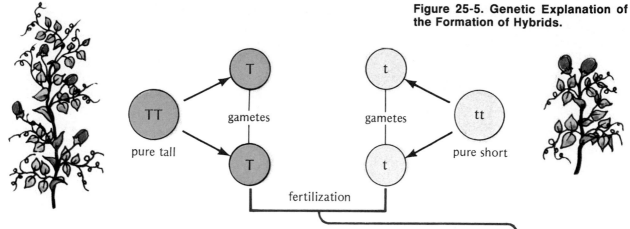

Figure 25-5. Genetic Explanation of the Formation of Hybrids.

experiments like those of Mendel. Bear in mind that these predictions apply only when large numbers of individuals are involved.

25-9 The Punnett Square

Let us consider what happens when a pure tall pea plant is crossed with a pure short plant. The body cells of the tall plant have two alleles for tallness. Their genotype is TT. When gametes form in this plant, each gamete receives one T allele. Its genetic composition can be shown by the single letter T (see Figure 25-5). The cells of the short plant have two alleles for the recessive trait of shortness. Their genotype is tt, and that of the gametes is t.

Suppose that we transfer pollen from the tall plant to the pistil of a short plant. Each sperm cell nucleus will be carrying one T allele. The egg cell in each ovule of the short plant will have one t allele. When fertilization occurs, the zygotes will all receive one T allele and one t allele, and their genotype will be Tt. The plants that develop from these zygotes will be hybrid tall.

A diagram called a **Punnett square** is a convenient way to show the results of any cross. The Punnett square for the cross we have just discussed is shown in Figure 25-6. In this diagram, the alleles of the possible male gametes are written at the heads of the columns of boxes. The alleles of the possible female gametes are written at the sides of the rows of boxes. (The positions of the male and female gametes can be interchanged.) In each box, we then write the allele combination of the zygote that forms when the allele at the top of the column and the allele at the left of the row are brought together.

In this simple case, where there is only one possible combination and all the zygotes are alike, the diagram seems an unnecessary complication. The results are 100 percent hybrid tall (Tt). However, the method is very useful in more complicated cases.

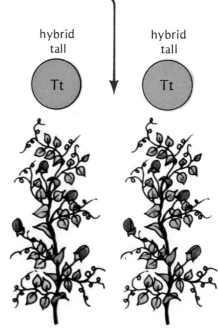

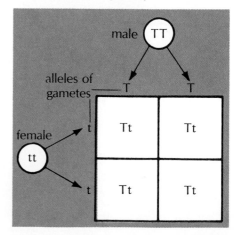

Figure 25-6. Punnett Square for Cross of Pure Dominant (Tall) with Pure Recessive (Short).

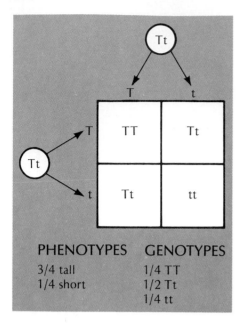

PHENOTYPES   GENOTYPES
3/4 tall   1/4 TT
1/4 short   1/2 Tt
                1/4 tt

Figure 25-7. Punnett Square for Crossing Two Hybrids. Of the zygotes produced, one-fourth are pure tall (TT), two-fourths are hybrid tall (Tt), and one-fourth are short (tt).

25-10   Punnett Square for a Hybrid Cross

We will use a Punnett square for a cross in which hybrid tall plants are either allowed to self-pollinate or are cross-pollinated. The genotype of these plants is Tt. Because they contain two different alleles (for plant height), they produce two types of gametes—one type with T and the other with t. Since the T and t alleles are present in equal numbers, the two types of gametes are produced in equal numbers. This is true for both male and female gametes, and it is an important fact for the discussion that follows.

The Punnett square for the fertilizations that occur between these gametes is shown in Figure 25-7. Each letter at the head of a column represents one type of male gamete that is formed. Each letter at the left of a row represents one type of female gamete. Remember that these types of gametes are produced in equal numbers.

We now come to the key idea of this analysis. Each box in the diagram represents a possible union of a male gamete with a female gamete. Since the types of gametes are present in equal numbers, each combination is just as likely to occur as any other. The laws of probability tell us that if a large number of pollinations and fertilizations occurs, all these possible combinations will occur in approximately equal numbers.

The Punnett square shows four possible combinations. All four will occur in equal numbers. Among a large number of offspring, 1/4 will be TT (pure tall), 2/4 (or 1/2) will be Tt (hybrid tall), and 1/4 will be tt (pure short). Therefore, with respect to genotype, the offspring ratio is 1:2:1. In terms of physical appearance, or phenotype, 3/4 will be tall and 1/4 will be short. Thus; the phenotype ratio of the offspring of this cross is 3:1 (3 tall to 1 short).

We see that the laws of probability, combined with a Punnett square, have enabled us to account for the results that Mendel obtained with his experimental crosses.

25-11   The Law of Independent Assortment

The hybrid cross discussed above is more correctly called a **monohybrid cross** because only one pair of contrasting traits is being studied. Mendel's first experiments involved only monohybrid crosses. In experiments on tallness and shortness, for example, he did not record the other traits of the plants involved. After a time, however, Mendel decided to follow two pairs of contrasting traits at the same time. From his previous experiments, he knew that yellow color (Y) was dominant over green color (y) in pea seeds, and that round seed shape (R) was dominant over wrinkled seeds (r). Mendel proceeded to make crosses in which he kept track of both seed color and seed shape.

As before, he started with plants that were pure for these traits. For one parent he used plants that were pure for both dominant traits: they produced yellow, round seeds. The other parent was pure for both recessive traits: they produced green, wrinkled seeds. He artificially pollinated one type of plant with pollen from the other type, and then observed the seeds that were produced. The results were as expected. All the seeds of the F_1 generation showed only the two dominant traits—that is, they were yellow and smooth. No green or wrinkled seeds appeared.

The next step was to plant these seeds and let the plants that grew from them self-pollinate. This would produce an F_2 generation of seeds. As expected, recessive traits reappeared in some of these seeds. Many seeds still showed both dominant traits. But some were yellow and wrinkled (dominant-recessive), some were green and smooth (recessive-dominant), and a few were green and wrinkled (recessive-recessive). A breeding experiment like this one, involving two traits, is called a **dihybrid cross.**

The actual numbers from one of these experiments are revealing. They are given in Table 25-1. Each trait considered by itself shows the 3:1 ratio expected in a monohybrid cross. There are 416 yellow seeds and 140 green seeds. The ratio of 416 to 140 is 2.97:1. There are 423 round seeds and 133 wrinkled seeds. This ratio is 3.18:1. Note also that there is about the same number of yellow, wrinkled seeds (dominant of one trait, recessive of the other) as green, smooth seeds (recessive of one dominant of the other).

From data of this kind, Mendel concluded that different traits were inherited independently of one another. This principle is known as the **law of independent assortment.** In modern terms, this means that during meiosis, *genes for different traits are separated and distributed to gametes independently of one another.* Today we know that this is not always true. The reasons why are discussed in Chapter 26.

25-12 Phenotype Ratios in a Dihybrid Cross

With a Punnett square we can predict the phenotype ratios expected in a dihybrid cross. We first construct the diagram for the cross between the pure dominant for both traits and the pure recessive for both traits (see Figure 25-8). Note that spaces are provided for four gametes from each parent. According to the law of independent assortment, four different but equally probable combinations of two alleles, one from each of the two genes involved, can end up in the same gamete. In this case, all four possible allele combinations in the gametes have the same genotype, but are the result of four different pairings. In the second cross, this point will be important.

As we expect, the phenotypes of the offspring in the F_1 generation are 100 percent dominant for both traits (yellow and smooth). The genotype is 100 percent hybrid for both traits (YyRr).

○	yellow-round seeds = 315
✿	yellow-wrinkled seeds = 101
●	green-round seeds = 108
✾	green-wrinkled seeds = 32

Table 25-1. Mendel's Results of a Dihybrid Cross.

Figure 25-8. Cross of Parents Pure for Two Contrasting Traits. All off-spring are hybrid dominant for both traits.

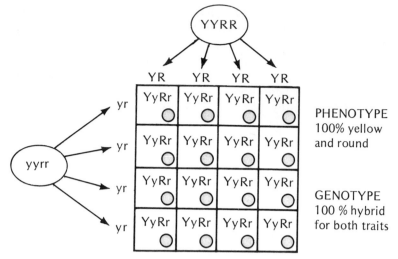

PHENOTYPE
100% yellow
and round

GENOTYPE
100 % hybrid
for both traits

Let us now construct the Punnett square for a cross between these dihybrids. This time the four possible gametes will be different: YR, Yr, yR, and yr. By the laws of probability, there will be equal numbers of the four types of gametes. The zygotes produced by this cross are shown in Figure 25-9.

Again by the laws of probability, all 16 of the possible zygotes will occur in equal numbers. The Punnett square shows ratios of the types of offspring produced when large numbers are involved. The phenotypes are as follows:

    9 yellow-round (dominant-dominant)
    3 yellow-wrinkled (dominant-recessive)
    3 green-round (recessive-dominant)
    1 green-wrinkled (recessive-recessive)

This phenotype ratio of 9:3:3:1 is the ratio that is observed in dihybrid crosses when the numbers of offspring are sufficiently large. Note that each trait considered by itself has the usual 3:1 phenotype ratio. There are 12 yellow seeds to 4 green; there are 12 round seeds to 4 wrinkled.

Figure 25-9. Predicting the Results of a Dihybrid Cross. The phenotype ratios agree fairly well with Mendel's experimental results.

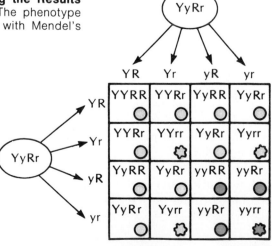

PHENOTYPES OF OFFSPRING

9 yellow-round
3 yellow-wrinkled
3 green-round
1 green-wrinkled

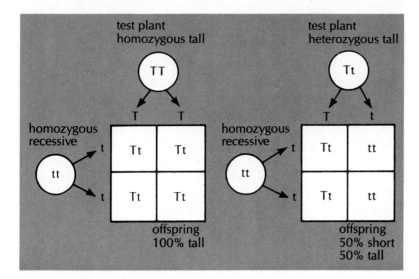

Figure 25-10. A Test Cross. An individual showing a dominant trait is crossed with a recessive. If any offspring show the recessive trait, the test individual must be hybrid.

25-13   The Test Cross

It is not possible to tell from appearance alone whether an individual showing a dominant trait is pure for the trait (homozygous) or hybrid (heterozygous). Breeders of plants and animals often need this information about parent stock. A procedure called a test cross can be used for this purpose.

In a **test cross**, the individual of unknown genotype is mated with an individual showing the contrasting recessive trait. The genotype of the latter individual is known—since it shows the recessive trait, it must be homozygous for it. The genotype of the unknown individual may be homozygous or heterozygous. The test cross will show which is the case.

To understand how the test cross works, let us take a tall pea plant as an example. A breeder wants to know whether the plant is homozygous (TT), or heterozygous (Tt). The unknown plant is crossed, by artificial pollination, with a short plant, which must be homozygous (tt). The Punnett squares in Figure 25-10 show the results of the two possible cases.

We see that if the unknown plant is pure tall, all offspring of the cross are tall. If the plant is heterozygous tall, half the offspring, on the average, will be short. That is, the test cross shows the presence of the recessive allele in the tall parent. The advantage of this method is that it does not require extensive testing and counting of phenotypes. Even a single short offspring will mark the tall parent as carrying the shortness allele. Thus, by crossing an individual of unknown genotype with a recessive individual and examining the offspring, it is possible to determine whether the unknown individual is homozygous or heterozygous

25-14   Incomplete Dominance

Many genes follow the patterns outlined by Mendel's laws, but many do not. In some organisms, both alleles contribute to

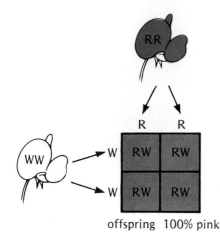

offspring 100% pink

Figure 25-11. Incomplete Dominance. The hybrids of the F_1 generation show a trait intermediate between the pure traits.

the phenotype of a heterozygous individual. This is known as **incomplete dominance,** or *blending inheritance.* For example, the inheritance of flower color in the Japanese four-o'clock plant does not follow the pattern of dominance. A cross between a plant with red flowers and one with white flowers results in offspring with pink flowers (see Figure 25-11). Note that genotypes for incomplete dominance can be written using the capital initial letter of each allele, since both alleles influence phenotype. In this case, red is represented by R and white by W. Individuals with red or white flowers are always homozygous (RR or WW). Individuals with a heterozygous genotype (RW) have an intermediate color. When two pink hybrid four-o-clocks are crossed, a 1:2:1 ratio of red-to pink-to white-flowered offspring is produced in the F_2 generation (see Figure 25-12).

In a variety of chicken called Andalusian, a cross between pure black and pure white chickens produces offspring that are blue. The feathers of the blue chickens do not possess blue pigment, but are arranged in tiny patches of black and white areas. When the blue fowl are crossed, the F_2 generation has a 1:2:1 ratio of black to blue to white chickens. Incomplete dominance is characterized by an F_1 generation with a phenotype different from that of either of the parents. The F_2 generation shows a phenotype ratio of 1:2:1 rather than the 3:1 ratio seen in normal Mendelian inheritance.

Another example of incomplete dominance is flower color in snapdragons. Also roan coat in horses and cattle, once thought to be caused by incomplete dominance, is now known to be another form of modified dominance called codominance.

25-15   Codominance

In **codominance,** two dominant alleles are expressed at the same time. This differs from incomplete dominance, in which neither allele is completely dominant or completely suppressed. The expression of both alleles in incomplete dominance results in an intermediate trait, or blending of the two traits. But in codominance, both alleles are expressed; there is no blending of traits. A cross between homozygous red shorthorn cattle and homozygous white shorthorn cattle results in heterozygous offspring with a roan coat. The roan coat consists of a mixture of red hairs and white hairs (see Figure 25-13). Since each hair is either entirely red or entirely white, the condition shows codominance.

Capital letters with superscripts are often used to represent genotypes in codominance. For example, the symbol C^R can represent the allele for red coat in shorthorn cattle, and the symbol C^W can represent the allele for white coat. The genotype for homozygous red coat is then symbolized as $C^R C^R$, and the genotype for homozygous white coat is $C^W C^W$. The heterozygous animal with a roan coat has a genotype of $C^R C^W$.

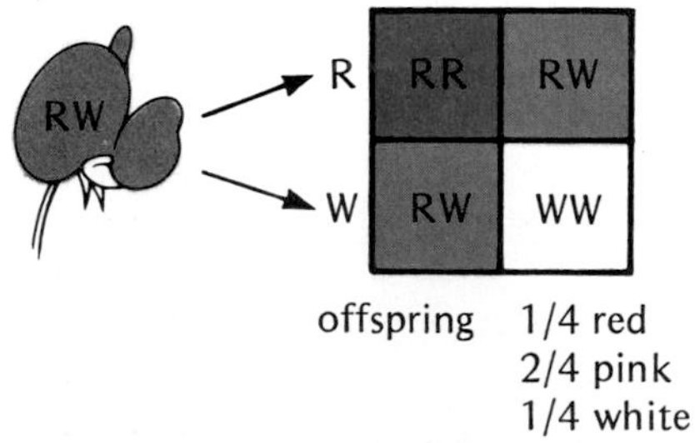

offspring   1/4 red
            2/4 pink
            1/4 white

Figure 25-12. Incomplete Dominance in a Hybrid Cross. One-fourth of the offspring are pure dominant, one-fourth are pure recessive, and two-fourths are hybrid intermediate.

Figure 25-13. Roan Coat. White hairs and red hairs in roan coat indicate the full expression of each dominant allele in different hairs.

Codominance also occurs in human heredity. Inheritance of the disease sickle-cell anemia is controlled by codominant alleles (see page 436). This disease results in abnormally shaped red blood cells due to abnormal hemoglobin. The sickle-cell condition produces serious effects. Blood vessels in the brain are sometimes clogged, reducing the oxygen supply and causing damage to brain cells. A heterozygous person, with one allele for normal hemoglobin and one allele for the sickle-cell condition, produces both types of red blood cells—normal and sickle shaped. The inheritance of blood type is another example of codominance found in humans. Blood type inheritance is discussed in the next section.

25-16 Multiple Alleles

For some traits more than two alleles exist in the species. They are referred to as **multiple alleles.** Although a single individual cannot have more than two alleles for each trait, different individuals can have different pairs of alleles when multiple alleles exist.

The alleles for human blood type are an example of multiple alleles for a trait. The ABO blood group system is described in Chapter 10, page 172. The existence of multiple alleles explains why there are four different blood types in this system. There are three alleles that control blood type, called A, B, and O. O is recessive. A and B are both dominant over O, but neither is dominant over the other. When A and B are both present in the genotype of an individual, both alleles are expressed.

The usual way to represent alleles in a multiple allele system is to use the capital letter I to represent a dominant allele and the lowercase i to represent a recessive allele. A superscript letter then identifies each particular dominant allele. Thus I^A represents the dominant allele A; I^B represents the dominant allele B; and i is understood to represent the recessive allele O.

Since there are three alleles, there are six possible genotypes: $I^A I^A$, $I^A I^B$, $I^A i$, $I^B I^B$, $I^B i$, and ii. Table 25-2 shows the blood types produced by each of these genotypes.

Rh blood factors are also an example of multiple alleles in human genetics (see page 174).

GENOTYPE	BLOOD TYPE
$I^A I^A$ or $I^A i$	A
$I^B I^B$ or $I^B i$	B
$I^A I^B$	AB
ii	O

Table 25-2. Multiple Alleles in the ABO Blood Group System. I^A and I^B are each dominant over i, but not over each other. When both dominant alleles are present, the blood type is AB. Type O blood is produced only when neither dominant allele is present (genotype ii).

Chapter Review

SUMMARY

- Genetics is the branch of biology concerned with how genes are transmitted from parent to offspring. Modern genetics developed from the scientific work of Gregor Mendel. From his experiments with heredity in pea plants, Mendel developed three laws of heredity —the laws of dominance, segregation, and independent assortment.

- Genes are located on the chromosomes in cell nuclei. The two chromosomes of a pair carry genes for the same traits. The different forms of a gene for a particular trait are called alleles. An individual may have two identical alleles or two different ones. The genetic makeup of an individual is called the genotype. The appearance of the individual due to the expression of the genotype is called the phenotype.

- Some traits do not follow Mendelian patterns of inheritance. Other patterns may involve incomplete dominance or codominance. Some traits are controlled by multiple alleles.

KNOW THE TERMS

allele	genetics	incomplete dominance	multiple alleles
codominance	genotype	law of dominance	phenotype
dihybrid cross	heterozygous	law of independent assortment	Punnett square
dominant trait	homozygous	law of segregation	recessive trait
gene	hybrid	monohybrid cross	test cross

SECTION QUESTIONS

Mendel's Principles of Heredity

1. Why are pea plants a good choice for genetic experiments?
2. What is a hybrid?
3. What is a dominant trait?
4. State Mendel's law of segregation.

Basic Concepts in Genetics

5. Define the term *allele*.

6. Define the terms *genotype* and *phenotype*.
7. What is a Punnett square used for?
8. Define the term *monohybrid cross*.
9. State the law of independent assortment.
10. How can you tell whether an organism is pure or hybrid?
11. Give two examples of codominance in humans.
12. Name a trait that is controlled by multiple alleles.

KNOW THE FACTS

Copy the number of each sentence below on a sheet of paper. Beside each number, write the terms(s) that complete(s) the sentence correctly.

1. _____ is the study of the ways in which hereditary information is transmitted from parents to offspring.
2. Pea plants hybrid for a pair of contrasting traits show only the _____ trait.
3. Genes are located on the _____ in cell nuclei.
4. The genotype Tt represents a(n) _____.

5. When hybrid tall pea plants are crossed, about _____ of the offspring are short.
6. The ratio of phenotypes typically produced in a dihybrid cross is _____.
7. A cross between red and white flowers that produces pink flowers illustrates _____.
8. Roan-colored cattle are produced by a form of gene expression known as _____.

UNDERSTAND THE CONCEPTS

9. What was Mendel's procedure in crossing pure plants showing contrasting traits?
10. What is meant by the F_1 generation?
11. Describe the appearance of the F_1 generation in Mendel's crosses of pure plants with contrasting traits.
12. How were Mendel's results explained by scientists in the early 1900s?
13. State the basic law of probability.
14. What phenotype and genotype ratios are observed in the offspring of a hybrid cross?
15. Describe the experiments that led to Mendel's law of independent assortment.
16. How is a test cross carried out?
17. Explain how codominance and incomplete dominance differ.
18. What are multiple alleles? How many alleles for one trait can an individual have?

THINK CRITICALLY

19. Do all individuals with the same phenotype have the same genotype? Explain.
20. How does the law of segregation explain Mendel's observation that the shortness trait in pea plants disappeared and reappeared from generation to generation?
21. In a monohybrid cross, the expected ratio of phenotypes differs from the expected ratio of genotypes. Explain.
22. If the two alleles controlling height in pea plants can yield two possible height phenotypes, then how many possible phenotypes can be produced by the three alleles controlling blood type in humans? Explain.
23. A mother and a father are each heterozygous for eye color. The couple has four children, all of whom have the recessive eye color. You might expect that three of the children would have the dominant eye color and only one would have the recessive eye color. Why did the actual phenotype ratios in this family differ from the expected ratios?

THINK CREATIVELY

24. Using your knowledge of meiosis, explain the genetic basis for the law of segregation.
25. Two women gave birth to girls in the same hospital at the same time. The nurses think they may have accidentally switched the babies' name tags and given the babies to the wrong set of parents. One baby, Jane, is blood type O. The other baby, Mary, is blood type A. The father in one set of parents, the Reds, is blood type A and the mother is type B. The father in the other set of parents, the Greens, is blood type AB and the mother is type O. Figure out which baby belongs to which set of parents.

FOR FURTHER INVESTIGATION

1. Grow and compare tall and dwarf marigolds.
2. Find out how commercial seed growers produce the various types of seeds that they sell. Present your findings to your class.
3. Write a report on one of the following career opportunities. See suggested procedures, p. 9, "For Further Investigation" Activity 3.
   a. Statistician   c. Animal breeder
   b. Geneticist
4. Outline the life and scientific work of one of the following scientists:
   a. Ruth Sagar   c. Virginia Apgar
   b. Hugo De Vries   d. R. C. Punnett

FOR FURTHER READING

Baltimore, David, "The Brain of a Cell," *Science 84,* November, 1984.

Brown, D., "Gene Expression in Eukaryotes," *Science,* February, 1981.

Miller, J.A., "Genetics of Body Plan: From Fly to Humans," *Science News,* July 14, 1984.

Steinberg, S., "Genes Shed Light on Photosynthesis," *Science News,"* August 13, 1983.

Chapter 26

MODERN GENETICS

An understanding of genetics is important to the success of selective breeding of animals such as horses.

DEVELOPMENT OF THE GENE-CHROMOSOME THEORY

Objectives:
1. State the chromosome theory.
2. Describe how sex is determined in humans.
3. Explain the terms *sex-linked trait, gene linkage, crossing-over,* and *multiple-gene inheritance.*

26-1 The Chromosome Theory

In 1902 W. S. Sutton, a graduate student at Columbia University, was studying the formation of sperm in the grasshopper. He observed the pairs of homologous chromosomes in diploid cells and the separation of the homologous chromosomes during spermatogenesis. He realized that the chromosomes that separated during meiosis were the same as the chromosomes that had united during the fertilization process that originally produced the animal.

After reviewing Mendel's work, Sutton began to think that the factors, or genes, of Mendel's theory were carried on the chromosomes. Sutton explained Mendel's dihybrid experiment with pea plants by saying that the alleles of the gene for seed color and the alleles of the gene for seed coat texture are on nonhomologous chromosomes. In this way independent assortment could take place. He published his research in a paper called "The Chromosomes in Heredity."

Although Sutton's work did not prove that the genes are carried on the chromosomes, it was a very important hypothesis in the understanding of genetics. The final proof that the genes are carried on the chromosomes was obtained through the work of the geneticist Thomas Hunt Morgan, also at Columbia University.

26-2   Sex Determination and Chromosomes

Around 1890 it was observed that the chromosomes in cells from males and females were identical except for one pair. Scientists suspected that these different chromosomes determined the sex of the organism. This hypothesis is now well confirmed. These two unmatched chromosomes are known as the **sex chromosomes;** the other chromosomes are called **autosomes** (*aw*-tuh-sohmz). The discovery of the sex chromosomes was important in the study of genetics because it linked a genetic property to the chromosomes.

There are 23 pairs of chromosomes in human body cells: 22 pairs of autosomes and 1 pair of sex chromosomes. The sex chromosomes are called X and Y. The cells of human females contain two X chromosomes. The cells of males contain one X chromosome and one Y chromosome. As human egg cells are produced in the female by meiosis, each egg cell receives one X chromosome (see Figure 26-1). There are, however, two types of sperm cells produced in the male—those that receive an X chromosome, and those that receive a Y. When fertilization occurs in humans, the zygote will be either XX or XY, depending on which type of sperm fertilized the egg. An XX zygote develops into a female; an XY zygote develops into a male. In humans, it is the sperm of the male that determines the sex of the offspring.

Not all animals have the same system of sex chromosomes as humans. In birds, butterflies, and some fish, the male has the two identical sex chromosomes, and the female produces two different types of gametes. In these animals, it is the egg of the female that determines the sex of the offspring.

26-3   T. H. Morgan and *Drosophila*

In the early 1900s Thomas Hunt Morgan began a study of genetics at Columbia University. He made great contributions to the understanding of genes and won a Nobel prize in 1933 for his work. One reason that Morgan's research was so successful was his choice of the fruit fly, *Drosophila* (droh-*sahf*-uh-luh), as his experimental animal.

The fruit fly is so called because it is often found around ripening fruits. It is a very useful organism for genetic experiments. It is only about 2 millimeters in length so that large numbers can be kept in a relatively small space. It is easy to raise in laboratory cultures. The fruit fly produces many offspring. A mating pair can produce more than 300 young. It also has a complete life cycle of about 14 days. So a geneticist is able to study many generations of flies in a short time.

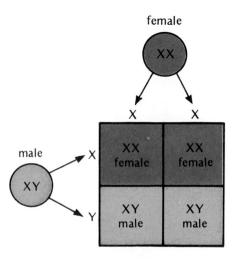

Figure 26-1. Sex Determination in Humans.

Figure 26-2. Fruit Flies. Both the female fly (top) and the male fly (bottom) have red eyes.

Another advantage to studying *Drosophila* is that it has only eight chromosomes. The cells in its salivary glands contain giant chromosomes, which can be easily observed under the microscope (see Figure 20-1, p331).

26-4   Sex-Linked Traits

Morgan examined thousands of fruit flies microscopically to find interesting traits to study (see Figure 26-2). The normal eye color of *Drosophila* is bright red. One day a white-eyed male fly appeared in the culture. Since he had never seen this trait before, he decided to investigate it. His first step was to mate the white-eyed male with a normal red-eyed female. All offspring of this mating showed red eyes, so Morgan concluded that the allele for white eyes is recessive.

If this cross obeyed the usual rules of Mendelian genetics, all the red-eyed flies of the F_1 generation would be heterozygous for eye color. If R represents the dominant allele for red eyes, and r the recessive allele for white eyes, the genotype of this generation should be Rr. To test this assumption, Morgan mated males and females of the F_1 generation. The F_2 generation did show the expected ratio of red eyes to white—three-fourths of the flies had red eyes, and one-fourth had white eyes. However, there was one peculiarity in the results—all the white-eyed flies were male. The females were all red-eyed. The inheritance of eye color seemed to have something to do with the sex of the offspring.

To find out more about what was happening, Morgan performed a kind of test cross. He mated the original white-eyed male with a red-eyed female from the F_1 generation. This time half the females had white eyes, and half had red. The males were also divided half white and half red.

When he thought about these results, Morgan knew that the Y chromosome is shorter than the X. It seemed reasonable to assume that some of the genes found on the X chromosome are missing from the Y chromosome. Morgan hypothesized that an allele for eye color is carried on the X chromosome of the fruit fly and that there is no corresponding allele on the Y chromosome. By this reasoning, a male fly will show the recessive allele for that trait. A female fly would have to have the recessive allele on both of its X chromosomes to show the trait.

By means of Punnett squares, we can show that Morgan's hypothesis accounts for the results of the crosses described above (see Figure 26-3). In these diagrams, X^R represents an X chromosome carrying the dominant allele for red eyes, X^r is an X chromosome with the recesive allele for white eyes; and Y is a Y chromosome with no gene for eye color.

Once a white-eyed female had been obtained, it was possible to make a further confirming test. Morgan crossed a white-eyed female with a red-eyed male. All the female

white-eyed male

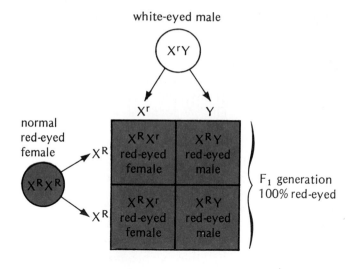

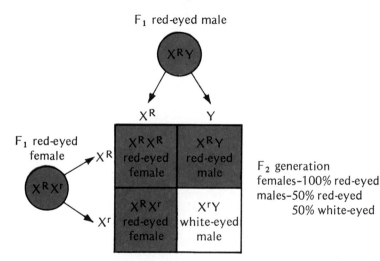

Figure 26-3. Inheritance of the White-Eye Trait in Drosophila. The allele for white eyes is recessive and is carried only on the X chromosome. *(Top)* A white-eyed male is crossed with a homozygous red-eyed female. Since all the offspring inherit the dominant red-eye allele from the female parent, all have red eyes. However, the females are heterozygous for eye color. *(Bottom)* A red-eyed male is crossed with a heterozygous red-eyed female. Since all the female offspring receive the dominant allele from the male parent, they are all red-eyed. However, the male offspring do not receive a gene for eye color from the male parent, but only from the female parent. Half the males receive the recessive allele and are white-eyed.

offspring were red-eyed; all the males were white-eyed. You may want to construct a Punnett square that will explain this result.

A trait that is controlled by a gene found on the sex chromosomes is a **sex-linked trait.** The chance of showing the trait is affected by the sex of the individual. Most sex-linked traits are determined by genes found on the X chromosome but not on the Y chromosome. Morgan's discovery of sex-linked traits was a strong confirmation of Sutton's hypothesis that genes are located on the chromosomes. It was also an important discovery in its own right, as it relates to the occurrence of several human diseases.

26-5   Sex-Linked Traits in Humans

Many human conditions and diseases are caused by abnormal recessive alleles of particular genes. The normal allele enables the body to perform some function that the abnormal

Frontier of Biology

Tests for the clotting activity of whole blood are routinely performed in laboratories.

Cloning the Clotting Factor

Victims of the most common form of hemophilia are unable to produce Factor VIII, a protein needed for normal blood clotting. Thus, they are subject to bleeding that can be crippling or fatal if not checked. Now, because of significant advances in molecular genetics, there is hope for controlling this problem.

Recently bioscientists, using human DNA, have isolated and cloned the DNA sequence, i.e., the gene, responsible for producing Factor VIII. This DNA sequence was inserted into the genetic machinery of cultured hamster and monkey kidney cells by recombinant DNA techniques (see pages 457-459). The cultured kidney cells obeyed the synthesis code of the Factor VIII gene and began producing the clotting factor in small quantities.

If further work goes as expected, there should be recombinant DNA Factor VIII available commercially before the end of the decade. Most hemophiliacs would then no longer need tranfusions of Factor VIII taken from donated blood, a procedure that is both risky and expensive.

allele does not. The term *defective allele* is often used to refer to the abnormal alleles that cause genetic diseases. Several of the known defective alleles in human genetics are sex-linked. Among the human diseases caused by defective sex-linked alleles are hemophilia, a disorder of the blood-clotting system, and muscular dystrophy, which results in the gradual destruction of muscle cells. A form of night blindness and color blindness are less serious sex-linked hereditary disorders.

Color blindness is a condition in which the individual cannot perceive certain colors, most commonly red and green. This condition is much more common in males than in females. Relatively few females suffer from color blindness, although they may be *carriers* for it. Carriers have the allele for color blindness on one X chromosome, but are not affected by it because the recessive defective allele is counteracted by a normal allele on the other X chromosome.

Every male receives an X chromosome from his mother and a Y chromosome from his father. If the mother is a carrier for color blindness, there is a 50 percent chance that she will transmit the X chromosome with the defective allele to any son she has (see Figure 26-4). Since the Y chromosome has no corresponding allele for color vision, when a son inherits an X chromosome with the defective allele, the allele is expressed and that son will suffer from color blindness. A daughter would be only a carrier if she received the defective allele from her mother and a normal allele from her father.

Since a father contributes only a Y chromosome to his sons, a color-blind father cannot transmit the color-blindness allele to his sons. He will, however, transmit this defective allele to all his daughters. If the mother in this case is a carrier of the defective allele, there is a 50 percent chance that a daughter will inherit the defective allele from the mother as well as from the father. Thus, on the average, half the daughters of such a mating will be color blind, and the other half will be carriers. Half the sons will also be color blind, but this result does not depend on the father's genotype. If both parents are color blind, all their offspring will be color blind, since neither parent is carrying a normal allele.

26-6   Gene Linkage

Every organism has thousands of genes. Every organism also has a certain small number of chromosomes in each body cell. Therefore many genes must be present on each chromosome. Genes located on the same chromosome are said to be *linked.*

If genes are linked on the same chromosome, they cannot be distributed independently during meiosis, and therefore they should not obey Mendel's law of independent assortment. Mendel arrived at the law of independent assortment only because the traits he studied happened to be controlled by genes located on different chromosomes.

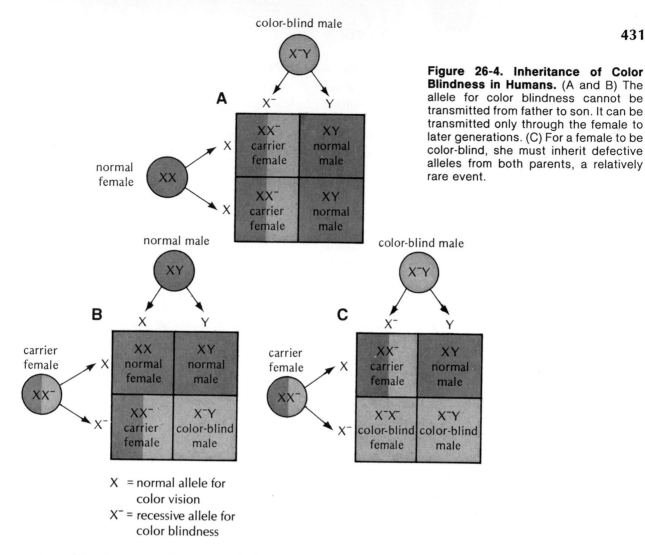

Figure 26-4. Inheritance of Color Blindness in Humans. (A and B) The allele for color blindness cannot be transmitted from father to son. It can be transmitted only through the female to later generations. (C) For a female to be color-blind, she must inherit defective alleles from both parents, a relatively rare event.

X = normal allele for color vision
X⁻ = recessive allele for color blindness

One of the first examples of **gene linkage** was found by R. C. Punnett and William Bateson in investigations at Cambridge University in 1906. They were studying the inheritance of two pairs of traits in pea plants: purple (dominant) and red (recessive) flowers, and long (dominant) and round (recessive) pollen grains. Plants pure for both dominant traits were crossed with plants pure for both recessives. The expected phenotype of 100 percent dominant for both traits in the F_1 generation was observed. However, when these dihybrids were crossed, they did not show the expected 9:3:3:1 phenotype ratios in the F_2 generation (see page 420). The results were much closer to the 3:1 ratio obtained from a single hybrid cross. The two dominant traits seemed to be staying together, as were the two recessive traits. They were not being distributed independently.

T. H. Morgan had obtained similar results with *Drosophila*. Certain traits seemed to be inherited together. Morgan took this to be further evidence that genes were carried on chromosomes, and that genes carried on the same chromosome were inherited together.

26-7   Crossing-Over

The difficulty with the hypothesis of linked genes was that the linkage did not seem to be perfect. In a small percentage of offspring in the F_2 generation, the linked genes had separated. In the Punnett-Bateson investigation, for example, there were some plants with purple flowers and round pollen, and some with red flowers and long pollen. But the numbers were far from the 9:3:3:1 ratios of Mendelian genetics. The actual ratios observed were fairly constant from one experiment to another, but they were hard to explain by any mathematical analysis.

Eventually, Morgan concluded that the reason for the unusual ratios was that pieces of homologous chromosomes were sometimes exchanged during meiosis, before the chromosomes separated to go to different gametes. He called this process **crossing-over** (see Figure 26-5). It is now known that crossing-over occurs during synapsis of the first meiotic division, when the four chromatids of each homologous chromosome pair are in close contact.

As a result of crossing-over, the chromosomes that go into the gametes have new gene linkages. They are not identical to the chromosomes in the parent cells. Crossing-over is an important source of variation in offspring.

Morgan reasoned that genes that are far apart on the same chromosome should become separated by crossing-over more often than genes that are close together. By studying the offspring ratios of dihybrid crosses for many different pairs of linked genes, Morgan was able to calculate mathematically how close or how far apart each particular pair appeared to be. In this way he was able to construct gene maps of the chromosomes in *Drosophila*. Each gene map showed the sequence of genes on the chromosome, based on inferences from the frequency with which the genes became separated by crossing-over.

26-8   Multiple-Gene Inheritance

Unlike the traits studied by Mendel, many traits in both plants and animals do not appear in two contrasting forms. For example, humans are not either tall or short. Instead human height shows continuous variation over a wide range from very short to very tall. The same is true of human skin color and the size of fruits and vegetables. Traits that vary in a continuous manner between two extremes are not controlled

Figure 26-5. Crossing-Over. During synapsis, segments of homologous chromatids may be interchanged. If the exchanged segments carry different alleles for certain traits, new gene combinations result.

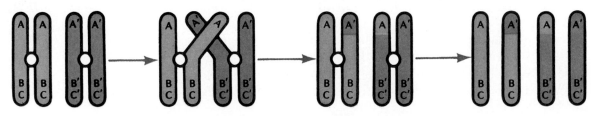

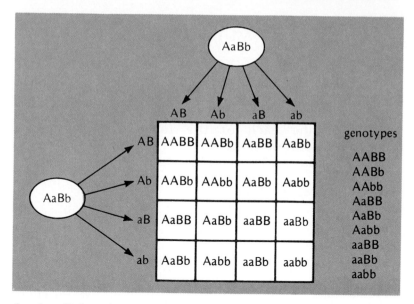

Figure 26-6. Multiple-Gene Inheritance. In multiple-gene inheritance in which there are two genes controlling a trait, there are nine different possible genotypes. There is a range of phenotypes between the pure dominant and pure recessive extremes.

by the alleles of a single gene. Instead, they are affected by the alleles of two or more different genes. When two or more independent genes affect the same characteristic, it is known as **multiple-gene,** or *polygenic,* **inheritance.**

The simplest case of multiple-gene inheritance would involve two genes, each with its own pair of alleles. The length of the ears in corn and the color of the kernels in wheat are both controlled by two genes. Using either one as an example, we can refer to the genes as Aa and Bb. With these two genes there can be four different possible gametes and nine different genotypes (see Figure 26-6). We can say that the greater the number of capital letters in the genotype, the larger the corn ear or the darker the wheat kernel. Thus, the largest corn ears or darkest wheat kernels would have the genotype AABB. The smallest ears and lightest kernels would have the genotype aabb. All other genotypes would show traits between these two extremes.

26-9   Environment and Heredity

Genes carry all the information for the development, structure, and metabolic processes of an organism. But the environment also plays a role in determining how the genes are expressed. For example, the Himalayan rabbit has white fur over most of the body, with black fur on the ears, nose, feet, and tail (see Figure 26-7). This pattern is produced by differences in temperature in various parts of the body. A gene causes the deposition of black pigment in the fur over parts of the body in which the temperature falls below 33°C. This can be illustrated by placing an ice pack on a shaved area on the back of a Himalayan rabbit. The new growth of fur is black. Genes carry the basic information for all traits, but the phenotypes of organisms can often be modified by environmental factors.

Figure 26-7. Effect of Body Temperature on Fur Color of the Himalayan Rabbit.

Frontier of Biology

Barbara McClintock at work in her laboratory.

Jumping Genes

Could segments of DNA spontaneously jump from one site to another on a chromosome, and influence the expression of their new neighboring genes? Yes. Contrary to the classical idea that genes are in fixed positions on chromosomes, such mobile elements, or "jumping genes," do exist. They were discovered by geneticist Barbara McClintock after decades of painstaking work analyzing the results of carefully planned genetic crosses in corn. McClintock was awarded the Nobel Prize for this work in 1983.

McClintock showed that some genes move during cell replication, taking a new position in or near another gene, and inactivating that gene. "Jumping genes" produce variations that offer a species new possibilities for evolution. Also, jumping genes are likely to be useful in genetic engineering. One jumping gene, for example, is already in use in fruitfly genetic engineering experiments. In addition, jumping genes may underlie the cell diversity that arises during development of organisms.

MUTATIONS

Objectives:
1. Explain the term *mutation.*
2. Distinguish between gene mutations and chromosome mutations.
3. Describe each of the following types of chromosomal mutation: translocation, inversion, addition, deletion, nondisjunction, and polyploidy.

26-10 Types of Mutations

Plant and animal breeders have known for a long time that new traits may suddenly appear in a strain of plant or animal. These traits can then be inherited according to Mendelian principles. A new trait that appears suddenly is called a **mutation** (myoo-*tay*-shun). The first individuals showing the new trait are called *mutants* (*myoot*-unts). Credit for the concept of mutation is given to the Dutch botanist Hugo De Vries, one of the scientists who rediscovered Mendel's work. De Vries' first observation of a mutation in living organisms was in a plant known as the evening primrose.

It is now known that there are two different types of mutation. One type is a **gene mutation,** where a new allele for an existing trait suddenly appears on the chromosome that carries the gene. The white-eyed male fruit fly that T. H. Morgan discovered was the result of a mutation of the gene for eye color. The nature of gene mutations is discussed in Chapter 27. The other type of mutation is a chromosomal mutation. **Chromosomal mutations** involve a change in the structure of an entire chromosome or a change in the chromosome number within the cells of the organism. The mutations observed by De Vries were chromosomal mutations.

For a mutation to be inherited in a sexually reproducing organism, it must be present in the DNA of a gamete. Thus, the mutation must occur in a gamete, or in any cell from which a gamete is derived. Mutations that occur in body cells cannot be transmitted to future generations, since these cells are not involved in reproduction.

26-11 Chromosomal Mutations

Changes in chromosome structure. Permanent changes in chromosome structure sometimes occur during meiotic cell division. As a tetrad forms during meiosis, the chromatids can become entangled and chromosome segments may be rearranged in several ways. These changes are not to be confused with crossing over. **Translocation** is the transfer of a chromosome segment to a nonhomologous chromosome. An **inversion** occurs when a piece of a chromosome is rotated so that the order of genes in the segment is reversed. **Addition** involves the breaking off of a chromosome segment and its attachment to its homologue. The homologue then has some genes repeated. **Deletion** occurs when a chromosome segment simply breaks off, resulting in the loss of some genes.

Nondisjunction. The misplacement of a whole chromosome can occur during meiosis. Thus an extra chromosome may be present in the new organism $(2n + 1)$ or an entire chromosome may be omitted $(2n - 1)$. This variation takes place when chromosomes that normally separate during meiosis remain together. This phenomenon is referred to as **nondisjunction** (non-dis-*junk*-shun).

Nondisjunction causes several serious genetic defects in humans. *Down's syndrome,* commonly known as *mongolism* (*mahn*-guh-liz-um), is the result of an extra chromosome (see Figure 26-8). A person afflicted with this condition has three number 21 chromosomes in each cell; he or she is mentally retarded and has physical abnormalities. Sexual development can be affected by nondisjunction of the sex chromosomes. One condition, called Turner's syndrome, is caused by the presence of only one X chromosome in the cells and it results in a female with underdeveloped sexual characteristics. In Klinefelter's syndrome, a male has two X's and a Y in each cell, which results in a normal male appearance, but underdeveloped sex organs.

Polyploidy. **Polyploidy** (*pahl*-ee-ployd-ee) is a condition found in plants in which the cells have some multiple of the normal chromosome number. For example, they may have a $3n$, $4n$, or even $5n$ number of chromosomes. Polyploidy occurs when the chromosomes fail to separate normally during mitosis or meiosis. Polyploid plants and their fruits are often larger than normal, and plant breeders sometimes use chemicals to develop polyploid plants (see Figure 26-9).

Figure 26-8. Down's Syndrome. This disorder results from an extra chromosome number 21.

HUMAN GENETIC DISEASES

Objectives:
1. Describe some of the difficulties that arise in studying human genetics.
2. Name three genetic diseases, and describe the cause and symptoms of each.
3. Describe how amniocentesis and karyotyping are used in the diagnosis of genetic diseases.

26-12 Difficulty of Studying Human Heredity

Although much is known about human genetics, the transmission of traits from one generation to another in humans cannot be studied in the same way it is in plants and other animals. The time between generations is too long, the number of offspring produced is too small, and no controlled experiments are possible.

Scientists have learned about certain genetic traits in humans by tracing the appearance of these traits in families over

Figure 26-9. Polyploidy. The strawberries in the upper row are from polyploid plants. Those in the lower row are from normal plants.

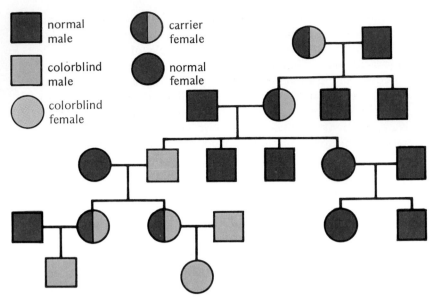

Figure 26-10. A Pedigree Chart Tracing Color Blindness in a Family.

eral generations. A pedigree chart shows the presence or absence of a particular trait in each member of each generation. Figure 26-10 shows a pedigree chart tracing the inheritance of color blindness in five generations of a family. The existence of female carriers of color blindness can be definitely shown only when the condition is found in her descendants.

26-13   Genetic Diseases

A number of human diseases are known to be caused by recessive, defective alleles. These alleles rarely cause symptoms in people who are carriers because there is also a normal allele present. Some sex-linked diseases were discussed on page 428. Among the other genetic diseases of humans are sickle-cell anemia, phenylketonuria, and Tay-Sachs disease.

Sickle-cell anemia is a disease in which the red blood cells have an abnormal hemoglobin molecule (see page 456). This in turn gives the cells an abnormal shape, which causes them to clump and block small blood vessels. The oxygen-carrying capacity of these cells is also decreased. A person with sickle-cell anemia suffers from oxygen deficiency, and also experiences pain and weakness. Sickle-cell anemia is found primarily in people of African descent. It has been found that carriers of the trait—those with one normal and one sickle-cell allele—are more resistant to malaria than people without the defective allele. Because it offers some protection from malaria, this allele has been maintained in African populations. Although carriers of the trait are not generally troubled by symptoms of the disease, such symptoms may arise occasionally as a result of severe stress. Screening for sickle-cell anemia is done by examination of the red blood cells.

Phenylketonuria, or PKU, is a disease in which an enzyme necessary for the normal breakdown of the amino acid phenylalanine is missing. Because of the missing enzyme, products of phenylalanine metabolism accumulate in the body, damaging the brain and causing mental retardation. In the past, it was not possible to diagnose PKU until the brain damage had occurred. Now, however, PKU can be diagnosed at birth by a simple test of the infant's urine. This is done routinely in most hospitals. Brain damage can then be avoided by a special diet low in phenylalanine.

Tay-Sachs disease, like PKU, results from the lack of a particular enzyme. In this case, it is an enzyme necessary for the breakdown of lipids in the brain. Without the enzyme, the lipids accumulate in the brain cells and destroy them. Tay-Sachs is a rare disease, but it is found in highest frequency among Jews of Central European descent. The allele for Tay-Sachs disease is recessive, and symptoms occur only in the homozygous condition. This disease appears before the age of 1 year and death occurs within several years. There is no treatment for Tay-Sachs disease at this time.

26-14 Genetic Counseling

Although no treatment is possible for many of the known genetic diseases, modern medical knowledge makes it possible to examine and counsel prospective parents and to give them an accurate idea about the risks they carry of having a child with a genetic disease. In some cases it is possible to perform tests that show whether or not the parents are carriers of genetic diseases.

26-15 Amniocentesis

Amniocentesis (am-nee-oh-sen-*tee*-sis) is a technique in which a long needle is inserted into the amniotic sac of a pregnant woman. A small sample of amniotic fluid, which contains some cells that have sloughed off the fetus, is withdrawn. The cells are then cultured and subjected to various tests. Cell metabolism can be checked for the presence or lack of a particular enzyme. If the fetus has Tay-Sachs disease, it can be detected in this way. The chromosomes of the fetus can be examined by a process known as **karyotyping** (kar-ee-oh-*typ*-ing). In karyotyping, a photograph is taken of a fetal cell undergoing mitosis. The photograph is then enlarged, and the chromosomes are arranged in pairs. This is possible because chromosome pairs differ from each other in length, shape, and position of the centromere. The karyotype of the fetus can then be compared with a normal human karyotype (see page 349). Sometimes a chromosome is missing. Sometimes an extra chromosome is present. The presence of an extra chromosome number 21 shows that the fetus has Down's syndrome (see Figure 26-11). The sex of the fetus, as well as any abnormalities of the sex chromosomes, can also be determined by karyotyping.

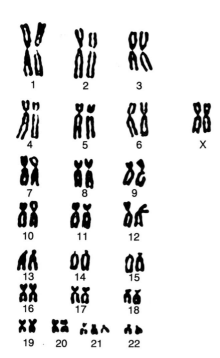

Figure 26-11. Karyotype of Down's Syndrome. Note that there are three number 21 chromosomes.

Figure 26-12. Animal Breeding. Modern strains of turkeys are the result of centuries of selective breedings.

GENETICS IN PLANT AND ANIMAL BREEDING

Objective:
   Describe the genetic techniques used by plant and animal breeders to improve their crops and animals.

26-16   Breeding Methods

People have always tried to improve their crops and domestic animals. They have tried to increase yields, upgrade quality, and expand growing and breeding areas. Today modern genetic principles are used to produce plants and animals with desirable traits (see Figure 26-12). Organisms with homozygous genes are necessary to establish a pure breeding line. A breeder can choose from several methods.

Selection. **Selection** is the choosing of animals and plants with the most desirable traits for mating. The breeder hopes to change the population by accumulating the desired characteristics. After mating occurs, the breeder then selects only the offspring with the desired traits for further mating.

Inbreeding. **Inbreeding** is the mating of closely related individuals to obtain desired results. The degree of closeness can vary. Self-pollination by plants is the closest possible hereditary relationship. In organisms that require cross-fertilization, the closest relationship would be brother-sister, mother-son, and father-daughter. Inbreeding is employed in raising domestic animals, such as fowl, sheep, cattle, and swine. It decreases variation for a particular trait in a population, and thus tends to increase the number of homozyous genes. Continued inbreeding and selection will eventually produce a line of animals that breeds nearly pure.

However, because inbreeding tends to increase the number of homozygous genes, it can also result in unwanted effects. Harmful, recessive alleles may be brought together by inbreeding and be expressed. This is why close relatives are prohibited from marrying in many societies.

Outbreeding. In **outbreeding**, individuals not closely related are mated. The purpose is to introduce new beneficial alleles into the population. Special traits are often found in hybrid crosses of two close species. These superior characteristics are called **hybrid vigor,** or *heterosis* (het-uh-*roh*-sis). One example of hybrid vigor is the mule, the offspring of a male donkey and a female horse. The mule is superior to its parents in physical endurance, strength, and resistance to disease. Mules, however, are usually sterile.

Another type of outbreeding is the mating of pure breeding lines within a species. White short-horned cattle and black Angus cattle have been crossed to produce offspring with superior beef and rapid growth.

Successful outbreeding followed by inbreeding may produce valuable new pure lines of plants and animals.

Mutations. Mutations are used by plant and animal breeders to improve their stock. Many fruits, such as the navel orange, pink grapefruit, McIntosh apple, and seedless grape, started as plant mutations. Once discovered, a plant mutation may be reproduced by vegetative propagation. This avoids the segregation of traits that would occur in sexual reproduction. Mutations are also valuable in animal breeding. For example, in mink ranching, the most valuable fur colors, platinum and black cross, originated as mutations.

Chapter Review

SUMMARY

- W. S. Sutton proposed the idea that genes are carried on the chromosomes. T. H. Morgan, who discovered sex-linked traits, proved that Sutton was right. Humans have 22 pairs of autosomes and 1 pair of sex chromosomes. Several human diseases are controlled by genes found on the sex chromosomes.

- Genes located on the same chromosome do not show independent assortment during meiosis. However, these linked genes may be separated by the crossing-over of chromosomes during synapsis. Crossing-over is an important source of genetic variation.

- Some traits, such as human skin color and height, are controlled by multiple genes, not just a single pair of genes. The environment may play a role in determining how genes are expressed.

- Various types of changes in chromosome structure can arise, generally as a result of abnormal meiosis. Such changes can produce chromosomal mutations. Another type of mutation is gene mutation.

- Among the genetic diseases of humans are sickle-cell anemia, phenylketonuria, and Tay-Sachs disease. These diseases are caused by defective recessive alleles. Symptoms of the diseases are found only in homozygous recessive individuals. Amniocentesis and karyotyping are techniques used to detect genetic diseases in developing fetuses.

- Plant and animal breeders use genetics to try to improve their stock. Methods of improvement include selection, inbreeding, outbreeding, and the use of mutations.

KNOW THE TERMS

addition	deletion	karyotyping	polyploidy
amniocentesis	gene linkage	multiple-gene inheritance	selection
autosome	gene mutation	mutation	sex chromosome
chromosomal mutation	hybrid vigor	nondisjunction	sex-linked trait
color blindness	inbreeding	outbreeding	translocation
crossing-over	inversion		

SECTION QUESTIONS

Development of the Gene-Chromsome Theory

1. What was W. S. Sutton's conclusion about the "factors" in Mendel's theories?
2. How is sex determined in humans?
3. What is one reason for the success of T. H. Morgan's genetics research?
4. Define the term *sex-linked trait*.
5. What is gene linkage?
6. In what process are pieces of homologous chromosomes exchanged during meiosis?
7. Name two human traits controlled by multiple genes.

Mutations

8. What is a mutation?
9. Name six types of chromosomal mutations.

Human Genetic Diseases

10. Name three human genetic diseases.
11. How can the cells of a fetus be examined?

Genetics in Plant and Animial Breeding

12. Name three methods used by breeders to improve yield and quality.
13. What method is used to reproduce a plant mutation?

KNOW THE FACTS

Copy the number of each statement below on a sheet of paper. Beside each number, write whether the statement is true or false. If the statement is false, replace the italicized word(s) with a term that will make the statement true.

1. The chromosomes in a cell that are not sex chromosomes are called *autosomes*.
2. About *two-thirds* of the offspring from a cross between XX and YY will be female.
3. Most *sex-linked* traits are determined by genes found on the X chromosome but not on the Y chromosome.
4. If a woman is a carrier for color blindness, her sons will have a *100%* chance of receiving the defective gene.
5. Crossing-over occurs during *replication* of the first meiotic division.
6. The influence of temperature on the fur color of the Himalayan rabbit illustrates the effect of *environment* on gene expression.
7. When a new allele for an existing trait suddenly appears, the event is called a *chromosomal* mutation.
8. Down's syndrome is the result of *polyploidy*.
9. The purpose of genetic counseling is to make parents aware of the risks they may carry of transmitting a *genetic* disease.
10. Special traits often found in hybrid crosses of two close species are called *heterosis*.

UNDERSTAND THE CONCEPTS

11. How did Sutton interpret the results of Mendel's dihybrid cross?
12. Explain what determines the sex of human offspring.
13. Give several reasons why *Drosophila* is useful for genetic experiments.
14. Explain why hemophilia and color blindness occur much more frequently in men than in women.
15. Why is crossing-over important?
16. What is a gene map, and how is a gene map constructed?
17. Explain the difference between a gene mutation and a chromosomal mutation.
18. Define the terms *translocation, inversion, addition*, and *deletion*.
19. Explain what happens in nondisjunction, and name some defects caused by nondisjunction.
20. What is polyploidy?
21. State some of the difficulties encountered in scientific studies of human heredity.
22. Name three genetic diseases of humans, and describe the effects of each.
23. Describe the techniques of amniocentesis and karyotyping.

24. Define the processes of selection, inbreeding, and outbreeding.
25. Why is marriage between close relatives usually prohibited?
26. How are mutations used by plant and animal breeders?

THINK CRITICALLY

27. If a boy's father is color blind, will the boy necessarily be color blind? Explain.
28. Why is it impossible for males to be carriers for sex-linked traits?
29. What kind of information does a karyotype provide? Can karyotyping be used to determine whether a fetus will be color blind? Whether it will have sickle cell anemia? Whether it will have Down's syndrome? Whether it will be a boy?
30. Compare sex determination in humans and in butterflies.
31. Explain how a near 3:1 phenotype ratio may appear in the F_2 generation of a dihybrid cross.
32. If a normal man marries a normal woman whose father is color blind, what are the chances that their sons and daughters will be color blind?

THINK CREATIVELY

33. Much of genetics research is aimed at understanding human genetics. But instead of doing genetics experiments on humans, researchers commonly use fruit flies. Explain why genetics research is done on flies and not on humans. Propose some explanations why information from experiments with flies can be used to understand human genetics.
34. Sometimes the gamete that a zygote receives from one or both parents has chromosomes that are not genetically identical to chromosomes in that parent's cells. Propose some explanations for the rearrangement of chromosomes. How would each rearrangement change the chromosome? How might this be a source of variation?

FOR FURTHER INVESTIGATION

1. Interview an obstetrician about the pros and cons of amniocentesis.
2. From hospitals or genetic counseling centers obtain sample human karyotypes showing different genetic diseases. Use them to prepare a bulletin board display.
3. Construct a pedigree of your family using one of the following traits, each of which is controlled by a single pair of alleles: (a) Tongue-rolling (the ability to roll one's tongue lengthwise into a U-shape). Rolling is dominant; nonrolling is recessive. (b) Type of ear lobes (free or attached). Free is dominant; attached is recessive.
4. Prepare a report on one of the career opportunities listed below.
   a. Genetic counselor   c. Seed grower
   b. Cell physiologist
5. Write a brief report on the life and contributions of one of the following scientists:
   a. Luther Burbank   c. Maxine Sanger
   b. Elizabeth Russel   d. Evelyn Witkin

FOR FURTHER READING

Brown, William L., "Hybrid Vim and Vigor," *Science 84,* November, 1984.

Chinnici, Madeline, "The Promise of Gene Therapy," *Science Digest,* May, 1985

Franklin, D., "Gene Defect Linked to a Common Dwarfism," *Science News,* May 12, 1984.

Fritz, Sandy, "Shocking Sickle Cells into Doughnuts?" *Scholastic Science World,* April 13, 1984.

Hapgood, Fred, "Fruitfly Fandango," *Science 84,* September, 1984.

Tetrault, S. M., "Hemophilia Gene Found!" *Scholastic Science World,* March 2, 1984.

Chapter 27
MOLECULAR GENETICS

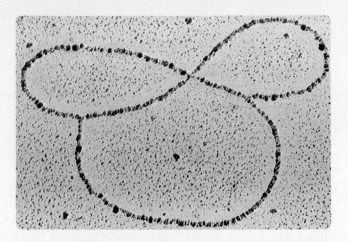

Early in this century, biologists debated whether DNA (shown here copying itself) could be the genetic material.

IDENTIFICATION OF THE GENETIC MATERIAL

Objectives:
1. Describe the experimental evidence proving that DNA carries the hereditary information.
2. Name the three components of a DNA nucleotide.
3. List the ways in which the chemical composition of RNA differs from that of DNA.
4. Describe the Watson-Crick model of the structure of DNA.
5. Describe the replication of a DNA molecule.

As a result of the work of Mendel, Morgan, and many other researchers in genetics, it became clear by 1950 that the chromosomes carry the hereditary information. It was also certain that the information is present in distinct units, and that these units, called genes, are arranged along the chromosomes like beads on a string. Still, no one knew what a gene was or how it worked. Without that knowledge, it could not be said that heredity and genetics were truly understood. This understanding came in the 1950s, when the chemical nature of the gene was discovered.

27-1 Protein vs. Nucleic Acids

Analysis of the material in the cell nucleus started in 1869 with the experiments of Friedrich Miescher, a Swiss biochemist. He isolated a material from the nuclei of fish sperm that he called *nuclein (noo*-klee-un). Work by other scientists showed that nuclein contained the usual elements of organic compounds—carbon, hydrogen, oxygen, and nitrogen—but it was also especially rich in phosphorus. When nuclein was shown to have an acidic nature, its name was changed to *nucleic acid.* Later research found two types of nucleic acid—deoxyribonucleic acid, or DNA, and ribonucleic acid, or RNA. DNA occurs only in the nuclei of cells. RNA is found mainly in the cytoplasm.

In the 1920s it was shown that the chromosomes contained DNA. It was already known that chromosomes contained proteins. The chemical structure of proteins was well understood. Although a few scientists suggested that DNA was the hereditary material, most scientists believed that only proteins were complex enough to carry genetic information. It was not until the 1950s that it became clear that the hereditary material of the chromosomes must be the DNA, not the protein. To understand how this came about, we must first consider experiments performed in 1928 by Frederick Griffith, an English bacteriologist.

Griffith's experiments. Frederick Griffith was trying to find a vaccine against pneumonia. Pneumonia is a disease caused by a type of bacteria called *pneumococcus* (noo-muh-*kahk*-us). Griffith knew that there are two types of pneumococcus (see Figure 27-1). One type, called Type S, is surrounded by an

Figure 27-1. Griffith's Experiment. (A) Live type S bacteria will kill the mouse. (B) Live type R bacteria are harmless. (C) Dead type S bacteria are harmless. (D) Dead type S are mixed with live type R. (E) The mixture kills the mouse, and live type S bacteria are present in the mouse's tissues. Griffith concluded that the type R bacteria had been transformed into type S.

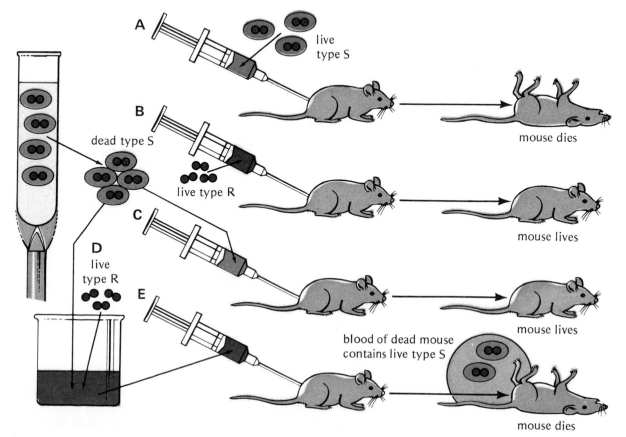

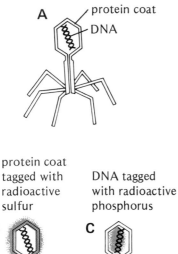

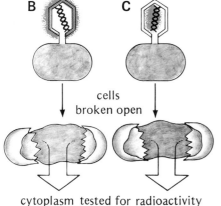

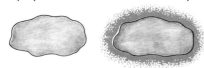

NO RADIATION   RADIATION

Figure 27-2. The Hershey-Chase Experiment. (A) Structure of one type of bacteriophage. (B) Bacteria infected by phage with protein coats tagged with radioactive sulfur. The cell contents do not become radioactive. (C) Bacteria infected by phage with DNA tagged with radioactive phosphorous. Cell contents become radioactive. Hershey and Chase concluded that a phage infects a bacterial cell by injecting its DNA into the bacterium. The protein coat remains outside.

outer covering called a *capsule.* Type S bacteria cause a severe case of pneumonia. The other type, called Type R, is not surrounded by a capsule. Type R bacteria do not cause pneumonia. If mice are injected with Type S bacteria, they develop pneumonia and die. Mice injected with Type R bacteria show no ill effects.

Dead Type S bacteria do not cause pneumonia when injected into mice. In Griffith's key experiment, he mixed dead Type S bacteria with live Type R. When he injected the mixture into mice, the mice developed pneumonia and died. Furthermore, the tissues of the dead mice were found to contain live Type S bacteria.

Remember that dead Type S bacteria alone do not cause pneumonia. Neither do live Type R alone. But when brought together, they do cause disease, and living Type S bacteria appear. Griffith concluded that some factor from dead Type S bacteria had transformed Type R bacteria into Type S. The transformed bacteria had acquired the ability to make smooth capsules and to cause pneumonia in mice.

Other researchers verified Griffith's results. They also succeeded in extracting material from the dead Type S bacteria that could transform Type R to Type S in a test tube.

Avery, MacLeod, and McCarty. In 1944, Oswald Avery, Colin MacLeod, and Maclyn McCarty of the Rockefeller Institute in New York identified the transforming material in Griffith's experiment as DNA. In other words, DNA had the capacity to give Type R bacteria new genetic traits. This was strong evidence that DNA is the genetic substance, but many scientists remained unconvinced. They still thought that protein must be the carrier of hereditary information. The conclusive evidence supporting DNA was obtained by Hershey and Chase in 1952.

Hershey and Chase. Alfred Hershey and Martha Chase made use of viruses called bacteriophages to resolve the DNA vs. protein argument. A *bacteriophage*, or *phage* for short, is a virus that infects bacteria. Hershey and Chase knew that this type of virus consists of a DNA core surrounded by a protein capsule (see Figure 27-2). They also knew that a phage attacks a bacterium by entering the bacterium and causing the production of hundreds of new phage particles inside the bacterial cell. The cell then ruptures and the new phage particles are released. These can in turn attack other bacterial cells. What Hershey and Chase wanted to find out was whether the whole phage entered the bacterium, or whether it was just the DNA or the protein portion. They decided to "tag" the protein and the DNA of the phage particles with different radioactive elements in hopes of answering this question.

DNA contains phosphorus in its chemical composition, but no sulfur. Virus protein contains some sulfur, but no phosphorus. Hershey and Chase devised a way of tagging the phage DNA with radioactive phosphorus and the protein coat with radioactive sulfur. One bacterial culture was then exposed to phages with radioactive DNA and another culture exposed to phages with radioactive protein. After large numbers of bacteria had become infected with phages, the cells were separated from the medium and their contents tested for radioactivity. The cells that had been infected by phages with radioactive DNA showed a large amount of radioactivity. The cells infected by phages with radioactive protein showed almost no radioactivity. This experiment proved that when phages infect bacteria, the phage DNA enters the cells, but the phage protein remains outside.

If phage DNA alone can cause bacteria to manufacture more phages, it must be the DNA that carries the genetic instructions for making phage. This experiment finally established DNA as the genetic material. The problem then became that of working out the chemical structure and functioning of DNA.

27-2 Composition of DNA

Most organic compounds have molecules made up of chemical groups of various kinds. For example, starch molecules are chains of sugar units bonded together; fats consist of fatty acids and glycerol; proteins are chains of amino acids. The first stage in analyzing an unknown organic compound is to find out what chemical groups it is made of. The second stage is to work out the structural arrangement of these groups in the molecule.

The chemical analysis of DNA was carried out in the 1920s by the biochemist P. A. Levene. Levene found that the very large DNA molecule is made up of the following chemical groups: (1) the 5-carbon sugar **deoxyribose** (dee-ahk-see-*ry*-bohs); (2) a phosphate group; and (3) four kinds of nitrogenous (nitrogen-containing) bases. Two of the four bases, **adenine** and **guanine,** are a type of compound called **purines** (*pyoor*-eenz); the other two, **cytosine** and **thymine,** are compounds called **pyrimidines** (pih-*rim*-uh-deenz).

Levene found that for each sugar unit there is one phosphate group and one nitrogenous base. He therefore concluded that the basic unit of DNA is a sugar, a phosphate, and one of the four nitrogenous bases. He called this unit a **nucleotide** (*noo*-klee-uh-tyd). Since there are four different bases, there are four different kinds of nucleotides.

27-3 Structure of DNA

After the chemical composition of DNA was known, the structure of the molecule remained to be worked out. This was accomplished in 1953 by James Watson, an American biochemist, and Francis Crick, an English physicist, working together at the Cavendish Laboratory in Cambridge, England. In arriving at their model of DNA, Watson and Crick made use of everything that was known about DNA. An important piece

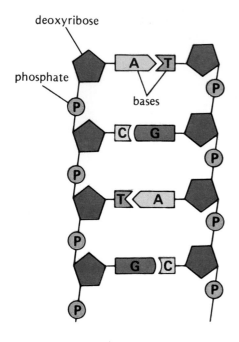

deoxyribose

phosphate

bases

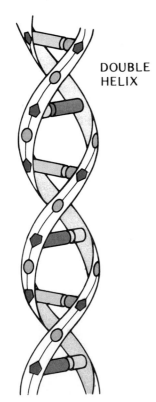

DOUBLE
HELIX

Figure 27-3. Watson-Crick Model of DNA.

of information came from Maurice Wilkins and Rosalind Franklin of Oxford University. They had made X-ray studies of crystals of DNA. These X-ray photographs showed that the repeating units in the crystal are arranged in the form of a **helix.** (A helix is the shape of a coiled spring.)

After trying many different arrangements of the chemical groups of DNA, Watson and Crick arrived at a model DNA molecule in which there are two chains of sugar-phosphate groups running parallel. Pairs of bases link the chains together like the rungs of a ladder (see Figure 27-3). The helix of the molecule is formed by twisting or coiling the ladder. Thus, the DNA molecule is a *double helix.*

Watson and Crick found that this model could be made to work only if the pairs of bases making each "rung" of the ladder is an adenine unit connected to a thymine, or a guanine connected to a cytosine. This model agreed with all the data for the DNA molecule. Besides, it explained a fact that other researchers had discovered—that the amount of adenine in DNA is always the same as the amount of thymine, and the amount of guanine is the same as the amount of cytosine. Furthermore, since the sequence of bases along the chain could vary, the sequence could be a code for genetic information.

Another important fact about this model is that the sequence of bases along one strand automatically determines the matching bases on the other strand. If we use capital letters A, T, G, and C to stand for the four bases, adenine, thymine, guanine, and cytosine, every A must be joined to a T and every G must be joined to a C. No other pairings are possible. Suppose, for example, that a sequence along one strand is AGGTTAC. The matching sequence along the second strand must be TCCAATG. The two strands are said to be *complementary.* Each strand is the complement of the other according to the A-T and G-C base pairing rule.

The double helix model of DNA was a great breakthrough in the science of genetics. Watson, Crick, and Wilkins received the Nobel prize in 1962 for this work.

27-4 Replication of DNA

One of the great questions of the gene-chromosome theory was, How can an exact copy of each chromosome be made during cell division? The double-helix model gave a simple answer. The base pairs that form the "rungs" of the model are held together by a weak type of bond called a *hydrogen bond.* If these bonds are broken, the two strands of the DNA molecule can separate like the halves of a zipper. The bases along each strand would then be exposed like the teeth of an opened zipper. If there are free nucleotides in the nucleus of the cell, their bases could be attracted to the complementary bases on each exposed strand. They could then join together to make a complete complementary strand exactly like the one

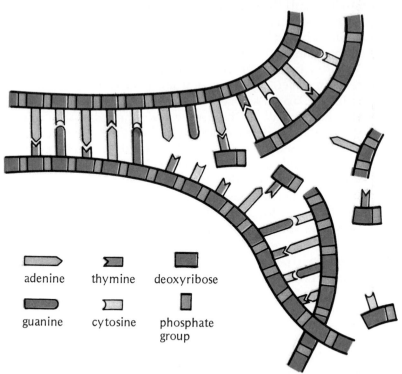

Figure 27-4. DNA Replication. DNA replication results in the formation of two double-stranded molecules exactly like the original DNA molecule.

adenine thymine deoxyribose

guanine cytosine phosphate group

that had been peeled away. Two double-stranded molecules of DNA exactly like the original molecule could be made in this way (see Figure 27-4). Experiments of many kinds have demonstrated that, under the action of special enzymes, this is exactly what happens in the living cell.

27-5 Composition and Structure of RNA

The composition of ribonucleic acid, RNA, is very similar to that of DNA, with two differences. The 5-carbon sugar in RNA is ribose, and in RNA the pyrimidine **uracil** is substituted for thymine. So the four bases found in RNA are adenine, guanine, cytosine, and uracil. Unlike DNA, which is double-stranded, RNA consists of only a single strand of nucleotides.

GENES, PROTEINS, AND CELLULAR ACTIVITY

Objectives:
1. Describe the experiments of Beadle and Tatum with *Neurospora*.
2. Explain the one gene, one polypeptide hypothesis.

27-6 Genes and Enzymes

Every chemical reaction in the living cell requires the presence of a specific enzyme. The enzymes that an organism needs are not present in its food. The organism must make all its enzymes. If the cell is unable to make one of its thousands of enzymes, its metabolism will be affected by the lack of this enzyme. The cell may be unable to function effectively, or it may even be unable to live without the enzyme.

The idea that the hereditary material acts by controlling the synthesis of cell enzymes first arose in the early 1900s. Sir Archibald Garrod, an English physician, studied certain diseases that he called "inborn errors of metabolism." He believed that these diseases are caused by the body's inability to make a particular enzyme, and that this inability could be inherited. In other words, the body cells normally have an allele that causes the production of the enzyme. In a person with the disease, the normal allele has been replaced by a defective allele. (Usually, the defective allele is recessive, and a person must be homozygous for the defective allele to develop the disease.)

Garrod's hypotheses came mostly from his study of the disease *alkaptonuria* (al-kap-tuh-*nyoor*-ee-uh). A patient with this disease excretes very dark urine. This is caused by the presence of a substance called *homogentisic acid* in the urine. Homogentisic acid is produced during the breakdown of two amino acids, phenylalanine and tyrosine, in the body. But it is usually then oxidized into another compound. A person who lacks an enyzyme necessary for the breakdown of homogentisic acid will excrete it, because the metabolic pathway is stopped after its production. Such a person is lacking the allele that controls the production of the necessary enzyme. Phenylketonuria (PKU) also results from a pair of defective recessive alleles and a missing enzyme (see page 436).

Garrod published his ideas in 1909, but they were largely ignored at the time. It was not until the 1930s and 1940s that their importance was realized.

27-7　The One Gene, One Enzyme Hypothesis

The best evidence that genes control the production of enzymes came from the experiments of George Beadle and Edward Tatum, two American scientists, in 1941. In their investigations, Beadle and Tatum used the red bread mold *Neurospora crassa* (See Figure 27-5). This mold can normally grow and reproduce in a medium containing just a few nutrients—sugar, a nitrogen compound, some mineral salts, and the vitamin biotin. This is called a *minimal medium.* From the medium, the mold can synthesize all the amino acids it needs to form its enzymes and other proteins.

Beadle and Tatum knew that irradiation with X rays could produce mutations in genes. When they exposed cultures of *Neurospora* to X rays, they found that many of the mold organisms could no longer grow in the minimal medium (see Figure 27-6). If amino acids were added to the medium, some of their organisms were able to survive. By adding amino acids, one at a time, to cultures of the irradiated mold, they

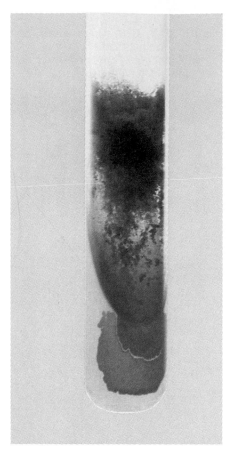

Figure 27-5. Red Bread Mold. The classic genetics experiments that led to the one gene, one enzyme hypothesis were performed using the fungus *Neurospora crassa*, shown here growing on medium in a culture tube.

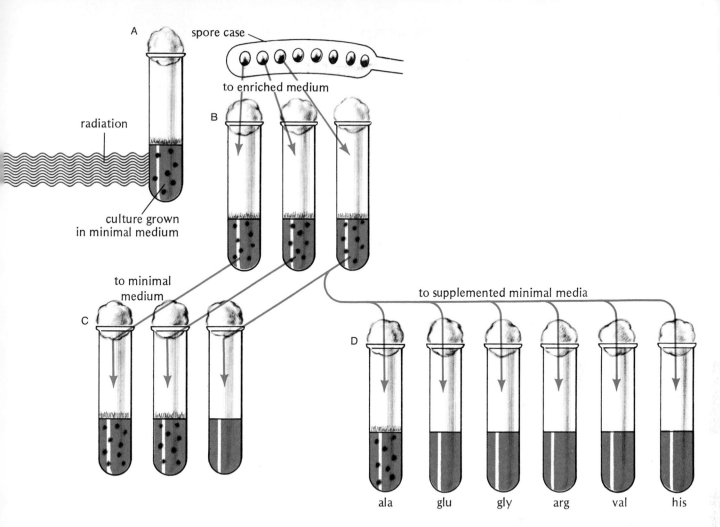

were able to separate out groups of organisms that needed one particular amino acid. The inability of the mold to produce a particular amino acid meant that the mold was not synthesizing an enzyme needed to make that amino acid. This meant, in turn, that the organism had lost the gene that directed the synthesis of that enzyme. The X rays had caused a mutation in the gene that normally causes the synthesis of the enzyme. From the results of these experiments, it was concluded that each gene produces its effects by controlling the synthesis of a particular enzyme. This is known as the *one gene, one enzyme hypothesis.*

All enzymes are proteins, but not all proteins are enzymes. Some proteins are hormones, some are materials needed for structural parts of the cell, some are needed for other purposes. Evidence shows that genes control the synthesis of all proteins, not just enzymes. Proteins are made up of polypeptides—long chains of amino acids (see page 55). Some proteins consist of two or more polypeptides linked and entwined to form the protein molecule. Hemoglobin, for example, is a protein made from two different kinds of polypeptide chains. The synthesis of each polypeptide is controlled by a different gene. Because of these facts, the one gene, one enzyme hypothesis was expanded

Figure 27-6. The Beadle-Tatum Experiment. (A) A spore case of *Neurospora* known to grow in a minimal medium was exposed to X rays. (B) Each spore was then removed from the case and placed in an enriched medium containing all basic nutrients and amino acids. Each spore produced a culture of mold. (C) Samples of each culture were tested in a minimal medium. Some samples did not grow in the minimal medium. (D) Samples of mold that would not grow in a minimal medium were then tested in other minimal media, each supplemented by a different amino acid. The mold grew in the medium that contained the amino acid it was no longer able to synthesize.

to the **one gene, one polypeptide hypothesis.** According to this modified hypothesis, each gene directs the synthesis of a particular chain.

PROTEIN SYNTHESIS

Objectives:
1. Explain how the sequence of nucleotides in DNA codes for the different amino acids.
2. Explain how the DNA code is transcribed into the

3. Describe the structure and function of tRNA.
4. Describe the assembly of a polypeptide.

27-8   The Idea of a Genetic Code

At the time that the Watson-Crick model of DNA was being accepted, it was generally agreed that each gene directs the synthesis of a particular polypeptide chain of amino acids. Therefore, the gene must have some way of specifying the order in which the amino acids should be assembled. It was not immediately clear from the Watson-Crick model how this might be done. One suggestion was that the polypeptides were assembled directly on the DNA strands. But no one could figure out how amino acids could match up with nucleotides, which is what would have to happen for direct synthesis. A more workable idea was that the sequence of bases along the DNA strands is a code that specifies the order of the amino acids. The code is then translated into a polypeptide by some intermediate mechanism. The second hypothesis was eventually shown to be correct.

What might the DNA code be? There are 20 amino acids in the proteins of humans and most other organisms. There must therefore be at least 20 different code "words" to specify these amino acids. There are only 4 different bases in DNA. How many base "letters" are needed to form the code words for 20 amino acids? From 4 bases, only 16 different 2-letter sequences can be made: AA, AT, AG, AC, TT, TA, TG, TC, etc. Therefore, the code words must be at least 3 letters long. From 4 bases, 64 different 3-letter sequences can be made. This is, of course, more than are needed. Research has shown that the code for specifying amino acids does consist of 3-base words, and that most of the amino acids are specified by more than one code word.

27-9   Messenger RNA

We know today that a gene is a long string of bases along the DNA molecule. Each successive group of three bases is a code that specifies a particular amino acid to be added to a polypeptide chain. The code also contains "punctuation"— code words that indicate where a polypeptide starts and

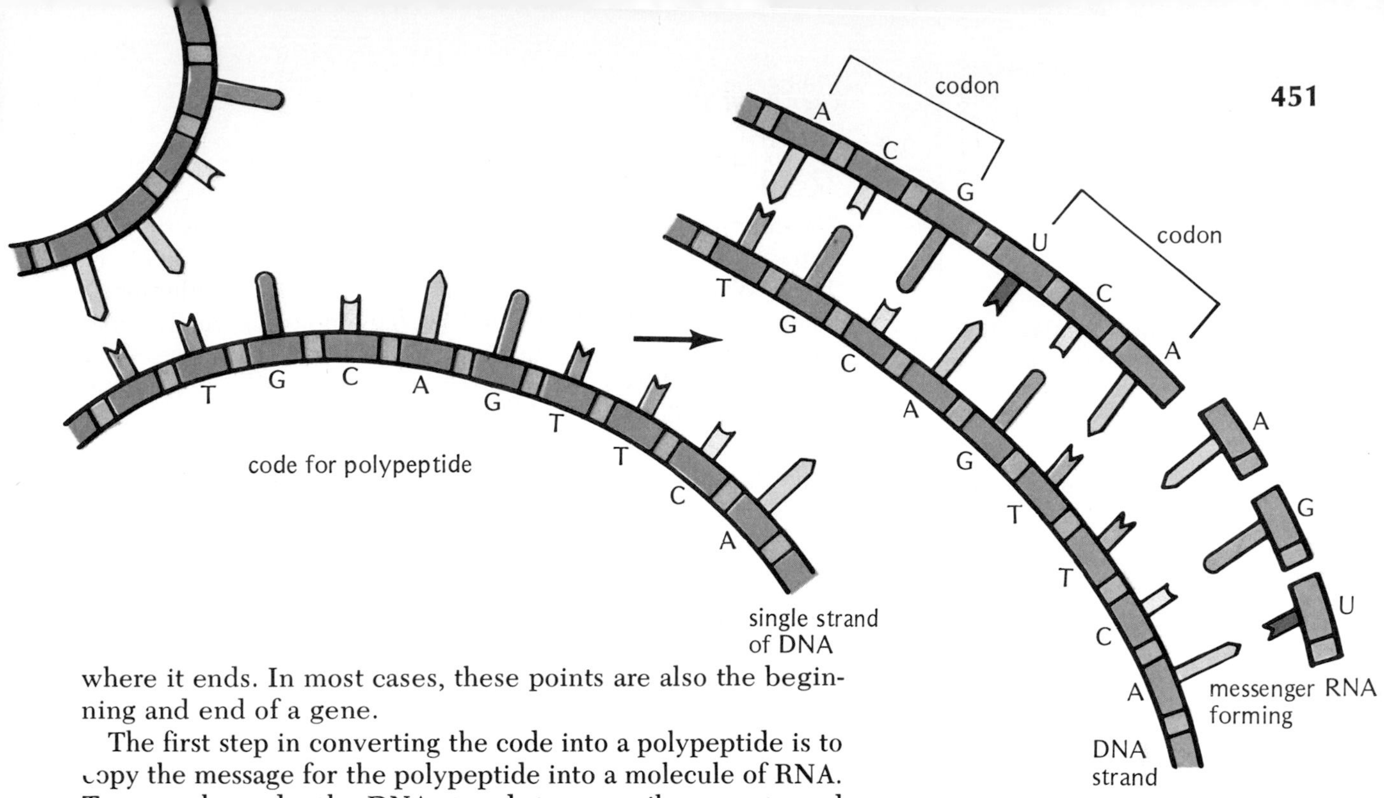

Figure 27-7. Transcription of a Gene. The code for each polypeptide is copied from one of the DNA strands into a strand of messenger RNA. The copying process is similar to DNA replication, except that uracil replaces thymine as a complement for adenine.

where it ends. In most cases, these points are also the beginning and end of a gene.

The first step in converting the code into a polypeptide is to copy the message for the polypeptide into a molecule of RNA. To copy the code, the DNA strands temporarily separate and serve as a pattern, or *template*, for RNA (See Figure 27-7). Complementary RNA nucleotides take their places along the exposed strands, in the same way that DNA is replicated. When the assembled RNA sequence reaches the end of the polypeptide message, it is detached from the DNA strand. The RNA strand is now a separate molecule carrying the complete message for a single polypeptide; although in complementary form; that is, each A of the DNA is represented by a U, each T by an A, each G by a C, and each C by a G. A strand of RNA of this type is called **messenger RNA**, or **mRNA**. The copying of a genetic message into a molecule of mRNA is called **transcription** (trans-*krip*-shun). Each group of three bases that specifies an amino acid is called a **codon** (*koh*-dahn). The complete genetic code is given in Table 27-1.

Table 27-1. The Genetic Code. Most of the amino acids are specified by more than one codon. For example, GCU, GCC, GCA, and GCG all code for the amino acid alanine.

Amino acid	Genetic code	Amino acid	Genetic code
phenylalanine	UUU, UUC	methionine	AUG
leucine	UUA, UUG, CUU, CUC, CUA, CUG	threonine	ACU, ACC, ACA, ACG
serine	UCU, UCC, UCA, UCG, AGU, AGC	asparagine	AAU, AAC
tyrosine	UAU, UAC	lysine	AAA, AAG
cysteine	UGU, UGC	valine	GUU, GUC, GUA, GUG
tryptophan	UGG	alanine	GCU, GCC, GCA, GCG
proline	CCU, CCC, CCA, CCG	aspartic acid	GAU, GAC
histidine	CAU, CAC	glutamic acid	GAA, GAG
glutamine	CAA, CAG	glycine	GGU, GGC, GGA, GGG
arginine	CGU, CGC, CGA, CGG, AGA, AGG	stop	UAA, UAG, UGA
isoleucine	AUU, AUC, AUA		

27-10   Transfer RNA

Messenger RNA is only one of three types of RNA that are formed by DNA. A second type is called **transfer RNA,** or tRNA. While mRNA may have thousands of nucleotides along its length, tRNA has only about 80. The molecule of tRNA has an odd shape, as shown in Figure 27-8. At one end there is a short tail. At this end, a particular amino acid can become attached. Each tRNA molecule will pick up only one type of amino acid, depending on the other nucleotides of its structure. There are at least 20 different forms of tRNA, one for each of the 20 different amino acids. At the other end of the tRNA molecule, there is a loop of exposed nucleotides. In this loop, there is a sequence of 3 bases, called an **anticodon,** that are complements of an mRNA codon. The codon that this anticodon matches is one that specifies the particular amino acid that this tRNA carries. Thus tRNA is a device for bringing a particular amino acid to a particular place specified by mRNA.

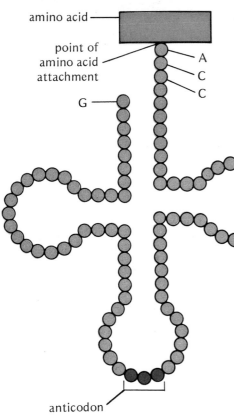

Figure 27-8. Transfer RNA. The codon that matches the anticodon of the tRNA calls for the particular amino acid that is attached to the tRNA.

amino acid

point of amino acid attachment

A

C

C

G

anticodon

27-11   Ribosomal RNA

Ribosomal RNA, or rRNA, is RNA that is formed by DNA in the nucleoli of the cell. A ribosome consists of protein and two subunits of rRNA, one larger than the other. The ribosomal protein is made in the cytoplasm and then migrates into the nucleus. In the nucleoli, the protein and the two subunits of rRNA are combined to form complete ribosomes.

27-12   Assembly of a Polypeptide

The synthesis of the three kinds of RNA, as well as the assembly of ribosomes, occurs in the cell nucleus. The RNA and ribosomes migrate through the nuclear pores to the cytoplasm. In the cytoplasm, there is a supply of all the amino acids needed to synthesize the cell's proteins. Here, the assembly of polypeptides for those proteins is carried out in accordance with the instructions carried by mRNA.

In the cytoplasm, amino acid molecules become attached to their specific varieties of tRNA (see Figure 27-9). Ribosomes become attached to each strand of mRNA at intervals along its length. Where a ribosome is attached to mRNA, a molecule of tRNA with the right anticodon temporarily becomes attached to the corresponding codon on the mRNA. The amino acid brought into position by the tRNA joins the last amino acid in the forming chain and separates from tRNA. The ribosome then moves along to the next codon. A new tRNA takes its place

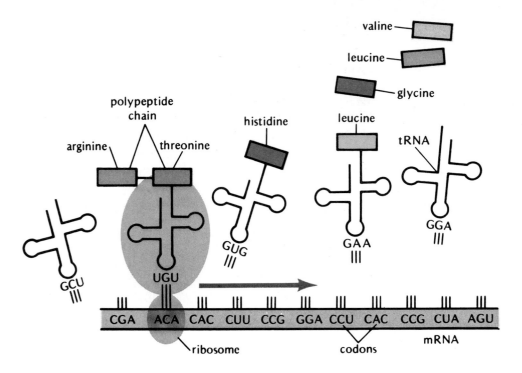

Figure 27-9. Protein Synthesis. As a ribosome moves into position at a codon of a messenger RNA, a transfer RNA with the complementary anticodon temporarily bonds to the codon. The tRNA adds its amino acid to the polypeptide chain, then detaches and moves away.

on the mRNA strand, and its amino acid joins the polypeptide chain. As the ribosome moves along, the tRNA that has served its purpose is released. It is now free to pick up another amino acid molecule and repeat its function. Amino acids continue to be added to the growing polypeptide chain until the ribosome reaches a "stop" codon. The polypeptide is then released and assembles itself into a complete protein molecule. By this remarkable system, all the cell's proteins are synthesized in the cytoplasm, while the chromosomes carrying the hereditary instructions for this synthesis remain in the nucleus.

Every step in the process of translating the genetic message into a polypeptide chain is assisted by a specific enzyme. There are enzymes that attach amino acids to tRNA. There are enzymes that attach tRNA to mRNA. There are enzymes that join the amino acids to the polypeptide chain. There are also enzymes in the nucleus that open up the DNA molecule for transcription, and others that assist in the assembly of RNA. All of these enzymes must themselves be specified by genes.

GENE CONTROLS AND GENE MUTATIONS

Objectives:
1. Explain the following terms: *operator, repressor, gene mutation,* and *mutagenic agent.*
2. Discuss the gene mutation that causes sickle-cell anemia.
3. Name two cytoplasmic organelles that can replicate.

4. Explain the following terms: *recombinant DNA, plasmid, transformation,* and *transduction.*
5. Explain how plasmids are used in transferring new genes to bacteria.
6. Describe the techniques currently used for cloning.

27-13 Control of Gene Transcription

Every cell in an organism has the complete set of genes characteristic of that organism. But even though all the cells of an organism have the same genes, different cells perform different functions and produce different proteins. Why is a particular set of genes activated in one cell, while a different set is activated in another cell of the same organism? One of the major questions that molecular biologists are trying to answer is how gene transcription is controlled.

In the early 1960s, the French biologists Francois Jacob, Jacques Monod, and André Lwoff discovered how the transcription of certain genes is controlled in the bacterium *Escherichia coli.* They were awarded a Nobel prize in 1965 for their work. Jacob, Monod, and Lwoff studied the production of the three enzymes used by the bacteria to digest the sugar lactose. They found that the enzymes are produced by the bacteria only when they are needed—that is, when lactose is present. Thus, enzyme production is turned on and off, depending on the needs of the cell.

Jacob, Monod, and Lwoff determined that production of the lactose-digesting enzymes is regulated by a cluster of genes (see Figure 27-10). The amino acid sequences of the enzymes are determined by three structural genes. A *structural gene* is

Figure 27-10. Gene Transcription in Bacteria. In *E. coli* the synthesis of lactose-digesting enzymes is controlled by a cluster of genes. The enzymes themselves are synthesized by structural genes. The activity of the structural genes is controlled by an operator gene, which in turn is controlled by a protein repressor coded for by a regulator gene.

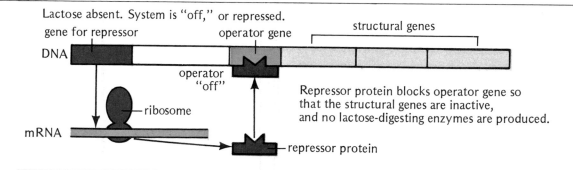

Lactose absent. System is "off," or repressed.

gene for repressor   operator gene   structural genes

DNA

operator "off"

Repressor protein blocks operator gene so that the structural genes are inactive, and no lactose-digesting enzymes are produced.

ribosome

mRNA

repressor protein

Lactose present. System is "on," or derepressed.

DNA

operator "on"

Structural genes "activated." Lactose-digesting enzymes produced.

lactose

Repressor protein inactivated by lactose.

mRNA

a DNA segment that codes for the production of a particular polypeptide.

The investigators found that the activity of the structural genes is controlled by an *operator gene,* a sequence of nucleotides found next to the structural genes. The structural genes cannot be transcribed unless the operator gene is in an active state. We can think of the operator as being switched "on" to cause transcription, or switched "off" to prevent transcription.

The activity of the operator is controlled by a protein called a *repressor.* The repressor is the product of yet another gene, called a *regulator gene.* When the repressor binds to the operator gene, transcription of the structural genes cannot start. The repressor protein is always present in the cell, and it is normally bound to the operator gene so that the operator is off. Lactose binds to the repressor protein, making it unable to bind to the operator gene. Therefore, when lactose is present, the operator gene is turned on, transcription of the structural genes proceeds, and the lactose-digesting enzymes are produced.

The digestion of the lactose reduces the amount present in the cell. When the amount of lactose becomes too small to inactivate the repressor, the repressor once again binds to the operator and switches it off. Transcription of the genes stops and the cell stops making the digestive enzymes. Thus the synthesis of the digestive enzymes is switched on when they are needed to digest lactose, and switched off when the lactose is gone and they are no longer needed. This is a clear example of control by *negative feedback* (see page 268).

Remember that the genes of a bacterium, a procaryote, are on a single chromosome in direct contact with the cytoplasm, not in a nucleus. The genetic control mechanisms in bacteria are probably simpler than in cells with nuclei and many chromosomes. Very little is known yet about the ways in which genes are switched on and off in eucaryotic cells.

27-14 Gene Mutations

Genes function by specifying the order of amino acids in a polypeptide chain for a certain protein. These instructions are coded into the sequence of bases along a DNA strand. Any change in this sequence is likely to change the message transcribed into mRNA and change the structure of a protein that the cell makes. Such changes are called **gene mutations** (see Figure 27-11). Once a mutation occurs in a DNA molecule, it is copied through all the later replications of the DNA. A mutation in a sex cell can be passed to future generations.

It is believed that gene mutations occur from time to time at random in all cells. Mutations in individual body cells are usually of no importance, since they are not likely to affect other cells or the functions of the organism as a whole. If a single cell loses the ability to make a certain protein, the cell may die, or it may obtain the protein from the intercellular

Figure 27-11. Mutation. The crossed bill on this robin is the expression of a mutation on a gene that affects bill development.

fluid. In either case, nothing noticeable happens. Mutations in sex cells are another matter. If a mutation is present in a gamete at the time of fertilization, all the cells of the embryo and the developed organism will have the mutation in at least half of their DNA.

Inherited mutations are usually recessive. Only about 1 in 100 gene mutations is dominant. Most mutations are harmful to the organism. The genes of a normal individual already meet the needs of the organism. Any change is likely to result in the production of a useless protein, or none at all, in place of one that is useful and necessary.

Causes of mutations. Mutations that produce observable changes in traits have been studied in *Drosophila* and in other organisms. Each type of mutation seems to occur at a definite, low rate in large populations. All the causes of natural mutation are not known. They may simply be the result of random errors in replication of the DNA.

Factors in the environment that cause mutations are called **mutagenic agents.** Hermann Muller, a student of T. H. Morgan, found that he could greatly increase the rate of mutation in fruit flies by exposing them to X rays. Other forms of radiation, and chemicals such as chloroform and mustard gas, are also known to be mutagenic agents. Natural mutations may be partly the result of mutagenic agents in the environment.

Types of gene mutations. There are various ways in which the base sequence of a gene may change and thus result in a mutation. An entire nucleotide may be added or removed at some point. Such a change would be quite drastic, since all the triplet codons beyond that point would be changed. The gene would probably be completely useless and the organism would be missing the protein it specifies. Alkaptonuria, PKU, and many other inherited diseases may be the result of gene mutations of this kind.

In other cases, one base could be substituted for another. This changes just one codon, and changes just one amino acid in the protein specified. Changing one amino acid may result in a protein that is only partially effective for its function.

Sickle cell anemia. Sickle cell anemia is caused by the change of one base in the gene that controls the production of one of the polypeptide chains in the hemoglobin molecule. There are about 300 amino acids in this chain. The change in one base changes the codon for one amino acid at a particular point in the chain. The normal codon is GAA, which places the amino acid glutamic acid in the chain. The mutant codon is GUA, which puts valine in place of glutamic acid. Hemoglobin made from the altered polypeptide does not carry oxygen as well as normal hemoglobin. The shape of the molecule is also different. It causes the red blood cells to have a distorted form that tends to make them catch and clump together in the small blood vessels (see Figure 27-12).

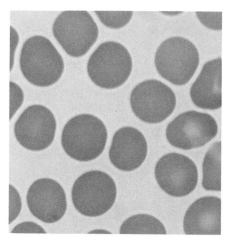

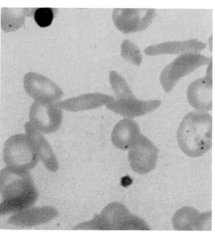

Figure 27-12. Normal and Sickle Red Blood Cells. (Top) Normal red cells are disk-shaped and thin in the center. (Bottom) Sickle cells are elongated and crescent-shaped.

27-15 DNA in Mitochondria and Chloroplasts

While most hereditary material is located in the nucleus of a cell, biologists have found that certain cell organelles carry genetic information. This is called *cytoplasmic DNA*. The DNA-containing organelles are chloroplasts and mitochondria. The nucleic acids in these organelles seem to code for the synthesis of materials needed for their functions—for photosynthesis and cellular respiration. The DNA in the nucleus still influences the organelles, however.

When a cell divides by mitotic division, each daughter cell receives about half the organelles in the parent cell. As the daughter cells grow, the mitochondria and chloroplasts reproduce themselves (see Figure 27-13). The DNA of these organelles also replicates to keep the new organelles supplied with their own DNA.

In the fusion of gametes in sexual reproduction, all the organelles of the zygote come from the egg cell, because of its much greater size. Thus while both parents contribute equally to the nuclear DNA of the offspring, all the cytoplasmic DNA comes from the female parent.

Because mitochondria and chloroplasts have their own DNA and are able to reproduce, some biologists speculate that these organelles were once free-living. At some early stage in the development of cells, they may have become incorporated into cells. They then became specialized for their functions inside cells, lost the DNA they no longer needed, and lost the capacity to survive outside cells.

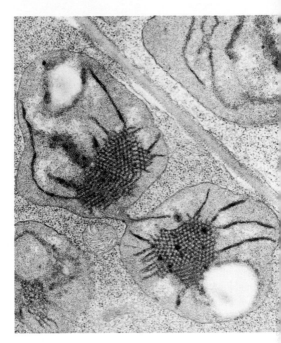

Figure 27-13. A Chloroplast Dividing.

27-16 Transformation and Transduction

Transformation and transduction are processes by which DNA is transferred from one bacterial cell to another. In **transformation,** living bacteria take in DNA from dead bacteria. The DNA causes traits of the dead bacteria to show in the living bacterial cells. In Griffith's experiments, type R bacteria were transformed by DNA from dead Type S bacteria. Transformation occurs in nature as well as in laboratory experiments. Pieces of DNA can also be transferred from one bacterial cell to another by viruses. This process is called **transduction.** Transduction occurs when a piece of bacterial DNA becomes incorporated into the virus particle. When the virus infects a new cell, it carries the piece of the DNA from its previous host cell.

27-17 Genetic Engineering

One of the most remarkable outcomes of the understanding of the gene has been the development of methods for changing the DNA of a cell. The altered DNA is called **recombinant DNA,** and the procedures for producing the altered DNA are often referred to as **genetic engineering,** or more popularly as *gene splicing.* The latter term is quite descriptive of the

Bacteria—Factories for Insulin Production

Early in the 1980s, human insulin of recombinant DNA origin was approved for the treatment of diabetes (see page 276) in the United States and several European countries. The insulin produced is virtually identical in structure and function to that produced in the body by the pancreas.

The recombinant-DNA insulin is produced by the process shown in Figure 27-14. The genes for human insulin production are inserted into the DNA of the bacterium *Escherichia coli* (see photo). Once inside the bacterium, these genes direct the host cell to produce human insulin. Commercial production is now so far advanced that processing containers as large as 10,000 gallons are routinely used. Today a constant, reliable, expandable supply of quality insulin is available. Prior to this development, diabetics faced an uncertain future, for insulin production from animal organs had been falling steadily for many years.

Insulin is the first of the many possible biologically active substances of recombinant DNA origin to find widespread use. Others important to humans will follow soon, and developments in plant breeding and animal husbandry will not be far behind.

methods being used at this time. They involve breaking a DNA molecule and inserting or attaching a new gene by means of a chemical "splice."

One of the long-range goals of genetic engineering is to correct genetic defects by transferring normal genes to cells that lack them. Hereditary diseases could possibly be treated in this way. Another goal is to give desired properties to plants and animals that are raised for food or other human purposes. However, at this time the techniques are limited to gene transplants in bacteria and other simple organisms.

Plasmids. Some of the methods of transferring genes to bacteria make use of transformation and transduction. Another important method involves small, ring-shaped segments of DNA called **plasmids.** Many bacteria either contain plasmids or will take plasmids into their cytoplasm from a surrounding medium. Inside the bacteria, the plasmids remain separate from the bacterial chromosome. However, the plasmids include genes that affect the metabolism and traits of the organism. For example, some plasmids have a gene for producing an enzyme that destroys penicillin. Bacteria containing these plasmids are resistant to penicillin; they are not killed by it. Plasmids are replicated along with the chromosomes at every cell division. Thus a single bacterium with a particular plasmid can produce large colonies of cells with the properties conferred by that plasmid.

To transfer a new gene to bacteria, plasmids are first obtained from bacterial cells. This is accomplished by crushing the bacteria and sorting the contents by centrifugation or other methods. The plasmids are placed in a solution containing the gene (DNA fragment) to be transplanted (see Figure 27-14). The genes are usually obtained from animals, although in some cases the genes have actually been made by chemically assembling nucleotides in the proper sequence. An enzyme called a *restriction enzyme* is then used to break open the plasmid ring. The free genes in the solution attach themselves to the open ends of the plasmid, thus closing the ring again. The plasmid now includes the new gene.

Bacteria are then exposed to the altered plasmids, and many of the bacteria will take them in. Once inside the bacterial cells, the transplanted genes begin to be expressed. The bacteria produce the protein specified by the gene. This protein may be any one of a number of desirable products that are difficult or expensive to obtain by other means. Among the proteins that are currently the object of research efforts are insulin, human growth hormone, and human interferon. Interferon is a substance produced by the body tissues that provides defense against virus infections and possibly against some forms of cancer. Several companies have formed in recent years to develop recombinant DNA technology on a commercial scale. Some of the new forms of bacteria produced by this research have even been patented.

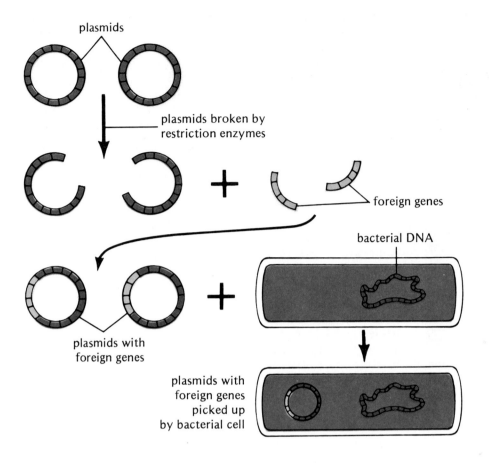

plasmids

plasmids broken by restriction enzymes

foreign genes

bacterial DNA

plasmids with foreign genes

plasmids with foreign genes picked up by bacterial cell

Figure 27-14. Using Plasmids to Transfer Foreign Genes to Bacterial Cells.

Dangers of recombinant DNA. Many scientists, including those working in the field, are aware of possible danger from research with recombinant DNA. In these experiments, new forms of microorganisms are produced. It is possible that an organism will be accidentally produced with the ability to cause an entirely new kind of human disease, against which the body will have no natural defenses. The escape of such an organism into the environment could lead to a massive, uncontrollable epidemic. To prevent this type of accident, the federal government and the scientists involved in recombinant DNA research have established rules and safeguards that must be observed. Since this is a new field and information is lacking, the actual risks and the necessary safeguards are not known. Also, compliance with rules ultimately depends on the efforts of individual workers. Because risks are involved, it will become ever more important to monitor safety and to update standards as recombinant DNA research expands.

27-18 Cloning

A **clone** is a group of individual organisms that have exactly the same genes. Organisms that reproduce asexually produce

Figure 27-15. Somaclonal Variations. Orange and yellow tomatoes have been produced by plants that are somaclonal variants of red tomato plants.

clones, since each offspring receives an exact copy of the genes of the parent. New plants produced by vegetative propagation are also clones.

Much research is now being directed toward the *cloning* (production of clones) of animals that normally reproduce sexually. Every body cell of an animal has a complete set of the genes that the animal started life with. In theory then, any of these cells should be able to develop into individuals identical to each other and to the parent.

Most of the work on cloning of animals has been done with frogs. The method involves the replacement of the haploid nucleus of a frog egg cell by a diploid nucleus from another frog cell. The egg cell is then allowed to divide and develop into a complete individual. The frog that results has the same genes as the original transplanted nucleus. If that nucleus came from a cell of an adult frog, the new frog would be its clone. However, it is very difficult to make this process work with the nucleus of an already fully differentiated cell. Apparently, too many of the genes are "turned off" and cannot be turned on again inside the egg cell. Most success is obtained by using nuclei from the cells of a frog embryo at the blastula stage. By transplanting nuclei from many cells of the same blastula, a number of genetically identical individuals can be obtained.

In 1981 a similar technique was applied successfully for the first time to a mammal. Nuclei from cells of the blastula of a mouse were transplanted to mouse egg cells from which the original nuclei had been removed. The altered egg cells were allowed to reach the blastula stage in a culture medium and were then transferred to the uteruses of female mice to complete their development.

One purpose of cloning experiments is to produce large numbers of genetically identical laboratory organisms for research. For example, animals with known and controlled heredity could be useful in the study of cancer, aging, birth defects, and the regeneration of damaged body parts. However, researchers have much to learn about cloning. Recent plant cloning studies have shown that spontaneous genetic changes can take place within a group of plants that theoretically should be genetically identical. This was observed when certain plants, cloned by tissue culture techniques from the cells of a single plant, exhibited traits that were different from those of the parent plant. This phenomenon, called *somaclonal variation*, has resulted in many unexpected and useful genetic variants (see Figure 27-15). Researchers expect that somoclonal variation will provide a means of obtaining new strains of crop plants faster than with conventional techniques of plant breeding. Some new strains of wheat, tomato, carrots and other crop plants derived by this method are currently undergoing field tests.

Chapter Review

SUMMARY

- The hereditary material of the chromosomes is DNA. DNA molecules are made up of nucleotides. Each molecule is in the form of a double helix. The two parallel chains of sugar-phosphate groups are linked by pairs of nitrogen bases. In replication, two DNA strands separate. Free nucleotides join with complementary bases on the exposed strands, thereby forming two double-stranded molecules identical to the original.

- Each gene directs the synthesis of a particular polypeptide chain. This information is encoded in the sequence of bases of the DNA molecule. Each type of amino acid is specified by a particular sequence of three bases. By transcription, the genetic information of the DNA is copied into mRNA. The mRNA passes from the nucleus into the cytoplasm.

- In the cytoplasm, ribosomes become attached to different parts of the mRNA. Molecules of tRNA carry amino acids to the mRNA. The amino acids are aligned in a sequence determined by the base sequence of the mRNA and joined to form polypeptides.

- Genetic engineering involves the deliberate altering of the DNA of living cells. The altered DNA is called recombinant DNA.

KNOW THE TERMS

adenine	genetic engineering	one gene, one polypeptide	thymine
anticodon	guanine	hypothesis	transcription
clone	helix	plasmid	transduction
codon	messenger RNA	purine	transfer RNA
cytosine	mutagenic agent	pyrimidine	transformation
deoxyribose	nucleotide	recombinant DNA	uracil
gene mutation		ribosomal RNA	

SECTION QUESTIONS

Identification of the Genetic Material

1. How does a bacteriophage infect a bacterial cell?
2. Name the components of a nucleotide.
3. How are the base pairs in a DNA molecule held together?

Genes, Proteins, and Cellular Activity

4. What happens when a person inherits a defective gene?
5. How does a gene produce its effect?

Protein Synthesis

6. How does genetic information get from DNA to the cytoplasm?
7. How are individual amino acids carried to a forming polypeptide?

Gene Controls and Gene Mutations

8. Name two mutagenic agents.
9. Name two cell organelles that contain DNA.
10. Define the term *plasmid*.

KNOW THE FACTS

Copy the number of each sentence below on a sheet of paper. Beside each number, write the term(s) that complete(s) the sentence correctly.

1. The basic unit of DNA is the _____.
2. In the DNA molecule, cytosine is always paired with _____.
3. Proteins, the building blocks of living material, are made up of long chains of amino acids called _____.

4. The copying of a· genetic message into a molecule of mRNA is called _____.
5. The sequence of three bases that are complements of a messenger RNA codon is called a(n) _____.
6. A(n) _____ consists of protein and two subunits of rRNA.
7. A(n) _____ gene is a DNA segment that codes for the production of a particular polypeptide.
8. In a process called _____, living bacteria take in DNA from dead bacteria.
9. _____ can be transferred from one bacterial cell to another by viruses.
10. A(n) _____ is a group of individual organisms that have exactly the same genes.

UNDERSTAND THE CONCEPTS

11. What conclusion did Griffith draw from his pneumococcus experiments? What further information was provided by the experiments of Avery, MacLeod, and McCarty?
12. How did Hershey and Chase demonstrate that DNA carries hereditary information?
13. Describe the Watson-Crick model of DNA.
14. Describe how a DNA molecule replicates.
15. Compare the chemical composition and structure of RNA with that of DNA.
16. What hypothesis did the experiments of Beadle and Tatum suggest? What is the expanded form of that hypothesis?
17. In what form is the hereditary information encoded in the DNA molecule?
18. Describe the synthesis of mRNA.
19. Describe the roles of mRNA, tRNA, and ribosomes in synthesizing a polypeptide.
20. Describe how the operator and repressor function in controlling the synthesis of lactose-digesting enzymes in *E. coli.*
21. What types of changes in the DNA can result in gene mutations?
22. How do genetic engineers use plasmids?

THINK CRITICALLY

23. Some scientists think that mitochondria may once have been free-living organisms. What evidence supports this hypothesis?
24. The sequence of bases of one strand of a DNA molecule is GACGTAC. What is the sequence of bases of the other strand?
25. Compare replication and transcription.
26. (a) How would protein synthesis and the organism be affected if a mutation changed the codon GAA to GAG? (b) If the codon GAA were changed to CAA? (c) If GAA were changed to UAA? (d) What would happen if the G were deleted from the codon?

THINK CREATIVELY

27. Propose an explanation for how the structure of tRNA is suited to its functions.
28. Suppose that you knew which gene or genes control the production of growth hormone. Suggest a way that you might produce the hormone in large quantities.

FOR FURTHER INVESTIGATION

1. Make a model of DNA or RNA using simple materials.
2. Find out what products genetic engineering companies are producing or planning to produce. What safety guidelines are followed?
3. Investigate one of the following careers:
   a. Genetic engineer
   b. Medical social worker
   c. Scientific writer
4. Write a brief report on the life and contributions of one of the following scientists:
   a. Harriet Creighton
   b. Beatrice Mintz
   c. Marie Daly
   d. Russell Brown

FOR FURTHER READING

Motulski, A. G., "Impact of Genetic Manipulation on Society and Medicine," *Science,* January, 1983.

Trachtman, Paul, "The Search for Life's Origins —and a First 'Synthetic Cell'," *Smithsonian,* June, 1984.

Issues in Biology

Gene Splicing

In June 1973, a group of scientists assembled in New Hampshire to learn a method of combining pieces of DNA taken from different species of organisms. This new technique, called genetic engineering or gene splicing, worried as well as excited the scientists. Applications of the technology seemed limitless. But what if genetically altered organisms such as bacteria accidentally "escaped" into the environment and upset the balance of nature or caused disease?

Two years later, scientists met at the Asilomar Conference Center in California to discuss how to regulate gene-splicing experiments. There they developed safety procedures for different types of DNA experiments. Their guidelines were adopted by the National Institutes of Health (NIH), a federal agency that funds university research. These regulations have governed gene-splicing research since 1976, but recently they were challenged.

In 1983, scientists proposed the first field test of genetically engineered organisms—bacteria developed to protect crops against frost damage. Normally, bacteria found growing on plants produce a protein that serves as a nucleus for the formation of ice crystals. Genetically altered "ice-minus" bacteria do not produce this protein. University scientists and a biotechnology firm each wanted to test these bacteria by spraying them on plants in California fields.

Concerned citizens filed a legal suit charging that the release of ice-minus bacteria in the environment could decrease rainfall, since they might replace the unaltered variety that forms the center of rain droplets. After two years of legal arguments, the courts ordered NIH to develop risk evaluation procedures for the release of genetically altered organisms into the environment. University scientists receiving NIH funds will be evaluated under the NIH procedures. However, private companies are not under the jurisdiction of NIH, since they do not receive federal funds.

At present, there are several other federal agencies regulating both biotechnology firms and universities. To coordinate these agencies and to help balance the positive aspects of bio-

The use of genetically altered bacteria may help prevent costly frost damage to crops.

technology with the unique risks, legislators have proposed "The Biotechnology Science Coordination Act of 1986." If enacted, this legislation will set up a special committee to investigate scientific problems, set guidelines, and review regulatory policies for genetic engineering.

---

1. What was the purpose of the Asilomar Conference? What event provoked a lawsuit challenging the Asilomar Conference guidelines?

2. Who are the various individuals or groups that might control gene-splicing experimentation? Should people with a financial interest in genetic engineering products be allowed to play a role in regulation? Give reasons for your answer.

3. In late 1985, the federal government approved a field test of "ice-minus" bacteria. In early 1986, local citizens blocked the test through zoning regulations. Do you think the public has a right to override federal approval? Give reasons for your answer.

UNIT 6
EVOLUTION

With a little imagination, this land iguana leisurely chewing on a leaf can seem to resemble a prehistoric animal. In fact, that thought is not so farfetched. This present-day reptile is indeed a close relative of reptiles that no longer roam the earth. One such group, the dinosaurs, predominated 200 million years ago. Today, only fossilized bones provide evidence of their existence. In this Unit, you will examine how a species' survival through the generations is linked to its ability to adapt to changing environmental pressures. You will see that this process of gradual change, called *evolution,* is responsible for the diverse life forms we know today. You will also learn that species that do not successfully adapt to environmental demands disappear from the earth.

Chapter 28

EVIDENCE OF EVOLUTION

Fossils of organisms like this beautifully preserved cephalopod are evidence of life forms that lived millions of years ago.

THE EVIDENCE OF FOSSILS

Objectives:

1. Explain the term *fossil*.
2. Describe at least five different processes by which fossils may be formed.
3. Explain how sedimentary rocks are formed and what the age relationships are among the layers of such rocks.
4. Explain what is meant by relative dating of rocks and fossils.
5. State the characteristics of an index fossil and explain how index fossils are used for relative dating of rocks.
6. State two important conclusions that can be drawn from the fossil record regarding the course of changes in living things over geologic time.
7. Name the chief method used to determine the actual age of rocks.
8. Explain what is meant by the geologic time scale.

The term *evolution* in its most general sense means a gradual change from one state to another. Since its formation about 4½ billion years ago, the earth itself has undergone continual change, a process called **geologic evolution.** Much evidence indicates that living things have also undergone continuous change since they first appeared on the earth, a process called organic evolution. This chapter is concerned with the various types of evidence of organic evolution and the theories that have been proposed to account for it. Organic evolution is a central and unifying theme of biology, encompassing the multitudinous changes in life forms that have occurred over the course of the earth's history, the current diversity of organisms, and the degree to which organisms have become adapted to various environments.

28-1 The Formation of Fossils

A **fossil** is the actual remains or any trace of an organism that lived at some time in the past. The study of fossils provided the first, and still provides the strongest, evidence of organic evolution. Fossils have been formed in many different ways. In some cases, an entire organism has been preserved with almost no decay, but in the great majority of cases, the soft tissues of the fossil organism have completely disappeared, and only the hard, decay-resistant parts, such as bones or shells, have been preserved.

Preservation in amber. Some trees produce a sticky, gumlike resin that hardens into a transparent yellow material called *amber*. Insects often become trapped and embedded in the resin, and they are found preserved in the amber (see Figure 28-1).

Preservation in ice. In very cold Arctic regions, the frozen remains of various animals have been preserved nearly intact for thousands of years. The 25,000-year-old remains of woolly mammoths are so well preserved that their flesh, skin, and hair are present.

Preserved hard parts. Although the soft tissues of animals quickly decay because of the activities of bacteria and fungi, the hard parts made mostly of mineral substances can remain unchanged for millions of years. Dinosaur bones estimated to be more than 100 million years old have been found (see Figure 28-2).

Photograph by Carolina Biological Supply Company

Figure 28-1. Insect Fossil Preserved in Amber.

Figure 28-2. Dinosaur Bones.

Figure 28-3. Petrified Trees.

Many animal skeletons have also been preserved in pools of tar in which the animals had been trapped. Thousands of such fossils have been found in the *La Brea tar pits* in Los Angeles. Although most of these animals lived less than 25,000 years ago, they include many now extinct species, such as the saber-toothed tiger and the mammoth.

Petrifaction. In some cases, a dead organism lies in a body of water containing a high mineral content. Gradually, the original substances of the organism are dissolved away and replaced by minerals from the water. By this process, which is called **petrifaction** (peh-truh-*fak*-shun), the remains of the organism are turned to stone. Sometimes only the exterior form of the structures of the organism are preserved in stone. In other cases, fine details of internal structure can be seen in the petrified fossil. Whole trees estimated to be 150 million years old have been preserved as stone fossils in the Petrified Forest in Arizona (see Figure 28-3). Many fossil bones are petrified—stone replicas of the original bones.

Molds and casts. By far the greatest number of fossils form on the bottoms of lakes and seas. The dead organism sinks and comes to rest in the sandy or muddy bottom. As additional particles of sand or mud accumulate on the bottom, the organism is gradually buried. The sand or mud later hardens into rock. Meanwhile, the remains of the organism decay, but its shape is preserved in the rock as a hollow form called a **mold.** Sometimes a mold later becomes filled with minerals, which in turn harden to form a rock. The hardened minerals form a **cast,** which is a copy of the external form of the original organism.

Imprints. Impressions made by living things in mud, such as animal footprints, may remain when the mud hardens into rock. The impression is called an **imprint.** Among the largest known imprints are dinosaur footprints (see Figure 28-4). Many imprints have also been left by thin structures, such as leaves.

Other traces. Some fossils are nothing more than traces of the passage of an animal over or through the rock material.

Worms, for example, have left fossils in the form of tubes in rock that hardened after the worms had burrowed through mud or soil.

28-2   Sedimentary Rocks

A very large fraction of all known fossils have been found in the kind of rock called **sedimentary** (sed-uh-*ment*-uh-ree) **rock.** To understand the importance of this fact, it is necessary to know how sedimentary rocks are formed. Most sedimentary rocks form on the bottom of shallow seas or on ocean bottoms along the shorelines of continents. Rivers flowing into these bodies of water carry fine particles of rock called *sediments.* These sediments are eroded, or worn away, from the land over which the rivers flow. When the river waters enter the sea, the sediments slowly settle to the bottom. This "rain" of sediments gradually builds up a deposit on the sea bottom, sometimes to very great depths. By various chemical processes, combined with the pressure exerted by the weight of the sediments, the material slowly hardens into rock.

This process may continue for tens of millions of years at any particular location. The size and mineral composition of the sediments being deposited by the rivers will usually change from time to time. Therefore, the sedimentary rock acquires a layered structure. Some layers may be formed from fine clay or silt. Others will be made of coarse sand particles. Different mineral content will give different colors or chemical properties to the various layers. Whatever the sequence of the layers may be, one statement can be made about them. The oldest layers, that is, those laid down first, are at the bottom. The youngest, or most recent, are at the top. The layers in between are arranged in a time sequence from older below to younger above (see Figure 28-5).

Geologists have concluded that the crust of the earth is constantly changing and shifting. Portions of the crust that are

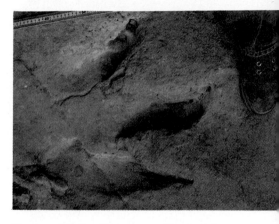

Figure 28-4. Dinosaur Footprints. Several cast type fossils of dinosaur footprints are evident in this photograph.

Figure 28-5. Deposition of Sediments. Streams flowing into a body of water carry fine rock particles called sediments. These sediments settle to the bottom and may gradually build up to a great thickness. The bodies of dead organisms that settle to the bottom may become fossils embedded in the sediments. The oldest fossils will be in the lowest layers and the youngest will be in the upper layers.

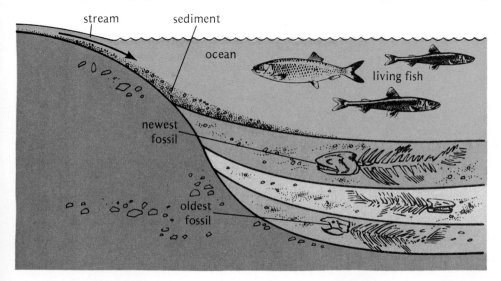

Figure 28-6. Sedimentary Rock. The layers of this rock formation were formed from sediments deposited under water. Shifts in the earth's crust then raised the rock layers without disturbing their order. Each layer is older than those above it.

under the seas at one time are later pushed up to form mountains and plateaus. Layers of sedimentary rock formed at some past time are thus exposed to view at many places on the earth (see Figure 28-6). Sometimes this exposure is simply the side of a mountain or plateau. In other cases the exposure occurs where a river has cut its way down through the layers. If the exposed sedimentary layers have not been greatly disturbed by the motions of the crust, they remain in their original sequence. The oldest are at the bottom, and the youngest are at the top. If these sedimentary layers contain fossils (as they usually do), they present a history of life that existed at a particular place during a particular time. This history of life is usually called the *fossil record*.

28-3 The Fossil Record

Relative dating. Wherever layers of sedimentary rock are exposed to view, they present a record of events that occurred during a certain time interval. If the rock layers are still in the original order of deposit, the lower layers were deposited earlier than the upper layers. Fossils in the lower layers represent organisms that lived at an earlier time than the fossils in upper layers. Any method of determining the order in which events occurred is called **relative dating.**

Correlation. Suppose a geologist finds a cliff made of sedimentary rock with five distinct layers of different texture and mineral composition. Then, a few kilometers away, another exposed cliff face of sedimentary rock is found. Examining the layers of this second formation, the geologist notices that the three top layers are exactly like the three bottom layers of the

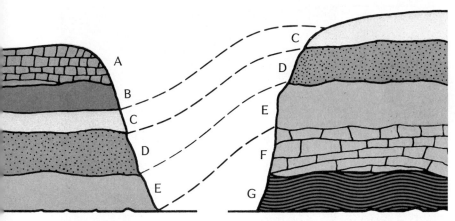

Figure 28-7. Correlation of Separate Rock Formations. Layers C, D, and E on the left have the same composition and thickness as layers C, D, and E on the right. Comparable layers on the left and the right were probably laid down at the same time. Layers F and G on the right are therefore older than layers A and B on the left.

first formation (see Figure 28-7). They have the same makeup and the same thickness in both places. It is reasonable to conclude that the layers were originally continuous and were deposited at the same time.

Suppose, now, that two more layers are visible below these three in the second cliffside. Those two layers must have been deposited before the other three. They must be older. In fact, they must be older than the bottom three layers of the first cliffside. By this process of matching, or **correlation,** we can show that certain rock layers in one place are older than certain rock layers in another place. It also follows that the fossils in the older layers are older than fossils in the younger layers.

Correlation of sedimentary rocks enables us to establish the relative dating of rocks and fossils in different places. Correlation by comparison of rock layers is, however, limited to a particular local region. The method runs up against a boundary where there are no nearby rocks to continue the correlation. The method can produce a fairly extended relative dating of the rocks and fossils of a region, but cannot provide a correlation with rocks in another section of the continent or another part of the world.

Index fossils. A study of fossils from many regions has shown that certain types of organisms seem to have appeared, flourished for a time over wide regions of the earth, and then disappeared. Rock layers containing fossils of such organisms must therefore have been formed during the period these organisms were in existence. By means of such fossils, it is possible to match the relative ages of sedimentary rocks at widely separated parts of the world. Fossils that permit the relative dating of rocks within a fairly narrow time span are called **index fossils.** Index fossils have enabled scientists to find rock sequences with overlapping time periods from the time of the first fossils up to the very recent past.

Characteristics of the fossil record. When the entire fossil record is studied, some important observations can be made. One is that the earliest organisms were relatively simple. As we travel up through the fossil record in time, we find

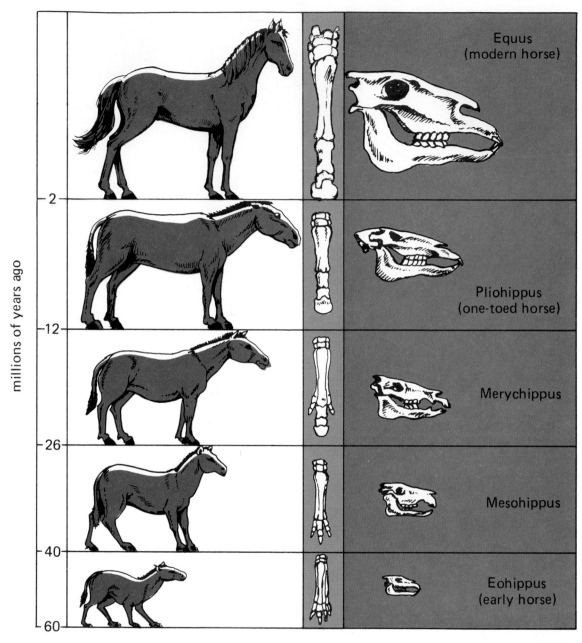

millions of years ago

- 2 — Equus (modern horse)
- 12 — Pliohippus (one-toed horse)
- 26 — Merychippus
- 40 — Mesohippus
- 60 — Eohippus (early horse)

Figure 28-8. Changes in the Horse as Indicated by Fossils of Different Ages.

the organisms becoming more and more complex. Another observation is that there seems to be a gradual transition from earlier forms to later ones. For example, changes in the structure of the horse have been traced from the first appearance of a horselike mammal through various modifications ending with the modern horse (see Figure 28-8). Many sequences of this kind in the fossil record indicate that later forms developed from earlier forms by a series of changes passed on from generation to generation. There are also many missing links or *transitional forms* between major groups of organisms that have not been found in the fossil record. However, the fossil record is still considered to be strong evidence of evolution—the gradual change of species by inherited variations.

28-4   Absolute Dating

Relative dating allows us to say that one type of organism lived earlier than another, but it does not tell us how much earlier. In other words, relative dating does not tell us the actual age of a rock or a fossil in years. Any method that does enable us to find out how long ago an event occurred is called **absolute dating.** Many methods of absolute dating have been tried, but scientists today consider radioactive dating to be the most accurate and reliable method.

Radioactive dating is based on the fact that certain elements have unstable atoms. The nuclei of these atoms tend to break down, or decay, changing to atoms of a different element. During this process, called radioactive decay, energy is given off in the form of radiation. This property of emitting radiation is known as *radioactivity* (see pages 30-31).

The rate at which a radioactive element decays is fixed and unchangeable. The time required for half the atoms of a sample of an element to decay is called the *half-life* of that element. For example, the half-life of uranium-238 is 4.5 billion years. If a rock containing uranium had been formed 4.5 billion years ago, only half the original amount of uranium would be left in the rock today. The other half would have changed to the final decay product of uranium, which is lead. By comparing the amount of lead in a rock with the amount of uranium, it is possible to calculate when that rock formed. Other radioactive elements and their decay products can also be used to date rocks by this method. The existence of different elements with radioactive isotopes often provides a cross-check on the accuracy of the calculation.

Radioactive dating methods cannot be applied to sedimentary rocks. The only types of rock they can be used on are *igneous* (ig-nee-us) rocks—rocks that formed when molten material in the crust cooled and hardened. However, the absolute age of sedimentary rocks can often be estimated by the age of igneous rocks that formed above, below, or within the sedimentary layers.

28-5   The Geologic Time Scale

Through a combination of absolute and relative dating of rocks, geologists have constructed a timetable of the earth's history, which is known as the **geologic time scale.** In this time scale, the earth's history is divided into major divisions called *eras*. Each era is subdivided into *periods* and *epochs*. Table 28-1 shows the main subdivisions of the geologic time scale, along with a brief summary of the types of organisms that appeared, flourished, or disappeared during each time interval.

Table 28-1. The Geologic Time Scale.

Era	Period (or Epoch)		Millions of years ago	Plant life	Animal life
CENOZOIC ERA — Age of Humans	Quaternary	Recent Epoch		Herbs dominant	Modern humans and modern animals
			—.01—		
		Pleistocene Epoch		Trees decrease; herbs increase	Early humans; large mammals become extinct
			—2.5—		
CENOZOIC ERA — Age of Mammals	Tertiary Period	Pliocene Epoch		Grasses increase; herbs appear	Mammals abundant; earliest humans appear
			—12—		
		Miocene Epoch		Forests decrease; grasses develop	Mammals increase; prehumans appear
			—26—		
		Oligocene Epoch		Worldwide tropical forests	Modern mammals appear
			—37—		
		Eocene Epoch		Angiosperms increase	Early mammals at peak
			—53—		
		Paleocene Epoch		Modern angiosperms appear	Early placental mammals appear; modern birds
			—65—		
MESOZOIC ERA — Age of Reptiles	Cretaceous Period			Conifers decrease; flowering plants increase	Large reptiles (dinosaurs) at peak, then disappear; small marsupials; toothed birds; modern fishes
			—136—		
	Jurassic Period			Conifers, cycads dominant; flowering plants appear	Large reptiles spread; first birds; modern sharks and bony fishes; many bivalves
			—190—		
	Triassic Period			Conifers increase; cycads appear	Reptiles increase; first mammals; bony fishes
			—225—		
PALEOZOIC ERA — Age of Amphibians	Permian Period			Seed ferns disappear	Amphibians decline; reptiles increase; modern insects
			—280—		
	Carboniferous Period			Tropical coal forests; seed ferns, conifers	Amphibians dominant; reptiles appear; rise of insects
			—345—		
PALEOZOIC ERA — Age of Fishes	Devonian Period			First forests; horsetails, ferns	Early fishes spread; amphibians appear; many mollusks, crabs
			—395—		
PALEOZOIC ERA — Age of Invertebrates	Silurian Period			First land plants	Scorpions and spiders (first air-breathers on land)
			—430—		
	Ordovician Period			Algae dominant	First vertebrates; worms; some mollusks and echinoderms
			—500—		
	Cambrian Period			Algae, fungi; first plant spores	Most invertebrate phyla; trilobites dominant
			—570—		
PRECAMBRIAN			?	Probably bacteria, fungi	A few fossils; sponge spicules; soft-bodied invertebrates

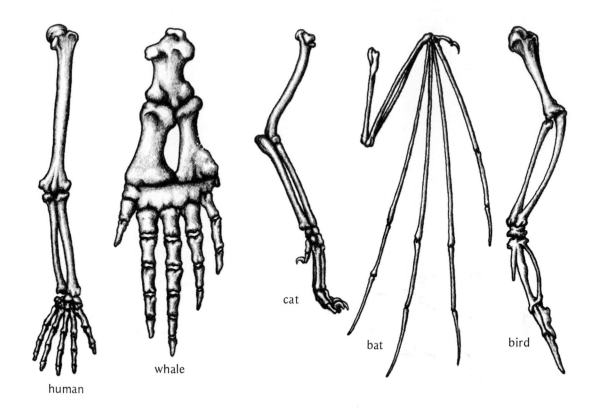

human   whale   cat   bat   bird

OTHER EVIDENCE OF EVOLUTION

Objective:
Explain how studies of comparative anatomy, embryology, and biochemistry provide evidence for evolution.

28-6   Evidence from Comparative Anatomy

Comparative anatomy is the study of structural similarities and differences among living things. The presence of certain types of similarities provides evidence about evolutionary relationships between organisms.

Figure 28-9 shows the structure of the arm and hand of a human, the flipper of a whale, the front leg of a cat, the wing of a bat, and the wing of a bird. These structures are quite different in external form. They are adapted to perform their functions in different ways. The human hand is adapted for grasping and the whale's flipper for swimming. The wings of bats and birds are both adapted for flying. Yet internally, the structures of these organs are surprisingly similar. They have the same number of bones arranged in a similar way. During embryonic development, these structures also form in similar ways. Parts of different organisms that have similar structures and similar embryonic development, but different forms and functions, are called **homologous structures.** Homologous

Figure 28-9. Homologous Structures. Although these organs function in different ways, they appear to have evolved from the same ancestral structure.

Paleontologist

Paleontologists locate, identify, and classify fossil organisms. Through the study of fossils, paleontologists learn about the life of the past and about changes in the earth itself. Paleontologists spend time in the field carefully unearthing fossils (see photo), and in the laboratory, analyzing and classifying them.

Paleontologists work at universities and museums. Some are employed by oil companies because oil deposits are often located in rocks that contain particular types of fossils. Many paleontologists have a specialized field of interest, such as invertebrate paleontology, vertebrate paleontology, or paleobotany.

Work as a paleontologist requires a bachelor's degree with courses in geology and paleontology. Most paleontologists also have advanced degrees.

structures are considered to be evidence of evolutionary relationships among the organisms that possess them.

The human, whale, cat, and bat are all mammals. For many reasons they seem to be related and are therefore classed together. We expect to find homologous structures among them. Homologous structures are evidence of evolution along similar lines. On the other hand, there are animals that have similar organs with similar functions, but that otherwise seem to be entirely different kinds of organisms. For example, birds and insects both have wings. In most other respects, they are very different in structure and development. When we examine the internal structure of bird wings and insect wings, we find no similarity at all. Structures that have similar external forms and functions but quite different internal structure are called **analogous structures.** If birds and insects evolved along quite different pathways, the fact that they have analogous structures, but not homologous ones, is understandable. Analogous structures are evidence of evolution along different lines.

Another type of evidence for evolutionary relationships is the presence of **vestigial** (ves-*tihd*-jee-ul) **structures** in modern animals. These structures are remnants of structures that were functional in an ancestral form. They are generally reduced in size and serve little or no function. In the human body, there are more than 100 vestigial structures, including the coccyx, the appendix, the wisdom teeth, and the muscles that move the nose and ears. The human coccyx is made up of fused vertebrae at the end of the spine. It is believed to be an evolutionary remnant of an ancestral reptilian tail. The appendix is believed to be the remnant of a large digestive sac from a vegetarian ancestor. Whales and pythons have vestigial hind leg bones embedded in the flesh of the body wall. Apparently, whales and snakes evolved from four-legged ancestors.

28-7   Evidence from Comparative Embryology

Comparison of the patterns of development of the embryos of different types of organisms can provide evidence of evolutionary relationships. Embryos of organisms believed to be closely related show similar patterns of development. Figure 28-10 illustrates various stages in the development of the fish, chicken, pig, and human. Note that in these vertebrates, there are many similarities during the early stages of embryonic development. For example, all the embryos have gill slits, two-chambered hearts, and tails. This similarity supports the idea that these organisms have a common evolutionary origin. As development continues, the embryos begin to resemble the adults of their type. The more closely related the animals, the longer they resemble each other during development.

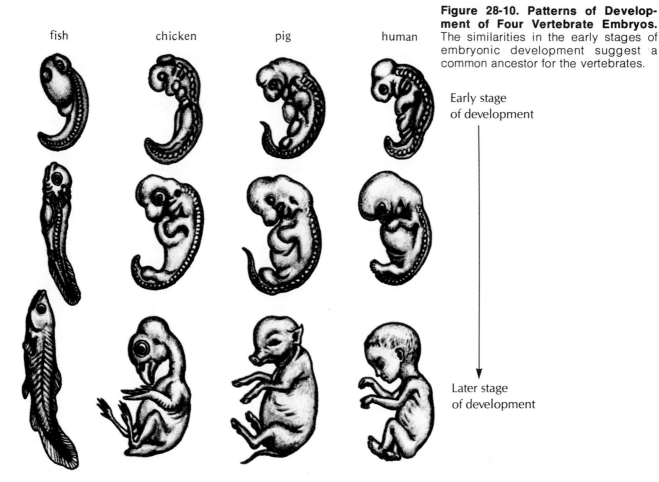

fish   chicken   pig   human

Figure 28-10. Patterns of Development of Four Vertebrate Embryos. The similarities in the early stages of embryonic development suggest a common ancestor for the vertebrates.

Early stage
of development

Later stage
of development

28-8 Evidence from Comparative Biochemistry and Immunology

Scientists have discovered that the closer the evolutionary relationship between organisms, the more alike the structure of their DNA and protein molecules. For example, the sequences of amino acids in the hemoglobin of closely related species are almost identical. The hemoglobins of humans and gorillas are the same except for one amino acid.

The degree of evolutionary relationship between different types of organisms can also be determined with the Nuttall test which is based on antigen-antibody reactions (see page 168.) For example, if human blood serum is injected into a rabbit, the rabbit produces antibodies against the proteins in the human blood. If serum from this sensitized rabbit is then mixed with human blood serum, a heavy, cloudy precipitate forms, showing an antigen-antibody reaction. The amount of the precipitate can be measured. Next, if serums from a chimpanzee, a baboon, and a pig are each tested individually with serum from the sensitized rabbit, the amount of precipitation will be found to vary. The amount of precipitation is an indica-

Figure 28-11. Lamarck's Theory of Acquired Characteristics. (A) Early giraffes had short necks. (B) When low-growing plants became scarce, giraffes stretched their necks to reach food. (C) The giraffes with stretched necks passed on their long-neck trait to their offspring.

A

B

C

tion of the similarity in protein structure between each of these animals and humans. The greater the amount of precipitate, the greater the similarity in protein structure, and the more closely the animal is related to humans.

EARLY THEORIES OF EVOLUTION

Objectives:
1. Outline Lamarck's theory of evolution.
2. Describe Weismann's experiment to show that acquired characteristics are not inherited.
3. Explain the principle of natural selection.
4. List the six main points of Darwin's theory of evolution.
5. State the chief weakness of Darwin's theory.
6. Explain the theory of punctuated equilibrium.

Up to this point in the chapter you have read some of the scientific evidence for believing that organic evolution did occur. However, the evidence for evolution does not explain how or why it occurred. The remainder of the chapter deals with theories of how evolutionary change is brought about.

28-9   Lamarck's Theory of Evolution

One of the first theories of evolution was presented by the French biologist Jean Baptiste de Lamarck in 1809. From his studies of animals, Lamarck became convinced that species were not constant, but evolved from preexisting species. He believed that evolutionary changes in animals were caused by their need to adapt to changes in the environment.

According to Lamarck's theory, evolution involved two principles. The first was his *law of use and disuse.* According to this principle, the more an animal uses a particular part of its body, the stronger and better developed that part becomes. Also, the less a part is used, the weaker and less developed it becomes. An athlete, for example, develops the strength of certain muscles by constant use. On the other hand, muscles that are not used tend to become smaller and weaker by disuse. The second part of Lamarck's theory was the *inheritance of acquired characteristics.* Lamarck made the assumption that the characteristics an organism developed through use and disuse of various parts of its body could be passed on to its offspring.

According to Lamarck, the long neck of the giraffe would have evolved in the following way (see Figure 28-11). The ancestors of modern giraffes had short necks and fed on grasses and shrubs close to the ground. As the supply of food near the ground decreased, the giraffes had to stretch their necks to reach leaves higher off the ground. Their necks then became longer from stretching, and this trait was then passed on to their offspring. In the course of generations, the giraffe's neck became longer and longer, thus giving rise to the modern giraffe.

28-10   Weismann's Experiment

From modern genetics, it is known that traits are passed from one generation to the next by genes in an individual's gametes. There is no way that these genes could be affected by the individual's life experiences or activities. Many experiments have been performed to look for evidence of such an effect, and all have failed. A famous example is the series of experiments performed by the German biologist August Weismann in the 1870s. Weismann cut the tails off mice for 22 generations. In each generation, the mice were born with tails of normal length. The acquired characteristic of shortened tails was not inherited.

28-11   Darwin

The name most closely connected with the theory of evolution is that of Charles Darwin (see Figure 28-12). Darwin was the son of a prosperous physician. At his father's urging he began to study medicine, but, finding the subject very unappealing, he gave it up. He then began to prepare for a career as a minister in the Church, but his real interest was in nature study—in observing the natural environment and collecting specimens.

In 1831 the British naval vessel H.M.S. Beagle was about to set out on a scientific expedition to chart the coastline of South America and some of the islands of the Pacific Ocean. Another purpose of the voyage was to collect specimens of wildlife from the lesser-known regions of this part of the world. Darwin learned that the captain of the Beagle was looking for someone to serve as a ship's naturalist. He applied for the position and was accepted. He was 22 years old when he sailed from England on a voyage that was expected to take 2 years, but actually lasted 5 years.

During those years, Darwin collected large numbers of specimens and made detailed observations of the regions through which he traveled. He left the ship several times and made inland journeys, rejoining it later. Darwin had plenty of time for thinking about what he saw. He also read *The Principles of Geology*, by Charles Lyell, the first volume of which was published shortly before Darwin left England. This book proposed that the earth was very old, that it had been slowly changing for millions of years, and that it was still changing. This idea led Darwin to think that perhaps living things also changed slowly over long periods of time.

There were several types of observations that particularly impressed Darwin as fitting in with this idea. One was that there was a gradual change in each species as he traveled down the coast of South America. For example, the ostrichlike

Figure 28-12. Darwin's Finches. Two of the finch species native to the Galapagos Islands are shown below.

Figure 28-13. Variation. Coloration is just one of many traits that show variation in these domestic ducks.

rheas that live in the latitudes around Buenos Aires are different from those found at the tip of South America. A second class of observations concerned the fossils that Darwin found. They were not the same as any of the living animals he observed. On the other hand, they had many similarities that suggested they might be related to modern forms.

The most significant of Darwin's observations, however, were those he made on the Galapagos Islands, which are in the Pacific Ocean about 1,000 kilometers from the coast of Ecuador. He found that there were many different species of finches living on these islands. These birds were very much alike, yet each species was slightly different from those on the next island or in another part of the same island (see Figure 28-12).

Darwin made similar observations about many plants, insects, and other organisms. Species on the Galapagos Islands resembled species on the mainland, but were always different in certain characteristics. He speculated that these organisms had originally reached the islands from the mainland. However, because of their isolation on the islands, the species had opportunities to develop special adaptations to each different region.

Darwin returned to England in 1836, convinced that evolution had occurred. He had a vast amount of detailed material that supported such a hypothesis, but he could offer no explanation of how evolution occurred. For that reason, he did not publish his ideas on evolution at once. Instead, he continued to collect and organize his data and to search for a reasonable theory of how evolution was brought about.

28-12   Natural Selection

Shortly after he returned to England, Darwin read *An Essay on the Principle of Population,* by Thomas Malthus. This essay greatly influenced Darwin's thinking and was to serve as the basis for his explanation of evolution. Malthus, a minister, mathematician, and economist, was concerned about the social problems of an increasing human population. Malthus reasoned that the human population tends to increase geometrically (2, 4, 8, 16, . . .). For example, if each pair of parents produced four children, the new generation would have 4 individuals to replace the two that had produced them. The next generation would have 8, the next 16, and so on. On the other hand, food production could at best be increased arithmetically (1, 2, 3, 4, . . .), by gradually increasing the amount of land under cultivation. According to this reasoning, the food supply could not keep up with the increase in population. The result was that millions of individuals had to die by disease, starvation, or war to keep a balance between the need for food and the supply.

Darwin realized that all organisms have the same potential for excess population growth. He was also familiar with the competition and struggle for existence that occurs everywhere in nature. In 1838 the idea came to him that organisms with favorable variations would be better able to survive and reproduce than organisms with unfavorable variations. He called this process **natural selection.** The result would be evolution, the formation of new species.

Darwin now had an explanation for evolution. Many of his friends in the scientific world urged him to publish a book on the subject before someone else reached the same conclusions and got all the credit. But Darwin would not be rushed. He insisted on building a strong case for his theory first. Then, in 1858, Darwin received an essay written by Alfred Russel Wallace, an English naturalist then working in Indonesia. Wallace had arrived at exactly the same conclusions as Darwin. Not knowing that Darwin had been thinking for years along the same lines, Wallace had simply sent the paper to Darwin for his opinion.

Darwin and Wallace agreed that Wallace's essay should be published along with a summary of Darwin's theory. Darwin then put his book into final shape and published it the next year, 1859, under the title *On the Origin of Species by Means of Natural Selection.* Darwin's book was well thought out and fully supported by examples. His theory of evolution was eventually accepted by most of the leading scientists of his time.

28-13 Darwin's Theory of Evolution

The main points of Darwin's theory can be summarized as follows:

1. ***Overproduction.*** Most species produce far more offspring than are needed to maintain the population. If all offspring lived long enough to reproduce, any one of the species would cover the earth in a fairly short time. This, of course, does not happen. Species populations remain more or less constant.

2. ***Struggle for existence.*** Since living space and food are limited, the offspring in each generation must compete among themselves, and with other species too, for the necessities of life. Only a small fraction can possibly survive long enough to reproduce.

3. ***Variation.*** In any species, the characteristics of the individuals are not exactly alike. They may differ in the exact size or shape of a body part, in strength or running speed, in resistance to a particular disease, and so on. These differences are called **variations.** Some variations may not be important. Others may affect the individual's chances of getting food, escaping enemies, or finding a mate. These are of vital importance (see Figure 28-13).

4. ***Survival of the fittest.*** Because of variations, some individuals will be better equipped to survive and reproduce than others. In the competition for existence, the individuals that are better adapted to their environment will have a greater

Frontier of Biology

Social Behavior in Dinosaurs?

Relatively new fossil evidence suggests that some dinosaurs exhibited social behavior not previously thought to occur until later forms of animals evolved. The evidence has been uncovered in a region of western Montana that 80 million years ago consisted of swamps and marshes, and was inhabited by fishes, amphibians, turtles, crocodiles, small primitive mammals, and some dinosaurs.

The evidence of social behavior consists of a densely-packed series of circular mud nests containing dinosaur eggs and egg fragments. Fossil skeletal remains of young dinosaurs also were found at the site (see photo). Paleontologists infer from this that parent dinosaurs guarded their eggs, and that after hatching they both fed and protected the young. In addition, it is thought that the dinosaurs may have lived in colonies, moved in herds, and communicated by sounds.

Not all paleontologists agree with these speculations, but this new fossil evidence is causing scientists to reevaluate the dinosaur lifestyle.

Figure 28-14. Darwin's Theory of Natural Selection. (A) Adult giraffes' necks varied in length. (B) When the environment changed, only the long-necked giraffes could reach food. (C) The short-necked giraffes died, leaving only the long-necked giraffes to reproduce.

chance of living long enough to reproduce. The phrase *"survival of the fittest"* is used to summarize this idea.

5. **Natural selection.** People who propagate plants and breed animals select individuals with desirable traits to be the parents of the next generation. Experience has shown that these desirable traits are usually passed on to the offspring. Further selection can then be used to produce additional improvements in the next generation. Darwin realized that survival of the fittest can act as a kind of natural selection, similar to the artifical selection of plant and animal breeders. Individuals with variations that make them better adapted to their environment survive and reproduce in greater numbers than those less fit. The offspring of the better adapted individuals inherit these favorable variations.

6. **Evolution of new species.** Over many generations, favorable variations gradually accumulate in the species and unfavorable ones disappear. Eventually the accumulated changes become so great that the net result is a new species.

28-14   Applying Darwin's Theory

Let us see how Darwin's theory would account for the evolution of the modern giraffe (see Figure 28-14). The original giraffe population had short necks and ate grass. However, some giraffes had longer necks than others. Those with longer necks could eat the lower leaves of trees as well as the grass. In times when grass was scarce, the longer-necked animals could obtain more food than the others and would therefore be more likely to survive and reproduce. Their offspring would inherit the favorable variation of a longer neck. The longer the neck of a giraffe, the higher it could reach for leaves on the trees. Therefore, as a result of natural selection, giraffe necks were slightly longer on the average in each succeeding generation. The modern long-necked animal is the result of this gradual process of evolution.

28-15   Weaknesses in Darwin's Theory

In general, Darwin's theory of natural selection gives a satisfactory explanation of evolution. However, there are weaknesses in his theory. One of these is that it does not explain the origin and transmissions of variations. Also, it does not distinguish between variations caused by hereditary differences and those caused by the environment, which are, of course, not inherited. For example, a plant growing in poor soil may be smaller than a plant of the same species growing in rich, fertile soil. Here, the differences in height are environmentally caused, and not a change that can be inherited.

28-16   Rate of Evolution

Scientists currently do not agree about the rate at which evolution or species formation occurs. According to Darwin's theory, new species arise through the gradual accumulation of small variations, and evolution occurs slowly, and continuously over many thousands and millions of years. This model is called **gradualism.**

Steven J. Gould and Niles Eldredge have proposed a different view of evolutionary change called **punctuated equilibrium.** According to this view, a species remains in equilibrium, staying the same for extended periods of time. This is supported by the fossil record which shows that each species seems to remain the same for thousands or millions of years. Then relatively suddenly, over a short length of time, this period of equilibrium is interrupted by the appearance in the fossil record of a new species. In other words, the long equilibrium period is interrupted or punctuated by a short period of rapid evolution. The gradualists believe that transitional forms between species are missing because they were less common, and thus few of them were preserved in the fossil record. The supporters of punctuated equilibrium argue that transitional forms are missing because evolution occurs rapidly over a relatively brief period on the geological time scale. Although the fossil record seems to support this new theory, the mechanisms that could produce new species over a short time interval are unknown. Figure 28-15 compares the Darwinian gradualistic model with the punctuated equilibrium model of evolution.

28-17 The Synthetic Theory of Evolution

In Darwin's time little was known about heredity and nothing about genetics. However, Darwin's basic theory has been combined by modern biologists with the findings of genetics and population biology into the **synthetic theory** of evolution (see Chapter 29). According to this modern theory, evolution is something that happens to populations, not to individuals. Indeed, evolution is now defined as a change in allele frequency within a population over a period of time. Nevertheless, as we shall see, individuals, not populations, are the units of natural selection.

Figure 28-15. Comparison of gradualism and punctuated equilibrium. A. The gradualism model sees evolution as proceeding more or less steadily through time. B. The punctuated equilibrium model views evolution as being concentrated in short periods of time (dotted lines) followed by long periods of little or no change. Note that both models result in the same number of species.

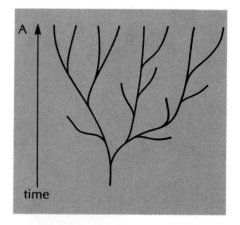

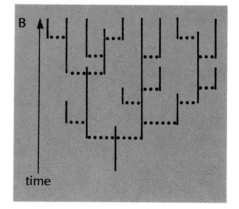

Chapter Review

SUMMARY

• Much evidence for organic evolution comes from the study of fossils. Fossils are found most commonly in sedimentary rock. Correlation of rock layers and the presence of index fossils may be used for the relative dating of fossils. Absolute dating of fossils is done by radioactive dating techniques. Other evidence of evolutionary relationships is provided by studies of immunology and comparative anatomy, embryology, and biochemistry.

- One of the first theories of evolution was that of Lamarck. Lamarck's theory was based on the law of use and disuse and the inheritance of acquired characteristics. Contemporary theory is based on the work of Darwin, which involves the concept of natural selection. According to this concept, organisms with traits that make them better adapted to their environment survive and reproduce in greater numbers than those lacking these traits.

- Scientists who are proponents of gradualism see evolution as proceeding steadily through time. Others propose a model called punctuated equilibrium, which views evolution as being concentrated in short periods of time, followed by long periods of little or no change.

KNOW THE TERMS

absolute dating	geologic time scale	mold	radioactive dating
analogous structures	gradualism	natural selection	sedimentary rock
cast	homologous structures	organic evolution	synthetic theory
correlation	imprint	petrifaction	variations
fossil	index fossil	punctuated equilibrium	vestigial structures
geologic evolution			

SECTION QUESTIONS

The Evidence of Fossils

1. What is a fossil?
2. Name six ways in which fossils can be formed.
3. In what kind of rock are most fossils found?
4. What is the fossil record?
5. What are index fossils?

Other Evidence of Evolution

6. Name three types of evidence, other than the fossil record, that support the theory of organic evolution.
7. Define *homologous structures*.
8. Name two analogous structures.

Early Theories of Evolution

9. Name the two principles involved in Lamarck's theory of evolution.
10. What is natural selection?
11. List the six main points of Darwin's theory of evolution.
12. What is the synthetic theory of evolution?

KNOW THE FACTS

Copy the number of each sentence below on a sheet of paper. Beside each number, write the term(s) that complete(s) the sentence correctly.

1. Insect fossils may be found preserved in _____.
2. The process by which the remains of an organism are turned to stone is called _____.
3. An impression made by an organism in mud that remains when the mud hardens to rock is a(n) _____.
4. In sedimentary rocks, fossils in the _____ layers represent organisms that are older than fossils in the _____ rock layers.
5. The process of matching rock layers in one location with rock layers in another location is called _____.
6. The actual age of a rock sample can be calculated by _____ _____.
7. _____ _____ is the name of the study of structural similarities and differences among living things.
8. _____ structures are the remnants of structures that were functional in some ancestral animal.
9. _____ viewed evolution as occurring gradually over many thousands and millions of years.
10. According to supporters of _____ _____, species stay the same for long periods of time, and then over a short period of time a new species evolves.

UNDERSTAND THE CONCEPTS

11. Explain the process of petrifaction.
12. Describe how sedimentary rock is formed.
13. Describe two characteristics of the fossil record.
14. What information is shown in the geologic time scale?
15. How do patterns of embryological development support evolutionary relationships?
16. How can comparative biochemistry and immunology be used in the study of evolutionary relationships?
17. How did August Weismann disprove the idea of the inheritance of acquired characteristics?
18. Describe three basic types of observations made by Darwin during his voyage on the Beagle that supported the idea of evolution.
19. Describe the main points of Darwin's theory of evolution.
20. What were the weaknesses in Darwin's theory of evolution?

THINK CRITICALLY

21. Explain how biologists use the existence of fossils to support the theory of evolution.
22. How has the combination of absolute and relative dating been used to establish the geologic time table?
23. In what way does the presence of homologous structures provide evidence about evolutionary relationships among organisms?
24. How have developments in modern genetics affected Lamarck's theory of evolution? Darwin's theory of evolution?

THINK CREATIVELY

25. Some people believe that species are fixed and unchanging and were placed on Earth in their present form. Do you think that there are any biologists who currently support this view? Why or why not?
26. The fact that evolution occurs gradually over time has hindered biologists' efforts to predict changes that may occur in a particular species. Suggest some possible ways that biologists could overcome these difficulties.

FOR FURTHER INVESTIGATION

1. Visit a natural history museum. Observe a fossil display that shows the fossil history of a group of organisms or relates one group of organisms to another. Make notes, sketches, or photographs for a poster, oral report, or written report.
2. Make a cast of leaves, twigs, footprints, or bones, using plaster of Paris or clay. In a short oral report relate this process to fossil formation.
3. Write a report on one of the career opportunities listed below. See suggested procedures, p. 9, "For Further Investigation" Activity 3.
   a. Geologist c. Analytical chemist
   b. Anatomist
4. Prepare a report on the life and contributions of one of the following scientists:
   a. Joan Steitz c. Kate Olivia Sessions
   b. Ernst Mayr d. Francisco J. Ayala

FOR FURTHER READING

Eicher, Don L., and others, *The History of the Earth's Crust*, Prentice-Hall, Inc., Englewood Cliffs, NJ, 1984.
Horner, J., "The Nesting Behavior of Dinosaurs," *Scientific American*, April, 1984.
National Geographic Society, *Giants from the Past* (Books for World Explorers), National Geographic Society, Washington, DC, 1983.
Simon, C., "Death Star," *Science News*, April 21, 1984.
Stanley, S., "Mass Extinctions in the Ocean," *Scientific American*, June, 1984.

Chapter 29

THE MODERN THEORY OF EVOLUTION

The well-developed eyes and legs of this shield back katydid are structural adaptations that have arisen over many generations.

VARIATION

Objectives:
1. Describe de Vries' contribution to Darwin's theory of evolution.
2. List the causes of variation in a species according to modern genetic theory.
3. What is *population genetics,* and explain its importance in modern evolutionary theory.
4. Explain evolution in terms of allele frequencies.
5. Explain the terms *gene pool* and *differential reproduction.*
6. State the Hardy-Weinberg law, and list the conditions under which this law holds true.

29-1   De Vries and the Mutation Theory

The Dutch botanist Hugo de Vries introduced the concept of mutation at the beginning of this century (see page 434). De Vries based his theory of mutation on research that he conducted over several years with the evening primrose (see Figure 29-1). In the course of this research, de Vries observed that occasionally a plant appeared with a totally new structure or form, which then bred true in later generations. De Vries considered each of these sudden changes in the hereditary material to be a mutation.

De Vries added the idea of mutation to Darwin's theory of evolution. This overcame one of the main weaknesses of Darwin's theory, which was a lack of explanation of how new traits could arise. De Vries claimed that the important changes leading to new species did not occur slowly over many generations. They occurred as sudden, large changes in heredity resulting from mutation. According to de Vries, a giraffe with a longer-than-normal neck would have been produced by a mutation. Since when grass was scarce, the long-necked giraffe and its offspring had an advantage over giraffes with necks of normal length, they survived and multiplied in greater numbers. Eventually, only the long-necked variety was left.

29-2 Sources of Variation

While mutations are the ultimate source of genetic variation, recombination resulting from sexual reproduction, and migration of individuals between populations also contribute to variation.

Gene mutations. In the modern theory of evolution, gene mutations are a major source of variation. The mutation of any particular gene is a rare event. Out of 10,000 gametes, only one may have a mutation of a particular gene. The mutation rate for that gene is said to be 1 per 10,000. On the other hand, each gamete has thousands of genes. Among those thousands of genes, it is very likely that at least one has mutated. Thus a few mutations are likely to be present in every zygote.

Most mutations are recessive. As a result, the mutant trait is usually hidden by the normal dominant trait. Because of the low frequency of gene mutations, it is very rare for mutant genes, i.e., the mutant alleles, to be brought together in the homozygous state. When this does occasionally happen, the effect is usually harmful to the individual. However, if environmental conditions change, mutant alleles may suddenly acquire usefulness to the species. Natural selection will then tend to gradually increase the frequency of this allele in the population.

Chromosomal mutations. Chromosomal mutations were described in Chapter 26 (page 434). Although these mutations do not produce new genes, they result in new combinations of genes in the organism. Since most physical traits are controlled by several genes, new gene combinations can give rise to new traits. Chromosomal mutations are another source of variation.

Recombination. The forming of new combinations of alleles resulting from (1) certain events that occur during meiosis, and (2) the fusion of two gametes to form a zygote is called **recombination.** During meiosis, crossing-over and independent assortment bring about recombination. Crossing-over involves the exchange of segments between homologous chromosomes, and results in new allele combinations. Independent assortment provides that alleles on nonhomologous chromosomes are randomly grouped, which is also allele recombination.

Immigration and emigration. Another source of variation may result from immigration into and emigration out of a population. As individuals move into a population, they may bring in

Figure 29-1. Evening Primroses. De Vries formulated his theory of mutation after observing this species of plant over many generations.

Figure 29-2. A Population of Penguins. According to the synthetic theory of evolution, it is a population that evolves over time, not individuals.

genes not already present. When individuals leave a population, they may remove some genes from the population. Migration, the movement of organisms from one area to another, tends to have its greatest effect on variations in small populations.

29-3   Population Genetics

The modern or synthetic theory of evolution stresses the importance of populations (see Figure 29-2). A **population** is a group of organisms of the same species living together in a given region and capable of interbreeding. According to the modern view of evolution, *individuals* do not evolve. Their genetic makeup remains the same throughout their lives. However, *populations* do evolve. Each population is made up of many individuals, each with its own unique assortment of alleles. As these individuals reproduce and die, the genetic makeup of the population as a whole may change. As its genetic makeup changes from generation to generation, the population evolves. The study of the changes in the genetic makeup of populations is called **population genetics.**

29-4   Allele Frequencies

Each individual of a population has a set of alleles that is not exactly the same as that of any other individual. Still, these individuals do have many of the same alleles. In the population as a whole, there are a certain number of alleles of each kind. Some alleles may be more common than others. For example, every individual in the population may have alleles for producing a particular enzyme. The *frequency* of that allele in the population is thus 100 percent. On the other hand, only one in a hundred individuals may have a certain mutant allele. Its frequency in the population is then 1/100, or 1 percent.

The total of all the alleles in a population is called the **gene pool.** At any given time, each allele occurs in the gene pool with a certain frequency. This frequency may be anywhere from 100 percent down to extemely low frequencies, such as 1 per 10,000 or 1 per 1,000,000. As time goes on, the allele frequencies in the gene pool may change as the result of natural selection. According to the synthetic theory, *evolution is gradual change of allele frequencies in a population.*

29-5   Differential Reproduction

As the result of mutations, new alleles are constantly appearing in every gene pool, resulting in variation among individuals. As variations appear, the environment acts as a screen that selects certain variations to be preserved and rejects others. Those individuals with favorable variations will survive longer and produce more offspring than those with unfavorable variations. Thus variation leads to **differential reproduction.** As a result of differential reproduction, certain allele frequencies will gradually increase and others will decline.

If the environment in which a population is living changes, the screening effect of natural selection will change. The frequency of alleles that give individuals an advantage under the new conditions will increase in the population. The frequency of alleles that are disadvantageous will decrease.

According to the synthetic theory the evolution of long-necked giraffes can be described in terms of differential reproduction and changes in allele frequencies (see Figure 29-3). In the original giraffe population, alleles for longer neck length were present, but at a low frequency. A change· in the enviroment may then have reduced the amount of grass available and increased the number of trees. Individuals with the alleles for longer necks would be able to obtain more food, would live longer, and would produce more offspring. In later generations, their offspring would be a larger fraction of the population. Therefore, the alleles they carried for long necks would be present at a greater frequency. Eventually, this frequency approached 100 percent, and only long-necked giraffes appeared in the population.

29-6   The Hardy-Weinberg Law

In Mendel's experiments with hybrid pea plants, there were two alleles for each trait that he studied. For example, there was the allele T that produced tall plants and the allele t that produced short plants. The frequencies of T and t in the hybrid plants were equal: 50 percent T and 50 percent t. When the hybrids reproduced, the offspring had a genotype ratio of 1:2:1 and a phenotype ratio of 3:1, but the allele frequencies in the offspring remained the same—50:50. You can check this statement by counting the T and t alleles in the Punnett square on page 418.

However, it is not necessary that two alleles in a population have the same frequency. One may be much more common than the other. Suppose, for example, that there are two alleles for a particular trait, such as eye color, in a certain species. Let us say that one allele produces white eyes; the other, red eyes. Let us not be concerned about dominance, or about the eye color of a hybrid. Let us just assume that the allele for white eyes is much more common in the population than the allele for red eyes—that 90 percent of the alleles are for white eyes, 10 percent for red. As these organisms mate and reproduce, what will happen to the allele frequencies for eye color as generation follows generation? It might seem logical that the much more common white-eye allele would eventually replace the red-eye allele altogether, and the allele frequency would become 100 percent white-eye.

In 1908, G. H. Hardy, an English mathematician, and W. H. Weinberg, a German physician, both considered this question and came to the same conclusion. They showed that the segregation and recombination of genes in sexual reproduction

Figure 29-3. Synthetic Theory of Evolution. In giraffes, the frequency of the allele for longer neck length increased gradually in the population over time.

Figure 29-4. Illustrating the Hardy-Weinberg Law. Assume that the frequency of allele p in a population is 90% and that of allele q is 10%. Then, out of every 10 sperm cells produced by the population, 9 will carry the p allele and 1 will carry the q. Likewise, of every 10 egg cells, 9 will carry p and 1 will carry q. The Punnett square shows the results of random fertilizations between these sperm and eggs. Of every 100 gametes formed, 81 are pp, 18 are pq, and 1 is qq. Let us find the total number of p;s and q's in these 100 gametes:

```
81 pp = 162 p's
18 pq =  18 p's and 18 q's
 1 qq =                2 q's
_____
Totals: 180 p's and 20 q's
```

We see that the ratio of p to q in the offspring generation is 180 to 20, or 9 to 1. This is the same as the ratio in the parent generation.

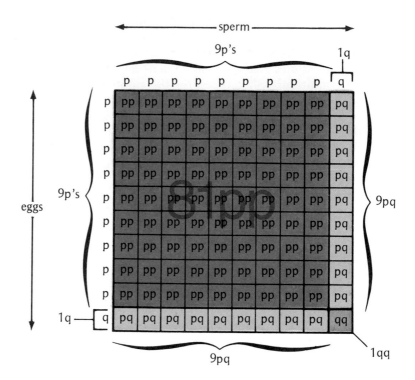

could not by itself change allele frequencies. If the frequency of allele p was 90 percent, and the frequency of its allele q was 10 percent, ordinary random mating would always produce a new generation with the same ratio of 90 percent p and 10 percent q. This is called the **Hardy-Weinberg law** (see Figure 29-4)

For the Hardy-Weinberg law to hold true, the following conditions must be met:

1. The population must be large. In a small population, alleles of low frequency might be lost, or the frequency changed, by the accidental death of a few individuals possessing those alleles.

2. Individuals must not migrate into or out of the population. Any individuals that did so might change the allele frequencies of the population.

3. Mutations must not occur. Mutations obviously change the frequencies of existing alleles.

4. Reproduction must be completely random. This means that every individual, whatever its genetic makeup, should have an equal chance of producing offspring.

29-7   The Hardy-Weinberg Law and Evolution

The preceding section lists four conditions necessary for the Hardy-Weinberg law to hold true. The first two of these might actually exist. Populations can be large enough, and migration can be practically zero under certain circumstances. However, the last two conditions almost never exist. Mutations are always occurring at fixed rates, thus changing allele frequencies. But more important, reproduction is not random. Differential reproduction is the rule, leading to natural selection and a resulting change in allele frequencies.

You may be wondering about the usefulness of a "law" that does not apply to any situation in the real world. The importance of the Hardy-Weinberg principle is that it enables us to demonstrate that evolution is occurring in a population. The law tells us that under certain conditions, allele frequencies would remain constant, and there would be no evolution. The simple fact that allele frequencies in a population are changing tells us that there are external factors causing them to change. In other words, the failure of the Hardy-Weinberg law in any given instance is a sign that evolution is occurring. The extent of the variation from the Hardy-Weinberg prediction is a measure of how rapid the evolutionary change is.

ADAPTATIONS

Objectives:
1. Explain the term *adaptation,* and name some different kinds of adaptations.
2. Explain the terms *camouflage, warning coloration,* and *mimicry.*

29-8 Types of Adaptations

An **adaptation** is any kind of inherited trait that improves the chance of survival and reproduction of an organism in a given environment (see Figure 29-5). The selecting force that chooses the best and most useful inherited variations is the environment itself. For example, in a population of plants, there may be a genetic variation in the amount of waxy cutin covering the leaves. Some plants may be heavily covered with this protective layer, while others are only thinly covered. Cutin is waterproof and protects the plant from drying out. If the climate becomes drier, then plants with a thicker cutin layer will be better able to survive and produce seeds, and differential reproduction will occur. The cutin in this case is an adaptation that has been "selected" by the environment. After many generations, alleles for this adaptation will accumulate in the gene pool. Eventually, only plants with a heavy cutin layer will remain in the population.

Structural adaptations are those that involve the body of the organism. The wings of birds and insects are structural adaptations for flight. The fins of fish and the webbed feet of ducks are structural adaptations for swimming. Leaves, by providing a large surface area, are an adaptation for photosynthesis. *Physiological adaptations* involve the metabolism of organisms. The protein web made by spiders and the poison venom made by snakes are examples of physiological adaptations. Still other adaptations involve particular behavior patterns. Of course,

Figure 29-5. Behavioral Adaptation in the Leaf-cutter Ants. The ability of these ants to cut and roll up tree leaves enables them to easily transport the leaves to their homes for food.

Figure 29-6. Male and Female Frigate Birds. The bright red pouch of the male frigate bird is an adaptation related to mating behavior.

many adaptations are combinations of various types of adaptations. For example, the mating behavior and migration of birds, the spawning of fish, and the hibernation of animals involve several types of adaptations (see Figure 29-6).

Many adaptations provide effective means of protection. In **camouflage,** the organism blends into the environment (see Figure 29-7). Flounders can become practically invisible against a variety of backgrounds. Striped tigers are hard to see among the shadows of grasses in their customary environment. In **warning coloration,** the colors of the animal actually make it easier to see. This is an advantage to certain insects that birds and other enemies find unpleasant to eat. If a young bird happens to eat one of these insects, it quickly learns to avoid that species in the future. The brightly colored monarch butterfly is an example of this kind of warning coloration (see Figure 29-8). In **mimicry,** one organism is protected against enemies by resembling another, unrelated species. Birds can eat the viceroy butterfly without unpleasant effects, but they tend to avoid it because it looks like the monarch butterfly, which they do find unpleasant. In another type of mimicry, the organism resembles some part of the environment and is ignored by its enemies (see Figure 29-9).

SPECIATION

Objectives:
1. Explain the terms *range* and *speciation*.
2. Describe the various ways in which speciation may occur.

29-9   Speciation and Geographic Separation

Each species is found in a particular region of the earth, which is called its **range.** The characteristics of a species are

Figure 29-7. Camouflage. (Left) A flounder against the ocean floor. (Right) A fawn half hidden in bushes.

Figure 29-8. Mimicry. (Left) A monarch butterfly. (Right) A viceroy butterfly.

Figure 29-9. Mimicry of Natural Environment. (Left) A grizzled mantis. (Below) A stick caterpillar on a cypress branch.

often different in different parts of its range. Differences in environmental conditions have exerted different selective pressures, leading to different adaptive characteristics. The leopard frog, *Rana pipiens,* for example, has a wide range extending over most of North America. Across this range the frogs gradually differ in such characteristics as body size, patterns of coloration, and the temperatures at which their embryos will develop. The species actually consists of separate populations with different gene pools. However, adjacent populations can mate and produce normal offspring. They are therefore called subspecies, or varieties, of the same species.

Leopard frogs at opposite ends of the range show the greatest differences in characteristics and in gene pools. In fact, frogs from widely separated regions cannot mate successfully. They are still considered to be the same species because there is continuous interbreeding among adjacent subspecies throughout the range. If, however, a population varies so much from its neighbors that it loses the ability to interbreed with them, a new species has developed. Under certain circumstances, one species can give rise to two or more species. This formation of new species is called **speciation** (spee-shee-*ay*-shun).

29-10 Types of Speciation

Isolation. Although a variety of factors are involved in speciation, one of the most important is isolation. *Isolation* refers to anything that prevents two groups within a species from interbreeding. Isolating a group of organisms has the effect of separating its gene pool from the gene pool of the rest of the species. It is generally believed that speciation is a two-step process involving first geographic isolation, followed later by reproductive isolation.

Geographic isolation occurs when a population is divided by some natural barrier, such as a mountain, desert, river or other body of water, or a landslide caused by an earthquake (see Figure 29-10). As a result, the gene pool of each group becomes isolated and the two can no longer intermix. Over a period of time, each group will become adapted to its particular environment. Through mutation, genetic recombination, and natural selection, a different gene pool will evolve in each group. When the differences between the isolated groups becomes sufficiently great, they will no longer be able to interbreed, even if they could get together. Now geographic isolation has been replaced by reproductive isolation.

Reproductive isolation can be produced by several mechanisms. Differences may arise between the two groups in courtship behavior, times of mating, or structure of the sex organs. Such changes make it unlikely that mating will occur. Other changes affect events after mating and involve the inability of sperm to fertilize eggs, the death of the embryo early in development, or the development of offspring that are sterile. According to most biologists, if two groups of organisms cannot interbreed successfully, they can be considered to be two different species.

Speciation by geographic and reproductive isolation is believed to have occurred in the case of the Kaibab squirrel and Abert squirrel. The Kaibab squirrel inhabits the north side of the Grand Canyon, and the Abert squirrel inhabits the south side. It is believed that these two squirrels evolved from a common ancestor. The Grand Canyon, acting as a geographical barrier, divided the ancestral population, which once occupied the entire area. After a long period of geographical isolation,

the Kaibab and Abert squirrels evolved. The two squirrels are similar in appearance, but are different species because they cannot interbreed.

Polyploidy. Speculation can also occur suddenly, when abnormal meiosis or mitosis results in polyploidy. Polyploids are organisms, usually plants, that contain more than the usual number of chromosome sets, for example, $3n$, $4n$, or more. When the offspring can interbreed only among themselves, they are considered to be a new species.

Adaptive radiation. The process by which an ancestral species evolves into a number of different species, each occupying a different habitat, is called **adaptive radiation.** This spreading, or radiation, of the organisms into different environments is accompanied by adaptive changes to the new ways of life.

For example, a single ancestral species may have migrated—radiated—into several different environments. If the descendants are successful, then through isolation, genetic variation, and natural selection, they will evolve a variety of adaptations to their new environments. After many generations, they will have evolved into several new species, each having certain adaptive traits. However, their common ancestry is indicated by the traits they share in common.

Darwin's finches are an example of adaptive radiation. In this case an ancestral type of finch probably arrived in the Galapagos Islands and then radiated into a variety of habitats and ways of life. The initial radiation involved living on the ground and living in trees. Further radiation occurred on the basis of food: some finches live on the ground and feed on seeds of varying size; some live in forests and feed on insects in trees; others feed mainly on cactus or berries; and one species lives in low bushes and feeds on insects. Without competition from other birds, the finches slowly radiated into and adapted to the various types of environment that were present.

Figure 29-10. Speciation through Geographic Isolation. (Left) A spring-dwelling Texas salamander. (Right) A cave-dwelling Texas salamander. Although they can no longer interbreed, these two species of central Texas salamanders are believed to share a common ancestor. The population was divided when one group took up residence in a cave. The differing selection pressures of the two environments resulted in the divergence of the species over time.

495

Marsupial mammals evolved by adaptive radiation in Australia because there were no placental mammals to compete with them for food and living space. On the other land masses of the world, where placental mammals did develop, almost all the marsupials became extinct. The placental mammals became dominant by natural selection and became varied by adaptive radiation.

Convergent evolution. One result of geographic isolation is that organisms that are not closely related may develop similar adaptations and come to resemble each other. The marsupial mouse looks very much like a placental rodent. There is also a marsupial that resembles a wolf (the Tasmanian wolf) and one that resembles a bear (the koala) (see Figure 29-11). These resemblances are only "skin deep." They evolved because of similar needs in similar environments, leading to the natural selection of similar structural adaptations. Natural selection that causes unrelated species to resemble one another is called convergent evolution.

Figure 29-11. Convergent Evolution. The koala bear is a marsupial that looks very much like a bear.

OBSERVED NATURAL SELECTION

Objectives:
1. Discuss industrial melanism and the information gained from the study of the peppered moth in England.
2. Describe how populations of antibiotic-resistant bacteria and DDT-resistant insects have arisen.

29-11 Industrial Melanism

Natural selection may take many thousands of years to produce a change in a population. However, in recent years some excellent examples of natural selection have given scientists an opportunity to study evolution in action. One of these illustrates the kind of adaptation called industrial melanism.

The peppered moth, *Biston betularia,* is found in wooded areas in England. Before the 1850s, most peppered moths were light in color. Black-colored moths, with a pigment called *melanin,* occurred but were very rare. During the years from 1850 to 1900, England became heavily industrialized. Where there was much industry, heavy smoke darkened the tree trunks and killed the light lichens growing on them. In these regions, by the 1890s, 99 percent of the peppered moths were black in color, while the light-colored variety were very rare. In the cleaner, nonindustrial areas of southern England, the light-colored moth continued to predominate.

An explanation for the change from light-colored to dark-colored moths can be found in natural selection. The light and dark color of the moth is genetically controlled. The dark color is a mutation that occurs at a constant low frequency. During daylight, peppered moths rest on tree trunks. Before England

Figure 29-12. Industrial Melanism. On the light tree (left) the lighter colored peppered moth is better camouflaged. On the dark tree (right) the darker moth is better camouflaged.

became industrialized, the light-colored moths blended in well with the lichens that covered the tree bark (see Figure 29-12). As a result of this camouflage, birds that feed upon the peppered moth could not easily find the light-colored moths. Of course, any dark-colored moths were easily seen and eaten. In this situation, the light-colored moths had a reproductive advantage. When the fumes and soot killed the lichens and blackened the trees, the light-colored moths were easy to see against the dark background of the tree trunks and became easy prey for birds. Now the dark-colored moths had a distinct advantage. The blackened trees offered them good camouflage. Through natural selection, more dark moths survived and reproduced than light-colored moths. During the years from 1850 to 1900, a period of 50 generations for peppered moths, the dark-colored moths became the more frequent color in the population.

In the 1950's, experiments were performed in England that attempted to test the above explanation. Light- and dark-colored peppered moths were released in both a polluted industrial area and in an unpolluted nonindustrial area. In the polluted area, where the trees were blackened with soot, more light-colored moths were eaten than dark-colored moths. In the unpolluted area, birds ate more dark-colored moths than light-colored moths.

This research on the color change in peppered moths shows that over a period of time a species can change gradually from one form to another. Two details of the evolutionary process are clearly illustrated. One is the presence of variability in the population. Both light-color and dark-color alleles are in the gene pool. The second detail illustrated is the effect of the changing environment in selecting one color trait over another. In nature, it is the trait that makes the moth best adapted to the environment that is preserved.

Industrial melanism is the name used for the development of dark-colored organisms in a population exposed to industrial air pollution. In the United States, the insects around many major cities are darker in color than the ones in the unpolluted countryside. Interestingly, since the 1950s air pollution control in England has resulted in an increase in the number of light-colored peppered moths.

29-12 Bacterial Resistance to Antibiotics

Antibiotics usually kill bacteria. However, once the use of antibiotics became common, resistant strains of bacteria began to appear. Antibiotics were no longer effective in killing those strains.

Scientists wanted to know how this resistance to antibiotics developed. One possibility was that exposure to an antibiotic caused certain bacterial cells to develop resistance to it. This would be similar to the immunity an individual acquires to a disease organism after recovery from the disease. Another possibility was that in a large population of bacteria, there are always a few individuals with resistance to the antibiotic. In an environment containing the antibiotic, only the resistant individuals will grow and reproduce. By natural selection, the strain with resistance becomes the common type.

In the early 1950s, Esther and Joshua Lederberg carried out a series of experiments that showed that the second explanation, natural selection, was the correct one. The Lederbergs worked with the common intestinal bacterium *Escherichia coli*, which is normally killed by the antibiotic streptomycin. The first step of their experiment was to spread a culture of the bacteria very thinly on an agar nutrient medium in a petri dish (see Figure 29-13). This had the effect of separating the culture into individual bacteria. Each bacterial cell then multiplied on the agar, forming a distinct colony. In each colony, all the cells were genetically alike since they had developed from a single original cell.

The Lederbergs now set out to look for cells resistant to streptomycin. It would have taken too much time to investigate each colony separately. Instead, they used a velveteen cloth to pick up bacteria from all the colonies at once. The cloth was then touched to a second agar plate that contained streptomycin, thus transferring bacteria from all the colonies to the agar. Usually, none of the transferred bacteria formed a colony; they could not survive and multiply in the streptomycin environment. Occasionally, however, a colony did grow on the streptomycin plate. When this happened, the Lederbergs knew which original colony the transferred cells had come from. They knew this because the velveteen cloth placed the bacteria in the same relative positions on the new agar as the colonies from which they were picked up. It was then a simple matter to test the original colony for streptomycin resistance.

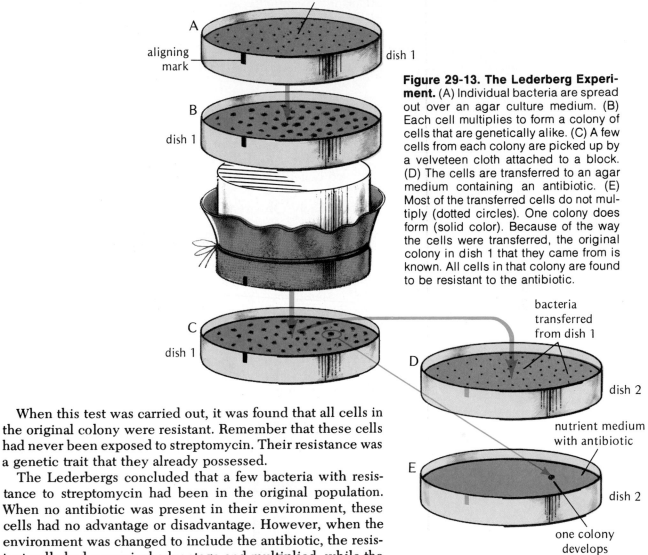

normal nutrient medium

A

aligning
mark

dish 1

B

dish 1

Figure 29-13. The Lederberg Experiment. (A) Individual bacteria are spread out over an agar culture medium. (B) Each cell multiplies to form a colony of cells that are genetically alike. (C) A few cells from each colony are picked up by a velveteen cloth attached to a block. (D) The cells are transferred to an agar medium containing an antibiotic. (E) Most of the transferred cells do not multiply (dotted circles). One colony does form (solid color). Because of the way the cells were transferred, the original colony in dish 1 that they came from is known. All cells in that colony are found to be resistant to the antibiotic.

bacteria
transferred
from dish 1

C

dish 1

D

dish 2

nutrient medium
with antibiotic

E

dish 2

one colony
develops

When this test was carried out, it was found that all cells in the original colony were resistant. Remember that these cells had never been exposed to streptomycin. Their resistance was a genetic trait that they already possessed.

The Lederbergs concluded that a few bacteria with resistance to streptomycin had been in the original population. When no antibiotic was present in their environment, these cells had no advantage or disadvantage. However, when the environment was changed to include the antibiotic, the resistant cells had a survival advantage and multiplied, while the normal type died out. The population became 100 percent streptomycin-resistant.

This experiment showed that the change in the environment had not caused the resistance to develop. It had acted only as a selector for organisms that already had the gene for resistance to streptomycin.

29-13 Insect Resistance to DDT

When DDT was first introduced, it was a very effective killer of insects, including serious pests such as mosquitos. Apparently, however, a small proportion of insects in various insect populations possessed a natural resistance to DDT. When the DDT-sensitive members of a population were killed by spraying, the DDT-resistant insects multiplied

Figure 29-14. Spontaneous Generation. It was once thought that frogs were formed from the mud of rivers.

rapidly, passing on their natural DDT-resistance to their offspring. Eventually, many insect populations were completely resistant to DDT.

The DDT did *not* create the resistance of the insects. Rather, the DDT acted as the environmental agent for the selection of the resistant strains.

EARLY BELIEFS ABOUT THE ORIGIN OF LIFE

Objective:

Describe some of the classic experiments that affected belief in the theory of spontaneous generation.

29-14   Early Observations

For thousands of years, it was believed that living organisms could arise spontaneously from nonliving matter over the course of a few days or weeks. This idea is the theory of **spontaneous generation,** or *abiogenesis* (ay-by-oh-*jen*-uh-sis). Belief in spontaneous generation was based on common observations. The ancient Egyptians, seeing frogs and snakes coming out of the mud of the Nile River, concluded that these animals were formed from the mud. The Greek philosopher Aristotle believed that an "active principle" was responsible for life. This active principle was thought to be present in mud. Thus, it was possible for animals to arise from the mud of rivers. Some other popular beliefs were that fleas and lice arose from sweat, mice arose from garbage, flies arose from decaying meat, and snakes and worms arose from horsehairs in water (see Figure 29-14).

29-15   A Recipe for Mice

In the early 1600s, the Belgian physician Jan Baptista van Helmont performed an experiment that seemed to support the idea of spontaneous generation. He placed wheat grains in a sweaty shirt. After 21 days, the wheat was gone and mice were present. Van Helmont reasoned that human sweat was the active principle that changed wheat grains into mice. Even though this was an uncontrolled experiment, his experimental "proof" gained wide acceptance among the scientists of his time.

29-16   Where Fly Larvae Come From

In the mid-1600s the Italian physician Francesco Redi struck the first great blow against the idea of spontaneous generation. It was a matter of common observation that whenever meat was left exposed to the air, maggots would soon appear on it. Maggots are the larvae of flies, but they were thought to be a kind of worm because of their shape and method of movement. It was widely believed at that time that the maggots developed by spontaneous generation from the decaying meat.

Redi doubted the truth of this common belief, and he decided to subject it to a scientific test. In reporting his results, he wrote:

> It being . . . the popular belief that the putrescence of a dead body, or the filth of any sort of decayed matter, engenders worms; and being desirous of tracing the truth in the case, I made the following experiment.

Redi's account of his experiments is a perfect example of the scientific method. He began with a series of careful observations. On the basis of his observations, he made certain hypotheses. He then tested his hypotheses by controlled experiments. The following is a brief summary of Redi's investigation.

He began by placing many different kinds of meat in open containers, and he closely observed the maggots that appeared on them (see Figure 29-15A). He watched the maggots consume the decaying meat, and he continued to observe them even after the meat was gone. He discovered that the maggots formed pupas, which then developed into flies of various kinds. Redi was apparently the first person to realize that maggots developed into flies.

This observation led Redi to recall that flies always gathered around the decaying meat. Everybody knew this, of course, but nobody had ever connected this observation with the maggots. Redi formed a hypothesis that the maggots developed from eggs laid on the meat by the flies. He then proceeded to test this hypothesis.

He placed some meat in open jars and other samples of the same meat in tightly sealed jars. This was a controlled experiment: The only variable was whether the jar was closed or open. Redi observed that flies entered the open jars and that maggots appeared on the meat. No maggots appeared on the meat in the closed jars (see Figure 29-15B).

This experiment proved only that the meat had to be exposed to develop maggots. It did not prove that the flies were the source of the maggots. Many scientists of the time claimed that fresh air was necessary for spontaneous generation, and by sealing the jars, Redi had prevented the needed air from reaching the meat.

Redi therefore performed another set of experiments in which the containers were covered by fine gauze (see Figure 29-16). The gauze allowed free circulation of air into the containers, but prevented flies from entering. Redi observed that the flies attempted to reach the meat by landing frequently on the gauze. The flies also deposited eggs on the gauze, which developed into maggots. But no maggots appeared inside the jars.

Figure 29-15. Redi's First Experiment. This experiment showed that meat had to be exposed to the environment to develop maggots.

A

Flies attracted by odor.

meat

rotting meat
Flies lay eggs on meat.

maggots on meat

meat gone
Maggots form pupas that develop into flies.

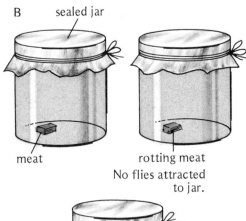

B   sealed jar

meat

rotting meat
No flies attracted to jar.

No flies or maggots in jar.

Figure 29-16. Redi's Second Experiment. This experiment showed that maggots arise in decaying meat from eggs laid by flies.

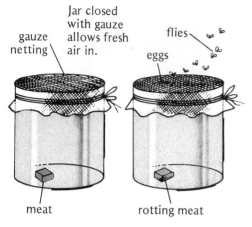

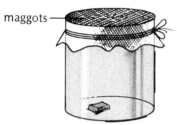

No flies or maggots in jar. Maggots on netting

Redi had shown conclusively that maggots did not arise spontaneously from decaying meat, but from eggs laid by flies. Scientists accepted this conclusion, but with the discovery of microorganisms, the whole question of spontaneous generation was thrown open again.

29-17   Spontaneous Generation of Microorganisms

At about the time that Redi was performing his experiments, Anton van Leeuwenhoek was making his simple microscopes and examining everything he could put under them. In 1677 he made the startling discovery of living things in a drop of water. Soon it was found that when hay or soil was placed in water that had no life in it to start with, millions of microorganisms appeared just a few hours later. Here, surely, was a clearcut case of spontaneous generation! Many scientists concluded that although larger animals might not be able to arise from nonliving matter, microscopic ones could. The controversy that Redi had almost put to rest flared up again and raged for the next 200 years.

29-18   The Boiled Soup Controversy

In 1745, John Needham, an English scientist, performed some experiments that reinforced belief in spontaneous generation of microorganisms. He boiled flasks of chicken, lamb, and corn broth for a few minutes to kill any microorganisms in them. Then he sealed the flasks. After several days he opened and examined the flasks and found them teeming with microorganisms. He repeated the experiment several times and always obtained the same results. Needham and other biologists concluded that the microorganisms developed by spontaneous generation.

29-19   Boiling Time Makes the Difference

About 20 years after Needham did his work, Lorenzo Spallanzani, an Italian scientist, challenged the concept of spontaneous generation of microorganisms. Like Needham, he set up flasks of chicken, lamb, and corn broth. However, he boiled the contents of the flasks for a much longer time. No living organisms appeared in the flasks.

Spallanzani claimed that Needham obtained organisms in his heated flasks because he had not heated them long enough to kill all the organisms originally present. Needham argued that Spallanzani had heated his flasks so long that he had destroyed the "vital principle" in the air that was necessary to bring about the generation of new organisms. The debate remained unsettled for almost another 100 years.

29-20   Disproving Spontaneous Generation

In 1860, the French chemist Louis Pasteur set out to disprove the theory of spontaneous generation. In his experi-

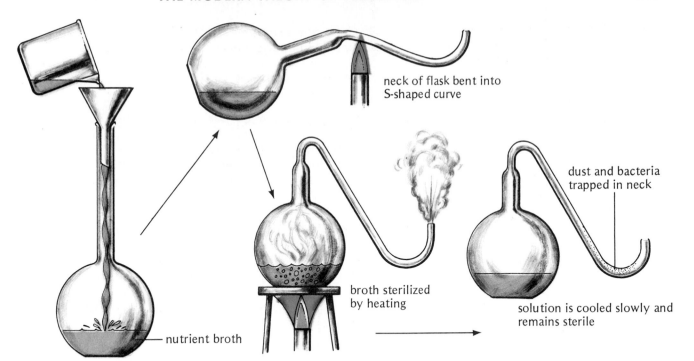

neck of flask bent into
S-shaped curve

dust and bacteria
trapped in neck

broth sterilized
by heating

solution is cooled slowly and
remains sterile

nutrient broth

ments he had to take into account the complaints about Spallanzani's experiments—that boiling destroyed the "force" needed for spontaneous generation and that the process required fresh air.

Pasteur thought that microorganisms and their spores were present in the air and that they became active and reproduced when they entered the nutrient broth. He claimed that the presence of air alone could not produce microorganisms in the broth. To test this theory, Pasteur filled flasks with nutrient broth and then heated the necks of the flasks and drew them out into a long S shape, leaving the ends open (see Figure 29-17). The contents of the flasks were then sterilized by boiling. Fresh air could reach the broth, but microorganisms and their spores were trapped in the long necks of the flasks. As long as the flasks were not disturbed, the contents remained sterile. Only when the flasks were tipped and some of the broth ran into the neck and became contaminated did microorganisms grow in the flasks. Pasteur's experiment finally put an end to the idea of spontaneous generation.

Figure 29-17. Pasteur's Experiment. This experiment showed that microorganisms that developed in a nutrient broth came from spores and microorganisms in the air.

MODERN THEORY OF THE ORIGIN OF LIFE

Objectives:
1. Describe the conditions thought to exist on the primitive earth according to the heterotroph hypothesis.
2. Describe the sequence of development of living things according to the heterotroph hypothesis.

3. Describe any experiments whose results seem to support the heterotroph hypothesis.

29-21 The Heterotroph Hypothesis

If, as most scientists believe, living organisms can now arise only from other living organisms, how did the first living things arise on earth? The most widely accepted theory of the origin of life is called the **heterotroph hypothesis.** This theory was formulated by a small group of scientists in the 1920s and 1930s. The scientist most widely credited with development of the heterotroph hypothesis was the Russian biochemist A. I. Oparin.

Primitive conditions on the earth. The heterotroph hypothesis assumes that the physical and chemical conditions on the earth billions of years ago were very different from those of the modern earth (see Figure 29-18). For example, the earth's atmosphere now consists almost entirely of nitrogen (N_2) and oxygen (O_2), with a small amount of carbon dioxide (CO_2). Chemists and geologists have concluded that the earth's primitive atmosphere consisted of hydrogen (H_2), water vapor (H_2O), ammonia (NH_3), and methane (CH_4). It is also assumed that the temperatures on the earth were much higher than at present. The oceans, when they first formed, were probably not much below the boiling point of water. The oceans of this period have been described as a "hot, thin soup," in which chemical reactions were likely to occur more rapidly than in the cooler waters of the modern earth.

Natural synthesis of organic compounds. Under the primitive conditions just described, the simple compounds in the atmosphere and dissolved in the oceans could have reacted to form

Figure 29-18. Early Conditions on the Earth Compared with Modern Conditions. On the primitive earth, the composition of the atmosphere was different from the modern atmosphere, the temperature was higher, and there were more sources of energy for producing chemical change.

PRIMITIVE EARTH

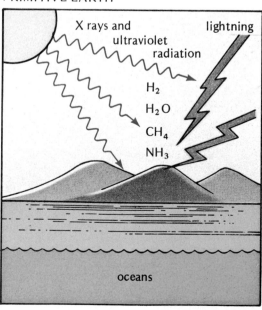

MODERN EARTH

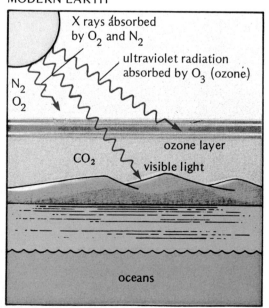

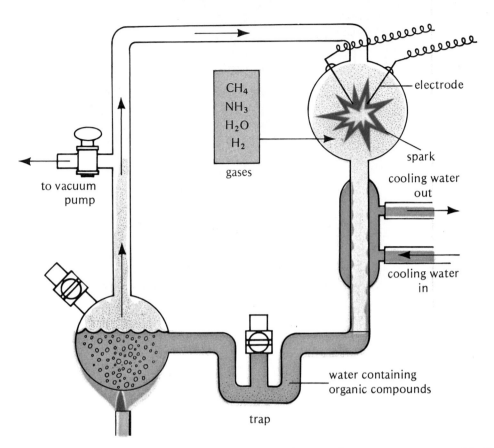

CH₄
NH₃
H₂O
H₂

gases

electrode

spark

cooling water out

cooling water in

to vacuum pump

water containing organic compounds

trap

more complex organic compounds. The synthesis of organic compounds from inorganic raw materials requires energy. Many sources of energy are thought to have been present on the primitive earth. There was heat given off by the earth itself; radiation from the decay of radioactive elements in the earth's crust; electrical energy from lightning; and ultraviolet light, visible light, and X rays from the sun. Under such conditions, there would have been adequate energy available for the breakdown and formation of chemical bonds. The first nucleotides, amino acids, and sugars could have been formed during this period. There are experimental results that support this hypothesis.

In 1953, Stanley Miller, a graduate student at the University of Chicago, designed an experiment simulating the conditions thought to be present on the primitive earth. His specially designed experimental apparatus contained four gases—hydrogen, water vapor, ammonia, and methane (see Figure 29-19). Boiling water in the apparatus forced these gases to circulate past sparking electrodes. Miller allowed the experiment to run for a week. At the end of that time, he analyzed the contents of the apparatus and found that it now contained urea, various amino acids, hydrogen cyanide, and organic acids, such as lactic and acetic acids. This experiment clearly demonstrated that organic substances, including amino acids,

Figure 29-19. Miller's Experiment Simulating Early Conditions on the Earth. A mixture of gases thought to resemble the primitive atmosphere was continuously passed through an electric spark. Water in the apparatus dissolved the new substances produced. After a time, the solution was found to contain many organic compounds.

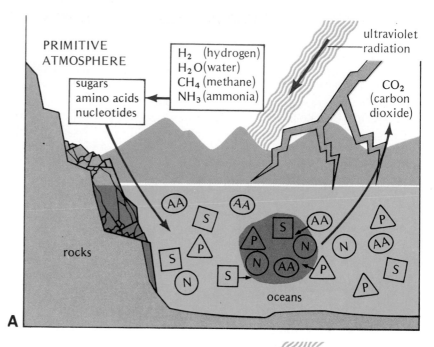

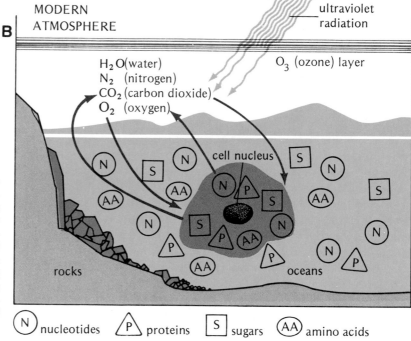

Figure 29-20. The Heterotroph Hypotheses. (A) In the early stages, coacervates absorbed organic nutrients from the physical environment. They obtained energy by anaerobic respiration, or fermentation. This released carbon dioxide into the atmosphere. (B) In later stages, autotrophs capable of producing nutrients by photosynthesis appeared. This added oxygen to the atmosphere and led to the development of aerobic respiration.

could have been produced in nature under the conditions assumed for the primitive earth.

The work of an American biochemist, Sidney Fox, showed that, given a supply of amino acids, proteins could also be formed by nonbiological processes. Fox heated a mixture of amino acids at temperatures above 100°C for different lengths of time. Analysis of the resulting compounds revealed the presence of proteins.

Aggregates of organic compounds. Oparin's heterotroph hypothesis suggests that protein complexes could develop into nonliving structures having some of the characteristics of life. Oparin proposed that proteinlike substances in the prehistoric oceans may have formed aggregates, or clusters, of large molecules (see Figure 29-20). He called such aggregates **coacervates** (koh-*as*-er-vayts). These complex structures were surrounded by a "shell" of water molecules, forming a sort of bounding membrane. The development of a limiting membrane made it easier for the internal contents of the structure to be chemically different from the external environment. It also kept various types of molecules in closer contact so that chemical reactions occurred more readily. Coacervates have been formed in the laboratory from proteins and other organic molecules.

Growth and reproduction. Oparin believed that within the coacervates, numerous chemical reactions occurred. As coacervates became more complex, they developed biochemical systems with the capacity to release energy from various types of organic (nutrient) molecules, which were absorbed from the environment. Coacervates, by absorbing material from the environment, grew in size. Eventually, they split in half, and each half would again grow. Such structures would be primitive living things. Oparin called them *heterotrophs* because they obtained nutrients from the environment.

Anaerobic respiration. Since the atmosphere of the primitive earth contained no free oxygen, it is assumed that these first organisms carried on some form of fermentation for the release of energy. This process resulted in the release of carbon dioxide into the oceans and atmosphere. As the number of heterotrophs increased, the supply of available nutrients in the environment decreased. Thus competition arose between existing heterotrophs. Any organism with biochemical machinery that enabled it to use different or more complex nutrients than most other heterotrophs had a distinct advantage. In this way, organisms containing more and more complex biochemical systems gradually developed.

Photosynthesis and aerobic respiration. Eventually, organisms developed that could use light energy directly for the synthesis of ATP. These were the first photosynthetic organisms. In these organisms, the use of light energy for the synthesis of ATP became coupled with reactions in which carbon dioxide and water were used in the synthesis of carbohydrates. These photosynthetic autotrophs further changed the environment by adding oxygen to the atmosphere.

The presence of oxygen led to the development of organisms with the capacity to carry on aerobic respiration. Aerobic respiration is much more efficient than fermentation in releasing energy from nutrients, so that aerobic organisms became dominant.

The activities of living organisms eventually altered the earth's environment so completely that the conditions that had originally led to the development of life were destroyed.

Frontier of Biology

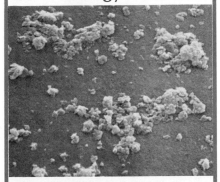

Crystals of bentonite, a type of clay, seen with a scanning electron microscope.

Did Life Evolve from Clay?

The heterotroph hypothesis holds that the first primitive organisms arose from clusters of large organic molecules. Now, however, there is an entirely new theory of the origin of life on earth.

The new theory proposes that the first organisms were inorganic crystals of clay. These minerals are produced by the weathering of hard rocks and would have been abundant on the early earth. Like all crystals, clay minerals self-assemble in specific patterns that are determined solely by the materials that compose them. Thus, these early organisms would have had the capacity for carrying information.

Occasionally, errors may have occurred during the assembly process, resulting in new, "mutated" forms. It is believed that those forms with favorable properties served as templates for organic molecules. Eventually, these more specialized organic compounds completely replaced the clay crystals.

Scientists are currently experimenting with clay crystals to gain evidence for this new theory.

Chapter Review

SUMMARY

- According to the modern, or synthetic, theory of evolution, variations and the appearance of new traits result from gene and chromosome mutations, crossing-over, recombination, and migration of organisms into and out of a population. According to the Hardy-Weinberg law, the frequency of genes within a population remains constant if the population is large, mating is random, there are no mutations, and there is no immigration or emigration. The fact that gene frequencies in populations change is evidence of evolution.

- Adaptations are inherited traits that improve an organism's chance of survival and reproduction in a given environment. They may be structural, physiological, or behavioral.

- Speciation, the development of new species, can result from geographic and reproductive isolation, polyploidy, and adaptive radiation. Convergent evolution results in unrelated species resembling one another.

- Studies of industrial melanism in the peppered moth show that over short periods of time natural selection can act in favor of certain

adaptations. Studies of resistance of bacteria to antibiotics and resistance of insects to DDT show that the resistance does not arise as a result of exposure to antibiotics or DDT. Instead, a small portion of the population had genes for resistance, and when the population was exposed to the antibiotic or DDT, it was the organisms with these genes that survived.

- Early theories of the origin of life often included the idea of spontaneous generation. The idea of spontaneous generation was tested by scientists for hundreds of years, and was finally disproved by the experiments of Louis Pasteur in the mid-1800s. The most widely accepted modern theory of the origin of life is the heterotroph hypothesis. According to this theory, the conditions of the primitive earth were much different from those of the modern earth in terms of the makeup of the atmosphere, energy sources, and temperature. It is thought that under those conditions primitive heterotrophic organisms that used some form of fermentation for energy arose by natural processes. From these first organisms all other forms of life developed.

KNOW THE TERMS

adaptation	gene pool	mimicry	reproductive isolation
adaptive radiation	geographic isolation	population	speciation
camouflage	Hardy-Weinberg law	population genetics	spontaneous generation
convergent evolution	heterotroph hypothesis	range	warning coloration
differential reproduction	industrial melanism	recombination	

SECTION QUESTIONS

Variation

1. Name the sources of variation within a species according to the synthetic theory.
2. What is a population?
3. Define the term *gene pool*.
4. Define the term *differential reproduction*.
5. List the conditions that must exist for the Hardy-Weinberg law to hold true.

Adaptions

6. Define the term *adaptation*.
7. Name two different types of adaptations and give an example of each.

Speciation

8. What is speciation?
9. Name the two steps involved in speciation.

10. What is adaptive radiation?

Observed Natural Selection

11. What is industrial melanism?
12. Who discovered how bacteria develop resistance to antibiotics?

Early Beliefs About the Origin of Life

13. What is spontaneous generation?
14. Whose experiments discredited the idea of spontaneous generation?

Modern Theory of the Origin of Life

15. What is the name of Oparin's theory of the origin of life?
16. Name the components of the atmosphere thought to have been present on the primitive earth.
17. List the sources of energy thought to have been present on the primitive earth.

KNOW THE FACTS

Copy the numbers from Column 1 on a sheet of paper. Select the letter for the term or phrase from Column 2 that matches each numbered item, and write it beside the number.

Column 1

1. gene frequency
2. gene pool
3. Hardy-Weinberg law
4. range
5. isolation
6. Darwin's finches
7. convergent evolution
8. Lorenzo Spallanzani's experiment
9. Stanley Miller's experiment
10. coacervates

Column 2

a. any barrier to interbreeding between two groups within a species
b. under certain conditions, the gene frequencies in a population will not change from generation to generation
c. an example of adaptive radiation
d. demonstrated that organic substances can be produced under conditions thought to have existed on the primitive earth
e. the total of all the genes in a population
f. the particular region on earth where a species is found
g. the mixing of two gene pools
h. the percentage of individuals in a population carrying a certain gene
i. boiled broth for a long time to kill microorganisms, and sealed the flasks; no microorganisms grew in the broth
j. a cluster of large proteinlike molecules
k. natural selection that causes unrelated species to resemble each other

UNDERSTAND THE CONCEPTS

11. How did De Vries explain (a) the appearance of new traits within a species and (b) the appearance of new species?
12. Why don't individuals evolve?
13. What is meant by the statement that the frequency of a particular gene in a population is 75 percent?
14. How is evolution defined according to the synthetic theory?
15. Why does differential reproduction affect gene frequency in a population?
16. In what way is the Hardy-Weinberg law useful?
17. Explain how camouflage, warning coloration, and mimicry each serve as a means of protection.
18. When are two groups of organisms considered to be two different species?
19. What are polyploids? How can polyploidy result in speciation?
20. What did the study of the peppered moth in England show?
21. How do bacteria develop resistance to antibiotics?
22. How did insect populations become resistant to DDT?
23. Briefly describe Redi's experiments on the origin of maggots in decaying meat.

24. How did van Leeuwenhoek's discovery of microorganisms affect the belief of scientists in spontaneous generation?
25. Describe the experiment by which Pasteur finally put an end to the idea of spontaneous generation.
26. Briefly describe the development of living things from inorganic compounds, according to the heterotroph hypothesis.

THINK CRITICALLY

27. What does the Hardy-Weinberg law show about the frequency of recessive traits?
28. What role does natural selection play in the formation of a new species?
29. Why should the control of air pollution in England have affected the numbers of light-colored peppered moths?
30. In what way does the existence of DDT-resistant insects support the synthetic theory of evolution?
31. What hypothesis was Stanley Miller testing when he designed an experiment simulating conditions that he thought to be present on the primitive earth?

THINK CREATIVELY

32. The heterotroph hypothesis is a hypothetical explanation of the origin of life on Earth. It lacks supporting evidence. In what areas might you search for supporting evidence?
33. Does the modern theory of evolution satisfactorily explain why ancestral populations are different in appearance from those we know today? Explain your answer.

FOR FURTHER INVESTIGATION

1. Visit a zoo, aquarium, or botanical garden. Observe (a) the different species and their adaptations, and (b) a group of related species. Use notes, drawings, and photographs to prepare a report on your observations.
2. Observe the birds in a local area, such as the woods, the seashore, or your own back yard. In particular, observe their feeding habits and beaks. Prepare a report on the birds' adaptations to the environment.
3. Use library resources to prepare a report on insect resistance to insecticides or bacterial resistance to antibiotics.
4. Prepare a report on one of the career opportunities listed below. See suggested procedures, p. 9, "For Further Investigation" Activity 3.
   a. Cytotechnologist
   b. Geographer
   c. Environmental engineer
5. Prepare a report on the life and contributions of one of the following scientists:
   a. Gertrude Cox
   b. A. I. Oparin
   c. Frederica de Laguna
   d. Theodosius Dobzhansky

FOR FURTHER READING

Cairns-Smith, A. G., "The First Organisms," *Scientific American*, June, 1985.

Hapgood, F., "The Importance of Being Ernst," *Science 84*, June, 1984.

Peterson, I., "Microsphere Excitement," *Science News*, June 30, 1984.

Stebbins, G., and Ayala, F., "The Evolution of Darwinism," *Scientific American*, July, 1985

Taylor, G. R., *The Great Evolution Mystery*, Harper & Row Pubs., Inc., 1983.

Issues in Biology

Land Use

As the human population increases, pressure to use land in new and varied ways also increases. In the United States, people are expanding urban and suburban areas, continually building roads, homes, factories, and offices. In countries such as the Philippines and Kenya, people are dredging and dynamiting coral reefs to carve out shipping lanes. In the rain forests that dot the equator, people are stripping the land for farming and cattle ranching. Even the Antarctic may not be safe from human incursion. There scientists have found deposits of copper, silver, and nickel that may be mined in the future.

One effect that development and use of land by people can have is an increase in the extinction rate of organisms. In nature, approximately 900,000 species become extinct in one million years. The activities of humans, however, have increased this rate by at least 400 times. This means that species become extinct, on average, at a rate of about one per day.

Extinction of species affects the process of evolution. Extinction can occur within a few decades or much more rapidly. In contrast evolution of new species generally takes much longer. Therefore, the extinction of organisms is outpacing the evolution of new ones, lessening the number of species in existence. This provides a smaller and smaller "base" of organisms from which new species can evolve.

The disturbance of natural environments by people may have some positive effects on the process of evolution. For example, when existing environments are changed, new environments are produced. Sometimes, new resources become available within an environment. The new environments and resources may allow some species to expand and to diversify. For example, a new species of moth that feeds exclusively on banana plants appeared after people introduced these plants in Hawaii about a thousand years ago.

Sometimes when a section of an ecosystem is destroyed, one portion of a population is separated from another. This happens, for example, when coral reefs are dredged. Evolution may then proceed differently in each of the separated

Many animal species are struggling to survive in environments that are being destroyed.

populations. Consequently a greater number of species may appear than if the population had remained intact.

At present, the number of extinctions caused by human activities is greater than the number of new species evolving. Most scientists agree that endangered species can be saved only by people actively cooperating with nature. They urge the governments of all countries to use current knowledge to retard the process of extinction and foster the processes of evolution. Such actions may include the establishment of wildlife preserves, improvement of damaged habitats, and the introduction of new resources such as food or shelter.

---

1. How is the extinction of species related to the constantly increasing size of the human population?

2. Is the current rapid extinction of plant and animal species a serious problem? Explain your reasoning.

3. Name one organism that is currently in danger of extinction due to human interference with the environment. Describe what has led to this situation. What steps, if any, are being taken to save this organism from extinction?

4. Suggest other methods of slowing extinction and/or enhancing evolution besides the methods given in this feature.

UNIT 7
DIVERSITY OF LIVING THINGS

From the white tip shark to the finger coral, this ocean reef near Hawaii is home to a great diversity of organisms. In this Unit, you will see that despite many differences, organisms can be grouped together according to common traits. You will also learn that these similarities often reflect a common evolutionary history.

Chapter 30

MONERANS, PROTISTS, AND VIRUSES

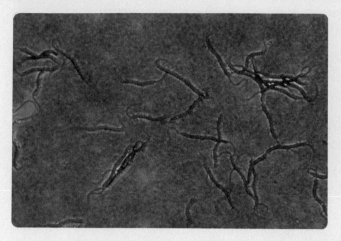

Bacteria, such as these spirilla, are members of the kingdom Monera.

KINGDOM MONERA

Objectives:

1. Name the two types of organisms found in the kingdom Monera.
2. Describe the general characteristics of procaryotic cells.
3. Describe the general characteristics of the blue-green algae.
4. Name and describe the three major groups of bacteria.
5. Describe the general structure of a bacterial cell.
6. Describe the different ways that bacteria obtain energy for their life processes.
7. Describe heterotrophic and autotrophic nutrition in bacteria.
8. Explain what happens during the different phases of growth of a bacterial culture.
9. Describe the rules by which it is determined whether a particular microorganism causes a particular disease.
10. List some of the beneficial activities of bacteria.

The *monerans* (muh-*ner*-uns), kingdom **Monera** (muh-*ner*-uh), and the protists (*proh*-tists), kingdom **Protista** (proh-*tist*-uh), include organisms that cannot be classified definitely either as plants or as animals. The viruses are an even more troublesome group. Biologists have not yet decided whether they should be considered to be living organisms. It is also unclear how the viruses are related in terms of evolution to living organisms. Whether viruses appeared before or after living cells is an unanswered question. For these reasons the viruses are studied as a separate group outside the classification system of living things.

30-1 Procaryotic Cells

The kingdom Monera includes only two types of organisms—blue-green algae and bacteria. The main feature of moneran cells, and what distinguishes them from the cells of all other organisms, is the absence of a distinct, membrane-bounded nucleus. Cells that lack such a nucleus are called **procaryotic** (proh-kar-ee-*aht*-ik). Thus monerans are called **procaryotes** (proh-*kar*-ee-ohts). Cells that do contain a membrane-bounded nucleus are called **eucaryotic** (yoo-kar-ee-*aht*-ik).

Moneran cells also lack the other membrane-bounded organelles that are usually present in eucaryotic cells. They do not have mitochondria, endoplasmic reticulum, Golgi bodies, lysosomes, or chloroplasts. They do contain ribosomes, but these are smaller than the ribosomes of eucaryotic cells. Although there is no distinct nucleus, procaryotic cells do contain DNA. The DNA is usually concentrated in one region of the cytoplasm and is not complexed with the proteins, called *histones*, that are associated with the DNA of eucaryotes. The major differences between procaryotic and eucaryotic cells are summarized in Table 30-1.

Some of the enzyme-controlled reactions that ordinarily take place in or on the organelles of eucaryotic cells take place on the inner surface of the cell membrane of procaryotes. Often, the cell membrane folds into the cyotplasm. In blue-green algae and photosynthetic bacteria, infoldings of the cell membrane may fill the cytoplasm. These infoldings carry the photosynthetic pigments.

Table 30-1. Comparison of Procaryotic and Eucaryotic Cells.

Cell structure	Procaryotic cells	Eucaryotic cells
Nuclear membrane	Absent	Present
Chromosomes	Contain DNA without histones	Contain DNA and histones
Endoplasmic reticulum	Absent	Present
Mitochondria	Absent	Present
Golgi apparatus	Absent	Present
Lysosomes	Absent	Present
Plastids	Absent	Present, in phototrophs
Flagella	Twisted strands of protein	Microtubules in 9 + 2 pattern
Cell membrane	Present	Present
Ribosomes	Present; smaller than eucaryote type	Present

A

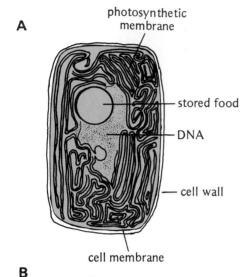

photosynthetic
membrane

— stored food

— DNA

— cell wall

cell membrane

B

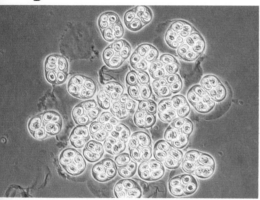

C

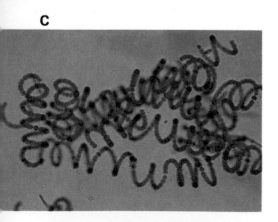

Figure 30-1. Blue-Green Algae. (A) Structure of typical cell of blue-green alga. (B) Cells of *Chroococcus*, which are surrounded by thickened cell walls. (C) *Anabaena*, a type of filamentous blue-green algae.

Procaryotes and eucaryotes differ in other ways. The procaryotes have cell walls, but the walls do not have the same chemical composition as the cell walls of plants. The flagella of procaryotes do not contain the 9+2 arrangement of microtubules found in the flagella of eucaryotic cells. Instead, they consist of parallel strands of protein twisted around one another like the strands of a rope.

30-2 Blue-Green Algae

The *blue-green algae*, phylum **Cyanophyta** (sy-uh-*nah*-fuh-tuh), are the simplest of the oxygen-producing photosynthetic organisms (see Figure 30-1). Members of this phylum contain a blue pigment, *phycocyanin* (fy-koh-*sy*-uh-nin), and the green pigment chlorophyll. About half the species are actually blue-green in color. Other species contain a number of additional pigments that make them red, yellow, brown, black, or green.

Blue-green algae are found in both fresh and salt water, as well as in soil and on rocks. A few species are found in natural hot springs where few other organisms can survive. Other species are found in icy Arctic waters. The Red Sea owes its name to the occasional appearance of huge populations of red-colored blue-green algae. Ponds or lakes that contain a rich supply of organic matter often develop large populations of blue-green algae. Because these algae thrive in polluted water, they are frequently an indication of the presence of organic pollutants.

The cytoplasm of the cells of blue-green algae generally contains storage granules filled with proteins and carbohydrates. The carbohydrates are stored as *polyglucan*, a compound similar to the glycogen of animal cells. The cells of the blue-greens do not contain the large, fluid-filled vacuoles characteristic of many plant cells. They also have no flagella. The cell walls are strengthened by a complex polysaccharide not found in eucaryotic cells. The outside of the cell walls is often surrounded by a protective jellylike layer, or *slime sheath*.

A few species of blue greens are found as single cells, but most form colonies in the form of plates, irregular clusters, or threadlike filaments. Some blue-green algae live together with fungi to form mixed organisms known as *lichens* (*ly*-kinz). (See page 533)

Filamentous blue-green algae take nitrogen from the atmosphere. Within the filaments are thick-walled, colorless cells called *heterocysts*. Research has demonstrated that the transformation of atmospheric nitrogen into a form usable by the organism takes place in these cells. The capacity of blue-green algae to fix atmospheric nitrogen plays an important role in maintaining the fertility of certain soils. For example, blue-green algae provide rice crops with a source of nitrogen, thereby reducing the need for artificial fertilizers.

Among the blue-green algae, reproduction is strictly asexual, taking place by binary fission. As the filaments or colonies grow, they break into smaller parts, often at the heterocysts. Each part can grow into a new colony. Some blue-green algae develop spores that can withstand harsh conditions.

30-3 Bacteria

Bacteria, phylum **Schizomycetes** (skiz-o-my-*seet*-eez), are, like the blue-green algae, procaryotes—their cells do not contain a distinct nucleus surrounded by a membrane, and they have no mitochondria, Golgi bodies, endoplasmic reticulum, or lysosomes. They do contain ribosomes. The hereditary material, DNA, is present in the cytoplasm in the form of one circular molecule.

Bacteria are found almost everywhere—in both fresh and salt water, in soil, in the air and in and on plants and animals. Like blue-green algal cells, bacterial cells are much smaller than the individual cells of plants and animals. In fact, they are amongst the smallest known living cells. About 2000 different kinds of bacteria have been identified.

Types of bacteria. Bacteria are divided into three major groups according to shape (see Figure 30-2). A spherical bacterium is called a **coccus** (*kahk*-us); a rod-shaped bacterium is called a **bacillus** (buh-*sil*-us); and a spiral or coiled bacterium is called a **spirillum** (spy-*ril*-um). In some species, chains or clumps of bacteria are formed when daughter cells do not separate after cell division. Cocci are found as single cells (*monococci*), in pairs (*diplococci*), in chains (*streptococci*), and in grapelike clusters (*staphylococci*). Bacilli are also found as single cells, pairs (*diplobacilli*), and chains (*streptobacilli*). Spirilla exist only as single cells (see Figure 30-4).

Structure of bacteria. Bacterial cells, like plant cells, are surrounded by a cell wall (see Figure 30-3). However, bacterial cell walls are made up of polysaccharide chains linked to amino acids, while plant cell walls are made up of cellulose, and other polysaccharides not linked to amino acids. (The antibiotic drug penicillin kills bacteria by inhibiting the formation of cell walls during cell division). Many bacteria secrete a slimy *capsule* around the outside of the cell wall. The capsule provides additional protection for the cell. Many of the bacteria that cause diseases in animals are surrounded by a capsule. The capsule prevents white blood cells and antibodies from destroying the invading bacterium. Inside the capsule and cell wall is the cell membrane. In aerobic bacteria, the reactions of cellular respiration take place on fingerlike infoldings of the cell membrane. Ribosomes are scattered throughout the cyotplasm, and the DNA is generally found in the center of the cell. Many bacilli and spirilla have flagella, which are used for locomotion in water. A few types of bacteria that lack flagella move by gliding on a surface. However, the mechanism of this gliding motion is unknown.

Figure 30-2. Types of Bacteria.

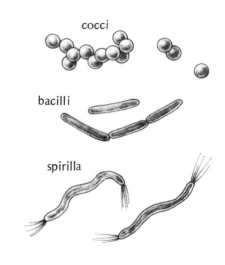

cocci

bacilli

spirilla

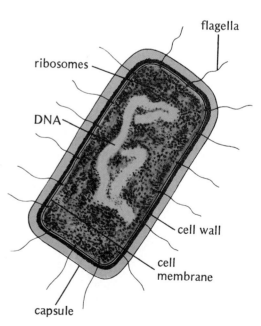

flagella

ribosomes

DNA

cell wall

cell membrane

capsule

Figure 30-3. Structure of a Bacterial Cell. In addition to a cell wall, many types of bacteria are surrounded by a slimy capsule.

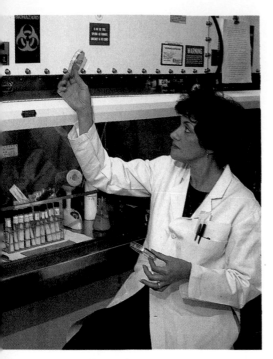

Figure 30-4. Classification of Bacteria. Observation of bacterial colonies growing in culture is an important aspect of identifying and classifying bacteria.

Life functions of bacteria. Most bacteria are aerobic—they require free oxygen to carry on cellular respiration. Some bacteria, called *facultative anaerobes (fak-ul-tayt-iv an-uh-rohbz)* can live in either the presence or absence of free oxygen. They obtain energy either by aerobic respiration when oxygen is present or by fermentation when oxygen is absent. Still other bacteria cannot live in the presence of oxygen. These are called *obligate (ob-lih-get) anaerobes.* Such bacteria obtain energy only by fermentation. *Clostridium botulinum,* a member of this group, causes *botulism* (bahch-uh-liz-um), the most dangerous kind of food poisoning. *C. botulinum* grows well in canned foods that have not been properly sterilized. Botulism is caused by the toxin produced by these bacteria.

Through fermentation, different groups of bacteria produce a wide variety of organic compounds. Besides ethyl alcohol and lactic acid, bacterial fermentation can produce acetic acid, acetone, butyl alcohol, glycol, butyric acid, propionic acid, and methane, the main component of natural gas.

Most bacteria are heterotrophic—they must obtain ready-made food from the environment. Heterotrophic bacteria are either saprobes or parasites. **Saprobes** feed on the remains of dead plants and animals, and ordinarily do not cause disease. They release digestive enzymes onto the organic matter. The enzymes break down the large food molecules into smaller molecules, which are absorbed by the bacterial cells. **Parasites** live on or in living organisms, and may cause disease.

A few types of bacteria are autotrophic—they can synthesize the organic nutrients they require from inorganic substances. Autotrophic bacteria are either photosynthetic or chemosynthetic. The photosynthetic bacteria contain chlorophylls (called *bacteriochlorophylls*) that are different from the plant chlorophylls. In bacterial photosynthesis, hydrogen is obtained from compounds other than water. Therefore, oxygen is not released by bacterial photosynthesis. One type of photosynthetic bacterium splits hydrogen sulfide, releasing pure sulfur. Chemosynthetic bacteria obtain energy by oxidizing inorganic substances, such as compounds of iron or sulfur, nitrites, and ammonia. The energy is used for the synthesis of organic compounds from carbon dioxide. The nitrifying bacteria in the nitrogen cycle oxidize ammonia or nitrites to nitrates, which can be used by plants as a source of nitrogen (see pages 651, 652).

Bacteria generally reproduce asexually by binary fission. The genetic material replicates, and the parent cell divides into two equal daughter cells. Under ideal conditions of food, temperature, and space, bacteria can divide about every 20 minutes. At this rate, in 24 hours one bacterial cell could theoretically produce a mass weighing about 2 million kilograms. However, such growth never occurs. Instead, the reproductive rate always slows because the food supply becomes used up and waste products accumulate.

Figure 30-5 shows a typical growth curve for a bacterial culture. It shows the number of bacteria in the culture plotted against time. The growth curve can be divided into four phases. In the *lag phase*, the bacteria are adjusting to their environment, and growth is slow. In the *exponential phase*, the bacteria are dividing very rapidly. In the *stationary phase*, the reproductive rate equals the death rate. In the *death phase*, the bacteria are dying off faster than they are reproducing.

Although bacteria usually reproduce asexually, sexual reproduction involving the transfer of chromosomes or chromosomal parts does occur occasionally. The three mechanisms of chromosome transfer are *conjugation*, *transformation*, and *transduction*.

Bacteria and disease. The idea that bacteria can cause disease—the **germ theory of disease**—was developed by the French scientist Louis Pasteur in the mid-1880s. Bacteria can cause disease in several ways. (1) The bacteria can become so numerous that they interfere with the normal functioning of the body. (2) In some diseases, bacteria destroy body cells and tissues. (3) Some bacteria produce toxins, or poisons, that interfere with the normal functioning of the body.

Robert Koch, a German physician who studied the causes of tuberculosis and anthrax, developed a set of rules to determine whether a specific organism is the cause of a specific disease. His rules are:

1. The suspected disease microorganism should always be found in animals with the disease and should not be found in healthy animals.

2. The microorganism must be isolated from the diseased animal and grown in pure culture (a culture containing only one kind of microorganism).

3. When microorganisms from the culture are injected into a healthy, susceptible animal, they must produce the disease.

4. The microorganism must be isolated from the experimentally infected animal, grown in pure culture again, and should be the same as the original microorganism isolated in step 2.

These rules are still used today. They have helped to establish which bacteria cause the diseases listed in Table 30-2.

Bacteria and decay. For every natural organic product, there is some variety of bacterium or fungus that can use it as a source of food and energy. Bacteria and fungi thus bring about the breakdown of organic materials, a process called *decay*. While decay is necessary for the recycling of materials in nature, it is often undesirable for human purposes. The decay of food by bacterial action causes it to rot or spoil and become unfit or harmful to eat.

In order to grow and reproduce, bacteria need food, moderate temperature, moisture, and, if aerobic, oxygen. Bacteria cannot grow if any of these conditions are absent. This informa-

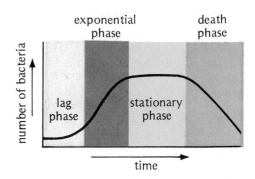

Figure 30-5. Growth Curve of a Bacterial Culture.

Table 30-2. Diseases Caused by Bacteria.

Disease	Bacterium
	COCCI
Boils, carbuncles	*Staphylococcus pyrogenes*
Gonorrhea	*Neisseria gonorrhoeae*
Meningitis	*Neisseria meningitidis*
Pneumonia	*Diplococcus pneumoniae*
Scarlet fever	*Streptococcus scarlatinae*
Strep throat	*Streptococcus pyrogenes*
	BACILLI
Botulism	*Clostridium botulinum*
Diphtheria	*Corynebacterium diphtheriae*
Plague	*Yersinia pestis*
Tetanus	*Clostridium tetani*
Typhoid fever	*Salmonella typhi*
	SPIRILLA
Cholera	*Vibrio comma*
Syphilis	*Treponema pallidum*

tion is used in protecting human foods against spoilage by bacteria. Table 30-3 summarizes some of the methods used in preserving food and the mechanisms by which each method accomplishes its action.

Beneficial activities of bacteria. Most bacteria are harmless, and, in fact, are necessary for the continuance of life. The bacteria of decay break down the tissues of dead animals and plants, and return oxygen, carbon, nitrogen, phosphorus, and sulfur to the air, soil, and water. These elements can then be used by other living things. The role of bacteria in the recycling of materials is discussed in Chapter 37.

Bacteria are very important in the preparation of certain foods, such as cheeses, sauerkraut, and pickles. They are also used in industry and agriculture. One group of bacteria, the actinomycetes, is responsible for the production of many useful antibiotics, including streptomycin.

KINGDOM PROTISTA

Objectives:
1. Compare and contrast the general characteristics of the euglenoids, the chrysophytes, and the dinoflagellates.
2. Describe the structure of diatoms and explain their importance in nature.

Method	Food preserved	Why effective
Freezing	Meat, vegetables, desserts	Stops growth and reproduction of bacteria
Refrigeration	Meat, eggs, butter, milk	Slows growth and reproduction of bacteria
Pasteurization (heating to moderate temperature followed by rapid cooling	Milk, egg products, apple juice, and other beverages	Almost all the bacteria are killed by the heat. Cooling slows the growth of remaining bacteria
Drying	Meats, grains, flour, starch, fruits, sugar, powdered milk, powdered eggs	Removes moisture required by bacteria for growth
Canning	Vegetables, fruits, meats	High temperature kills all bacteria; sealed container prevents entrance of new bacteria
Preservatives: Salt Sugar Lactic acid (from fermentation) Vinegar	Meats Fruits Cucumbers (pickles) and cabbage (sauerkraut Vegetables	High concentrations of sugar and salt osmotically dehydrate bacteria; acid conditions prevent bacterial growth

3. Describe the structure and life processes of the euglena.
4. Describe the general characteristics of each of the four phyla of protozoa—the sarcodines, ciliates, zooflagellates, and sporozoans.
5. Describe the structure of foraminiferans and radiolarians, and explain their importance in nature.
6. Describe the life cycle of *Plasmodium,* the organism that causes malaria.
7. Describe the general characteristics and life cycles of the slime molds

Table 30-3. Methods of Preserving Food.

Members of the kingdom Protista are all either unicellular or very simple multicellular organisms. Protists are eucaryotes—their cells contain a distinct, membrane-bounded nucleus and many different types of cytoplasmic organelles. The organisms that comprise this kingdom are extremely varied. There are both phototrophic and heterotrophic forms. The phototrophic protists are included among the algae—a general term that includes all the oxygen-evolving photosynthetic organisms except the land plants (see Chapters 24 and 31). Protists of this type are placed in three phyla. The heterotrophic protists include motile, animal-like forms called protozoa, nonmotile forms, and fungus-like forms. Protists that are het-

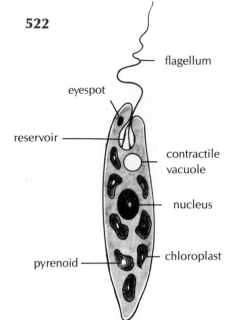

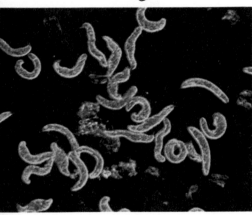

Figure 30-6. Euglena. The green color of euglenas is caused by the presence of chlorophyll.

erotrophic have been classified into six phyla. In some protists, reproduction is asexual and in others it is sexual.

30-4   Phylum Euglenophyta—The Euglenoids

The *euglenoids* (yoo-*glee*-noyds) of the phylum **Euglenophyta** (yoo-gleen-*ah*-fuh-tuh) show both plantlike and animal-like characteristics. Like plants, they contain chloroplasts and can carry on photosynthesis. Like animals, the cells have one or two flagella that are used in locomotion. Also like animals, they lack cell walls. However, inside the cell membrane there is a grooved, flexible **pellicle** (*pel*-uh-kul) made up of protein. The pellicle gives the organism a definite shape. Euglenoids are found mainly in freshwater lakes, streams, and ponds.

The best-known euglenoids are the bright green *euglenas* (see Figure 30-6). The euglena is an oval-shaped, unicellular organism. The cell has a large, central nucleus and numerous small chloroplasts. The chloroplasts contain chlorophylls a and b, as well as several other pigments. When light is available, euglenas carry on photosynthesis. However, in the absence of light, they live as heterotrophs, absorbing dissolved nutrients from the environment. Food, in the form of starchlike *paramylum* (par-*am*-uh-lum), is stored in a structure within each chloroplast called the *pyrenoid* (*py*-ruh-noyd).

Euglenas have one large flagellum that is used in movement and one short flagellum that is inactive. The bases of the flagella are within an inpocketing called the *reservoir*. Next to the reservoir within the cell is a contractile vacuole, which excretes excess water into the reservoir and out of the cell. Near the reservoir is the red-orange eyespot, or *stigma*, which is sensitive to light. The stigma enables the euglena to detect light intensity and direction and to position itself for maximum photosynthesis.

30-5   Phylum Chrysophyta—Yellow-Green and Golden-Brown Algae and Diatoms

The *chryosphytes* (*kris*-uh-fyts), phylum **Chrysophyta** (kris-*ah*-fuh-tuh), are mostly unicellular organisms that contain large amounts of the yellow-brown carotenoids and fucoxanthins. These pigments give the cells their characteristic colors. Chlorophyll is also present. **Yellow-green** and **golden-brown algae** are mostly freshwater organisms, while **diatoms** (*dy*-uh-tahmz) are found in both fresh and salt water. Members of this phylum store food as oils or as a starchlike carbohydrate called *chrysolaminarin* (kris-uh-lam-uh-*nar*-in). The cell walls, or shells, of these organisms contain compounds of silicon that make them rigid. Yellow-green and golden-brown algae have one or two flagella. Diatoms lack flagella, but move by cytoplasmic streaming.

The diatoms are the most numerous members of this phylum. They are tremendously abundant in the oceans, where they serve as a source of food for fish and other aquatic animals. Each diatom contains a nucleus and one or more chloroplasts. These organisms usually reproduce asexually, but sexual reproduction does occur.

The shells of diatoms are made up of two halves that fit together like the top and bottom of a box (see Figure 30-7). Microscopic examination of these shells shows an amazing variety of forms. When diatoms die, their shells sink to the ocean floor. In some places, the shells have accumulated in layers hundreds of meters thick, forming rocklike deposits known as *diatomaceous* (dy-uh-tuh-*may*-shus) *earth*. Some of the deposits formed millions of years ago are now on land. Diatomaceous earth is mined and used in metal polishes, toothpaste, insulation, and filters.

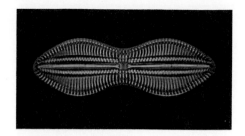

Figure 30-7. Diatom.

30-6 Phylum Pyrrophyta—The Dinoflagellates

The *dinoflagellates* (dy-noh-*flaj*-uh-layts), phylum **Pyrrophyta** (py-*rah*-fuh-tuh), are a group of unicellular algae found mainly in the oceans. Some types are photosynthetic, while others are heterotrophic. The photosynthetic dinoflagellates, along with diatoms, serve as the major source of food for many aquatic animals. Many dinoflagellates have a cellulose shell made up of armorlike plates (see Figure 30-8). They all have two flagella—one running in a beltlike groove around the middle of the organism and the other extending from one end of the organism. Dinoflagellates have a twirling or rolling motion in the water. In these organisms food is stored as oil or starch. Reproduction is asexual.

The photosynthetic dinoflagellates contain chlorophyll, and some contain other pigments as well. They therefore vary in color from yellow-green to brown and red. Some of the red dinoflagellates produce poisonous substances. Occasionally, these organisms undergo a population explosion, producing a "red tide" that kills many fish.

Figure 30-8. Dinoflagellates.

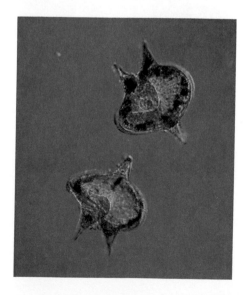

30-7 The Protozoa

Protozoa are animal-like microscopic organisms. Most are unicellular, but there are a few simple colonial forms. Protozoa are found in fresh and salt water, in the soil, and in the bodies of other organisms. Most are motile, moving by means of pseudopods, flagella, or cilia. All protozoa are heterotrophic—they must obtain food from the environment.

The life processes of two common protozoans—ameba and paramecium—are discussed in Unit 2.

On the basis of their method of locomotion, protozoa are divided into four phyla: the Sarcodina, the Ciliata, the Mastigophora, and the Sporozoa.

Figure 30-9. A Radiolarian. The pseudopods of the radiolarian are thin and pointed.

Figure 30-10. Stentor. In the stentor, the cilia are in clumps called *membranelles*.

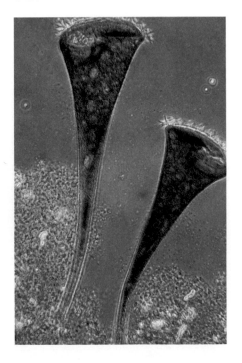

30-8   Phylum Sarcodina—Ameboid Protozoans

The *sarcodines*, phylum **Sarcodina** (sar-kuh-*dy*-nuh), are protozoans that move and capture prey by means of "false feet," or pseudopods. Members of this group are found in both fresh and salt water. A few are disease-causing parasites. The best known of the sarcodines are the amebas, unicellular organisms that constantly change shape.

Amebic dysentery is a disease caused by a parasitic type of ameba. This species is common in tropical areas. It lives in the human large intestine and feeds on the intestinal walls, causing bleeding ulcers. The disease is spread when some of the amebas form cysts, which pass out of the body with the digestive wastes. A person becomes infected by drinking or eating contaminated water or food. Amebic dysentery can be treated with drugs. It can be eradicated only by proper sewage disposal.

Unlike amebas, which are surrounded only by a cell membrane, some sarcodines are surrounded by shells. Among these are *foraminiferans* (fuh-ram-uh-*nif*-un-runz), which have calcium-containing shells, and *radiolarians* (rayd-ee-oh-*lehr*-ee-unz), which have silicon-containing shells (see Figure 30-9). Both are abundant in the oceans. When these organisms die, their shells drop into the mud of the ocean bottom. In some places, the accumulation of tremendous numbers of foraminiferan shells has formed huge chalk deposits. The white cliffs of Dover on the English coast were formed in this way. Radiolarian shells make up much of the bottom ooze in some parts of the oceans, and they are also an important part of certain silicon-containing rocks.

30-9   Phylum Ciliata—the Ciliates

The *ciliates*, phylum **Ciliata** (sil-ee-*ah*-tuh), are found in both fresh and salt water. They are the most complex protozoans. In addition to the paramecium, the ciliates include vorticella, stentor, and didinium (see Figure 30-10). The cells of ciliates are highly structured, showing a wide variety of organelles. Members of this group have many hairlike cilia. In some ciliates, the cilia are attached together in rows, forming structures called *cirri* (*sihr*-ry). In others, the cilia are in clumps, forming structures called *membranelles*. The coordinated beating of the cilia, cirri, or membranelles, enables the organism to move through the water.

Ciliates have a protective outer covering called a pellicle. Some ciliates have structures called *trichocysts* (*trik*-uh-sists) beneath the pellicle. Trichocysts are barbed structures that are discharged for defense or to aid in capturing prey. Also beneath the pellicle is a system of contractile fibers, similar to muscle fibers.

Ciliates have an oral groove through which food particles enter the organism. The movement of food into the oral groove is aided by the beating of the cilia. At the base of the oral groove, the food is enclosed in a vacuole, where it is digested. Some ciliates have contractile vacuoles, which collect and excrete excess water from the cell. Most reproduction in ciliates is asexual by binary fission. However, sexual reproduction by conjugation also occurs .

Ciliates differ from other protozoa in having two nuclei. The large macronucleus controls normal cell metabolism. The smaller micronucleus functions only in sexual reproduction. Ciliates can live without the micronucleus, but not without the macronucleus.

30-10   Phylum Mastigophora—The Zooflagellates

The *zooflagellates* (zoh-uh-*flaj*-uh-luhts), phylum **Mastigophora** (mas-tuh-*gahf*-uh-ruh), are thought to be the most primitive of the protozoans. Although some zooflagellates are free living, most live in the bodies of animals and plants. Members of this group move by the beating of long, whiplike flagella. Some have only one flagellum, while others have many. The flagella have the typical 9+2 arrangement of microtubules (see page 76). Zooflagellates reproduce both asexually and sexually.

Among the zooflagellates is *Trypanosoma gambiense* (trypan-uh-*sohm*-uh *gam*-bee-enz), which causes African sleeping sickness (see Figure 30-11). The parasite multiplies in the blood, releasing toxins. The symptoms of the disease include weakness, sleepiness, and fever. If left untreated, the victim eventually dies. Although the protozoan lives in the blood of wild African mammals, it does not harm them. It is spread to humans and domestic animals by the bite of the tsetse fly.

Another zooflagellate is *Trichonympha* (trik-uh-*nim*-fuh), which lives in the digestive tract of the termite. Termites do not have the enzymes necessary to break down wood, but *Trichonympha* does. Thus, the zooflagellate breaks down the wood eaten by the termite, and both organisms absorb and use the nutrients.

Figure 30-11. *Trypanosoma gambiense.* This zooflagellate causes African sleeping sickness.

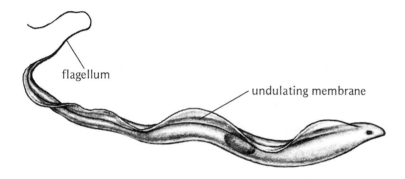

flagellum

undulating membrane

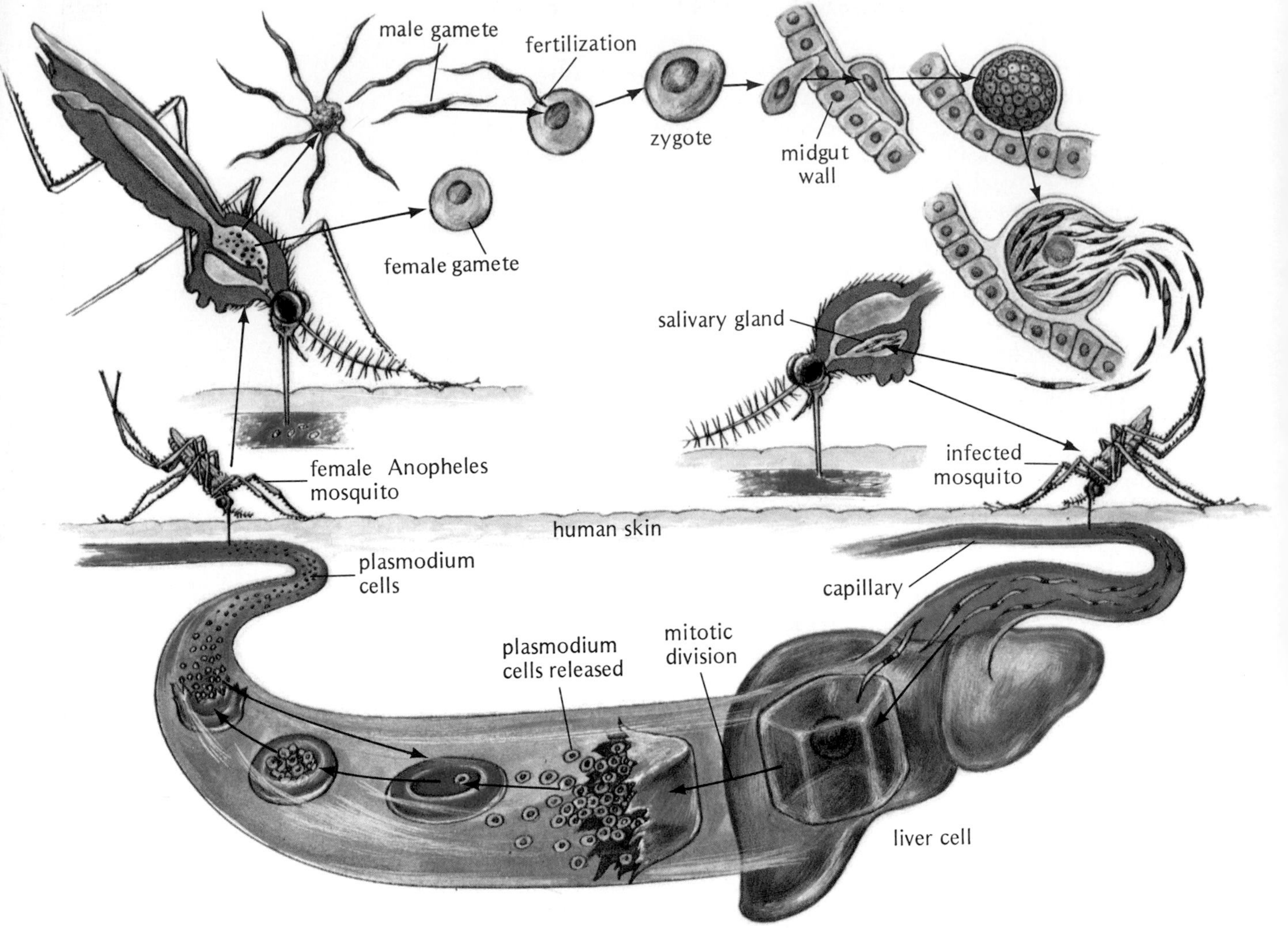
male gamete
fertilization
zygote
midgut wall
female gamete
salivary gland
female Anopheles mosquito
infected mosquito
human skin
plasmodium cells
capillary
plasmodium cells released
mitotic division
liver cell

Figure 30-12. Life Cycle of the Malarial Parasite.

30-11 Phylum Sporozoa—The Sporozoans

Members of the phylum **Sporozoa** are nonmotile. All are parasitic protozoans. They obtain nutrients from the bodies of their hosts. All members of this phylum produce spores during the asexual phase of their complicated life cycles. The best known sporozoans are the members of the genus *Plasmodium* (plaz-*mohd*-ee-um), which cause malaria in humans (see Figure 30-12). The parasite is transmitted to humans by the bite of the female *Anopheles* (uh-*nahf*-uh-leez) mosquito. When an infected mosquito pierces the skin to obtain a blood meal, *Plasmodium* cells are injected into the human bloodstream. The cells multiply asexually within human tissues, forming spores. The spores eventually invade the red blood cells and multiply further. Every 48 to 72 hours they break out of the red blood cells and invade new ones. The breakdown of the red blood cells and the release of cell wastes into the blood cause the fever and chills of malaria.

After a period of time, some spores develop into gametocytes. When the infected person is bitten by a mosquito, the gametocytes pass into the mosquito with the blood. If it is a female *Anopheles* mosquito, the gametocytes develop into gametes in the mosquito's stomach. Fertilization occurs, forming a zygote. The zygote divides, forming thousands of infective cells. These cells migrate into the tissues of the mosquito, including the salivary glands, where they are ready to infect the next victim. Malaria can be treated with drugs such as quinine and chloroquine, but the most effective way to prevent malaria is to destroy the *Anopheles* mosquito.

30-12   The Slime Molds

The *slime molds* are an unusual group of organisms that show both protozoa-like and fungus-like stages in their life cycle. They are most commonly found on decaying matter in cool, damp places in forests.

The *true slime molds* belong to the phylum **Myxomycota** (*mix*-uh-my-*kaht*-uh). In the most commonly observed stage of their life cycle, they look like giant amebas, or slimy masses, generally white, yellow, or red in color (see Figure 30-14). This stage is called the *plasmodium*. The cytoplasm of the plasmodium contains many nuclei not separated by cell membranes. The plasmodium is ameboid, and feeds by engulfing bits of organic matter with pseudopods as it creeps along the forest floor. When conditions for growth become unfavorable, the plasmodium stops moving around and develops stalked, spore-producing structures called *fruiting bodies* (see Figure 30-13). Within the fruiting bodies, haploid spores are produced by meiosis. The spores are eventually released, and if they land in a moist, suitable environment, they germinate to form flagellated gametes. Two gametes join to form a diploid

Figure 30-13. Fruiting Bodies of a Slime Mold.

Figure 30-14. Life Cycle of a Slime Mold.

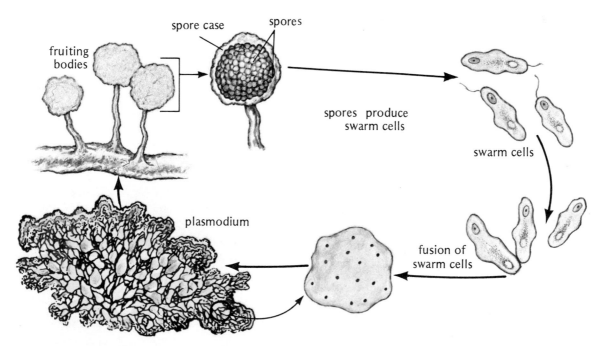

fruiting bodies

spore case   spores

spores produce swarm cells

swarm cells

fusion of swarm cells

plasmodium

zygote, which becomes ameboid. The nucleus of the zygote undergoes repeated mitotic divisions, and becomes a new plasmodium.

Slime molds of the phylum **Acrasiomycota** (uh-*krayz*-ee-oh-my-*kaht*-uh) are called the *cellular slime molds*. In this group, the spores give rise to separate, haploid, ameboid cells. The individual ameboid cells move about and feed. They also divide repeatedly, producing new, daughter haploid cells. When food becomes scarce, these individual cells come together to form a *pseudoplasmodium*. Within the pseudoplasmodium, unlike the true plasmodium, the individual, membrane-bounded cells are distinguishable. The pseudoplasmodium forms fruiting bodies that produce spores. Apparently there is no diploid phase in the life cycle of the cellular slime molds.

VIRUSES

Objectives:
1. Describe the basic structure of a virus.
2. Explain how viruses replicate within a host cell.
3. Explain the term *bacteriophage.*
4. Describe the body's defenses against viral infections.

Viruses are unique. They do not fit with any other group in the classification of living organisms. Although much is known about their structure and their method of replication, scientists still cannot decide if viruses are living or nonliving. Viruses are not made up of cells. They cannot reproduce, or replicate, unless they are inside a host cell.

30-13   Viral Structure and Reproduction

Viruses range in size from 0.01 to 0.3 microns. A virus consists of a nucleic acid core surrounded by a protein coat (see Figure 30-15). The virus shown in the diagram is one that infects bacteria. Other viruses have different shapes, but still consist of a protein coat and a nucleic acid core. The nucleic acid may be single- or double-stranded DNA, or it may be RNA. Viruses do not contain any internal structures or enzyme systems. Outside a host cell, viruses appear to be completely nonliving.

A cell can be infected by a particular type of virus only if it has receptors for the virus protein coat. In some types of virus infections, the entire virus, including both protein coat and nucleic acid, enter the host cell. In others, the protein coat of the virus remains outside the cell and only the nucleic acid enters.

Most viruses, upon entering a host cell, take over the cell's biochemical machinery and use it to produce more viruses. In DNA-containing viruses, the viral DNA serves as a template

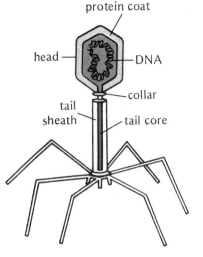

protein coat

head

DNA

collar

tail sheath

tail core

Figure 30-15. Structure of a Bacteriophage.

for producing more viral DNA. It also produces viral mRNA to direct the synthesis of viral proteins. If the viral genetic material is RNA, this RNA directs the production of more viral RNA and acts as its own mRNA. Among the proteins synthesized by the viral mRNA are enzymes that can lyse, or break down, the cell membrane of the host cell. After a number of new viruses have been assembled in the host cell, the cell membrane (and cell wall, if any) is broken, or lysed, and the viruses are released. Each new virus can infect another cell.

A virus that infects bacteria is called a **bacteriophage** (bak-*teer*-ee-uh-fayj). Some bacteriophages behave like the viruses described above. They take over the machinery of the bacterial cell, replicate themselves, and lyse the bacterial cell wall. Other bacterial viruses behave differently. When the viral DNA enters the cell, it becomes part of the bacterial chromosome. When the bacterial chromosome replicates during cell division, the viral DNA replicates too. When the bacterial cell divides, the two resulting daughter cells each contain a copy of the viral DNA along with the bacterial chromosome. The viral DNA may remain harmless through many generations, but eventually it replicates, producing new viruses that lyse and destroy the cell.

30-14 Viruses and Disease

Many human diseases are caused by viruses, including the common cold, polio, chicken pox, measles, and influenza. The human body can protect itself from viruses in several ways. The immune response to a virus occurs when lymphocytes in the blood produce antibodies that destroy the virus (see page 166). Some lymphocytes also react with virus-infected cells and destroy them. In this way no new viruses can be transmitted to healthy cells. The body also produces a substance called *interferon* when infected by a virus (see page 170). Interferon provides protection against all types of viruses. Much scientific research is now being done on interferon in search of a cure for diseases such as cancer and multiple sclerosis. Doctors also use vaccines to prevent certain virus-caused diseases, such as polio and measles (see page 168). The vaccine stimulates the production of antibodies against the disease without causing the disease. If the disease-causing virus enters the body, it is immediately attacked and destroyed by the antibodies.

Frontier of Biology

Healthy (left) and viroid-infected (right) tomato plants.

Viroids

Scientists have discovered disease-causing agents in plants and animals that are much smaller and simpler than viruses. One such agent, called a viroid, consists of small pieces of single-stranded RNA with no protein coating. Viroids are known to infect tomato, potato, cucumber, and coconut.

The size of the viroid RNA is about one tenth that of the DNA or RNA in viruses. This size is too small to code for even one small enzyme. Scientists do not yet understand how such a small molecule can replicate within a host cell. Another problem is how viroids cause disease; one theory is that they interfere with gene regulation in the host cells.

So far, viroids have been found only in plants. However, similar subviral agents are involved in some animal diseases. A type of cancer in hamsters is caused by a small DNA molecule with no protein coat. Another subviral particle called the prion is implicated in the animal disease scrapie. Other diseases as yet unexplained may be caused by such particles.

Chapter Review

SUMMARY

- The kingdom Monera includes organisms with the least complicated cellular organization. The members of this group, blue-green algae and bacteria, are procaryotic. The blue-green algae are among the simplest photosynthetic organisms.

- The bacteria are divided into three groups based on shape. Members of these groups vary in their methods of nutrition and respiration. Bacteria cause many diseases in humans, but they also cause decay and so participate in the recycling of materials in nature.

- The kingdom Protista includes unicellular and multicellular algae, protozoa, and slime molds. Members of this kingdom are eucaryotic.

- Viruses have no place in the current biological classification scheme. Viruses are smaller than bacteria, and they are dormant outside of living cells. Within a host cell, a virus can replicate itself. Viruses cause many diseases.

KNOW THE TERMS

Acrasiomycota	diatom	Myxomycota	saprobe
bacillus	eucaryote	parasite	Sarcodina
bacteriophage	Euglenophyta	pellicle	Schizomycetes
Chrysophyta	germ theory of disease	procaryote	spirillum
Ciliata	golden-brown algae	Protista	Sporozoa
coccus	Mastigophora	protozoan	yellow-green algae
Cyanophyta	Monera	Pyrrophyta	virus

SECTION QUESTIONS

Kingdom Monera

1. Name the two types of organisms in the kingdom Monera.
2. What is a procaryotic cell?
3. List six structures not found in procaryotic cells.
4. Name the simplest photosynthetic organism.
5. List the types of bacteria.

Kingdom Protista

6. List nine phyla in the kingdom Protista.
7. Which of the nine phyla can carry on photosynthesis?
8. Which of the nine phyla are heterotrophic?

Viruses

9. Where do viruses reproduce?
10. What is a bacteriophage?

KNOW THE FACTS

Copy the number of each sentence below on a sheet of paper. Beside each number, write the term(s) that complete(s) the sentence correctly.

1. Cells that contain a membrane-bounded nucleus are called _____ cells.
2. In blue-green algae, folds of the cell membrane contain pigments for _____.
3. Some blue-green algae live together with fungi to form _____.
4. Many kinds of blue-green algae form long threadlike chains called _____.
5. Bacteria generally reproduce asexually by _____ _____.
6. The ameboid protozoans move by means of _____.
7. Ciliates have an outer protective covering called a _____.
8. African sleeping sickness is caused by the zooflagellate _____ _____.
9. The slime mold plasmodium produces spores in structures called _____ _____.
10. A virus consists of a nucleic acid core surrounded by a _____ _____.

UNDERSTAND THE CONCEPTS

11. Summarize both heterotrophic and autotrophic nutrition in bacteria.
12. What rules did Robert Koch establish for determining whether a particular disease is caused by a particular microorganism?
13. What important function do bacteria have in nature?
14. In what ways do euglenoids resemble plant cells, and in what ways do they resemble animal cells?
15. Describe the structure of a diatom. What happens to the shells of dead diatoms?
16. List the major characteristics of dinoflagellates.
17. Name three types of sarcodines.
18. Name the two nuclei found in ciliates, and state the functions of each.
19. Briefly describe the life cycle of the malarial parasite, *Plasmodium.*
20. Describe the structure and life cycle of the true slime molds.
21. How does a virus use a host cell?
22. How does the human body combat viral infections?

THINK CRITICALLY

23. Would you consider viruses living or nonliving? Give your reasons.
24. A veterinarian suspects that an apparently new feline disease is caused by a specific type of bacterium. Describe a set of procedures for proving this hypothesis.
25. Compare the ways that bacteria and viruses can harm an organism after they infect it.
26. What would happen if all the bacteria in a forest suddenly died?

THINK CREATIVELY

27. From your knowledge of the life cycle of the malaria parasite, think of possible plans for eliminating the disease, and propose your best plan. Why do you think your plan would be effective?
28. Several members of a family become very ill and are diagnosed as having botulism. A public health official goes to the family's home and finds several jars of home canned food that have swollen lids. The official also finds an empty canning jar in the garbage. If you were the official, how would you write a report describing the way in which the family contracted the disease? What might be the significance of the swollen lids? What are your recommendations for avoiding bacterial food poisoning?

FOR FURTHER INVESTIGATION

1. Did eucaryotic cells develop from procaryotic cells? Were cell organelles once separate living organisms? Try to arrive at answers to these questions on the basis of library research.
2. It has been suggested that, because of their complex organization, protozoans should be called *acellular* rather than *unicellular.* Use a library to find further support for this view.
3. Investigate one of the following careers:
   a. Invertebrate zoologist
   b. Virologist
   c. Bacteriologist
4. Outline the life and contributions of one of the following scientists:
   a. Harold Amos
   b. Alice Evans
   c. Dorothy McClendon
   d. Anna Williams

FOR FURTHER READING

Dixon, Bernard, "Arthritis Virus," *Science 84,* June, 1984.

Dixon, Bernard, "Attack of the Phages," *Science 84,* June, 1984.

Godson, G. N., "Molecular Approaches to Malaria Vaccines," *Scientific American,* May, 1985.

Kusinitz, M., "The World's Most Dangerous Viruses," *Scholastic Science World,* Apr. 26, 1985.

Chapter 31
PLANTS AND FUNGI

These fruiting bodies of the angel's wing fungus are the structures within which sexually formed spores are produced.

KINGDOM PLANTAE—THE PLANTS

Objectives:

1. Describe the basic characteristics of the green algae.
2. Discuss the evolutionary relationship thought to exist between green algae and land plants.
3. Describe the general characteristics of the brown algae, and list some of the specialized structures found in large brown algae.
4. Describe the general characteristics of the red algae.
5. Name two useful substances obtained from red algae.
6. Name three types of plants found in the phylum Bryophyta.
7. Describe the general characteristics of the bryophytes.
8. Name five types of plants found in the phylum Tracheophyta.
9. Briefly describe the general characteristics of the whisk ferns, club mosses, and horsetails.
10. Describe the general structure of a fern.
11. Describe the general characteristics of the gymnosperms, and name four members of this group.
12. Describe the general characteristics of the angiosperms.

31-1   General Characteristics of Plants

The plants, kingdom Plantae, include the land plants as well as the green, the brown, and the red algae. The land plants, with their complex structural organization, are thought to have evolved from much simpler algal-like ancestors. Among the existing algal groups, the green algae, which include unicellular, colonial, and multicellular forms, are most similar to the land plants. For the most part, green algae and land plants have the same kinds of chlorophyll, the same food storage polysaccharide, i.e., starch, and the same polysaccharides in their cell wells. These similarities suggest that the land plants and the green algae share a common evolutionary ancestry. Because of this relationship, the green algae are classified in the plant kingdom, even though the many unicellular forms would appear to belong to the kingdom Protista. The brown and the red algae, although not closely related to the land plants, are multicellular and exhibit some degree of tissue and structural specialization. For this reason they also are included in the plant kingdom.

The members of the plant kingdom that constitute the land plants are divided into two groups—the *bryophytes* and the *tracheophytes*. The bryophytes include mosses, liverworts, and hornworts. These plants do not have vascular, or conducting, tissues. They are relatively short plants and usually grow in areas where there is an abundant supply of water. The tracheophytes include horsetails, ferns, gymnosperms, and flowering plants. Members of this group have well-developed vascular tissues for transport.

Life on land presents a number of problems that do not exist for aquatic organisms. The most immediate problems are obtaining and conserving water. Land plants must be able to obtain water, transport it to all its cells, and control the evaporation of water from its tissues. Land plants also need supporting tissues to enable them to stand upright against the force of gravity, and many of them need special reproductive mechanisms that enable the sperm to reach the egg without swimming through water.

31-2   Phylum Chlorophyta—The Green Algae

The *green algae*, phylum **Chlorophyta** (klor-*ah*-fuh-tuh), are found in salt and fresh water and in moist places on land. This group includes unicellular, colonial, and multicellular forms. Most green algae have a cell wall composed of cellulose and contain chlorophylls a and b in chloroplasts. Some green algae have flagella, which are used in movement.

Chlamydomonas (klam-uh-duh-*moh*-nus) is a typical unicellular green alga (see Figure 31-1). This freshwater organism has two flagella of equal length, which are used in locomotion. There is one chloroplast and a pyrenoid for starch synthesis. There are two contractile vacuoles near the bases of the

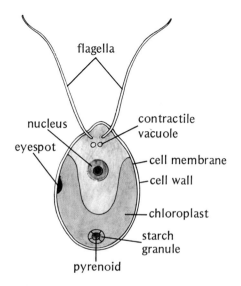

Figure 31-1. Structure of *Chlamydomonas.*

A

B

C

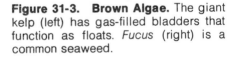

Figure 31-2. Green Algae. (A) *Ace-tabularia.* (B) *Halimeda.* (C) *Valonia.*

Figure 31-3. Brown Algae. The giant kelp (left) has gas-filled bladders that function as floats. *Fucus* (right) is a common seaweed.

flagella. Unlike other green algae, *Chlamydomonas* has a cell wall made up of a compound containing carbohydrate and protein, instead of cellulose. Reproduction is usually asexual. Multicellular green algae include filamentous forms, such as spirogyra (see page 354), and other, more complex forms (see Figure 31-2).

31-3 Phylum Phaeophyta—The Brown Algae

The *brown algae*, phylum **Phaeophyta** (fee-*ah*-fuh-tuh), include many of the common seaweeds. Members of this group are all multicellular, and range in size from microscopic to more than 50 meters in length. They are found mainly in cold ocean waters. The brown algae contain chlorophyll, which functions in photosynthesis, as well as other pigments that give them their brown color. Brown algae have cellulose in their cell walls, and they store food in the form of a polysaccharide or as oil. Their life cycles show an alternation of generations (see page 391).

Some brown algae that live along the shoreline have root-like structures that anchor them to rocks, while others found on the ocean surface have gas-filled structures that function as floats (see Figure 31-3). The surface of the so-called Sargasso Sea, which is an area stretching across the Atlantic Ocean from

the West Indies to the coast of Africa, is densely covered by several types of floating brown algae that belong to the genus *Sargassum.*

31-4 Phylum Rhodophyta—The Red Algae

The *red algae,* phylum **Rhodophyta** (roh-*dah*-fuh-tuh), like the brown algae, include many common seaweeds (see Figure 31-4). Red algae are found in warmer waters and at greater depths then brown algae. They generally grow attached to rocks or other surfaces. Most red algae are multicellular, but they are never as large as the largest brown algae. The chloroplasts of red algae contain chlorophyll and several other pigments. Many red algae are reddish in color, but others are black, green, yellow, or purple. Red algae have complex life cycles, including an alternation of generations. The cell walls of the red algae contain cellulose and other substances, including *agar,* which has a number of industrial uses. Agar is used as a thickener in foods, including ice cream, and it is used as a medium on which bacteria and fungi are grown in laboratories. *Carrageenan* (kar-uh-*ghe*-nun), another product of red algae, is used as a stabilizing agent to prevent separation of food mixtures. It is used, for example, in chocolate milk to prevent separation of the milk and the chocolate.

31-5 Phylum Bryophyta—Mosses, Liverworts, and Hornworts

The phylum **Bryophyta** (bry-*ah*-fuh-tuh) includes *mosses, liverworts,* and *hornworts* (See Figure 31-5). These are nonvascular land plants. Bryophytes have no specialized conducting tissues. Transport of materials through the plant takes place by diffusion, which is relatively slow and inefficient. Therefore, members of this group must live where water is plentiful. They are found on the forest floor, on damp rocks, in swamps and bogs, and near streams. Without xylem, bryophytes also have little in the way of supporting tissues. For this reason, most are very short, ranging from 1 to 5 centimeters in height.

In many bryophytes, some branch filaments of the young plant grow downward and enter the soil, where they function as roots. These **rhizoids** anchor the plant and absorb minerals and water. Other branches grow upward, forming stemlike shoots and leaves. However, the cells in the rhizoids, shoots, and leaves are all similar. Thus, these structures are not true organs.

In the bryophyte life cycle, the haploid gametophyte is the prominent form, i.e., the dominant generation. The diploid sporophyte generation is small, short-lived, and dependent on the gametophyte for its nutrition. The life cycle of mosses is shown in Figure 24-2 (page 392). In mosses and other bryophytes, the sperm must swim to the egg through water. Thus these plants still retain this feature indicative of their ancestral origins.

Figure 31-4. Red Algae. (Top) Coralline algae. (Bottom) Irish moss.

Figure 31-5. Liverworts. Liverworts and other bryophytes have no specialized conducting tissues and must live where water is abundant.

Figure 31-6.   Whisk Fern. Whisk ferns are the oldest known vascular plants, but they are lacking both true leaves and true roots.

Figure 31-7.   Club Moss. Living club mosses are generally small, but prehistoric members of this group were the size of trees.

31-6   Phylum Tracheophyta—The Vascular Plants

The *vascular plants*, phylum **Tracheophyta** (tray-kee-*ah*-fuh-tuh), are a diverse group that includes most of the dominant modern land plants. Vascular plants include the whisk ferns, club mosses, and horsetails, as well as the ferns, conifers, and flowering plants. All tracheophytes contain the vascular tissues xylem and phloem in the sporophyte generation. In the tracheophytes, the sporophyte generation is dominant and the gametophyte is small and short-lived.

The vascular plants are divided into two groups—the spore-dispersing plants and the seed plants. The spore-dispersing plants include the whisk ferns, club mosses, horsetails, and ferns. Fertilization in these plants requires water. The seed plants include the gymnosperms and the angiosperms. In these plants water is not required for fertilization.

31-7   The Whisk Ferns

The **whisk ferns** are the oldest known vascular plants. Fossil evidence indicates that this group was widespread about 400 million years ago, but there are only a few modern living species. These species, which live only in warm climates, are found from South Carolina to Florida. Members of this group are not really ferns. They do not have either true leaves or true roots. The plant body of the sporophyte consists of an underground stem anchored by rhizoids, which absorb water and minerals. Above ground, the stems are green and carry on photosynthesis (see Figure 31-6). As the stems grow, they split into two branches, so that the ends of the stems are Y-shaped. Sporangia form at the tips of some branches. Within the sporangia, haploid spores are produced by meiosis. Upon release, some of the spores germinate, giving rise to small inconspicuous gametophytes that bear both male and female reproductive organs i.e., the antheridia and archegonia, respectively (see pages 392-394). After fertilization occurs, the resulting zygote develops into a new sporophyte.

31-8   The Club Mosses

The **club mosses** were one of the dominant forms of plant life during the Carboniferous, or coal-forming, period of the earth about 300 million years ago. However, there are only a few remaining small genera of club mosses. Some of the prehistoric forms were as large as trees and formed forests. Living club mosses are mostly small, reaching about 20 centimeters in height (see Figure 31-7). However, a few tropical species may reach heights of 90 centimeters and look like bushes.

Club moss sporophytes have true roots, stems, and leaves. Like the whisk ferns, the stems branch so that the ends are Y-shaped. At the tips of some branches, groups of spore-producing structures form conelike *strobili* (*stroh*-bil-ly).

Spores released from the strobili give rise to gametophytes, which bear the reproductive organs. Fertilization results in a zygote that develops into the sporophyte.

Some club mosses are evergreens and are used for Christmas decorations. Ground pine and ground cedar are club mosses found in forests in the United States. One species from Mexico is known as the "resurrection plant." When dry, this club moss curls into a gray ball. However, when water is added, it opens, forming an attractive green plant.

31-9   The Horsetails

The **horsetails** include only about 20 living species of plants. They represent the remains of a group of plants that flourished during the Carboniferous period. Some ancient horsetails were the size of trees, reaching 30 meters in height. The remains of these and other plants of that period were eventually transformed into coal. Modern horsetails are generally less than 1 meter in height.

Horsetails are common in shaded woods and around streams, swamps, and ponds (see Figure 31-8). The sporophytes have true roots and leaves. The stems are green and hollow. The leaves grow only at specific points along the stem, forming "collars" of leaves. Cone-shaped strobili form at the ends of some stems. Haploid spores produced by meiosis in the strobili are released and give rise to small, inconspicuous gametophytes, which bear the reproductive organs. Following fertilization, the zygote gives rise to the sporophyte.

The stems of horsetails contain crystals of silicon, which made them useful to early settlers for scouring pots and pans. For this reason they are also known as *scouring rushes*.

31-10   The Ferns

The **ferns** were most abundant during the Carboniferous period, as were the other spore-dispersing plants. There are now about 9,000 living species of ferns (see Figure 31-9). They are particularly abundant in tropical rain forests, but are also

Figure 31-8.   Horsetails.

Figure 31-9.   Ferns. When the leaves of ferns first emerge from the soil, they are curled into the form of a fiddlehead (left). The tiny leaflets of a mature fern give it a feathery appearance (right).

found in cooler climates. Some tropical tree ferns have a woody, unbranched trunk and may reach heights of more than 15 meters. Such trees may have leaves 4 meters long. The ferns of cooler climates are much smaller. They have horizontal stems called rhizomes that grow just beneath the surface of the soil. Hairlike roots grow from the rhizomes deeper into the soil. The only visible parts of these ferns are the leaves, or fronds, that grow up from the rhizome. When the leaves first emerge from the soil, they are coiled in a bud called a *fiddlehead*. The fiddlehead gradually uncoils and develops into a mature frond. The fronds are generally divided into tiny "leaflets" that give them a feathery appearance.

The internal structure of ferns is similar to that of seed plants. Ferns contain xylem and phloem. Their roots have a root cap and show the growth zones found in the roots of higher plants. Fern stems have no cambium, so they show little or no growth in diameter.

Ferns reproduce both sexually and asexually. Sexual reproduction in ferns is discussed in Chapter 24 (page 393). In asexual, or vegetative, reproduction, the rhizome grows through the soil, branching and producing new fronds at the tip of each branch. Older portions of the rhizome die, leaving separate rhizomes each of which continues to grow.

31-11   The Seed Plants

The seed plants have become the dominant and most successful group of land plants. There are more than 250,000 existing species, ranging in size from the giant redwood tree to the tiny duckweed, a water plant with leaves only a few millimeters wide. There are two major groups of seed plants—the gymnosperms and the angiosperms. The gymnosperms are a diverese group in which the seeds are relatively exposed, i.e., they are not contained within a specialized organ. The angiosperms are the flowering plants, and their seeds are enclosed within fruits. In both groups, the seed is surrounded by a protective seed coat, and contains stored food that nourishes the young seedling during germination until it can function independently.

31-12   The Gymnosperms

The *gymnosperms* are nonflowering seed plants most of which bear their seeds on the upper surface of scales that collectively form a cone-shaped structure. The gymnosperms have true roots, stems, and leaves. The stems contain cambium, which causes growth in stem diameter. The gymnosperm plant is the sporophyte generation. The life cycle of gymnosperms is discussed in Chapter 24 (page 394).

Fossil evidence shows the presence of gymnosperms as early as 350 million years ago. By about 250 million years ago they were the dominant form of plant life. There are now about 700 living species of gymnosperms. The conifers are the

Figure 31-10.   Redwood Tree. Some redwood trees are more than 3,000 years old.

most important group of gymnosperms. Two other gymnosperm groups are the cycads and the ginkgoes.

Conifers. The **conifers,** or evergreens, are the the best known of the gymnosperms. Members of this group are cone-bearing plants with leaves in the form of needles. In most conifers, the leaves remain green throughout the year. The conifers include pine, spruce, fir, hemlock, redwood, sequoia, cedar, and cypress trees. These trees show wide geographic distribution. In colder regions they are the dominant trees of the forest. At high altitudes, pine and spruce are most abundant.

Sequoias and redwoods include some of the oldest-living and largest trees in the world (see Figure 31-10). Some are between 3,000 and 4,000 years old and are more than 90 meters tall. Pine, spruce, and fir trees are widely used as Christmas trees, and they and other conifers are used for lumber.

Cycads. The **cycads** (*sy*-kuds) look like palm trees except that they have cones. Members of this group are generally slow-growing and may live to be more than 1,000 years old. Several species may reach heights of 15 meters. In some, the ovules are the size of large eggs and the cones weigh as much as 45 kilograms. Cycads grow in tropical and semitropical regions. The only cycad found in the United States is *Zamia*, which is found in Florida (see Figure 31-11).

Ginkgoes. **Ginkgo,** or maidenhair, trees are the only living representatives of a once numerous group. This species has survived primarily because the trees were cultivated as ornamental and shade trees. Few survive in the wild. Ginkgo trees, which may reach heights of more than 30 meters, are very hardy. They can survive with limited water supplies and in the presence of air pollution.

Figure 31-11. A Cycad.

31-13   The Angiosperms

The *angiosperms*, the flowering plants, are the most successful of all living land plants. This group includes about 250,000 species, many of which are used for food. Flowering plants are found in all types of climates and environments. Some live in the desert where there is almost no water, and others live completely underwater.

In the angiosperms, the flower serves a reproductive function, since it contains the structures that produce spores by meiosis. The angiosperm plant is the sporophyte, while the gametophytes are reduced to only a few cells. Fertilization is followed by the development of a seed, which is enclosed in a fruit. The life cycle of angiosperms is discussed in Chapter 24 (page 396).

The angiosperms are divided into two major groups—the *dicots* and the *monocots.* The seeds of dicots contain two seed leaves, or cotyledons, whereas the seeds of monocots have only one (see page 401). The monocots incude the grasses, palms, lilies, sedges, irises, orchids, and various aquatic plants. The

	Family	Representative species
Dicots	Magnolia	magnolia and tulip trees
	Rose	roses, hawthorns, flowering quince, flowering almond, apples, pears, strawberries, blackberries, raspberries, apricots, cherries, peaches, plums
	Beech	beech, oak, and chestnut trees
	Parsley	parsley, carrots, celery, parsnips, dill, caraway, fennel, poison hemlock, anise
	Mustard	mustard, cabbage, broccoli, kale, cauliflower, brussels sprouts, turnips, horseradish, rutabaga
	Heath	heaths, heather, rhododendrons, mountain laurel, blueberries, huckleberries, cranberries, wintergreen
	Pea	peas, soybeans, lima beans, peanuts, clover, alfalfa, wisteria, sweet peas, black locust, rosewood
	Composite	sunflowers, dandelions, asters, dahlias, marigolds, zinnias, lettuce, artichoke, endive
	Nightshade	potato, tomato, tobacco, eggplant, red pepper, petunia
	Mallow	hollyhock, okra, cotton
	Mint	spearmint, peppermint, lavender, rosemary, thyme, sage
Monocots	Lily	tiger lily, easter lily, lily of the valley, day lily, onion, leek, chive, garlic, asparagus, tulip, crocus
	Grass	rice, wheat, corn, rye, barley, oats, sugar cane, bamboo, buffalo grass, Kentucky bluegrass
	Palm	coconut palm, date palm

Table 31-1. Major Families of Dicots and Monocots.

dicots are much more numerous than monocots. Table 31-1 lists some of the major families of dicots and monocots and representative members of each.

KINGDOM FUNGI

Objectives:
1. Describe the general characteristics of fungi.
2. List the common names of the fungi phyla. State the distinguishing characteristics of each phylum, and name two or three of its members.
3. Describe both asexual and sexual reproduction in the bread mold *Rhizopus*.
4. Describe the structure and growth of a mushroom.
5. Describe the structure of a lichen.

The kingdom **Fungi** includes familiar organisms, such as yeasts, molds, and mushrooms, as well as rusts, smuts, and other less familiar organisms, Fungi are nongreen organisms that absorb needed nutrients from the environment. Most fungi are saprobic, obtaining their nutrients from the remains of dead plants and animals. They secrete digestive enzymes onto the food and then absorb the digested nutrients. The fungi, along with the bacteria, play a key role in decomposing dead organisms and releasing the minerals and other substances they contain for reuse by other organisms. Some fungi are parasitic. They obtain nutrients from the living organisms on which they live.

31-14 General Characteristics of Fungi

Fungi vary greatly in size. Some are microscopic, while others weigh several kilograms. The bodies of most fungi consist of threadlike filaments called **hyphae** (*hy*-fee) (singular, hypha). As the hyphae grow, they frequently branch, eventually forming a tangled mass called a **mycelium** (my-*see*-lee-um) (plural, mycelia). In some fungi, the cytoplasm within the hyphae is not divided by any cell walls. The continuous cytoplasm contains several nuclei. Such hyphae are said to be *multinucleate.* In other fungi, the hyphae are divided by incomplete septa, or cross walls, so that the hyphae are partly compartmentalized, but the cytoplasm is still continuous. Each compartment may contain more than one nucleus. The cell walls of most fungi are composed of chitin, not cellulose. Fungi reproduce both asexually and sexually by means of spores.

Based more or less on the pattern of sexual reproduction that they exhibit, the 80,000 species of fungi are grouped into four phyla. These are the conjugation fungi, the water molds, the sac fungi, and the club fungi. There is also a fifth group, called the *Fungi Imperfecti,* which includes thousands of fungi that cannot be properly classified because their pattern of sexual reproduction is unknown. On the basis of their pattern of asexual reproduction, it is thought that most members of this group are sac fungi.

31-15 Phylum Zygomycota—The Conjugation Fungi

The *conjugation fungi,* phylum **Zygomycota** (zy-goh-my-*kaht*-uh), all produce a special type of thick-walled spore that develops from a zygote during sexual reproduction. Another type of spore is produced asexually. Most of the conjugation fungi are saprobes, but some are parasites on plants, insects, or other fungi. The hyphae of the conjugation fungi lack cross walls, but cross walls do form during the production of gametes and spores. The common bread mold *Rhizopus* is a typical member of this group.

Rhizopus grows on the surface of bread and fruit as a cotton-like mass of filaments (see Figure 31-12). The whitish or grayish mycelium consists of several kinds of hyphae. Root-like hyphae called rhizoids anchor the fungus, secrete digestive enzymes, and absorb nutrients. Other hyphae, called **stolons,** grow in a network over the surface of the food. The stolons give rise to still another type of hyphae that grow up-

ward from the surface of the food. These reproductive hyphae are called *sporangiophores.* At the tip of each sporangiophore, a round spore case, or sporangium, develops. Numerous spores form within each sporangium. At maturity, when the cases open, the spores are released. Those that land in favorable environments germinate and form new mycelia.

Reproduction in bread mold is usually asexual by spore formation. However, under certain conditions, bread molds reproduce sexually by conjugation. The pattern of conjugation is similar to that found in spirogyra, an alga (see page 354).

Conjugation occurs when hyphae of different strains touch. Following contact, the tips of both hyphae enlarge, and cross walls form behind the tips. These partitioned-off ends are now the gamete-producing structures. The two strains of bread mold are called "plus" and "minus." One tip contains several plus nuclei, while the other contains several minus nuclei. At the point of contact, the end walls of the two touching hyphae disintegrate, and the nuclei of opposite strains fuse to form a number of diploid nuclei. A hard wall forms around the nuclei and their associated cytoplasm to produce a thick-walled zygospore, which is resistant to harsh environmental conditions. When conditions become favorable, the zygospore germinates. Only one diploid nucleus remains, and this nucleus undergoes meiosis. Meiosis produces four nuclei, three of which degenerate. The remaining haploid nucleus gives rise to a sporangiophore, which in turn produces spores asexually.

Figure 31-12. Life Cycle of Bread Mold. The bread mold *Rhizopus* can be found growing on the surfaces of bread and fruit.

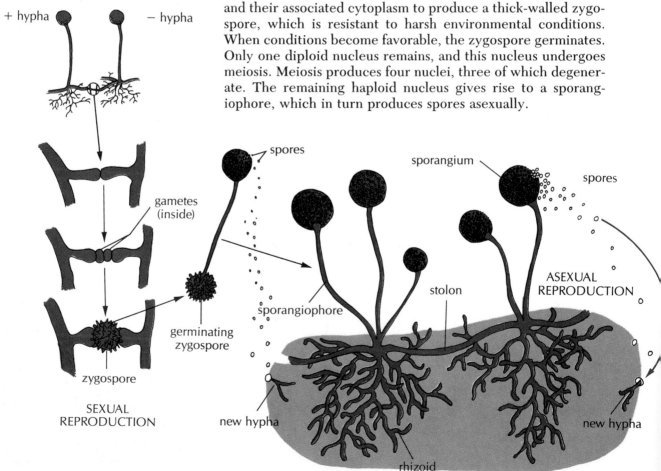

31-16   Phylum Oomycota—The Water Molds

The *water molds*, members of the phylum **Oomycota** (*oh*-uh-my-*kaht*-uh), are mostly aquatic saprobes, but a few are parasites of fish. Also, a few species are parasites of land plants and cause severe economic damage. The most damaging of the water molds has been the *late blight fungus*, which destroyed the potato crops of Ireland from 1845 to 1847. The resulting famine caused about 750,000 deaths and the emigration of about half the population of the country. Downy mildew of grapes and beets is also caused by water molds.

The water molds differ from other fungi in several basic ways. They are the only group with motile, flagellated spores. They are the only group in which the male and female gametes are structurally different. The male gametes are sperm, and the female gametes are eggs. Unlike the other fungi, the cell walls of the water molds contain cellulose, not chitin. In most species, the hyphae have no cellular partitions. And finally, in the life cycle of water molds, it is the diploid stage that is prominent.

31-17   Phylum Ascomycota—The Sac Fungi

The *sac fungi,* phylum **Ascomycota** (*as*-koh-my-*kaht*-uh) are the largest group of fungi. Included in the sac fungi are cup fungi, powdery mildews, morels, truffles, blue and green molds, and yeasts.

Sac fungi produce two kinds of spores, each of which can give rise to new organisms under the proper conditions. Spores produced as a result of sexual reproduction are called *ascospores*. Usually eight, but occasionally four, ascospores develop inside a saclike *ascus*, which serves as a sporangium. Spores produced asexually are called *conidia*. Conidia are formed in chains at the tips of specialized reproductive hyphae called *conidiophores*.

Except for the yeasts, which are unicellular, the sac fungi are multicellular. Hyphae of multicellular sac fungi are divided by cross walls. Holes in the cross walls permit cytoplasm and nuclei to move from one compartment of the hypha to the next. Each compartment has one to several nuclei.

The cup fungi are saprobic and grow on dead organic matter (see Figure 31-13). The visible portion of the fungus is the cup-shaped *fruiting body*, which contains the spore-bearing sacs, or *asci*. However, beneath the surface of the soil is a large mycelium made up of many hyphae.

The unicellular yeasts are not typical of the Ascomycota. Yeasts reproduce by budding and also by spore formation (see page 339). In spore formation, the yeast cell itself functions as an ascus. Yeasts are economically important because they are used in the manufacture of alcohol, alcoholic beverages, and breads.

Some Ascomycota cause plant diseases, including Dutch

Figure 31-13.   Cup Fungi. Cup fungi grow on decaying organic matter.

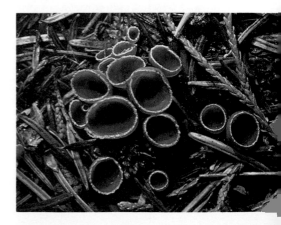

Figure 31-14.   A Morel.

Figure 31-15.   A Mushroom of the Genus *Russula*.

elm disease, chestnut blight, and ergot. Ergot is a disease of wheat and rye caused by a parasitic species. Ergot poisoning results from eating flour made from infected plants. Modern methods of flour production have eliminated this problem.

Truffles and morels are ascomycetes that are edible and are considered great delicacies. Truffles grow several centimeters below the surface of the soil. They are spherical, brown fruiting bodies that range from about 1 to 7 centimeters in diameter. In France, where truffles have been used in cooking for many hundreds of years, pigs and dogs are trained to locate them by their odor. Morels, which are also known as sponge or honeycomb fungi, are common in many areas of the United States. The stem and distinctive cap are the fruiting body (see Figure 31-14). The asci are located within the folds of the cap.

31-18   Phylum Basidiomycota—The Club Fungi

The *club fungi*, phylum **Basidiomycota** (buh-*sid*-ee-uh-my-*kaht*-uh), include most of the large and prominent fungi seen in fields and woods. Mushrooms, toadstools, bracket fungi puffballs, and various parasites, such as rusts and smuts, are club fungi (see Figure 31-15).

In the club fungi, sexual reproduction involves the production of spores called *basidiospores*. These spores are formed in an enlarged, club-shaped reproductive structure, the *basidium*, at the end of a specialized hypha. Some club fungi also produce spores asexually. As in the Ascomycota, the hyphae of the Basidiomycota are divided by incomplete cross walls. The cells of the hyphae may contain one or two nuclei.

The most familiar of the club fungi are the mushrooms. The mushroom is actually a fruiting body, the spore-producing part of the fungus. The main part of the mycelium grows beneath the surface of the ground, living as a saprobe on the remains of plant and animal matter. The mycelium may live for many years, slowly growing through the soil. Only when growing conditions are favorable do mushrooms grow up above the surface.

A mushroom consists of a stalk, or *stipe*, and a *cap* (see Figure 31-16). Mushrooms begin to develop on the underground mycelium as small knobs. As the cap pushes up through the soil, it is kept closed and protected by a thin membrane that connects the edges of the cap to the stalk. Once above ground, the membrane breaks, and the cap expands. The part of the membrane that remains attached to the stalk is called the *annulus*.

The undersurface of the cap contains many *gills*, which radiate out from the center of the stalk like wheel spokes. Each gill consists of many hyphae that are pressed closely together. On the sides of the gills are the basidia, each bearing four basidiospores. One mushroom can produce over one billion spores.

Many types of mushrooms are edible, but others are extremely poisonous. It takes an expert to distinguish between the edible and poisonous species. Never eat mushrooms that you find growing in the wild.

Rusts are club fungi that produce rust-colored spores during one phase of their life cycle. Rusts are parasites on wheat, barley, oats, and other crop plants. Each year they cause millions of dollars worth of damage to these crops. Smuts are similar to rusts. Their name refers to the black and dusty-looking mass of spores that they form within the tissues of the host plant. Smuts attack corn, wheat, oats, barley, and rye.

31-19   Lichens

A **lichen** (*ly*-ken) is made up of two types of organisms—an alga and a fungus—living together. The algal cells are embedded within the mycelium of the fungus. The fungus is usually a sac fungus, while the alga may be a green alga or a blue-green alga. Through photosynthesis, the alga provides nutrients for the fungus. The fungus provides the alga with water, essential elements, and protection from intense light and dryness. Lichens reproduce when fragments of existing lichens break off, blow away, and start growing independently.

Some lichens are crustlike and resemble spots of paint; some are flat, but curled at the edges like leaves; and some are shrublike and have branches (see Figure 31-17). Lichens grow on the bark of trees, on rocks, and on soil. They are very hardy organisms and can exist for months without water. In Arctic regions they serve as food for caribou, musk ox, and other animals. Lichens are usually the first organisms to grow on bare rock. They gradually break the rock down, beginning the process of soil formation.

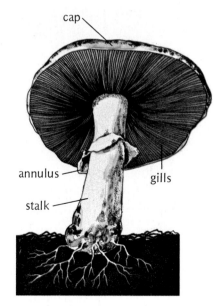

Figure 31-16.   Structure of a Mushroom.

Figure 31-17.   Lichens.

Chapter Review

SUMMARY

- The green algae include both unicellular and multicellular forms. Members of this group contain chlorophyll in chloroplasts and have cell walls composed of cellulose. It is thought that the higher plants evolved from the green algae. Most common seaweeds are either brown algae or red algae. All red and brown algae are multicellular.

- The bryophytes are land plants that lack vascular tissues. They are generally small and grow where moisture is abundant. Tracheophytes are vascular plants. They are divided into two groups, the spore-bearing tracheophytes and the seed-bearing plants.

- Most fungi consist of a tangled mass of hyphae that form a mycelium. In most, the cell walls are composed of chitin. The fungi can reproduce both asexually and sexually. Many fungi are saprobes, and others are parasites.

KNOW THE TERMS

Ascomycota	cycad	lichen	Tracheophyta
Basidiomycota	fern	mycelium	whisk fern
Bryophyta	Fungi	Oomycota	Zygomycota
Chlorophyta	gingko	Phaeophyta	
club moss	horsetail	Rhodophyta	
conifer	hypha	stolon	

SECTION QUESTIONS

Kingdom Plantae—The Plants

1. From what group of algae did the land plants probably arise?
2. List the three levels of complexity found in green algae.
3. List two economically valuable substances produced by red algae.
4. Name three kinds of bryophytes.
5. Name two tissues that are common to all vascular plants.
6. How are materials transported in mosses?
7. List four spore-bearing tracheophytes.
8. Name three groups of gymnosperms.

Kingdom Fungi

9. List the four major phyla in the kingdom Fungi.
10. What two organisms make up lichens?

KNOW THE FACTS

Copy the numbers of each statement below on a sheet of paper. Beside each number, write whether the statement is true or false. If the statement is false, replace the italicized word(s) with a term that will make the statement true.

1. Brown and red algae are frequently found attached to *rocks*.
2. Mosses absorb minerals and water with structures called *roots*.
3. Club mosses and horsetails produce spores in structures termed *fiddleheads*.
4. Some tropical ferns may be *15 meters* high.
5. Seeds of angiosperms are enclosed in *cones*.
6. The seeds of *cycads* are found in cones.
7. The reproductive organ of the angiosperms is the *strobilus*.
8. Fungi are composed of threadlike filaments of cells called *hyphae*.
9. Fungi are grouped into phyla based on their pattern of *asexual* reproduction.
10. Mushrooms are *spore-producing* fungi.

UNDERSTAND THE CONCEPTS

11. What problems exist for land plants that do not exist for aquatic plants?
12. Describe the structure of *Chlamydomonas*.
13. Compare the general characteristics of red and brown algae.
14. Discuss the general characteristics of the bryophytes.
15. Discuss the general characteristics of the tracheophytes.
16. Discuss reproduction in ferns.
17. What are the basic features of conifers?
18. Name the two major groups into which the angiosperms are divided, and explain the significance of the names.
19. Discuss the general structure of fungi.
20. In what ways do the water molds differ from other types of fungi?
21. Describe the structure of a mushroom.
22. What important role do lichens play in nature?

THINK CRITICALLY

23. Compare the way bryophytes, tracheophytes, and fungi obtain nutrients and water.
24. Why are green, red, and brown algae classified in the plant kingdom rather than with the other algae in the kingdom Protista?
25. Would you expect to find bryophytes in a dry environment? Explain your answer.
26. Land plants face conditions that are different from those faced by aqueous plants. What are these conditions? How have land plants adapted to them?

THINK CREATIVELY

27. The antibiotic penicillin is a natural secretion of a certain kind of fungus, a green mold called *penicillium*. Penicillin kills bacteria. Propose a possible explanation for why molds have evolved a way to kill bacteria.
28. Many plants discussed in this chapter contain pigments in addition to chlorophyll. Red algae, for example, contain certain pigments not present in other algae. Red algae also live at depths in the ocean where other algae could not survive. Using your knowledge of the function of chlorophyll, propose some possible explanations why red algae can live at these greater depths.

FOR FURTHER INVESTIGATION

1. Collect examples of several major plant groups. Take the entire plant, if possible. Dry the samples as directed by your teacher and mount them on white paper. Add information about the plant.
2. Add 3 teaspoons of soil to 50 mL of water in a small flask. Place the flask in a window and note whether any algae develop. If so, try to identify them. Repeat the experiment with other soil samples.
3. Prepare a report on one of the career opportunities listed below. See suggested procedures, p. 9, "For Further Investigation" Activity 3.
   a. Mycologist   c. Plant taxonomist
   b. Plant ecologist
4. Outline the life and contributions of one of the following scientists:
   a. Letitia Oberg   c. Heinrich DeBary
   b. James Henderson   d. Esther Lederberg

FOR FURTHER READING

Mohlenbrock, Robert, "Ancient Bristlecone Pine Forest, California," *Natural History*, May, 1985.

Picket-Heaps, J., *New Light on the Green Algae* (Carolina Biology Reader), Carolina Biological Supply Co., Burlington, NC, 1982.

Schultz Jack, "Tree Tactics," *Natural History*, May, 1983.

Sharnoff, Sylvia Duran, "Lowly Lichens Offer Beauty—and Food, and Drugs, and Perfume," *Smithsonian*, April, 1984.

Chapter 32
INVERTEBRATES–SPONGES TO MOLLUSKS

This ocean reef is composed of invertebrate animals called corals.

THE ANIMAL KINGDOM

Objectives:
1. Describe the basic characteristics of animals.
2. Explain the difference between vertebrates and invertebrates.
3. Distinguish between radial symmetry and bilateral symmetry.

32-1 Basic Characteristics of Animals

The animal kingdom is the largest of the five kingdoms. Animals are multicellular organisms that must obtain food from the environment. Most have nervous and muscular systems that enable them to move. Most animals reproduce sexually, but some of the simpler forms also reproduce asexually. In some animals the young have the same basic features as the adult, but in others, the young are very different from the adult. In such cases, the young forms are known as **larvae** (*lar*-vee). The larvae undergo a series of developmental changes that produce the adult form.

The branch of biology that deals with the study of animals is called **zoology** (zoh-*ahl*-uh-jee), and scientists that study animals are called zoologists (zoh-*ahl*-uh-jists). Zoologists divide the animal kingdom into about 30 major groups, or *phyla*. The nine largest phyla contain the majority of species, and it is these phyla that we will study. On the basis of the presence or absence of a backbone, animals are divided into two groups—**vertebrates,** animals with backbones, and **invertebrates,** animals without backbones.

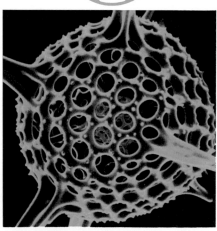

Figure 32-1. Spherical Symmetry. In spherical symmetry, any cut passing through the center of the sphere divides the organism into two equal parts. A radiolarian skeleton shows spherical symmetry.

32-2 Symmetry

The bodies of most animals show *symmetry* (*sim*-uh-tree). This means that the body can be cut into two halves that have matching shapes. A few organisms, including amebas and most sponges, are *asymmetrical* (ay-suh-*meh*-trih-kul)—that is, there is no way that the organism can be cut into two matching halves.

There are different kinds of symmetry. **Spherical symmetry** is found in a few protists. These organisms are in the shape of a sphere, and any cut passing through the center of the sphere divides the organism into matching halves (see Figure 32-1).

In **radial** (*rayd*-ee-ul) **symmetry,** there is a central line, or axis, running the length of the animal from top to bottom or from front to rear. Any cross section at right angles to the central axis shows repeating structures arranged around the center like spokes in a wheel (see Figure 32-2). Cross sections at different levels are not alike, but any lengthwise cut down the center divides the animal into matching halves. The hydra shows radial symmetry. One end of the animal has a mouth and tentacles. The other end is closed and rounded. But any lengthwise cut down the center divides the animal into matching halves, like the halves of a vase. Animals showing radial symmetry are generally either sessile or they drift with the water currents.

In **bilateral** (by-*lat*-uh-rul) **symmetry,** the organism varies both from top to bottom and from front to back (see Figure 32-3). The human body shows bilateral symmetry. In this type of symmetry, there is only one way to cut the body into two symmetrical halves. Each half is a mirror image of the other. Bilaterally symmetrical animals have fixed right and left sides. There are special terms that describe other positions on bilaterally symmetrical animals. **Dorsal** (*dor*-sul) refers to the upper side or the back of the animal; **ventral** (*ven*-trul) is the lower or belly side of the animal. The front or head end of the animal is **anterior,** while the rear or tail end is **posterior.**

Figure 32-2. Radial Symmetry. An adult starfish shows radial symmetry.

Figure 32-3. Bilateral Symmetry. Frogs, like humans, show bilateral symmetry. There is only one way to cut the organism into two symmetrical halves.

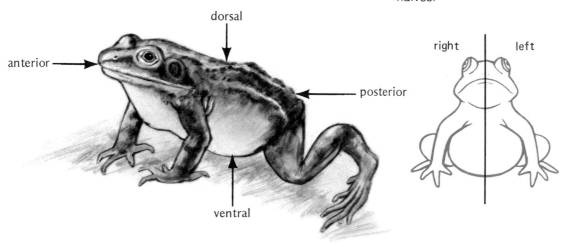

Figure 32-4. Sponges. Sponges are the simplest multicellular animals.

PHYLUM PORIFERA—THE SPONGES

Objectives:
1. Name the phylum to which sponges belong.
2. Describe the general structure of a sponge.
3. Explain how the following life processes are carried out in the sponge: nutrition, excretion, respiration, and reproduction.

32-3   General Characteristics

The *sponges*, phylum **Porifera** (puh-*rif*-uh-ruh), are the simplest multicellular animals. *Porifera* means "pore bearing." Sponges are pierced by many **pores,** or holes, through which water moves continuously. All sponges are aquatic. Most are found in salt water, but a few live in fresh water. Although the larvae are free swimming, adult sponges are *sessile*—that is, they live attached to something, usually shells or rocks on the ocean floor. Some sponges are found in clusters, or *colonies.* Some colonies look like plants, with individuals branching from a common stem. Other sponges live singly.

Members of this group vary widely in size and shape. Most are asymmetrical. Some are the size of a pearl, while others are the size of a bathtub. Simple sponges are shaped like a hollow, upright cylinder or vase. More complex sponges have folds in the body walls, while still others have complex systems of canals and chambers within the body walls. Many sponges are gray or black, but others are bright red, yellow, orange, or blue (see Figure 32-4).

32-4   Structure and Life Functions

Sponges have a simple level of organization. Although their cells show specialization and are present in layers, they do not form true tissues. The sponge body is composed of three layers (see Figure 32-5). The outer layer, which consists of thin, flat cells, is pierced by numerous pores. These pores allow water, dissolved oxygen, and food particles (microscopic plants and animals) to enter the sponge. The inner layer, which lines the central cavity, contains specialized cells called **collar cells.** These cells have a collar of cytoplasm that extends out from the cell into the central cavity. Extending out through the collar of each cell is a flagellum.

Between the outer and inner cell layers is a middle layer of jellylike material that contains wandering ameboid cells. Embedded in the jellylike material of many sponges are small skeletal structures called **spicules** (*spik*-yoolz), which are secreted by some of the ameboid cells. Spicules provide support and give shape to the sponge. Sponges are classified according to their chemical makeup. One group of sponges has spicules composed of calcium compounds; another group has spicules composed of silica. The third group has a network of tough, flexible fibers made up of a protein-containing substance called **spongin.** In the past, sponges with spongin skeletons were widely used for household cleaning and as bath sponges.

The pores of the sponge serve as *incurrent openings*, allowing water to enter the body of the sponge. Water is drawn into the sponge and circulated in the central cavity by the beating of the flagella of the collar cells. From the central cavity, water passes out of the sponge through the osculum. The **osculum** (*ahs*-kyoo-lum) is a large opening at the top (unattached end) of the sponge, which serves as the *excurrent opening*.

As water passes through the sponge, food particles are captured, ingested, and digested by the collar cells. Some partly digested food is picked up from the collar cells by the ameboid cells of the middle layer. Digestion is completed in the ameboid cells, which then carry the nutrients to other parts of the sponge.

Wastes diffuse out of the cells into the central cavity of the sponge and leave with the water through the osculum. Gases are exchanged by diffusion between the cells and the water. Although sponges have no specialized nerve or muscle cells, some of the cells surrounding the incurrent pores respond to harmful substances in the water by closing the pores.

Sponges can reproduce sexually or asexually. In sexual reproduction, both male and female gametes are formed in the same sponge. However, self-fertilization does not occur. Mature sperm leave the sponge through the osculum, and are drawn into other sponges through their pores. The eggs are found in the jellylike middle layer. After fertilization, the zy-

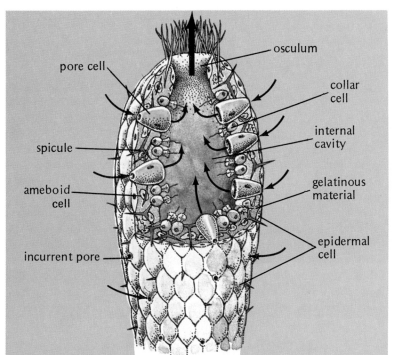

Figure 32-5. Structure of a Sponge. There is a constant flow of water through the body of the sponge. It enters through the pores and leaves through the osculum.

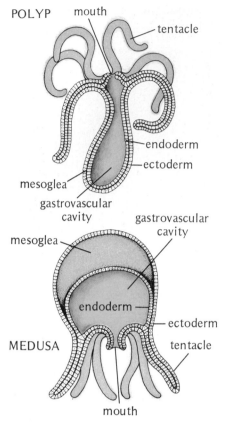

POLYP
mouth
tentacle
endoderm
ectoderm
mesoglea
gastrovascular cavity

mesoglea
gastrovascular cavity
endoderm
ectoderm
MEDUSA
tentacle
mouth

Figure 32-6. Body Forms of Coelenterates. The polyp form (top) is found in hydra. The medusa form (bottom) is commonly seen in jellyfish.

gote begins cleavage. However, the stages of embryonie development in sponges are unlike those of any other animal. Eventually, a free-swimming larva develops. The larva passes through the inner cell layer and leaves the mother sponge through the osculum. After a time the larva becomes attached to the ocean floor and develops into an adult sponge.

Asexual reproduction usually occurs by budding. Groups of cells on the parent sponge divide to form buds. The buds eventually break off and grow into new individuals. When unfavorable conditions arise, some freshwater sponges form reproductive structures called **gemmules** (*jem*-yoolz). The gemmule consists of a group of cells enclosed by a tough outer covering. When conditions again become favorable, each gemmule develops into a new sponge. Sponges also have a remarkable capacity for regeneration. They can be cut up into small pieces, and each piece will grow into a new sponge.

PHYLUM COELENTERATA—HYDRAS, JELLYFISH, AND CORALS

Objectives:
1. Name some representative animals of the phylum Coelenterata.
2. Describe the two body forms found among coelenterates and name a coelenterate showing each body form.
3. Describe the structure and life functions of the coelenterates.
4. Describe the life cycle of *Aurelia*.

32-5 General Characteristics

The *coelenterates* (suh-*lent*-uh-rayts), phylum **Coelenterata** (suh-*lent*-uh-rah-tuh), show a more complex level of organization than the sponges. This phylum includes hydras, jellyfish, corals, and sea anemones (uh-*nem*-uh-neez). Coelenterates are aquatic. Hydras live in fresh water, but most other coelenterates are marine. There are two general body forms found among the coelenterates (see Figure 32-6). The **polyp** (*pahl*-ip) form is usually sessile and has a cylindrical body with a mouth and tentacles at the upper free end. Corals and hydras are examples of polyps. The other form, the **medusa** (muh-*doo*-suh), is shaped like an upside-down bowl, with the mouth and tentacles facing downward. The medusa is usually free swimming. Jellyfish show the medusa body form. Although the two body forms look different, they possess the same basic structure —a hollow sac with a single opening, the mouth, surrounded by tentacles. Most adult coelenterates show radial symmetry.

32-6   Structure and Life Functions

The coelenterates show a tissue level of organization. There are two cell layers, the ectoderm and endoderm, which are separated by a jellylike material composed largely of protein called the **mesoglea** (mez-uh-*glee*-uh). In the medusa forms, the mesoglea makes up most of the body wall. The ectoderm cells contain contractile fibers. Movement is acccomplished by contraction of these fibers. However, for the medusas, the free-swimming forms, the strength of these contractions is not great enough to overcome the movement of the water. Thus, medusas drift with currents in the water.

Specialized stinging cells called **cnidoblasts** (*nyed*-uh-blasts) are characteristic of coelenterates. They are used for defense and capturing food. Within the cnidoblasts are **nematocysts,** (*nem*-uh-tuh-sists), which are small, fluid-filled capsules containing a coiled thread. When a cnidoblast on a tentacle is stimulated by pressure, the nematocyst is discharged. The thread uncoils and entangles the prey. Some nematocysts contain poison, which is injected into the prey and paralyzes it. Once the prey is captured, the tentacles stuff it into the mouth. The structure and function of cnidoblasts in the hydra are discussed on page 130.

The internal body cavity of coelenterates is called the **gastrovascular cavity.** Its single opening serves as both a mouth and an anus. Extracellular digestion takes place in the cavity. This is accomplished by enzymes secreted into the cavity by some of the cells of the endoderm. When the food is partially digested, it is engulfed by the endoderm cells, where digestion is completed within food vacuoles. Thus digestion is both extracellular and intracellular.

No respiratory or excretory system is found in coelenterates. Oxygen is obtained and wastes are excreted by diffusion. The first true nerve cells are found in the coelenterates. The nerve cells form a *nerve net* that sends impulses in all directions. There is no brain in these animals, but the movement of the tentacles shows coordination.

32-7   Corals

Many of the structures and life functions of polyps are described in the sections on the hydra in Unit 2. *Corals* (*kor*-ulz) are small polyps that grow in colonies (see Figure 32-7). Corals are surrounded by a hard, calcium-containing skeleton, which they secrete. In warm, shallow parts of the ocean, islands and large coral reefs are formed by massive colonies of corals.

32-8   Life Cycle of *Aurelia*

Aurelia (or-*eel*-yuh) is a common jellyfish. Its life cycle includes both medusa and polyp forms (see Figure 32-8). The jellylike body of the medusa is the form commonly seen on

Figure 32-7.   Corals. Corals are small polyps that grow in colonies. Unlike hydras, they are surrounded by a hard skeleton.

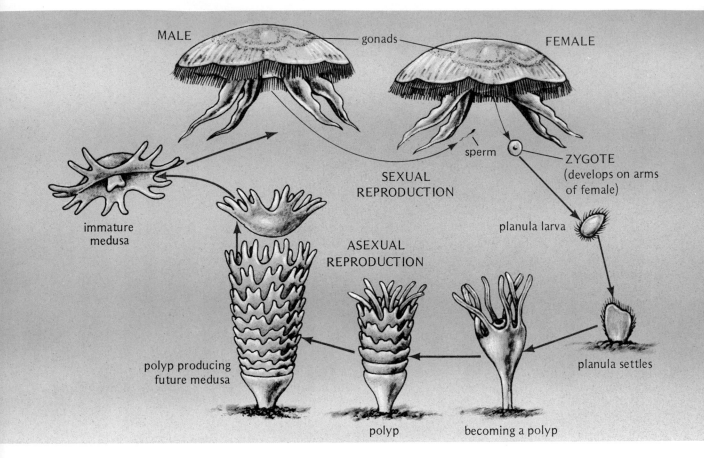

MALE — gonads — FEMALE

sperm

ZYGOTE
(develops on arms
of female)

SEXUAL
REPRODUCTION

planula larva

immature
medusa

ASEXUAL
REPRODUCTION

polyp producing
future medusa

planula settles

polyp   becoming a polyp

Figure 32-8.   Life Cycle of *Aurelia*.

beaches. Protective tentacles hang from the edge of the um-
brellalike body. The sexes are separate in *Aurelia*, but the
male and female look alike. Sperm from the male medusa are
released into the surrounding water. Some sperm cells enter
the gastrovascular cavity of a female medusa, where fertilization occurs. Early development occurs while the zygote is
attached to the female. The zygote develops into a small,
oval-shaped, ciliated larva called a **planula** (*plan*-yuh-luh).
The planula is free swimming for some time. It then becomes
attached by one end to a rock or some other structure on the
ocean floor. The larva develops a mouth and tentacles at the
unattached end and becomes a polyp. The polyp grows, eventually reproducing asexually to form medusas. This occurs in
the fall and winter, when a series of horizontal divisions make
the polyp look like a stack of saucers. One by one, the saucer-
shaped structures break off from the top and grow into full-
sized medusas.

The alternation of the medusa form with the polyp form is
characteristic of some coelenterates. The medusa stage reproduces sexually by the production of eggs and sperm, and it
gives rise to the polyp stage. The polyp stage reproduces
asexually by budding and gives rise to the medusa stage.

PHYLUM PLATYHELMINTHES—THE FLATWORMS

Objectives:
1. Name the phylum to which flatworms belong, and name a representative animal from each of the three classes of flatworms.
2. Describe the digestive, excretory, and nervous systems in planaria.
3. Explain how reproduction occurs in planaria.
4. Describe the structure and life cycle of a blood fluke.
5. Describe the structure and life cycle of a tapeworm.

32-9   General Characteristics

The *flatworms*, phylum **Platyhelminthes** (plat-ee-hel-*min*-theez), are the simplest animals showing bilateral symmetry. In addition, the flatworms are the simplest invertebrate group showing definite head and tail regions. These animals are called flatworms because their bodies are flattened. There are three major groups of flatworms—free-living flatworms, such as planaria (pluh-*nehr*-ee-uh); parasitic flukes; and parasitic tapeworms. Free-living flatworms are usually aquatic, and are found in both fresh and salt water.

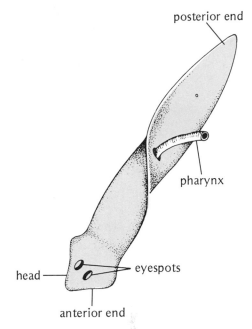

Figure 32-9.   Planaria.

32-10   Structure and Life Functions

The body of the flatworm is composed of three distinct tissue layers—ectoderm, mesoderm, and endoderm. These tissues are organized into organs and organ systems. Thus, the flatworms are also the simplest animals showing organ and organ system levels of organization.

Planaria. We will use *planaria*, class Turbellaria (ter-buh-*lehr*-ee-uh), as an example of a typical flatworm.

Planaria are found in freshwater streams and ponds, where they cling to the bottoms of leaves, rocks, and logs. These animals are gray, brown, or black in color and about 5 to 25 millimeters in length (see Figure 32-9). The triangular head contains a pair of *eyespots*. Although the eyes cannot actually detect images, they are sensitive to light, which the animal avoids.

Planaria can move about freely, and a piece of liver placed in a stream will be covered with them in a few hours. Moving planaria appear to be gliding over a surface because the underside of the body is covered with microscopic cilia that propel the animal. Muscles enable them to change their shape or their direction of movement.

The planarian has a digestive system consisting of a mouth, pharynx, and a highly branched intestine (see Figure 32-10). The muscular **pharynx** is a tube that can be extended through the mouth opening for eating. The mouth is located at the

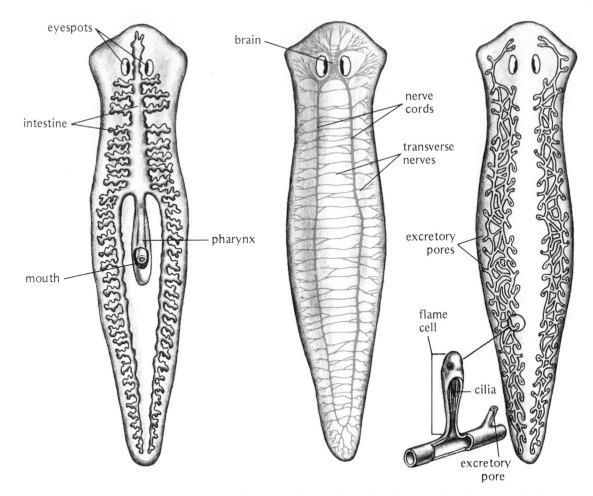

Figure 32-10.   Internal Structure of a Planarian.

midline on the underside of the body. Planaria feed on living or dead small animals. The pharynx can suck small bits of food into the digestive cavity. The intestine is highly branched. Most digestion takes place within food vacuoles in the cells lining the intestine. Digested food diffuses to all cells of the body. Indigestible materials are expelled through the pharynx and mouth.

Planaria have no skeletal, circulatory, or respiratory system. Oxygen and carbon dioxide simply diffuse into and out of individual cells. However, they do have an excretory system consisting of a series of tubules that run the length of the body. Side branches of the tubules have cells called *flame cells* that remove excess water and liquid wastes from the body and pass them into ducts. The contents of the ducts pass out of the worm through small *excretory pores* on the dorsal surface.

The nervous system includes a small brain beneath the eyespots. From the brain, two nerve cords run the length of the body along either side. Connecting transverse nerves make the nervous system look like a ladder. This ladderlike nervous system enables the planarian to respond to stimuli in a coordinated manner.

Planaria have a well-developed reproductive system. Although they are hermaphroditic, self-fertilization does not occur. Instead, two planaria mate and exchange sperm. Fertilization is internal, and a short time later, the fertilized eggs are shed in capsules. In a few weeks, the eggs hatch into tiny worms, which grow into adults. The planarian can regenerate an entire animal from a fairly small segment. It can also reproduce asexually by fission, separating its tail end from its head end. Each half regenerates the missing structures.

Flukes. *Flukes* are parasitic flatworms of the class Trematoda (trem-uh-*tohd*-uh). The body of the fluke is covered by a thick cuticle that protects the parasite from the enzymes of its host. Flukes have suckers by which they attach themselves to the tissues of their host. They do not need a well-developed digestive system because the food obtained from the host has already been broken down.

The blood fluke is a typical fluke. In humans, this parasite causes a disease called *schistosomiasis* (shis-tuh-soh-*my*-uh-sis). The adult fluke is about 1 centimeter long and lives in the blood vessels of the human intestine (see Figure 32-11). Here it lays thousands of eggs that pass out of the body with digestive wastes. If the eggs land in water, they hatch into free-swimming larvae. They then enter the bodies of snails, where they reproduce asexually. The new individuals leave the snails and infect streams, rice paddies, and irrigation ditches. Upon contact with humans, the flukes bore through the skin and start

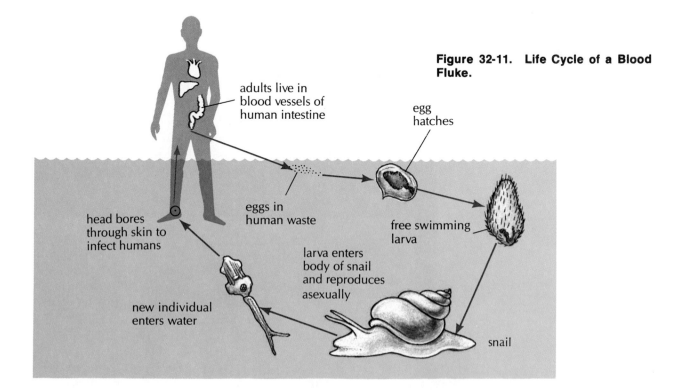

Figure 32-11.   Life Cycle of a Blood Fluke.

adults live in blood vessels of human intestine

egg hatches

eggs in human waste

free swimming larva

head bores through skin to infect humans

larva enters body of snail and reproduces asexually

new individual enters water

snail

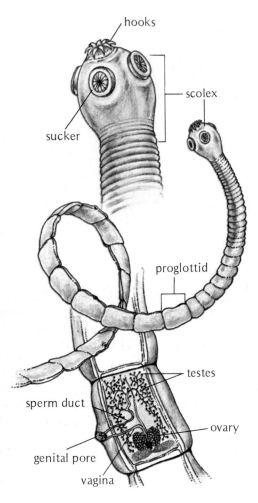

hooks

scolex

sucker

proglottid

testes

sperm duct

ovary

genital pore

vagina

Figure 32-12. Structure of a Tape-worm.

their reproductive cycle again. The blood fluke causes loss of blood, diarrhea, and much pain.

Tapeworms. *Tapeworms* are parasitic flatworms of the class Cestoda (ses-*tohd*-uh). The beef tapeworm, which can infect humans, is a long, ribbonlike flatworm (see Figure 32-12). Adults may be from 4 to 9 meters in length. These worms have excretory and nervous systems and a highly developed reproductive system. They lack a mouth and digestive system. Tapeworms live as parasites in the intestine, and absorb digested food through their skin. The suckers on the knoblike head, or *scolex* (*skoh*-leks), hold the tapeworm in place. Some tapeworms, such as the human pork tapeworm, have hooks as well as suckers.

Below the head and neck are square body segments called **proglottids** (proh-*glaht*-idz). These segments are produced continuously by budding from the neck region. Essentially, proglottids are reproductive structures, producing both sperm and eggs. Periodically, the end segments, filled with over 100,000 fertilized eggs, break off and pass out of the host in the feces. If cattle eat food contaminated with eggs, the eggs develop into larvae in the intestine. The larvae burrow into blood vessels and are carried to the muscle, where they form a dormant capsule.

Humans can become infected when they eat undercooked beef. The capsule surrounding the larva is digested, releasing the small tapeworm. The tapeworm then attaches itself to the wall of the human intestine, and the cycle begins again. Human tapeworms cause illness by absorbing needed nutrients, and may actually obstruct the passage of food through the intestine.

PHYLUM NEMATODA—THE ROUNDWORMS

Objectives:
1. Describe the general characteristics of nematodes.
2. Describe the life cycles of the following roundworms and how they affect humans: trichina, filaria, pinworm, and hookworm.

32-11   General Characteristics

The phylum **Nematoda** (nem-uh-*tohd*-uh) consists of slender, bilaterally symmetrical *roundworms.* Their elongated, cylindrical bodies are tapered at both ends and are covered by a tough cuticle. Roundworms range in length from less than 1 millimeter to more than a meter. Many roundworms are free living, while others are parasitic. The free-living forms are found in fresh water, salt water, and in soil. They feed on algae, plant sap, and decaying organic matter. The parasitic forms live on or in most kinds of plants and animals. The actual number of roundworms present in the environment is tremendous. It has been estimated that a million or more *nematodes* (*nem*-uh-tohdz) are present in one shovel load of garden soil.

32-12 Structure and Life Functions

Roundworms, unlike flatworms, have two openings to their tubular digestive system. Food is taken in through the mouth at the anterior end, and undigested material passes out through the *anus* at the posterior end. Roundworms are the simplest animals having a complete digestive system with two openings and a tube-within-a-tube body plan.

Nematodes have no circulatory or respiratory system. They do have a simple excretory system as well as a nervous system. Well-developed muscles located in the body wall enable nematodes to move in a characteristic whiplike fashion.

Nematodes have well-developed reproductive systems. The sexes are separate, and fertilization occurs within the body of the female. In free-living forms the fertilized eggs, which are surrounded by a thick shell, are deposited in soil. The newly hatched young resemble the adults.

32-13 Parasitic Roundworms of Humans

Trichina, filaria, pinworm, and hookworm are parasitic roundworms that infect humans.

Trichina (trih-*ky*-nuh) is the nematode that causes *trichinosis* (trik-uh-*noh*-sis) in humans. Adult trichina worms live in the intestines of hogs (see Figure 32-13). When these worms reproduce, the resulting larvae invade the muscles of the hog. They grow to about 1 millimeter in length, and then curl up and become enclosed in hard cysts. When pork that

Figure 32-13.   Life Cycle of *Trichina.*

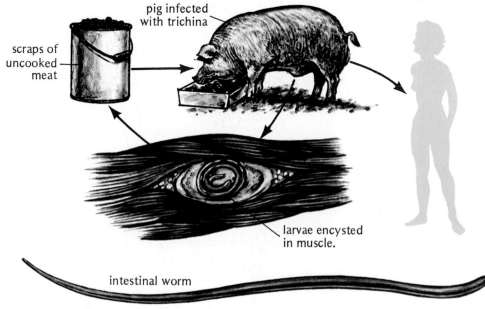

scraps of uncooked meat

pig infected with trichina

larvae encysted in muscle.

intestinal worm

Raccoons—Risky Neighbors

The raccoon, a charming if pesky neighborhood wild animal, poses a disease threat to humans. In addition to rabies, which is epidemic among raccoons in parts of North America, these animals may carry an intestinal roundworm that can infect humans. This parasite, *Baylisascaris procyonis,* has caused fatal infections in other wildlife and in a small number of children.

The roundworm's eggs, which are excreted in raccoon feces, can remain infective for a long time. Infection in humans, especially in children, can occur when they put contaminated hands or objects into their mouths. The eggs eventually hatch into larvae that migrate to certain body organs, particularly the brain, eyes, and spinal cord.

Doctors recommend that children and pets not be allowed into areas frequented by raccoons. People who must visit such areas should always wash their hands immediately after contact with dirt or waste materials.

has not been cooked well enough to kill the organisms is eaten by a human, digestive enzymes release the larvae from the cysts. The larvae develop into adults in the human intestines and reproduce sexually. The new larvae then move through the blood vessels and muscles just as the larvae did in hogs. The movement of the worms through muscle causes intense pain and can also cause permanent damage to the muscle. Trichinosis can be easily prevented by cooking pork thoroughly. Hogs become infected when they are fed infected scraps of uncooked meat. Because of better sanitary procedures used today for raising hogs, trichinosis is no longer very common.

Filaria (fuh-*lehr*-ee-uh) *worms* cause a disease known as *elephantiasis* (el-uh-fun-*ty*-uh-sis). These worms are carried by a species of mosquito found in tropical and subtropical regions. The worms are spread to humans by the bite of an infected mosquito. In the human body filaria worms invade the lymphatic system, blocking lymph vessels, and causing fluid to accumulate and tissues to swell. The affected area of the body often becomes abnormally enlarged, and the tissues involved become badly damaged. Within the lymph tissues, the worms reproduce sexually, producing larvae that enter the bloodstream. A mosquito becomes infected when it bites an infected person. The larvae mature within the mosquito, and the infection is spread by the bite of the infected mosquito.

Pinworms are one of the more common parasitic roundworms. They are tiny worms most often found in children. Adult pinworms live in the large intestine. The female worms deposit their eggs in the anal region. The presence of the eggs causes itching. When the child scratches, some eggs get on the fingers. Children reinfect themselves when they put their unclean fingers in their mouths. Pinworms live only a few weeks. Thus, if reinfection can be prevented by cleanliness, the pinworms disappear from the intestine within a short time.

Hookworm is a nematode that most commonly infects people in warm climates who walk barefoot on contaminated soil. The hookworm lives in the small intestine, and its eggs leave the body in the feces. When sewage disposal is inadequate, the eggs hatch into larvae on the ground, where people have contact with them. The larvae bore through the skin of bare feet. In the body, they are carried to the lungs by the circulatory system. They bore through the lungs, are coughed up, swallowed, and pass again to the small intestine, where they suck blood from the intestinal wall. Symptoms of hookworm infection include anemia and lack of energy.

Diseases caused by parasitic worms are widespread, but many can be controlled by good personal hygiene, proper sanitation, and thorough cooking of food. Some drugs are also useful in controlling these parasites.

PHYLUM ANNELIDA—THE SEGMENTED WORMS

Objectives:
1. Describe the general characteristics of members of the phylum Annelida.
2. Compare and contrast the structure of the marine worm *Nereis* with that of the earthworm.
3. Explain how leeches obtain food.

32-14 General Characteristics

The most familiar of the worms are those of the phylum **Annelida** (uh-*nel*-uh-duh), the *segmented worms.* This phylum includes the earthworm, class Oligochaeta (ahl-ig-oh-*keet*-uh), and the leech, class Hirudinea (hir-yuh-*din*-ee-uh). The most striking characteristic of the *annelids* (*an*-uh-lidz) is the division of the body into separate sections, or segments. Segmented worms are found in both salt and fresh water and on land. Most of these worms are free living, but a few are parasites. Annelids range in length from less than 1 millimeter to more than 2 meters.

32-15 Structure and Life Functions

Annelids are bilaterally symmetrical. Their bodies are divided into segments, or *metameres* (*met*-uh-meerz), both externally and internally. This type of segmentation is called *metamerism* (muh-*tam*-uh-riz-um). Annelids are the simplest invertebrates having a closed circulatory system. In addition, like the more complex animals, they have a tube-within-a-tube body plan. The digestive tract, which is lined with endoderm, is the inner tube and is open at both ends—mouth and anus. The body wall makes up the outer tube and is covered with ectoderm. A fluid-filled body cavity is found between the two tubes. This cavity is called a **coelom** (*see*-lum) and is lined with mesoderm (see Figure 32-14).

Nereis. In most ways the structure and life functions of the marine sandworm *Nereis* (*nehr*-ee-is), class Polychaeta (pahl-ee-*keet*-uh), are very similar to those of the earthworm, which were described in Unit 2 on animal maintenance. However, there are a few important differences between these two animals.

Nereis lives at tide level (the intertidal zone) and emerges at night and crawls along the sand or swims in the shallow sea. During the day it stays in a temporary burrow in mud or sand with its head poking out. *Nereis* is green in color and is composed of about 200 similar segments (see Figure 32-15). The first two segments form a distinct head. The first segment, which is called the *prostomium* (proh-*stoh*-mee-um), has two short tentacles, two pairs of small eyes, and two other appendages called *palps*. The second segment, which is called the

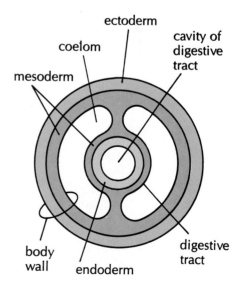

Figure 32-14. The Coelom. The coelom is a fluid-filled cavity found between the inner and outer body tubes of annelids and more complex animals.

**Figure 32-15. Structure of the
Marine Sandworm *Nereis*.**

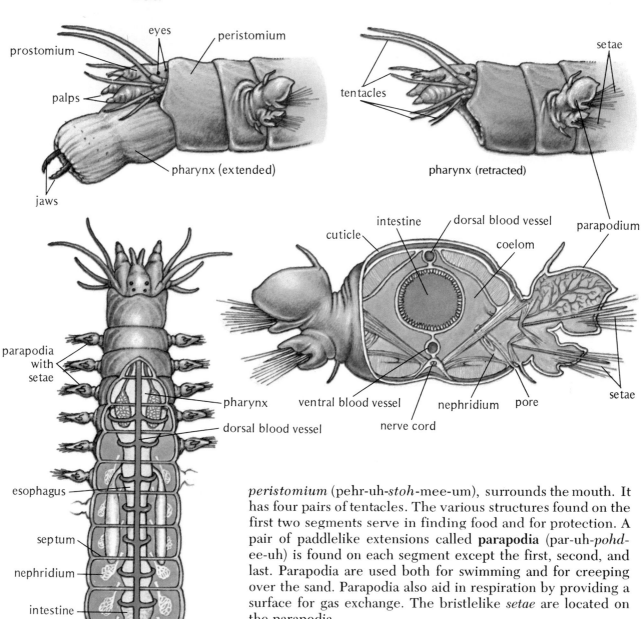

peristomium (pehr-uh-*stoh*-mee-um), surrounds the mouth. It
has four pairs of tentacles. The various structures found on the
first two segments serve in finding food and for protection. A
pair of paddlelike extensions called **parapodia** (par-uh-*pohd*-
ee-uh) is found on each segment except the first, second, and
last. Parapodia are used both for swimming and for creeping
over the sand. Parapodia also aid in respiration by providing a
surface for gas exchange. The bristlelike *setae* are located on
the parapodia.

Nereis eats small animals, which it captures by extending its
pharynx out through its mouth. The pharynx has a pair of hard,
pointed jaws that grasp the food. As the jaws are pulled back
into the mouth, the food is swallowed. The food passes into
the esophagus and then to the intestine, where it is digested.
Undigested food is eliminated through the anus on the last
segment.

Circulation, excretion, and respiration in *Nereis* are basically the same as in the earthworm. The nervous system is also
similar.

In *Nereis*, sexes are separate. During the mating season, eggs and sperm develop in the body cavity, or coelom. Eventually they pass out through the nephridia or break through the body surface into the sea. Fertilization is external, and the zygote develops into a free-swimming, ciliated **trochophore** (*troh*-kuh-for) larva (see Figure 32-16). As the larva develops, the mouth and segments with parapodia appear. Eventually the young worm settles to the ocean bottom and begins the adult mode of life.

Leeches. *Leeches* are mostly freshwater animals that are parasites of vertebrates. Some are found in moist soil. Most live on the blood of their prey (see Figure 32-17). The segmentation characteristic of annelids is not very prominent in leeches. Leeches have suckers at both their anterior and posterior ends. In feeding, the leech attaches itself to its host with its hind sucker. Then it attaches the anterior sucker, which surrounds the mouth and three small jaws. The jaws break through the host's skin. The saliva of the leech contains an enzyme that prevents the host's blood from clotting while it is being sucked up. The leech can ingest many times its own body weight of blood in one feeding. When the leech is full, it drops off the host and remains inactive for long periods, while the blood, which has been stored in the digestive tract, is gradually digested. Leeches are hermaphrodites, but cross fertilization takes place when two leeches exchange sperm. The fertilized eggs develop in water or soil.

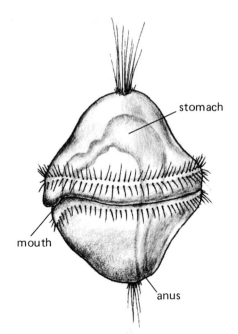

Figure 32-16.   A Trochophore Larva.

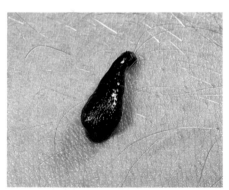

Figure 32-17.   A Leech.

PHYLUM MOLLUSCA—THE MOLLUSKS

Objectives:
1. Name a representative animal from each class of mollusks.
2. Describe the general characteristics of mollusks.
3. Explain the functions of each of the following mollusk structures: the foot, mantle, and radula.
4. Describe respiration, nutrition, circulation, excretion, and reproduction in clams.
5. Describe some of the ways in which gastropods and cephalopods differ from bivalves.

32-16   General Characteristics

The phylum **Mollusca** (mahl-*us*-kuh) is a highly successful animal group. They are the second largest animal phylum, next to the arthropods. Oysters, clams, snails, squids, and octopuses are familiar *mollusks*. Mollusks are found in salt water, in fresh water, and on land. Members of this group vary greatly in size and shape (see Figure 32-18). They range from tiny snails 1 millimeter long to giant squids, which can reach 16 meters in length and weigh 2 tons. The giant clam of the

Figure 32-18. Nudibranch Mollusks.

South Pacific Ocean can be 1.5 meters long and weigh 250 kilograms.

Many types of mollusks are used by humans for food. Among them are oysters, clams, scallops, mussels, snails, squids, and octopuses. Pearls from oysters are used in jewelry, and mother-of-pearl is used in buttons and decorative objects. On the other hand, some snails and slugs feed on crops and are highly destructive.

There are three major classes of mollusks: the class Bivalvia (by-*valv*-ee-uh) includes mollusks with two-part shells, such as clams, oysters, and mussels; the class Gastropoda (ga-*strahp*-uh-duh) includes mollusks with a single shell, such as snails; and the class Cephalopoda (sef-uh-*lahp*-uh-duh) includes mollusks with little or no shell, such as squids and octopuses. Many marine mollusks have a trochophore larva similar to the trochophore larva of marine annelids. This is thought to indicate an evolutionary relationship between the two groups.

32-17   Structure and Life Functions

Although adult mollusks vary widely in appearance, they do share a number of common characteristics. They are bilaterally symmetrical and are composed of three tissue layers. They also have a true coelom. All mollusks have a soft body that houses all the organ systems—the digestive system, heart, nervous system, reproductive system, and so on. The foot, mantle, shell, and radula are structures found only in mollusks.

The large, ventral, muscular **foot** functions in locomotion. In clams, the foot is used to burrow or plow through wet sand or mud. The snail uses its foot to creep over rocks or plants. The foot of the squid and octopus is divided into tentacles and covered with suckers. The tentacles are used for seizing and holding prey.

The **mantle** is a fold of skin that surrounds the body organs. In the squid and octopus, the muscular mantle is used for locomotion. In mollusks with shells, the mantle is a glandular tissue that secretes part of the shell.

The **radula** (*rad*-joo-luh) is a rasping, tonguelike organ found in all mollusks except bivalves. The radula has many rows of teeth and can extend out of the mouth to scrape food from an object and bring it into the digestive system. Some snails use the radula to drill holes in the shells of other mollusks. They then suck out the soft body of the mollusk for food.

The bivalves. Bivalves (*by*-valvz), such as clams, scallops, oysters, and mussels, have a shell made up of two parts. The smooth, shiny, innermost layer of the shell, which is just outside the mantle, is called *mother-of-pearl* (see Figure 32-19). In certain bivalves, pearls are produced when an irritating substance, such as a grain of sand, gets between the mantle

Figure 32-19.   Oyster with Pearl.

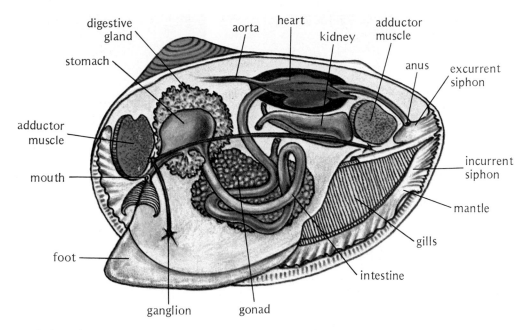

digestive gland

aorta

heart

kidney

adductor muscle

anus

excurrent siphon

stomach

adductor muscle

mouth

incurrent siphon

mantle

gills

foot

intestine

ganglion

gonad

Figure 32-20. Structure of a Clam.

and the shell. The mantle walls off the irritant by secreting layers of mother-of-pearl around it. Eventually, a pearl is formed.

In terms of its life functions, the clam is a typical mollusk. Thus it will be discussed here as representative of the phylum.

The two halves of the clam's shell can be held firmly closed by two strong *adductor* muscles (see Figure 32-20). When the muscles relax, an elastic hinge keeps the shell open. Usually, the shells are partly open with two tubes extending into the water. One tube, the *incurrent siphon* (sy-fun), carries water containing food particles into the mantle cavity. The water is kept in motion by the beating of cilia on the gills. As the water moves over the gills, the exchange of respiratory gases occurs between the blood in the gills and the water. Oxygen diffuses through the gills and into the blood, and carbon dioxide diffuses from the blood into the water. Food particles in the water are trapped by mucus on the gills. The water then flows out of the mantle cavity through the *excurrent siphon.*

Food particles stuck in the mucus on the gills are transported by the cilia into the mouth and then into the rest of the digestive system. Animals that feed by filtering water through their bodies are called *filter feeders.* They feed on organic particles and dead and decaying microscopic organisms in the water.

The clam has an open circulatory system. It consists of a heart and vessels. When the blood reaches the body tissues, it flows out of the vessels and into the body spaces, or *sinuses,* where it bathes the body tissues. From the sinuses, the blood flows into vessels that carry it to the gills. After the exchange of respiratory gases, the blood flows back to the heart.

 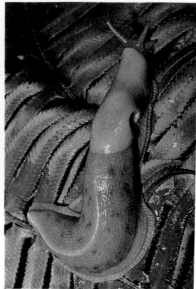

Figure 32-21. Gastropod Mollusks. The garden snails (left) have a single shell, while the slug (right) lacks a shell.

The clam has a pair of kidneys that remove organic wastes from the blood and empty them into the water leaving through the excurrent siphon. The nervous system consists of three pairs of ganglia connected by nerves to the foot and body organs. Sensory cells enable the clam to respond to chemical changes in the water, to touch, and to light.

In clams the sexes are separate. Sperm leave the male through the excurrent siphon. They then enter the female through her incurrent siphon. The eggs are held on the gills, where they are fertilized. The young bivalves pass through one or more distinct larval stages before reaching the adult form.

The gastropods. Snails, whelks, abalones (ab-uh-*loh*-neez), conches (*kahn*-chez), and slugs make up the largest group of mollusks, the **gastropods** (*gas*-truh-pahdz) (see Figure 32-21). Most gastropods have a single shell, which is often coiled. A few, such as the slug, lack a shell. Some are aquatic; some are terrestrial.

The common garden snail has a head with tentacles, eyes, and a mouth (see Figure 32-22). The head is connected to the foot. The shell is on top of the foot. For protection, all soft parts of the body can be drawn into the shell. Land snails have simple lungs rather than gills. Air is drawn into the mantle cavity and gas exchange occurs through the mantle.

Land snails usually travel at night when the air is moist. They slide along on a layer of mucus secreted by the foot. To keep from drying out during the day, the snail generally withdraws into its shell and seals the opening with mucus. The land snail feeds by rubbing its radula against plant material. As the pieces of plant are shredded, they are taken into the mouth.

Figure 32-22. Structure of a Snail.

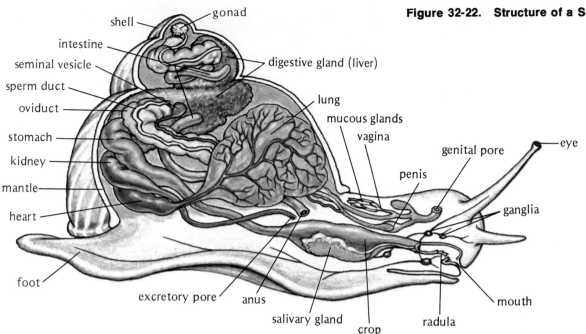

The cephalopods. Squids, octopuses, and cuttlefish are **cephalopods** (*sef*-uh-luh-pahdz). They are very different in appearance from other mollusks (see Figure 32-23). The most obvious difference is that most have either no shell (the octopus) or a small internal shell (the squid and cuttlefish). Only a few, such as the nautilus, are enclosed in a shell.

In cephalopods, the mouth is surrounded by tentacles. The tentacles are used to gather food and manipulate objects. The streamlined bodies of cephalopods are adapted for rapid swimming. They swim by expelling a jet of water from their mantle cavity. They have a well-developed nervous system with a large brain. The eye of the octopus is similar to the eye of vertebrates, and works in the same way. In times of danger, some cephalopods, such as squids and octopuses, discharge an inky fluid. This "smoke screen" distracts the enemy and enables the animal to escape.

Figure 32-23. An Octopus. The octopus has no shell.

Chapter Review

SUMMARY

- The sponges, phylum Porifera, are the simplest multicellular animals. Sponges are pierced by numerous pores through which water containing food and oxygen flows.

- The coelenterates, phylum Coelenterata, are radially symmetrical and have a tissue level of organization.

- The flatworms, phylum Platyhelminthes, are the simplest animals with bilateral symmetry and with definite head and tail regions.

- Roundworms, phylum Nematoda, are bilaterally symmetrical. They are the simplest animals having a complete digestive system.

- The segmented worms, phylum Annelida, are bilaterally symmetrical, and their bodies are divided into segments.

- The mollusks, phylum Mollusca, are bilaterally symmetrical and have three tissue layers.

KNOW THE TERMS

Annelida	gastropod	osculum	radula
anterior	gastrovascular cavity	parapodium	spherical symmetry
bilateral symmetry	gemmule	pharynx	spicule
bivalve	invertebrate	planula	spongin
cephalopod	larva	Platyhelminthes	trochophore
cnidoblast	mantle	polyp	ventral
Coelenterata	medusa	pore	vertebrate
coelom	mesoglea	Porifera	zoology
collar cell	Mollusca	posterior	
dorsal	nematocyst	proglottid	
foot	Nematoda	radial symmetry	

SECTION QUESTIONS

The Animal Kingdom

1. List the three kinds of body symmetry.

Phylum Porifera—The Sponges

2. How does water enter the body of a sponge?
3. What structures provide support to the sponge?

Phylum Coelenterata—Hydras, Jellyfish, and Corals

4. Name four coelenterates.
5. Name the two body forms found in the phylum Coelenterata.

Phylum Platyhelminthes—The Flatworms

6. What type of symmetry do flatworms have?
7. List the three major groups of flatworms.

Phylum Nematoda— The Roundworms

8. Where are roundworms found?
9. List some parasitic roundworms that infect humans.

Phylum Annelida— The Segmented Worms

10. What is the most striking characteristic of the annelids?
11. Where are annelids found?

Phylum Mollusca— The Mollusks

12. Name an organism from each of the three major classes of mollusks.
13. Where are mollusks found?

KNOW THE FACTS

Copy the numbers from Column 1 on a sheet of paper. Select the letter for the term or phrase from Colum 2 that matches each numbered item, and write it beside the number.

Column 1

1. dorsal
2. ventral
3. cnidoblasts
4. flame cell
5. bivalves

Column 2

a. part of the planarian excretory system
b. the upper side or back of the animal
c. stinging cells that contain nematocysts
d. have shells lined with mother-of-pearl
e. the lower or belly side of an animal

UNDERSTAND THE CONCEPTS

6. Compare radial and bilateral symmetry, as applied to the bodies of animals.
7. Briefly describe nutrition, respiration, and excretion in sponges.
8. What are the three layers of a coelenterate body?
9. Outline the life cycle of *Aurelia*.
10. Describe feeding and digestion in planaria.
11. In a brief statement, detail the general structure of roundworms, including symmetry.
12. Describe the body plan of an annelid.
13. Describe the structure and function of the foot, mantle, and radula of mollusks.

THINK CRITICALLY

14. What measure can you take to prevent tapeworm and trichina infections? Why is this measure effective?
15. How are garden snails adapted to life on land? Are they completely adapted? Explain.
16. In the reproduction of most animals, one zygote develops into one organism. In the coelenterate *Aurelia*, one zygote leads to the development of many medusae. Explain.
17. Compare the way adult leeches and flukes are adapted to life as parasites.

THINK CREATIVELY

18. From your knowledge of the life cycle of the blood fluke, propose a method for preventing the infestation of this parasite.
19. In this chapter the phyla are ordered from simple to complex. Discuss what you think are the most important advances in complexity in the progression of these phyla.

FOR FURTHER INVESTIGATION

1. Obtain planaria. Fill a clear glass dish with water. Cover half the dish with cardboard, so that it will be in darkness. Place planaria in the exposed side of the dish. After an hour, in which side of the dish are the planaria? Do these results show positive or negative phototropism?
2. Investigate one of the following careers:
   a. Parasitologist   c. Invertebrate zoologist
   b. Shellfish harvester
3. Outline the life and contributions of one of the following scientists:
   a. Katharine Foot   c. Gloria Hollister
   b. Samuel Nabrit   d. Wendell Stanley

FOR FURTHER READING

Foot, Jeff, "Jellyfish, Sunny Side Up," *Natural History*, February, 1985.

Rotman, Jeff, "Friends and Anemonies," *Natural History*, April, 1985.

Chapter 33

INVERTEBRATES— ARTHROPODS AND ECHINODERMS

The butterfly is a member of the phylum Arthropoda and the class Insecta.

PHYLUM ARTHROPODA

Objectives:
1. List the five classes that make up the phylum Arthropoda.
2. Describe the general characteristics of the arthropods.

33-1 Arthropods—The Most Numerous Animals

The phylum **Arthropoda** (ar-*thrahp*-uh-duh) includes such common animals as flies, bees, beetles, mosquitoes, butterflies, spiders, ants, crabs, lobsters, and shrimp. The *arthropods* are the most biologically successful and abundant of all animal groups. There are more arthropod species than all other species of organisms put together. There are about 400,000 known species of plants and about 250,000 species of animals other than arthropods. But there are more than 1 million known species of arthropods. Arthropods are found in all regions of the earth and are of great importance to humans.

The phylum Arthropoda is divided into five classes. These are Crustacea, Chilopoda, Diplopoda, Arachnida, and Insecta. The characteristics of each class will be described separately later in the chapter.

33-2 General Characteristics of Arthropods

In many ways, arthropods are the most advanced invertebrates. They are bilaterally symmetrical and have a small coelom.

Figure 33-1. A Prawn Molting.

Although the phylum Arthropoda consists of a large number of dissimilar species, all arthropods share a number of common features.

1. Arthropods have jointed legs. The limbs of arthropods are composed of several pieces that are connected together at hinged joints. These joints are controlled by opposing sets of muscles, and they allow much freedom of movement. Different arrangements of these jointed limbs, or appendages, allow such varied functions as crawling, swimming, hopping, jumping, flying, grabbing, digging, and biting.

2. Arthropods have exoskeletons composed of chitin, a carbohydrate, and protein. The tough, lightweight exoskeleton protects the soft body parts within. The exoskeleton is also waterproof and prevents excessive water loss, enabling many arthropods to live successfully on land. Because the exoskeleton is nonelastic and cannot grow, young arthropods must periodically undergo a process called **molting** (see Figure 33-1). During molting, the exoskeleton is shed and replaced by a new, larger one. Growth takes place before the new exoskeleton hardens. Until the new exoskeleton hardens, the young animal is vulnerable, since it is unable to move or defend itself. Therefore, many arthropods hide until their new exoskeleton has hardened.

3. Like annelids, all arthropods are segmented. However, the body segments are usually modified and fused to form specific body regions. In most arthropods, there is a head, **thorax** (*thor*-aks), and **abdomen** (*ab*-duh-men). The head is well developed and is always composed of six segments. It contains a mouth that is specialized for chewing or sucking. The thorax is the middle region of the arthropod, and the abdomen is the posterior region. While the head always con-

tains six segments, the number of segments in the thorax and abdomen varies greatly from one group of arthropods to another.

4. Arthropods have a well-developed nervous system. There is a distinct brain and a ventral nerve cord located beneath the digestive system. Arthropods have a variety of sense organs, including eyes, organs of hearing, sensory cells sensitive to touch, and antennae that are sensitive to touch and chemicals.

5. Arthropods have an open circulatory system. There is a dorsal tubular heart located above the digestive system. Arteries carry blood away from the heart to the body spaces, where it bathes the tissues directly. The blood eventually reenters the heart through openings in it sides.

CLASS CRUSTACEA—THE CRUSTACEANS

Objectives:
1. Describe the basic characteristics of the class Crustacea, and name four members of this group.
2. Describe the external structure of the crayfish.
3. Describe the following life processes in the crayfish: nutrition, excretion, circulation, and respiration.
4. Describe the nervous system and sense organs of the crayfish.
5. Describe reproduction in the crayfish.

33-3   General Characteristics of Crustaceans

The class **Crustacea** (krus-*tay*-shuh), the *crustaceans*, includes lobsters, crayfish, crabs, shrimp, waterfleas, sow bugs, barnacles, and many others (see Figure 33-2). Most crusta-

Figure 33-2. Crustaceans. The hermit crab (left) lives in an empty shell. The purple anemone on the shell feeds on the crab's leftovers. (Right) Goose barnacles.

ceans are marine, but some live in fresh water. A few, such as the sow bug, live on land in moist places. Crustaceans vary in size from microscopic water fleas to huge crabs with leg spans of 3.5 meters. Microscopic crustaceans are the main source of food for many larger marine animals. Crustaceans are characterized by the presence of two pairs of antennae located on the head.

33-4 The Crayfish—External Structure

Crayfish, which can be found in freshwater streams, lakes, and swamps, are typical crustaceans, showing many of the characteristics of their class. They are covered by an exoskeleton hardened with lime. At the joints, where bending occurs, the exoskeleton is softer and thinner, and also folded. The crayfish body has two main regions (see Figure 33-3). At the anterior end, the segments of the head and thorax are fused to form the **cephalothorax** (sef-uh-luh-*thor*-aks). The part of the exoskeleton that protects and covers the dorsal and side surfaces of the cephalothorax is called the *carapace* (*kar*-uh-pays). The seven segments posterior to the cephalothorax form the abdomen. The paddle-shaped last segment of the abdomen is called the *telson* (tel-sun).

The various paired appendages of the crayfish have specific functions. Starting at the anterior end, the first pair of appendages are the *antennules* (an-*ten*-yoolz), which function in touch, taste, and balance. Next come the *antennae* (an-*ten*-ee), which are also used for touching and tasting. The *mandibles* (*man*-duh-bulz), or jaws, crush food by moving from side to side. The two pairs of *maxillae* (mak-*sil*-ee) handle food. The three pairs of *maxillipeds* (mak-*sil*-uh-pedz) function in touch and taste, and also handle food. The large first legs are called *chelipeds* (*kihl*-uh-pedz). Their grasping claws are used to catch foods and for defense. Behind the chelipeds are four pairs of

Figure 33-3. External Structure of the Crayfish.

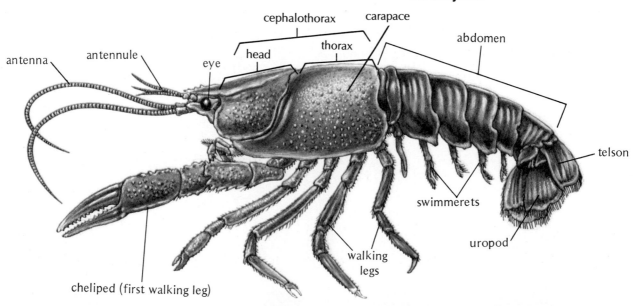

walking legs. On the abdomen are *swimmerets* (swim-uh-*rets*), which are used in swimming. In females they are used to carry the developing eggs. The last pair of appendages are the broad *uropods* (*yur*-uh-pahdz). The uropods, along with the telson, form a fan-shaped tail that is used for rapid backward movement. When the crayfish senses danger, the powerful abdominal muscles whip the tail forward under the abdomen causing the crayfish to shoot backward.

33-5   The Crayfish—Internal Structure and Life Functions

Nutrition. The crayfish feeds on dead animals or on living animals that it catches with its powerful chelipeds. The food is crushed by the mandibles and passed to the mouth by the maxillae and maxillipeds. The mouth leads into a short esophagus (see Figure 33-4). From the esophagus, food passes into the stomach, where it is chewed up by chitinous teeth in a structure called the *gastric mill.* The finely ground food particles are digested by enzymes, then passed into the digestive glands and absorbed into the blood. Undigested material passes through the intestine and out the anus.

Excretion. The excretory organs of the crayfish are called the *green glands.* They are located in the head region. The green glands remove wastes from the blood, and these wastes are excreted from the body through an opening near the base of the antennae.

Circulation and respiration. The open circulatory system consists of a dorsal heart surrounded by a cavity called the *pericardial* (pehr-uh-*kard*-ee-ul) *sinus.* Blood in the pericardial

Figure 33-4. Internal Structure of the Crayfish.

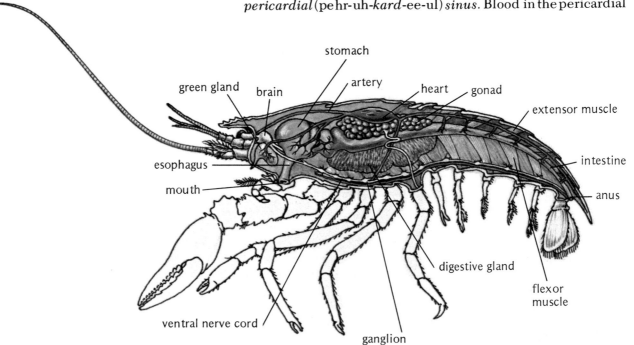

sinus enters the heart through three pairs of valves called *ostia* (*ahs*-tee-uh). When the heart contracts, the ostia close, and blood is pumped out through arteries to all parts of the body. There are no capillaries or veins. The arteries open into spaces, or sinuses, among the body tissues. There the blood bathes the cells directly. Oxygen and nutrients from the blood diffuse into the cells, and carbon dioxide and wastes from the cells diffuse into the blood. Eventually, the blood collects in the *sternal* (*stern*-ul) *sinus*. From there, it is channeled to the gills, where it picks up oxygen and gets rid of carbon dioxide. From the gills, the blood returns to the pericardial sinus. Dissolved in the plasma of the colorless blood is **hemocyanin** (hee-moh-*sy*-uh-nin), a copper-containing respiratory pigment that aids in the transport of oxygen.

The gills, where the exchange of respiratory gases occurs, are delicate, plumelike structures. They are located in *gill chambers* on each side of the thorax. The gill chambers are protected by the carapace. Water is kept flowing through the gill chambers by the movement of the second maxillae.

Nervous regulation. The nervous system of the crayfish resembles that of the annelids in form. The brain, which is in the head, is connected by nerves to the eyes, antennules, and antennae. Extending from the brain, two nerves circle the esophagus and join ventrally to form a double, ventral nerve cord. As the ventral nerve cord runs posteriorly, it enlarges into ganglia in each segment. From these ganglia, nerves branch to the appendages, muscles, and other organs.

The sensory organs of the crayfish are varied and well developed. They include a pair of *compound eyes* located at the ends of movable stalks. Each eye contains about 2,000 visual units. Each unit contains a lens system that, unlike the human eye, cannot focus at different distances. Such an eye is very sensitive to movement and offers a wide angle of vision. However, it produces only a crude image.

The crayfish has two kinds of small sensory hairs that are found on the appendages and other parts of the body. One type of hair is sensitive to touch. The other is sensitive to chemicals, providing information equivalent to the human senses of taste and smell.

The sense organs of equilibrium, or balance, are found in sacs called *statocysts* (*stat*-uh-sists), which are located at the bases of the antennules. Each statocyst contains sensory hairs and grains of sand. When the crayfish moves, the sand grains move, stimulating some of the sensory hairs. From the stimulated hairs, impulses pass to the brain. The brain interprets the information and initiates impulses that enable the crayfish to adjust its position and maintain its equilibrium. Each time the animal molts, the sand grains are shed along with the exoskeleton. New sand grains are picked up when the new exoskeleton forms.

Figure 33-5. Female Crayfish with Eggs and with Newly Hatched Young.

Reproduction. In crayfish, sexes are separate. Mating takes place in the fall. The male uses his first pair of swimmerets to transfer sperm from his body to the *seminal* (*sem*-in-ul) *receptacle* of the female. The sperm are kept in the receptacle until spring, when the female lays several hundred eggs that have been fertilized by the stored sperm. The eggs attach to the female's swimmerets (see Figure 33-5). The waving of the swimmerets back and forth keeps the embryos well supplied with oxygen. After 5 to 6 weeks the eggs hatch, but the young remain attached to the mother for several more weeks. During this time, the young crayfish begin to molt. Crayfish live for 3 to 5 years.

Regeneration. If a crayfish injures an appendage, it can shed the injured limb at a joint. This process of self-amputation, which is called *autotomy* (aw-*taht*-uh-mee) prevents excessive loss of blood. Gradually, with each molt, the lost appendage grows back. Regeneration in crayfish is limited to the appendages and eyes.

CLASSES CHILOPODA AND DIPLOPODA— THE CENTIPEDES AND MILLIPEDES

Objectives:
1. Name the members of the classes Chilopoda and Diplopoda.
2. Describe the general characteristics of centipedes.
3. Describe the general characteristics of millipedes.

33-6 General Characteristics of the Chilopoda

Centipedes, or "hundred-leggers," belong to the class **Chilopoda** (ky-*lahp*-uh-duh). Actually, some centipedes have more than 150 pairs of legs, but 30 to 35 pairs is most common. A centipede has a distinct head made up of six segments. The

Figure 33-6. A Centipede.

head is followed by a long, wormlike, slightly flattened body made up of many similar segments (see Figure 33-6). Centipedes live on land and are commonly found in dark, damp places, such as under logs or stones.

In the centipedes, all body segments except the one behind the head and the last two have one pair of legs. The head has one pair of antennae and various mouthparts. Centipedes feed mainly on insects. The centipede bites its victim with *poison claws*, which are on the first body segment. Small centipedes are harmless to humans. The common house centipede is about 2.5 centimeters long. At night, it searches for food, eating cockroaches, bedbugs, and other insects.

33-7   General Characteristics of the Diplopoda

Millipedes, or "thousand-leggers," belong to the class **Diplopoda** (dih-*plahp*-uh-duh). They do not have a thousand legs, but they may have more than 300 pairs (see Figure 33-7). Like a centipede, a millipede has a distinct head and a long, wormlike body made up of many segments. Except for the last two segments, millipedes have two pairs of legs per segment. The head bears a pair of antennae and various mouthparts. Millipedes, unlike centipedes, do not have poison claws. Whereas centipedes can move rapidly, millipedes move much more slowly. They feed mainly on decaying plant material. When they are disturbed, millipedes usually roll themselves into a ball. Many have "stink" glands that give off an offensive odor.

Figure 33-7. A Millipede. The millipede is curled around a twig.

CLASS ARACHNIDA—THE ARACHNIDS

Objectives:
1. Name four members of the class Arachnida.
2. Describe the general characteristics of arachnids.

33-8   General Characteristics of the Arachnids

The *arachnids*, members of the class **Arachnida** (uh-*rak*-nih-duh), include spiders, scorpions, ticks, mites, and daddy

A

C

longlegs (see Figure 33-8). Some arachnids are annoying and even dangerous to humans and other animals. Mites and ticks live as temporary parasites on the skin of many animals, including humans, dogs, chickens, and cattle. Mites often cause terrible itching. Ticks are carriers of several diseases, including Rocky Mountain spotted fever and Texas cattle fever. Scorpions sting with their tail. While the sting is very painful, it is usually not fatal to humans. Spiders are generally harmless. In fact, they are often helpful because they feed on insects. The poisonous spiders of the United States are the black widow and the brown recluse. Spiders rarely bite unless they are disturbed.

33-9   Structure and Life Functions of Arachnids

Most arachnids live on land, and many resemble insects. The body of an arachnid consists of a cephalothorax and an abdomen. These animals do not have either antennae or chewing jaws. They have six pairs of jointed appendages, all on the cephalothorax (see Figure 33-9). The first pair of appendages are the fang-like *chelicerae* (kuh-*lis*-uh-ree), which are used to pierce the prey. The body fluids of the prey are then drawn into the spider's mouth by the action of the *sucking stomach*. Usually, poison glands associated with the chelicerae inject a poison that paralyzes the prey. The second pair of appendages, the *pedipalps* (*ped*-uh-palps), are sensitive both to chemicals and to touch. They also hold food and are used by the male in reproduction. The next appendages are the four pairs of walking legs.

The respiratory organs of the arachnids are called **book lungs.** Located in chambers on the underside of the abdomen, they consist of a series of leaflike plates containing blood vessels. Air drawn into the chambers through slits in the abdo-

B

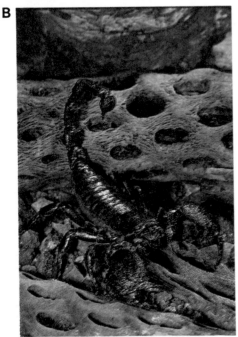

Figure 33-8. Arachnids. (A) Huntsman spider. (B) Scorpion. (C) Daddy longlegs.

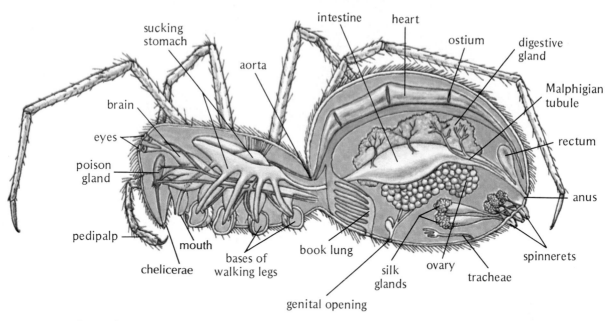

Figure 33-9. Structure of an Arachnid.
The body of an arachnid is divided into
a cephalothorax and an abdomen, and
there are four pairs of legs.

men circulates between the plates. Gas exchange occurs
between the blood in the plates and the air in the chamber.
Oxygen and carbon dioxide are transported in the blood between the body cells and the book lungs. Although some in-
sectlike tracheae, or air tubes, are present, they play only a
minor role in respiration.

In spiders and some other arachnids, the pedipalps of the
male are modified for sperm transfer. Following elaborate
courtship behavior, the male uses the pedipalps to place the
sperm in the seminal receptacle of the female. In spiders, as
the female lays the eggs, they are fertilized by the stored
sperm, and wrapped in a cocoon. In some species the female
carries the cocoons until the young hatch (see Figure 33-10).

Figure 33-10. Wolf Spider. Female
wolf spider with egg case (left) and with
newly hatched young (right).

Spiders—Safer in Chaotic Webs?

Which spider web is more evolutionarily advanced—the beautiful orb web to the right, or the chaotically arranged cobweb above? For over a century, biologists have thought the orb web to be superior. Now, some scientists suspect that the chaotic cobweb may offer important advantages over the symmetrical orb.

Suppose an orb web is damaged. The spider must make immediate repairs, because even minor damage destroys the web's integrity. While making repairs, the spider is unprotected from predators. Even after the web has been repaired, the spider must station itself at the center, still exposed, to wait for prey.

With a dense, chaotic web, however, minor damage does little structural harm. The spider can make repairs when it is safe. This web offers the spider more protection than an orb web does.

So, at least in spider webs, beauty and near-perfect geometry may not represent the highest evolutionary attainment.

Figure 33-11. Spider in Web.

In other spider species the eggs in their cocoons are deposited on the ground. In other types of arachnids, sperm are not transferred into the body of the female by the male. Instead, the sperm are enclosed in a case and deposited on the ground. The case is then taken up by the female into a special body opening called a *gonopore*.

In spiders and one other small group of arachnids, there are three pairs of *spinnerets* (spin-uh-*rets*) at the end of the abdomen. Spinnerets are used to spin silk produced by silk glands within the abdomen. As the fluid protein is squeezed out of the spinnerets, it hardens into a thread. Spiders use these threads for many purposes. Some use them to construct webs in which they capture prey (see Figure 33-11). Threads are also used to line nests and to make cocoons for the fertilized eggs. Spiders also use threads as a means of transportation. They can lower themselves from trees on a thread.

CLASS INSECTA—THE INSECTS

Objectives:

1. List several reasons for the enormous success of insects as land animals.
2. Describe some of the structural variations in the mouthparts, legs, and body forms found among insects.
3. Describe the external structure of the head, thorax, and abdomen of the grasshopper.
4. Describe sexual reproduction in insects.
5. Compare and contrast complete and incomplete metamorphosis in insects.
6. Name two members of each of the six major insect orders.

7. Discuss some of the advantages and disadvantages of chemical and biological methods of insect control.

33-10 General Characteristics of the Insects

Biologically, the *insects,* class **Insecta** (in-*sek*-tuh), are the most successful group of animals. There are more than 900,000 known species. Nearly all insects are land animals, although a few live in fresh water and a few in salt water. Insects range in size from tiny beetles 0.25 millimeters long to some large tropical moths with a wingspan of 30 centimeters. Most insects, however, are less than 2.5 centimeters long.

There are several reasons for the remarkable success of insects.

1. Insects are the only invertebrates capable of flying. The ability to fly allows them to travel over great distances in search of food. It enables them to escape from their enemies and to spread into new environments.

2. Among the insects there is tremendous variation in how they are adapted for feeding and reproduction. These adaptations allow insects to exist in all types of environments and to obtain nourishment from many sources.

3. Insects have a very high rate of reproduction. A single female can lay hundreds or even thousands of eggs at a time. These eggs develop rapidly and in turn may produce millions of offspring during a year.

4. Insects are generally small, which means that they do not need large areas in which to live.

33-11 Structural Variations Among Insects

All insects have three separate body regions—the head, thorax, and abdomen (see Figure 33-12). On the head is one

Figure 33-12. Structure of the Dragonfly. Like all insects, the body of the dragonfly is divided into a head, thorax, and abdomen.

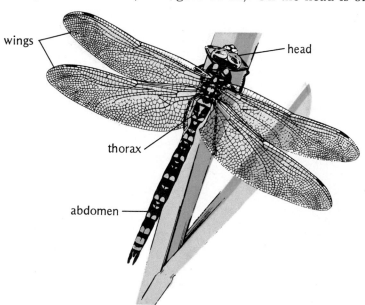

A

B

C

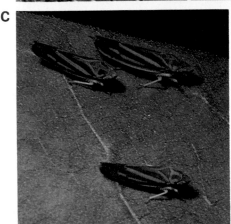

D

Figure 33-13. Insects. (A) Praying mantis. (B) Walking stick. (C) Leafhoppers. (D) Bee.

pair of antennae, several mouthparts, and in most, compound eyes. On the thorax are three pairs of walking legs. In flying insects, the wings are also located on the thorax. The abdomen has up to eleven segments, with no leglike appendages.

The structure of the grasshopper, which is discussed later in this chapter, shows the general characteristics of the insect class. However, as mentioned previously, many insects have highly specialized structures that enable them to feed on a particular plant or animal or to live in a particular environment. Let us look briefly at some of these adaptive modifications (see Figure 33-13).

Mouthparts. The structure of an insect's mouthparts reflect the way in which it obtains food. Mouthparts are of two basic types. Some insects, such as grasshoppers, have chewing mouthparts (see page 583). Others, such as bees, have sucking mouthparts, which are usually in the form of a tube. Some insects have needlelike projections that enable them to pierce the tissues of animals and plants and suck their juices. In butterflies, the coiled siphoning tube uncoils to suck nectar from flowers. Houseflies have sponging and lapping mouthparts.

Body form. Insects vary greatly in body form. Cockroaches have flattened bodies that are suited for living in cracks and crevices. Beetles have thick, plump bodies. Damsel flies and walking sticks have long slender bodies. Moths are covered with hairs that may serve to protect them from cool evening temperatures. The hairs or bristles on bees help in the collection of pollen.

Legs. The legs of insects show many types of modifications. For example, water bugs and some beetles have paddle-shaped legs that are used in swimming. The walking legs of honeybees are modified for the collection of pollen. The forelegs of the praying mantis are modified for grasping prey.

33-12 The Grasshopper—A Representative Insect

Like all insects, the body of the grasshopper is divided into three sections—the *head, thorax,* and *abdomen.* The head is made up of six fused segments. Two large compound eyes similar to those of the crayfish are located on the sides of the head (see Figure 33-14). In addition, the grasshopper also has three *simple eyes,* or *ocelli* (oh-*sel*-ee), located between the compound eyes. The simple eyes do not form images. They are only sensitive to light and dark. On the front of the head is a pair of jointed antennae. The antennae are sensitive to smell and touch.

The mouthparts used in chewing are located outside the mouth. These structures are adapted for eating leafy vegetation. The upper lip, or *labrum,* and the lower lip, or *labium,* function in holding the food (see Figure 33-15). The *mandibles,* or crushing jaws, are lined with rough-edged chitinous teeth. In biting off and chewing food, the mandibles move from side to side. Behind the mandibles is a second pair of jaws called the *maxillae.* These structures hold the food and pass it to the mandibles. Sensory palps on both the maxillae and labium feel and taste the food. Beneath the lower lip is a tonguelike organ.

The thorax is composed of three segments—the *prothorax,* the *mesothorax,* and the *metathorax* (see Figure 33-16). Each segment bears a pair of legs that are structurally similar. Each leg has five segments. The last segment is called the *tarsus,* or foot. On the tarsus are pads that enable the grasshopper to cling to smooth surfaces and claws that enable it to climb rough surfaces. The first two pairs of legs are for walking. The third pair of legs is larger than the first two and is modified for jumping.

Attached to the last two segments of the thorax are two pairs of wings. The outer pair, the fore wings, is hard and serves as a protective covering for the inner pair of wings, the hind wings.

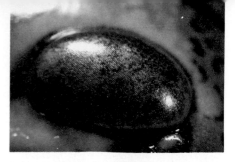

Figure 33-14. Compound Eye of the Grasshopper.

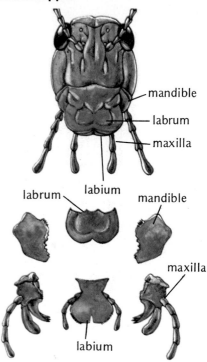

Figure 33-15. Mouthparts of the Grasshopper.

Figure 33-16. External Structure of the Grasshopper.

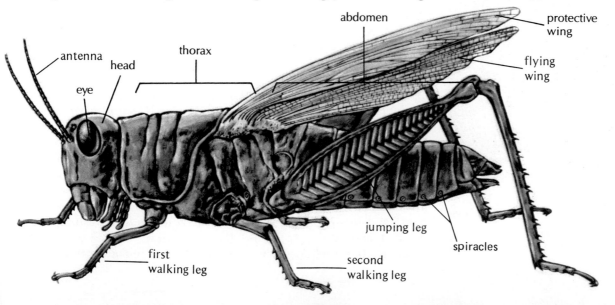

It is the flexible hind wings that are used in flight. When not in use, the hind wings are folded like fans. The thin membranes of the hind wings contain veins that serve to strengthen them.

The abdomen consists of ten segments. Along the lower sides of the abdomen and thorax are ten pairs of spiracles, which open into breathing tubes, or tracheae. Located on either side of the first abdominal segments are the *tympana* (*tim*-puh-nuh), the organs of hearing. Each tympanum consists of an oval, flat membrane that vibrates when hit by sound waves. The last segment of the abdomen is modified for reproduction.

The internal structure of the grasshopper and its life functions have been discussed in Unit 2. For a discussion of the digestive system, see page 132; for the circulatory system, see page 146; for the respiratory system, see page 181; for the excretory system, see page 197; for the musculoskeletal system, see page 213; for the nervous system, see page 238.

33-13   Reproduction in Insects

All insects reproduce sexually. Eggs are produced in the ovaries of the female, and sperm are produced in the testes of the male. When grasshoppers mate, the male transfers sperm into the body of the female. The sperm are stored in the seminal receptacle of the female. When the eggs leave the ovary of the female, they enter the oviduct, where fertilization occurs. They then pass out of the body of the female. On the end of the abdomen of the female is a hard, four-pointed organ called the **ovipositor** (*oh*-vee-pahz-it-er). It is used to dig holes in the ground in which the eggs are deposited. Although the eggs are laid in the fall, they do not hatch until spring.

33-14   Development in Insects

In a few insects, eggs hatch directly into miniature adults. The young molt several times, growing larger each time. In most species, however, insects undergo distinct changes as they develop from eggs to adults. This series of changes is called **metamorphosis** (met-uh-*mor*-fuh-sis), and the process is under hormonal control.

Incomplete metamorphosis. The eggs of some insects, such as grasshoppers, crickets, and cockroaches, undergo **incomplete metamorphosis.** In this type of development, the eggs hatch into **nymphs** (nimfs). The nymph resembles the adult, but lacks certain adult features. The grasshopper nymph looks like the adult, but it lacks wings and reproductive structures (see Figure 33-17). Nymphs molt several times. With each molt they become larger and more like the adult. In incomplete metamorphosis, the three stages of development are the egg, nymph, and adult.

Complete metamorphosis. The eggs of most insects undergo

Figure 33-17. An Immature Grasshopper. Grasshopper nymphs lack the wings and reproductive structures of the adult.

complete metamorphosis. Among the insects exhibiting complete metamorphosis are moths, butterflies, beetles, bees, and flies. In this type of development, the eggs hatch into segmented, wormlike larvae. These larvae are commonly known as *caterpillars* (kat-er-pil-erz), *maggots* (mag-uts), or *grubs.* During this active stage, the larva eats and grows. After several molts, the larva passes into a resting stage called the **pupa** (*pyoo*-puh). The pupa is surrounded either by a cocoon or by a case made from its outer body covering. During the pupal stage, the tissues of the larva are reorganized into the adult form. When the changes are complete, the case or cocoon splits open, and the adult emerges. In complete metamorphosis, the four stages of development are the egg, larva, pupa, and adult.

The development of the cecropia (sih-*kroh*-pee-uh) moth is typical of insects that undergo complete metamorphosis. It includes the egg, larva, pupa, and adult stages (see Figure 33-18). The stages of metamorphosis are controlled by the interaction of three hormones—brain hormone, molting hormone, and juvenile hormone.

The egg hatches into the larva, in this case a caterpillar. As the caterpillar eats and grows, neurosecretory cells in the brain secrete a hormone called *brain hormone*. Brain hormone stimulates production of *molting hormone* by an endocrine gland in the thorax. Molting hormone stimulates periodic molting of the exoskeleton. The transformation of the larva into more mature forms is inhibited by a hormone called *juvenile hormone.* Juvenile hormone is produced by endocrine glands near the brain. As long as juvenile hormone is secreted, the larva can molt, but it will not change into the next stage, the pupa. At the end of the larval period, the secretion of juvenile hormone decreases. At the time of the next molt, the larva forms a pupa. During the pupal stage, the insect appears inactive, but great changes in body form are occurring. At the end of pupation, the adult moth emerges.

A recent approach to insect control involves the use of substances similar to juvenile hormone. These substances prevent the metamorphosis of larvae into adults, which prevents the insects from reproducing.

33-15 Classification of Insects

The branch of biology that deals with the study of insects is called **entomology** (ent-uh-*mahl*-uh-jee). The scientists who study insects are called *entomologists*(ent-uh-*mahl*-uh-jists). Entomologists divide the class Insecta into twenty-seven orders. Of these twenty-seven, only six are of major importance. The six major orders are the **Hymenoptera** (hy-muh-*nahp*-tuh-ruh), **Orthoptera** (or-*thahp*-tuh-ruh), **Coleoptera** (kohl-ee-*ahp*-tuh-ruh), **Lepidoptera** (lep-uh-*dahp*-tuh-ruh), **Diptera** (*dip*-tuh-ruh), and **Hemiptera** (heh-*mip*-tuh-ruh). Table 33-1 shows the basic characteristics of these and other insect orders.

Figure 33-18. Development of the Cecropia Moth. (A) Adult female laying eggs. (B) Larva. (C) Pupa. (D) Adult.

Table 33-1. Classification of Insects

Order	Examples	Mouthparts	Wings	Characteristics/Habitat
Anopleura	sucking lice	sucking	none	Parasites of mammals. Feed by sucking blood of their hosts, including humans. Their bites are irritating, and they spread disease.
Coleoptera	beetles (diving beetles, fireflies, bark beetles, ladybird beetles, Junebugs, carpet beetles, Japanese beetles)	chewing	usually 2 pairs	Largest insect order. Found in all habitats. Many feed on plants and are serious pests.
Collembola	springtails	chewing	none	Small insects found in leaf litter, on rotting logs, on beaches, and on surface of pond water. Some species are jumpers.
Diptera	flies (houseflies, black flies, mosquitos, midges, gnats, horseflies)	sucking	1 pair	Found in a wide variety of habitats. Some feed on plants, others are parasites, and still others feed on insects. Many types are pests. Some damage plants, some transmit animal diseases.
Ephemeroptera	mayflies	vestigial	2 pairs	Small or medium-sized, found in and around ponds and streams. Adults live only a day or so, and do not eat.
Hemiptera	bugs (water bugs, water striders, bedbugs, assassin bugs, stinkbugs)	sucking	none or 2 pairs	Very large group. Most terrestrial; some aquatic; few parasitic. Some feed on plants, others prey on insects.
Homoptera	cicadas, aphids, leafhoppers, spittlebugs, planthoppers, whiteflies, lac insects	sucking	none or 2 pairs	Feed on plants. Many cause serious damage, and some transmit diseases. Lac insects are the source of lac, from which shellac is made.
Hymenoptera	bees, wasps, ants, sawflies	bees: sucking wasps, ants, and sawflies: chewing	none or 2 pairs	Large order whose members live in a variety of habitats, mainly on vegetation, particularly flowers, and on the ground. Some are parasites of other insects. Ants and some wasps and bees are social insects. They live in colonies in which members are divided into several castes, each serving a particular function. Honeybees are very important in pollination of many types of plants.

Order	Examples	Mouthparts	Wings	Characteristics/Habitat
Isoptera	termites	chewing	none or 2 pairs	Small social insects that feed mainly on wood. Termites damage or destroy buildings and other objects made of wood.
Lepidoptera	butterflies and moths	sucking, with coiled sucking tube	usually 2 pairs	Found on vegetation. The larvae of this group are caterpillars, which feed on plants and often do serious damage. Adults commonly feed on plant nectar and may serve to pollinate the plants they visit. Salivary glands of larvae produce silk used to make cocoon. Silk is produced by silkworm moths.
Mallophaga	chewing lice	chewing	none	Parasites of birds and mammals (but not humans).
Odonata	dragonflies, damselflies	chewing	2 pairs	Found around water; feed on mosquitos and other small insects.
Orthoptera	cockroaches, crickets, grasshoppers, katydids, walking sticks, praying mantis	chewing	usually 2 pairs	Large insects found on ground or on low vegetation. Many make noise by rubbing body parts together. Many members of this group feed on plants and can do great damage. Cockroaches are pests in buildings.
Siphonaptera	fleas	sucking	none	Small parasites on birds and mammals. Fleas are pests, attacking domestic animals and humans. A few types of fleas transmit disease, including bubonic plague.
Thysanura	silverfish, bristletails	chewing	none	Small insects. Bristletails found in leaf litter, under logs, etc. Silverfish found in cool, damp places, often pests in buildings.

An entomologist examining a hornworm that is defoliating a tomato plant.

Entomologist

Entomologists are biological scientists who study insects. Some entomologists investigate insect anatomy, physiology, development, and behavior. Others may concentrate in applied-science areas, such as insects and agriculture, insects as human disease carriers, and apiculture—the breeding and culture of bees. Because insects are so widespread and their influence in nature and on humans is so great, entomologists must have a broad background in biological and physical sciences.

Graduates with a bachelor's degree can find jobs as technicians in research laboratories or in field testing and inspecting. With a master's degree, higher level opportunities exist. Those with a doctorate in entomology qualify for university teaching and research positions, and for administrative jobs.

33-16   Economic Importance of Insects

Insects are so widespread and so numerous that they affect many aspects of daily life. Each year, insects cause billions of dollars of damage to crops. Insects spread many plant diseases, such as Dutch elm disease and corn smut. They also transmit animal diseases: mosquitoes carry malaria, yellow fever, and elephantiasis; houseflies carry dysentery and typhoid fever; tsetse (*seet*-see) flies carry African sleeping sickness; lice carry typhus; and fleas carry plague. Insects also destroy property: termites destroy wood; moths and carpet beetles damage clothing, fabrics, furs, and carpets; silverfish destroy paper; and weevils, cockroaches, and ants ruin food.

Insects also serve some valuable functions. Various insects are necessary for the pollination of important crop plants. For example, bees pollinate the flowers of apple and pear trees, clover, and berries. Products obtained from insects include honey from bees; lac, which is used to make shellac, from lac insects; and silk from silkworm moths.

Some insects destroy other insects that are harmful to humans and human property. Ladybird beetles eat scale insects, which injure orange and lemon crops. The praying mantis eats almost any insect it can catch. Wasps, by laying their eggs in caterpillars, eventually kill them. Aquatic bugs eat mosquito larvae. Insects also serve as a source of food for birds, frogs, and fish. Finally, some insects act as scavengers, eating dead plant and animal remains.

A major problem for scientists has been to find ways of controlling harmful insects without harming other insects or animals. Chemical insecticides poison the environment and kill both harmful and helpful insects. They are dangerous to other animals, including humans. In addition, in time, insect populations become resistant to chemical controls.

Many scientists believe that biological methods of insect control are safer than chemical insecticides. Biological controls include: sterilizing males and releasing them; developing resistant plants; introducing specific predators and parasites that destroy only harmful insects; and using insect sex attractants (pheromones) to lure insects into traps.

PHYLUM ECHINODERMATA— THE SPINY-SKINNED ANIMALS

Objectives:
1. Name three members of the phylum Echinodermata.
2. Describe the general characteristics of echinoderms.
3. Explain why echinoderms are considered to be more closely related to the vertebrates than other invertebrate phyla.

4. Describe the structure of the water-vascular system of the starfish and explain how it is used in locomotion and feeding.
5. Describe respiration, excretion, and reproduction in the starfish.

Figure 33-19. Echinoderms. Common echinoderms include the sea cucumber (left) and the sea urchin (right).

33-17   General Characteristics of the Echinoderms

The phylum **Echinodermata** (ih-ky-nuh-der-*mah*-tuh) includes starfish, sea urchins, sea cucumbers, and sand dollars (see Figure 33-19). These animals are all marine, and live mainly on the ocean floor. Some are sessile, but most are motile. The larvae are bilaterally symmetrical, but the adults are radially symmetrical. *Echinoderms* have a well-developed coelom.

Almost all echinoderms have an internal skeleton that serves both for support and protection. The skeleton consists of hard, calcified plates that are embedded in the body wall. Spiny projections on the plates stick out through the skin. These projections give echinoderms their spiny-skinned appearance.

In all the invertebrates that we have studied so far, the first opening of the digestive system formed in the embryo is the mouth, which is formed from the blastopore (see page 368). The opening for the anus breaks through later opposite the mouth. In the echinoderms the pattern is reversed. The blastopore becomes the anus, and the mouth forms later opposite the anus. This pattern of development is characteristic of vertebrates, and is thought to show a possible evolutionary relationship between echinoderms and more complex animals.

The starfish is representative of the phylum, so we will use it as an example to study the structure and life functions of echinoderms.

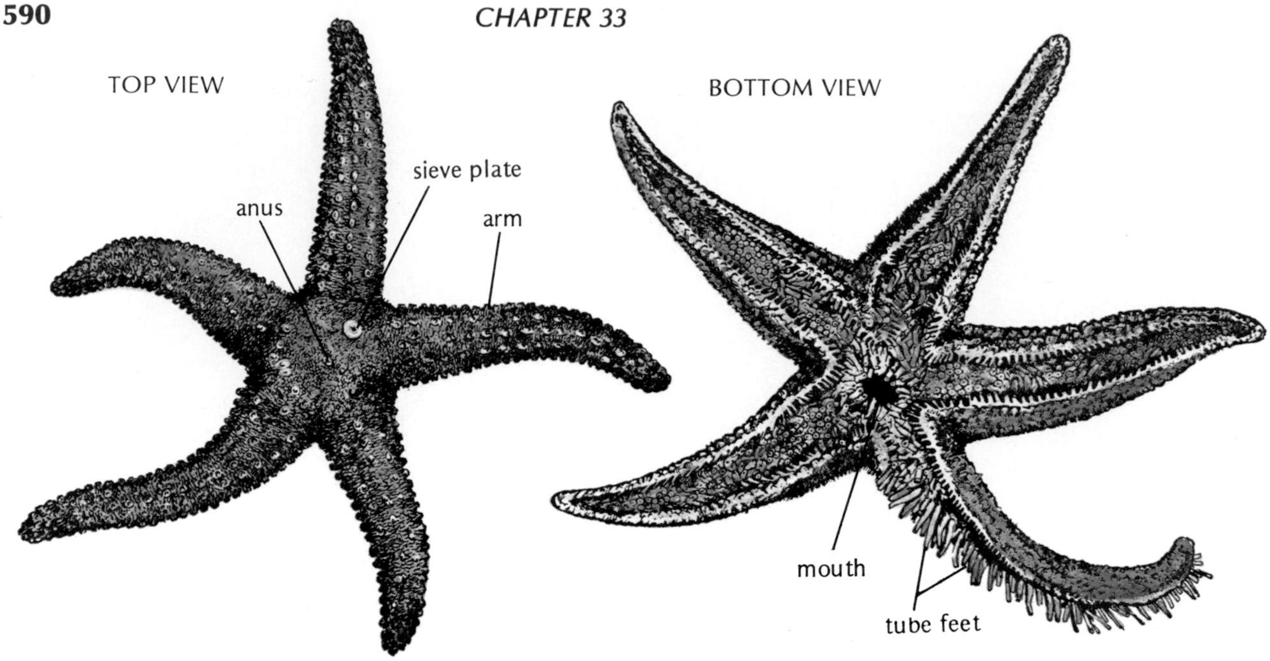

TOP VIEW

anus

sieve plate

arm

BOTTOM VIEW

mouth

tube feet

Figure 33-20. External Structure of the Starfish.

33-18   Structure and Life Functions of the Starfish

The body of the starfish consists of a *central disk* from which the arms, or rays, radiate (see Figure 33-20). Most starfish have five arms, but some have as many as twenty.

Locomotion and food-getting in starfish involve a system called the **water-vascular system,** which is found only in echinoderms (see Figure 33-21). On the dorsal surface of the starfish is an opening called the *sieve plate.* Sea water enters through the sieve plate and passes through the *stone canal* into the *ring canal.* A *radial canal* runs into each arm from the ring canal. Connected to each radial canal are many small, tubular structures called **tube feet.** Each tube foot has a bulblike structure at one end and a sucker at its tip. The bulbs are within the body of the starfish, but the tube feet extend out

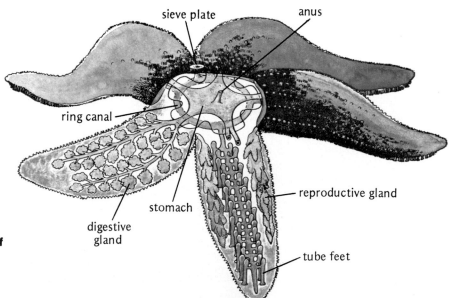

sieve plate

anus

ring canal

reproductive gland

stomach

digestive gland

tube feet

Figure 33-21. Internal Structure of the Starfish.

from the ventral, or bottom, surface of the arms (see Figure 33-22). When the bulb contracts, water is forced into the tube, causing it to elongate. When the tube foot touches a surface, its sucker holds fast. When the tube foot contracts, or shortens, water is forced back into the bulb, and the starfish is pulled forward. Movement of the animal requires the coordinated action of hundreds of tube feet.

Starfish feed on clams and oysters. They use their water-vascular system to pry open their prey. In feeding, the starfish wraps its arms around both sides of the mollusk, attaches tube feet to each shell, and pulls (see Figure 33-23). Eventually, the mollusk tires, and its shell opens slightly. The stomach of the starfish is then extended out through the mouth, and inserted into the small opening between the mollusk's shell. (The starfish can insert part of its stomach into an opening as small as 0.1 millimeter.) Enzymes secreted by the stomach partly digest the soft body of the mollusk. The food is then taken into the stomach, and the stomach is pulled back into the starfish. Food passes from the stomach into the digestive glands in the arms, where digestion is completed.

Respiration in the starfish occurs by diffusion of gases across the skin gills and tube feet. *Skin gills* are small, fingerlike structures that extend out from the body surface. They are filled with coelomic fluid. Many materials are distributed by the fluid in the coelom, which bathes the body organs and supplies them with nutrients and oxygen and removes wastes. Excretion takes place by diffusion through the body surface.

Sexes are separate in the starfish. Gametes are shed through openings in the central disk into the water, where fertilization occurs. The fertilized egg develops into a bilaterally symmetrical, free-swimming larva. After several weeks, the larva attaches to a solid surface and develops into a small starfish.

Starfish have an amazing ability to regenerate missing parts. An entire new body can grow from as little as a single arm and a tiny part of the central disk.

Figure 33-22.   Tube Feet of the Starfish.

Figure 33-23.   Starfish Feeding on an Oyster.

Chapter Review

SUMMARY

- Members of the phylum Arthropoda have jointed legs, a chitinous exoskeleton, and a segmented body.

- The class Crustacea includes lobsters and crayfish. The crayfish, a typical crustacean, has two main regions—the cephalothorax and the abdomen.

- The class Chilopoda consists of centipedes, whose wormlike bodies have one pair of legs on most segments.

- The class Diplopoda consists of millipedes, which have two pairs of legs on most segments.

- The spiders, class Arachnida, have a two-part body consisting of a cephalothorax, an abdomen, and six pairs of jointed appendages.

- The insects, class Insecta, have three distinct body regions and three pairs of legs.

- All the members of the phylum Echinodermata are marine. Echinoderms have a calcified internal skeleton and are spiny-skinned.

KNOW THE TERMS

abdomen	complete metamorphosis	hemocyanin	nymph
Arachnida	Crustacea	Hymenoptera	Orthoptera
Arthropoda	Diplopoda	incomplete metamorphosis	ovipositor
book lung	Diptera	Insecta	pupa
cephalothorax	Echinodermata	Lepidoptera	thorax
Chilopoda	entomology	metamorphosis	tube foot
Coleoptera	Hemiptera	molting	water-vascular system

SECTION QUESTIONS

Introduction to the Arthropods

1. Name the five major classes of the phylum Arthropoda.
2. Name the body regions of most arthropods.

Class Crustacea—The Crustaceans

3. Name four members of the class Crustacea.
4. Name the two main body regions of the crayfish.

Classes Chilopoda and Diplopoda— The Centipedes and Millipedes

5. Name the members of the classes Chilopoda and Diplopoda.

Class Arachnida—The Arachnids

6. Name three members of the class Arachnida.
7. What do spiders eat?

Class Insecta—The Insects

8. List four reasons for the biological success of insects.
9. What is metamorphosis?
10. List the six major orders of insects.

Phylum Echinodermata— The Spiny-Skinned Animals

11. Name four echinoderms.
12. Where are echinoderms found?

KNOW THE FACTS

Copy the number of each sentence below on a sheet of paper. Beside each number, write the term(s) that complete(s) the sentence correctly.

1. Flies, beetles, butterflies, spiders, crabs, and shrimp belong to the phylum _____.
2. The symmetry of arthropods is _____.
3. The arthropod's soft body parts are protected by a(n) _____.
4. The dorsal heart of the crayfish is surrounded by _____ _____.

5. The excretory organs in the crayfish are the _____ _____.

6. The respiratory organs of the arachnids are _____ _____.

7. In arachnids, the organs that are sensitive to chemicals and to touch are called _____.

8. In the grasshopper, the organs of hearing are the _____.

9. In incomplete metamorphosis, the eggs hatch into _____.

10. In the starfish, locomotion and foodgetting involve the _____ _____.

UNDERSTAND THE CONCEPTS

11. Describe five characteristics shared by all arthropods.
12. Describe the basic characteristics of the class Crustacea.
13. Describe the functions of the appendages of the crayfish.
14. Describe reproduction in the crayfish.
15. Describe the structure and feeding habits of centipedes. Of millipedes.
16. Describe the basic characteristics of the class Arachnida.
17. Describe reproduction in spiders.
18. Describe the basic characteristics of the class Insecta.
19. Describe the grasshopper's legs and wings.
20. In what ways are insects harmful? Helpful?
21. Describe the characteristics of echinoderms.
22. Why are echinoderms thought to be more closely related to vertebrates than to other invertebrates?
23. Describe the structure of the water-vascular system of the starfish.

THINK CRITICALLY

24. Compare incomplete and complete metamorphosis.
25. What would happen if a spider's silk glands and spinnerettes were removed?
26. Butterflies are pests as larvae but are beneficial as adults. Explain.
27. When a starfish pries open the shell of a clam or oyster, the mollusk resists. Even if the shell opens only slightly, however, the starfish gets its meal. Explain.

THINK CREATIVELY

28. Farmers' crops are being destroyed by insects. The farmers come to you, an entomologist, for advice. What would you suggest as possible pest-control methods? Which method would you recommend most highly? Why?
29. Since starfish were eating many clams and oysters, divers were hired to go down to the shellfish beds and chop the starfish into pieces. After fishermen had harvested the shellfish, they found even more empty clam and oyster shells than before. Suggest a possible explanation.

FOR FURTHER INVESTIGATION

1. In a glass jar, raise a moth or a butterfly caterpillar to maturity. The glass jar should contain leaf-bearing twigs and fresh grass in order to sustain the insect. How long does the caterpillar take to build the cocoon? How long is the insect in the cocoon? What does the insect look like when it leaves the cocoon?

2. Investigate one of the following careers.
   a. Entomologist
   b. Seafood store owner
   c. Biological photographer
3. Prepare a report on the life and contributions of one of the following scientists:
   a. Vivian Chambers
   b. Alexander Agassiz
   c. Nina Matikashvilli
   d. Leon Roddy

FOR FURTHER READING

Batra, S., "Solitary Bees," *Scientific American*, February, 1984.

Headstrom, Richard, *Adventurer with Insects*, Dover Pubns., New York, 1982.

Chapter 34

VERTEBRATES—FISHES TO REPTILES

This long-nosed butterfly fish belongs to the large class of vertebrates called the bony fishes.

PHYLUM CHORDATA—THE CHORDATES

Objectives:
1. Name the three subphyla included in the phylum Chordata.
2. List the three basic characteristics that are present in all chordates.
3. Briefly describe the structure and life functions of tunicates and lancelets.
4. List the basic characteristics of the subphylum Vertebrata.
5. Explain the terms *ectothermic* and *endothermic*.

The phylum **Chordata** (kor-*dahd*-uh) is divided into three subphyla. The largest of these is the subphylum **Vertebrata** (verd-uh-*brahd*-uh), which includes the vertebrates. The other two chordate subphyla are the **Urochordata** (*yur*-uh-kor-*dahd*-uh) and the **Cephalochordata** (*sef*-uh-loh-kor-*dahd*-uh). The members of these two subphyla do not have backbones and are considered to be more primitive than vertebrates.

34-1 General Characteristics of Chordates

At some time in their life, all *chordates* show the following three characteristics, which distinguish them from all other animals.

1. Chordates have a dorsal, hollow nerve cord.

2. Chordates have a flexible, rodlike, internal supporting structure called a **notochord** (*noht*-uh-kord). The notochord, which is dorsal to the digestive tract, is found in the embryos of all chordates. In the urochordates and cephalochordates, it remains throughout life as the only supporting structure. In most vertebrates, it is replaced early in embryonic development by cartilage or bone. The cartilage or bone forms a supporting backbone, or vertebral column.

3. Chordates have paired **gill slits** in the throat region. In land-dwelling chordates, the gill slits are seen only during embryological development. In certain chordates, such as the fishes, the gill slits function in respiration throughout life.

34-2 Characteristics of Urochordates and Cephalochordates

The *urochordates* are soft-bodied, marine animals called *tunicates*. Adult tunicates are sessile animals that obtain food and oxygen from water that flows through their bodies (see Figure 34-1). Water enters the mouth, or incurrent siphon. It then passes into the pharynx and through the gill slits in the walls of the pharynx, where gas exchange occurs. The water then passes into a chamber called the atrium and out the excurrent siphon. The gill slits also trap food particles, which then pass into the digestive system. Adult tunicates lack a dorsal, hollow nerve cord and notochord. Larval tunicates, unlike adults, show all three chordate characteristics. They are motile and resemble tadpoles. Eventually the larva settles to the ocean floor and develops into an adult.

The *cephalochordates* are small, marine animals called *lancelets*. The most common member of this group is *amphioxus* (am-fee-*ahk*-sus). Lancelets generally live buried in the sand with only their anterior end exposed. Adult lancelets show the three characteristic chordate structures (see Figure 34-2). As in the tunicates, water enters the body through the mouth and passes into the pharynx and through the gill slits, where gas exchange occurs. Food particles do not pass

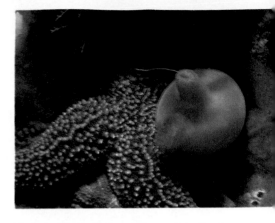

Figure 34-1. A Starfish and a Tunicate.

Figure 34-2. Internal Structure of a Lancelet. Adult lancelets show the characteristics of a chordate—they have a dorsal, hollow nerve cord, a notochord, and paired gill slits.

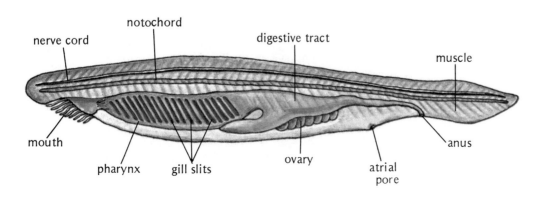

through the gill slits. Instead, they enter the digestive system directly. Water leaves the body through the atrial pore.

34-3   Characteristics of Vertebrates

The vertebrates are the most numerous and complex chordates. The basic characteristic distinguishing vertebrates from other chordates is the presence of a spinal column made up of vertebrae. This structure serves as the basis for an internal supporting skeleton and allows flexibility and movement. In adult vertebrates, the spinal column surrounds or replaces the notochord.

In addition to their backbone, vertebrates share a number of other characteristics.

1. The anterior part of the dorsal, hollow nerve cord is enlarged into a brain.

2. The body is generally divided into a head, neck, and trunk. The head contains the brain and various sense organs.

3. In most vertebrates, a tail is present at some stage of development.

4. There is a jointed, internal skeleton.

5. There are two pairs of appendages.

6. There is a heart with two to four chambers. The circulatory system is closed, and the red blood cells contain hemoglobin.

7. In aquatic vertebrates, gas exchange takes place in the gills, while in land vertebrates it occurs in the lungs.

8. There is a large body cavity, or coelom, containing the organs of digestion, excretion, and reproduction, as well as the heart and lungs.

9. The body covering, the skin, consists of at least two layers. The skin often forms accessory structures, such as glands, scales, feathers, hair, nails, claws, horns, and hoofs.

The subphylum Vertebrata is divided into seven classes. These are the jawless fishes, cartilaginous fishes, bony fishes, amphibians, reptiles, birds, and mammals.

34-4   Body Temperature in Vertebrates

Fishes, amphibians, and reptiles are *cold-blooded,* or **ectothermic** (ek-tuh-*ther*-mik), animals. Their body temperature varies with the temperature of the environment. Birds and mammals, on the other hand, are *warm-blooded,* or **endothermic** (en-duh-*ther*-mik). Their body temperature remains relatively constant regardless of the temperature of the environment. The normal body temperature of birds ranges between 40°C and 43°C. In mammals, it ranges from 36.5°C to 39.8°C. Warm-blooded animals can survive and be active in cold environments. They maintain a constant internal temperature by varying their metabolism rate to produce more heat, or less, as needed. Cold-blooded animals that live in areas with cold seasons become inactive or hibernate during the cold weather.

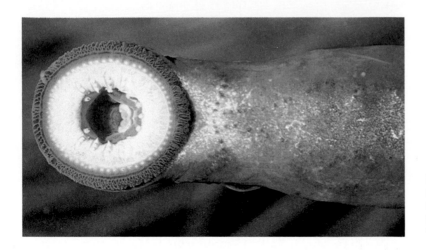

Figure 34-3. A Lamprey. Lampreys use their suckerlike mouth to attach themselves to other fish. They use their teeth to gnaw a hole in the body of their victim.

CLASS AGNATHA—THE JAWLESS FISHES

Objectives:
1. Name two members of the class Agnatha.
2. Describe the structure and life cycle of lampreys.

34-5 General Characteristics of Jawless Fishes

The class **Agnatha** (ag-*nath*-uh), the *jawless fishes,* includes only the *lampreys* and *hagfish.* These are the most primitive of all living vertebrates. They have long, snakelike bodies and smooth skin with no scales. They have two single fins and a tail fin. They lack the paired fins, true jaws, and scales of other fishes. The skeleton of jawless fishes is made up of cartilage, and the notochord persists throughout life. Sexes are separate, and fertilization is external.

34-6 Lampreys and Hagfish

Lampreys are found in both fresh and salt water. They are parasites, and obtain food by attaching themselves with their round, suckerlike mouth to the bodies of other fish (see Figure 34-3). Once attached, they use the teeth on their tongue to gnaw a hole in the body of their victim. The lamprey then sucks the blood and body fluids of the fish.

Lampreys shed their eggs, or spawn, in freshwater streams. The eggs are fertilized by the male, and they hatch into larvae about 1 centimeter long. The larvae live in the mud of the streams, maturing into adults in 3 to 7 years. The adult lives only a year or two. However, adult lampreys can do great damage to fish populations.

Hagfish are found only in salt water. They feed on dead fish, worms, or other small invertebrates that live on the ocean floor. Hagfish are also called "slime eels" because their skin glands release large amounts of mucus if they are disturbed. Hagfish do not have a larval stage in their development.

CLASS CHONDRICHTHYES— THE CARTILAGINOUS FISHES

Objectives:
1. Name three members of the class Chondrichthyes.
2. Describe the general characteristics of the cartilaginous fishes.

34-7   General Characteristics of Cartilaginous Fishes

Class **Chondrichthyes** (kahn-*drik*-thee-eez), the *cartilaginous* (kard-ul-*aj*-uh-nus) *fishes*, includes sharks, rays, and skates. Almost all members of this group are found in salt water. They range in size from small sharks less than 1 meter in length to whale sharks 15 meters long. Manta rays may be 6 meters across and weigh over 1,200 kilograms. In members of this group, the skeleton is made up entirely of cartilage, and traces of the notochord are present in the adult. Unlike the jawless fishes, the cartilaginous fishes have movable upper and lower jaws equipped with several rows of sharp teeth. These biting jaws enable the cartilaginous fishes to eat a wide variety of food. Like all fishes, members of this class have a two-chambered heart.

34-8   Skates, Rays, and Sharks

Skates and rays have flattened, winglike bodies with whiplike tails (see Figure 34-4). The rippling motion of their pectoral fins gracefully propels them through the water. They live on the ocean floor and feed on worms, mollusks, and crustaceans. Stingrays have poison stingers in their tails, which they use for defense. Electric rays produce a large electric charge, which they use to stun their prey.

Figure 34-4.   A Reef Stingray.

Figure 34-5. Sharks. (Left) A bonnethead shark. (Below) Teeth of a shark.

Sharks are streamlined fish that swim by moving their trunk and powerful tail from side to side (see Figure 34-5). Swimming forces water through the mouth, over the gills, and out through five to seven pairs of gill slits. The shark obtains the oxygen it needs from this flow of water. If a shark is caught where it cannot move, in a net, for example, it will die from lack of oxygen. Fertilization is internal in the shark. In some species, the embryos develop within the body of the mother and are born live. In others, the eggs are covered with a leathery coat before they are released from the body of the female.

The sense organs of the shark are well developed, particularly those for smell and vibration. Water entering the two nostrils passes through the *olfactory sacs*, which are sensitive to various chemicals and can detect the presence of food. The **lateral line,** which extends along each side of the body, is an organ sensitive to vibration. Most sharks are meat eaters, and are active hunters. However, the two largest sharks, the basking shark and the whale shark, are filter feeders, and obtain food by straining microorganisms from the water.

The skin of the shark is covered with embedded, toothlike *placoid* (*plah*-koyd) *scales*, which make it so tough it can be used as sandpaper. Unlike the scales of bony fishes, these scales do not overlap one another.

CLASS OSTEICHTHYES—THE BONY FISHES

Objectives:
1. Name three members of the class Osteichthyes.
2. Describe the general characteristics of the bony fishes.
3. Describe the respiratory and circulatory systems of the bony fishes.
4. Describe the digestive and excretory systems of the bony fishes.
5. Explain how a bony fish adjusts the density of its body to maintain its level in the water.

Figure 34-6.   A Pufferfish.

34-9   General Characteristics of Bony Fishes

The class **Osteichthyes** (ahs-tee-*ik*-thee-eez), the *bony fishes*, is the largest class of fishes. Members of this group have bony skeletons, paired fins, and protective overlapping scales. They are found in both fresh and salt water all over the earth. Bony fishes vary greatly in size, ranging from the Philippine goby, which is 10 millimeters long, to swordfish, which may be more than 4 meters long.

Many adaptations for protection are found among the bony fishes. The pufferfish, for example, is covered with sharp spines. In times of danger, it inflates itself with air or water so that its spines stand out (see Figure 34-6). Flying fish have a pair of winglike pectoral fins. To escape their enemies, they leap out of the water and glide through the air for distances of 100 meters or more. The large South American electric eel can stun or kill its enemies with a strong electric charge.

Bony fishes also show various types of protective coloration. Many are brightly colored so that they blend in with their surroundings. Some, such as flounders, can change color by varying the concentration of pigment in their pigment cells.

34-10   Structure and Life Functions of Bony Fishes

The bony fishes vary widely in structure, from the moray eel, which looks much like a snake, to the sea horse (see Figure 34-7). Most, however, are streamlined animals, like the perch. Their fins are made up of skin webbing, and are usually supported by bone or cartilage ribs. Most bony fishes swim by side-to-side movements of the body and tail. The fins aid in maintaining balance and in controlling the direction of movement.

Figure 34-7.   Bony Fishes. Although most fish resemble the perch in form, sea horses and moray eels are also fishes.

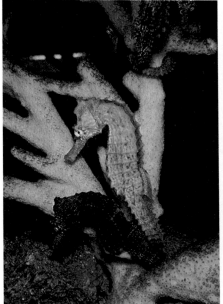

Figure 34-8. External Structure of the Perch.

Bony fishes usually have a pair of well-developed eyes, two nostrils, and lateral lines on each side of the body (see Figure 34-8). There are usually four pairs of gills, which lie on each side of the body under a protective bony flap called the *gill cover,* or **operculum** (oh-*perk*-yuh-lum). Water moves in through the mouth, passes over the gills, and then flows out of the body. The movement of muscles in the mouth and gill covers maintains the flow of water over the gills. Bony fishes have a two-chambered heart, consisting of an atrium and a ventricle. Blood travels from the heart to the gills, where oxygen is picked up and carbon dioxide is given off. The blood is then distributed through blood vessels to all parts of the body before it returns to the heart.

Most of the body of the fish is muscle. Along the ventral side is a small space containing the digestive, excretory, and reproductive organs (see Figure 34-9). The digestive system consists of the mouth, pharynx, esophagus, stomach, intestine, liver, gallbladder, pancreas, and anus. The gills are located on the sides of the pharynx. Attached to the short intestine are three tubular structures called *pyloric caeca* (*see*-kuh). They aid in absorption of digested materials. Some nitrogenous

Figure 34-9. Internal Structure of the Perch.

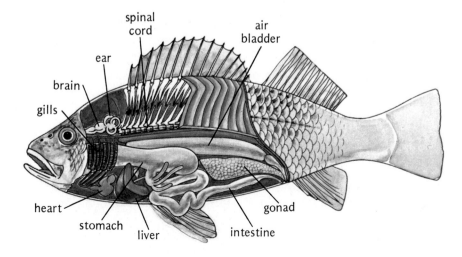

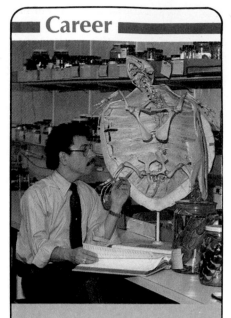

Career

Museum Manager

University science museums and natural history museums hire managers to collect, index, and maintain good collections of biological specimens from all over the world. Their job is to make these specimens available for researchers or the public.

These persons, called collection managers, curators, or registrars, may specialize in a botanical or zoological area. Their responsibilities vary; they often arrange for exchanges of specimens with other museums or other countries, order supplies, and manage the budget. They maintain the proper environment for preserving the specimens. Some also have research and teaching functions.

Museum managers usually have bachelor's or master's of science degrees. They may start as museum technicians to acquire experience. People with doctorate degrees can function in a research-oriented capacity. The field is not large, but it offers unique opportunities to those who find the work fascinating.

wastes are filtered from the blood by the two kidneys. These wastes, in the form of urea, pass through the ureters to the urinary opening. However, most of the nitrogenous wastes are excreted by the gills in the form of ammonia. Bony fishes have a complex nervous system. Ten pairs of cranial nerves extend from the brain, and spinal nerves radiate from the spinal cord.

All fish are slightly heavier than water. To keep from sinking, they must have some type of flotation device, or they must keep swimming to maintain their level in the water. Most bony fishes have a gas-filled sac called the **swim bladder**, or *air bladder*, in the upper part of their body cavity. This bladder acts as a float to regulate the buoyancy of the fish. By increasing or decreasing the amount of gas in the bladder, the fish can change the density of its body, enabling it to remain suspended in the water at any depth. In lungfish, which are air-breathing fish, the swim bladder serves as a lung.

As in vertebrates in general, the sexes are separate in bony fishes. The male has testes and the female has ovaries. Fertilization and development are most commonly external. The female deposits eggs in the water, and the male then discharges *milt*, a sperm-containing fluid, over the eggs.

CLASS AMPHIBIA—THE AMPHIBIANS

Objectives:
1. Name three members of the class Amphibia.
2. List the major characteristics of amphibians.
3. Describe the external structure of the frog.
4. Describe the circulatory and respiratory systems of the frog.
5. List the sense organs and the parts of the brain of the frog and describe their functions.
6. Describe metamorphosis in the frog.

34-11   General Characteristics of Amphibians

The class **Amphibia** (am-*fib*-ee-uh), the *amphibians*, includes frogs, toads, salamanders, and newts. Some amphibians live their entire adult lives on land. Others are found only in or around water. In any case, reproduction and development of most amphibians must take place in water or in a moist place. It is thought that amphibians evolved from air-breathing, lunged fishes, and were the first land-dwelling vertebrates.

In addition to their need of water for reproduction, amphibians share the following characteristics.

1. The skin is generally thin and contains mucus-secreting glands.

2. There are two pairs of limbs, which are used for walking, jumping, and/or swimming.

3. There is a pair of nostrils connected to the mouth cavity.

4. The heart has three chambers—two atria and one ventricle.

5. The young generally show a distinct larval form, and gradually develop adult characteristics.

There are two major groups of amphibians—the tailed amphibians, such as salamanders, and the tailless amphibians, such as frogs. A third group consists of small, tropical, wormlike animals that burrow in moist soil.

The tailed amphibians include salamanders and newts. (Newts are actually a type of salamander.) These animals have long bodies, long tails, and two pairs of short limbs (see Figure 34-10). Most salamanders range from 8 to 20 centimeters in length. However, the Japanese giant salamander, which is the largest living amphibian, may reach a length of 1.5 meters. Salamanders feed on fish, snails, insects, worms and other salamanders. Some are entirely aquatic, while others live under rocks or logs or in other moist places. They are active only at night. The aquatic salamanders retain their gills, which are used for breathing. The mudpuppy is a well-known salamander that lives in the streams and lakes of the eastern United States. Both the mudpuppy and the *axolotl* (*ak*-suh-lahd-ul), which is a salamander found in the Rocky Mountains and Mexico, are actually larval forms that can reproduce sexually (see Figure 34-11).

The tailless amphibians include frogs and toads. As adults, they have a short, squat body and lack a tail. Their large, powerful hind-legs are modified for jumping.

Toads have a dry, rough, warty skin (see Figure 34-12). They can live on land far away from water. Toads burrow or take shelter during the day, and come out to feed at night, when it is cooler and more humid. Some toads live in the desert, but like most amphibians, they need water for reproduction. During the winter, toads hibernate by burrowing into the ground. During *hibernation*, life processes slow down, and the animal is inactive.

Figure 34-10. Blue-Spotted Salamander.

Figure 34-11. Axolotl. The gills of the axolotl remain throughout life.

Figure 34-12. A Toad. Unlike frogs, toads can live away from water.

Frogs have a thin, moist skin that is loosely attached to the body. They generally live near ponds, streams, swamps, or other bodies of water. During the winter, they hibernate in the mud at the bottom of pools and streams. Frogs and toads eat insects and worms, while the larval forms, called **tadpoles**, eat aquatic plants.

Frogs and toads have many enemies, including snakes, birds, and turtles. Among their protective adaptations are their coloring, which provides good camouflage, and their ability to leap. They often dive underwater to escape their enemies. In addition, glands in their skin produce secretions that are unpleasant-tasting or poisonous to their enemies.

34-12   Structure of the Frog

The organ systems of the frog are similar to those of most other vertebrates, including humans. For this reason, they are often studied in detail in biology courses.

External features of the frog. The frog has a short, broad body with two short forelimbs and two long, muscular hind limbs (see Figure 34-13). The hands have four fingers and are not webbed, while the feet have five webbed toes and are adapted for jumping and swimming. The upper surface of the frog is yellow-green to green-brown in color, while the underside is whitish. This coloring allows the animal to blend into its surroundings. The skin can also change color to some extent to further camouflage the animal.

Two large, movable eyes protrude from the head. They permit vision in all directions. Each eye is protected by three

Figure 34-13.   External Structure of the Frog.

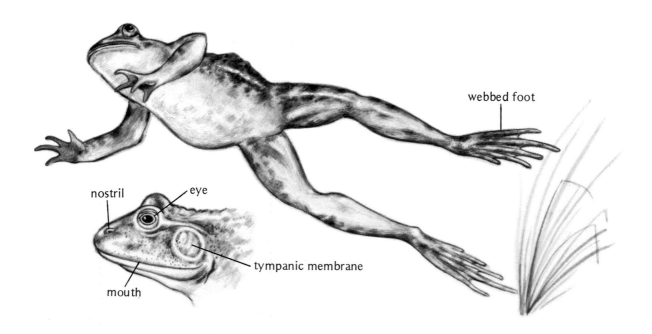

eyelids—the upper eyelid, the lower eyelid, and the **nictitating** (*nik*-tuh-tayt-ing) **membrane.** The transparent nictitating membrane permits the frog to see underwater. Behind each eye is a round eardrum called the **tympanic membrane,** which picks up sound waves from air or water. Two nostrils on the tip of the head enable the frog to breathe air while the rest of the body is floating underwater.

The mouth. The mouth of the frog is very large. The sticky tongue is attached at the front end of the lower jaw. The frog can rapidly flip out its tongue and catch insects in flight. The food sticks to the tongue, which is then pulled back into the mouth. Teeth along the edge of the upper jaw and on the roof of the mouth aid in gripping the food. From the mouth, the food is forced down the opening of the esophagus in the back of the throat. The glottis, the opening that leads to the lungs, is also in the back of the throat.

The digestive system. Food passes down the esophagus into the stomach, where digestion begins (see Figure 34-14). The partially digested food then passes through the pyloric valve into the small intestine. The pancreas and liver secrete digestive juices that pass through ducts into the small intestine. Most digestion and absorption take place in the small intestine. Undigested food passes from the small intestine into the large intestine and then into the **cloaca** (kloh-*ay*-kuh). The cloaca empties to the outside of the body through the anal opening. The cloaca also serves as a passageway for urine and for eggs and sperm.

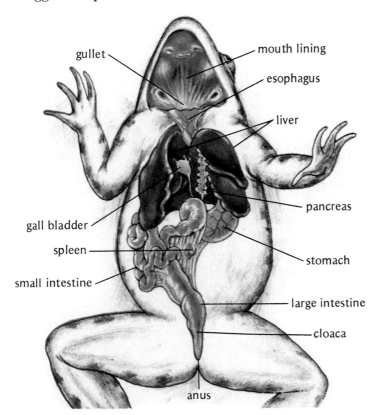

Figure 34-14. Digestive System of the Frog.

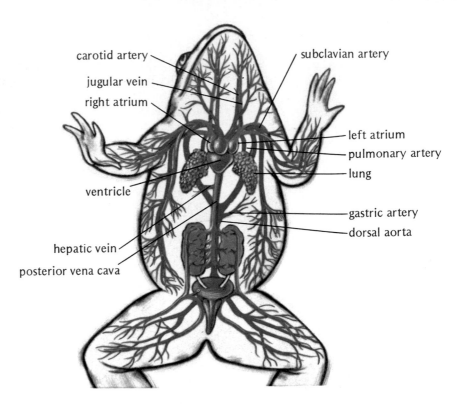

carotid artery

subclavian artery

jugular vein

right atrium

left atrium

pulmonary artery

lung

ventricle

gastric artery

dorsal aorta

hepatic vein

posterior vena cava

Figure 34-15. Circulatory System of the Frog.

The circulatory system. The frog has a three-chambered heart made up of two thin-walled atria and one muscular ventricle (see Figure 34-15). Blood leaving the ventricle enters a large blood vessel that branches immediately into two arteries. Each of these divides into many smaller arteries, and eventually into capillaries. Blood from the capillaries is returned to the heart through the veins. Blood from the lungs is carried to the left atrium by the right and left pulmonary veins. This blood is oxygenated only when the frog is breathing air with its lungs. Blood from all the other parts of the body is returned through three large veins into a thin-walled sac. Blood from the sac enters the right atrium. Both the right and left atria empty blood into the ventricle. Thus, blood pumped out by the ventricle is a mixture of oxygenated blood from the left atrium and deoxygenated blood from the right atrium.

The respiratory system. The respiratory system of the adult frog includes the lungs, the lining of the mouth, and the skin. All of these structures have thin, moist surfaces and are richly supplied with blood vessels.

The frog uses its lungs to meet most of its oxygen requirements. The two lungs are elastic sacs with thin walls. Air is forced into the lungs by the pumping action of muscles in the floor of the mouth. The floor of the mouth is lowered, and air is drawn into the closed mouth through the nostrils. Then the nostrils are closed, the floor of the mouth is raised, and air is forced through the glottis into the lungs. Exchange of oxygen and carbon dioxide occurs in the capillaries of the lungs. The thin roof of the mouth also serves as a respiratory surface. The thin, moist skin of the frog serves as a respiratory surface

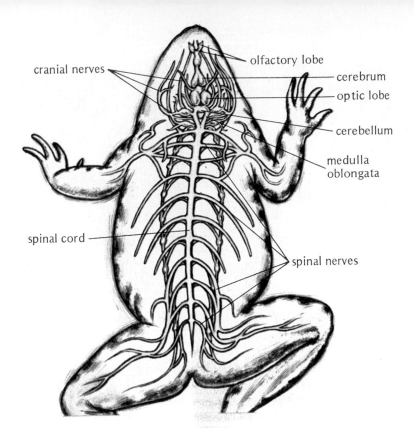

cranial nerves

olfactory lobe

cerebrum

optic lobe

cerebellum

medulla oblongata

spinal cord

spinal nerves

Figure 34-16. Nervous System of the Frog.

either in air or in water. This is especially important when the frog remains underwater for long periods of time. Also, when the frog is hibernating over the winter, the body metabolism is reduced so that skin respiration alone can provide all the oxygen needs of the animal.

The nervous system. Like humans, frogs have a central nervous system and a peripheral nervous system (see Figure 34-16). The central nervous system of the frog consists of the brain and spinal cord. The brain is connected to various parts of the head and abdomen by ten pairs of cranial nerves. The spinal cord, which is encased in bony vertebrae, is connected to various parts of the body by ten pairs of spinal nerves. The cranial nerves and the spinal nerves and their branches make up the peripheral nervous system.

The frog brain is divided into the following parts: the olfactory lobes, which function in smell; the cerebrum, which receives and interprets sensory information and controls voluntary muscles; the optic lobes, which function in vision; the cerebellum, which coordinates muscle action; and the medulla, which connects the brain to the spinal cord and controls many reflexes. The sense organs of the frog include the eyes, tympanic membranes for hearing, inner ears for balance, taste buds on the tongue, odor-sensitive nerve endings in the nasal passages, and sensory nerve endings in the skin.

The excretory system. Most of the carbon dioxide produced by the frog is excreted through the skin, but other metabolic wastes are excreted by the kidneys. The pair of kidneys are located in the back of the body cavity on either side of the spine (see Figure 34-17). Wastes filtered from the blood form

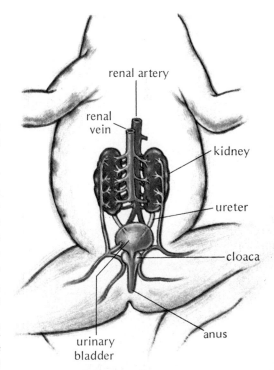

renal artery

renal vein

kidney

ureter

cloaca

anus

urinary bladder

Figure 34-17. Excretory System of the Frog.

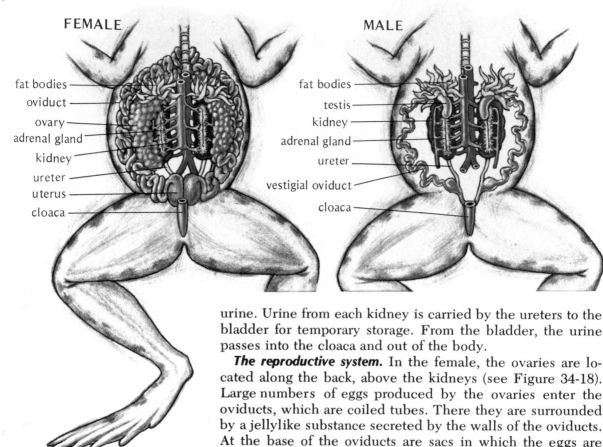

FEMALE

fat bodies
oviduct
ovary
adrenal gland
kidney
ureter
uterus
cloaca

MALE

fat bodies
testis
kidney
adrenal gland
ureter
vestigial oviduct
cloaca

Figure 34-18. Reproductive System of the Frog.

urine. Urine from each kidney is carried by the ureters to the bladder for temporary storage. From the bladder, the urine passes into the cloaca and out of the body.

The reproductive system. In the female, the ovaries are located along the back, above the kidneys (see Figure 34-18). Large numbers of eggs produced by the ovaries enter the oviducts, which are coiled tubes. There they are surrounded by a jellylike substance secreted by the walls of the oviducts. At the base of the oviducts are sacs in which the eggs are stored until they are released from the body through the cloaca.

In the male, the testes are small, yellowish, bean-shaped organs located in the back just above the kidneys. Sperm produced in the testes pass to the kidneys through microscopic tubules. From the kidneys, the sperm are carried by the ureters to the cloaca. During mating, the sperm are discharged from the male through the cloaca.

34-13 Fertilization and Development in Frogs

Fertilization in frogs is external. During mating, the male clasps the female with his short front legs. This is known as *amplexus* (am-*plek*-sus) (see page 361). As the eggs leave the body of the female, the male releases sperm over them, so that many are fertilized.

After 6 to 9 days, the eggs hatch into tadpoles (see Figure 34-19). They are fishlike, with no legs, a long tail, and gills. The tadpole has a two-chambered heart. Metamorphosis of the tadpole into the adult frog involves the development of legs, the absorption of the tail, the disappearance of gills, and the development of lungs and a three chambered heart, as well as still other changes. The leopard frog completes its metamorphosis in about 3 months, while bullfrogs take 2 or 3 years to complete the process.

Figure 34-19. Development of the Frog. (A) A mass of eggs. (B) Newly hatched tadpoles. (C) Tadpole with limbs. (D) Adult frog.

CLASS REPTILIA—THE REPTILES

Objectives:

1. Explain why reptiles are better adapted to life on land than amphibians.
2. List the general characteristics of reptiles.
3. Compare and contrast the external structures of crocodiles and turtles.
4. Describe the major characteristics of lizards and snakes.

34-14   General Characteristics of Reptiles

The *reptiles,* class **Reptilia** (rep-*til*-ee-uh), include crocodiles, alligators, turtles, tortoises, lizards, and snakes. Reptiles are very well adapted for life on land. Unlike amphibians, they do not require water for reproduction. Fertilization is internal. The fertilized egg is enclosed in a thick, leathery, waterproof shell that protects it from drying out (see page 372). Unlike amphibians, reptiles do not have gills at any stage in their life cycle, and they do not undergo metamorphosis.

Figure 34-20. Newly Hatched Crocodiles. The newly hatched young look like miniature adults.

When reptiles hatch from eggs, they look like miniature adults (see Figure 34-20).

In addition to their shelled eggs, reptiles share a number of other characteristics.

1. The skin of reptiles is dry and covered with scales. This waterproof covering protects them from excessive water loss and from predators.

2. Except for snakes, reptiles have two pairs of legs. Most reptiles have five clawed toes on each leg. The legs are adapted for climbing, running, or paddling.

3. In most reptiles, there is a three-chambered heart consisting of two atria and one partly divided ventricle. This partial separation of the ventricle decreases the mixing of oxygenated and deoxygenated blood in the heart, thereby increasing the amount of oxygen carried to the body cells. Crocodiles and alligators have four-chambered hearts.

4. Reptiles have well-developed lungs that are protected by a rib cage.

5. Nitrogenous wastes are execreted mainly as uric acid, so that the urine of many reptiles is a semisolid paste. This is an excellent adaptation for conserving water.

From the fossil record, it appears that reptiles were once a highly successful group. Dinosaurs were reptiles. Prehistoric reptiles were a diverse group. There were swimming reptiles,

Figure 34-21. A Tuatara.

flying reptiles, reptiles that walked on four legs, and reptiles that walked on two legs. Today, however, there are only four orders of living reptiles. One of these orders has only one member, the *tuatara*, which is a lizardlike animal found only in New Zealand (see Figure 34-21). This primitive reptile has an extra eyelike structure on the top of its head.

34-15   Crocodiles and Alligators

Crocodiles and alligators are the largest living reptiles. They range in length from 2.5 meters to more than 7 meters. They are found in lakes, swamps, and rivers in tropical regions all over the world. Both alligators and crocodiles have long snouts, powerful jaws with large teeth, and long, muscular tails (see Figure 34-22). The tails are used in swimming. These two types of reptiles look very much alike, but the arrangement of their teeth is slightly different, and the American alligator has a much broader snout than the American crocodile. In both alligators and crocodiles there are nostrils at the tip of the snout. This allows the animals to lie submerged in water, with only the tip of the snout and the eyes projecting above the surface.

Alligators and crocodiles feed on animals that they capture with their massive, toothed jaws. Crocodiles are more vicious and aggressive than alligators. They will attack large animals, including humans, cattle, and deer. It is the less aggressive alligator that is most commonly found in the southern United States. Their hides are used for leather goods. Overkilling brought some species close to extinction, but protective laws have allowed the populations to increase again.

34-16   Turtles

Turtles are found on land and in both fresh and salt water. Land-dwelling turtles are sometimes called tortoises. The

◼ Sidelight ◼

Rare Reptile Rescued

The fish-eating gharial, one of the world's rarest and least understood crocodiles, is on the verge of extinction. The population of this creature, native to hot northern India wastelands, is down from many thousands to about 200 breeding adults. For generations, people have slaughtered them for their hides or killed them while fishing. Their eggs, considered to be delicacies, have been taken indiscriminately. Their habitats have been destroyed, mainly by damming rivers.

The Indian government is now trying to save the gharial. Eggs are being collected and hatched safe from predators. In addition, hatchlings from the wild are collected, protected, and then returned when they are old enough to fend for themselves. Finally, several gharial sanctuaries have been set aside.

By these measures, the Indians hope to save this only surviving member of an entire family of crocodilians—a creature whose anatomy, physiology, and behavior holds clues to reptile evolution.

Figure 34-22.   An American Alligator.

Figure 34-23.   Eastern Box Turtles.

body of a turtle is enclosed in protective shells (see Figure 34-23). The upper shell is called the *carapace,* and the lower shell is called the *plastron.* For defense, the legs, tail, neck and head of some turtles can be pulled completely inside the shell. Turtles feed on plants and small animals. They have no teeth, but they grab and tear their food with the hard, sharp edges of their beak.

Land-dwelling turtles are slow moving. Their short legs have claws that are used in digging. In sea turtles, the legs are paddle-shaped and are used in swimming. All turtles, including ocean-dwelling turtles, lay their eggs on land in holes that they dig with their hind legs.

Some marine turtles reach lengths of 2 meters and weights of more than 500 kilograms. Some land turtles have reached weights of more than 180 kilograms. Turtles may live to be more than 100 years old.

34-17   Lizards and Snakes

Lizards and snakes belong to the same order, but there are many differences between them. Most lizards are four-legged, while snakes have no legs. Lizards have movable eyelids and external ear openings, while snakes have immovable eyelids and no external ear openings. In both lizards and snakes, the skin is covered with scales and is shed periodically. The scales of the lizard are almost uniform in size, while those of the snake vary in size. The scales on the back and sides of snakes are small. But on the belly there is a single row of large scales that act as cleats and give the snake traction as it moves.

Lizards. Lizards are an extremely diverse group. They are found in deserts, in forests, and in water. The smaller lizards feed on insects, worms, spiders, and snails. The larger ones may also eat eggs, small birds, other lizards, and small mammals. A few lizards feed on plants. Many lizards can shed their tail if seized by an enemy. The tail wiggles, distracting the other animal, and the lizard escapes. A new tail is regenerated in a short time.

A

B

C

Figure 34-24. Lizards. (A) The Komodo dragon is the largest of the lizards. (B) Anole. (C) Gecko.

The gecko is a small lizard that has sticky toe pads that allow it to walk on vertical surfaces and upside down (see Figure 34-24). It catches insects with a flick of its long, sticky tongue. The American chameleon, the anole, has a remarkable ability to change color and blend in with its surroundings. The Gila monster is a highly colored lizard found in the deserts of the southwestern United States. Its bite is poisonous, but rarely fatal to humans. The largest lizard is the Komodo dragon of Indonesia. It weighs over 100 kilograms and may be 3 meters long. The Malaysian flying lizard has skin extensions on its sides that enable it to glide from tree to tree.

Snakes. Although snakes in general have a bad reputation, only about 200 of the 2,500 known species are poisonous. Snakes are actually more helpful than harmful because they kill large numbers of rodents.

Snakes are widely distributed in nature. They are found on the ground, in trees, and in both fresh and salt water. They are most abundant in tropical areas. The body of a snake consists of the head, trunk, and tail (see Figure 34-25). The trunk contains the body cavity with the elongated internal organs. The digestive tract is essentially a straight tube running from the mouth to the anus. The tail is the portion of the body following the anus. The skeleton has a large number of vertebrae and ribs.

Snakes have special sense organs that are used in hunting food. The forked tongue of the snake picks up odor-bearing particles. These are identified by the *Jacobson's organs* in the roof of the mouth. Snakes are deaf to airborne sounds, but there are sense organs within the skull that respond to vibrations in the ground. Some snakes are *pit vipers.* They have heat-detecting pit organs on their head, between the nostrils and the eyes. With these organs they can accurately track and strike warm-blooded prey, even at night or in deep burrows.

Snakes feed on mice, rats, frogs, toads, insects, fish, and other small animals, depending on where they live. Some snakes eat only living animals, swallowing them alive, while others kill their prey before they swallow it. Large snakes,

Figure 34-25. A Western Rattle-snake.

Figure 34-26. Fangs of a Diamond-back Rattlesnake.

such as pythons, boas, and king snakes, coil their body around their victim and crush or strangle it to death. Some snakes poison their victims.

Snakes can swallow animals that are much larger in diameter than they are. This is possible because the structure of the jaw allows the mouth to open very wide. Furthermore, the ribs are unattached at one end, allowing the body cavity to expand. Swallowing is a slow process. The teeth point backward so that the prey cannot pop out of the mouth, and the windpipe is projected forward so that breathing is not obstructed. After a large meal, a snake may go for weeks or months without eating.

Poisonous snakes have a pair of specialized teeth called *fangs* (see Figure 34-26). The fangs are connected to salivary glands, which produce a poison, or venom. Some venoms are *neurotoxins*, which attack nervous tissues. They cause paralysis of muscles and affect the action of the heart and lungs. Other venoms, called *hemotoxins*, break down red blood cells and blood vessels. When a snake bites, the venom is conducted into the victim by the fangs. Some snakes have hollow fangs that act like hypodermic needles, injecting the venom. In others, the fangs are grooved, and the venom passes into the victim by capillary action. The poisonous snakes of the United States include rattlesnakes, water moccasins, copperheads, and coral snakes. The best known and most common snake is the garter snake, which is harmless.

Chapter Review

SUMMARY

- The phylum Chordata includes the subphyla Urochordata, Cephalochordata, and Vertebrata. All chordates, at some stage in their life, have a dorsal, hollow nerve cord, a notochord, and paired gill slits.

- The urochordates and cephalochordates are small groups of soft-bodied, marine animals.

- The vertebrates are the most numerous and complex chordates. They have a spinal column made up of vertebrae. The vertebrates include jawless fishes, cartilaginous fishes, bony fishes, amphibians, reptiles, birds, and mammals.

- The jawless fishes include lampreys and hagfish, which are the most primitive vertebrates.

- The cartilaginous fishes include skates, rays, and sharks. Members of this class have skeletons made up of cartilage and movable upper and lower jaws.

- The bony fishes have skeletons of bone, paired fins, and overlapping scales.

- Amphibians generally live in and around water. All members of this class need water for reproduction and development. Development generally involves metamorphosis. The tailed amphibians include salamanders and newts. The tailless amphibians include frogs and toads.

- The reptiles include crocodiles, alligators, turtles, lizards, and snakes. Reptiles are well adapted for life on land. Fertilization is internal, and the egg is enclosed in a thick, leathery, waterproof shell. Reptiles do not have gills at any stage in their life cycle, and they do not undergo metamorphosis.

KNOW THE TERMS

Agnatha	cloaca	nictitating membrane	swim bladder
Amphibia	ectothermic	notochord	tadpole
Cephalochordata	endothermic	operculum	tympanic membrane
Chondrichthyes	gill slit	Osteichthyes	Urochordata
Chordata	lateral line	Reptilia	Vertebrata

SECTION QUESTIONS

Phylum Chordata—The Chordates

1. Name the subphyla of the phylum Chordata.
2. List the characteristics that distinguish chordates from other animals.
3. What basic characteristic distinguishes vertebrates from the other chordates?
4. What classes make up the vertebrates?

Class Agnatha—The Jawless Fishes

5. Name the two types of jawless fishes.
6. What are the feeding habits of lampreys and hagfish?
7. Where are lampreys and hagfish found?

Class Chondrichthyes— The Cartilaginous Fishes

8. Name three members of the class Chondrichthyes.
9. List the general characteristics of the class Chondrichthyes.
10. What organisms do skates and rays eat?
11. What are the protective mechanisms of stingrays and electric rays?
12. What is the function of the olfactory sacs in the shark?

Class Osteichthyes—The Bony Fishes

13. Name three members of the class Osteichthyes.
14. List the general characteristics of the bony fishes.
15. What structures aid in maintaining balance and in controlling the direction of movement in bony fishes?

Class Amphibia—The Amphibians

16. Name the two main groups of amphibians and give an example of each.
17. What is the function of the nictitating membrane in the frog?
18. What is the tympanic membrane?
19. Name the respiratory surfaces of the frog.

Class Reptilia—The Reptiles

20. Name four members of the class Reptilia.
21. What are the upper and lower shell of the turtle called?
22. Name the poisonous snakes of the United States.

KNOW THE FACTS

Copy the numbers from Column 1 (page 616) on a sheet of paper. Select the letter for the term or phrase from Column 2 that matches each numbered item, and write it beside the number.

Column 1	Column 2
1. notochord	a. structures that aid in absorption of digested materials
2. ectothermic	b. dry, rough, warty skin
3. endothermic	c. body temperature remains fairly constant
4. lamprey	d. a flexible, rodlike, internal supporting structure
5. lateral line	e. transparent eyelid for seeing underwater
6. placoid scales	f. skin of shark
7. operculum	g. specialized teeth called fangs
8. pyloric caeca	h. the passageway for urine, eggs, sperm, and undigested food
9. ammonia	i. parasite that attaches itself to fish with its suckerlike mouth
10. toads	j. gill cover
11. nictitating membrane	k. an organ found in fish that is sensitive to vibrations
12. cloaca	l. land-dwelling turtles
13. tadpole	m. small and fishlike, with a long tail, gills, and no legs
14. tortoises	n. body temperature varies with the temperature of the environment
15. poisonous snakes	o. nitrogenous waste excreted by the gills
	p. the sperm-containing fluid produced by male fish

UNDERSTANDING THE CONCEPTS

16. Describe the structure of lancelets.
17. Describe the general characteristics of vertebrates.
18. Describe the general characteristics of the jawless fishes.
19. Describe the external structure of skates, rays, and sharks.
20. Describe the respiratory system of the bony fishes.
21. What is the function of the swim bladder in fish?
22. Describe the characteristics of amphibians.
23. How do frogs catch insects?
24. Trace the path of food through the digestive system of the frog, and state the function of each part.
25. Explain why the frog's heart pumps both oxygenated and deoxygenated blood to the body.
26. Describe the frog's reproductive system.
27. Describe the metamorphosis of a tadpole into an adult frog.
28. Describe the characteristics of reptiles.
29. Describe the external structure of crocodiles and alligators.
30. Describe the special sense organs that a snake uses in hunting.
31. How do snake venoms affect the bite victim?

THINK CRITICALLY

32. Why have biologists classified tunicates as vertebrates rather than as members of the phylum Porifera?
33. Why do lampreys feed by gnawing a hole in the bodies of other fish rather than trapping and ingesting fish?
34. In what ways would the adult whale shark be similar to an adult flounder? In what ways would the shark and flounder differ?
35. In what ways are snakes better adapted for life on land than are frogs?
36. How does the fact that reptiles are cold-blooded limit their geographic distribution?
37. What characteristics have contributed to the biological success of the vertebrates as a group?

THINK CREATIVELY

38. Propose a hypothesis to explain why reptiles, once a highly successful group, have only four living groups today.
39. How would you change the internal and external body of a land-based reptile if you expected it to be able to fly?

FOR FURTHER INVESTIGATION

1. Fish are fun to raise and watch! Set up an aquarium to study goldfish. Feed the fish and watch them eat. Can you use food to train the fish to respond to light or sound? How do the fish use their fins and tail in swimming? How often do the gill covers move? What is the relationship of the opening of the mouth to the moving of the gill covers? How are the scales arranged on the body? Write up your observations and experiments. Present your findings in an oral report to the class.

2. Do library research on the treatment of poisonous snake bites. Write up your findings in the form of a feature article for a magazine or newspaper.

3. Visit an aquarium or a tropical fish store. Select five fish that interest you. Write a report about these fish. For each fish be sure to include its common and scientific name, and a description of its habitat, body shape, color, and behavior.

4. Using field guides, identify some of the kinds of fish, amphibians, and reptiles living in your local area. Present your finding in an oral report to the class.

5. Prepare a report on one of the career opportunities listed below. See suggested procedures, p. 9, "For Further Investigation" Activity 3.
   a. Zoologist
   b. Fishery worker
   c. Tropical fish store worker
   d. Marine biologist

6. Write a brief report on the life and contributions of one of the following scientists:
   a. Agnes Stroud
   b. Thomas Julian Huxley
   c. Eugenie Clark
   d. Charles Turner

FOR FURTHER READING

Carr, Archie, *So Excellent a Fishe: A Natural History of Sea Turtles*, revised ed., Charles Scribner's Sons, New York, 1984.

Crews, D., and Garstka, W. R., "The Ecological Physiology of a Garter Snake," *Scientific American*, November, 1982.

Myers, C. W., and Daly, J. W., "Dart-Poison Frogs," *Scientific American*, February, 1983.

Nelson, J., "*Fishes of the World*," John Wiley, New York, 1984.

Scott, Jack Denton, *Alligator*, Putnam Pub. Group, New York, 1984.

Webb, P., "Form and Function in Fish Swimming," *Scientific American*, July, 1984.

Wilson, E. O., "In Praise of Sharks," *Discover*, July, 1985.

Chapter 35

VERTEBRATES— BIRDS AND MAMMALS

These pelicans feed on fish that they catch with their long, sharp beaks.

CLASS AVES—THE BIRDS

Objectives:
1. List the major characteristics of birds
2. Describe the structure and functions of feathers.
3. Describe the respiratory and circulatory systems of birds.
4. Describe the digestive, excretory, and nervous systems of the bird.

35-1   General Characteristics of Birds

The *birds*, class **Aves** (*ay*-veez), are a very successful animal group. Members of this class are found in almost all types of environments. The single characteristic that distinguishes birds from all other animals is the presence of feathers. Birds are thought to have evolved from reptiles, and the feathers are thought to be modified scales. Birds do have reptile-like scales on their legs and feet.

In addition to the presence of feathers, birds share a number of other characteristics:

1. The body is usually spindle-shaped and divided into a head, neck, trunk, and tail.

2. There are two pairs of limbs. The forelimbs are wings, which in most birds are used for flying. The hind limbs are legs that are adapted for perching, walking or swimming, or prey-catching, depending on the particular life-style of the bird.

3. The bones are strong and light, and many are filled with air spaces.

4. The circulatory system is well developed and includes a four-chambered heart.

5. The respiratory system is highly efficient and consists of lungs connected to air sacs.

6. The mouth is in the form of a horn-covered beak or bill. There are no teeth.

7. The excretory system does not include a urinary bladder.

8. Fertilization is internal. The large, shell-covered eggs are incubated by the parents, and at hatching, the young are cared for by the parents.

9. Birds are warm-blooded, and their body temperature is relatively high.

The beaks and feet of birds show adaptations for different ways of life. The pelican uses its long, sharp beak for catching fish. The cardinal uses its strong beak to crack open seeds. The hooked beak of the hawk enables it to tear its food (see Figure 35-1). The woodpecker uses its beak to bore into trees and extract insects. A duck scoops and strains its food from mud with its beak. The ostrich and other ground-dwelling birds have sturdy feet and toes that enable them to run. Ducks and geese have webbed feet that are useful in swimming. The position of the toes and the presence of sharp claws enable woodpeckers to cling to the sides of trees. Grasping feet with sharp claws or talons are characteristic of falcons and hawks. The ability to grasp is also well developed in perching birds. The tendons of the feet are arranged so that when the bird lands on a branch, the weight of the body forces the toes to grasp the branch. These birds can sleep without falling off their perch.

Figure 35-1. Birds. (A) Ostriches. (B) Hawk. (C) Woodpecker.

Figure 35-2. Male and Female Peafowl. In many birds, including peafowl, the males are much more brightly colored than the females.

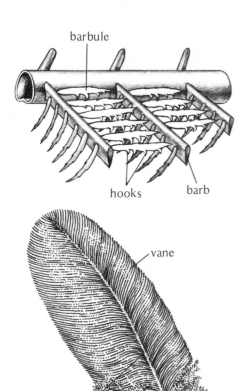

barbule

hooks   barb

vane

rachis

quill

Figure 35-2. Male and Female Peafowl. In many birds, including peafowl, the males are much more brightly colored than the females.

35-2 Feathers

Feathers are lightweight and flexible, yet incredibly tough. They provide a body covering that protects the skin from wear, supports the bird in flight, and provides insulation from the weather. Feathers grow from follicles in the skin. As the feather grows in the follicle, pigments are deposited in the epidermal cells making up the feather. The color pattern of the feathers is typical of the species. In many species, the male and female differ in coloring, with the male generally brighter (see Figure 35-2). The difference in coloring between sexes plays a role in the mating behavior of birds.

Figure 35-3 shows a typical feather. The flat area, the *vane*, is supported by a central shaft, or *rachis* (ray-kus). The hollow part of the shaft that is attached to the skin follicle is called the *quill*. Each vane consists of numerous, closely spaced *barbs*. The barbs spread out diagonally from the shaft. Each barb has numerous *barbules*. The barbules of one barb overlap the barbules of an adjacent barb, and they are held together by tiny hooks on the barbules themselves. When neighboring barbs become separated, the bird can zip them together with its beak.

Feathers grow only on certain parts of the skin known as *feather tracts*. When fully grown, feathers are not living structures. Usually in the late summer, molting occurs. The feathers are shed and replaced by new feathers. Molting is usually a gradual process so that no part of the body is ever completely without feathers.

There are several different types of feathers. The elongated *contour feathers* are the type shown in Figure 35-3. They cover, insulate, and protect the body. Contour feathers that extend beyond the body are called *flight feathers*. Those on the wings support the bird in flight, while those on the tail serve as a rudder for steering. *Down feathers* have a short

Figure 35-3. Structure of a Feather. The photo shows the barbs and barbules of a gull feather.

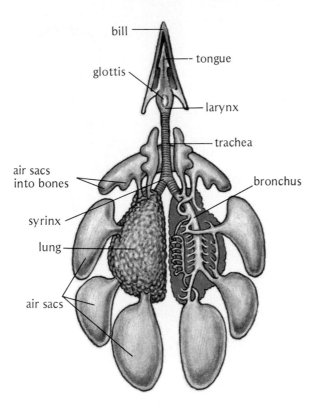

bill

tongue

glottis

larynx

trachea

air sacs
into bones

bronchus

syrinx

lung

air sacs

Figure 35-4. The Respiratory System of the Bird.

shaft with long barbs. They are soft because the barbules lack hooks. In ducks, geese, and other water birds, down feathers are present beneath the contour feathers.

Birds have oil glands near the base of their tail. They use their beaks to take oil from the gland and spread it over the feathers. The oil makes the feathers waterproof.

35-3 Internal Structure of Birds

Respiratory and circulatory systems. The unique and highly efficient respiratory system of birds provides the large amounts of oxygen needed for flight. Pouching out from the small lungs are *air sacs* (see Figure 35-4). These sacs occupy space between the internal organs and even run into the cavities of the larger bones. Air enters the respiratory system through the nostrils and passes down the trachea, which divides into two bronchi. One bronchus enters each lung. The bronchi pass through the lungs to the posterior air sacs. Thus, oxygen-rich air entering the respiratory system passes through the lungs to the posterior air sacs without any exchange of respiratory gases. A system of small air tubes leads from the posterior air sacs into the lungs. The air tubes subdivide many times and make close contact with blood capillaries in the lungs. Oxygen-rich air from the posterior sacs is forced through the fine air tubes in the lungs, and gas exchange occurs with the blood. The air, now oxygen-poor, enters the anterior air sacs. From these sacs, it passes back up the trachea and out of the

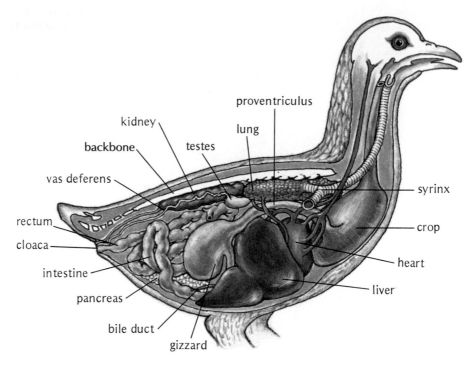

Figure labels: kidney, backbone, vas deferens, rectum, cloaca, intestine, pancreas, bile duct, gizzard, testes, proventriculus, lung, syrinx, crop, heart, liver

Figure 35-5. The Internal Structure of the Bird.

body. The one-way flow of air through the lungs for gas exchange increases the efficiency of the system.

The circulatory system of birds is similar to that of humans. There is a four-chambered heart with complete separation of oxygenated and deoxygenated blood.

Digestive system. Birds eat large amounts of food—a consequence of their high rates of metabolism and the energy demands of flight. They feed on seeds, fruits, insects, worms, and in some cases, small reptiles and mammals. Some small birds take in an amount of food equal to 30 percent of their body weight each day.

Food is taken into the mouth, mixed with saliva, and passed down the esophagus to the crop, where it is stored and softened (see Figure 35-5). From the crop, it passes into the first portion of the stomach, the *proventriculus* (proh-ven-*trik*-yuh-lus), where it is partially digested by gastric juice. It then passes to the gizzard, the second part of the stomach. The gizzard is a thick-walled, muscular organ that may contain small stones. Stones found in the gizzard have been swallowed by the bird. In the gizzard, the food is ground up and thoroughly mixed with the gastric juices. Next, the food moves into the intestine, where digestion is completed and nutrients are absorbed into the bloodstream. Undigested food enters the short rectum and leaves the body through the cloaca. The genital ducts and the ureters from the kidneys also open into the cloaca.

Excretory system. Nitrogenous wastes, in the form of uric acid, are removed from the blood by the kidneys. There is no urinary bladder, and these wastes pass through the ureters to the cloaca. They combine with the fecal matter in the cloaca to form a whitish, semisolid material.

Nervous system. The brain of the bird is relatively large. The cerebellum, which is involved in muscle coordination, is well developed and enables the bird to perform precise movements in flight. In most birds, the senses of smell and taste are poorly developed, but the senses of sight, hearing, and balance are highly developed.

Reproductive system. There are no external sex organs in birds. During mating, the sperm are transferred from the male to the female by contact of the cloacas. After fertilization in the female's reproductive tract, a protective shell is deposited around each egg. The female deposits her eggs in a nest, and they are incubated until hatching.

CLASS MAMMALIA—THE MAMMALS

Objectives:
1. List the major characteristics of mammals.
2. Name the three different kinds of mammals.
3. List the major orders of placental mammals, and name some members of each.

35-4 General Characteristics of Mammals

The *mammals*, class **Mammalia** (muh-*mayl*-ee-uh), include many familiar animals—cats, dogs, bats, monkeys, horses, cows, deer, whales, and also humans. Members of this group are found all over the earth, in both cold and warm climates. Most are land dwelling, but a few, such as the whale, porpoise, and seal, are found in the oceans. Mammals range in size from the tiny pygmy shrew, which is less than 5 centimeters long and weighs less than 5 grams, to the giant blue whale, which may be 30 meters long and weigh more than 100,000 kilograms.

Two characteristics distinguish mammals from all other vertebrates: (1) mammals nourish their young with milk produced by mammary glands; and (2) the body covering of mammals is hair. The amount of hair varies greatly. In whales and porpoises, just a few whiskers are found around the mouth. In many other mammals, the hair is in the form of a thick coat of fur.

Mammals also share several other characteristics. Like birds, they are warm-blooded and have a four-chambered heart. An internal muscular wall, the diaphragm, separates the chest cavity from the abdominal cavity. The cerebrum of the brain is more highly developed than in any other group, and mammals are therefore the most intelligent animals.

Mammals have highly differentiated teeth. The structure and arrangement of the teeth vary from group to group, depending on feeding habits. The four types of teeth are the

Sidelight

Bird Songs and Speech

Scientists are currently investigating why some bird species imitate other bird calls and sounds they hear, while most species are limited to their own sounds. They know that birds' repertoires of songs are learned, not genetically determined. Most birds learn their species' songs at an early age from adult members. Others, such as mockingbirds, sparrows, catbirds, and starlings, imitate other birds' sounds or even car horns.

Some birds imitate human speech. The myna bird's vocabulary can include 50 words plus 15 to 20 sentences. Starlings can be taught to speak and to whistle familiar tunes.

So far, researchers have learned that the ability to make sounds is controlled by an area in the front of the brain. This forebrain is generally larger in males than in females, correlating with the fact that males tend to do most of the singing as part of their mating behavior.

Scientists also know that bird sounds are produced by the syrinx—the equivalent of the human voice box, but much simpler. Surprisingly, some of the bird species that are the best speakers have the simplest syrinxes.

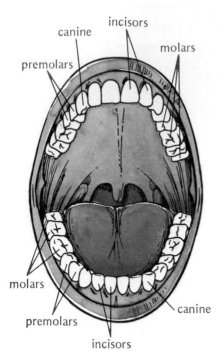

Figure 35-6. The Teeth of Mammals. Mammals have differentiated teeth, including incisors, canines, premolars, and molars.

incisors (in-*syz*-erz), which are for cutting; the **canines** (*kay-nynz*), which are for tearing; and the **premolars** (pree-*mohl-erz*) and **molars,** which are for grinding (see Figure 35-6).

Except for a few egg-laying mammals, all mammals give birth to living young. The number of offspring produced at each birth is fewer than in most other animals. However, because the young are protected and cared for by the parents, they have a better chance of survival.

There are three different kinds of mammals—the **monotremes,** the **marsupials,** and the **placental mammals.** The monotremes are the egg-laying mammals (see page 374). They are the most primitive and reptilelike of the mammals. The duckbill platypus and spiny anteater of Australia are the only living monotremes. The marsupials are the pouched mammals, such as the kangaroo, opossum, and koala. Marsupials are born at a very tiny, immature stage, and complete their development in their mother's pouch (see page 374). Marsupials were once much more numerous and widespread than they are today. Wherever placental mammals arose, the marsupials eventually died out. Only in Australia did marsupials become the dominant form of mammals. The largest and most successful group of mammals is the placentals. In the placental mammals the developing young are retained within the uterus of the female until embryonic development is completed. The young are born in a stage of development more advanced than that in the marsupials.

35-5 Kinds of Placental Mammals

There are about fifteen different orders of placental mammals. Members of these groups range from tiny bats to enormous whales. The major orders of placental mammals are discussed below.

Insect-eating mammals. Moles, hedgehogs, and shrews are insect-eating mammals, members of the order **Insectivora** (in-sek-*tiv*-uh-ruh) (see Figure 35-7). Insectivores (in-sek-tuh-

Figure 35-7. The Hedgehog.

vors) are generally small, mouselike animals. Many live underground. They feed on ants, grubs, beetles, and other insects.

Rodents. Mice, rats, beavers, porcupines, squirrels, hamsters, and guinea pigs are all members of the order **Rodentia** (roh-*dench*-ee-uh), the largest order of placental mammals (see Figure 35-8). Their sharp, chisel-like incisor teeth are used for gnawing. These teeth grow continuously to replace the ends that wear away. Rodents reproduce rapidly. Many are serious pests, destroying food and carrying disease.

Lagomorphs. Rabbits and hares are members of the order **Lagomorpha** (lag-uh-*mor*-fuh). Like rodents, they are gnawing animals that feed on plants. Both rabbits and hares have long ears and fluffy tails (see Figure 35-9). Newborn rabbits cannot see or move around, and they have no fur. Newborn hares, on the other hand, are covered with fur and become active within a few hours. Both rabbits and hares move by hopping, using their powerful hind legs. They are among the fastest-moving mammals.

Figure 35-8. Rodents. (A) Porcupine. (B) Beaver. (C) Guinea pig.

Figure 35-9. A Snowshoe Hare.

Figure 35-10.   Bats. Bats are the only true flying mammals.

Figure 35-11.   Bottle-Nosed Dolphin. Dolphins are intelligent animals and can be trained to do various kinds of tricks.

Flying mammals. Bats, members of the order **Chiroptera** (ky-*rahp*-tuh-ruh), are the only mammals capable of real flight. The wing of a bat consists of four long fingers covered by a membrane of skin. The first finger is used for grasping, as are the small hind legs. At rest, bats hang upside down from a perch by their hind legs (see Figure 35-10). Bats are generally active at night.

The most common bats feed on insects, while others feed on fruit, pollen, or small animals. The vampire bat, which is found in Central and South America, preys mainly on cattle. To obtain blood, the bat bites off a small piece of skin and then laps up the blood. The total amount of blood lost is very small, and the wound itself is generally not serious. However, the transmission of disease by bat bites can be a problem.

Bats use a sonarlike system of echo location to find their way around in the dark and to locate their prey. They produce high-frequency sound waves that bounce off any object they strike, producing an echo that the bat can hear. The distance to the object is determined by the time interval between the emission of the sound and the return of the echo.

Aquatic mammals. Whales, dolphins, and porpoises are aquatic mammals, members of the order **Cetacea** (see-*taysh-ee*-uh). These animals are well adapted to life in the ocean. Although they are air breathers, they can remain underwater for long periods of time by holding their breath. The forelimbs of cetaceans are modified as flippers (see Figure 35-11). There are no hind limbs. Cetaceans swim by moving their powerful tails up and down through the water. Like other mammals, cetaceans give birth to live young, which are fed on milk from the mammary glands.

Porpoises, dolphins, and some whales have teeth and feed on fish. The largest whales feed on plankton, the small organisms that float in the oceans. Plankton is strained from the water by a series of horny plates called *whalebone.* Blue whales, which feed on plankton, are the largest animals that have ever lived.

Mammals without teeth. Anteaters, armadillos, and sloths belong to the order **Edentata** (ee-den-*tah*-duh). In these animals the teeth are either very small or completely lacking. Members of this order are found mainly in Central and South America. Anteaters and sloths are covered by long hair, while armadillos are covered by hard plates (see Figure 35-12). Sloths spend much of their time hanging on trees. They feed on leaves and young shoots. Anteaters and armadillos feed primarily on ants, termites, and other insects. They both have long claws and long tongues. They use their claws to break open anthills and termite mounds and their tongues to lick up the insects.

Mammals with trunks. The order **Proboscidea** (proh-buh-*sid*-ee-uh) includes only African and Asiatic elephants. The muscular trunk of the elephant is formed from a greatly elongated upper lip and nose. The trunk is used to bring food to the mouth. The huge ivory tusks of the elephant are actually greatly enlarged upper incisor teeth. Elephants feed on plants. They are the largest living land animals. To maintain their huge bodies, elephants must feed for up to 18 hours a day.

Hoofed mammals. Mammals with feet in the form of hoofs are called *ungulates* (*ung*-yoo-lets). The ungulates are divided into two orders depending on whether the hoofs have an odd or even number of toes. Those with an even number belong to the order **Artiodactyla** (*art*-ee-uh-*dak*-tuh-luh). This order includes pigs, deer, antelopes, sheep, cattle, hippopotamuses,

Figure 35-12. Mammals without Teeth. Both the anteater (left) and the armadillo (right) feed mainly on ants, termites, and other insects.

Figure 35-13. Hoofed Mammals. The hoofed mammals, or ungulates, include (A) camels, (B) giraffes, (C) rhinos, and (D) hippos.

giraffes, and camels (see Figure 35-13). Ungulates with an odd number of toes belong to the order **Perissodactyla** (puh-*ris*-uh-*dak*-tuh-luh). This order includes horses, rhinoceroses, and tapirs.

All ungulates are herbivores, or plant eaters, and tend to feed in herds. Their flattened teeth can crush and grind tough plant material. Some ungulates, such as cattle, sheep, camels, and deer, are *ruminants (roo*-muh-nents). Their stomachs have four chambers. When grazing, they store large amounts of food in a chamber of the stomach called the **rumen** (*roo*-men). Later, they bring the food back up into their mouths and chew it thoroughly before swallowing it for a second time.

Meat-eating mammals. The order **Carnivora** (kar-*niv*-uh-ruh) includes cats, dogs, bears, skunks, walruses, and other meat-eating mammals (see Figure 35-14). Some carnivores, such as the bear, eat plant material as well as meat. Most carnivores are strong and fast moving and have sharp claws. Their power-

ful jaws and large teeth are specialized for seizing, cutting, and tearing meat. They have a well-developed sense of smell. Carnivores are generally intelligent, and much of their hunting behavior is learned.

Walruses, sea lions, and seals are aquatic carnivores. They feed mainly on fish. Their limbs are modified as flippers, and their body shape is adapted for swimming.

Primates. Humans, apes, and monkeys are members of the order **Primates** (pry-*mayt*-eez). All *primates (pry*-mayts) have well-developed grasping hands that enable them to handle and manipulate objects (see Figure 35-15). Their fingers and toes have flat nails instead of claws. Except for humans, gorillas, and baboons, which live on the ground, most primates live in trees. Primates eat both plant material and meat. Primates are the most intelligent of the mammals. Their brains are large and complex, and their sense of sight is well developed.

Figure 35-14. Meat-Eating Mammals. The meat-eating mammals, or carnivores, include bears and walruses.

Figure 35-15. Primates. Primates include orangutans (left) and chimpanzees (right).

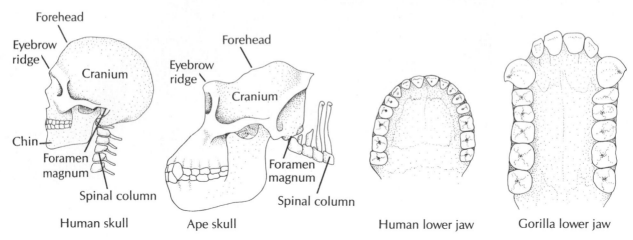

Figure 35-16. Comparison of Human and Ape Skulls and Jaws. The gorilla's brain capacity is about 450 cm³ while that of the human is about 1450 cm³.

HUMAN ORIGINS

Objectives:

1. Describe the characteristics that distinguish humans from other primates.
2. Describe the humanlike characteristics of *Ramapithecus*.
3. Describe the characteristics of each of the species of *Australopithecus*.
4. Describe the characteristics of *Homo habilis* and *Homo erectus*.
5. Compare and contrast the major characteristics of Neanderthals, Cro-Magnons, and modern humans.

35-6 Identifying Human Fossils

The branch of science that attempts to trace the development of the human species is called **anthropology** (an-thruh-*pahl*-uh-jee). Anthropology deals with human physical, social, and cultural development, and with the study of the origin of humans. Few areas of scientific research have produced more confusion and disagreement than the interpretation of the human fossil record. This record is fragmentary. Often, it consists of a few teeth or scattered pieces of bone. Occasionally, a complete jawbone, skull, pelvis, or thigh bone is found. Putting these bone fragments together into a complete picture of an organism is like trying to do a jigsaw puzzle when all the pieces are the same color, many pieces are missing, and you don't know what the finished puzzle is supposed to look like. Dating the fossils is also difficult. Their ages must be inferred from the age of the rocks in which they are found, and accurate measurements by absolute dating methods are not always possible.

Figure 35-17. *Sivapithecus* Lived Between 17 Million and 8 Million Years Ago. This specimen is the most complete skull known.

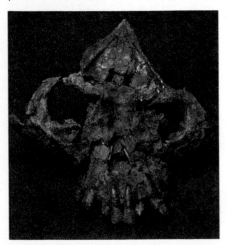

Humans, apes, and monkeys are all primates. They are structurally similar in many ways. However, there are several characteristics that distinguish humans from other primates.

1. *The size and shape of the skull.* The human brain is much larger than that of other primates. To accommodate the brain, the human skull is generally larger than that of other primates and has a unique shape. The cranium, or brain case, is higher and more rounded than that of other primates (see Figure 35-16). In addition, humans have a relatively flat, vertical forehead, while other primates have a sloping forehead with heavy, bony eyebrow ridges.

2. *The jaws and teeth.* Primates other than humans generally have heavy jawbones that tend to have a rectangular shape, while the jawbones of humans are lighter and are typically U-shaped in front. Also, humans have distinct chins, while the other primates are chinless. Human teeth are generally smaller than those of other primates.

3. *The pelvis and foramen magnum.* Another unique characteristic of humans is their ability to walk on two legs in an upright position. This is called **bipedal locomotion.** With the exception of birds and kangaroos, most other animals walk on four legs. There are several structural adaptations connected with bipedal locomotion. The pelvis is adapted for upright posture. The back of the pelvis is thick and strong and serves as a site of attachment for the long muscles of the legs. The bowl shape of the pelvis helps to support the internal organs. The S-shaped spinal column places the center of gravity over the pelvis and legs.

The **foramen magnum** (fuh-*ray*-men *mag*-num) is the opening in the skull where the spinal cord enters. In humans, this opening is under the skull. Its location allows the head to be balanced on top of the spinal column. In other primates, the foramen magnum is toward the back of the skull, which means that the skull is held forward and tends to face downward. In fossils, the location of the foramen magnum reveals whether a primate had bipedal locomotion.

Modern humans, and humanlike fossils that exhibited bipedal locomotion, are called *hominids.* The only hominids alive today are humans.

35-7 Search For Our Earliest Ancestors

From the fossil record, it is thought that apes began to evolve around 30 million years ago. Based on fossil and biochemical evidence, scientists believe that humans and apes evolved from a common ancestor.

For a long time it has been suggested that the human lineage could be traced to the fossil remains of *Ramapithecus* or its close relative *Sivapithecus* (see Figure 35-17). These chimpanzee-like animals lived in Africa, Asia, and Europe between 17 million and 8 million years ago. Their teeth and jaws were

Career

Physical Anthropologist

Physical anthropologists study humans as biological organisms. They observe remains of human ancestors to see how the human body evolved in different environments. They are concerned with variations in individuals, populations, and racial groups.

To become a physical anthropologist, extensive post-graduate study is usually required, including anatomy, genetics, and evolutionary biology—particularly of the primates.

Because of this broad knowledge, physical anthropologists often work in cross-disciplinary areas of research. They may do field work in remote areas, write, or teach. They can be consultants in a wide variety of practical fields such as health, clothing design, and equipment design. Employment in this field is generally with universities or research organizations; other jobs are found in government agencies, museums, and consulting firms.

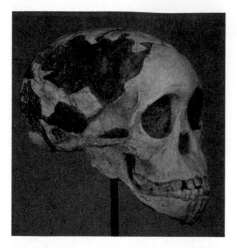

Figure 35-18. Skull of *Australopithecus africanus*.

humanlike; however, the rest of the skull resembled that of an orangutan.

Biologists do not agree on where *Ramapithecus* and its relatives fit into the evolution of humans. According to one view, they may be common ancestors of all apes and humans. Some authorities believe that they are most likely ancestral orangutans. However, most experts agree that *Ramapithecus* and its relatives are not the first prehumans.

35-8 Fossil Evidence of Human Origins

Australopithecus. In 1924, workers in a limestone quarry in South Africa found some skulls embedded in the rock. Most of the skulls were those of monkeys, but one skull displayed some human characteristics. It resembled the skull of a child about 5 years old. The brain size was greater than an ape's, but much less than that of a modern human. The position of the foramen magnum indicated that the primate was bipedal. Finally, the teeth were more humanlike than apelike. Raymond Dart, a famous anthropologist, named the new species *Australopithecus africanus* (aus-truh-luh-*pith*-uh-kus af-ruh-*kan*-us), which means "ape of southern Africa." He believed that *Australopithecus* was more humanlike than apelike and represented an early type of hominid (see Figure 35-18).

In 1936, Dr. Robert Brown discovered the remains of an adult *Australopithecus.* Since then, hundreds of such fossils have been found and the genus has been divided into several species.

It is believed that *Australopithecus africanus* lived between 3 million and 2 million years ago. Members of this group were about 1 meter tall and weighed about 25 kilograms. They could stand and walk upright. Their brain size was somewhat larger than that of a gorilla's, in proportion to body size.

In 1938, Robert Brown found a fossil of a species that was similar to *A. africanus*, but larger and more muscular. He named this massively built but related species *Australopithecus robustus* (roh-*bus*-tus). *A. robustus* was a little over 1.5 meters in height and weighed about 65 kilograms. The jaw of *A. robustus* was heavier than that of *A. africanus*, and the teeth were larger. Extensive pitting in the molars of *A. robustus* suggested that they fed on vegetation containing sand. The teeth of *A. africanus* do not show this pitting, and it is therefore thought that they were meat eaters.

A. robustus lived between 2.2 and 1.4 million years ago. Most experts believe that this hominid was not the ancestor of modern humans, but became extinct.

In 1974, Donald Johanson and Maurice Taieb discovered the bones of a small female *Australopithecus.* Johanson called her Lucy (see Figure 35-19). Although she had an ape-size brain and jaw, the pelvis clearly showed she was bipedal. Then in 1975, they found the fossilized bones of a group of adults and children, apparently all killed at the same time, possibly by a

Figure 35-19. Lucy, *Australopithecus afarensis*.

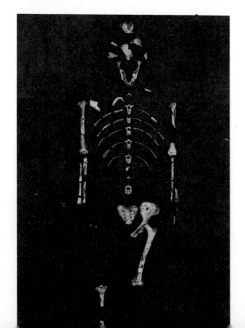

flash flood. The group was called the First Family. All these prehuman fossils are between 3.8 and 2.8 million years old and were named *Australopithecus afarensis.*

At the present time, scientists cannot agree on how many species of *Australopithecus* there were or whether or not they were the ancestors of human beings. However, scientists do agree that bipedal locomotion apparently evolved before an increased brain size.

Homo habilis. Since 1959, fossils found in East Africa by Louis and Mary Leakey (see Figure 35-20) and their son Richard indicate that other hominids lived at the same time as *Australopithecus.* Compared to *Australopithecus,* these hominids had more humanlike teeth and a larger brain. Found with these other fossils were pebbles chipped to form sharp-edged tools. Because they were toolmakers, these fossils have been classified as *Homo,* the same genus as modern humans. They have been named *Homo habilis (hoh-*moh *hab-*uh-lus), which means "handy man" (see Figure 35-21). *Homo habilis* is thought to have lived between 2.2 and 1.6 million years ago.

Homo erectus. The first remains showing truly human characteristics appear in the fossil record about 1.5 million years ago. These hominids, thought to be descendants of *Homo habilis,* are classified as *Homo erectus* (uh-*rek-*tus) (see Figure 35-22). Fossil bones, tools, and living sites of *H. erectus* have been found in Asia, Africa, and Europe. *H. erectus* was the first user of fire. Members of this species lived in groups. Their brain size, though larger than that of *H. habilis,* was significantly smaller than that of modern humans. It is thought that *H. erectus* survived until 350,000 to 250,000 years ago and that they gave rise to the earliest members of the species *Homo sapiens* (*say-*pee-inz), the species of modern humans.

Neanderthals. The Neanderthals (nee-*an-*der-thals) were an early type of *Homo sapiens,* and are classified as *H. sapiens neanderthalensis.* The Neanderthals first appeared about 130,000 years ago. Their fossils have been found throughout

Figure 35-21. Hand and Skull of *Homo habilis.* The hand shows that *H. habilis* had good manual dexterity.

Figure 35-20. Mary and Louis Leakey at Work.

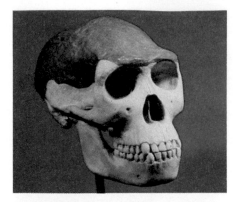

Figure 35-22. *Homo erectus* Skull.

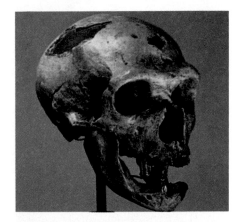

Figure 35-23. Neanderthal Skull.

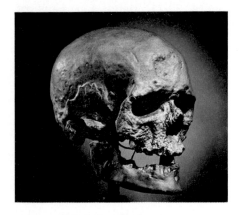

Figure 35-24. Cro-Magnon Skull.

Figure 35-25. A Cro-Magnon Cave Painting.

Europe, Africa, and Southeast Asia. These humans were only about 1.5 meters tall, but powerfully built. Their faces had a heavy, bony eyebrow ridge. According to skull measurements, their brain size was as large as or slightly larger than that of modern humans, but was shaped differently (see Figure 35-23).

Neanderthals lived in family groups in caves or in simple shelters built of rocks. They used fire and produced a variety of stone tools. It appears that some of these tools were used to scrape hides, which were then used to make clothing. Tools were also used to kill large animals, such as mammoths and woolly rhinoceroses, which were trapped in pits lined with wooden spikes. The Neanderthals buried their dead in a ritualistic fashion, sometimes with weapons and food.

Cro-Magnons. About 35,000 years ago, the Neanderthals disappeared from the fossil record and were replaced by the **Cro-Magnons** (kroh *mag*-nuns) (see Figure 35-24). Scientists do not know what happened to the Neanderthals. They may have been killed off by the more advanced Cro-Magnons, or possibly the two groups interbred and the Neanderthals lost their distinct identity.

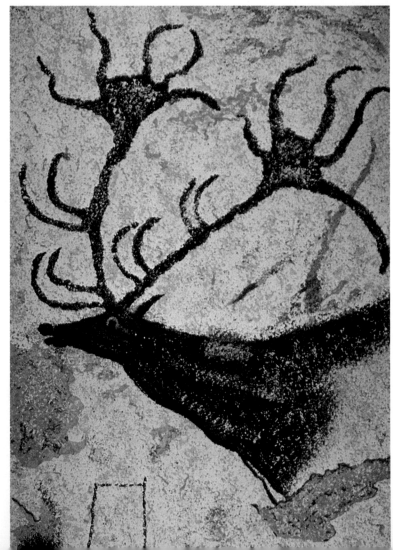

The skeletons of Cro-Magnons were like those of modern humans, and their brain size was about the same. They lived not only in caves, but also in dwellings built of rock, wood, and hides. They made finely chipped stone and bone tools, including axes, knives, awls, chisels, and scrapers. They also made fishhooks, needles, and spear points. They wore clothing sewn from animal skins. On the walls of caves in France are paintings by Cro-Magnons of the animals they hunted (see Figure 35-25). These drawings may have had some spiritual significance. The Cro-Magnons buried their dead in a ritualistic manner. Often, the body was covered with dye and buried with food and personal articles.

Most of the evolutionary changes in the human species up to the Cro-Magnons apparently were physical changes (see Figures 35-26, 35-27). Since the Cro-Magnons, however, changes are thought to have been mainly behavorial and cultural rather than physical. It is believed that the Cro-Magnons migrated to various parts of the world. The different groups, being geographically isolated, gave rise to the three primary human races—Negroid (black), Mongoloid (yellow), and Caucasoid (white).

Figure 35-26. An Artist's Representation of *Homo erectus* (A), Neanderthal (B), and Cro-Magnon Figures (C).

A

B

C

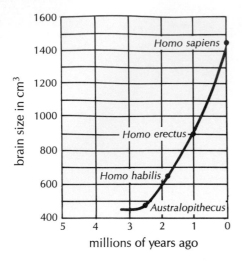

Figure 35-27. Increase in Brain Volume in the Course of Hominid Evolution.

35-9   Interpreting the Fossil Evidence

Because fossil evidence is limited, the ancestry of humans is still vague. Often there are large and significant gaps in the fossil record. Therefore, as new fossils are discovered and interpreted, the human evolutionary sequence is revised. Figure 35-28 shows two possible patterns of human evolution that have been proposed by different scientists.

Recent studies by molecular geneticists indicate that as different species evolve from a common ancestor, their DNA sequences change at a fairly constant rate. In other words, by comparing the DNA sequences of particular genes in related species whose ages are already known from fossil evidence the relative rates of change in the DNA can be assessed. This can also be done indirectly by comparing changes in the amino acid sequences of similar proteins. This measurement can serve as a genetic or *molecular clock*. It has been shown that there are fewer differences in similar proteins between closely related species than between distantly related species. Thus, the number of base differences in the DNA of related species can be used as a measure of the time at which the species diverged from a common ancestor.

Evidence based on the molecular clock indicates that the split between humans and apes occurred about 5 or 6 million years ago. Fossil evidence suggests that the split occurred between 12 million and 6 million years ago. However, since so few humanlike fossils have been discovered from this period, much about our evolutionary past is as yet unknown.

Figure 35-28. Two Hypotheses for Human Evolution. The scheme on the left has been proposed by Donald Johanson; the scheme on the right has been proposed by Richard Leakey. White areas represent gaps for which there is no fossil information.

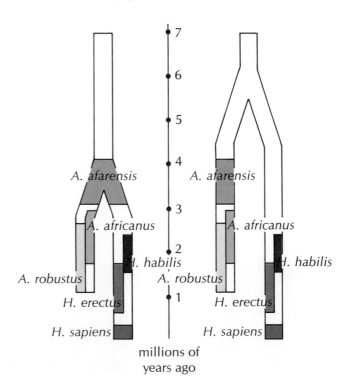

millions of years ago

Chapter Review

SUMMARY

- Birds have feathers, distinguishing them from all other animals. In most birds, the wings are used for flight. Fertilization is internal in birds, and the egg is enclosed in a shell. The young are cared for by the parents.

- The mammals include monotremes, marsupials, and placental mammals. Members of this group nourish their young with milk produced by mammary glands. The body covering of mammals is hair.

- The most successful mammals are the placentals, whose young remain within the uterus of the female until embryonic development is complete.

- The largest order of placental mammals is the rodents—rats, mice, beavers, hamsters, and squirrels.

- The only mammals capable of true flight are the bats.

- Aquatic mammals include whales, dolphins, and porpoises.

- There are two orders of hoofed mammals, or ungulates. Ungulates with an even number of toes include pigs, sheep, cattle, and camels. Those with an odd number of toes include horses and rhinoceroses. The ungulates are all herbivores.

- The carnivores include cats, dogs, bears, seals, and other meat-eating animals.

- The primates—monkeys, apes, and humans—are the most intelligent animals.

- There are several characteristics that distinguish humans from other primates. However, the finding and identifying of human fossils is difficult. The fossil record is fragmentary and there is much disagreement as to its interpretation.

- The earliest known fossil displaying some human characteristics is *Ramapithecus*. Another prehuman fossil primate group is *Australopithecus*.

KNOW THE TERMS

anthropology	Chiroptera	Mammalia	Primates
Artiodactyla	Cro-Magnons	marsupial	Proboscidea
Australopithecus	Edentata	molar	*Ramapithecus*
Aves	foramen magnum	monotreme	Rodentia
bipedal locomotion	*Homo Sapiens*	Neanderthals	rumen
canine	incisor	Perissodactyla	
Carnivora	insectivora	placental mammal	
Cetacea	Lagomorpha	premolar	

SECTION QUESTIONS

Class Aves—The Birds

1. Name the single characteristic that distinguishes birds from all other animals.
2. Name three ways that birds use their beaks.
3. List three different types of feathers.

Class Mammalia—The Mammals

4. What is a mammal?
5. Name the four types of teeth in mammals.
6. Name the three different kinds of mammals.
7. What is the largest order of placental mammals?
8. To what order do the flying mammals belong?
9. To what order do whales, dolphins, and porpoises belong?
10. What are ungulates?

Human Origins

11. What is anthropology?
12. What is bipedal locomotion?
13. List the names of three species of *Australopithecus*.
14. Name another prehuman that lived at the same time as *Australopithecus*.
15. Which fossil humans or prehumans probably used tools?
16. Which fossils are classified as *Homo sapiens*?

KNOW THE FACTS

Copy the number of each statement below on a sheet of paper. Beside each number, write whether the statement is true or false. If the statement is false, replace the italicized word(s) with a term that will make the statement true.

1. Birds are *warm-blooded,* and have a high body temperature.
2. Ducks have *grasping* feet that are useful in swimming.
3. Birds *molt,* that is, shed their feathers.
4. The circulatory system of birds is *similar* to that of humans.
5. During mating, sperm are transferred from the male bird to the female by the *penis*.
6. *Canines* are teeth which are used for cutting.
7. *Incisors* are teeth which are used for tearing.
8. *Premolars and molars* are used for grinding.
9. The *placental mammals* are the largest and most successful group of mammals.
10. Rabbits and hares are *rodents*.
11. The largest whales feed on *plankton*.
12. The order Carnivora includes cats, bears, and *walruses*.
13. The *orbit* is the opening in the skull where the spinal cord enters.
14. Most scientists agree that *brain size* evolved before *bipedal locomotion*.
15. *Homo habilis* was the first user of fire.

UNDERSTANDING THE CONCEPTS

16. Describe the general characteristics of birds.
17. Describe the functions and structure of feathers.
18. Trace the path of air through the respiratory system of a bird.
19. Why do birds need large amounts of food?
20. Describe the structure and function of the digestive system of birds.
21. Name three members of the order Primates and list their major characteristics.
22. What characteristic is shared by all hominids?
23. Why are *Ramapithecus* and its relatives no longer considered to be human ancestors?
24. Why is *Australopithecus* considered to be more humanlike than apelike?
25. Why is *Homo habilis* considered to be more advanced than *Australopithecus*.
26. Why is *Homo erectus* considered an early type of human?
27. Why are Neanderthals considered to be *Homo sapiens?*
28. What evidence indicates that Neanderthals and Cro-Magnons lived in organized communities?
29. Describe the characteristics of Cro-Magnons.
30. Why do scientists disagree about how humans evolved?

THINK CRITICALLY

31. How can you explain the fact that the placentals are the most successful group of mammals?
32. Compare and contrast reproduction and embryonic development in monotremes, marsupials, and placental mammals.
33. In order for vertebrates to become adapted for flight, body weight must be reduced. In what ways is this achieved in birds?
34. What assumptions have been made by anthropologists about the intelligence of early human types?

THINK CREATIVELY

35. What explanations can you offer for the development of bipedal locomotion in early humanlike types?

36. Suggest some possible reasons why Cro-Magnons would bury their dead in a ritualistic manner.

FOR FURTHER INVESTIGATION

1. Prepare a bulletin board or chart showing the different types of hominids.

2. Report to the class on one of the following unusual mammals: vampire bat, blue whale, or duckbill platypus.

3. Do library research on the methods used by scientists to excavate and date hominid fossils. Write up your findings in the form of a feature article for a magazine or newspaper.

4. Do some investigative research on the fraudulent Piltdown Man. Write up your findings about this hoax in the form of an exposé.

5. Prepare a report on one of the career opportunities listed below. See suggested procedures, p. 9, "For Further Investigation," Activity 3.

   a. Dental hygienist   **c.** Veterinarian

   b. Anthropologist   **d.** Dog groomer

6. Prepare a report on the life and contributions of one of the following scientists:

   a. Margaret Mead

   b. W. Montague Cobb

   c. Mary and Louis Leakey

   d. Donald Johanson

FOR FURTHER READING

Bower, Bruce, "Catching Up with China's Past," *Science News*, May 18, 1985.

Day, M. H., *The Fossil History of Man* (Carolina Biological Reader), Carolina Biological Supply Co., Burlington, NC, 1984.

National Geographic Society, *Book of Mammals*, 2 vols., National Geographic Society, Washington, DC, 1981.

National Geographic Society, *The Wonders of Birds*, National Geographic Society, Washington, DC, 1983.

Natural History, September, 1983. Entire issue devoted to birds.

Pilbeam, D., "The Descent of Hominoids and Hominids," *Scientific American*, March, 1984.

Rensberger, Boyce, "Bones of Our Ancestors," *Science 84*, April, 1984.

Chapter 36
BEHAVIOR

To attract females during courtship, the male peacock displays his brilliantly colored tail feathers.

THE NATURE OF BEHAVIOR

Objectives:

1. Distinguish between behavioral response and physiological response.
2. Explain how behavior is related to stimuli.
3. Give examples of differing perceptions of stimuli and explain the importance of responding only to particular stimuli.
4. Describe the relationship between heredity, structure, the nervous system, and behavior.
5. Explain the role of biological clocks in certain cycles of behavior.

36-1 Stimuli and Behavior

An organism's environment continually changes. These changes may involve one or more external factors, including heat, light, carbon dioxide, oxygen, moisture, and the activities of other organisms. Environmental changes also may involve internal factors, such as thirst or hunger. Any change in the external or internal environment is called a **stimulus** (plural, **stimuli**).

In living organisms, metabolic processes run best when internal conditions remain constant. Living things maintain constant internal conditions by physiological or behavioral responses to stimuli. When a hungry dog smells food, it salivates. Secreting saliva is a physiological response. The dog may then actively hunt for the food. That response is behavioral. A person sweats when hot. If this response is not sufficient to cool the body, the individual may then remove outer clothing. Sweating is a physiological response. Removing outer clothing is a form of behavior. **Behavior** is the series of activities performed by an organism in response to stimuli. While stimuli also may result in physiological responses within an organism, such responses usually are not considered to be behavior.

The behavior of each species is different from that of others. In flight, a robin usually does not respond to the sight of a rabbit. But another bird, such as a hawk, may respond by capturing and eating the rabbit.

Behavior aids in the survival of the individual and of the species. When a rabbit sees an attacking hawk, it runs first in one direction and then abruptly in another. This behavior may confuse the attacker and allow the rabbit to escape.

36-2 Perceiving and Responding to Stimuli

An organism is exposed to countless environmental changes involving sound, light, chemicals, movement, and many other factors. But stimuli are not the same for every kind of organism. That is, one organism may not perceive something that another does perceive. One example involves light. The honeybee can see ultraviolet light along with blue-violet and purple. But humans are unable to see ultraviolet light (see Figure 36-1). Because of its form of vision, the bee can distinguish between white light with ultraviolet light and white light without ultraviolet light. The white light a bee usually sees contains ultraviolet light. Therefore, a bee's "white" and a human's "white" are different.

Another type of environmental factor that can change involves chemicals. Here, too, organisms differ in their perceptions. The female gypsy moth releases a chemical sex attractant. Male gypsy moths are able to detect minute quantities of this chemical from great distances, which enables them to find females for mating. Dogs display excellent chemical senses. Their outstanding ability to follow a chemical trail is well known. In comparison, humans have a poor sense of smell.

Many organisms, especially bats, have a keen sense of hearing. Bats feed on moths and other night-flying insects. A bat produces very high-pitched sounds that are inaudible to humans. These sounds bounce off objects. The bat is able to detect the echoes and determine whether an object is an obstacle or a moving prey. Having processed this information, the bat responds by directing its flight accurately toward the insect or around the obstacle. Some moths are able to hear the bat sounds. They respond by taking evasive action and sometimes avoid being eaten (see Figure 36-2).

Due to a constant barrage of stimuli of many kinds, an organism must respond only to signs or "messages" that are significant to it. A frog flicks out its tongue to catch small dark objects that move (see Figure 36-3). It does not respond to stationary objects. A spider in its web responds only to violent

Figure 36-1. Perception of Light. (Top) Silverweed flower as seen by a human. (Bottom) Silverweed flower as seen by a honeybee. Honeybees are able to see untraviolet light, whereas humans are not. Thus, the same flower is perceived differently by different species.

Figure 36-2. Response to Stimuli.
Bats use their keen sense of hearing to search for insects at night. The echoes of high-pitched cries emitted by a bat are used to guide its flight. Some moths can hear bat cries and avoid capture.

web vibrations caused by a trapped insect and not to web movements caused by wind. Responding only to particular messages is important when quick action is necessary to capture food or avoid danger. Each "pertinent" message triggers a specific behavior pattern that is unique to the species involved.

36-3   Heredity and Behavior

The behavior of an organism is dependent on its form and structure. The cheetah has a body structure that permits it to run swiftly to catch prey (see Figure 36-4). The robin escapes predators by flying away. Humans and other organisms respond in ways that are suited to their bodies.

Behavior is affected by all body systems. The nervous system, endocrine system, muscles, and skeleton all influence an organism's responses. The more complex an organism's nervous system and structure are, the more complex is its behavior. A frog's behavior is more complex than a grasshopper's. The behavior of a chimpanzee is more complex than that of a frog. Human behavior is the most complex of all.

The development of an organism's body structure, nervous system, and behavior patterns is dependent on its heredity. DNA carries a "blueprint" for the development of body form and structure. Also included in the blueprint is a "program" for behavior that uses the body form and structure effectively for continued survival. For example, within a spider's DNA are instructions for building the kind of web that its species constructs.

Figure 36-3. Significant Stimulus. A frog responds to a small object that moves, but not to a stationary object.

Behavior occurs in populations as well as in individual organisms. One goose cannot fly in a "V" formation. This form of goose behavior requires a group (see Figure 36-5). Instructions for this pattern of flight are coded in the DNA of each individual goose. A complex sequence of events links the DNA codes of individuals to their behavior as a group of excited, honking geese flying in a "V" formation. This behavior pattern is characteristic of geese and is one function of their body systems.

Responses to stimuli depend not only on muscles and skeleton but also on the ability to perceive and interpret the stimuli. Sense organs receive "information" about environmental conditions. The incoming information is "processed" by the nervous system, which then determines the responses to be made by the organism. Heredity determines the forms of information that can be perceived, how the perceived information is interpreted, and the responses that can occur. Heredity also determines the coordinated pattern of muscular movement that forms the resulting behavior sequence.

All multicellular animals except the sponge have a nervous system. The simplest nervous systems occur in the group that includes the hydra, jellyfish, and sea anemone. The members of this group have a nervous system consisting of cells that form a *nerve net* (see page 236). A nerve net produces little or no centralization or coordination of activity. In the sea anemone, if a tentacle touches a small piece of food, only that tentacle bends toward the mouth. If the prey is large and struggling, the stimulus spreads over the nerve net, and other tentacles join in the response.

The flatworm exhibits more complex behavior. A flatworm moves by the beating of cilia located on the lower body surface and also by rippling and crawling motions of the body. This animal's nervous system includes enlarged ganglia at the forward end of paired nerve cords (see page 556). Removal of these ganglia, or simple brain, stops the crawling activity.

Figure 36-4. Cheetah Chasing Prey. The behavior of an organism is dependent on its body structure.

Figure 36-5. Candian Geese in Flight. Some behavioral activities, such as flying in a "V" formation, occur at the population level.

Crawling requires the coordination of muscles, with the brain acting as a center for coordination. The rudimentary brain in flatworms represents the simple form of this structure. In higher animals, the brain is more complex. In all animals with brains, the brain coordinates complicated behavioral sequences.

36-4 Cycles of Behavior

The behavior of an individual organism may vary over time. Certain behaviors may be repeated over a particular time period. For example, activities of many organisms seem to occur only at certain times each day. Field mice are active at night and quiet during the day. Flowers of the common morning-glory open during the day and close at night. Hawks hunt by day, and owls at night. Paper wasps are active during the day but return to the hive at night. June beetles are active at night but relatively inactive during the day. The activities of these organisms seem to be influenced by a *rhythm,* or cycle, of approximately 24 hours.

Early investigations into biological rhythms were conducted with fiddler crabs and involved a physiological process. These animals usually become darkly colored during the day and pale at night. For purposes of investigation, some crabs were placed in rooms with complete darkness and constant temperature and humidity. Yet, the regular 24-hour cycle of color changes continued.

Physiological and behavioral cycles occurring over a period of about 24 hours are called **circadian** (sur-*kay*-dee-un) **rhythms.** This term comes from the Latin words *circa* (about)

Figure 36-6. Biological Rhythm. The willow ptarmigan is dark in color during the warm season (left), and light in color during the snowy winter (right).

and *dies* (day). Circadian rhythms are so regular that the activities of many organisms are said to be controlled by a "biological clock." Although a circadian rhythm is inborn, a biological clock may be "reset" by environmental stimuli. In fact, the cycle of day and night continually resets biological clocks. If an organism is kept under daylight conditions for a long period, its clock is affected. The clock gradually becomes out of phase with the actual day-night cycle. Suppose an insect's inborn cycle is actually 23 hours. If the insect is kept under daylight conditions for ten days, its clock will not reset each day and, on the tenth day, will be ten hours out of phase with the normal daily cycle.

A similar disruption of daily cycle is experienced by someone who flies by jet from San Francisco to London. Upon arrival, the person is still oriented to the daily cycle in San Francisco. Most people in London are sleeping when this person is wakeful, hungry, and ready to work. However, after a few days, this person's biological clock will be reset to London time and our traveler's activities will coincide with the London pattern.

Some animal phenomena follow monthly or even yearly cycles (see Figure 36-6). The grunion is a small fish that lives along the Pacific coast. Each year from April to June, this fish lays its eggs in the wet sand of the beach during the three or four days of the highest monthly tides. Animals such as the ground squirrel and black bear hibernate during the colder months of each year. Experiments with ground squirrels kept under constant environmental conditions showed that the animals entered hibernation without environmental stimuli. This indicates that they, too, are influenced by biological clocks.

INNATE BEHAVIOR

Objectives:
1. Describe some innate behavior patterns in plants and protists.
2. Explain the mechanism and importance of reflexes.
3. Explain the concept of instinct and give several examples of instincts.
4. Describe several factors that can influence instinctive behavior.

36-5 Behavior of Plants and Protists

Any form of behavior that has not been learned is **innate behavior,** or inborn behavior. Most innate behavior aids survival and reproduction. Innate behavior results from impulse pathways built into the nervous system. Instructions for the built-in impulse pathways are carried in the DNA of the individual. These instructions are common to a given species and are passed from parent to offspring as an inherited trait. An

Figure 36-7. Innate Behavior. The leaves of the "sensitive plant" are normally open (left), but quickly close up after they are touched (right).

organism cannot "choose" to perform an innate behavior—it occurs automatically.

Innate behavior is found in most organisms. In simple organisms, such as the paramecium, sea anemone, and flatworm, behavior is almost entirely innate. However, in more complex animals, only part of the behavior is innate. The remainder consists of learned behavior. (Even an earthworm can learn to turn right or left repeatedly in a T-shaped maze.)

Plants also have inborn responses to stimuli. In plants, as discussed in Chapter 19, simple growth movements toward or away from stimuli are called *tropisms* (see page 321). These movements may involve the roots, stems, or leaves. Environmental factors such as light, gravity, water, heat, and chemicals act as stimuli. Like the sponge, plants do not have a nervous system. Tropisms are controlled by hormones and may take hours or even days to occur.

Some plants exhibit rapid responses. Leaves of the "sensitive plant," a type of mimosa, quickly fold and droop after being touched (see Figure 36-7). Leaves of the Venus's-flytrap rapidly close when sensitive hairs on the surface of the leaf are touched. An insect may be trapped as a result (see Figure 17-12, page 295). Rapid responses in plants are not controlled by hormones, but are brought about by changes in turgor pressure in certain cells.

One characteristic of cells is their sensitivity to stimuli. The ameba and the paramecium do not have a nervous system, but they are able to respond to environmental changes. When a paramecium bumps into an obstacle, it stops. Then it reverses its ciliary beating and backs away. The paramecium then turns and goes forward again. If the paramecium hits the same obstacle, it repeats the back-up and turn. Eventually it avoids the obstacle (see Figure 36-8).

In a similar fashion, the ameba avoids intense light by turning away. But it pursues a food particle until it has engulfed the food. If the ameba loses actual contact with the food, it can still sense the location of the food by chemical stimuli (see Figure 36-9).

Any movement by a simple animal or a protist toward or away from a particular stimulus is called a **taxis**. The movement of an ameba away from strong light is a *negative* taxis. The euglena, a protist containing chloroplasts, moves toward light—a *positive* taxis.

36-6   Reflexes

As an animal develops, neurons develop connections that form a system. For the most part, neurons do not change their connections with other nerves once the system is formed. These fixed pathways in the nervous system are the basis for a type of innate behavior called the **reflex** (see page 259). A reflex involves a *receptor* (sense organ) that detects stimuli and an *effector* (muscle or gland) that produces a reaction. Nerve cells connecting the receptor and effector complete the nerve pathway called the *reflex arc.* A given reflex arc always produces the same response. Reflex actions are simple, quick, and automatic.

Reflexes occur in all animals with a nervous system. If you touch a hot object, a reflex response causes quick withdrawal of your hand. A flatworm subjected to electric shock automatically contracts. If a frog's toe is pinched, the leg is always drawn away. If you rub the hind area on a dog's back, it responds by scratching. Reflexes protect by helping to prevent injury and by helping an organism react to environmental changes. Reflexes also aid in the general functioning of an organism. In complex animals, reflexes account for only a small portion of

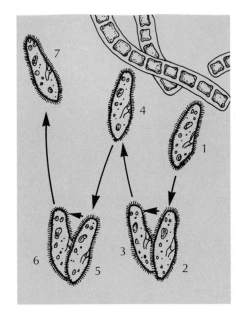

Figure 36-8. Negative Taxis. On encountering an obstacle, a paramecium backs away (1→2), and then goes forward (3→4). If the obstacle is still in its way, the process is repeated (4→5, 6→7).

Figure 36-9. Taxis in the Ameba. An ameba avoids strong light by moving away from the stimulus (left), and pursues food particles by moving towards the stimulus (right).

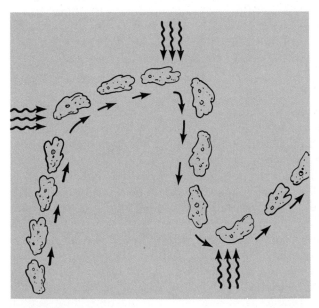

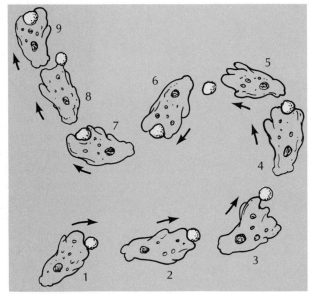

Figure 36-10. Series of Reflex Actions. When a praying mantis sees a fly, a three-step series of reflex actions occurs. First, the mantis's head turns towards the insect (left); then, its body orients in line with the head (middle); and finally, it strikes, capturing the fly with its front legs (right).

overall behavior. In simple animals, reflexes account for a great part of the total behavior.

Reflex arcs are sometimes linked to produce a complicated series of reflex actions. The behavior of the praying mantis in catching food is an example. When a fly or other insect appears in the mantis's field of vision, it turns its head to face the insect. This is the first reflex. Then the mantis orients its body in the same direction as the head—the second reflex. If the fly is close enough, the mantis instantly strikes, grasping the fly with its front legs. The strike—the third reflex—takes only a fraction of a second (see Figure 36-10).

The stimulus triggering the turning of the mantis's head is the sight of the fly. The subsequent stimulation of receptors in the neck of the mantis results in the orientation of the body to the position of the head. The strike follows the stimulus of alignment of the head and body. Thus, this series of reflex actions depends on a succession of particular stimuli.

36-7   Instincts

Certain behavior patterns in animals involve a complicated set of unlearned activities that occur in response to a stimulus or series of stimuli. Although complex, these behavior sequences are innate and are performed automatically. One example of this kind of behavior is nest building in birds. Such a complex, inherited behavior sequence is called an **instinct.** In contrast, a taxis and a reflex are simple forms of behavior that usually are limited to a single response.

Instincts are associated mostly with either individual survival or species survival. They often involve activities related to feeding, defense, or reproduction. The chief advantage of instincts is that they provide an animal with ready-made "answers" to its problems of survival. This is important for an animal with a short life span, because no time is required to learn vital responses.

Instincts are found primarily in vertebrates and complex invertebrates. Each species displays its own characteristic instinctive behaviors, which are performed similarly by all members. The migration of salmon up the same river in which they were hatched, the communication "dances" of bees, the migration patterns of geese, and the construction of a hanging nest by the Baltimore oriole are instincts unique to those organisms.

Insects and spiders are examples of animals whose behavior is almost entirely instinctive. A spider's construction of its intricate web is an instinct. A type of spider can be identified as easily by its web as by its anatomy (see Figure 36-11). Four basic types of webs are spun by spiders. Within each type, every species exhibits its own unique pattern of construction.

Some spiders perform courtship rituals before mating. A male jumping spider may perform a certain "sidestep" dance in front of his mate. An orb-weaving male spider may "strum" on the strands of a female's web before approaching her. These ritualistic acts are instinctive and appear to communicate the male's intent to mate. Usually such behavior prevents his being eaten by the female.

The life cycle of an insect occurs in several stages (see page 585). Each stage has its own set of instincts. For example, the june beetle larva shuns light. However, the adults are attracted to light, often scraping loudly against the screens of lighted windows.

In insects and spiders, certain complex acts are performed only once, but correctly, without experience. The caterpillar of the gypsy moth climbs upward when hungry. Just before entering the pupa stage, it spins a particular type of cocoon in a series of steps performed only once in its life. If a female spider builds a silken egg case but misses the opening when laying her eggs, she still completes the case and guards it even though it is empty.

Fish exhibit instinctive behavior as part of their nesting activities. The male sunfish scoops out a shallow, saucerlike nest in the bottom sediments of a pond or lake. He removes all the pebbles, leaving a layer of sand. After the female lays her eggs in the nest and they are fertilized, the eggs adhere to the sand. Care of the eggs is carried out entirely by the male. He fans the eggs with his tail and drives predators away from the nest until the eggs hatch.

In an instinct, often one activity triggers the next. That is, each activity in a behavior sequence may depend on the previous activity, as in a "chain reaction." For example, the reproductive behavior of the three-spined stickleback, a fish, is composed of a sequence of ordered stimuli and responses. After establishing a territory (discussed in Section 36-16), the male builds a nest. If an egg-laden female enters his territory, the male performs a "zigzag" courtship dance. The female re-

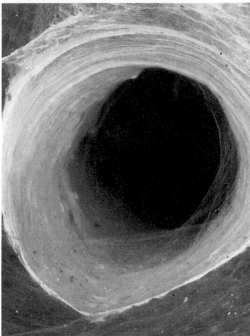

Figure 36-11. Spider Webs. In spiders, web construction is an instinct. A spider can be identified by the type of web it builds.

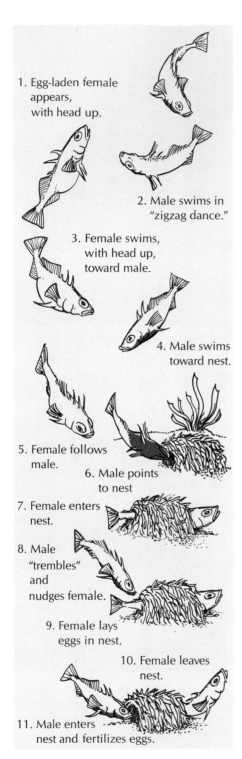

1. Egg-laden female appears, with head up.

2. Male swims in "zigzag dance."

3. Female swims, with head up, toward male.

4. Male swims toward nest.

5. Female follows male.

6. Male points to nest

7. Female enters nest.

8. Male "trembles" and nudges female.

9. Female lays eggs in nest.

10. Female leaves nest.

11. Male enters nest and fertilizes eggs.

Figure 36-12. Mating Behavior of the Three-Spined Stickleback. The ordered sequence of behavior is dependent on hormones and triggered by sight stimuli.

sponds by swimming toward the male. The male then swims toward the nest, and the female follows him. The male then points to the entrance to the nest with his head. This act stimulates the female to enter the nest. Her presence in the nest stimulates the male to "tremble" and nudge her at the base of the tail. His trembling and nudging stimulate her to lay eggs. The female leaves the nest, and the male enters and fertilizes the eggs (see Figure 36-12).

36-8   Factors Controlling Instincts

Many physiological factors influence instincts. These factors all relate to a loss of internal balance or other body changes. The animal responds with behavior that makes it possible for internal balance to be restored. For example, lack of nutrients upsets an animal's internal balance. This upset is translated into the sensation of hunger. The animal responds with feeding behavior. In another example, blood composition is the physiological factor responsible for the sensation of thirst, leading the animal to drink water. Thus, instinctive behavior triggered by the presence of food or water, for example, is an action that restores internal balance. Once homeostasis is restored, the behavior ceases.

Reproductive, or sex, hormones are the physiological factors that lead to courtship, mating, and care of young. These hormones may act directly on specific organs, such as gonads, causing them to produce eggs or sperm (see page 355). These changes, along with a high level of reproductive hormones, prepare the individual for reproduction. Sight of a mate under these conditions usually stimulates courtship behavior, which ultimately results in mating.

In some animals, once mating occurs, reproductive behavior stops. However, in other animals, parental care of eggs or young is stimulated by the continued presence of reproductive hormones and the presence of offspring. For example, the hormone prolactin influences parental feeding in doves. Doves feed their young "pigeon milk," a thick, white substance produced in the bird's crop. The "milk" is composed of sloughed epithelial cells lining the crop. Young doves are fed this material for a short time after hatching.

Hormones may also influence behavior by acting on the central nervous system. Female canaries, unlike males, usually do not sing. But if a pellet of male sex hormone (testosterone) is placed under the skin of a female, she will sing a typical canary song until all the hormone is metabolized.

Experiments with thirsty goats have disclosed the involvement of the brain, as well as hormones, in some instincts. When a goat is thirsty, the deficiency of water in its blood stimulates cells in its hypothalamus. The *hypothalamus* is a portion of the brain to which the *pituitary gland* is attached. A message from the hypothalamus is passed into the pituitary gland, which

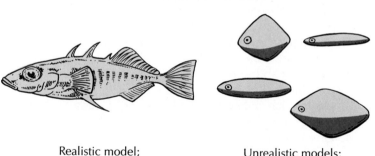

Realistic model;
lacks red belly

Unrealistic models;
with red belly

Figure 36-13. Models of Male Stickle-backs. In experiments with stickle-backs, it was found that models without red bellies were attacked much less often than those with red bellies. This was true even when the models with red bellies were unrealistically shaped. From this, it was concluded that the red color of a male's belly is what stimulates aggressive behavior in another male.

secretes a hormone. The hormone causes the blood to reabsorb more water from the filtrate passing through the tubules of the nephrons in the kidneys (see page 202). While this physiological means of conserving water takes place, the goat looks for water to drink.

Reproductive behavior and parental care of offspring also are thought to be controlled initially by the hypothalamus and the pituitary gland. The hypothalamus or pituitary is triggered by information from the internal or external environment. For example, in many birds and mammals with seasonal reproductive cycles, increasing day length stimulates the hypothalamus. The hypothalamus in turn stimulates the pituitary gland to produce sex hormones. Increasing temperature also may initiate seasonal production of sex hormones in vertebrates.

Another external factor that can trigger the hypothalamus is a visual stimulus. For example, if a female ring dove sees a male, the visual image stimulates cells in her hypothalamus, which in turn activates her pituitary gland. Hormones from the pituitary gland cause growth of the ovaries and secretion of the female hormone estrogen. The female then lays eggs. Normally, the hormone level of a female ring dove kept in isolation remains low. But a female can be induced to lay eggs without seeing a male if she is given an injection of hormones.

Once internal conditions have been altered by hormones, the animal becomes responsive to external factors that do not ordinarily stimulate it. Specific environmental stimuli can then initiate various forms of reproductive behavior. For example, hormones motivate the male three-spined stickleback to establish a territory and build a nest. Once the territory has been established, seeing actions of a mate provides the stimulus for reproductive behavior in both the male and the female, as illustrated in Figure 36-12. The male stickleback also guards his territory against the intrusion of other males. When other males approach, he becomes aggressive and drives them away. During the mating period, the belly of a male becomes red. It is the red color on the belly of another male that directly stimulates the aggressive behavior (see Figure 36-13).

LEARNED BEHAVIOR

Objectives:
1. Distinguish between learned behavior and innate behavior.
2. Explain habituation and habit formation, and give examples of each.
3. Distinguish between classical conditioning and operant conditioning.
4. Describe the process of imprinting and explain its significance.
5. Explain the concept of insight and relate it to learning.

36-9 Experience and Learning

Learned behavior is behavior that changes as a result of experience. Experiences are "stored" in the brain as memory and can be recalled. In learning, a recalled experience is used to help modify behavior in a new situation. Unlike innate behavior, learning may permit the animal to choose responses that are appropriate to the stimuli in any new situation. As a result of learning, an animal can adapt to change.

While innate behavior is controlled by genes, learned behavior is not controlled directly by genes. Heredity determines the type and complexity of the nervous system, which controls ability to learn. Animals with the most complex nervous systems exhibit the greatest capacity to learn. Animals with relatively long life spans and long periods of parental care show mostly learned behavior as adults. In some animals, parents actually teach their offspring certain behaviors, such as hunting in lions.

Learning has several forms. The simplest type of learning is called **habituation.** In this type of learning, an animal learns not

Figure 36-14. Classical Conditioning. Conditioning involves associating a new stimulus with a response. A hungry dog usually salivates at the sight or smell of food. Pavlov substituted the sound of a bell. Eventually, the dog salivated in response to the bell.

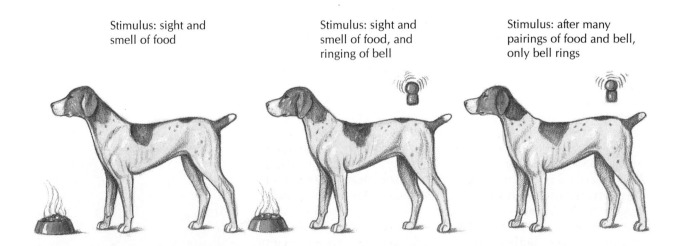

Stimulus: sight and smell of food

Stimulus: sight and smell of food, and ringing of bell

Stimulus: after many pairings of food and bell, only bell rings

Response: salivation

Response: salivation

Response: salivation

to respond to repeated "unimportant" stimuli. Squirrels in a park eventually become accustomed to people and will venture quite close to them. Crows will learn to ignore a harmless scarecrow in a field.

Humans and other animals can learn to perform many complex activities with little or no thought. Such an act, which is first learned and then, by frequent repetition, becomes automatic, is called a **habit.** Dressing, writing, talking, tying shoelaces, typing, and dancing are all habits. Each of these activities is first performed slowly, with concentration, and often with difficulty. Through repetition, its performance eventually requires little or no conscious effort. The development of a series of actions into a habit makes it automatic, easier and faster to perform, and more accurate.

36-10 Conditioning

Conditioning is a simple type of learning that changes behavior through forming new associations. One type, called *classical conditioning,* was first studied by the Russian physiologist Ivan Pavlov (1849-1936). In classical conditioning, a new stimulus is paired with the stimulus and response of a simple reflex action. The new stimulus, which does not normally cause the reflex reponse, becomes associated with the response by a process of reinforcement or reward. This process results in the substitution of the new stimulus for the original one.

Dogs normally salivate when they smell or see food. Secretion of saliva is the reflex response. In studies carried out by Pavlov, a bell was rung (new stimulus) every time dogs were given food (old stimulus). The association of the new stimulus (bell) with the reflex response (salivation) was reinforced by presenting food immediately after ringing the bell. After a while, the dogs would salivate upon hearing the bell without the presence of food (see Figure 36-14).

In Pavlov's experiment, the food was the *unconditioned stimulus.* The ringing bell was the *conditioned stimulus.* Salivation became a *conditioned response.* House pets often become conditioned in a similar manner. Pet owners know that the sound of the refrigerator door or can opener can cause their pets to be quite attentive and to salivate.

Operant conditioning is a type of conditioning in which animals learn to "operate" or do something by associating the action with a reward. The animals may learn to push a lever, open a door, respond to a command, or perform other kinds of actions. In this case, the conditioned response is a behavior that produces the reward. An animal first must be *motivated* to seek the reward by performing the activity. The motivation is usually hunger.

B. F. Skinner, a psychologist, constructed a special cage with a food-release mechanism to study operant conditioning. A rat placed in the cage eventually learns that pressing a bar releases

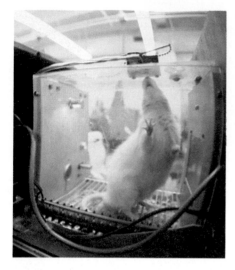

Figure 36-15. Operant Conditioning. (A) After an initial period of trial-and-error, a hungry rat learns to associate pressing the bar with the reward of food. (B) By rewarding an animal with food only when it performs correctly, a trainer can teach the animal to perform tricks.

a pellet of food (see Figure 36-15A). At first the rat explores its cage. This leads to a period of trial and error before the rat accidentally performs the correct act—pressing the bar. Food is the reward for pressing the bar. By rewarding the rat for pressing the bar, the rat is more likely to repeat the act. The rat learns to associate the action of pressing the bar with the reward of food. Because of the initial period of exploration, operant conditioning is also called *trial-and-error learning*.

Trainers teach animals to perform tricks by rewarding them for desired behavior and punishing them for undesired behavior. To the animal, the absence of an expected reward is the same as a punishment. Some sea mammals, such as porpoises, sea lions, and whales, will perform tricks at a trainer's command when rewarded with a fish (see Figure 36-15B). Hunger is the motivation for doing the trick. During training, the animal is given a fish only after the trick is performed correctly. A poor performance results in no reward.

Figure 36-16. Imprinting. Young swans imprinted on their mother (left); other swans imprinted on Konrad Lorenz (right).

36-11 Imprinting

One simple type of learning that occurs in young animals of certain species was discovered in 1935 by Konrad Lorenz, an Austrian biologist. He found that newly hatched ducks, geese, and chickens follow and form a strong attachment to the first moving object they see. If the moving object makes sound, it is more likely to be followed. Forming an attachment to an object or environment soon after hatching or birth is called **imprinting**. This form of learning is rapid and cannot be reversed.

Imprinting in birds occurs several hours after hatching. The young bird will follow the object even over obstacles. Ordinarily, the first object a young bird sees is its mother. Imprinting on the mother bird helps the young bird survive. This behavior quickly establishes a bond between the mother bird and her young, and helps the young birds recognize others of their kind (see Figure 36-16).

If eggs are hatched under experimental conditions in an incubator, the young birds may imprint on a foreign object, such as a person, a mechanical object, or a dog. The young birds will follow the object when it moves around. Once the period of imprinting has passed, about 36 hours after hatching, the young birds cannot imprint on another object. For example, mature mallard ducks that imprinted on a "decoy" mother duck will court and attempt to mate with the decoy. At maturity, geese and other birds that imprinted on foster parents of another species try to mate with members of the foster species.

Although imprinting was first described in birds, it is now known to occur in other animals. Animals whose young are able to stand and walk shortly after birth, such as buffalo, deer, sheep, and goats, are capable of imprinting. Puppies that have human contact during the sixth and seventh weeks after birth are easily trained and become good pets. However, if puppies have no human contact until after their fourteenth week, they rarely make friendly pets. Scientists speculate that imprinting plays an important part in the ability of migrating salmon and other types of fish to return to the stream in which they were hatched.

36-12 Insight

Insight is the ability to "create" a solution to an unfamiliar problem without a period of trial and error. The animal surveys a new situation and uses memory of past experiences to "plan" a response. Insight involves the application of past learning to a new experience. Through reasoning, the animal is able to solve a problem different from any previously encountered. Insight is found only in complex vertebrates.

One of the best-known studies of insight involves chimpanzees. A hungry chimpanzee is released in a room with boxes scattered around the floor and a bunch of bananas hanging from the ceiling out of reach. The chimp finds that it cannot reach

Sidelight

A female slave-making ant *Polyergus breviceps*, holding a pupa from a raided colony of *Formica gnava*

Symbiosis Among Ants

The western slave-making ant, *Polyergus breviceps*, equipped with jaws specialized for fighting only, makes domestic slaves of another ant species. During the summer, female warriors of *Polyergus* attack the nests of *Formica gnava*, and steal the pupae. A single colony may take as many as 30,000 *Formica* pupae per year.

Some of the captured pupae are eaten, while others emerge as adults in the slave-makers' nest, quickly becoming imprinted with the odor of the new nest. The slaves seem to accept their captors as sisters, and some even join them in raids against their own species. Most of the time, however, the slave ants are occupied in building new *Polyergus* nests, foraging for insects, feeding the queen, and tending her brood— tasks the slave-makers are not physically equipped to do. The slave-makers, it seems, are totally dependent on their servants for their survival.

Figure 36-17. Insight. Chimpanzees use insight to get bananas suspended from the ceiling. They first try to reach the bananas by jumping, but then stack the boxes and climb up to get them.

the bananas by jumping. Eventually, it piles the boxes on top of each other under the bananas and then climbs the boxes to reach them (see Figure 36-17). Reasoning has resulted in the correct response to a new situation. Chimpanzees and monkeys are often successful at solving problems on the first exposure to a new situation. Most other animals, including dogs, fail at first.

The ability to reason is most highly developed in humans. Insight is involved in much human behavior. At first, young children solve problems by trial and error and by imitation. This helps them in the mastery of many motor skills, such as tying shoes and putting on and buttoning clothes. As children mature and learn, they begin to use insight to solve problems. Insight in people is enhanced by the ability to exchange ideas through speech and written symbols. These skills give each person the ability to use someone else's experiences to solve problems—an ability that is unique in the animal kingdom.

SOCIAL BEHAVIOR

Objectives:
1. Describe several forms of helpful social behavior.
2. Explain the roles of conflict and dominance hierarchies in animal groups.
3. Describe three types of signals used by animals and give an example of each type.
4. Explain the function of territoriality and the role of communication in maintaining territories.

5. Explain the organization of a honeybee society and describe how these bees communicate with one another.

36-13   Helpful Behavior

Animals often encounter other animals in their environment. Interactions occur both between individuals of the same species and between animals of different species. Many environmental factors bring animals together in a group. A street light is a stimulus that attracts a variety of insects. The rich African grassland draws grazing animals such as the zebra, wildebeest, and antelope to feed side by side. A water hole may be a gathering place for many species. These groups of mixed animal species, called *aggregations*, are not social. They are together merely by chance.

Social behavior consists of both helpful and hostile interactions between animals belonging to the same species. Helpful social behavior includes mating behavior, family interactions, and activities by larger groups. Mating behavior brings a female and a male together, and results in fertilization of eggs. This form of social behavior may involve courtship as well as actual mating. *Courtship* is a form of communication that signals a readiness to mate and prevents conflict.

Family interactions involve helpful relationships between parents and young. The interactions between members of a family are the basis for the providing of food, shelter, and defense for the young. The interactions usually require certain stimuli. Birds incubate their eggs and later feed their chicks. A gull incubates the eggs only when they are visible and when certain hormones are produced in the parent.

The needs of the young are often satisfied as a result of behavior sequences in which certain forms of behavior stimulate other forms of behavior among family members. Many birds will not feed their young unless the chicks "communicate" in a form of behavior called *begging*. Begging is usually done by opening the mouth widely. This stimulates the parent to place food in the chick's mouth. Initially, the young are stimulated to beg when the parent's head appears over the edge of the nest or by the jolt of the adult landing on the nest. Sea gull chicks peck at a red spot on the parent's beak when begging (see Figure 36-18). The parent then regurgitates food, picks some up, and presents it to the chick.

Interactions occur within larger groups such as herds of animals, schools of fish, and flocks of birds. Individuals can cooperate in groups as long as they can communicate with one another. Information is passed between members of a group by sound signals, visual signals, and chemical signals.

Species that live in groups often depend on the group for survival. A group of animals is more alert than a single individual. When one member senses danger, it communicates it to the whole group. The group then tries to escape the danger.

Figure 36-18. Begging Behavior. A herring gull chick begs for food by pecking at a red spot on its parent's beak.

Figure 36-19. Aggressive Behavior.

Figure 36-20. Pecking Order. A rooster's rank within its group determines when it will get food or drink.

Groups also offer various forms of protection against attack by predators. Male musk oxen form a protective ring around the young and females. Some animals attack in groups as a form of defense. Small birds will attack crows and hawks in groups—a behavior called *mobbing*. Hunting in groups is practiced by wolves, lions, and wild dogs.

36-14 Conflict and Dominance Hierarchies

Close association among animals of the same species can result in conflict instead of cooperation. Individuals seek to fulfill their requirements for food, water, space, and mates. A limited supply of these factors may lead to competition in which an individual attempts to satisfy its own needs at the expense of other members of its species. Many animals resolve this competition by aggressive behavior. *Aggression* is threatening or fighting another animal to force it away from something it already possesses or is trying to obtain.

There are numerous forms of aggression. Animals may bite, butt, kick, or claw one another. However, aggressive behavior among members of a species seldom causes serious injury or death. More often, "symbolic" threatening behavior results in a "winner." Such displays are instinctive and clearly understood by other species members. In threat displays, animals assume aggressive postures and show the contrasting or brightly colored parts of their bodies. Robins display their red breasts. Fish display colored body parts or puff themselves up.

When actual fights occur, they are mostly symbolic and cause very little injury to the rivals. Poisonous male snakes wind themselves together during a bout, and each attempts to butt the other's head with its own. The snake that becomes fatigued first retreats from the fight. Although the snakes have fangs, they never bite each other. Rival male bighorn sheep butt their heads together, resulting in spectacular fights (see Figure 36-19). The sounds of their butting heads can be heard for a long distance.

The animal that loses a fight may simply run away. In some cases, it signals defeat by a *subordination ritual.* The signal for submission used by a wolf or dog is to present its neck to the winner. This display stops further aggression by the victor. Its position of superiority over the losing animal has been established. Winning a fight has special results for the victor. The animal achieves *dominance,* or better access to contested resources, such as food, water, space, and mates.

In some animals that live in organized groups, or *societies,* fighting establishes a **dominance hierarchy,** or ranking, within the group. Individuals with a high rank have first choice of necessities. In duck and chicken societies, a *pecking order* is established by pecking action. Those birds with the highest standing have uncontested access to food, water, and the roost (see Figure 36-20). Pecking order reduces tension in the group because there is less fighting over who gets what first. Due to their lower position in the group, subordinates must wait their turn to drink or eat. If no food is left, the subordinates go without nourishment. For members of the lowest rank, survival is most difficult.

In baboons, dominance hierarchy is more complicated than a sequence of individuals with decreasing dominance. A group of baboons, called a *troop,* is governed by a clique of dominant males. Any member of the ruling clique that is challenged by an outsider is supported by the other members of the governing group. This helps keep the troop stable by preventing frequent changes. The clique of dominant males protects the troop against attack by predators.

36-15   Communication

Communication plays an important role in both helpful and hostile social behavior. The male and female of many animal species are brought together by *signals.* The signals sent out by both sexes include visual signals, sound signals, and chemical secretions. Visual signals are common among fish and birds. These signals include movement and posture as well as displays of certain body parts. The zigzag dance of the male stickleback causes the female to approach and be led to the nest. The male mallard duck courts by displaying his brightly colored plumage (see Figure 36-21). The female identifies herself with a signal. She may beg food from the male, which will signal him not to attack her as he would another male during the reproductive period. Examples of visual signals during aggression were given in the previous section.

Frontier of Biology

Dr. Katherine Payne with a young elephant.

Elephant Communication

In addition to audible rumbles, growls and trumpeting, Asian elephants make infrasonic calls—calls at frequencies that are below the range of human hearing. The calls are at 14-24 Hz, last 10 to 15 seconds, and appear to be used in communication. They were discovered by Dr. Katherine Payne, a researcher who noticed that she occasionally felt a throbbing in the air near elephants. Recalling the sensation caused by thunder, she guessed that the elephants might be vocalizing at very low frequencies. Her guess was confirmed by recording with equipment sensitive to low frequency sound, and by observing that when a low frequency call was being recorded, an area on the calling elephant's forehead flutters.

Elephants live in a highly organized society. Often, field observers have noticed coordinated behavior among elephants that are separated from each other by large distances, and have wondered how the coordination was achieved. It may be that the answer lies in elephants' ability to make very low frequency calls, since such sounds are particularly well suited to travel long distances.

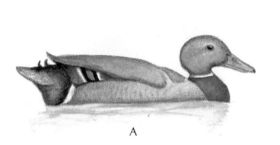

A   B   C

Figure 36-21. Courtship Display. To attract a mate, a male mallard duck displays his brightly colored feathers. (A) Normal swimming. (B) "Head up, tail up" display. (C) "Down up" display.

Sound signals are important among insects, frogs, and birds. The male *Aedes* mosquito is attracted to the sounds produced by the wings of the female while in flight. Male crickets attract females with sound signals made by rubbing their wings together. Male toads and frogs have characteristic songs that attract the females to the pond or bog. People in northeastern United States know that spring is near when they hear the song of the small tree frog *Hyla crucifer* (commonly called the spring peeper). Male birds such as the robin, meadowlark, wood thrush, and vireo produce distinctive high-pitched songs as a signal to the female. The songs of these birds enable individuals to recognize mates of their own species.

Chemical secretions are used by many animals as signals. Such secretions are called **pheromones** (*fehr*-uh-mohnz). These chemicals influence the behavior of other members of the same species. Pheromones can act as sex attractants. The female silkworm moth releases a pheromone so strong that it attracts males from a distance as great as three kilometers. Gypsy moths, cockroaches, and many other insects produce pheromones that act as sex attractants.

36-16 Territoriality

A **territory** is an area defended by an individual against intrusion by members of the same species. Claiming a territory is another aspect of social behavior. Territorial behavior usually takes place during the breeding season and is often limited to males. Maintaining a territory affords an animal the needed space to acquire food, court a mate, and raise a family.

To defend its territory, an individual may spend long periods of time in a conspicuous place. The animal may also "announce" ownership with certain forms of communication. In some birds, such as the thrushes, a male will choose an unoccupied area and then sing loudly and vigorously to stake his claim (see Figure 36-22). The loud singing warns away other males but attracts females. Usually, the loudest-singing male maintains the largest territory. A singing duel between competing males often can resolve a boundary dispute, with the

Figure 36-22. Territoriality. The loud singing of the male thrush marks its territory, and warns other males to keep out.

loudest male being the victor.

Some mammals use pheromones to mark territory. Deer have pheromone-secreting glands in their hooves. Male antelopes have similar glands close to their eyes (see Figure 36-23). The civet, a cat, has pheromone-secreting glands around its anus. Beavers have musk glands. Dogs and wolves mark their ''turf'' with urine. Bears rub against trees, leaving a distinctive odor.

Primates show variation in the establishment of territory. The tree-living howler monkey of Central America displays strong group territoriality. A troop consists of several dozen monkeys. They defend the boundaries of their territory by sessions of howling, which discourages intrusion by other troops (see Figure 36-24). The rhesus, an old-world monkey, is also territorial and will drive off intruders with active threat displays and, if necessary, ferocious attacks. Chimpanzee and gorilla troops live on a large range, but they show no defense of territory. Different troops may intermingle without causing disturbances.

Territoriality has several advantages. Due to territories, groups or individuals are evenly distributed throughout the available area. This enables an animal species to use the habitat and available food supply efficiently. Dividing a habitat into territories tends to reduce conflict between members of a species. In some cases, especially in birds, position of a territory helps attract a mate.

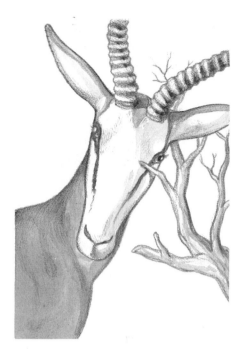

Figure 36-23. Pheromones. A male antelope claims his territory by marking twigs with a secretion produced by a gland near his eye.

36-17 Honeybee Societies

Insect societies are found among termites, ants, and bees. In an insect society, all effort is directed toward the survival of the group. The activities of most insect societies are centered around one female, the *queen.* All members of the group are offspring of the queen.

A honeybee society involves a complex organization and division of labor (see Figure 36-25). The queen is usually the

Figure 36-24. Territoriality. A troop of howler monkeys defends its territory as a group; their loud howling scares away other troops.

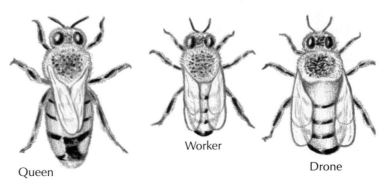

Queen   Worker   Drone

Figure 36-25. Honeybee Society. (Left) Bees at work in a hive. (Right) The three types of bees that live in a hive are the queen, the worker, and the drone.

only reproductive female. She is the focus of hive activity. The colony continues as a group as long as she is healthy and functioning. A queen mates only once, with several *drones*, or male bees, during a "nuptial" flight. The drones develop from unfertilized eggs and live for only a short time after mating with the queen bee. From the single mating flight, the queen stores enough sperm to fertilize the thousands of eggs she will lay for the colony. Most of these eggs will hatch into sterile females called *worker bees*. Worker bees carry on the essential activities that maintain the hive, including producing honey, feeding larvae, and protecting the hive.

Chemical signals are one form of bee communication. Even the status of the queen's health is passed to members of the hive by a chemical signal. This signal originates from the queen as a secretion. It is passed to workers attending her, and then to others in the hive. Chemical signals help maintain the organization of the hive.

Workers at the hive entrance fan hive odor outward, which guides foraging workers home. After a forager locates a food source, it uses visual and other signals to communicate the location of the food to other workers in the hive. The work of Karl von Frisch, a German scientist, helped explain this form of communication between honeybees. In his experiments, he placed sheets of paper smeared with honey near a hive. Eventually the bees discovered the honey. Von Frisch noticed that when one bee discovered the honey, others would come in a short time. Somehow the other bees were informed by the first bee.

Von Frisch set up a hive with glass sides so he could observe the scout bees returning from a new food supply. A bee that landed at the new food supply was marked with a little paint to help identify her. Upon returning to the hive, the bee fed several other workers. Then she performed a "dance" on the inner wall of the honeycomb. Other workers near her became excited and followed with antennae held close to her. One by one, the other workers left the dancer and in a short time appeared at the location of the food. The dance pattern, called the *round dance* by von Frisch, consists of circling first in one direction and then in the other direction (see Figure 36-26A). The round dance is repeated many times. This dance seems to inform other workers that food is nearby, while the bee passes on the scent of the flower to the workers. However, neither direction nor distance of the food is communicated by the round dance.

Von Frisch set up another experiment. He used two dishes of sugar water scented with lavender oil. He placed one dish at 10 meters from the hive and the other at 300 meters from the hive. The foraging bees that discovered the dish at 10 meters returned to the hive and danced the round dance. Workers returning from the dish 300 meters away performed a different dance. Von Frisch called this dance the *waggle dance*. In this dance, the bee runs along the wall of the hive in a straight line for a short distance while wagging her abdomen from side to side. She then circles back, runs forward again, circles in the opposite direction, and runs forward again. This "figure eight" motion is repeated several times (see Figure 36-26B). Distance of the food is communicated by the number of straight runs and the number of waggles given in a 15-second time period. As distance increases, the number of straight runs decreases while the number waggles increases. The waggle dance appears to be used to communicate food distances greater than 50 meters.

The direction of the food source is indicated by the direction of the waggle dance on the honeycomb wall. If the food is located in the direction of the sun, the dancer travels vertically up the wall of the honeycomb on the straight run. If the food is in a direction away from the sun, the dance is directed down the honeycomb wall. If the food is located at some angle between the line from the hive to the sun, the straight run is oriented at the same angle relative to a vertical line. Bees are thus able to translate information concerning the distance and direction of food into the speed and angle of a dance. This system of communication is but one other example of behavior that is an adaptation for species survival.

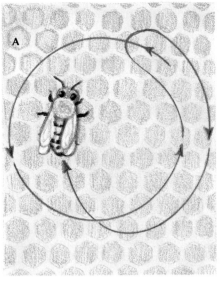

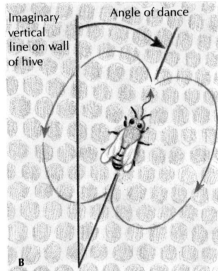

Figure 36-26. Bee Communication. (A) The round dance informs the bees of a hive that food is nearby. (B) The waggle dance indicates the direction and distance of the food from the hive.

Chapter Review

SUMMARY

- Behavior is a series of activities that occur in response to a stimulus.

- Many animals exhibit inherited cyclic behavior patterns that vary over the course of a day, month, or year. It is thought that these patterns are regulated by some sort of internal "biological clock."

- Some behavior patterns are innate and some are learned. Reflexes and instincts are innate behaviors.

- Learned behavior results from experience and involves some choice of responses to a given stimulus. Habituation, imprinting, conditioning, habits, and insight are all learned behaviors.

- Social behavior consists of interactions of animals of the same species. Among the factors affecting social behavior are sight, sound, and chemical signals; the dominance hierarchy; and territoriality. Ants, termites, and bees are insects that show highly organized social behavior.

KNOW THE TERMS

behavior	habituation	learned behavior	taxis
circadian rhythm	imprinting	pheromone	territory
conditioning	innate behavior	reflex	
dominance hierarchy	insight	social behavior	
habit	instinct	stimulus	

SECTION QUESTIONS

Nature of Behavior

1. List some environmental factors important in behavior.
2. Define the term *behavior*.
3. How does behavior aid an individual or species?
4. What is the role of heredity in behavior?
5. How does an organism sense changes in the environment?
6. What are circadian rhythms?

Innate Behavior

7. Define the term *innate behavior*.
8. What is a taxis?

9. What is the chief advantage of instincts?

Learned Behavior

10. List some forms of learned behavior.
11. Which animals exhibit the greatest capacity to learn?
12. How does a habit become automatic?

Social Behavior

13. Define the term *social behavior*.
14. What is a dominance hierarchy?
15. What signals bring together the male and female of a species during courtship?
16. What are three insects that form complex societies?

KNOW THE FACTS

Copy the number of each of the following statements on a sheet of paper. Beside each number, write whether the statement is true or false. If the statement is false, replace the italicized word(s) with a term that will make the statement true.

1. A *response* is a reaction to a stimulus.
2. All multicellular animals except the *hydra* have a nervous system.
3. Cycles of behavior may be *longer* than 24 hour rhythms.
4. Leaves of the sensitive plant fold *slowly* after being touched.
5. An ameba moving toward light is *negatively* phototactic.
6. Nerve cells *between* the receptor and effector complete the reflex arc.
7. An instinct is *learned* behavior.
8. Fish exhibit *instinctive* behavior during nesting activities.
9. *Reproductive* behavior is thought to be controlled initially by the hypothalamus and the pituitary gland.
10. The simplest type of learning is called *instinct*.
11. Trial and error conditioning is also called *operant* conditioning.
12. The ability of higher animals to solve problems is known as *conditioning*.
13. Mixed groups of animals are referred to as *interactions*.
14. A group of animals is generally *less* alert than a single individual.
15. A group of baboons is called a *pride*.
16. *Hormones* are also known as sex attractants.
17. A *territory* is a home area defended by an individual.
18. The waggle dance of bees informs other worker bees that food is *nearby*.

UNDERSTAND THE CONCEPTS

19. How does a bat determine whether an object is an obstacle or a moving prey?
20. Describe evidence supporting the existence of innate biological clocks.
21. What function is served by innate biological clocks?
22. Describe the function of the receptor and the effector in producing a reflex.
23. What physiological factors lead an animal to courtship, mating, and care of young?
24. Explain the difference between innate behavior and learned behavior.
25. What are conditioned responses?
26. Briefly describe Pavlov's experiment in conditioning dogs.
27. Define *insight* and give an example.
28. Describe the types of social behavior.
29. What is a dominance hierarchy, and what are the advantages of this type of social organization?
30. Describe the various types of signals found in animal groups.
31. In what way is the establishment of territories a useful form of social behavior?
32. Briefly describe the social organization of a beehive.

THINK CRITICALLY

33. Animals tend to behave in a way that will aid the survival of the species. Explain.
34. In what way are genetically determined behaviors different from more complex learned behaviors?
35. Some biologists believe that lower vertebrates such as fish are capable of learning. What important assumption must these biologists have made?
36. How does a species benefit from social behavior?
37. Explain how Pavlov's concept of classical conditioning is different from Lorenz's concept of imprinting.

THINK CREATIVELY

38. Design an organism that is clearly a plant, yet would exhibit some form of learning. What types of behavioral activity would you expect your plant to perform?
39. People often argue that cats are smarter than dogs, yet most cats will not perform tricks. Explain. Construct an argument to show that monkeys are smarter than dogs.

FOR FURTHER INVESTIGATION

1. There is much to learn about the bee as a social insect. Visit a beekeeper at an apiary to learn how colonies are maintained. Go to the library for more information on apiculture.
2. Find a spider in its web. Does it respond to presence? (Can it see you?) Play a radio near the animal, high volume, and then lower the volume. Does it respond to sound? What effect has a bright light on this animal? Blow gently on the web. Are there any observed responses? Gently touch the web with a stick. What happens? Catch an insect and toss it into the web. What happens when the trapped insect struggles? Closely observe this spider's behavior with its prey. Accurately record your observations. Try the same thing with a different kind of spider. Are the responses the same? Make a chart and list the stimuli and the spider's responses to the stimuli. Record any activity you think is instinctive behavior. For further reference, read Fabre, J.H., *The Life of the Spider*, 1912, or Kaston, B.J., *How to Know the Spiders*, William C. Brown & Co., 1978.
3. Prepare a report on one of the career opportunities listed below. See suggested procedures, p. 9, "For Further Investigation" Activity 3.
   a. Ethologist
   b. Behavioral psychologist
   c. Psychiatric nurse
   d. Horse trainer
4. Prepare a report on the life and contributions of one of the following scientists.
   a. Konrad Lorenz
   b. Karl Von Frisch
   c. Donald R. Griffin
   d. Niko Tinbergen

FOR FURTHER READING

Fellman, Bruce, "A Clockwork Gland," *Science 85*, May, 1985.

Ghiglieri, Michael P., "The Social Ecology of Chimpanzees," *Scientific American*, June, 1985.

Hinde, R. A., and Hinde, J. S., *Instinct and Intelligence*, 2nd ed. (Carolina Biology Reader), Carolina Biological Suppy Co., Burlington, NC, 1980.

Jolly, Alison, "Can Animals Think? A New Science That Sees Animals as Conscious Beings," *Smithsonian*, March, 1985.

Scheller, R., and Axel, R., "How Genes Control an Innate Behavior," *Scientific American*, March, 1984.

Weatherhead, P., "The Bird's Communal Connection," *Natural History*, February, 1985.

Issues in Biology

Preserving Genetic Diversity

Like begets like. Parent organisms pass on copies of their genes, producing offspring like themselves. The species continues to survive. However, more than genetic "sameness" is needed for species survival. Genetic diversity is required too. Diversity among the members of a species provides the "raw material" on which natural selection acts—allowing some organisms to survive during environmental stress, while others perish.

Genetic uniformity has become a trademark of modern agriculture. Consumers want products with certain characteristics, such as large, juicy oranges or seedless grapes. In addition, farmers want crops that grow rapidly, mature uniformly, and are easy to harvest. In response to these demands, plant breeders have used selective breeding to develop crops with a narrow range of desired characteristics. However, valuable qualities such as hardiness, resistance to disease, and adaptability to varying climates, traits which are maintained in natural, wild populations of plants, are sometimes lost by selective breeding. Furthermore, the diverse "wild" varieties of certain crop plant species are facing extinction as more wild habitats disappear and as farmers turn to the cultivation of the often higher-yielding varieties developed through modern breeding programs.

The danger of losing the genetic diversity of crops is illustrated by the Irish potato blight of the mid-1800s. Ireland's potato crop lacked genetic diversity. When disease struck, the entire crop was lost. As a result, more than a million people starved to death. If the crop had been genetically diverse, part of it might have survived.

Modern agriculture tries to cope with plant disease by breeding varieties resistant to specific pests, and by using chemical pesticides or biological controls. However, these methods do not always work, and as recent history has shown, disaster can still strike. In just a few days in 1970, more than half the corn crop of the United States was lost to southern corn leaf blight.

Today, scientists can manipulate genes to produce organisms with certain desired traits. Some

In the United States, the once varied corn stock has been replaced by genetically similar hybrids.

plant breeders look to genetic engineering to help decrease the vulnerability of genetically similar crop plants. Plants with the required traits could be produced quickly using the technology of genetic engineering, and transported wherever they were needed. However, the technique is very expensive. Furthermore, scientists have not yet developed techniques for manufacturing new plant genes. They can obtain genes for splicing only from existing plant stocks.

Efforts are now being made to prevent the genes of many crop plants from becoming extinct. Some countries and the United Nations have established seed banks that protect some, but not all, crops. By preserving the genetic diversity of crop plant species, these seed banks will play a critical role in the future course of the world's agriculture.

---

1. What is genetic diversity? What factors have led to a loss of genetic diversity in crop plants?

2. Why is the loss of genetic diversity in crop plants considered to be a serious worldwide problem?

3. Could genetic engineering alone be used to prevent events like the potato and corn crop losses described in this essay? Explain.

4. Various groups now claim ownership of particular crop gene resources. What group(s) might have legitimate ownership rights? Why?

UNIT 8
ECOLOGY

The mushrooms and plants in this photograph live in close quarters on this forest floor. We might wonder how the members of this community coexist. How does each species impact on others around it? Do they compete for available resources such as water? Do they cooperate and share resources? Do they interact in other ways? The same questions can be posed for any region where organisms live together, even for the earth as a whole. In this Unit, you will learn that the earth is a delicately balanced system with limited space and resources, and inhabitants that are interdependent. You will examine the interactions between organisms and their environment, and see how they result in a flow of energy and a continual cycling of materials.

Chapter 37

ORGANIZATION IN THE BIOSPHERE

Scavengers like these African vultures play an important role in the ecology of their environment.

ABIOTIC FACTORS IN THE ENVIRONMENT

Objectives:
1. List the abiotic factors in the environment.
2. Describe how light, temperature, and precipitation vary with position on the earth's surface.
3. Describe the process of soil formation.

All types of living organisms have adaptations that enable them to survive in a particular environment. They may show adaptations for food-getting and reproduction, as well as for avoiding predators. Living organisms are affected by physical factors in their environment, such as the availability of water, temperature variation and range, the amount of light, and the composition of the soil. The physical environment is also affected by the organisms that live in it. For example, certain organisms affect the breakdown of rock to soil, and plant growth contributes to the filling in of ponds. Finally, organisms are affected by the other organisms living in the same area. The branch of biology that deals with the interactions among organisms and between organisms and their environment is called **ecology** (ih-*kahl*-uh-jee).

In studying the interaction between organisms and their environment, both the living and nonliving factors must be considered. The **biotic** (by-*aht*-ik), or living, **factors** include all the living organisms in the environment and their effects, both direct and indirect, on other living things. The **abiotic** (ay-by-*aht*-ik), or nonliving, **factors** include water, oxygen, light, temperature, soil, and inorganic and organic nutrients.

The abiotic factors determine what types of organisms can survive in a particular environment. For example, in deserts there is very little available water, and the temperature can vary daily from very hot to cold. Only plants that are adapted to these conditions, such as sagebrush and cactus, can survive. Other types of plants, such as corn, oak trees, and orchids, cannot survive in deserts. They grow in other environments with different abiotic conditions to which they are adapted.

37-1   Light

The energy for almost all living things on earth comes directly or indirectly from sunlight. The amount of sunlight striking a given area of the earth's surface varies with latitude. *Latitude* is the distance north or south of the equator. Both the *intensity,* or strength, of sunlight and the *duration,* or length, of daylight vary with latitude. Areas around the equator receive sunlight of the strongest intensity, while areas around the North and South Poles receive light of the weakest intensity (see Figure 37-1). Areas at the equator receive about 12 hours of daylight throughout the year. At the North and South Poles, the sun never rises above the horizon during the six winter months of each year. During the summers, the sun never sets. In regions between the equator and the poles, the relative lengths of day and night vary with the season, with more hours of daylight in the summer and fewer in the winter. These variations in the amount of sunlight striking the earth are caused by the daily rotation of the earth, the movement of the earth around the sun, and the tilt of the earth's axis.

The intensity and duration of sunlight are basic factors affecting the growth and flowering of plants (see page 323). Some plants require high light intensity and long days, while others grow where the light intensity is low and the days

Figure 37-1. Intensity of Sunlight at Different Latitudes. In this diagram, each ray represents the same amount of light. Note that a given amount of surface is struck by many more rays near the equator than near the poles.

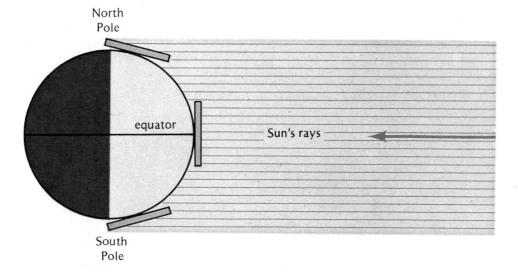

North Pole

equator

Sun's rays

South Pole

Career

Agronomist

Agronomists apply the principles of the soil and plant sciences to soil management and the raising of field crops such as wheat, potatoes, alfalfa, and cotton. In addition, agronomy in concerned with special-purpose plants such as grasses for home plots, recreational areas, and highway embankments. The agronomist is primarily interested in matching soil quality and nutrients to plants in such a way as to produce maximum yields without depleting the soil. Some of the problems that agronomy is concerned with are the nutritional quality and yield of various crop plants, the role of water in agricultural soils, disease resistance of crop species, and the domestication of wild plants for food.

Agronomists must be well versed in all aspects of soil and plant science. This usually requires a college degree. Most job opportunities in agronomy are in the sections of the continent where large-scale agriculture is the major economic activity.

short. In many animals, migration, hibernation, and reproductive behavior are influenced by the relative lengths of day and night.

Light conditions also vary in aquatic environments. Light is absorbed as it passes through water. Thus the amount of light present decreases with increasing depth. The layer of water through which light penetrates is called the *photic* (*foh*-tik) *zone*. Approximately 80 percent of the earth's photosynthesis takes place in the photic zone. Below the photic zone is the *aphotic* (ay-*foh*-tik) *zone*, where there is no light. Except for a few chemotrophs, organisms that live in the aphotic zone are all heterotrophs deriving their energy from organisms that drift or migrate down from the photic zone.

37-2   Temperature

Temperature patterns on the earth's surface vary with latitude and with altitude. *Altitude* is the vertical distance below or above sea level. The temperature pattern of a region may also be affected by the presence of nearby major geographic features, such as a mountain or an ocean.

The warmest average temperatures on the earth's surface occur around the equator. Traveling north or south of the equator, the average temperatures drop. The North and South Poles are the coldest regions on earth. Temperatures also drop with increasing altitude. Thus, the tops of high mountains may be snow-covered even at the equator.

37-3   Water

The release of water from the atmosphere in such forms as rain, snow, dew, and fog is called *precipitation*. The annual amount of precipitation varies from one region to another on the earth's surface. Annual precipitation patterns are related both to latitude and to altitude, and are also influenced by local features, such as mountains and large bodies of water. Areas around the equator are generally hot and very humid, and there is relatively heavy rainfall throughout the year. Because of the pattern of airflow over the earth's surface, most deserts are found around latitudes 30° north and 30° south of the equator. In these regions there is a very brief rainy season. There may be almost no rain at all the rest of the year. Still further north and south of the equator are *temperate* regions with hot summers and cold winters. Rainfall is relatively abundant in these regions. The polar regions are very cold, and precipitation is in the form of snow.

37-4   Soil and Minerals

Soil consists of both inorganic and organic materials. The inorganic material is mostly rock particles broken off from larger rocks by the action of water and wind—a process known as *weathering*. Alternate freezing and thawing of water helps

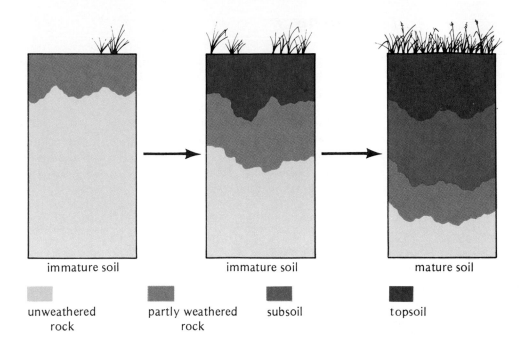

immature soil   immature soil   mature soil

unweathered   partly weathered   subsoil   topsoil
rock   rock

to crack the rock and break off pieces. Soluble minerals in the rock dissolve in water, breaking down the rock still further. Lichens (see page 545) and other soil-forming organisms also act to break down rock. When these organisms die, their remains are intermingled with the rock particles, thus adding organic matter to the developing soil. Plants may take root in the thin soil, and when they die, their remains add more organic matter.

The minerals present in soil depend partly on the type of rock from which the soil was formed and partly on the types of organisms living in the soil. The amount of precipitation determines the extent to which minerals will be retained in, or washed out of, the soil.

As soil development proceeds, three distinct layers form (see Figure 37-2). The uppermost layer, called *topsoil*, includes organic matter and living organisms. Plant "litter," such as fallen leaves and twigs, overlies the topsoil and gradually blends into it. The dark, rich organic matter in the topsoil is called **humus** (*hyoo*-mus). It is formed from the decay of dead plants and animals. The living organisms of the topsoil include plant roots, as well as earthworms, insects, and many other animals and protists. The organisms of decay—bacteria and fungi—are also found in this layer.

Beneath the topsoil is a layer of *subsoil*. The subsoil consists of rock particles mixed with inorganic compounds, including mineral nutrients. Water-soluble materials from the topsoil are constantly carried downward into the subsoil by the downward movement of water. The bottommost layer of the soil consists of bits of rock broken off from the parent bedrock below.

There are many types of soils. They are classified according to their organic content, mineral composition, pH, and size of

Figure 37-2. Three Stages in the Development of Soil. The forces of weathering and the action of certain small organisms gradually break down bedrock into fine particles. The products and remains of organisms add organic matter to the rock particles, forming soil.

the rock particles. Sandy soil has the largest particles, silt has particles of intermediate size, and clay is made up of very small particles. Water drains too quickly through sand and too slowly through clay. In general the best soils for plants to grow in consist of a mixture of clay and larger particles. However, different types of plants grow best in different types of soil. Some plants require well-drained, sandy soils, while others do best in clayey soils. Also some plants thrive in acid soils, but others need alkaline soils.

BIOTIC ORGANIZATION

Objective:
Explain the terms *population, community, ecosystem,* and *biosphere.*

37-5   Populations, Communities, and Ecosystems

In studying organisms in nature, ecologists generally focus their attention on a particular group of organisms in a particular type of natural setting. The simplest grouping of organisms in nature is a **population,** which includes all individuals of a particular species within a certain area. All the black oak trees in a forest make up a population. All the bullfrogs in a pond make up a population. Populations can also be considered as parts of larger groups. All the populations of different organisms within a given area make up a **community.** For example, all the frogs, fish, algae, plants, and other living things in and around a pond make up a pond community.

An **ecosystem** includes a community and its physical environment. In an ecosystem, both the biotic and abiotic factors are included. There is an ongoing exchange of materials between the nonliving and living parts of an ecosystem. All the ecosystems of the earth are linked to one another. Organisms move from one ecosystem to another. Water and other inorganic substances pass from one ecosystem to another. Also, organic compounds, with their stored energy, are transferred between ecosystems.

37-6   The Biosphere

The portion of the earth in which living things exist is the **biosphere.** Compared to the diameter of the earth, the biosphere is a very thin zone. It is about 20 kilometers in thickness, extending from the ocean floor to the highest point in the atmosphere where life is found. The biosphere includes portions of the *lithosphere,* which is the solid part of the earth's surface; the *hydrosphere,* which includes the water on and under the earth's surface and the water vapor of the air; and the *atmosphere,* which is the mass of air surrounding the earth.

NUTRITIONAL AND ENERGY RELATIONSHIPS IN AN ECOSYSTEM

Objectives:

1. Explain the terms *herbivore, carnivore, omnivore, predator, scavenger,* and *saprobe.*
2. List the different types of symbiotic relationships and describe each of them.
3. Explain the roles of producers, consumers, and decomposers in an ecosystem.
4. Describe the feeding relationships in an ecosystem in terms of food chains and food webs.
5. Explain the flow of energy in an ecosystem using the concepts of a pyramid of energy and a pyramid of biomass.

Figure 37-3. Herbivores. The prairie dog is just one of many herbivores that inhabit grasslands of western North America.

37-7 Autotrophic and Heterotrophic Nutrition

An ecosystem includes all kinds of organisms—microorganisms, plants, and animals. These organisms interact on many levels, but their nutritional and energy relationships are among the most important.

Autotrophs are organisms that can synthesize all the organic nutrients they need from inorganic compounds. Most autotrophs carry on photosynthesis; however, a few carry on chemosynthesis. Directly or indirectly, autotrophs provide all the food of heterotrophs—those organisms, including animals, that cannot synthesize their own nutrients.

Heterotrophs are divided into several groups, depending on what they eat and how they obtain their food. Heterotrophs include herbivores, carnivores, omnivores, and saprobes (see Figure 37-3).

Herbivores (*her*-buh-vorz) are animals that feed only on plants. Rabbits, cattle, horses, sheep, and deer are herbivores. **Carnivores** (*kar*-nuh-vorz) are animals that feed on other animals. Among the carnivores, some are predators and some are scavengers. **Predators** (*pred*-uh-terz), such as lions, hawks, and wolves, attack and kill their prey and feed on their bodies. **Scavengers** (*skav*-en-jerz) feed on dead animals they find. Vultures and hyenas are scavengers. **Omnivores** (*ahm*-nih-vorz) are animals that feed on both plants and animals. Humans and bears are omnivores. **Saprobes** are organisms that obtain nutrients by breaking down the remains of dead plants and animals. Many bacteria and fungi function as saprobes.

37-8 Symbiotic Relationships

Symbiotic relationships are those in which two different types of organisms live in a close association with each other such that at least one of the organisms benefits. There are three types of symbiotic relationships: mutualism, commensalism, and parasitism.

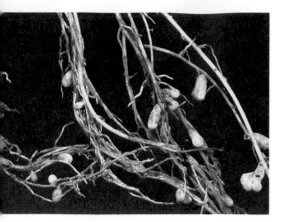

Figure 37-4. Root Nodules of a Legume.

Figure 37-5. Mistletoe. A fir tree is being parasitized by this species of mistletoe.

In **mutualism** (*myooch*-uh-wuh-liz-um), both organisms benefit from their association. For example, termites have cellulose-digesting microorganisms living in their digestive tracts. Without these microorganisms, termites could obtain no nutrients from the wood they eat. The termites, on the other hand, provide the microorganisms with food and a place to live. Cows have a similar association with microorganisms that live in their digestive tracts.

Lichens consist of both algal and fungal cells, and both types benefit from this association. It allows them to live in environments in which neither could survive alone. The algae produce food by photosynthesis for themselves and for the fungi. The fungi provide moisture and the structural framework and attachment sites in which the algae grow.

Peas, clover, and alfalfa are *legumes.* Legumes have nodules on their roots in which certain bacteria grow (see Figure 37-4). The bacteria convert nitrogen gas from the air in the soil into forms usable by the plants. In this relationship, the plants are supplied with the nitrogen compounds they need, while the bacteria are given an environment in which they can grow and reproduce.

In **commensalism** (kuh-*men*-suh-liz-um), one organism benefits from a symbiotic relationship and the other is not affected. For example, the remora is a small fish that lives attached to a shark by a sucker. It detaches itself to eat the scraps left over from the shark's feeding. Thus the shark provides the remora with food. As far as is known, the remora neither helps nor hurts the shark. Barnacles may attach themselves to the large body surface of a whale. Barnacles are sessile and rely on water currents to bring them food. The movements of the whale provide them with a constantly changing environment and food supply. The whale is not affected by the presence of the barnacles.

In **parasitism** (*par*-uh-suh-tiz-um), one organism benefits from a symbiotic relationship while the other one is harmed. The organism that benefits is called the *parasite,* while the organism that is harmed is the *host.* Some parasites cause only slight damage to their hosts, while others eventually kill the host. Tapeworms, for example, are parasites that live in the digestive tracts of various animals. There they are provided with nutrients and a suitable environment in which to grow and reproduce. However, the host is harmed by the presence of the tapeworms. The loss of nutrients and tissue damage caused by the worm can cause serious illness. There are parasitic plants that grow on other plants. Two examples of plant parasites are mistletoe (see Figure 37-5) and Indian pipe (see Section 17-10).

Symbiotic relationships, particularly those involving mutualism or commensalism, are not always permanent. Also, it is not always possible to say definitely whether a particular organism is helped or harmed by such a relationship. For example, in many environments the algal cells of a lichen can survive perfectly well without the fungal cells. The fungal cells, on the other hand, may not be able to survive alone.

37-9 Producers, Consumers, and Decomposers

In all but a few small ecosystems, the autotrophs are plants and other photosynthetic organisms. They trap energy from sunlight and use it for the synthesis of sugars and starch. These substances can be converted to other organic compounds needed by the plant, or they can be broken down for energy. Heterotrophs cannot use any form of energy for their life processes except chemical energy stored in organic compounds. These organic nutrients must be obtained from the bodies of other organisms—either plants or animals. Since autotrophs (phototrophs and chemotrophs) are the only organisms in an ecosystem that can produce organic compounds (food) from inorganic compounds, they are called **producers.** Since heterotrophs must obtain nutrients from other organisms, they are called **consumers.**

Saprobes play an important role in an ecosystem. They function as *organisms of decay,* or **decomposers.** They break down the remains of dead plants and animals, releasing substances that can be reused by other members of the ecosystem. In this way many important substances are recycled in an ecosystem.

37-10 Food Chains and Food Webs

Within an ecosystem, there is a pathway of energy flow that always begins with the producers. Energy stored in organic nutrients synthesized by the producers is transferred to consumers when the plants are eaten. Herbivores, which feed on plants, are the primary, or *first-order consumers.* The carnivores that feed on the plant-eating animals are secondary, or *second-order consumers.* For example, mice feed on plants and are first-level consumers. The snake that eats the mouse is a second-level consumer, while the hawk that eats the snake is a third-level consumer. Since many consumers have a varied diet, they may be second-, third-, or higher-level consumers, depending on their prey. Each of these feeding relationships forms a **food chain,** a series of organisms through which food energy is passed (see Figure 37-6).

Feeding relationships in an ecosystem are never just simple food chains. There are many types of organisms at each feeding level, and there are always many food chains in an ecosystem. These food chains are interconnected at various points, forming a **food web** (see Figure 37-7).

At every level in an ecosystem there are decomposers. The decomposers make use of the wastes and remains of all organisms in the system. They use the energy in these materials for their own metabolism. At the same time, they break down

Figure 37-6. A Simple Food Chain. The grass is a producer; the field mouse is a first-order consumer; and the owl is a second-order consumer. The arrows show the flow of energy in the food chain.

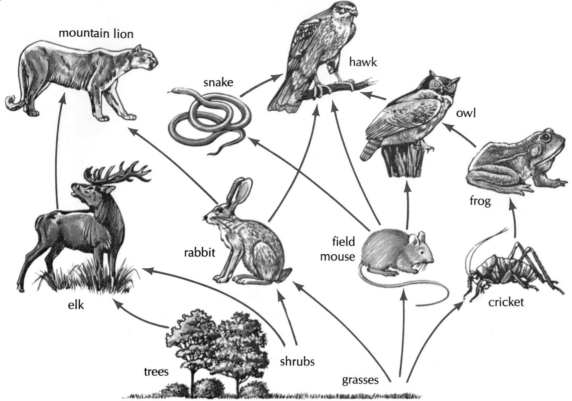

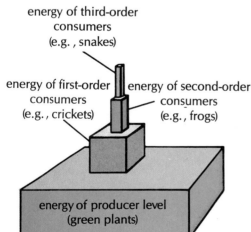

Figure 37-7. A Simple Food Web. Each organism is usually part of several different food chains. The same organism (for example, the hawk) can be a second-level consumer in one chain, a third-level consumer in another, and a fourth-level consumer in still another.

Figure 37-8. The Pyramid of Energy in an Ecosystem. At each level, the energy available is only about 10 percent of the energy at the level below it.

organic compounds into inorganic ones and make substances available for reuse in the system. The decomposers can be thought of as the final consumers in every food chain and food web.

37-11 Pyramids of Energy and Biomass

The amount of energy available in a food web decreases with each higher feeding level. The reason for this is that only a small fraction of the energy taken in as food becomes stored as new tissue. Much of the food ingested is not digested and absorbed. Furthermore, a large part of the energy in the food is used for respiration and maintenance. This energy is lost as heat. As a result, only about 10 percent of the energy taken in at any feeding level is passed upward to the next feeding level.

The amount of available energy in an ecosystem is commonly shown in the form of a pyramid—the **pyramid of energy** (see Figure 37-8). The greatest amount of energy is present in the producers—the base of the pyramid—and the least energy is present at the top of the pyramid—the highest-level consumers. Because the amount of available energy decreases so steeply, there are generally no more than four or five feeding levels in an ecosystem.

Since the total amount of energy available decreases with each higher feeding level, the total mass of living organisms that can be supported at each level decreases, too. This relationship can also be represented by a pyramid. This relationship, known as the **pyramid of biomass,** shows the relative mass of the organisms—the *biomass*—at each feeding level. The greatest amount of biomass is in the lowest level, the producers. The least is found in the highest level of consumers.

CYCLES OF MATERIALS

Objective:

> Describe each of the following biogeochemical cycles: the nitrogen cycle, the carbon and oxygen cycles, and the water cycle.

In all ecosystems cycling of materials occurs between living things and the environment. Organisms incorporate certain substances from the environment into their bodies. When these organisms die, their bodies are broken down by decomposers, and the substances returned to the environment. If these substances were not returned to the environment, their supply would eventually become exhausted. The cycles of materials between living things and the environment are called *biogeochemical cycles*. Nitrogen, carbon, oxygen, and water are among the substances involved in such cycles.

37-12   The Nitrogen Cycle

Nitrogen is an important element in living things. It is a basic component of amino acids, which form proteins, and of nucleotides, which form nucleic acids. Nitrogen gas makes up almost 80 percent of the earth's atmosphere. However, most organisms are unable to make use of nitrogen gas directly. Their supplies of nitrogen must be in the form of nitrogen compounds. Most plants can utilize nitrogen only in the two inorganic forms, ammonia, NH_3, and nitrate, (NO_3^-). Usually nitrate is the major source of nitrogen for plants. From nitrate and ammonia, plants can synthesize their own organic nitrogen-containing compounds, e.g., proteins and nucleic acids. In contrast, animals lack this ability. They can utilize nitrogen only in an organic form. Thus, animals must ingest plants or other animals to meet their nitrogen needs.

Nitrogen in the wastes and in the remains of organisms must be made available to living plants for reuse. This is accomplished through the activity of decomposers that break down the complex organic compounds in plant and animal remains. During decomposition, most of the nitrogen in organic compounds is released as ammonia. Some of this may be taken up directly by plants, but most is quickly converted by **nitrifying bacteria** to nitrite (NO_2^-) and finally nitrate. The nitrate then is available for uptake again by plants.

Not all nitrate in the soil and in water remains as nitrate until taken up by plants. **Denitrifying bacteria** derive energy for their life processes by converting nitrite and nitrate to nitrogen

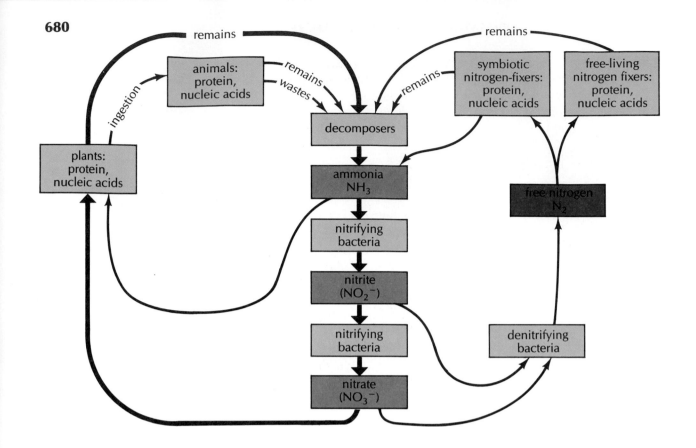

Figure 37-9. The Nitrogen Cycle. There are acutally two interlocking nitrogen cycles. In the main cycle, ammonia and nitrate are converted to plant and animal proteins, which are then broken down again to ammonia and nitrate. The nitrogen remains in compound form throughout this cycle. In the secondary cycle, inorganic nitrogen compounds are broken down to free nitrogen by denitrifying bacteria. Free nitrogen is returned to compound form by nitrogen-fixing organisms.

gas, N_2. This form of nitrogen, which is released into the atmosphere, cannot be used by plants and animals. However, nitrogen gas can be changed to a form available to plants. A few kinds of bacteria and blue-green algae convert nitrogen gas directly to ammonia through a process called **nitrogen fixation.** Some of these **nitrogen fixers** are free-living. The ammonia they produce is used to synthesize their own nitrogen-containing compounds. Other nitrogen-fixers are symbiotic. They fix nitrogen only when living in close association with a host plant (see page 676). In these symbiotic associations, the nitrogen fixers utilize the ammonia themselves and also supply some directly to the host plant. When the nitrogen fixers die, their nitrogen is recycled through decomposition.

Figure 37-9 shows the various pathways of the nitrogen cycle. The nitrogen cycle keeps the level of usable nitrogen in the soil fairly constant. The nitrogen cycle also occurs in lakes, streams, and oceans. Most of the nitrogen being cycled remains in compound form. Only a small fraction is cycled through the atmosphere.

37-13 The Carbon and Oxygen Cycles

Carbon in the form of carbon dioxide makes up about 0.03 percent of the atmosphere. Carbon dioxide is also found dissolved in the waters of the earth. In the course of photosynthesis, carbon dioxide from the atmosphere is incorporated

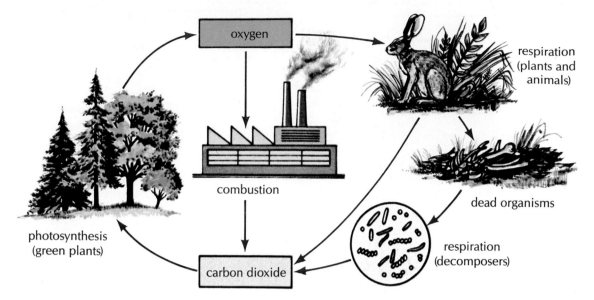

into organic compounds, a process known as *carbon fixation.* Some of these organic compounds are broken down during cellular respiration by the photosynthetic organisms, releasing carbon dioxide back into the atmosphere. If the plants or other photosynthetic organisms are eaten by animals, the carbon compounds pass through a food web. At each level, some are broken down by cellular respiration, releasing carbon dioxide into the atmosphere. Finally, the remains of dead plants and animals and animal wastes are broken down by decomposers, releasing carbon dioxide.

In the **carbon cycle,** carbon dioxide is removed from the atmosphere by photosynthesis, and it is returned to the atmosphere by cellular respiration (see Figure 37-10). These two processes are normally in balance, maintaining a relatively constant level of carbon dioxide in the atmosphere. However, the burning of fossil fuels (oil, coal, and natural gas) also releases carbon dioxide. Because of the increasing use of these fuels, there has been a gradual increase in the carbon dioxide content of the atmosphere since the mid-1800s. The long-term effects of this change are not known. However, some scientists think that it will result in an increase in temperature on the earth's surface. This would occur because the atmospheric carbon dioxide absorbs heat from the earth that would otherwise be radiated away into space.

Oxygen makes up about 20 percent of the earth's atmosphere. During photosynthesis, water molecules are split into hydrogen and oxygen. The hydrogen is used in the formation of carbohydrates, and the oxygen is released into the atmosphere. Animals, plants, and many protists use oxygen in cellular respiration and release carbon dioxide. Thus, in the **oxygen cycle,** oxygen is released into the atmosphere by the process of photosynthesis and removed from the atmosphere by cellular respiration.

Figure 37-10. The Oxygen and Carbon Cycles. Carbon dioxide is removed from the air by photosynthesis and returned by cellular respiration and the burning of fossil fuels. Oxygen is removed from the air by cellular respiration and burning and returned by photosynthesis.

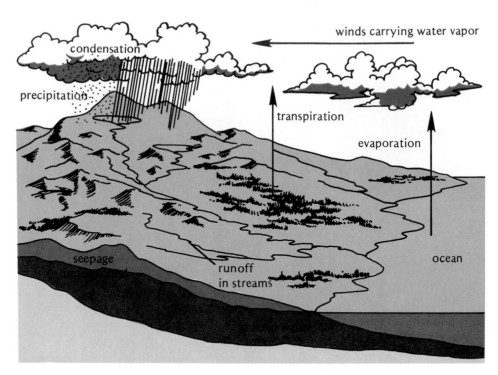

Figure 37-11. The Water Cycle. Water from the earth's surface enters the atmosphere in the form of water vapor through the processes of evaporation and transpiration. It returns to the surface by condensation and precipitation.

37-14   The Water Cycle

The cycling of water on the earth is almost entirely a physical process. Wherever water is exposed to the air, it continuously evaporates—escapes into the air in the form of water vapor. Plants also contribute to this loss of water to the air by the process of transpiration. However, there is a limit to the amount of water vapor the air can hold. Through various physical processes, excess water vapor condenses to form clouds and falls back to the earth's surface as precipitation.

This cycling of water between the surface of the earth and the atmosphere is called the **water cycle** (see Figure 37-11). Unlike the other cycles we have examined, no chemical changes are involved and no truly biological processes enter into it. It is true that some water is broken down chemically to hydrogen and oxygen during photosynthesis. This water is restored by cellular respiration. However, the amount of water involved in the photosynthesis-respiration cycle is only a small fraction of the total amount that passes through the water cycle.

COMPETITION IN ECOSYSTEMS

Objectives:
1. Explain the terms *habitat* and *niche*.
2. Compare and contrast interspecific and intraspecific competition in an ecosystem.

37-15 Habitat and Niche

Each type of organism within an ecosystem has a particular part of the environment in which it lives. This is its **habitat.** For example, slime molds live on the damp floors of forests. This is their habitat. Because of the complex interactions that occur within an ecosystem, each species also plays a particular role. The role of a species in an ecosystem is its **niche.** An organism's habitat is part of its niche, but only part. Also included are how, when, and where it obtains nutrients, its reproductive behavior, and its direct and indirect effects both on the environment and on other species within the ecosystem.

37-16 Intraspecific and Interspecific Competition

In a balanced ecosystem, each species occupies its own niche. It occupies a particular territory (its habitat) and obtains nutrients in a particular way. Competition arises when the niches of two species overlap. The greater the overlap—the more requirements the two species have in common—the more intense the competition. Competition between two different species is called **interspecific competition.** As the resources being competed for become more scarce, the competition becomes more intense. Eventually one of the species is eliminated from the ecosystem, leaving the more successful species to occupy the niche.

Competition also occurs between members of the same species. This is called **intraspecific competition.** The intensity of the competition between members of the same species is affected by such things as population density and the availability of needed resources. If conditions become very harsh, those individuals with the most helpful adaptations will survive, while the less-well-adapted individuals will not.

MAINTENANCE AND CHANGE IN ECOSYSTEMS

Objectives:
1. Describe the conditions necessary for a stable, self-sustaining ecosystem.
2. Explain the terms *ecological succession, dominant species, climax community, primary succession,* and *secondary succession.*
3. Describe primary succession on land leading to development of a forest community.
4. Describe succession in lakes and ponds leading to development of a forest community.

37-17 Maintenance in an Ecosystem

For an ecosystem to be stable and self-sustaining certain conditions must exist. (1) There must be a constant source of energy. For almost all ecosystems on earth the source of

energy is light from the sun. Only a few ecosystems are based on chemosynthesis. In those ecosystems, the producers derive energy for the synthesis of organic compounds from chemical reactions involving various inorganic compounds. (2) There must be organisms within the ecosystem that can use incoming energy (light) for the synthesis of organic compounds. This role is filled by green plants and algae, which are the producers of the ecosystem. (3) There must be a cycle of materials between living organisms in the ecosystem and the environment. The producers incorporate inorganic compounds from the environment into organic compounds, which may then pass through a food chain or food web. Eventually, however, the decomposers break down the remains of dead organisms, releasing the inorganic substances back into the environment for reuse.

37-18   Ecological Succession

Although ecosystems appear stable, they do undergo change with time. Change occurs because the living organisms present in the ecosystem alter the environment. Some of the changes tend to make the environment more suitable for new types of organisms and less suitable for the existing organisms. Thus, the original organisms in an ecosystem are gradually replaced by other types. A new community replaces the original community in the ecosystem. Over time, this community is gradually replaced by still another community. The process by which an existing community is gradually replaced by another community is called **ecological succession.** In general, in land environments, ecological succession depends upon the types of plants that are present at any given time. Plants determine the type of community that develops because plants are the producers. The types of animals that can survive in the community depend, directly or indirectly, on the types of plants.

During each stage of ecological succession, a few species exert the greatest effect on the environment and on other members of the community. These species are called the **dominant species.** The conditions imposed on the environment by the dominant species determine the types of other species that can survive in each successive community.

Succession of one community by another continues until a mature, stable community develops. Such a community is called a **climax community.** In an ecosystem with a climax community, the conditions continue to be suitable for all the members of the community. The climax community remains until it is upset by a catastrophic event, such as a fire, flood, or volcanic eruption. After the destruction of a climax community, succession begins again and continues until a new climax community develops.

Succession that occurs in an area that has no existing life, for

EARLY PLANT
FORMS   INTERMEDIATE FORMS   CLIMAX FOREST

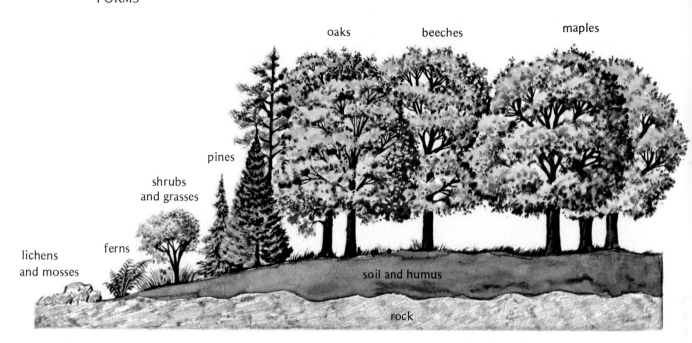

example, on bare rock, is called **primary succession.** Succession that occurs in an area in which an existing community has been partially destroyed and its balance upset is called **secondary succession.**

Succession on land. Primary succession occurs on land in areas that are initially nearly lifeless (see Figure 37-12). Such conditions exist on rocky cliffs, sand dunes, newly formed volcanic islands, and newly exposed land areas. Primary succession is a very slow process because it must begin with the formation of soil.

Soil forms very slowly over thousands of years (see Section 37-4). By the process of weathering, large rocks are gradually broken into smaller and smaller pieces. Eventually, some of the rock is broken down into small particles. The first organisms to inhabit an area are called *pioneer organisms.* Such organisms generally include bacteria, fungi, and lichens. They break down the rock still further and add organic matter to the developing soil. Lichens are adapted to exposed conditions. They become attached to irregularities in the surface of the rock by rootlike rhizoids. They secrete acids that dissolve the rock. Some lichens die, and their remains are added to the soil. Mosses appear in areas where a little soil has accumulated. The mosses may shade the lichens, causing them to die and thus adding more organic material to the still primitive soil.

Eventually, grasses and annual plants grow in the areas where organic material has accumulated. When these plants die, the soil becomes richer. Small shrubs begin to grow, and their roots break rocks apart. The shrubs may shade the

Figure 37-12. Stages of Primary Succession. The sequence of stages is represented from left to right. In an actual succession, only one stage is present at any given time.

A

B

C

D

Figure 37-13. Ecological Succession in a Pond. A pond may gradually change to dry land supporting a forest community.

grasses, killing them. Tree seedlings may take root. The trees eventually shade out the shrubs. The seedlings that grew among the shrubs probably required a fair amount of sunlight. Thus, when they become mature trees, there may not be enough sun on the forest floor for seedlings of the same type to survive. However, seedlings of other trees may grow well in the shade. In this way, one community of trees will be succeeded by another community with different types of trees. After many thousands of years, a climax community will develop. Climax communities are usually described in terms of their dominant plant forms.

The dominant plants of a climax community are determined by the physical factors of the environment. Where there is adequate rainfall and suitable soil, the climax community is likely to be a forest. However, if there is not enough water to support a forest, the climax community can consist of grasses or some other type of plant.

Animal life changes with the plant communities. For example, as a succession proceeds toward a forest community, animals that live among grasses and shrubs will eventually be replaced by animals that live on the forest floor and at varying levels in the trees.

Secondary succession occurs in areas in which the climax community has been destroyed. For example, a forest may be cut down in order to clear the land for farming. If, after being farmed for awhile, the land is left untended, a new succession will begin, ending eventually in another forest climax community. In secondary succession, the area already has existing soil. Since the sequence does not begin with soil formation, the process is much faster than primary succession. A climax community may become reestablished after a few hundreds of years, rather than the thousands originally needed for the primary succession.

Succession in lakes and ponds. Lakes and ponds may also pass through stages of ecological succession, eventually developing into a forest climax community (see Figure 37-12). The process begins when sediment, fallen leaves, and other debris gradually accumulate on the lake bottom, decreasing its depth. Around the edges of the lake, sphagnum moss and many of the rooted plants, such as cattails, reeds, and rushes, grow out into the shallower water. They gradually extend the banks inward, decreasing the size of the lake. As the lake fills in, it becomes rich in nutrients that can support a large population of organisms. The increased number of plants and animals contribute organic material to the sediment, which hastens the filling-in process. As succession continues, the lake becomes a marsh. Still later, the marsh fills in, forming dry land. Land communities replace aquatic forms. Over a period of time, the filled area becomes part of the surrounding community.

Chapter Review

SUMMARY

- Ecology deals with the interactions between organisms and their environment. The environment has both nonliving, or abiotic, and living, or biotic, factors. In a given area, all the organisms and their physical environment together make up an ecosystem.

- Autotrophs are organisms that synthesize all the nutrients they need. Heterotrophs feed on other organisms. Sometimes two different types of organisms are closely associated in a symbiotic feeding relationship that benefits at least one of them. Mutualism, commensalism, and parasitism are the three major types of symbiotic relationships.

- In an ecosystem, the autotrophs are the producers and the heterotrophs are the consumers. The saprobes act as decomposers. The path of energy flow in an ecosystem forms a food chain. Energy flows from the producers, to the various levels of consumers, and finally to the decomposers. All the food chains in an ecosystem are interconnected, forming a food web.

- The amount of energy in an ecosystem is greatest at the producer level and least at the highest level of consumers. This is represented as the pyramid of energy. Biomass—the relative mass of the organisms—also is greatest at the producer level and least at the highest level of consumers. This is represented as the pyramid of biomass.

- In all ecosystems there are cycles in which materials are exchanged between the organisms and their environment. The most important of these cycles are the nitrogen, carbon, oxygen, and water cycles.

- Ecosystems can change when the environment is altered. The original organisms can be replaced by others in an ecological succession.

KNOW THE TERMS

abiotic factor	dominant species	mutualism	primary succession
biotic factor	ecological succession	niche	producer
biosphere	ecology	nitrifying bacteria	pyramid of biomass
carbon cycle	ecosystem	nitrogen cycle	pyramid of energy
carnivore	food chain	nitrogen fixation	saprobe
climax community	food web	nitrogen fixers	scavenger
commensalism	habitat	omnivore	secondary succession
community	herbivore	oxygen cycle	symbiotic relationship
consumer	humus	parasitism	water cycle
decomposer	interspecific competition	population	
denitrifying bacteria	intraspecific competition	predator	

SECTION QUESTIONS

Abiotic Factors in the Environment

1. What is ecology?
2. List some common abiotic environmental factors.
3. Define the term *latitude*.
4. What are some geographic features that influence temperature patterns?
5. List two forms of precipitation.
6. Which environmental factors cause the weathering of rock?

Biotic Organization

7. What is a population?
8. Define the term *biosphere*.

Nutritional and Energy Relationships in an Ecosystem

9. Name two important groups of saprobes.
10. List three types of symbiotic relationships.

11. Which kind of organisms are always at the base of a food chain?
12. Which level of an energy pyramid contains the most energy?

Cycles of Materials

13. Name three biogeochemical cycles.
14. What kind of organisms return soil nitrogen to the atmosphere?

Competition in Ecosystems

15. Define the term *niche*.
16. Define the term *habitat*.

Maintenance and Change in Ecosystems

17. By what process do ecosystems change?
18. What is any group of organisms that is the first to inhabit an area?

KNOW THE FACTS

Copy the number of each sentence below on a sheet of paper. Beside each number, write the term(s) that complete(s) the sentence correctly.

1. An ecosystem includes a community and its _____ environment.
2. When two different organisms live in close association so that at least one benefits, the relationship is termed _____.
3. In the feeding relationship called _____, one organism benefits and the other is not affected.
4. A food web results from interconnected _____.
5. The relative mass of organisms at each feeding level is called _____.
6. In the nitrogen cycle, certain bacteria called _____ convert nitrites to nitrates.
7. In the carbon cycle, carbon dioxide is removed from the atmosphere by _____.
8. The kind of competition that occurs between two different species is called_____.
9. An existing community is gradually replaced by another community through the process of _____.
10. The mature, stable community that finally develops as a result of ecological succession is called the _____ community.

UNDERSTAND THE CONCEPTS

11. Discuss the effect of latitude on the intensity and duration of sunlight received at the earth's surface.
12. Describe soil formation, including the three layers found in mature soil.
13. Describe biotic organization in terms of populations, communities, and ecosystems.
14. Explain the difference between a predator and a scavenger and give examples of each.
15. Describe the different parts of the biosphere.
16. Describe the three types of symbiotic relationships and give an example of each.
17. Summarize the structures of a food chain and a food web.
18. Describe the nitrogen cycle.
19. Describe the oxygen cycle.
20. Trace the path of the water cycle.
21. Under what circumstances is an ecosystem stable and self-sustaining?
22. Describe primary succession both on land, beginning with rock, and in a pond, leading to a forest community.

THINK CRITICALLY

23. (a) In North America, most ski slopes are built on north-facing slopes rather than south-facing slopes. Why does this plan result in a longer ski season? (b) Why would farmers in the northern hemisphere be wise to plant crops that required lots of sunlight on south-facing slopes?
24. What type of soil would be best for lining a land-fill site designed to store hazardous wastes?
25. If the intensity of sunlight was drastically reduced for several weeks by smoke and ash from an erupting volcano, how would each of the following members of nearby ecosystems be affected: (a) sweet grass, (b) rabbit, (c) hawk?
26. Why do farmers plant alfalfa, clover, or other legumes on fields that are lying fallow, or are not being used to grow a cash crop?

THINK CREATIVELY

27. Suggest some characteristics that plants would need in order to grow successfully in far northern latitudes.
28. What special adaptations might an animal need to survive in areas that (a) were always very hot; (b) were always very cold; (c) had daily temperature fluctuations from very hot to very cold?

FOR FURTHER INVESTIGATION

1. Find an area near your home where a new community is replacing an original community. What plants and animals are found in the changing community? Can you determine the dominant species? What will the climax community be? Use field guides as a resource.
2. Write a report on one of the following career opportunities.
   a. Ecologist
   b. Environmental chemist
   c. Soil conservationist
3. Prepare a report on the life and contributions of one of the following scientists:
   a. Ann Haven Morgan
   b. Lillie Rose Minoka-Hill, M.D.
   c. Frederick Lafayette

FOR FURTHER READING

Baggett, James, "The Greenhouse Effect: Will the 1990's Be Hotter Than July?" *Scholastic Science World*, January 6, 1984.

Eliot, John, "A North Woods Park Primeval: Isle Royale," *National Geographic*, April, 1985.

Gore, Rick, "Our Restless Planet Earth," *National Geographic*, August, 1985.

Whittaker, R. H., "Careers in Life Science and Ecology," *Scholastic Science World*, October 19, 1984.

Chapter 38

BIOMES OF THE EARTH

The tundra of Canada's Yukon Territory is home to these caribou bulls.

TERRESTRIAL BIOMES

Objectives:
1. List the major terrestrial biomes of the earth and specify the location of each.
2. Describe the climatic factors that characterize each of the terrestrial biomes.
3. Name the dominant plant and animal types of each biome.

The type of climax community that can develop in a land area is determined by the climate and other physical conditions of that area. Areas that are similar in climate and other physical conditions develop similar types of climax communities. The term **biome** (*by*-ohm) refers to a large geographical region showing a particular type of climax community. In the case of a land, or terrestrial, biome, the climax community is defined by its dominant type of plant life. For example, one biome may consist of climax communities of grasses. Another may contain evergreen trees. The species may vary from one part of a biome to another, but the general type of plant life, or vegetation, is the same throughout. The major terrestrial biomes are the tundra, taiga, deciduous forest, grassland, desert, and tropical rain forest.

The term *biome* is also applied to communities that develop in aquatic environments. Ecologists refer to freshwater biomes, or communities of organisms inhabiting lakes and streams, and to saltwater, or marine, biomes.

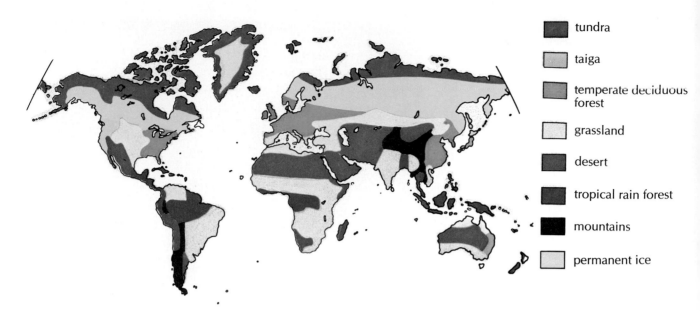

■	tundra
▢	taiga
■	temperate deciduous forest
□	grassland
■	desert
■	tropical rain forest
■	mountains
▢	permanent ice

Figure 38-1. Biomes of the World.

38-1   The Tundra

The **tundra** (*tun*-druh) is a region south of the ice caps of the Arctic and extending across North America, Europe, and Siberia (see Figure 38-1). (In the Southern Hemisphere, the latitudes that would be tundra are oceans.) The tundra is characterized by a low average temperature and a short growing season—about 60 days. During the long, cold winters, the ground is completely frozen. During the short summer, only the topmost layer of soil thaws. The layers beneath, which remain frozen, are called **permafrost** (*per*-muh-frost). The average precipitation in the tundra is only about 10 to 12 centimeters a year. However, because of the low rate of evaporation, the region is wet with bogs and ponds during the warm season.

Vegetation in the tundra is limited to lichens, mosses, grasses, sedges, and shrubs (see Figure 38-2). Because of the short growing season and the permafrost, there are almost no trees. The vegetation that does grow in the tundra is adequate to support a limited number of animal species. Animals found in the tundra include reindeer, musk oxen, caribou, wolves, Arctic hares, Arctic foxes, lemmings, snowy owls, and ptarmigans, which are a type of bird.

During the warm season, a great number of flies and mosquitos appear in the region. Various types of birds, including sandpipers, ducks, and geese, migrate to the tundra during the summer season. Here, these migratory birds can nest and breed in safety, because of the relative absence of predators. During their breeding season, the birds feed on the growing vegetation and the abundant insects.

Figure 38-2. The Tundra. (Top) Tundra in the summer. (Bottom) Tundra in the winter.

38-2   The Taiga

Moving south across the tundra, the vegetation gradually changes. Groups of stunted trees appear in sheltered places. Farther south, the trees become larger and closer together, eventually giving way to evergreen forests. This belt of evergreen forest, which extends across North America, Europe, and Asia, is the **taiga** (*ty*-guh). The taiga has cold winters in which the ground is covered by deep snow. However, the growing season is longer than that of the tundra—about 120 days. The summer days are warmer than in the tundra, and the ground thaws completely. As in the tundra, there are many ponds and bogs. Pines, firs, and spruce are the dominant vegetation (see Figure 38-3). However, some deciduous trees (those that shed their leaves) are also present. These include willows and birches. There are also shrubs and herbaceous plants.

Figure 38-3. The Taiga. In the taiga, pines, firs, and spruce are the dominant vegetation, and there are many ponds.

Animals of the taiga include moose, wolves, bears, lynx, deer, elks, wolverines, martens, snowshoe hares, porcupines, and various rodents, birds, and insects.

38-3 The Temperate Deciduous Forest

Regions south of the taiga show variations in rainfall, so that there is not a single type of biome that stretches in a belt across these latitudes. South of the taiga in eastern North America and in Europe are regions of **temperate deciduous forest** (see Figure 38-4). In this type of biome the summers are generally hot and humid, and the winters are cold. Rainfall averages 75 to 150 centimeters a year.

The species present in deciduous forests vary with the local rainfall. Common trees of deciduous forests include oak, maple, hickory, beech, chestnut, and birch. Smaller trees and shrubs are also present, as well as herbaceous plants, ferns, and mosses.

Figure 38-4. A Temperate Deciduous Forest in Summer. Common trees of the deciduous forest include oak, maple, hickory, beech, and birch.

Figure 38-5. Grasslands. In the past, pronghorn antelope were found in great numbers in the grasslands of North America.

Animals of the deciduous forest include wolves, gray foxes, bobcats, deer, raccoons, squirrels, and chipmunks, as well as a wide variety of birds and insects.

38-4   Grasslands

Grasslands, or prairies, are found in North America, Asia, South America, and Africa. They occur in both temperate and tropical climates. Grasslands usually cover large areas in the interior of a continent. They develop where rainfall ranges from 25 to 75 centimeters a year. This quantity of rainfall cannot support a deciduous forest, and grasses become the dominant form of vegetation (see Figure 38-5). The soil of the grasslands is often deep and rich, and such areas have become the most productive farmlands of the earth.

The natural vegetation of the grasslands includes many species of grasses and wildflowers. In wetter areas near rivers the vegetation may be quite dense and include various shrubs.

Animals of the North American grasslands include coyotes, badgers, rattlesnakes, prairie dogs, jackrabbits, and ground squirrels. In the past, great herds of bison and pronghorn antelope were common. Now, most have been replaced by domesticated cattle and sheep. In Africa, the grasslands are populated by zebras, giraffes, gazelles, and other large grazing animals. Predators, such as lions, that feed on the grazers are also present. There are fewer types of birds in the grasslands than in the deciduous forest. There are meadowlarks, ring-necked pheasant, prairie chickens, hawks, and owls. There are many insects, but the grasshopper populations in particular may be huge.

38-5   Deserts

Deserts occur in regions that are too dry to support grasses. Rainfall is usually less than 25 centimeters a year. In North

Figure 38-6. The Desert. (Left) The Sonoran Desert of Arizona. (Above) The fennec, a small desert fox of Africa.

America there is a desert extending from Mexico north to the eastern part of Washington. Huge areas of desert are also found in South America, Africa, Asia, and Australia. Temperatures in the desert vary widely in the course of a day. During the day, it is very hot. At night, however, the temperature may drop steeply, sometimes as much as 30°C. Some deserts have almost no vegetation at all, while others have a variety of plants (see Figure 38-6).

Plants found in the desert have special adaptations for the conservation of water and for the completion of their reproductive cycles. Most have widespread, shallow roots that enable them to absorb the maximum amount of water when it is available. Many desert plants, such as cacti, store water in their tissues. Many live only a short time. They sprout, flower, and produce seeds during the brief rainy periods, which may last only a few days. Plants characteristic of the deserts of North America are cactus, yucca, mesquite, sagebrush, and creosote bush.

Like desert plants, desert animals show a wide variety of adaptations for survival in the harsh environment. Most are active at night, spending the hot days in burrows in the ground or hidden in any available shade. Many desert rodents can survive with very little drinking water. They manage mostly on the water produced by cellular metabolism and water present in the plants they eat. The fennec, which is a small desert fox, spends its days in a burrow, coming out only at night to feed on birds and other small animals. Its long ears provide surface area for getting rid of excess body heat. Also found in the desert are snakes, lizards, spiders, and insects.

Figure 38-7. Tropical Rain Forest. The floor of the tropical rain forest is in constant shade from the dense tree cover above.

38-6 Tropical Rain Forests

Tropical rain forests are found in areas around the equator. In these regions the climate is uniform throughout the year. There is a constant supply of rainfall, which may total between 200 and 400 centimeters a year. Rain falls nearly every day, and the humidity is consistently high. Temperatures remain constant at about 25°C throughout the year. Tropical rain forests contain an enormous variety of plants and animals.

Within a tropical rain forest, the tree cover is so dense that little light reaches the ground (see Figure 38-7). The treetops form a canopy about 50 meters high. Below the canopy are shorter trees that can grow in the shade. The trees of the rain forest have shallow root systems that enable them to absorb nutrients from the thin layer of wet soil. Many have braces, or buttresses, that extend out from the trunks to the ground. Like prop roots, they help to keep the tree standing upright.

Organic materials decay very quickly in this warm, humid environment. Minerals released by decomposition are rapidly taken up again by the plants through mycorrhizae. Materials not absorbed by the plants are quickly washed away by the frequent rains. Therefore, in a tropical rain forest there is little organic matter stored in the soil. Most of the nutrients in this biome are found within the living organisms. Because of the basically poor soil, land cleared of a tropical rain forest cannot support crops for more than a year or two.

Figure 38-8. Bromeliads and Orchids. The bromeliads (left) and orchids (right) are both epiphytes.

Among the hundred or more different species of trees found in the rain forest, there are many with large, broad leaves. In addition to the trees there are thick vines, called *lianas*, that are attached to the tree trunks and grow up through the treetops. The roots of these vines are in the ground. There are also many *epiphytes* (*ep*-uh-fyts), which are plants that grow on other plants, but are not parasites. Various orchids, cacti, and ferns are epiphytes (see Figure 38-8). The roots of some epiphytes absorb moisture from the air. Others, such as the bromeliads, have leaves that form cups at their bases. Water-absorbing structures pick up moisture trapped in the leaves. On the floor of tropical rain forests are plants that are tolerant of almost complete shade.

Tropical rain forests have a wide variety of animal species, many of which show adaptations that enable them to live at a particular level in the trees (see Figure 38-9). Monkeys, bats, squirrels, and parrots and other birds feed on fruits and nuts in the treetops. Flying squirrels leap from one tree to another. Snakes and lizards live in the branches of the trees, as do opossums and porcupines. Rodents, tapirs, antelope, deer, and other large animals live on the forest floor. Spiders and insects are present at all levels. There are ants, termites, bees, butterflies, and moths.

Figure 38-9. Animals of the Rain Forest. Squirrel monkeys and parakeets are among the many animals that live in the trees of rain forests.

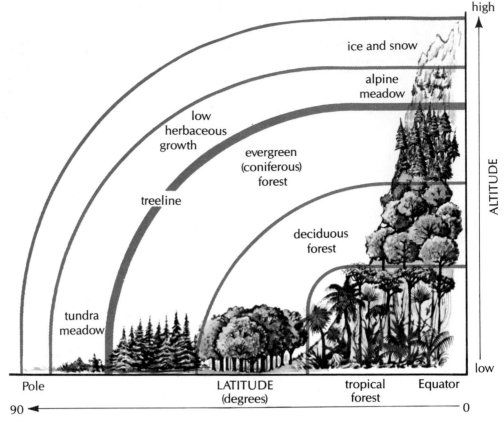

ice and snow

alpine
meadow

low
herbaceous
growth

evergreen
(coniferous)
forest

treeline

deciduous
forest

ALTITUDE

tundra
meadow

low

Pole

LATITUDE
(degrees)

tropical
forest

Equator

90 ◄

0

Figure 38-10. Effects of Altitude on Climax Vegetation.

38-7 Effects of Altitude on Climax Vegetation

With exceptions as noted, the terrestrial biomes of the earth are distributed in irregular belts, more or less in sequence according to latitude. However, mountainous regions are usually omitted from the biome classifications. The reason for this is that increasing altitude generally produces climatic effects similar to increasing latitude. Thus, the sides of mountains may show a succession of plant communities that change with increasing altitude. These communities will have many characteristics in common with those of specific biomes. For example, the climatic conditions and types of plant life near the top of a mountain may resemble those of the tundra. Lower down, evergreen forests that are characteristic of the taiga will appear. This relationship between higher altitude and higher latitude is shown in Figure 38-10.

AQUATIC BIOMES

Objective:

Describe the different types of aquatic biomes, and name some representative organisms of each.

38-8 Physical Factors in Aquatic Biomes

The problems of life in aquatic biomes are somewhat different from those in terrestrial biomes. For one thing, there is no problem about the availability of water. However, in fresh water, excess water must be excreted by organisms, while in salt water, excess salt may be excreted. Temperature variation in the course of a year is much less in aquatic environments than it is on land. Temperatures in the oceans show the least variation, while those in lakes and ponds show more of a change. Other physical factors that affect living things in aquatic biomes are the amounts of oxygen and carbon dioxide dissolved in the water, the availability of organic and inorganic nutrients, and light intensity.

38-9   The Marine Biome

Since all the oceans of the earth are interconnected, they are considered to form a single marine, or saltwater, biome. Conditions and life forms vary gradually from one region of the marine biome to another, but without the clearcut differences of the terrestrial biomes.

Characteristics of the marine biome. The marine biome is a continuous body of water that covers more than 70 percent of the earth's surface. Because of the heat capacity of water, the oceans can absorb solar heat energy during warm seasons and hold it during cold seasons. As a result, ocean temperatures remain relatively stable. The oceans also have a stabilizing effect on average temperatures of land areas. Temperatures on the earth would vary much more than they do if the oceans did not exist. The aquatic environment of the oceans is stable in other respects, too. In any given region, the supply of nutrients and the concentration of dissolved salts remain relatively constant.

Although environmental conditions tend to remain constant in any particular region of the marine biome, they do vary from region to region. In particular, the salt content varies from one place to another. It is lower where large rivers bring fresh water into the ocean and higher where high atmospheric temperature causes rapid evaporation. In general, salt concentrations in the ocean are very similar to those in living cells. Marine organisms therefore do not usually have the problem of water balance that freshwater organisms face.

Although temperatures remain fairly constant throughout the year in any given part of the marine biome, there is a variation with latitude. Ocean temperatures vary from near 0°C in the polar regions to 32°C near the equator.

Organisms of the oceans. The marine biome supports a very great variety of life forms (see Figure 38-11). Some marine organisms are sessile and live attached to the ocean floor or to various other fixed surfaces. Sessile organisms include sponges, sea anemones, corals, and barnacles. Organisms that live on the ocean floor are called **benthos.** Starfish, clams, worms, snails, and crabs are benthic organisms. Small organisms that float near the surface and are carried by ocean currents are called **plankton.**

Figure 38-11. Diversity of Life in the Marine Biome. This tropical ocean reef supports a great variety of marine life forms. At further depths, however, conditions are not as favorable for life, and far fewer marine species are found.

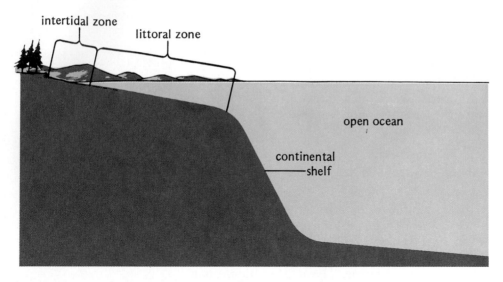

Figure 38-12. Zones of the Ocean.

Planktonic organisms include protozoa and algae, tiny crusta-ceans called copepods, the larvae of various animals, small jellyfish, and worms. Photosynthetic planktonic organisms, called **phytoplankton,** are the major producers of the oceans. Nonphotosynthetic planktonic protists and planktonic animals are called **zooplankton.** Both phytoplankton and zooplankton make up the lowest level of the complex marine food web. Many types of animals, from small worms to whales, feed on plankton. Free-swimming organisms that live in the oceans are called **nekton.** Nektonic organisms include squid, fishes, tur-tles, seals, and whales.

Zones of the oceans. The oceans are divided into several zones based mainly on depth (see Figure 38-12). The **inter-tidal zone** is the area along the shoreline that is covered by water at high tide and uncovered at low tide. Various types of seaweeds—red and brown algae—are abundant in this zone. On sandy beaches, clams, crabs, sand fleas, and worms live in the sand. Many types of birds live along the shore, including gulls, terns, and sandpipers. On rocky coasts, algae, barnacles, mussels, and starfish cling to the rocks.

Beyond the intertidal zone is the **littoral zone,** which in-cludes the relatively shallow waters above the continental shelf. The gently sloping continental shelf extends out from the edge of the continent for about 300 kilometers. This zone contains nutrients from the continents carried into the oceans by rivers and streams. Because the water is shallow, light reaches all the way to the ocean floor in the littoral zone. The littoral zone contains many different forms of life. In many places there are large populations of algae, as well as fish, oysters, mussels, crabs, barnacles, worms, and sea cucumbers.

Beyond the continental shelf is the zone of the open ocean. Here the water is very deep, and light does not reach the ocean floor. The upper layer of the open ocean is occupied

■ Frontier of Biology ■

Underwater Communities Use Geothermal Energy

Although it has long been known that various microorganisms obtain energy by chemosynthesis, it was thought that energy for all communities of organisms was provided by photosynthesis. However, in 1977, marine biologists and oceanographers investigating the Galapagos Rift in the eastern part of the Pacific Ocean discovered a new type of community, one based on chemosynthesis.

The Galapagos Rift is an area in the ocean floor where molten material from the core of the earth comes up through cracks, or vents, in the earth's surface. On meeting the cold water, the molten material, called *magma*, solidifies to form a porous, black lava.

In most parts of the open ocean, the floor is dark and existing organisms are specialized heterotrophs that feed on organic matter drifting down from the water's surface. However, around the vent of the Galapagos Rift, about 2½ kilometers beneath the surface, are unique communities of mussels, clams, crabs, worms, and other life forms.

The energy source for organisms of the vent communities is *geothermal*—heat given off from the core of the earth. Near the vents, water percolates through the porous lava and becomes saturated with minerals. Heat from the earth's core super-boils the water and spews it back into the ocean through cracks in the lava. These boiling plumes can reach 350°C. The heat changes sulfate in the rock to hydrogen sulfide. Bacteria of the vent communities use the hydrogen sulfide in combination with oxygen and carbon dioxide to synthesize organic compounds. This chemosynthetic process serves the same functions for vent communities as photosynthesis does for communities that are exposed to sunlight. The chemosynthetic vent bacteria are the producers of this community and are the base of the food chain.

Among the animals of the vent communities

Tube worms growing in a dense colony near a marine geothermal vent.

are various mollusks and giant tube worms, some 1.5 meters long. Many of these animals have highly specialized symbiotic relationships with the chemosynthetic vent bacteria. The animals supply the bacteria with sulfides, carbon dioxide, and water. The bacteria supply the animals with carbohydrates. The mollusks have colonies of the bacteria growing on their gills. The structure of the tube worms appears to have developed around the presence of the bacteria. There is no digestive tract. Instead, they have many tentacles through which they absorb nutrients from the water. Within their bodies is a specialized organ called a *trophosome,* which is made up of bacterial cells and small blood vessels. The exchange of materials between the worm and the bacteria occurs in the trophosome.

The environment of the vent communities is unlike any other on the modern earth. In fact, in some ways, the conditions are similar to those hypothesized for the primitive earth at the time life arose. There is abundant energy in the form of heat, and the sea at the vents is tremendously rich in nutrients, both inorganic and organic. Perhaps these communities will provide biologists with new information about the origin of life.

mainly by plankton. In this zone there are also large fish, including sharks, as well as porpoises, squids, and whales. Below the zone of photosynthesis, the organisms are all heterotrophs. They feed on organic matter that drifts downward from the photosynthetic zone above.

38-10 Freshwater Biomes

Freshwater biomes can be divided into two basic types— running water (streams) and standing water (lakes, ponds, swamps, and bogs). The volume of water in these biomes is very much smaller than that of the marine biome. As a result, the temperature variations in freshwater biomes are generally larger. Organisms living in fresh water must be able to adapt to greater seasonal variations than those living in the ocean. They also have the problem of maintaining water balance. In a freshwater environment, water enters living cells by osmosis (see page 82). Freshwater organisms usually need a mechanism for removing excess water by active transport. The contractile vacuoles of the ameba and paramecium are an example of such a mechanism.

Streams. In fast-moving streams, the bottom consists mainly of rocks and gravel. Most organisms are found in calmer, shallow areas near the banks of the stream . Here , algae grow on rocks and there are many insects and insect larvae. Fish and microscopic floating algae are found both in running water and in the calmer pools. Where streams are slow-moving, muddy sediment accumulates on the bottom. Many animals live in the bottom mud, including aquatic insects and their larvae, worms, snails, and crayfish. Raccoons, birds, and other animals that live along the banks catch fish and other animals from the stream (see Figure 38-13).

Lakes and ponds. Lakes and ponds are bodies of standing water. Lakes are generally larger than ponds and are deep enough that light does not reach the bottom in all parts. Ponds are generally shallow enough so that light does reach the bottom throughout.

Around the shores of a lake is a zone of shallow water in which light reaches the bottom. In this zone, cattails, bulrushes, and other plants grow above the surface of the lake. These plants have roots in the lake bottom. In deeper water out from the shore there are floating plants, such as water lilies, which are also rooted in the bottom. Many types of animals are found in the bottom in the shallow water zone. There are insect larvae, crayfish, worms, hydra, clams, and snails. Free-swimming animals include diving beetles, mosquito larvae, giant water bugs, fish, frogs, salamanders, turtles, and snakes. On the surface there may be water striders, water boatmen, and whirligig beetles.

In the deep, open waters of the lake where light does not

Figure 38-13. Raccoon Fishing in Stream.

reach the bottom, the main producers are microscopic algae (phytoplankton) that float near the surface. Zooplankton is also present. These floating, microscopic, heterotrophic organisms are the primary consumers in a complex food web. The planktonic organisms are eaten by small fish, which are eaten by larger fish, and so on.

Life in ponds is much the same as that in the shallow waters of lakes.

Swamps and bogs. Swamps are low, wetland areas in which the vegetation includes shrubs and trees. Many types of plants and animals are found in wetlands. Wetlands are also important as nesting sites for water birds.

Bogs are shallow bodies of water that contain large growths of sphagnum moss. The moss and other factors create an acid environment in which the rate of decay is slowed. With decay slowed, the cycling of nitrogen through the ecosystem is reduced. Several plants common in bogs are insectivorous. These include pitcher plants and sundews.

Chapter Review

SUMMARY

- Biomes are large geographical areas showing a particular type of climax community. The type of vegetation found in a biome is determined by climate and other physical conditions. The two basic types of biomes are terrestrial and aquatic.

- The major terrestrial biomes are tundra, taiga, deciduous forest, grassland, desert, and tropical rain forest. They occur in this order between the poles and the equator.

- The tundra has a low average temperature and a short growing season. There are almost no trees. The dominant animals are reindeer, musk oxen, caribou, wolves, Arctic hares and foxes, lemmings, snowy owls, and ptarmigans.

- The taiga is mainly evergreen forest. The dominant animals are moose, wolves, bears, lynx, and elks. There are also many rodents, birds, and insects.

- Temperate deciduous forest has hot summers and cold winters. The dominant animals

include wolves, bobcats, deer, raccoons, and squirrels, as well as many birds and insects.

- Deserts are too dry to support grasses. Days are very hot and nights are very cold. Cacti, snakes, lizards, spiders, and insects are common in deserts.

- Tropical rain forests have almost daily rainfall. Lianas, which are thick vines, and epiphytes, which grow on other plants, are among the many plants. Monkeys and birds live in the treetops, larger animals live on the forest floor, and spiders and insects live everywhere.

- The major aquatic biomes are freshwater and marine, or saltwater, biomes. The marine biome includes all the oceans of the world. Freshwater biomes include streams, lakes and ponds, swamps, and bogs. Organisms living in fresh water must be able to maintain water balance and adjust to significant variations in temperature.

KNOW THE TERMS

benthos	littoral zone	plankton	tropical rain forest
biome	nekton	taiga	tundra
grassland	permafrost	temperate deciduous forest	zooplankton
intertidal zone	phytoplankton	tropical deciduous forest	

SECTION QUESTIONS

Terrestrial Biomes

1. Define the term *biome*.
2. How long is the growing season on the tundra?
3. What vegetation characterizes the taiga?
4. Name some common trees of the deciduous forest.
5. In what kinds of climates do grasslands usually develop?
6. List some plants found in North American deserts.
7. List some types of plants common to tropical rain forests.
8. Why are mountainous regions omitted from biome classifications?

Aquatic Biomes

9. Name the two basic kinds of aquatic biomes.
10. How do plankton move from one place to another in the ocean?
11. What are the two basic types of freshwater biomes?

KNOW THE FACTS

Copy the number of each sentence below on a sheet of paper. Beside each number, write the term(s) that complete(s) the sentence correctly.

1. Land biomes are characterized and named by the _____ _____.
2. The land biome that borders the tundra is the _____.
3. The land biome in which the climate displays seasonal variation, rainfall is moderate, and most trees shed their broad leaves in the fall is called _____ _____ _____.
4. The environmental factor most directly responsible for the distinctive differences among deserts, grasslands, and forests is total annual _____.
5. Plants such as cacti have become adapted to their arid habitat by storing _____ in their tissues.
6. The biome that is located near the equator is called _____ _____ _____.
7. An increase in altitude produces climatic effects similar to an increase in _____.
8. The most stable environmental conditions on the earth occur in the _____ biome.
9. The maintenance of water balance is essential to the life of organisms that live in the _____ biome.

UNDERSTAND THE CONCEPTS

10. List the tundra's physical characteristics.
11. Describe the principal vegetation and animal life of the tundra.
12. Describe the location and physical characteristics of the taiga.
13. Identify the principal vegetation and animal life of the taiga.
14. Describe the location and physical characteristics of temperate deciduous forests.
15. Identify the vegetation and animal life of temperate deciduous forests.
16. Describe the physical characteristics of grasslands.
17. Identify the vegetation and animal life of the grasslands.
18. Describe the physical characteristics of deserts.
19. Identify the vegetation and animal life of deserts.
20. Describe the location and physical characteristics of tropical rain forests.
21. Describe the vegetation and animal life of tropical rain forests.
22. How does altitude affect climax vegetation?

23. List examples of sessile, free-floating, and free-swimming marine organisms.
24. What is the role played by photosynthetic planktonic organisms in the marine biome?
25. Describe the zones of the oceans.
26. Identify the physical characteristics, vegetation, and animal life of streams.
27. Describe the physical characteristics, vegetation, and animal life of lakes and ponds.
28. Summarize the general characteristics of swamps and bogs.

THINK CRITICALLY

29. Marine algae of the intertidal zone are alternately exposed to many hours of direct sunlight and air followed by an equal number of hours of submersion in salt water. What special adaptations would help the algae cope with these harsh conditions?
30. Of what advantage is each of the following desert plant adaptations: (a) petals only at the very tips of the highest branches; (b) flowers only in the early spring; (c) flowers that bloom only at night?
31. Given the physical characteristics of the desert biome, why would bats be good pollinators?
32. Classify each biome that you studied according to its suitability for: (a) growing crops, (b) building new cities, and (c) maintaining wildlife preserves.

THINK CREATIVELY

33. Propose some evidence to convince most biologists that the first forms of life arose in the oceans.
34. In the benthic zones of oceans, far below the depth to which sunlight penetrates, many types of species thrive. Suggest some special characteristics that would enable species to inhabit the benthos. Diagram a food web to which these organisms might belong.

FOR FURTHER INVESTIGATION

1. Demonstrate lake stratification, which occurs in spring and summer when the water becomes warmer. You will need a two-quart glass baking dish, salt, red food coloring, a thin rubber siphoning tube, and an electric fan. In a separate container, mix one tablespoon of salt in one pint of cold water. Add a few drops of food coloring. Fill the glass dish one-third full with warm tap water. Let the water become still. Carefully siphon the red salt water underneath the warm water. You should have two distinct water layers, demonstrating how the dense, cooler water remains at the bottom if the water is undisturbed. Use the fan to blow air across the surface of the water. How does this affect the layers of water? What does this mean for the oxygen and nutrients in the water? How does lake stratification affect plants and animals living in the lake?

2. Write a report on one of the career opportunities listed below.
   a. Range manager   c. Demographer
   b. Game warden

3. Prepare a report on the life and contributions of one of the following scientists:
   a. Ruth Patrick
   b. Alfred Russell Wallace
   c. May E. Chinn, M.D.
   d. Sylvia Earle Mead

FOR FURTHER READING

Cusack, Michael, "Careers in Oceanography and Marine Science," *Scholastic Science World*, October 19, 1984.

Gore, Rick, "No Way to Run a Desert," *National Geographic*, June, 1985.

Perry, Donald R., "The Canopy of the Tropical Rain Forest," *Scientific American*, November, 1984.

Reyinga, Wilhelmina, "The Changing Earth," *Scholastic Science World*, October 19, 1984.

Chapter 39

HUMAN ECOLOGY

Large areas of land are altered for the cultivation of rice and many other crop plants.

CAUSES OF ENVIRONMENTAL DAMAGE

Objectives:
1. Discuss the importance of human population control in improving the quality of human life.
2. Explain the terms *limiting factor* and *carrying capacity*.
3. Describe how urbanization and poor farming practices have damaged the environment.
4. List the major types of water pollutants and describe the ways in which they damage the environment and/or human health.
5. List the major types of air pollutants and describe the ways in which they damage the environment and/or human health.
6. Discuss the problem of land pollution.
7. Describe the problems that can arise from the use of chemical pesticides and from the importation of organisms into new environments.

39-1 Human Use of the Environment

In the past, there was relatively little concern about the effects of human activities on the environment. Forests were cut down, rivers were dammed, soil erosion was allowed to proceed unchecked, and wastes from mines and other industries were dumped on the land, into waterways, and into the air. Within the last 20 years or so, however, there has been increasing recognition of the fact that the environment cannot be used thoughtlessly any longer. It is evident that human activities have damaged the environment, and the damage may be dangerous and permanent. In response to this awareness, human activities in many areas are now devoted to restoring the environment. Rivers that had been so polluted that they contained no fish have now been cleaned up. In some cities where the air was dangerously polluted, it is now somewhat cleaner.

Human ecology deals with the relationship between humans and the environment. In this chapter we will discuss some of the most important aspects of this relationship.

39-2 Human Population Growth

Many of the most serious environmental problems of today are related to the tremendous increase in the human population in recent decades. In 1850, the population of the earth was estimated to be about 1 billion. Within 80 years, by about 1930, the population had doubled, reaching 2 billion. It doubled again, reaching 4 billion, by the mid-1970s. Note that the time required for the doubling of the population has been getting shorter. It is estimated that by the year 2,000, the human population will reach 7 billion.

The human population cannot continue to grow indefinitely. As in other natural populations, it will eventually reach a point at which the environment cannot support any greater size. The unavailability of food, water, space, or some other necessity acts as a **limiting factor** for every population and halts any further growth. The size of a population that can be supported by the environment is called the **carrying capacity** of the environment. At some point in the future, human population growth must stop because the earth will reach its carrying capacity and will not be able to support any more humans.

A population remains the same size if the birth rate and death rate are equal and no changes result from migration. In this century, the death rate in the industrialized countries has declined sharply because of improvements in medical care, food production, and sanitation. In many of these countries there has also been a decline in the birth rate, resulting in a stable, but older, population. In a few, the birth rate has dropped below the death rate, resulting in a shrinking population. In the underdeveloped countries, the birth rate remains very high. The death rate in most of the underdeveloped countries has dropped because of improved conditions; thus the continued high birth rate is causing a rapid growth in the populations. However, many people in the underdeveloped nations are barely surviving. Food production is not increasing as fast as the population. Any failure in crop production in these countries could result in large numbers of deaths from starvation.

Frontier of Biology

Harvested seaweed, a major source of food from the ocean, is hung out to dry.

Farming Earth's Waters

Freshwater farming (aquaculture) and ocean farming (mariculture) are emerging as major sources of food for a hungry world. As the term "farming" indicates, plants and animals are not just taken from the water, but species are regulated and cultivated.

Marine products now available or being developed commercially include salmon, abalone, oysters, clams, scallops, mussels, and lobsters as well as edible seaweeds. The salmon industry alone annually harvests fish worth more than $3.5 million.

In the freshwater sector, catfish and trout lead the way. Other organisms in production include crayfish, freshwater prawns, and hard clams. Research on the feasibility of raising freshwater mussels is under way.

Experts agree that both mariculture and aquaculture hold great promise for feeding the world's growing population.

Directly or indirectly, the problem of human population growth affects everyone. If food is allowed to become the limiting factor in human population growth, then starvation will become the major means of population control in many parts of the world. One way to avoid this situation is to reduce the birth rate to the level that will maintain the population at its present size. This is the level of *reproductive replacement*, at which the number of births equals the number of deaths over a period of time.

Along with population control, steps could be taken to reduce the level of wasteful consumption by the industrialized nations. More resources would then be available for use by the underdeveloped countries. Strict application of conservation measures in farming, lumbering, mining, and water use could ensure the production of food and other needed materials at a constant level. Food production could also be increased. The use of fertilizers, pesticides, and irrigation, as well as the development of crops with higher yields, would increase the food supply. New sources of food could be developed—from the oceans, for example. Most ecologists feel, however, that no matter what steps are taken, the food supply will eventually become inadequate if the current rate of population growth continues.

39-3   Urbanization

Population increases coupled with technological advances have resulted in the careless destruction of many ecosystems. As the population has increased, patterns of land use have changed. There has been a shift from rural (farming) areas to the cities. Movement of the population to cities, or **urbanization,** has resulted in the destruction of productive farmland, as former farms were turned into housing developments and shopping centers. Such growth has also destroyed or endangered other ecosystems, such as wetlands, that had previously been untouched. These changes have destroyed the natural habitats of many species of plants and animals.

39-4   Poor Farming Practices

In a natural ecosystem, dead plants cover the ground. They decompose and form rich humus that is added to the soil. In farmland, the crops are harvested each year, and most of the plant parts are removed from the fields. Thus, nutrients from the soil taken up by the crop plants are removed from the field. If these nutrients are not returned, the soil becomes less fertile, and crop yield drops. In the past when this happened, the fields were abandoned, left only with a covering of poor soil. When fields are left without a cover of vegetation, heavy rains or winds can carry away the topsoil. In many areas, overgrazing by herds of cattle and sheep left former grasslands without a cover of vegetation (see Figure 39-1).

Figure 39-1. Soil Erosion. Without a protective covering of vegetation, the topsoil is washed away, and the land becomes useless for cultivation.

39-5   Pollution

Adding anything to the environment that makes it less fit for living things is called **pollution.** Pollution of the environment has increased with population growth and industrial development. Gaseous wastes from cars and trucks, the burning of fuels, and industrial gases have polluted the air. Sewage and industrial wastes dumped into streams and rivers have polluted the waterways. The land has been polluted by tremendous quantities of solid wastes generated by industry and by the population in general. Some of the industrial wastes are highly toxic.

39-6   Water Pollution

In industrialized countries, enormous quantities of water are used each day by individuals and by industry. However, much of the available water is polluted (see Figure 39-2). The major sources of water pollution are discussed below.

1. Many *organic wastes* are materials of plant and animal origin. These materials are generally **biodegradable** (by-oh-duh-*grayd*-uh-bul)—that is, they can be broken down by bacteria and other decay organisms into simpler substances. Sewage and wastes from canning, brewing, meat packing, and paper mills are major sources of organic materials in waterways. If organic wastes are added in small quantities, bacteria and other decay organisms break them down, keeping the water clean. However, the breakdown of these materials uses oxygen from the water. If sewage and other organic materials are present in large quantities, the oxygen content of the water becomes seriously reduced. This kills off fish and other types of aquatic organisms.

Some organic wastes are plant nutrients. When these substances are present in large quantities, they stimulate the growth of algae and aquatic plants. In lakes, the presence of nutrients can hasten the process of succession. As the or-

Figure 39-2. An Example of Water Pollution. The wastes dumped into this stream have killed the fish.

ganisms die, material is added to the lake bottom and reduces its depth. Growth around the shores reduces the size of the lake. This accelerated aging process is called **eutrophication** (yoo-truh-fuh-*kay*-shun).

The nutrients occasionally cause an explosive growth of the algae populations. Only the topmost layer of algae receives adequate light and oxygen, and the lower layers die. When they decay, the oxygen content of the lake is reduced, killing off other forms of life.

Various synthetic organic chemicals, such as pesticides, fertilizers, and detergents, are poisonous to aquatic life. At the same time, fertilizers and detergents contain plant nutrients. The net effect is to upset the natural balance of an ecosystem and possibly to destroy it.

2. *Inorganic chemicals* are dumped into waterways by mining and other industrial processes. These substances add to the cost of purifying water for human use. Some wastes contain metals, particularly mercury and lead, that are toxic to humans and other animals (see Figure 39-3).

When dumped into waterways, mercury, lead, and some pesticides are picked up first by small aquatic plants and algae. These are eaten by first-level consumers. Because the number of plants and algae eaten by these consumers is large, the toxic substances accumulate in their bodies. In the food web, larger second-level consumers eat many first-level consumers. The toxic substances then accumulate in higher concentrations in the bodies of the second-level consumers. As the food chain proceeds, each higher level of consumers accumulates larger quantities of toxic substances. This process is called **biological magnification.** At the end of the food chain where the concentrations are highest, the animals are most harmed by the pesticide or chemicals. In some cases this has been humans. People in Japan who rely heavily on fish in their diet have suffered mercury poisoning from mercury that had been dumped into the ocean. Through biological magnification, it accumulated in high concentrations in the bodies of large food fish.

3. *Disease-causing microorganisms* may enter the water from untreated sewage and wastes from farm animals. Contamination of water by sewage can be detected by testing for the presence of the bacterium *Escherichia coli*. These organisms, as well as other infectious bacteria and viruses, live in the intestines of warm-blooded animals and are found in their wastes.

4. Changes in the water temperature in streams and rivers can kill fish and other organisms living there. This type of pollution, called **thermal pollution,** occurs when water is taken from a stream and used for cooling various types of industrial equipment. The cold stream water is run through pipes next to pipes containing hot water from the plant. Heat is transferred from the hot water to the cold water, and the

Figure 39-3. Water Purity. The purity of water samples can be determined with a spectrophotometer.

Figure 39-4. Air Pollution.

stream water, now heated, is returned to the waterway. The warmed stream water, in addition to the direct effects it has on living organisms, holds less oxygen than the cold water. Nuclear power plants in particular require great amounts of water for cooling.

5. Other forms of water pollution involve oil spills and the presence of radioactive wastes. Oil is toxic to all forms of aquatic life, even killing many types of bacteria. Water birds die when they ingest the oil in trying to clean it off their feathers. Radioactive wastes are produced by nuclear reactors, mining, and the processing of radioactive materials. Exposure to relatively small amounts of radioactivity can be harmful.

39-7   Air Pollution

Air pollution is a problem in industrialized countries with large urban populations and many cars. In the United States alone, more than 200 million metric tons of pollutants are released into the atmosphere each year (see Figure 39-4).

Some pollutants are **aerosols.** They consist of tiny solid particles or liquid droplets that remain suspended in air. Dust and smoke are aerosols. Aerosol particles scatter sunlight, reducing the amount of light reaching the earth's surface, and thus lowering the surface temperature.

Some pollutants are gases, which mix with the air. Sulfur dioxide (SO_2) is a pollutant produced by the burning of coal and oil that contain sulfur. In the atmosphere, sulfur dioxide may react chemically to form sulfuric acid, a harsh irritant to the respiratory system. Sulfuric acid dissolved in rainwater forms "acid rain," which can gradually destroy stone buildings and other structures. It can also lower the pH of lakes and ponds, killing many of the organisms they contain or affecting their ability to reproduce (see pages 40 and 41).

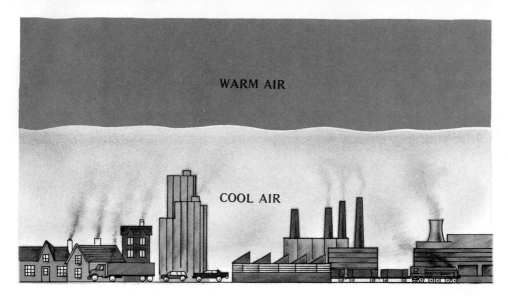

WARM AIR

COOL AIR

Figure 39-5. Temperature Inversion. In a temperature inversion, a layer of cool air becomes trapped beneath a layer of warm air.

Hydrogen sulfide (H_2S) is a pollutant produced by several industrial processes, including the refining of oil and the manufacture of paper pulp. This gas, which has an odor like rotten eggs, is mainly a nuisance at low concentrations, but can be toxic at high concentrations.

Carbon monoxide (CO) is produced by the burning of gasoline, coal, and oil. It combines readily with the hemoglobin of the red blood cells and reduces its capacity to carry oxygen. In low concentrations, carbon monoxide can cause drowsiness and slow reaction time. In high concentrations, it causes death.

Nitrogen oxide (NO) and nitrogen dioxide (NO_2) are produced by the burning of gasoline, oil, and natural gas. When nitrogen dioxide is exposed to sunlight, it turns a dirty brownish color. Reactions in the atmosphere between nitrogen oxide, oxygen, and ultraviolet light produce ozone (O_3), which is also a pollutant.

Hydrocarbons, which are compounds of hydrogen and carbon, are produced by the burning of gasoline, coal, oil, natural gas, and wood. Several hydrocarbons, such as formaldehyde and acetaldehyde, irritate the eyes, nose, and throat, but most are not dangerous at existing levels. However, hydrocarbons react with nitrogen oxides in the presence of sunlight to form what is known as *photochemical smog*, the type of smog found in Los Angeles. This type of smog, which occurs in dry, warm climates, is highly irritating to the lungs and eyes. It also damages plants. The major component of photochemical smog is a compound known as PAN.

The air layer closest to the earth's surface is generally the warmest layer, and the air temperature drops with increasing altitude. Under these conditions, the less dense, warmer air rises, carrying pollutants away from the earth's surface. In a **temperature inversion,** a layer of cooler, denser air becomes trapped below a layer of warmer air (see Figure 39-5). The warm air acts as a lid, preventing the upward movement of air from the earth's surface. Pollutants accumulate in the cool layer, sometimes reaching very high concentrations. The condition lasts until the air masses move away.

39-8   Land Pollution

As cities have grown, land pollution has become an ever-increasing problem. Even small cities produce many tons of solid waste, or refuse, every day. Two acceptable ways of disposing of refuse are in sanitary landfills and by incineration (burning).

A *sanitary landfill* is a large area where the refuse is dumped into a trench. It is compacted (made as small as possible) and covered over with dirt. However, as cities have grown, it has become increasingly difficult to find land for this purpose.

Burning refuse in large furnaces, or incinerators, is another method of disposal. Incinerators must be equipped with pollution control devices, or they release large quantities of pollutants into the air. After burning, the ashes must still be disposed of in sanitary landfills. Some cities are conducting experiments in which they are using steam produced by the burning of refuse to generate electricity.

39-9   Pesticides

Pesticides, used indiscriminately, have contaminated the air and water in many places. They have also disrupted food chains, killing organisms that are not pests. Some widely used pesticides have been found after years of use to be dangerous. This is true of DDT, which was found to be highly toxic to many animals, including humans. DDT sprayed on plants was washed off by rainwater and carried into streams and rivers. Eventually it entered the oceans, where it was taken up by the plankton. DDT is not readily biodegradable, and through biological magnification it became concentrated in the bodies of the higher-level consumers. The interconnected nature of the world's ecosystems can be illustrated by the fact that DDT has been found in the bodies of polar bears and in the ice of the Antarctic. DDT also has been found to collect in the fatty tissues of humans.

An additional problem with pesticides is that frequently populations of the organisms they were intended to kill become resistant to them. The resistance is an inherited trait, so that the pests are then even more difficult to control.

39-10   Disruption of Existing Ecosystems

In a balanced ecosystem, the number of organisms at each level in a food chain is controlled by the number of organisms at the next higher feeding level. Thus, for example, the number of insects is controlled by the organisms that feed on them. When an organism is removed from its natural ecosystem and introduced into a new ecosystem, there may be no

Figure 39-6. Gypsy Moth Damage. Gypsy moth caterpillars feed on the leaves of many different types of trees, often stripping the tree completely bare.

predator to control its numbers. This has happened in a number of cases where insects and other organisms have accidentally or intentionally been introduced into new environments in which they have no natural enemies. The Japanese beetle, the fungus that causes Dutch elm disease, and the gypsy moth were all imported into North America. With few natural enemies, they. have spread, doing great damage to plants (see Figure 39-6). Human diseases, such as influenza, are also carried by travelers from one part of the world to another.

RESTORING THE ENVIRONMENT

Objectives:
1. Describe some of the efforts that are being made to control pollution.
2. Explain how soil erosion occurs.
3. Describe how each of the following techniques is used in soil conservation: cover crops, strip cropping, terracing, contour farming, windbreaks, dams, crop rotation, and fertilizers.
4. Discuss methods of forest and wildlife conservation.
5. Describe several biological methods of pest control.

In many countries, programs have been introduced that would improve the lives of their citizens and halt the deterioration of the environment. There are programs aimed at family planning to slow the rate of population growth. Other programs deal with disease control and sanitation. In terms of the environment itself, there are national and international programs aimed at pollution control, conservation of natural resources, and preservation of existing species. Various methods of maintaining and restoring the environment are discussed in the following sections.

39-11 Controlling Pollution

Efforts are being made in many places to control pollution of the air, water, and land. In some countries where much of the air pollution is caused by exhaust from automobiles, the introduction of emission controls and the use of unleaded gasoline have reduced pollution. Waste gases from industrial processes are being treated in various ways to remove the most serious pollutants before the gases are released into the atmosphere.

A major factor in the reduction of water pollution involves the use of sewage treatment plants, where the sewage is broken down by bacteria before being released into waterways. Where these plants have been built, the waterways are much cleaner. However, there is a great need for many additional plants. Although some of the most toxic industrial wastes are no longer being dumped into waterways, others are still pouring into lakes, streams, and rivers. The dumping of wastes into the oceans by coastal nations, along with wastes carried into the oceans by rivers, threatens the future productivity of these huge bodies of water.

Some efforts are being made to control the dumping of wastes on land. In many areas there are special sites for the disposal of toxic wastes. However, since the wastes remain toxic for long periods of time, there is always a problem with leakage and contamination of surrounding areas. An extremely difficult problem exists with the disposal of radioactive wastes from nuclear reactors. These wastes must be stored so that the radioactivity is safely absorbed by surrounding materials, and so that leakage will not occur for the thousands of years during which the wastes remain radioactive.

39-12 Conserving Natural Resources

Natural resources are materials in the environment that are used by humans either for their life processes or for cultural activities. These resources can be divided into two types— renewable and nonrenewable. **Renewable natural resources** include air, water, soil, sunlight, and living things. Careless human activities can disrupt the natural events that replace renewable resources. **Nonrenewable natural resources** are those that can be taken from the earth only once. Coal, oil, natural gas, metals, and minerals are nonrenewable natural resources. Some products made from nonrenewable resources can be reprocessed and used again for their original purpose. This is called **recycling** (see Figure 39-7).

39-13 Conserving Soil

Although soil is a renewable resource, the process of soil formation is very slow. It may take thousands of years to yield a few centimeters of topsoil. Therefore, it is important to prevent the loss of soil. The major cause of soil loss is **erosion—** the removal of soil by wind and water. Wind action blows the soil away, occasionally causing dust storms. After rainstorms, water running over the surface of the land carries soil into nearby streams. Soil conservation involves the prevention of erosion and the loss of nutrients from the soil. The following techniques are used in soil conservation (see Figure 39-8).

1. **Cover crops** are crops planted to cover a whole field and that have fibrous roots that form a dense mat in the soil. This mat prevents soil erosion. Commonly used cover crops include clover, alfalfa, oats, and wheat. Crops that are planted in rows, such as corn, beans, and cabbage, do not prevent erosion of the exposed soil between the rows of plants.

2. **Strip cropping** is a conservation practice in which cover crops are planted between strips of row crops. Thus no exposed soil is left open to erosion.

Figure 39-7. Recycling. Aluminum from cans can be reprocessed and used again.

contour plowing   terracing

strip cropping   windbreak

Figure 39-8. Some Soil Conservation Practices.

3. **Terracing** is used on the sides of hills. Flat areas, or terraces, are dug in the hillside, providing areas for planting. Each terrace has a boundary made up of an earth bank held in place by plants and rocks. Terracing prevents surface water from running directly down the hill, carrying the soil with it.

4. **Contour farming** is used on uneven landscapes. In contour farming, the rows are plowed across the slopes, following the contour of the land. The mounds of earth formed by the plow and the plants prevent water from running straight down the slopes.

5. **Windbreaks** are used to prevent wind erosion. Windbreaks usually consist of rows of trees. Poplar trees are commonly used for this purpose.

6. **Dams** are often built in eroded areas to slow down the running of water and reduce or prevent further erosion. Dams are also a major means of water conservation. Large amounts of water collect behind the dam. This water can be used for drinking water, irrigation, and recreation, as well as for the generation of electricity.

7. **Crop rotation** involves growing different crops in succeeding years. Since each plant has its own mineral requirements, planting different crops prevents the reduction of soil nutrients, which is known as *soil depletion*. Legumes, such as clover, are rotated along with other crops to restore nitrates to the soil.

8. **Fertilizers** are used to replace essential soil materials removed by crops. Both natural fertilizers, such as manure, and commercial chemical fertilizers are widely used.

39-14   Conserving Forests

Forests, which supply a wide variety of materials for human use, are a renewable natural resource. However, like soil, replacement of forests is a slow process, and poor tree-cutting practices can cause permanent damage to the forest ecosystem. In addition to furnishing wood, trees are also used for the production of paper, charcoal, turpentine, and rayon. Forest soils hold large quantities of water, and the trees and undergrowth of the forest prevent soil erosion.

As populations have grown, the need both for cleared land and for forest products has increased. As a result, in many parts of the world the amount of forest land is shrinking. In an attempt to raise productivity and ensure future supplies, the following conservation practices are being applied to remaining forests.

1. *Sustained-yield tree farming* involves cutting down trees in only certain areas of a forest, leaving surrounding areas untouched. In *block cutting*, square areas of forest are cut. Reseeding of the cut section takes place naturally by seeds coming from the surrounding forest. In *strip cutting*, strips of trees are cut between strips of untouched forest. In *selective harvesting*, certain trees are marked and cut, leaving the others undisturbed.

2. In *reforestation* programs, cut areas are planted with seeds or seedlings of a particular type. These are generally fast-growing, disease-resistant varieties that will produce good-quality lumber. In all forestry programs, undesirable, diseased, or dead trees are removed to allow space for growth of good timber.

39-15   Conserving Wildlife

The growth of cities and suburbs has led to the destruction of the natural habitats of many types of plants and animals. Indiscriminate hunting has brought about the extinction of a few species and the near-extinction of many others. The passenger pigeon was a bird that was found in large numbers in North America until the mid-1800s. A prime target of bird hunters, the huge flocks were killed off, and the last known passenger pigeon died in the early 1900s. Many other species of birds, as well as whales and other large mammals, are now in danger of becoming extinct. Several plant species have also become extinct, and others are endangered.

Concern over the possible extinction of various species of animals and plants has resulted in wildlife conservation practices that are being carried out in many areas. These include the following:

Career

Forester

A forester is a person involved in the management of forest lands. In addition to the wood that trees provide, forests are important to the water supplies of many areas, as homes for a wide variety of wildlife, and as recreation areas.

Foresters are involved in all aspects of forest use. Working for government agencies or private companies, foresters plan both the harvesting and planting of trees so that lumber will be continuously available. They work to control plant diseases and pests that damage the trees. They fight forest fires and work to prevent soil erosion and flooding. Foresters are also involved in the management of forest wildlife, maintaining a balance between available food and water and animal populations, and of recreational areas.

For a career in forestry, a person should have a bachelor's degree with courses in forestry and biology and should enjoy outdoor work.

Frontier of Biology

Bengal tiger in a zoo.

Saving Endangered Animal Species

Zoo curators and geneticists are teaming up to establish breeding populations of threatened animal species. Some species exist only as zoo populations, so it is no longer possible to obtain replacements from the wild. Thus, it has become necessary to develop breeding plans that will provide sufficient genetic diversity to assure the long-range survival of each species. To accomplish this, worldwide cooperation and coordination among zoos has begun.

Some 30 species have been selected for breeding programs. To date, however, only a few, including the Siberian tiger, Speke's gazelle, Przewalski's horse, and lion tamarin, are being managed intensively. The first animal to be bred under the new guidelines is the Siberian tiger. This creature, endangered in the wild, is thought to be the least likely to survive in its dwindling native habitat. Some fifty North American zoos are participating, and there are plans to increase the tiger population's genetic diversity by introducing animals from Russian and Chinese zoo populations.

1. Hunting and fishing laws have been established that restrict the sex, size, and number of prey that can be taken, and limit the hunting season.

2. Game and bird preserves have been established where no hunting is allowed.

3. Game fish are being bred in fish hatcheries and used to restock heavily fished lakes and streams. This keeps the populations at a reasonable level, but also allows recreational fishing.

4. Restricted use of pesticides and herbicides limits the number of accidental deaths caused by these chemicals.

5. Legal protection for endangered species has made it possible for some species that were near extinction to begin to show a population increase. This is true of the bison, egret, and whooping crane. Other endangered species are still decreasing in numbers.

39-16 Controlling Pests Biologically

Although chemical pesticides have been of great importance in controlling damage to agricultural crops, they have also created some serious ecological problems. Many chemical pesticides are not readily broken down in nature, so they accumulate in the environment. Plants and animals not intended as targets have been contaminated and harmed by them. Chemical pesticides have been developed that break down within a few days to harmless substances. Such pesticides will not accumulate. On the other hand, they have to be applied more frequently, which makes them more expensive and difficult to use.

As an alternative to chemical pesticides, various biological methods of pest control have been discovered. These methods are more specific than the chemical pesticides, and have much less of an effect on the environment in general.

1. In some areas, natural enemies have been imported to control certain pests. For example, ladybugs have been used to control aphids, and a wasp that preys on the alfalfa weevil has been used to control that insect pest. In introducing one organism to control the population of another organism, it is important to know in advance whether or not there is any way to control the population of the introduced organism.

2. Various insect larvae, including gypsy moth caterpillars and mosquito larvae, can be controlled by infection by a particular type of bacterium. Viruses have been used against worms that attack vegetable crops.

3. Another technique used in pest control is crop rotation. Planting different crops in succeeding years can remove the favored food source of a pest organism and thereby decrease the pest population.

4. **Pheromones** (fehr-uh-mohnz) are a type of animal secretion that serve as sex attractants between members of a species. Scientists have developed pheromones that are used to lure

insects into traps where they are exposed to contact poisons. In this way insecticides can be used without contaminating the environment.

5. Another method of insect control involves the release of sterile males into the population. The males, which have been sterilized by exposure to radiation, mate with the females, but no offspring result.

39-17   Key to the Future

Pollution is a pressing societal issue, one that directly affects the future survival of all earth's living organisms. Yet, although science has accumulated the facts and developed various technologies to stop pollution, it is difficult to devise a comprehensive plan to deal with environmental problems. Any solution usually will require significant social and cultural changes, not easy to produce. The views and attitudes of any society are based on a system of values deemed important to that society. Judgments are based on values that are not within the realm of science, which normally deals with physical evidence and ideas, principles, and theories based on that evidence. Thus, environmental problems cannot be left to the scientist alone. Furthermore, decisions about such important issues should not be made solely by one group—every member of every community should be involved.

Some people are already trying to preserve and improve the environment voluntarily. Such actions would improve our surroundings if taken by large numbers of individuals. But well-meaning people may not have enough information to make the correct choices, while many' others show little concern about their surroundings, and continue with their destructive habits.

In addition, the actions of individuals are only a small part of the problem. It is people in groups—in towns, cities, and industries—who produce the greatest effects on the environment. Often industries will not voluntarily reduce their polluting activities because the costs of pollution abatements are high, a factor which reduces profits. Municipalities and states that have industries are hesitant to set strict pollution standards for fear of placing excessive financial burdens on the companies. Ultimately, if costs become too high to operate an industry profitably, the industry may move, producing local unemployment and decreasing tax revenues. Also the major causes of pollution are not limited to industries. Municipalities themselves often degrade the environment with inefficiently operated sewerage plants and poorly managed landfills. The reasons are the same—cost factors. Efficient operation increases cost, which in turn affects taxes, and this touches all members of the community. Yet well-informed individuals know that failure to stop pollution will also endanger the community.

One method of controlling pollution is through legislation. At present there are many laws regulating pollution in the United States and Canada. But laws that regulate effluents, emissions, landfills, heat, and noise often do not prevent pollution. Frequently judgments against offenders are merely small fines, unimportant to large corporations and imposed only after long court proceedings. Thus the legislative approach has not proven very effective in dealing with the problem. Some states are now proposing new economic incentives in the form of lower taxes to industries that reduce pollution.

Perhaps the most promising way to influence people is by educating them. In successful environmental education, individuals would obtain the essential facts, identify the relevant values, analyze the effects of different values in decision-making processes, and predict the consequences of various choices. Once people realize that certain consequences are unacceptable, they may recognize that individual and collective behavior must be modified.

Well-informed citizens know that the problem of pollution *must* be solved if the earth is to remain a safe, stable place for future inhabitants. They understand that informed voters in a democratic society can bring out an enlightened government. A government supported by its constituents could force compliance with strong, firmly enforced laws that are based on an understanding of earth's delicately balanced biosphere. With such insight, the life-sustaining conditions of our earth could be preserved for all the living organisms that will follow us.

Chapter Review

SUMMARY

- The rapidly growing human population is putting a strain on the earth's environmental resources. The size of the population that can be supported by the environment—its carrying capacity—is limited.

- Much productive farmland has been lost through poor farming practices and urbanization. Urbanization has also caused the destruction of the natural habitats of some plant and animal species.

- Some human activities are damaging to the environment. They include cutting down forests, damming rivers, and allowing soil erosion to proceed unchecked. The dumping of industrial and other wastes has caused some pollution of the land, the water, and the air.

- Water pollution is caused by the dumping of toxic substances, such as lead and mercury, into waterways; the oxygen-absorbing decay of organic matter; and the introduction of disease-causing microorganisms from untreated sewage, oil from oil spills, and radioactive wastes from nuclear reactors.

- One major type of air pollution results from aerosols, whose suspended particles block sunlight. Some toxic gases pollute by mixing with the air.

- Efforts are being made to control pollution and conserve natural resources. Sanitary landfill, or covered dumping, and burning in incinerators are two methods of disposing of solid wastes. Various techniques are being used to restore and protect farmland and forests. Biological methods of pest control provide an alternative to the use of chemical pesticides.

KNOW THE TERMS

aerosol	crop rotation	limiting factor	strip cropping
biodegradable	dam	nonrenewable natural resource	temperature inversion
biological magnification	erosion	pheromone	terracing
carrying capacity	eutrophication	pollution	thermal pollution
contour farming	fertilizer	recycling	urbanization
cover crop	human ecology	renewable natural resource	windbreak

SECTION QUESTIONS

Causes of Environmental Damage

1. What is human ecology?
2. List some past human activities that damaged the environment.
3. What is the major contributing factor to the serious environmental problems of today?
4. Define the term *carrying capacity*.
5. What term refers to the movement of population into the cities?
6. List some of the major sources of water pollution.
7. What do aerosols consist of?
8. List some polluting gases that mix with air.
9. Name two acceptable ways of disposing of refuse.

Restoring the Environment

10. What are the two major types of natural resources?
11. List some methods used in soil conservation.
12. Name two conservation practices being used to protect forests.
13. List some of the principal methods of wildlife conservation.
14. Name some biological controls used in place of chemical pesticides.

KNOW THE FACTS

Copy the numbers from Column 1 on a sheet of paper. Select the letter for the term or phrase from Column 2 that matches each numbered item, and write it beside the number.

Column 1

1. limiting factor
2. pollution
3. biodegradable
4. biological magnification
5. temperature inversion
6. photochemical smog
7. sanitary landfill
8. DDT
9. recycling
10. selective harvesting

Column 2

a. makes environment less fit for living things
b. cooler, dense air trapped below warmer air
c. compacted refuse covered with dirt
d. unavailability of food
e. contains PAN
f. reprocessing of nonrenewable resources
g. capable of being broken down by bacteria
h. forest conservation practice
i. pesticide that persists in the environment
j. increase in amount of toxic materials at higher levels of food chain

UNDERSTAND THE CONCEPTS

11. How do changes in birth and death rates affect population growth in industrialized and nonindustrialized countries?
12. What could happen if human population growth continues at the present rate?
13. How has the shift of populations from rural to urban areas affected the environment?
14. How have poor farming practices ruined former farmlands?
15. Describe the harmful effects of organic wastes as water pollutants.
16. Define the term *biological magnification*.
17. What is thermal pollution?
18. Name the major air pollutants, and describe how each is harmful.
19. What happens in a temperature inversion?

20. Describe some of the problems that can arise from the use of chemical pesticides.
21. What is the danger of importing an organism from one environment into a new environment?
22. Describe some of the current programs for reducing water, air, and land pollution.
23. Explain the difference between renewable and nonrenewable natural resources, and give some examples of each.

24. Describe five farming techniques used to prevent soil erosion.
25. Identify some techniques used in forest conservation to ensure future supplies of lumber.
26. List five wildlife conservation practices.
27. What are some of the advantages of biological pest control compared with those of chemical pesticides? Give five examples of biological pest control.

THINK CRITICALLY

28. Explain how the breakdown of large amounts of organic matter upsets the natural balance of a lake ecosystem.
29. Compare farming methods that destroy resources with farming methods that conserve resources.
30. Discuss the ecological advantages of limiting population growth.

31. A person who ate fish from a lake adjacent to farmlands might ingest large amounts of pesticides. How might pesticides have concentrated in the fish through the process of biological magnification?
32. How can industry reduce its contribution to air and water pollution?

THINK CREATIVELY

33. Some environmentalists use the greenhouse effect as a model to explain some possible consequences of air pollution. The greenhouse effect is caused by the buildup of carbon dioxide from air pollution, which traps heat in the earth's atmosphere. Propose possible world-wide consequences of this atmospheric heating.
34. Discuss ways in which urbanization can take place without destroying the environment.

FOR FURTHER INVESTIGATION

1. Visit a water treatment plant. Compare the method of treatment in the plant you visit with either the trickling filter or the activated sludge method of treatment.
2. Prepare a report on the life and contributions of one of the following scientists:
   a. Dixy Lee Ray
   b. Michiko Ishimuri
   c. Rachel Carson

3. Write a report on one of the career opportunities listed below. See suggested procedures, p. 9, "For Further Investigation" Activity 3.
   a. Pollution technician
   b. Urban and regional planner
   c. Pollution control engineer
   d. Air quality engineer

FOR FURTHER READING

Bassett, Libby, "The Roots of Famine," *Scholastic Science World,* February 15, 1985.
Boraiko, Allen, "Storing Up Trouble: Hazardous Waste," *National Geographic Magazine,* March, 1985.
Brown, Lester, and others, "State of the Earth 1985," *Natural History,* April, 1985.

Carson, Rachel, *Silent Spring,* Houghton Mifflin Co., Boston, 1962.
Fox, Robert, "The World's Urban Explosion," *National Geographic Magazine,* August, 1984.
Grover, H. D., "The Climatic and Biological Consequences of Nuclear War," *Environment,* vol. 26, 1984.

Issues in Biology

Vanishing Habitats

Tropical rain forests—areas of high temperature, high rainfall, and lush vegetation—cover only about 6 percent of the earth's surface. Yet rain forests provide homes for about 50 percent of the earth's total animal and plant species. Today, the existence of many of these lush forests is threatened. They are being cut down and burned at an alarming rate.

In Australia, two-thirds of the rain forests have already been destroyed. Since 1950, Guatemala has lost 65 percent of its rain forests. El Salvador has cleared about 93 percent of its forest areas. Scientists estimate that over two-thirds of the remaining rain forests in the world will be gone by the year 2000. If this happens, about one-fifth of the world's total plant and animal populations will die.

The rain forests are being cleared for many reasons. Huge tracts of forest have been stripped to grow certain crops such as coffee, bananas, and sugar cane. Other areas have been converted into pastures to raise beef cattle inexpensively. Some forests are cut down piecemeal to provide firewood for about one-third of the world's population.

The death of the rain forests means the extinction of thousands of species of plants and animals. Species of trees and of herbs whose value to humans has yet to be investigated may be lost forever. Plants that can be used as alternate fuels or for medicines face extinction. Species of animals not yet named may die. In fact, one or more species becomes extinct every day.

The ecology of the rain forest is already changing. Crops grown in the rain forest soil are quickly depleting its already sparse nutrients. Heavy rains falling directly on the stripped land further leach its nutrients and erode the soil. Also, less water evaporates into the atmosphere from these stripped areas. Some scientists say that this lowered evaporation may result in a sparser cloud cover and less rain. They warn that the change in the ecology of the rain forest could change temperature patterns and water cycles around the world.

To save the rain forest from vanishing, ecologists propose such measures as replanting and

Some farmers use "slash-and-burn" agriculture, destroying the rain forest to raise crops or cattle.

conservation programs. Retention of large areas of undisturbed forest would help to preserve plant and animal species. Planting small areas of shade-requiring crops within the forest would help maintain the natural vegetation.

The vanishing rain forest is an international problem. Countries can help each other by sharing technologies such as satellite photography, financial and organizational support, and basic research on the water, carbon, and mineral cycles. The peoples of the world can work together to prevent the loss of a resource of incalculable ecological, economic, and aesthetic value.

---

1. Explain why many scientists consider the loss of tropical rain forests a serious ecological problem.

2. Name another ecological problem that is international in scope. Explain why that problem exceeds national boundaries. What are some possible solutions to this problem?

3. Describe two ways, other than the ones mentioned in the essay, in which countries might help each other tackle the problem of the vanishing rain forest.

4. If laws need to be passed to protect the rain forests, who should pass them? Would the laws need to be national or international? Why? How might such laws be enforced?

THE SI SYSTEM OF MEASUREMENT

The abbreviation SI refers to the International Metric System (formally, Système Internationale d'Unités). This widely used system of measurement is conveniently based on units of 10. Tables of SI base units, their multiples and submultiples, and selected Metric/English conversions are presented below. Also included are notes on temperature and temperature conversions, and heat energy.

SI BASE UNITS

To Measure	SI Base Unit Used	Common Multiples and Submultiples	Approximate Size
Length	meter (m)	meter = 1 m kilometer 1 km = 1000 m centimeter 1 cm = 0.01 m millimeter 1 mm = 0.001 m micron 1 μm = 10^{-6} m (micrometer) angstrom 1 Å = 10^{-10} m	1 m—height of a doorknob 1 km—length of 5 city blocks 1 cm—width of a paper clip 1 mm—thickness of a dime 1 μm—diameter of a bacterium 10 Å—length of an amino acid
Mass	gram (g)	gram = 1 g kilogram 1 kg = 1000 g milligram 1 mg = 0.001 g	1 g—mass of a paper clip 1 kg—mass of a pair of adult shoes 1 mg—mass of a grain of rice
Volume	liter (L)	liter = 1 L milliliter 1 mL = 0.001 L cubic centimeter 1 cm³ (also cc) ≈ 1 mL	1 L—capacity of a water pitcher 1 mL (1 cm³)—capacity of an eye dropper

METRIC PREFIXES

Prefix	Symbol	Meaning	Multiples and Submultiples
atto-	a-	quintillionth	10^{-18}
femto-	f-	quadrillionth	10^{-15}
pico-	p-	trillionth	10^{-12}
nano-	n-	billionth	10^{-9}
micro-	μ-	millionth	10^{-6}
milli-	m-	thousandth	10^{-3}
centi-	c-	hundredth	10^{-2}
deci-	d-	tenth	10^{-1}
deka-	dk-, da-	ten	10
hecto-	h-	hundred	10^{2}
kilo-	k-	thousand	10^{3}
mega-	M-	million	10^{6}
giga-	G-	billion	10^{9}
tera-	T-	trillion	10^{12}

SOME METRIC/ENGLISH CONVERSIONS

To Obtain	Multiply	By
Feet	Meters	3.2808
Miles	Kilometers	0.6214
Ounces	Grams	0.0353
Pounds	Kilograms	2.2046
Liquid quarts	Liters	1.0567
Fluid ounces	Milliliters	0.0338
Meters	Feet	0.3048
Kilometers	Miles	1.6093
Grams	Ounces	28.3495
Kilograms	Pounds	0.4536
Liters	Liquid quarts	0.9463
Milliliters	Fluid ounces	29.5735

TEMPERATURE

The SI base unit for temperature is the kelvin (K). However, as a matter of convenience, the degree Celsius (°C) is more commonly used.

SOME SAMPLE TEMPERATURES

Scale	Water Freezes	Water Boils	Range
K	273	373	100
°C	0	100	100
°F	32	212	180

Temperature Conversion Formulas

$$°C = K - 273 \qquad K = °C + 273$$
$$°C = 5/9(°F - 32) \qquad °F = (9/5)°C + 32$$
$$°F = 9/5(K - 273) + 32 \qquad K = 5/9 (°F - 32) + 273$$

HEAT ENERGY

1 calorie (cal) = The amount of heat needed to raise the temperature of 1 g of water 1 °C (also called the small calorie or gram calorie)

1 Calorie (Cal) = 1 kilocalorie, or 1000 cal (also called the large calorie or kilogram calorie)

CLASSIFICATION OF ORGANISMS

KINGDOM MONERA

Monerans are the simplest organisms. Most are single-celled, although some form colonies. Their cells are procaryotic—they lack nuclear membranes, mitochondria, chloroplasts, and other membranous organelles. Reproduction is mainly asexual by fission.

Phylum Cyanophyta
The blue-green algae contain chlorophyll and other pigments and carry on photosynthesis. Most are aquatic. Some are unicellular, but others are colonial. Examples: *Nostoc, Oscillatoria, Gleocapsa, Anabaena.*

Phylum Schizomycetes
Bacteria are single-celled organisms. Some are found as pairs or chains of cells. Bacteria are classified according to shape: bacilli are rodlike; cocci are spherical; and spirilla are spiral. Most are saprobic or parasitic. A few are photosynthetic or chemosynthetic. Examples: *Escherichia, Diplococcus, Streptococcus, Staphylococcus, Spirocheta, Treponema.*

KINGDOM PROTISTA

Protists are unicellular or very simple multicellular organisms. Their cells are eucaryotic, containing a membrane-bounded nucleus and a variety of cytoplasmic organelles. Some protists are phototrophic—while others are heterotrophic.

Phylum Euglenophyta
The euglenoids are unicellular, photosynthetic organisms with a light-sensitive eyespot. They are found mainly in fresh water. Locomotion is by means of a single flagellum. Reproduction is asexual. Example: *Euglena.*

Phylum Chrysophyta
The yellow-green algae, golden-brown algae, and diatoms are mainly unicellular, photosynthetic organisms. Yellow-to-brown pigments mask the chlorophyll and give these organisms their characteristic colors. Food is stored as an oil or as a starchlike carbohydrate. They are found in fresh and salt water. Examples: *Botrydium, Chrysamoeba, Pinnularia.*

Phylum Pyrrophyta
The dinoflagellates are unicellular, photosynthetic algae with two flagella; most are marine. Their cell walls contain cellulose. Reproduction is asexual. Examples: *Gonyaulax, Gymnodinium.*

Phylum Sarcodina
The sarcodines are unicellular freshwater or marine protozoans that use pseudopods for locomotion and/or for capturing prey. Of the sarcodines, amebas are surrounded only by a cell membrane; foraminiferans are surrounded by a calcium-containing shell; and radiolarians

by a silicon-containing shell. Examples: *Amoeba, Entamoeba, Globigerina, Pelomyxa.*

Phylum Ciliata
Ciliates are complex, unicellular protozoans that move by means of cilia. They are found in both fresh and salt water. The cells contain a micronucleus and a macronucleus. Reproduction is both asexual and sexual. Examples: *Paramecium, Stentor, Tetrahymena, Vorticella.*

Phylum Mastigophora
The zooflagellates are unicellular protozoans that move by means of flagella. Some are free-living, but most are parasitic. Examples: *Trypanosoma, Trichonympha.*

Phylum Sporozoa
The sporozoans are unicellular, spore-forming protozoans. They are nonmotile parasites with a life cycle that includes two hosts. Examples: *Plasmodium, Toxoplasma.*

Phylum Myxomycota
The true slime molds have a life cycle in which there is an ameboid, multinucleate plasmodium stage and a fungus-like, spore-producing, fruiting-body stage. Slime molds are found on damp soil, rotting logs, and in leaf litter. Example: *Physarum.*

Phylum Acrasiomycota
The cellular slime molds have a life cycle in which one stage consists of many separate ameboid cells and the other stage consists of a pseudoplasmodium, an aggregate of many individual cells. The pseudoplasmodium gives rise to spore-producing fruiting bodies. Example: *Dictyostelium.*

KINGDOM PLANTAE

Plants are generally nonmotile, multicellular, photosynthetic organisms. Their cells contain plastids and are surrounded by cell walls. Chlorophylls and carotenoids are present in chloroplasts. Most plants have specialized tissues and organs. Reproduction may be asexual or sexual. Sexual reproduction in many plants involves an alternation of generations with diploid sporophyte and haploid gametophyte stages.

Phylum Chlorophyta
The green algae are chiefly aquatic, and include unicellular, colonial, and multicellular forms. Some have flagella. Chloroplasts contain chlorophylls *a* and *b*; food is stored as starch in plastids. Multicellular forms show little structural differentiation. Examples: *Chlamydomonas, Chlorella, Protococcus, Volvox, Spirogyra, Ulva, Ulothrix.*

Phylum Phaeophyta
The brown algae are multicellular marine seaweeds and kelps that contain the brownish pigment fucoxanthin as well as chlorophylls *a* and *c*. Food is stored as the

carbohydrate laminarin. Some cells are motile, containing two flagella. Examples: *Sargassum, Macrocystis, Fucus, Laminaria.*

Phylum Rhodophyta
The red algae are mainly marine and include both unicellular organisms and multicellular seaweeds. In these algae, the chlorophyll is often masked by red pigments. Food is stored as a special form of starch. The life cycle is complex, but includes no motile cells. Examples: *Porphyra, Polysiphonia, Chondrus.*

Phylum Bryophyta
The bryophytes are small multicellular land plants that lack xylem and phloem, and do not have true leaves, stems, or roots. Bryophytes are found usually in moist areas, and water is needed for fertilization. The gametophyte generation is dominant; the sporophyte generation is reduced in size and is dependent on the gametophyte. Dispersal is by means of spores.

Class Musci In mosses, the gametophyte generation consists of small, erect plants that have tiny leaf-like structures arranged spirally around a stalk. Examples: *Sphagnum, Polytrichum.*

Class Hepaticae In liverworts, the gametophytes are low with flattened and thallus-like or leaf-like structures. Examples: *Marchantia, Riccia.*

Class Antherocerotae In hornworts, the gametophyte is thallus-like; the sporophyte is cylindrical. Example: *Anthoceros.*

Phylum Tracheophyta
The vascular plants contain xylem and phloem and have true leaves, stems, and roots. The sporophyte generation is dominant, and the gametophyte generation is greatly reduced. Chlorophylls *a* and *b* are present, and food is stored as starch in plastids. Tracheophytes are the dominant land plants.

Subphylum Psilopsida
In whisk ferns, the highly branched vascular stems lack true leaves and roots. Whisk ferns are rare plants that are found mainly in warm regions. Example: *Psilotum.*

Subphylum Lycopsida
Club mosses have small leaves arranged in a spiral. Spores are found at the tips of some branches in conelike strobili. Examples: *Lycopodium, Selaginella.*

Subphylum Sphenopsida
Horsetails have small leaves arranged in whorls at specific points along the stems. Conelike strobili form at the ends of some stems. Example: *Equisetum.*

Subphylum Pteropsida
This group includes the ferns, gymnosperms, and angiosperms. These plants have relatively large expanded leaves or are derived from plants with leaves of that type.

Class Filicineae Ferns have fronds that grow up from horizontal underground stems. Sori are found on the backs of the leaflets of some fronds. The independent gametophyte generation consists of a small prothallus. The sperm are motile, and water is required for fertilization. Examples: *Polypodium, Dryopteri, Osmunda.*

Class Gymnospermae Gymnosperms are the plants that bear seeds not enclosed in a fruit. The tiny gametophytes grow on the dominant sporophyte. Sperm are enclosed in a pollen tube, so water is not needed for fertilization.

Subclass Coniferophyta Conifers, or evergreens, are cone-bearing trees with needlelike or scalelike leaves. Examples: pines (*Pinus*), spruce (*Picea*), hemlocks (*Tsuga*), firs (*Abies*), redwoods (*Sequoia*).

Subclass Cycadophyta Cycads are tropical, palmlike gymnosperms. Examples: *Cycas, Zamia.*

Subclass Ginkgophyta Ginkgo, or maidenhair, trees, have fan-shaped leaves. The only surviving species is *Ginkgo biloba.*

Class Angiospermae Angiosperms are flowering plants whose seeds are enclosed in an ovary that ripens into a fruit. The tiny gametophytes grow on the dominant sporophyte. Sperm are enclosed in a pollen tube so that water is not needed for fertilization.

Subclass Monocotyledonae Monocots have an embryo with a single cotyledon; leaves with parallel veins; flower parts in threes or sixes; and vascular bundles scattered throughout the stem tissue. Primarily herbaceous plants. Examples: grasses, including rye (*Secale*), corn (*Zea*), and wheat (*Triticum*); lilies (*Lilium*); tulips (*Tulipa*); orchids (*Orchis*).

Subclass Dicotyledonae Dicots have an embryo with two cotyledons; veins of leaves in form of network; flower parts in fours or fives; vascular tissue organized in concentric ring. Includes both herbaceous and woody plants. Examples: oaks (*Quercus, Lithocarpus*), maples (*Acer*), magnolias (*Magnolia*), cucumbers (*Cucumis*), carrots (*Daucus*), roses (*Rosa*).

KINGDOM FUNGI

Fungi are eucaryotic, heterotrophic organisms that absorb nutrients from dead or living organisms. A few are unicellular, but most are multicellular and are made up of masses of threadlike hyphae. In most, the cell walls are composed of chitin. Reproduction can be either asexual or sexual.

Phylum Zygomycota
Conjugation fungi are terrestrial; their cell walls are made of chitin. They reproduce sexually by conjugation and asexually by spore formation. Examples: *Rhizopus, Phycomyces.*

Phylum Oomycota
Water molds are mainly aquatic and have flagellated spores. Their cell walls contain cellulose. Example: *Saprolegnia.*

Phylum Ascomycota
The sac fungi include both aquatic and terrestrial forms. Their cell walls are made of chitin. Sexual reproduction

results in the formation of ascospores; asexual reproduction results in the formation of spores called conidia. This group includes cup fungi, yeasts, powdery mildews, truffles, morels, and blue and green molds. Examples: *Saccharomyces, Aspergillus, Penicillium, Neurospora*.

Phylum Basidiomycota
The club fungi are terrestrial. Their cell walls are made of chitin. Sexual reproduction involves the formation of basidiospores. This group includes mushrooms, bracket fungi, puffballs, rusts, and smuts. Examples: *Amanita, Lycoperdon, Phragmidium*.

Fungi Imperfecti
In the Fungi Imperfecti, the pattern of sexual reproduction is unknown. Most members of this group show the other characteristics of the Ascomycota. Example: athlete's foot fungus *Trichophyton*.

KINGDOM ANIMALIA

Animals are multicellular, heterotrophic organisms with specialized tissues. Most are motile. Their cells are eucaryotic and lack cell walls. Reproduction is mainly sexual.

Phylum Porifera
Sponges are sessile, aquatic animals; most are marine. Their asymmetrical bodies have two cell layers and are pierced by pores; they are stiffened by skeletal elements called spicules. Reproduction is both asexual and sexual. Examples: *Grantia, Scypha, Euplectella*.

Phylum Coelenterata
In coelenterates, the radially symmetrical body is saclike and is made up of two cell layers. There are two body forms—the polyp and the medusa. The digestive cavity has a single opening surrounded by tentacles containing stinging cells. Coelenterates are all aquatic, most are marine. Some coelenterates, such as corals, are colonial. Reproduction is sexual in the medusa stage and asexual in the polyp stage. Examples: hydra (*Hydra*), jellyfish (*Aurelia, Obelia, Physalia*), corals (*Gorgonia*), and sea anemones (*Actinia*).

Phylum Platyhelminthes
The flatworms have flattened, bilaterally symmetrical bodies made up of three tissue layers. The digestive system has only one opening.

Class Turbellaria Free-living flatworms with eyespots. Examples: *Planaria, Dugesia*.

Class Trematoda Flukes are parasitic flatworms, usually with suckers. Examples: *Schistosoma, Fasciola*.

Class Cestoda Tapeworms are parasitic flatworms without digestive systems. Example: *Taenia*.

Phylum Nematoda
Roundworms have long, cylindrical bodies; there is a digestive system with both a mouth and an anus. Most are parasitic. Examples: *Ascaris, Necatur, Trichinella*.

Phylum Annelida
Segmented worms have a body made up of many similar segments. They have a well-developed coelom, a complete digestive tract, a closed circulatory system, and a ventral nervous system.

Class Polychaeta Mostly marine worms. They have a well-developed head. Example: *Nereis*.

Class Oligochaeta Includes terrestrial and aquatic worms. Members of this group, including earthworms, have poorly developed heads. Examples: *Lumbricus, Tubifex*.

Class Hirudinea Leeches are parasitic annelids with suckers at one or both ends of the body. Example: *Hirudo*.

Phylum Mollusca
Mollusks have a soft, unsegmented body, often with a muscular foot, mantle, and radula. The digestive, circulatory, and nervous systems are well developed.

Class Bivalvia Bivalves include clams, oysters, mussels, and scallops. These mollusks have a two-part, hinged shell and no head or radula. Examples: *Mytilus, Pecten, Teredo*.

Class Gastropoda Gastropods include snails, slugs, and whelks. These mollusks have a head with tentacles; most have a spiral shell. Examples: *Limax, Helix, Busycon*.

Class Cephalopoda Cephalopods have a large head surrounded by arms, or tentacles. The octopus has no shell, the squid has an internal shell, and the nautilus has an external shell. The nervous system is particularly well-developed. Examples: octopus (*Octopus*), squid (*Loligo*), and nautilus (*Nautilus*).

Phylum Arthropoda
Arthropods have a segmented body with paired, jointed appendages and an exoskeleton composed of chitin.

Class Crustacea Crustaceans have two pairs of antennae. Most are aquatic and respiration is by gills. Examples: lobsters (*Homarus*), crabs (*Cancer*), crayfish (*Cambarus*), water fleas (*Cyclops, Daphnia*).

Class Chilopoda Centipedes have one pair of antennae, many body segments, and one pair of legs on most body segments. Example: *Scolopendra*.

Class Diplopoda Millipedes have one pair of antennae, many body segments, and two pairs of legs on most body segments. Example: *Glomeris*.

Class Arachnida Arachnids have no antennae, two body regions, four pairs of legs, and book lungs. Examples: spiders (*Argiope*), scorpions (*Chelifer*).

Class Insecta Insects have one pair of antennae, three body regions, three pairs of legs, and tracheal respiration; many have two pairs of wings. Group includes flies, ants, beetles, fleas, lice, bees, and roaches. (See pages 586–587 for a table of insect classification.)

Phylum Echinodermata
Echinoderms have a water-vascular system, an internal skeleton, and a spiny skin. Adults are radially symmetrical. All are marine. Examples: starfish (*Asterias*), sea urchins (*Arbacia*), sea cucumbers (*Cucumaria*), sand dollars (*Echinarachnius*).

Phylum Chordata
At some stage of development chordates have a notochord, paired gill slits, and a dorsal, hollow nerve cord.

Subphylum Urochordata
Adult tunicates are soft, saclike, sessile, marine animals. Larvae are free-swimming. Examples: *Ciona*, *Appendicularia*.

Subphylum Cephalochordata
Lancelets are small, fishlike, marine animals. A notochord is present in adults. They have prominent gill slits. Example: *Branchiostoma*.

Subphylum Vertebrata
Vertebrates have an enlarged brain and a spinal column made up of vertebrae that enclose the dorsal nerve cord.

Class Agnatha The jawless fishes, which include the lampreys and hagfish, have a cartilaginous skeleton, a snakelike body, and smooth skin without scales. They lack true jaws. Examples: *Petromyzon*, *Myxine*.

Class Chondrichthyes The cartilaginous fishes have a skeleton composed of cartilage, movable jaws, scales, and fins. Examples: sharks (*Squalus*), skates (*Raja*).

Class Osteichthyes The bony fishes have a skeleton made of bone, movable jaws, overlapping scales, paired fins, and an air bladder. Examples: salmons and trouts (*Salmo*), carps (*Cyprinus*), perches (*Perca*), codfish (*Gadus*).

Class Amphibia Most amphibians have moist, smooth, scaleless skin and four limbs. Water is needed for reproduction. Aquatic larvae have gills and undergo metamorphosis. Adults are usually terrestrial and have lungs and a three-chambered heart. Examples: frogs (*Rana*), toads (*Bufo*), salamanders (*Necturus*, *Triturus*).

Class Reptilia The reptiles have dry skin and a scale-covered body with four limbs (absent in snakes). Fertilization is internal. Their eggs have a leathery shell and protective membranes. Most reptiles live and reproduce on land. They have lungs and a three-chambered heart with a partially divided ventricle. Examples: turtles (*Chelydra*, *Terrapene*), crocodiles (*Crocodylus*), alligators (*Alligator*), snakes (*Crotalus*).

Class Aves Birds have feathers and their front limbs are wings. Their eggs have a hard shell. They have a four-chambered heart and are warm-blooded. Examples: robins and thrushes (*Turdus*), chickens (*Gallus*), ducks (*Anas*), sparrows (*Passer*, *Melospiza*), starlings (*Sturnus*).

Class Mammalia Mammals nourish their young with milk produced by mammary glands. Their body covering is hair or fur. They have a four-chambered heart and are warm-blooded.

Subclass Prototheria Monotremes are egg-laying mammals. Examples: duckbill platypus (*Ornithorhynchus*), spiny anteater (*Tachyglossus*).

Subclass Metatheria Marsupials are pouched mammals, found mainly in Australia. Examples: kangaroos (*Macropus*), opossums (*Didelphis*), koalas (*Phascolarctos*).

Subclass Eutheria The placental mammals include most living mammals. Developing embryos receive nourishment from the mother's circulatory system by means of a structure called the placenta.

Order Insectivora moles (*Scalopus*), shrews (*Sorex*)

Order Rodentia rats (*Rattus*), mice (*Mus*), squirrels (*Sciurus*)

Order Lagomorpha rabbits (*Sylvilagus*), hares (*Lepus*)

Order Chiroptera bats (*Myotis*)

Order Cetacea whales (*Balaena*), dolphins (*Delphinus*), porpoises (*Phocaena*)

Order Edentata anteaters (*Myrmecophaga*), armadillos (*Dasypus*)

Order Proboscidea elephants (*Elephas*, *Loxodonta*)

Order Artiodactyla camels (*Camelus*), sheep (*Ovis*), pigs (*Sus*), cattle (*Bos*)

Order Perissodactyla horses (*Equus*), rhinoceroses (*Rhinoceros*)

Order Carnivora cats (*Felis*), dogs (*Canis*), bears (*Ursus*), raccoons (*Procyon*)

Order Primates humans (*Homo*), chimpanzees (*Pan*), orangutans (*Pongo*), monkeys (*Macacus*)

GLOSSARY

a

abdomen: In *arthropods,* the posterior region. In *mammals,* the region between the diaphragm and pelvis.

abiotic factor: A physical factor of the environment, such as water, air, light, or temperature.

ABO blood group: A group of blood types (A, B, AB, and O). Each type is identified by the presence of certain antigens on the surface of red blood cells.

abscisic acid: An organic compound that influences the shedding of leaves and the seasonal slowing down of plant activities.

absolute dating: Any method that enables scientists to find out how long ago an event occurred.

absorption: The passage of materials across a cell membrane into the cell; the process by which usable materials are taken into an organism.

acid: A compound that produces an excess of hydrogen ions in a water solution.

acquired immunity: Immunity that develops after birth.

Acrasiomycota: A phylum of protists called cellular slime molds; their life cycle includes a stage as separate ameboid cells and a stage as a pseudoplasmodium—an aggregate of many cells; cellular slime molds.

active site: The region on an enzyme where the reaction it catalyzes takes place.

active transport: A process in which the movement of materials across a cell membrane requires the expenditure of cellular energy.

adaptation: An inherited trait or modification that improves the chance of survival and reproduction of an organism in a given environment.

adaptive radiation: The process by which an ancestral species evolves into a number of different species, each occupying a different habitat or ecological niche.

addition: The breaking-off of a segment of a chromosome and its attachment to the homologous chromosome.

adenine: A nitrogenous base found in DNA and RNA.

adenosine diphosphate: See **ADP.**

adenosine triphosphate: See **ATP.**

adrenal gland: An endocrine gland that secretes hormones that help the body deal with stress.

ADP (adenosine diphosphate): The lower-energy compound remaining after one phosphate group is removed from ATP.

aerobic respiration: Respiration requiring the presence of free oxygen, in which glucose is completely oxidized to carbon dioxide and water.

aerosol: Very small solid particles or liquid droplets suspended in air.

afterbirth: The placenta and the amnion, which are expelled from the uterus after birth of the baby.

agglutination: A process in which red blood cells clump together.

Agnatha: A class of vertebrates having a cartilaginous skeleton, snakelike body, and smooth skin; the jawless fishes.

air sac: The structure at the end of a bronchiole comprised of a cluster of alveoli.

alimentary canal: The digestive tube; the passageway through which food moves from mouth to anus.

allantois: In *bird and reptile eggs,* a saclike extraembryonic membrane that grows out of the digestive system of the embryo and controls gas exchange and collects metabolic wastes; in *placental mammals,* an extraembryonic membrane that forms part of the umbilical cord.

allele: One of the two or more forms of the gene for a specific trait.

allergy: A disorder caused by the release of histamine by the body cells following an antigen-antibody reaction.

alternation of generations: A life cycle of some plants that involves a multicellular haploid generation alternating with a multicellular diploid generation.

alveolus (pl. alveoli): One of the small, cup-shaped cavities in the air sacs where gas exchange occurs.

amino acid: The structural unit of proteins; contains a carboxyl group (—COOH), an amino group (—NH$_2$), and a side chain.

amino group: A chemical group composed of two hydrogen atoms and one nitrogen atom, found in amino acids.

amniocentesis: A technique in which amniotic fluid, which contains fetal cells, is withdrawn from the amniotic sac of a pregnant woman so that the cells can be examined for the presence of genetic abnormalities.

amnion: In both shelled eggs and mammals, a fluid-filled extraembryonic sac that surrounds the embryo; provides a watery environment and protects the embryo.

amniotic fluid: The fluid that fills the amnion.

Amphibia: A class of land and water dwelling vertebrates having moist, smooth, scaleless skin and four limbs; they need water for reproduction; amphibians.

anabolism: The synthesis of materials needed for life processes in an organism.

anaerobic respiration: Respiration in the absence of free oxygen, in which glucose is partially oxidized.

analogous structures: Structures found in different types of organisms that are similar in function or outward appearance, but are dissimilar in basic structure or embryonic development.

anal pore: The opening through which indigestible wastes are ejected from a paramecium.

anaphase: The stage of mitosis during which the daughter chromosomes move to opposite poles.

anemia: A disorder in which the blood contains too few red blood cells or insufficient hemoglobin.

angiosperm: A flowering plant.

Animalia: One of the five kingdoms, comprised of multi-cellular, usually motile, heterotrophic organisms; animals.

Annelida: A phylum of animals with bodies made up of many similar segments; segmented worms.

anterior: Pertaining to the front, or head, end of a bilaterally symmetrical animal.

anther: The saclike structure of a stamen in which pollen grains are produced.

anthropology: The branch of science that studies human origins and humans' physical, social, and cultural development.

antibody: A protein produced by leukocytes, which reacts with a specific foreign substance, or antigen, and inactivates it.

anticodon: A sequence of three bases on a tRNA molecule that pairs with the complementary three-nucleotide codon of a mRNA molecule during protein synthesis.

antigen: Any substance that can cause a response of the immune system.

anus: The opening of the digestive tube through which undigested materials are eliminated from the body.

aorta: The major artery carrying oxygenated blood away from the heart.

aortic arch: A heartlike blood vessel in the earthworm.

appendicitis: Inflammation of the appendix.

appendicular skeleton: The division of the human skeleton that includes the arms, legs, pectoral girdle, and pelvic girdle.

appendix: A small, fingerlike pouch found where the small intestine joins the large intestine.

Arachnida: A class of arthropods having no antennae, two body regions, four pairs of legs, and book lungs; includes spiders and scorpions; arachnids.

artery: A blood vessel that carries blood away from the heart to the organs and tissues of the body.

Arthropoda: A phylum of animals having a segmented body with paired, jointed appendages and an exoskeleton; arthropods.

Artiodactyla: An order of hoofed mammals having an even number of toes; includes camels and deer.

Ascomycota: The largest phylum of fungi, both aquatic and terrestrial; sac fungi.

asexual reproduction: A type of reproduction in which there is only one parent; all offspring are genetically identical to the parent.

assimilation: The incorporation of materials into the body of an organism.

aster: A star-shaped structure formed during mitosis or meiosis in animal cells by fibers extending from the centrioles.

atom: The smallest particle of an element that has the properties of that element; consists of an arrangement of electrons revolving around a nucleus.

atomic mass: The total number of protons and neutrons in the nucleus of an atom.

atomic number: The number of protons in the nucleus of an atom; the number that identifies an element.

ATP (adenosine triphosphate): The compound in which energy released by cellular respiration is stored.

atrium (pl. atria): One of the upper, thin-walled chambers of the heart; auricle.

auditory canal: The passage leading from the outer ear to the middle ear.

auditory nerve: The nerve which carries impulses from the inner ear to the brain during the process of hearing.

Australopithecus: A genus of fossil bipedal mammals found in southern Africa, showing more human than ape characteristics.

autoimmune disease: A disease in which the tolerance of the immune system breaks down, and antibodies and sensitized lymphocytes develop in response to the body's own antigens.

autonomic nervous system: A division of the peripheral nervous system consisting of motor fibers from the brain and spinal cord that serve the internal organs of the body; not under voluntary control.

autosome: A chromosome other than a sex chromosome.

autotroph: An organism capable of synthesizing its needed organic nutrients from inorganic substances.

auxin: A hormone that affects the growth of all types of plant tissues.

Aves: A class of warm-blooded vertebrates; that have feathers, a four-chambered heart, front limbs as wings, and eggs with hard shells; birds.

axial skeleton: The division of the human skeleton that includes the skull, vertebrae, ribs, and breastbone.

axon: A long, thin fiber that carries nerve impulses away from the cell body of a neuron.

b

bacillus: A rod-shaped bacterium.

bacteriophage: A virus that infects bacteria.

ball-and-socket joint: A joint that permits movement in all directions.

bark: The protective, outermost layer of a woody stem or root.

base: A compound that produces an excess of hydroxyl ions when dissolved in water.

Basidiomycota: A phylum of terrestrial fungi that sexually reproduce utilizing a special, club-like structure called a basidium; club fungi.

behavior: The series of activities performed by an organism in response to stimuli.

benthos: The organisms living on the ocean floor; benthic organisms include clams, snails, and crabs.

bilateral symmetry: A type of symmetry in which there is only one longitudinal section that will divide the organism into two parts that are mirror images of each other.

bile: A fluid secretion of liver cells that aids in the breakdown of fats.

binary fission: The simplest form of asexual reproduction, in which a unicellular parent organism divides into two approximately equal cells.

binomial nomenclature: The two-word system that identifies each kind of organism by use of its genus and species names.

biodegradable: Able to be broken down by bacteria and other decay organisms into simpler substances.

biological magnification: The process that results in substances accumulating in larger and larger quantities in the bodies of organisms at each higher level of a food chain.

biology: The study of living things.

biome: A large geographical region showing a particular type of climax vegetation.

biosphere: The portion of the earth in which living things exist.

biotic factor: An organism in an environment and its effects on other living things.

bipedal locomotion: The ability to walk on two legs in an upright position.

bivalve: A member of the class Bivalvia, including clams, oysters, mussels, and scallops; a mollusk having a two-part, hinged shell and no head or radula.

blade: The thin, flat, expanded part of a leaf.

blastocoel: The fluid-filled cavity in a blastula.

blastopore: The opening in a gastrula created by the gastrulation process; becomes an opening to the digestive system in the adult organism.

blastula (pl. blastulae): A stage of development in which the embryo consists of a single layer of cells surrounding a fluid-filled cavity.

book lungs: Respiratory organs of the arachnids, consisting of leaflike plates in which gas exchange occurs.

Bowman's capsule: A double-walled, cup-shaped structure surrounding the glomerulus in the kidney.

brain: A group of specialized nerve cells that control and coordinate the activities of a nervous system.

bronchial tube: One of the branches of a bronchus.

bronchiole: One of the finest branches of the bronchial tubes; ends in an air sac.

bronchus (pl. bronchi): A cartilage-ringed tube that branches from the trachea and enters a lung.

Bryophyta: A phylum of land plants lacking specialized conducting tissues; these mosses, liverworts, and hornworts grow in moist areas; bryophytes.

budding: A type of asexual reproduction in which the parent organism divides into two unequal parts.

bulb: A short underground stem with thickened storage leaves; can give rise to new plants by vegetative reproduction.

C

calorie: The amount of heat that will raise the temperature of 1 g of water 1°C. (The large Calorie, used to measure the energy contents of foods, is equal to 1,000 calories.)

calyx: The complete circle of sepals in a flower.

camouflage: A protective adaptation that enables an organism to visually blend into the environment.

canine: A type of tooth specialized for tearing food.

capillary: A microscopic blood vessel that connects the smallest arteries to the smallest veins.

capillary action: The upward movement of a liquid in a tube of narrow diameter.

carbohydrate: A compound of carbon, hydrogen, and oxygen in which the ratio of hydrogen to oxygen to carbon is about 2:1:1.

carbon cycle: The pathways by which carbon is circulated through the biosphere.

carbon fixation: The process in which carbon dioxide is incorporated into organic compounds by the processes of photosynthesis and chemosynthesis.

carboxyl group: —COOH; the characteristic chemical group of organic acids.

Carnivora: An order of flesh-eating mammals; includes cats, dogs, bears, and seals; carnivores.

carnivore: An animal that feeds on other animals; order Carnivora.

carrying capacity: The maximum size of a population that can be supported by an environment.

cartilage: A type of flexible connective tissue.

cast: A type of fossil formed when a mold becomes filled with minerals and hardens, producing a copy of the external features of an organism.

catabolism: All the processes that result in the breakdown of complex substances in the body.

catalyst: A substance that increases the rate of a particular chemical reaction without being changed itself.

cell: The basic unit of structure and function in living things; the smallest unit in living things that shows the characteristics of life.

cell body: The part of a nerve cell that contains the nucleus cyton.

cell membrane: The structure that separates the interior of a cell from the surrounding environment and controls the passage of materials into and out of the cell; plasma membrane.

cell plate: A structure formed during cytokinesis in a plant cell that divides the cell in half, forming part of the new cell walls of the daughter cells.

cell theory: The theory that states that all living things are made of cells and that cells arise only from other cells.

cellular respiration: The process by which energy stored in food is released by cells.

cell wall: The rigid structure, often composed of polysaccharides that encloses the cells of plants and various microorganisms.

central nervous system: The division of the nervous system that includes the brain and spinal cord.

centrifugation: The process of separating materials of different densities in a centrifuge.

centrifuge: A device in which materials of different densities can be separated from one another by whirling them at high speed in a cylinder.

centriole: A cylindrical organelle found near the nucleus in animal cells that is involved in mitosis.

centromere: The region of attachment of two sister chromatids.

Cephalochordata: A subphylum of chordates; small, fish-like, marine animals with a notochord present in adults; lancelets.

cephalopod: A member of the class Cephalopoda, including the octopus, squid, and nautilus; a mollusk having a distinct head and tentacles.

cephalothorax: The anterior portion of some arthropods, made up of the fused segments of the head and thorax.

cerebellum (pl. cerebella): A part of the brain located below the rear part of the cerebrum; coordinates voluntary movements.

cerebral cortex: The outer layer of the cerebrum; the gray matter of the brain.

cerebral hemisphere: One of the two halves of the cerebrum, which are partially separated from each other by a deep groove.

cerebrum: The largest part of the human brain.

cervix: The narrow neck of the uterus.

Cetacea: An order of nearly hairless marine mammals having paddle-like forelimbs; includes whales, dolphins, and porpoises; cetaceans.

chemical bond: A force of attraction between atoms that holds them together in compounds.

chemical equation: A written representation of a chemical reaction.

chemical reaction: The process in which chemical bonds of substances are broken and the atoms form new bonds, producing different substances.

chemosynthesis: A form of autotrophic nutrition in which energy for synthesizing organic compounds is obtained from inorganic compounds rather than from light.

chemotroph: An autotroph that carries on chemosynthesis.

Chilopoda: A class of arthropods with one pair of antennae, many body segments, and one pair of legs on most body segments; centipedes.

Chiroptera: An order of mammals capable of real flight; bats.

chitin: The polysaccharide that makes up the exoskeleton of arthropods.

chlorophyll: The major photosynthetic pigment of plants and algae.

Chlorophyta: A phylum of mainly aquatic plants; green algae.

chloroplast: A plastid that contains chlorophyll and is the site of photosynthesis in eucaryotic cells.

cholesterol: A steroid found in animal cells; plays a role in the buildup of fatty deposits in arteries.

Chondrichthyes: A class of vertebrates including sharks and skates, having a cartilaginous skeleton, movable jaws, scales, and fins.

Chordata: A phylum of animals having at some stage of development a notochord, paired gill slits, and a dorsal, hollow nerve chord; chordates.

chorion: The membrane that surrounds the embryo and the other extraembryonic membranes in mammals, birds, and reptiles.

choroid coat: The darkly pigmented middle layer of the eye.

chromatid: One of the two strands of a doubled chromosome.

chromatin: The material of which chromosomes are composed.

chromatography: A process used to separate and analyze mixtures of chemical substances.

chromoplast: A plastid that contains pigments other than chlorophyll.

chromosomal mutation: A change in chromosome structure, resulting in new gene combinations.

Chrysophyta: A phylum of algal-like protists; chrysophytes are mostly unicellular and contain large amounts of yellow-brown pigment.

chyme: The thin, soupy liquid produced from food by the stomach.

Ciliata: A phylum of protists containing the most complex protozoans, which have an abundance of hairlike cilia; ciliates.

cilium (pl. cilia): A short, hairlike organelle at the surface of a cell, with the capacity for movement.

circadian rhythm: A physiological or behavioral cycle that repeats approximately every 24 hours.

circulation: The movement of materials within a cell or between parts of an organism.

class: A group of related orders.

cleavage: In a fertilized egg, the first series of cell divisions that occur without growth and continue until the cells of the embryo are reduced to the size of the cells of the adult organism.

climax community: A mature, stable community that is the final stage of ecological succession.

cloaca: In *reptiles, birds, amphibians,* and many *fishes,* the cavity into which the intestinal and genitourinary tracts empty. In some *invertebrates,* a cavity serving as an excretory, respiratory, and reproductive duct.

clone: A group of individual organisms that have identical genetic makeups.

closed circulatory system: A circulatory system in which blood is always confined in vessels.

clotting: The solidification of blood.

club moss: Small, spore-dispersing tracheophytes with true roots, stems, and leaves.

cnidoblast: A stinging cell found in coelenterates, which is used for defense and capturing food.

coacervate: According to the heterotroph hypothesis, an aggregate of large proteinlike molecules; thought to have developed into the first forms of life on the primitive earth.

coccus: A spherical bacterium.

cochlea (pl. cochleae): The organ of hearing, found in the inner ear, consisting of coiled, liquid-filled tubes.

codominance: A type of inheritance in which two dominant alleles are expressed at the same time without blending of traits.

codon: A group of three bases in an mRNA molecule that specifies a particular amino acid.

coelom: The fluid-filled body cavity between the body wall and the digestive tube.

coenzyme: A nonprotein, organic substance necessary to the functioning of a particular enzyme.

cold-blooded: See **ectothermic.**

Coleoptera: The largest insect order, having front wings modified to form a horny covering for hind wings; beetles.

collagen: A fibrous structural protein that is a constituent of connective tissue.

collar cell: A type of flagellated cell found in the inner layer of a sponge.

colloidal dispersion: A mixture in which the solute particles are larger than molecules or ions, but are too small to settle out; colloid.

color blindness: A sex-linked trait in which an individual cannot perceive certain colors.

commensalism: A type of symbiotic relationship in which one organism benefits from the association and the other is not affected.

community: All the different populations within a given area.

complete metamorphosis: The type of development in most insects; involves the stages of larva, pupa, and adult.

compound: A substance made of two or more kinds of atoms combined in definite proportions.

compound microscope: A microscope with two lenses or lens systems—an ocular and an objective.

concentration gradient: The difference in concentration between a region of greater concentration and a region of lesser concentration.

conditioning: A simple form of learning in which behavior is changed through association.

conducting tissue: See **vascular tissue.**

cone: A structure in the *retina of the eye* responsible for color vision. In *gymnosperms,* the seed-bearing, or pollen-bearing, structure.

conifer: Subclass Coniferophyta of the gymnosperms; cone-bearing seed plants with needlelike or scalelike leaves.

conjugation: A form of sexual reproduction found in protists; the individual organisms appear to be identical, but are of different mating types.

connective tissue: A type of tissue that supports other body tissues and binds tissues and organs together.

consumer: A heterotroph; an organism that obtains nutrients from other organisms.

contour farming: A method of farming in which rows are plowed horizontally across slopes, following the contour of the land, and acting to reduce the flow of water down the slopes.

controlled experiment: An experiment set up in duplicate, with a single factor changed in one of the setups.

convergent evolution: The evolution of outward similarities in organisms that are not closely related, because they have to meet similar problems in their habitats.

cork: A protective plant tissue that covers the surface of woody stems and roots.

cork cambium: The meristematic tissue that produces cork.

corm: A short, vertical underground stem containing stored food; it can give rise to new plants by vegetative reproduction.

cornea: The transparent part of the sclera in the front of the eye through which light enters.

corolla: The complete circle of petals in a flower.

coronary circulation: The subdivision of the systemic circulation that supplies blood to the tissues of the heart.

corpus luteum: A progesterone-secreting yellow body in the ovary, formed when luteinizing hormone causes a ruptured follicle to fill with cells.

correlation: The process of matching by which geologists determine the relative ages of rock layers and fossils in a local region.

cortex: The outer region or layer of a plant or animal organ or structure.

corticosteroid: A type of hormone produced by the adrenal cortex, synthesized from cholesterol.

cotyledon: A modified leaf of a seed plant embryo, which often provides nourishment for the developing seedling.

covalent bond: A chemical bond formed by the sharing of electrons.

cover crop: A crop planted over a whole field instead of in rows; used to prevent soil erosion.

cranial nerve: A nerve connected directly to the brain.

cranium: The upper part of the skull, which houses and protects the brain.

Cro-Magnons: A type of prehistoric human, considered to be the same as modern humans; replaced the Neanderthals about 35,000 years ago.

crop: In birds and many invertebrates, a thin-walled organ that temporarily stores food from the esophagus.

crop rotation: A method of farming in which different

crops are grown on a field in successive years to prevent the reduction of soil nutrients.

crossing-over: The process in which pieces of homologous chromosomes are exchanged during synapsis in the first meiotic division.

Crustacea: A class of mostly aquatic arthropods having two pairs of antennae; includes lobsters, crabs, shrimp, and barnacles; crustaceans.

cuticle: The layer of cutin that covers plant epidermis.

cutting: Any vegetative part of a plant used to produce a new plant by artificial vegetative reproduction.

Cyanophyta: A phylum of monerans; blue-green algae, the simplest of all photosynthetic, oxygen-producing organisms.

cycad: Subclass Cycadophyta of the gymnosperms; tropical plants resembling ferns or palm trees.

cytokinesis: The division of the cytoplasm of the cell after mitosis or meiosis; the cell divides into two parts, each containing one of the newly formed nuclei and half of the other contents of the parent cell.

cytokinin: A plant hormone that stimulates cell division and growth.

cytoplasm: The watery material between the nucleus and the cell membrane of a cell.

cytosine: A nitrogenous base found in DNA and RNA.

d

dam: A barrier built to hold back flowing water.

dark reactions: The series of reactions in photosynthesis in which carbon fixation occurs and which do not require light.

decomposer: An organism of decay.

dehydration synthesis: A type of reaction in which two molecules are bonded together by the removal of a water molecule.

deletion: A type of chromosomal alteration in which a portion of a chromosome and the genes it contains is lost.

dendrite: A short, branched part of a neuron specialized for receiving nerve impulses and transmitting them to the cell body.

denitrifying bacteria: Anaerobic bacteria that convert nitrates and nitrites to nitrogen gas, which is released into the atmosphere.

deoxyribose: A 5-carbon sugar found in DNA.

dermis: The layer of skin beneath the epidermis, consisting of elastic connective tissue.

desert: A biome in which there is too little rainfall to support trees or grasses; may show great variation in temperature between day and night.

development: The orderly series of changes that occur as an organism grows to maturity.

diabetes mellitus: A condition caused by an insufficient concentration of insulin in the blood.

diaphragm: The muscle that forms the floor of the chest cavity.

diastole: The period of relaxation during the heartbeat cycle.

diatom: A member of the phylum Chrysophyta; a unicellular, silica-shelled organism found largely in salt water.

diatomic molecule: A molecule formed when two atoms of the same element form a covalent bond, such as O_2.

dicot: A plant whose seeds have two cotyledons.

differential reproduction: The idea that individuals with favorable variations survive longer and produce more offspring than those without the variations, thus causing certain allele frequencies to gradually increase or decline within a population.

differentiation: The series of changes that transforms unspecialized embryonic cells into the specialized cells, tissues, and organs that make up an adult organism.

diffusion: The movement of molecules or particles from an area of greater concentration to an area of lesser concentration.

digestion: The breakdown of complex food materials into simpler forms that can be used by the organism.

dihybrid cross: A genetic cross in which two pairs of contrasting traits are studied.

dipeptide: A type of molecule formed when two amino acids are joined by a peptide bond.

diploid: Having two of each type of chromosome; two times the haploid number of chromosomes.

Diplopoda: A class of arthropods with one pair of antennae, many body segments, and two pairs of legs on most body segments; millipedes.

Diptera: A widespread insect order having one pair of functional, membranous wings; includes flies.

disaccharide: A double sugar formed by joining two monosaccharides by dehydration synthesis.

disjunction: The separation of homologous chromosomes during anaphase I of meiosis.

DNA (deoxyribonucleic acid): The nucleic acid that contains the hereditary information.

dominance hierarchy: A ranking within a group of animals that is established through fighting or displays of aggression.

dominant species: The species that exert the greatest effects on the environment and on other members of the community.

dominant trait: The trait that appears in the offspring of a cross between two pure individuals showing contrasting forms of the trait.

dormancy: A period during which growth and other metabolic activities stop or are severely reduced.

dorsal: Pertaining to the upper side or the back of a bilaterally symmetrical animal.

double fertilization: In flowering plants, the fertilization of the egg and of the two polar nuclei to form the diploid zygote and the triploid endosperm nucleus, respectively.

eardrum: See **tympanic membrane.**

Echinodermata: A phylum of marine animals having a water-vascular system, an internal skeleton, and a spiny skin; echinoderms.

ecological succession: The process by which an existing community in an ecosystem is gradually replaced by another community.

ecology: The branch of biology that deals with all the interactions between organisms and their environment.

ecosystem: A community and the physical environment that it occupies.

ectoderm: The outer layer of cells in a simple animal or embryo; one of the germ layers of an animal embryo.

ectothermic: Having a body temperature that varies with the temperature of the environment; cold-blooded.

Edentata: An order of mammals having only molars or no teeth at all; includes anteaters, sloths, and armadillos.

endothermic: Having a body temperature that remains relatively constant regardless of the temperature of the environment; warm-blooded.

effector: A muscle or gland; responds to a stimulus.

egestion: The elimination of undigested material from the digestive tract.

ejaculation: The release of semen from the urethra.

electron: A negatively charged particle found in the space outside the nucleus of an atom.

electron transport chain: A series of oxidation-reduction reactions in which most of the energy produced from the breakdown of glucose is transferred to ATP.

electrophoresis: A technique that uses an electric field to separate and analyze mixtures of chemical substances whose particles have an electrical charge.

element: A substance made entirely of one kind of atom.

elongation zone: In plants, a region behind the meristematic zone of the root, in which the cells produced in the meristematic zone grow longer.

embryo: A multicellular organism in the early stages of development.

embryonic induction: The process by which one group of cells (the organizer) induces another group of cells to differentiate.

embryo sac: The mature female gametophyte of a flowering plant.

empirical formula: A formula that shows the atoms in a compound in their simplest proportions.

endocrine gland: A ductless gland.

endoderm: The inner layer of cells in a simple animal or embryo; one of the germ layers of an animal embryo.

endodermis: In plants, the innermost layer of the cortex of the root.

endoplasmic reticulum: A system of membrane-enclosed, fluid-filled canals that form a network through the cytoplasm of a cell.

endoskeleton: A skeleton composed of bone and/or cartilage located within the body walls.

endosperm: The tissue that develops from the endosperm nucleus, often serving as a food supply for the plant embryo.

energy level: One of the regions around the nucleus of an atom in which an electron may move; each level is associated with a specific energy value.

entomology: The branch of biology that deals with the study of insects.

enzyme: A protein that acts as a catalyst, increasing the rate of a specific chemical reaction.

epicotyl: The part of a plant embryo above the point of attachment of the cotyledons; gives rise to the terminal bud, leaves, and stem.

epidermis: In *plants,* a protective tissue that forms the outer layer of leaves, green stems, and roots; in *animals,* the outer layer of skin consisting of layers of tightly packed epithelial cells.

epididymis: A storage area for sperm on the upper, rear part of the testis.

epiglottis: A flap of tissue that covers the trachea during swallowing, so that food passes only into the esophagus.

epinephrine: A hormone produced by the adrenal medulla; a neurotransmitter produced by some nerve cells; adrenaline.

epithelial tissue: A type of tissue that covers body surfaces and lines body cavities and organs.

erosion: The removal of soil by the action of wind and/or water.

erythrocyte: A hemoglobin-containing cell in blood that carries oxygen to the body tissues and carbon dioxide to the lungs; red blood cell.

esophagus (pl. esophagi): The tube that is the passageway for food from the mouth to the stomach.

estrogen: A hormone secreted by the ovaries that promotes development of female secondary sex characteristics and regulates the reproductive cycle.

ethylene: An organic compound that stimulates flowering in some plants and hastens the ripening of fruit.

eucaryote: A cell containing a membrane-bounded nucleus.

Euglenophyta: A phylum of protists; euglenoids show both plantlike and animal-like characteristics.

Eustachian tube: The tube extending between the middle ear and the throat that equalizes the pressure between the middle ear and the environment.

eutrophication: An accelerated aging process in a lake or pond, in which the body of water fills in with plant remains and is reduced in size.

evolution: The theory that life arose by natural processes at an early stage of the earth's history and that complex organisms developed from simple organisms by a process of gradual change.

excretion: The process by which the wastes of cellular metabolism are removed from an organism.

exhalation: The phase of breathing in which air is expelled from the lungs.

exocrine gland: A gland that discharges its secretions into a duct.

exoskeleton: A skeleton found on the outside of the body, enclosing the soft parts.

extensor: A muscle that extends a joint.

external fertilization: The process in which eggs are fertilized outside the body of the female.

extraembryonic membrane: In shelled eggs of reptiles and birds, any one of four membranes outside the embryo but inside the shell

facilitated diffusion: A process by which certain molecules diffuse quickly across a cell membrane.

family: A group of related genera.

fatty acid: A type of organic molecule having a carbon chain with at least one carboxyl group attached to it; one of the end products of the digestion of fats.

feces: Undigested and indigestible food material that is solidified in the large intestine and then eliminated from the body.

fern: Any of a class of spore-dispersing tracheophytes; Filicineae.

fermentation: Following glycolysis, the conversion of pyruvic acid to an end product with no further release of energy.

fertilization: The union of an egg cell nucleus and a sperm cell nucleus to form a zygote.

fertilizer: A material used to provide or replace soil nutrients.

fetus: The developing baby after about the second month of pregnancy.

filament: The stalklike part of a stamen that supports the anther.

flagellum (pl. flagella): A long, hairlike organelle at the surface of a cell, with the capacity for movement.

flexor: A muscle that bends a joint.

follicle: A structure in the ovary in which the mature egg develops.

food chain: A series of organisms through which food energy is passed in an ecosystem.

food web: A complex relationship formed by interconnecting and overlapping food chains in an ecosystem.

foot: A large ventral, muscular structure that functions in locomotion in mollusks.

foramen magnum: The opening in the skull where the spinal cord enters.

fossil: The remains or traces of an extinct organism.

fraternal twins: Two individuals formed when two eggs are fertilized at the same time; twins that are genetically different.

fruit: A structure that develops from the ovary and other associated flower parts after fertilization and that contains the seeds.

fundamental tissue: A tissue involved in the production and storage of food and in the support of the plant; parenchyma, collenchyma, and sclerenchyma.

Fungi: One of the five kingdoms; its members are saprobic or parasitic, mostly multicellular, and usually consist of filaments.

gallbladder: The organ that stores bile produced by the liver.

gamete: A haploid cell that fuses with another haploid cell to form a zygote; a sperm cell or egg cell.

gametogenesis: The process by which gametes develop.

gametophyte generation: The multicellular, haploid, gamete-producing generation in a plant showing an alternation of generations

ganglion: A group of cell bodies and interneurons that switch, relay, and coordinate nerve impulses.

gastric juice: The digestive secretion of glands in the stomach, containing hydrochloric acid and pepsin.

gastropod: A member of the class Gastropoda, including snails, slugs, and whelks; a mollusk having a head with tentacles and a one-piece, straight, or spiral shell.

gastrovascular cavity: The internal body cavity of a coelenterate.

gastrula (pl. gastrulae): In animals, an early stage of embryonic development during which the second germ layer is formed.

gastrulation: The process in which the cells on one side of a blastula move in to form the two-layered gastrula.

gene: A distinct unit of hereditary material found in chromosomes; a sequence of nucleotides in DNA that codes for a particular tRNA, rRNA, or polypeptide.

gene linkage: Genes located on the same chromosome; they are not independently assorted, but instead are generally distributed together during meiosis.

gene mutation: A change in the sequence of the bases in a gene, which changes the structure of the polypeptide that the gene codes for.

gene pool: The total of all the alleles in a population.

genetic engineering: The process of producing altered DNA, usually by breaking a DNA molecule and inserting new genes.

genetics: The branch of biology concerned with the ways in which hereditary information is transmitted from parents to offspring.

genotype: The genetic makeup of an individual.

genus: A group of closely related species.

geographic isolation: The first stage of speciation, in which a population of organisms is prevented from interbreeding with other populations of that species by a natural barrier.

geologic evolution: The process of continual change that the earth undergoes.

geologic time scale: A timetable devised by geologists that describes the earth's geological history.

germ layers: The three embryonic cell layers—the ectoderm, mesoderm, and endoderm—that give rise to all tissues and organs of animals.

germ theory of disease: The idea that bacteria and other microorganisms can cause disease.

gestation period: The length of a pregnancy.

gastrovascular cavity: The internal body cavity of a coelenterate.

gibberellin: A hormone that affects plant growth as well as the development of fruits and seeds.

gill: In *aquatic animals,* a thin layer of tissue richly supplied with blood vessels that is the respiratory organ. In some *fungi,* a reproductive structure that consists of many hyphae pressed closely together.

gill slit: A structure found in pairs in the throat region of all chordates during some part of their lives.

ginkgo: Subclass Ginkgophyta of the gymnosperms; the maidenhair tree with fan-shaped leaves—the only surviving species.

gizzard: In birds and many invertebrates, a thick-walled grinding organ that crushes food released from the crop.

gliding joint: A joint that permits limited flexibility in all directions.

glomerulus (pl. glomeruli): A cluster of capillaries in the nephron of a kidney.

glucagon: The hormone secreted by the pancreas that increases the blood-glucose level.

glycerol: An alcohol that reacts with fatty acids to form fats; one of the end products of the digestion of fats.

glycogen: A polysaccharide that is the main food storage compound in animals.

glycolysis: The series of reactions in which a glucose molecule is converted into two molecules of pyruvic acid with a net gain of 2 ATP.

golden-brown algae: Members of the phylum Chrysophyta; mostly fresh-water organisms.

Golgi body: An organelle consisting of stacks of membranes forming flattened sacs in the cytoplasm, which serves as a storage center for proteins synthesized by a cell.

gonad: In animals, a specialized organ in which gametes develop.

gradualism: Darwin's theory of evolution, in which new species arise through gradual changes in their characteristics, and thus evolution occurs slowly over millions of years.

grafting: A type of artificial vegetative propagation accomplished by permanently joining a part of one plant to another plant.

grassland: A biome in which there is not enough rainfall to support trees and the dominant form of vegetation is grasses; prairie.

growth: The process by which living organisms increase in size.

guanine: A nitrogenous base found in DNA and RNA.

guard cell: In leaves, a specialized epidermal cell that regulates the opening and closing of the stomates.

gullet: The part of the paramecium where food particles enter the cell.

gymnosperm: A seed plant whose seeds are not enclosed within a fruit.

h

habit: Learned behavior that becomes automatic.

habitat: The particular part of the environment in which an organism lives.

habituation: The simplest type of learning; the animal learns not to respond to repeated "unimportant" stimuli.

haploid: Having half the diploid number of chromosomes; *n* or monoploid.

Hardy-Weinberg law: The principle that sexual reproduction by itself does not change allele frequencies in a population.

Haversian canal: A cavity in bone that contains the blood vessels and nerves that serve the osteocytes.

helix: A shape like a coiled spring, used to describe the structure of DNA molecules.

Hemiptera: A large order of insects—mostly terrestrial, some aquatic; bugs.

hemocyanin: A copper-containing pigment that carries oxygen in the blood of some invertebrates.

hemoglobin: A red, iron-containing pigment in the red blood cells of vertebrates that increases the oxygen-carrying capacity of the blood.

hemophilia: A hereditary disease in which one or more of the clotting factors are missing from the blood.

hepatic-portal circulation: A subdivision of the systemic circulation that transports blood from the digestive tract to the liver.

herbaceous stem: A stem that is soft, green, and juicy.

herbivore: A heterotroph that feeds only on plants.

hermaphrodite: An individual organism that possesses both testes and ovaries.

heterotroph: An organism that cannot synthesize its own food and must obtain it ready-made.

heterotroph hypothesis: The hypothesis that the first organic compounds were formed by natural chemical processes on the primitive earth and that the first lifelike structures developed from coacervates and were heterotrophs.

heterozygous: Having two different alleles for a trait.

hinge joint: A joint that permits back-and-forth motion in one plane, such as the elbow and knee.

homeostasis: The condition of a stable internal environment in an organism.

homologous pair: A pair of chromosomes having the same size and shape and carrying alleles for the same traits.

homologous structures: Structures found in different kinds of organisms that have the same basic arrangement of parts and a similar pattern of embryonic development.

Homo sapiens: The species of modern humans.

homozygous: Having two identical alleles for a trait.

hormone: A substance that is secreted by a gland directly into the bloodstream and that produces a specific effect on a particular tissue.

horsetail: A spore-dispersing member of the tracheophytes, having a hollow green stem and a collar of leaves at intervals along the stem.

human ecology: The study of the relationship between humans and the environment.

humus: The dark, rich organic matter in topsoil formed from the decay of dead plants and animals.

hybrid: An individual that is heterozygous for a particular trait; an individual produced by a cross between members of two closely related species.

hybrid vigor: Superior characteristics that are often found in hybrids produced by a cross of two closely related species; heterosis.

hydrolysis: The process by which molecules are broken apart by the addition of water molecules.

Hymenoptera: A large varied order of colonial insects; includes bees, wasps, and ants.

hypersecretion: An excess of a hormone.

hypertonic solution: A solution whose concentration of solutes is higher than that of a cell placed in it.

hypha (pl. hyphae): A threadlike filament many of which make up the bodies of most fungi.

hypocotyl: The part of a plant embryo between the radicle and the point of attachment of the cotyledons.

hyposecretion: A deficiency of a hormone.

hypothalamus: The part of the human brain located below the thalamus; controls body temperature, blood pressure, and emotions.

hypothesis: A possible explanation of an observed set of facts.

hypotonic solution: A solution that contains a lower concentration of dissolved substances than that of a cell placed in it.

identical twins: Two individuals formed when one fertilized egg divides in half at an early stage of development, producing two organisms with the same genetic makeup.

immovable joint: A joint in which the bones are fitted tightly together and cannot move.

immune response: The reaction of the immune system to the presence of foreign cells or molecules.

immunity: The ability of the body to resist a disease.

implantation: The attachment of the embryo to the uterine lining, in placental mammals.

imprint: A type of fossil formed when an impression made in mud by a living thing is preserved when the mud is transformed into rock.

imprinting: In some animals, the forming of an attachment to an organism, object, or other environmental factor soon after hatching or birth.

impulse: A region of electrical and chemical change that passes along the cell membrane of a neuron.

inborn immunity: Immunity that is present at birth.

inbreeding: A breeding method in which closely related individuals are mated to retain or strengthen certain desirable traits.

incisor: A type of tooth specialized for cutting food.

incomplete dominance: A type of inheritance in which neither of a pair of contrasting alleles is dominant over the other, and the heterozygous individual is intermediate in phenotype; blending inheritance.

incomplete metamorphosis: A type of development in some insects in which there is no larval stage.

independent assortment: The principle of genetics stating that the alleles of genes on nonhomologous chromosomes are inherited independently of one another.

index fossil: The fossil of an organism that was common in many areas, but which existed for only a short period of time; used in relative dating.

indicator: A substance that changes color when the pH of a solution goes above or below a certain value.

industrial melanism: The development of dark-colored organisms in a population exposed to severe, soot-laden air pollution.

inferior vena cava: A large vein that collects blood from the lower half of the body and returns it to the right atrium of the heart.

ingestion: The taking in of food from the environment.

inhalation: The phase of breathing in which air is drawn into the lungs.

innate behavior: Behavior determined by heredity.

inorganic compound: A compound that does not contain carbon and hydrogen.

Insecta: A class of arthropods having no antennae, three body regions, three pairs of legs, and tracheal respiration; insects.

Insectivora: An order of generally small, primitive mammals that feed mainly on insects; includes moles, shrews, and hedgehogs.

insight: Creating a solution to an unfamiliar problem without a period of trial and error.

instinct: A complex, inborn behavior pattern.

insulin: A hormone secreted by the pancreas that lowers blood-glucose levels.

intercellular fluid: The colorless, watery fluid that bathes all the cells of the body; interstitial fluid.

interferon: A protein produced by body cells in response to attack by viruses.

internal fertilization: The process in which eggs are fertilized within the body of the female.

interneuron: A neuron that relays impulses from one neuron to another.

interphase: The stage of the cell reproductive cycle lasting from the end of one mitotic cycle to the beginning of the next.

interspecific competition: Competition between two different species in an ecosystem.

intertidal zone: The biome along the ocean shoreline that is covered by water at high tide and uncovered at low tide.

intestinal juice: A secretion of the cells of the walls of the small intestine, containing digestive enzymes.

intestine: The organ in which most digestion and the absorption of food occurs.

intraspecific competition: Competition between members of the same species in an ecosystem.

inversion: A type of chromosomal alteration in which a portion of a chromosome is rotated, resulting in the reversal of the order of the genes in that segment.

invertebrate: Any animal without a backbone.

ion: An atom or group of atoms with an electrical charge.

ionic bond: The force of attraction between two ions in a chemical compound.

iris: The round, colored part of the eye formed from the choroid layer; controls the size of the pupil.

irritability: The capacity of a cell or organism to respond to stimuli.

islets of Langerhans: The endocrine portion of the pancreas, consisting of clusters of hormone-secreting cells.

isotonic solution: A solution that contains the same concentration of dissolved substances as does a living cell placed in it.

isotope: An atom that differs from other atoms of the same element by the number of neutrons in its nucleus.

joint: A point in the skeleton where bones meet.

karyotyping: A technique for examining the chromosome makeup of an individual.

kidney: One of a pair of organs in vertebrates that excrete nitrogenous wastes and regulate the blood's chemical balance.

kilocalorie: The amount of heat needed to raise the temperature of 1 kg of water 1°C; 1,000 calories or 1 Calorie.

kingdom: A group of related phyla; the largest category in classification systems.

Krebs cycle: The biochemical pathway in which a two-carbon compound is broken down, releasing carbon dioxide, hydrogen, and energy.

labor: The slow, rhythmic contractions of the uterine muscles during childbirth.

lacteal: A small lymph vessel found in the center of a villus.

Lagomorpha: An order of plant-eating mammals having short tails and two pairs of upper incisors, one behind the other; includes rabbits and hares.

large intestine: The final section of the digestive tract; it serves three functions: reabsorption of water, absorption of vitamins, and the elimination of undigested and indigestible material from the digestive tract.

larva (pl. larvae): An early developmental stage of some animals after hatching; must undergo metamorphosis to reach the adult form.

larynx: The voice box; connects the pharynx with the trachea.

lateral bud: A bud in the upper angle where a leaf joins a stem; axillary bud.

lateral line: A row of sensory organs along each side of the body in fishes and some amphibians, for detecting vibrations.

law of dominance: The principle of genetics stating that when organisms pure for contrasting traits are crossed, all their offspring will show the dominant trait.

law of segregation: The genetic principle stating that the alleles of a gene occur in pairs and are separated from each other during meiosis and are recombined at fertilization.

layering: A type of artificial vegetative propagation, accomplished by covering part of a growing plant with soil.

leaf: A usually thin, flat, outgrowth of a stem; carries out photosynthesis.

learned behavior: Behavior that develops as a result of experience.

lens: In the eye, the structure behind the iris that focuses light on the retina.

lenticel: An opening in cork tissue that allows the exchange of respiratory gases between the atmosphere and the plant tissues.

Lepidoptera: An insect order having two pairs of broad, membranous wings; butterflies and moths.

leucoplast: A colorless plastid in which glucose is converted to starch.

leukocyte: A nucleated blood cell that serves as part of the body's defense against disease; white blood cell.

lichen: An organism consisting of an alga and a fungus living symbiotically; they grow on soil, rocks, and tree trunks.

ligament: A tough, fibrous band of connective tissue that holds the bones together at a movable joint.

light reactions: In photosynthesis, a series of reactions requiring light in which water or some other compound is oxidized and ATP and $NADPH_2$ are produced.

light system: The mirror and other parts of a microscope that direct light through the specimen.

limiting factor: A condition of the environment that limits the growth of a population, such as limited availability of food, water, space, or some other necessity.

lipid: An organic compound other than a carbohydrate, consisting of carbon, hydrogen, and oxygen; a fat, oil, or wax.

littoral zone: The biome between the intertidal zone and the continental shelf; the water is relatively shallow and light reaches the ocean floor.

liver: An organ that secretes bile and removes toxic substances from the blood.

lung: In vertebrates, an organ specialized for the exchange of gases between the blood and the atmosphere.

lymph: The fluid inside the lymph vessels.

lymph node: A lymphatic gland that plays an important role in the body's defense against disease.

lymphatic system: A system of vessels that returns excess fluid and proteins from the intercellular spaces to the blood.

lymphocyte: A white blood cell that recognizes and destroys antigens present in the body tissues.

lysosome: A small, saclike organelle that contains hydrolytic enzymes.

m

magnification: The amount of enlargement of an image that a lens or a microscope produces.

Malpighian tubule: The excretory organ of grasshoppers and other insects.

Mammalia: A class of warm-blooded vertebrates that have a four-chambered heart, are covered with hair or fur, and nourish their young with milk; mammals.

mantle: A fold of skin that surrounds the body organs in mollusks and secretes the shell of shelled mollusks.

marrow: The soft tissue that fills the hollow spaces in bone.

marsupial: Nonplacental mammal in which the fetus is born at a very immature stage and completes its development in a pouch on the mother's body.

mass number: See **atomic mass.**

Mastigophora: A phylum of protists containing the most primitive protozoa, called zooflagellates; they move by means of flagella.

maturation zone: The region behind the elongation zone of the root in which cells differentiate.

mechanical system: The structural parts of a microscope excluding the light system.

medulla: The part of the brain beneath the cerebellum and continuous with the spinal cord; controls involuntary activities.

medusa: The body form of free-swimming coelenterates.

meiosis: Cell division in diploid cells that results in haploid cells; reduction division.

menstrual cycle: The hormone-controlled cycle in the human female, lasting about a month, in which an egg matures and is released from the ovary and the uterus prepares to receive it.

menstruation: The last stage of the menstrual cycle, marked by the shedding of some of the uterine lining, the unfertilized egg, and a small amount of blood through the vagina, which occurs about once a month in the human female.

meristem: In a plant, a region or tissue composed of cells that undergo or are capable of repeated cell division.

meristamatic tissue: Plant tissue whose cells undergo, or are capable of, repeated cell division; meristem.

meristematic zone: A region of actively dividing cells just behind the root cap.

mesoderm: The germ layer between the endoderm and ectoderm.

mesophyll: A layer of photosynthetic tissue found between the epidermal layers of a leaf.

messenger RNA (mRNA): The type of RNA that carries the code for a polypeptide from DNA to the ribosomes where it is translated.

metabolism: All the chemical reactions of the life processes of an organism.

metamorphosis: The series of changes that certain types of organisms undergo as they develop from a larva or nymph to an adult.

metaphase: The stage of mitosis or meiosis during which the centromeres of the chromosomes are lined up at the equatorial plane.

metric system: A decimal system of weights and measures based on the meter, liter, gram, and Celsius degree.

microdissection: Operations done under a microscope on living cells, using very small instruments.

microfilament: Long, threadlike strands found in the cytoplasm of some cells, involved in movement.

micropyle: A small opening in the ovule through which the pollen tube grows.

microscope: An instrument that makes very small objects appear larger so they can be studied.

microtubule: A long, cylindrical organelle found in cilia and flagella.

mimicry: A protective adaptation in which one species is protected from its enemies by its resemblance to another species.

mitochondrion: An oval membrane-enclosed organelle in which most of the reactions of cellular respiration occur.

mitosis: The process by which the nucleus of a cell divides, while maintaining the chromosome number.

mixture: A combination of substances in which the substances are physically mingled but are not chemically bonded to each other.

molar: A type of tooth specialized for grinding food.

mold: *A type of fossil* formed when sediment in which an organism is embedded hardens, preserving the shape of the organism after its remains decompose. A *kind of fungus.*

molecular formula: A formula that shows the atomic composition of a molecule.

molecule: An uncharged group of atoms held together by covalent bonds.

Mollusca: A phylum of invertebrates having soft, unsegmented bodies, often enclosed in a mantle; mollusks.

molting: The process in which an exoskeleton or other outer covering is shed and replaced by a new one.

Monera: The kingdom that includes the simplest one-celled organisms—the bacteria and blue-green algae; monerans.

monocot: A flowering plant whose seeds have one cotyledon.

monohybrid cross: A genetic cross in which only one pair of contrasting traits is studied.

monosaccharide: The simplest type of carbohydrate, with the empirical formula CH_2O; a simple sugar.

monotreme: Any of the order of mammals, Prototheria; they lay eggs and have one discharge opening for the digestive and urinary tracts; includes the duckbill platypus.

morula (pl. morulae): An early stage of animal development in which the embryo consists of a solid ball of cells formed by cleavage of the fertilized egg.

moss: Any of a class of bryophytes; small, simple, green plants that grow in moist environments; Musci.

motor neuron: A nerve cell that carries impulses from the spinal cord and brain toward an effector.

multiple alleles: Three or more different forms of a gene, each producing a different phenotype.

multiple-gene inheritance: The type of inheritance in which two or more pairs of genes affect the same characteristic; polygenic inheritance.

muscle tissue: A tissue consisting of cells that have the capacity to contract and exert a pull.

muscle tone: The state of partial contraction in which all muscles are kept.

mutagenic agent: A material or environmental factor that causes mutations.

mutation: The appearance of a new allele on a chromosome.

mutualism: A symbiotic relationship in which both organisms benefit from their association.

mycelium: A tangled mass of hyphae.

myelin: A white, fatty substance produced by Schwann cells on some axons.

Myxomycota: A phylum of protists with characteristics of both protozoa and fungi during their life cycles; slime molds.

n

nasal passage: Hollow space in the nose through which air flows from the nostril to the pharynx.

natural selection: The process whereby organisms with favorable variations survive and produce more offspring than less well-adapted organisms.

navel: A scar formed at birth when the umbilical cord is cut and tied.

Neanderthals: An early type of *Homo sapiens* that first appeared about 100,000 years ago.

negative feedback: A regulatory mechanism that returns a condition to its normal value.

nekton: Free-swimming marine organisms, including fishes, turtles, and whales.

nematocyst: The capsule within a cnidoblast containing a coiled, hollow thread that is discharged when the cnidoblast is stimulated.

Nematoda: A phylum of invertebrates with cylindrical bodies covered by a heavy cuticle; roundworms.

nephridium (pl. nephridia): The organ of excretion in the earthworm and other annelids.

nephron: The functional unit of the kidney.

nerve: A bundle of axons, or fibers, that are bound together by connective tissue.

nerve net: A type of nervous system found in the hydra; the nerve cells are formed into an irregular network through which coordinated movement can occur.

neuron: A cell specialized for the transmission of impulses; a nerve cell.

neuromuscular junction: The junction between motor neurons and muscle fibers.

neurotransmitter: A substance released from the synaptic knob into the synaptic cleft that initiates impulses in adjacent neurons.

neutralization: The reaction of an acid and a base to produce a neutral solution.

neutron: An electrically neutral particle found in the nuclei of atoms.

niche: The particular way in which a species functions in an ecosystem.

nictitating membrane: A transparent kind of eyelid present in many vertebrates.

nitrifying bacteria: Bacteria that can convert ammonia to nitrite and nitrate.

nitrogen cycle: The pathways by which nitrogen is circulated through the biosphere.

nitrogen fixation: The process by which nitrogen-fixing organisms produce nitrogen compounds from the gaseous nitrogen of the atmosphere.

nitrogen fixers: Bacteria and blue-green algae that can produce nitrogen compounds from the gaseous nitrogen of the atmosphere.

nomenclature: The system for naming organisms.

nondisjunction: The failure of homologous chromosomes to separate normally during meiosis, producing gametes or spores with one more or one less chromosome than normal.

nonrenewable natural resource: A resource that can be used only once, such as coal, oil, and minerals, and cannot be replaced.

norepinephrine: An excitatory neurotransmitter; noradrenaline.

notochord: A flexible, rodlike, internal supporting structure found in all chordates during some part of their lives.

nucleic acid: A molecule made up of repeating units called nucleotides, which form the genetic code for transmitting hereditary information; DNA or RNA.

nucleolus: A dense, granular body that is found in the nucleus of cells and that is a site of RNA production.

nucleotide: The basic unit of nucleic acids, containing a sugar, a phosphate group, and one of four nitrogenous bases.

nucleus: In a eucaryotic *cell,* a large, membrane-enclosed organelle that contains the cell's DNA. In an *atom,* the central core of the atom, containing protons and neutrons.

nutrient: A substance that can be used in metabolism for energy, for growth and repair, or for regulation.

nutrition: The process by which materials from the environment are taken into an organism and changed into usable forms.

nymph: The young of an insect with incomplete metamorphosis; it resembles the adult but lacks certain features.

olfactory cell: A receptor for smell located in the mucous membrane lining the upper nasal cavity.

omnivore: A heterotroph that feeds on both plants and animals.

one gene, one polypeptide hypothesis: The hypothesis that every gene directs the synthesis of a particular polypeptide chain; originally called the one gene, one enzyme hypothesis.

oogenesis: The formation of eggs.

Oomycota: A phylum of mainly aquatic fungi with flagellated spores and distinctly male and female gametes; water molds.

ootid: The large, haploid daughter cell produced by the meiotic division of the secondary oocyte; matures into an egg.

open circulatory system: A circulatory system in which blood is not always enclosed in blood vessels, but flows into open spaces to bathe the tissues.

operculum: A protective, bony flap that covers the gills of bony fishes; gill cover.

optic nerve: The nerve that carries impulses from the receptors in the retina of the eye to the brain.

optical microscope: A microscope that uses light rays and transparent lenses to produce an enlarged image; light microscope.

optical system: The lenses of a compound microscope.

oral groove: The opening in the paramecium through which food is ingested.

order: A group of related families.

organ: A body part composed of specialized tissues, performing a specific function.

organ system: A group of organs that works together to perform a general function.

organelle: A specialized structure in the cytoplasm of a cell that carries out a specific function.

organic compound: A compound that contains carbon along with hydrogen; found in nature only in the bodies and products of living organisms.

organic evolution: The process of continual change that occurs in species over time.

organism: An individual living thing.

Orthoptera: A large order of insects that exhibit incomplete metamorphosis and have biting mouthparts; they inhabit the ground or low vegetation; includes cockroaches and grasshoppers.

osculum: An opening at the unattached end of a sponge that serves as the excurrent opening.

osmosis: The diffusion of water across a semipermeable membrane from a region of high concentration of water to a region of low concentration of water.

osmotic pressure: The increase in pressure resulting from the flow of water in osmosis.

ossification: The process by which cartilage is replaced by bone in the skeletons of most vertebrates.

Osteichthyes: A class of vertebrates having a bony skeleton, movable jaws, overlapping scales, paired fins, and an air bladder; bony fishes.

osteocyte: A bone-forming cell entrapped in a small cavity within the bone substance.

outbreeding: A breeding method in which individuals not closely related are mated to introduce new beneficial alleles into the population.

oval window: The membrane between the middle and inner ear, connected to the eardrum by three small bones.

ovary: In *animals,* the female gonad, which produces egg cells; in *flowering plants,* the basal part of the pistil, which contains ovules and later, seeds, and which develops into a fruit.

oviduct: A tube that carries the egg away from the ovary.

ovipositor: A tubular organ on the end of the abdomen of female insects, used to deposit eggs.

ovulation: The release of an egg from an ovary.

ovule: In seed plants, a structure within the ovary that contains a female gametophyte and that develops into a seed after fertilization.

ovum (pl. ova): Egg cell.

oxidation: A type of chemical reaction in which an atom or molecule loses electrons or hydrogen atoms.

oxidation-reduction reaction: A reaction in which one substance is oxidized and another substance is reduced.

oxygen cycle: The pathways of oxygen in the biosphere.

oxygen debt: The amount of oxygen needed to oxidize the lactic acid produced in muscle cells during exercise.

pacemaker: A specialized group of cells in the wall of the right atrium that initiates contraction of the heart by electrical impulses.

palisade cells: The regularly arranged, tightly packed cells filled with chloroplasts that make up the upper layer of the mesophyll of the leaf.

pancreas: An organ that is both an exocrine gland and endocrine gland and that secretes digestive juice and the hormones insulin and glucagon.

pancreatic juice: The digestive secretion of the pancreas containing sodium bicarbonate, amylase, proteases, and lipases.

parapodia: Paired, paddlelike extensions found on each segment of some annelids; used for swimming and creeping.

parasite: A heterotroph that obtains nutrients from the living organism in or on which it lives.

parasitism: A symbiotic relationship in which one organism benefits from the association and the other is harmed.

parasympathetic nervous system: The division of the autonomic nervous system that slows down the functioning of various body systems.

parathyroid gland: One of four small glands embedded in back of the thyroid that secrete parathormone.

parthenogenesis: The development of an unfertilized egg into an adult organism.

passive transport: A process by which materials move across cell membranes without the expenditure of cellular energy.

pedicel: The stalk that bears a single flower.

pellicle: A grooved, flexible proteinaceous structure found inside the cell membrane of some protists.

pepsin: A protein-digesting enzyme in gastric juice.

peptide bond: The bond formed between two amino acids by dehydration synthesis.

pericardium: The tough, protective membrane surrounding the outside of the heart.

periosteum (pl. periostea): A tough membrane covering the outside of bones, except at joints.

peripheral nervous system: The division of the nervous system that includes all the neurons and nerve fibers outside the brain and spinal cord.

Perissodactyla: An order of hoofed mammals having an uneven number of toes on each foot; includes horses and rhinoceroses.

peristalsis: The alternate waves of contraction and relaxation in the walls of the alimentary canal.

permafrost: The lower layers of the soil in the tundra that remain frozen throughout the year.

petal: One of the usually showy flower structures located between the sepals and the stamens.

petiole: The structure that attaches the leaf to the stem of a plant.

petrifaction: The process by which the body of a dead organism is slowly replaced by dissolved minerals.

pH: A unit that indicates the concentration of hydrogen ions in a solution; a measure of the acidity of a solution.

Phaeophyta: A phylum of plants that includes multicellular marine seaweeds and kelps; brown algae.

phagocytosis: The process in which large particles or small organisms are ingested into a cell.

pharynx: The throat.

phase-contrast microscope: An instrument with an optical system that uses phase shifts in light passing through living cell structures to make those structures visible.

phenotype: The physical traits that appear in an individual as a result of its genetic makeup.

pheromone: A type of animal secretion that serves as a means of communication between members of the same species.

phloem: The tissue that conducts food and other dissolved materials throughout the body of a vascular plant.

photon: A particle of light.

photoperiodism: The response of a plant to the changing duration of light and darkness during the year.

photosynthesis: The process by which organic compounds are synthesized from inorganic carbon, i.e., CO_2, in the presence of light in most autotrophic organisms.

phototroph: An organism that carries out photosynthesis.

phylum: The largest or most inclusive group within a kingdom.

phytoplankton: Photosynthetic organisms that float near the surface of water.

pigment: A substance that absorbs only certain wavelengths of light; a substance that has color.

pineal gland: A pea-sized gland attached to the base of the brain that produces melatonin.

pinocytosis: The process in which liquids or very small particles from the surrounding medium are taken into a cell by an inpocketing of the cell membrane.

pistil: The part of a flower that contains the ovules and through which pollen tubes grow.

pith: The center of a herbaceous dicot system, made up of parenchyma cells.

pituitary gland: The endocrine gland attached to the hypothalamus that controls the activities of many other endocrine glands in the body.

pivot joint: A joint that permits rotation from side to side as well as up-and-down movement.

placenta: In mammals, a temporary organ through which the fetus receives food and oxygen from the mother's body and gets rid of wastes.

placental mammal: A mammal in which a placenta forms during development of the embryo.

plankton: Organisms that float in a body of water.

Plantae: One of the five kingdoms; its members are mostly multicellular and photosynthetic; plants.

planula: The small, ciliated larva of many coelenterates.

plasma: The liquid portion of blood, consisting mostly of water and dissolved proteins.

plasmid: A small, circular segment of DNA that is found in bacteria and that stays separate from the bacterial chromosome; used in genetic engineering.

plasmolysis: The shrinking of cytoplasm resulting from loss of water by osmosis in a cell placed in a hypertonic solution.

plastid: A membrane-enclosed organelle found in the cells of some protists and almost all plants; includes chloroplasts, chromoplasts, and leucoplasts.

platelet: A small, round or oval blood cell fragment that triggers the blood-clotting process.

pleura (pl. plurae): A two-layered membrane that encloses the human lung.

pollen grain: The male gametophyte of seed plants.

pollen tube: The tubelike outgrowth of the pollen grain through which the sperm nuclei pass to the ovule.

pollination: The transfer of pollen from an anther to a stigma of a flower.

pollution: The addition of anything to the environment that makes it less fit for living things.

polymer: A large molecule consisting of chains of repeating units.

polyp: The sessile body form of a coelenterate.

polypeptide: A chain of amino acids joined by peptide bonds.

polyploidy: A condition in which the cells have some multiple of the normal chromosome number.

polysaccharide: A long chain of repeating sugar units formed by joining simple sugars by dehydration synthesis.

pons: A part of the brain that serves as a relay system linking the spinal cord, medulla, cerebellum, and the cerebrum.

population: A group of organisms of the same species living together in a given region and capable of interbreeding.

population genetics: The study of the changes in the genetic makeup of populations.

pore: A tiny opening found in plant leaves and animal skins through which fluids are absorbed or discharged.

Porifera: A phylum of the simplest multicellular animals; aquatic, immobile animals with an outer layer pierced by many pores; sponges.

posterior: Pertaining to the rear or tail end of a bilaterally symmetrical animal.

predator: A carnivore that captures and feeds on prey.

pregnancy: In mammals, the period during which the developing embryo is carried in the uterus.

premolar: A type of tooth specialized for grinding food.

primary root: The first structure to emerge from a sprouting seed.

primary succession: Succession that occurs in an area that had no previously existing life.

Primates: An order of mammals having grasping hands and flexible feet, each with five digits; includes humans, apes, monkeys, and lemurs.

primitive gut: The cavity within the gastrula of an embryo that eventually forms the digestive tract.

Proboscidea: An order of mammals having tusks and long, flexible, tubelike snouts; includes elephants.

procaryote: A cell that lacks a distinct, membrane-bounded nucleus; a moneran; a bacterium or blue-green alga.

producer: An organism that produces organic compounds from inorganic compounds; an autotroph.

product: A substance produced by a chemical reaction.

progesterone: A hormone secreted by the ovaries that helps to regulate the menstrual cycle and maintains the uterus during pregnancy.

proglottid: Any of the segmentlike divisions of a tapeworm's body.

prophase: The stage of mitosis or meiosis in which the chromosomes and spindle appear, and the nuclear membrane disappears.

prostaglandin: A local hormone that produces its effects on the cells in which it is synthesized, without entering the bloodstream.

protective tissue: Any tissue that helps shield a plant from injury.

protein: A compound consisting of one or more chains of amino acids.

Protista: A kingdom that includes simple, mostly unicellular, eucaryotic organisms; protists.

proton: A positively charged particle found in the nucleus of all atoms.

protozoan (pl. protozoa): Protists that are usually motile, e.g., amebas and paramecia.

pseudopod: In certain cells, a temporary projection of the cell surface that enables the cell to engulf particles.

pulmonary circulation: The pathways in which blood flows between the heart and the lungs.

pulse: The expansion in the diameter of an artery that can be felt each time the left ventricle contracts.

punctuated equilibrium: A theory of evolution stating that a species remains the same for a long time, and then evolves rapidly during a short time interval.

Punnett square: A diagram, used in genetics, to show the results of a cross.

pupa: The resting stage of metamorphosis in which the tissues of an insect are organized into the adult form.

pupil: The opening in the center of the iris of the eye, which allows light to enter the eye.

purine: A type of nitrogenous base found in DNA and RNA; adenine and guanine.

pyramid of biomass: The relative mass of organisms at each feeding level in an ecosystem.

pyramid of energy: The relative amount of available energy at each feeding level in an ecosystem.

pyrimidine: A type of nitrogenous base found in DNA and RNA; thymine, cytosine, and uracil.

Pyrrophyta: A phylum of photosynthetic, mostly marine protists; dinoflagellates.

r

radicle: The root portion of a seed embryo.

radial symmetry: A type of symmetry in which any section through and parallel to the central axis of the organism divides it into similar halves.

radioactive dating: A dating method based on the rate of disintegration of radioactive isotopes; used to determine the age of rocks and fossils.

radioactivity: The property of giving off subatomic particles and/or radiation when an atom changes to another isotope or element.

radioisotope: A radioactive isotope.

radula: A rasping, tonguelike organ in mollusks.

Ramapithecus: A chimpanzee-like animal found as fossil remains; at one time thought to be one of the first pre-humans.

range: The particular region of the earth where a species is found.

reactant: Any of the substances participating in a chemical reaction.

receptacle: The expanded end of the pedicel, to which the flower parts are attached.

receptor: In a nervous system, a specialized structure sensitive to a certain type of stimulus; a sense organ.

recessive trait: The trait that is masked in the offspring of a cross between two pure individuals showing contrasting forms of the trait.

recombinant DNA: DNA that has been altered by genetic engineering.

recombination: The formation of new combinations of alleles resulting from crossing-over and independent assortment during meiosis, and from gamete fusion.

rectum: A structure in which undigested food (feces) is stored prior to elimination from the body.

recycling: The process of reusing materials rather than discarding them as waste.

red blood cell: See **erythrocyte.**

reduction: A type of chemical reaction in which an atom or molecule gains electrons or hydrogen atoms.

reflex: An involuntary, automatic response to a given stimulus, not involving the brain.

reflex arc: The pathway over which the nerve impulses travel in a reflex.

refractory period: The brief recovery period during which the cell membrane of a neuron cannot be stimulated to carry impulses.

regeneration: The regrowth of lost body parts by an animal.

regulation: The processes by which an organism maintains a stable internal environment in a constantly changing external environment.

relative dating: A technique in which the relative ages of layers of sedimentary rocks are determined, allowing the relative ages of the fossils in the layers to be determined.

releasing factor: A hormone that is produced by the hypothalamus and that controls the release of a hormone from the anterior pituitary.

renal artery: One of the vessels that bring blood to the kidneys.

renal circulation: A subdivision of the systemic circulation that carries blood to and from the kidneys.

renal vein: One of the vessels through which blood flows from the kidneys.

renewable natural resource: A natural resource, such as air, water, soil, sunlight, and living organisms, that can be replaced by natural processes.

reproduction: The process by which living things produce new organisms of their own kind.

reproductive isolation: The loss of ability to interbreed successfully by two groups of a population that have been separated geographically for a long time.

Reptilia: A class of cold-blooded vertebrates with dry skin, scales, four limbs, lungs, and a three-chambered heart; fertilization of eggs is internal; reptiles.

resolution: The ability of a microscope to show two points that are close together as separate images; resolving power.

respiration: The process by which organisms obtain the energy they need by releasing chemical energy stored in nutrients.

respiratory surface: A moist surface through which the exchange of respiratory gases takes place.

retina: The innermost layer of the eye, on which an

image is projected by the lens.

Rh factor: One of a group of antigens found on the surface of red blood cells.

rhizome: A thick, horizontal stem containing stored food, which forms new plants by vegetative reproduction.

Rhodophyta: A phylum of plants that includes unicellular organisms and multicellular seaweeds; red algae.

ribosomal RNA (rRNA): A type of RNA transcribed from DNA in the nucleolus and found in the ribosomes.

ribosome: An organelle that is the site of protein synthesis in a cell.

RNA (ribonucleic acid): The nucleic acid that is transcribed from DNA.

rod: A structure in the retina of the eye responsible for black-and-white vision.

Rodentia: The largest order of placental mammals, having sharp incisors for gnawing; includes rats, mice, and squirrels; rodents.

root: A structure containing vascular tissue adapted for anchoring a plant and absorbing water and dissolved substances.

root cap: A thimble-shaped group of cells that form a protective covering for the root tip.

root hair: A hairlike extension of a root epidermal cell that increases the surface area for absorption.

root pressure: The osmotic pressure in the xylem of a root.

roughage: Indigestible material in food; fiber.

rumen: In ruminants, the chamber of the stomach in which food is stored.

runner: A horizontal stem with long internodes that forms independent plants by vegetative production; a stolon.

S

saliva: The secretion of the salivary glands.

salivary amylase: The enzyme in saliva that hydrolyzes starch into maltose; ptyalin.

salivary gland: A gland that secretes saliva into the mouth.

salt: A compound other than water produced by a neutralization reaction between an acid and a base.

saprobe: An organism that obtains nutrients by breaking down the remains of dead plants and animals.

Sarcodina: A phylum of protists comprised of protozoans that move and capture prey by using pseudopods; sarcodines.

saturated fat: A fat formed from fatty acids in which all carbon-to-carbon bonds are single bonds.

scavenger: A carnivore that feeds on dead animals that it finds.

Schizomycetes: A phylum of monerans; the bacteria.

Schwann cell: A type of cell that surrounds axons and forms the myelin sheath.

scientific method: A universal approach to solving problems, in which a problem is defined, a hypothesis is formed about the cause, and an experiment is designed and carried out to prove or disprove the hypothesis.

sclera: The tough, fibrous, white, outer layer of the eye.

scrotum (pl. scrota): A sac of skin outside the body wall in which the testes of the male are located.

sebaceous gland: A gland in the skin that produces oily secretions.

secondary root: A branch off of a primary root.

secondary sex characteristic: A characteristic, such as body hair, muscle development, broadened pelvis, or voice depth, controlled by the male and female sex hormones, but not essential to the reproductive process.

secondary succession: Succession that occurs in an area in which an existing community has been partially destroyed and its balance upset.

sedimentary rock: A type of rock formed from layers of particles that settled to the bottom of a body of water, often containing fossils.

seed: In seed plants, the structure formed from the ovule following fertilization; contains the plant embryo, stored nutrients and a seed coat.

seed coat: A tough, protective covering around a seed that develops from the wall of the ovule.

selection: A technique in which only those animals and plants with the most desirable traits are chosen for breeding.

selective permeability: A characteristic of a cell membrane that allows some substances to pass freely through the membrane, while others can pass through to a slight extent or not at all.

semen: The mixture of sperm and fluids released during ejaculation.

semicircular canals: A system of loop-shaped tubes in the inner ear that enable the body to maintain balance.

sensory neuron: A nerve cell that carries impulses from a receptor toward the spinal cord and brain.

sepal: One of several leaflike structures at the base of a flower.

seta (pl. setae): One of the tiny bristles on the body segments of annelids, used in locomotion.

sex chromosome: One of two unmatched chromosomes that determine the sex of an individual; represented as X and Y.

sex-linked trait: A trait that is controlled by a gene found on one of the sex chromosomes.

sexual reproduction: A form of reproduction in which a new individual is produced by the union of the nuclei of two specialized sex cells, i.e., gametes, usually from two separate parent organisms.

simple microscope: A magnifying glass.

skeletal muscle: Muscle that is attached to bone and is involved in locomotion and voluntary movement; striated muscle.

small intestine: The part of the digestive tract where most chemical digestion and almost all absorption occurs.

smooth muscle: Muscle tissue made up of individual cells, not marked by striations, and not under voluntary control.

social behavior: Helpful and hostile interactions between animals of the same species.

sodium-potassium pump: An active transport mechanism that pumps sodium ions out of, and potassium ions into, a nerve cell; sodium pump.

solute: A substance dissolved in a solvent.

solution: A mixture, usually liquid, in which one substance, in the form of molecules or ions, is uniformly distributed through another substance.

solvent: The liquid substance that makes up the bulk of a solution.

somatic cell: A body cell, as distinguished from a sex cell.

somatic nervous system: The division of the peripheral nervous system that contains sensory and motor neurons that connect the central nervous system to skeletal muscles, skin, and sense organs.

speciation: The formation of new species.

species: All organisms of one kind that can interbreed in nature.

spectrophotometry: A method that uses an instrument that measures the intensity of light at different wavelengths, given off, or absorbed, by a substance.

spermatogenesis: The formation of sperm in the testes.

spermatogonium (pl. spermatogonia): A diploid cell in the testis, from which sperm are formed through meiosis and differentiation.

sperm cell: The male gamete.

spherical symmetry: A type of symmetry in which any cut passing through the center of the organism divides it into matching halves.

sphincter: A ring of muscle that acts as a valve.

spicule: A small skeletal structure embedded in the middle layer of sponges that provides support and gives shape to the sponge.

spinal column: In vertebrates, the series of vertebrae connected by cartilage discs that surrounds and protects the spinal cord; the backbone.

spinal cord: The cord of nervous tissue in vertebrates that extends down from the brain, running through the vertebrae of the spinal column.

spinal nerve: A nerve connected to the spinal cord.

spindle: A structure formed by fibers during mitosis.

spiracle: One of several paired openings through which air enters and leaves the body of terrestrial arthropods.

spirillum: A spiral or coiled bacterium.

spongy mesophyll: The lower portion of mesophyll in a leaf, consisting of irregularly shaped, chloroplast-filled cells separated by large air spaces.

spontaneous generation: The idea that living things regularly arise from nonliving matter; abiogenesis.

spore: A specialized reproductive cell that can give rise to a new organism.

sporophyte generation: The diploid, spore-producing generation in a plant with an alternation of generations.

Sporozoa: A phylum of protists comprised of nonmotile, parasitic protozoans; sporozoans.

stamen: The organ of a flower that bears pollen grains.

starch: A polysaccharide that is the main food storage compound in plants.

stem: The leaf-bearing structure of a vascular plant.

stereomicroscope: A microscope with an ocular and an objective for each eye, which provides a three-dimensional image of the specimen being viewed; binocular microscope.

stigma: In a *pistil,* the enlarged, sticky knob on top of a style that receives the pollen. In *protists,* an eyespot.

stimulus (pl. stimuli): Any factor that causes a receptor to trigger impulses in a nerve pathway, resulting in a change of activity.

stolon: In *fungi,* a hypha that grows over the surface of food; in *vascular plants,* a runner.

stomach: The organ of the digestive tract in which food is temporarily stored and partially digested.

stomate: An opening in the epidermis of leaves that allows the exchange of respiratory gases between the internal tissues of the leaf and the atmosphere.

striated muscle: See **skeletal muscle.**

strip cropping: A conservation practice in which cover crops are planted between strips of row crops, leaving no soil open to erosion.

structural formula: A molecular formula that shows how the atoms in a molecule are bonded to one another.

style: In flowers, the part of the pistil between the stigma and the ovary.

substrate: The substance upon which an enzyme acts.

superior vena cava: The large vein that collects blood from the upper half of the body and returns it to the right atrium of the heart.

suspension: A mixture that separates on standing.

sweat gland: A gland composed of a tiny coiled tube that opens to the surface of the skin and secretes perspiration.

swim bladder: In bony fishes, a gas-filled sac that acts as a float to regulate the buoyancy of the fish; air bladder.

symbiotic relationship: A relationship in which two different types of organisms live in a close association that benefits at least one of them.

sympathetic nervous system: The division of the autonomic nervous system that generally accelerates body activities.

synapse: The region where nerve impulses pass from one neuron to another.

synthesis: A process in which simple substances are combined chemically to form more complex substances.

synthetic theory: A modern theory of evolution stating that populations evolve, rather than the individuals within populations.

systemic circulation: The circulatory pathways that carry blood from the heart to all parts of the body except the lungs.

systole: The period of contraction during the heartbeat cycle.

tadpole: The larval form of a frog or toad.

taiga: A biome with cold winters and warm, moist summers in which the climax flora are evergreen vegetation.

taste bud: A taste receptor on the tongue.

taxis: Any movement by a simple animal or a protist toward or away from a particular stimulus.

taxonomy: The branch of biology that deals with the classification and naming of living things.

telophase: The stage of mitosis during which the chromosomes uncoil, the spindle and asters disappear, and the nuclear membrane reforms.

temperate deciduous forest: A biome in which the climax vegetation is deciduous trees; characterized by hot, humid summers and cold winters.

temperature inversion: A situation in which a layer of cooler, denser air becomes trapped below a layer of warmer air.

tendon: A strong band of connective tissue that attaches skeletal muscle to bone.

terminal bud: The bud at the tip of a plant stem.

terracing: A method of altering land for cultivation, in which flat areas are cut into the sides of a hill to prevent soil erosion from water running over the surface.

territory: An area defended by an individual against intrusion by members of the same species.

test cross: A genetic cross in which a test organism showing the dominant trait is crossed with one showing the recessive trait; used to determine whether the test organism is homozygous dominant or heterozygous.

testis (pl. testes): The male gonad, which produces sperm and secretes male sex hormones.

testosterone: A male sex hormone secreted by the testes; stimulates development of the male reproductive system and promotes male secondary sex characteristics.

thalamus: A part of the brain that serves as a relay center.

theory: An explanation that applies to a broad range of phenomena.

thermal pollution: A type of pollution in which warmed water, which has been used to cool industrial equipment, is returned to a stream or river; the change in water temperature kills fish and other organisms.

thorax: In *arthropods,* the middle region of the body. In *mammals,* the region between the neck and abdomen.

threshold: The minimum sensitivity level of a nerve cell; impulses below this level do not initiate responses.

thymine: A nitrogenous base found in DNA.

thymus gland: A gland located in the upper chest cavity that is involved in immunity.

thyroid: The endocrine gland that is located in front of the trachea and that secretes thyroxine and calcitonin.

thyroxine: An iodine-containing hormone that is secreted by the thyroid and that regulates the rate of metabolism in the body.

tissue: In multicellular organisms, a group of cells that are similar and are organized into a functional unit; usually integrated with other tissues to form an organ.

tissue culture: A technique for maintaining living cells or tissues in a culture medium outside the body.

trachea (pl. tracheae): The tube through which air passes from the pharynx to the lungs.

Tracheophyta: The phylum of vascular plants; contain the water-conducting and food-conducting tissues—xylem and phloem; tracheophytes.

transcription: The copying of a genetic message from a strand of DNA into a molecule of RNA.

transduction: The process in which pieces of DNA are transferred from one bacterial cell to another by viruses.

transfer RNA (tRNA): The type of RNA that carries a particular amino acid to mRNA at the ribosome in protein synthesis.

transformation: The transfer of DNA from dead, ruptured bacteria to living bacterial cells.

translocation: In *plants,* the movement of dissolved materials. In *genetics,* the transfer of a chromosome segment to a nonhomologous chromosome.

translocation: The movement of dissolved materials through a *plant.* In *genetics,* the transfer of a chromosome segment to a nonhomologous chromosome.

transmission electron microscope: A high-magnification instrument that passes an electron beam through a very thin specimen to create an image.

transpiration: The loss of water vapor from a plant through the stomates of the leaves.

transpiration pull: The chief process by which water moves through the xylem of a plant.

transport: All the processes by which substances pass into or out of cells and circulate within the organism.

trochophore: A type of free-swimming, ciliated larva.

tropical rain forest: A biome found around the equator in which there is a constant supply of rainfall and the temperature remains at about 25°C throughout the year.

tropism: A growth response in a plant caused by an environmental stimulus that comes primarily from one direction.

tube foot: In echinoderms, one of many water-filled tubes ending in a suction disk; used in locomotion, feeding, and respiration.

tuber: An enlarged portion of an underground stem that can grow into a new plant by vegetative reproduction.

tundra: A biome characterized by a low average temperature, permafrost, and a very short growing season.

turgor pressure: The pressure against a plant cell wall resulting from the osmotic flow of water into the cell.

tympanic membrane: A delicate membrane stretched across the inner end of the auditory canal of the ear; eardrum.

typhlosole: A longitudinal fold in the intestinal wall of some animals that increases the surface area of the intestine.

umbilical cord: In placental mammals, the structure that connects the fetus and the placenta.

unsaturated fat: A fat formed from a fatty acid in which there is one or more double or triple carbon-carbon bonds.

uracil: A nitrogenous base that is found in RNA but not in DNA.

urbanization: The transformation of a rural area to a city environment.

urea: A nitrogenous waste formed from ammonia and carbon dioxide.

ureter: A tube that carries urine from a kidney to the bladder.

urethra: The tube that carries urine from the bladder to the outside of the body.

uric acid: A dry, nitrogenous waste product excreted by birds, reptiles, and insects.

urinary bladder: A sac-like organ where urine is stored before being excreted.

urinary system: The system involved in the production and excretion of urine, including the kidneys, bladder, and associated tubes.

urine: An excretory liquid composed of water, urea, and salts.

Urochordata: A subphylum of chordates that are soft, saclike, sessile, marine animals; tunicates.

uterus: The thick, muscular, pear-shaped organ in the female mammal in which the embryo develops.

vaccine: An injection of dead or weakened bacteria or viruses or modified bacterial toxins that produces an active immunity.

vacuole: A membrane-enclosed, fluid-filled cavity in a cell.

vagina: The structure leading from the uterus to the outside of the body in mammalian females; the birth canal.

valve: A flaplike structure that permits body fluids to flow in only one direction, or that opens and closes a tube or opening.

variation: A characteristic in an individual that differs from the typical characteristic of other individuals of the same species.

vascular bundle: A structure within a stem containing parallel strands of xylem and phloem; may also contain cambium.

vascular cambium: The meristematic layer of cells that causes growth in width of a stem or root.

vascular cylinder: The central core of the root, which contains xylem and phloem; central cylinder.

vascular tissue: The xylem and phloem of a plant; conducting tissue.

vas deferens: The tubes that carry sperm from each testis to the urethra.

vegetative reproduction: The process in which undifferentiated plant cells divide mitotically and then differentiate to form an independent plant; vegetative propagation.

vein: In *leaves,* a structure that contains the vascular tissues. In *animals,* a blood vessel that carries blood from the body tissues to the heart.

ventral: Pertaining to the lower or belly side of a bilaterally symmetrical animal.

ventricle: One of the lower, thick-walled chambers of the *heart;* a space within the human *brain* that is filled with cerebrospinal fluid.

vertebra (pl. vertebrae): One of the bones of the spinal column that surrounds and protects the spinal cord.

Vertebrata: A subphylum of chordates having an enlarged brain and a spinal column made up of vertebrae that enclose the dorsal nerve chord; vertebrates.

vertebrate: Any animal with a backbone, including mammals, fishes, birds, reptiles, and amphibians; see **Vertebrata.**

vestigial structure: A nonfunctional structure in an organism that is a remnant of a structure that was functional in some ancestral form of the organism.

villus (pl. villi): A small, fingerlike projection of the lining of the small intestine.

virus: An extremely small particle of DNA or RNA surrounded by a protein coat and capable of reproducing itself inside a living cell.

vocal cords: Two pairs of membranes that are stretched across the interior of the larynx, and which, when air passes over them, can be controlled to make sounds.

warm-blooded: See **endothermic.**

warning coloration: A protective adaptation in which the bright colors of an organism make it easy to recognize.

water cycle: The cycling of water between the surface of the earth and the atmosphere.

water-vascular system: The locomotion and food-getting system in echinoderms.

whisk fern: A spore-dispersing member of the tracheo-phytes that lacks leaves and roots.

white blood cell: See **leukocyte.**

windbreak: A row of trees used to prevent wind erosion.

woody stem: A stem containing wood.

xylem: The tissue that conducts water and minerals from the roots upward through the plant, and helps to support the plant.

y

yellow-green algae: Members of the phylum Chrysophyta; mostly unicellular, fresh-water organisms.

yolk: Stored food in an animal egg.

yolk sac: In *shelled eggs,* the extraembryonic membrane that surrounds the yolk, containing blood vessels that transport food to the embryo; in *mammals,* an extraembryonic membrane that forms part of the umbilical cord.

zoology: A branch of biology that deals with the study of animals.

zooplankton: Small animals and nonphotosynthetic protists that float near the surface of water.

Zygomycota: A phylum of terrestrial fungi capable of reproducing sexually and asexually; conjugation fungi.

zygospore: A zygote covered by a thick, protective wall.

zygote: The diploid cell resulting from fusion of two gametes.

INDEX

g

h

l

PHOTOGRAPHY CREDITS

KEY TO PHOTO SOURCE ABBREVIATIONS

Animals, Animals: (AA). Bruce Coleman, Inc.: (Coleman). Carolina Biological Supply Co.: (Carolina BSC). Grant Heilman Photography: (Heilman). Odyssey Productions: (Odyssey). Oxford Scientific Films: (Oxford). Peter Arnold, Inc.: (Arnold). Photo Researchers, Inc.: (PRI).

KEY TO PHOTO POSITION IN TEXT
T = Top. B = Bottom. C = Center. L = Left.
R = Right.

Cover: J. Holmes. Detail repeated on page i.
Frontis: T. McHugh (PRI). Detail repeated in Table of Contents.

UNIT 1□xiv-1: M. Kage (Arnold). Detail repeated in Table of Contents. **Chapter 1□2:** T. McHugh (PRI). **3T:** F. Muller (Arnold). **3B:** J. Howard (Positive Images). **5:** B. Kent (AA). **6:** J. Dermid. **7T:** J. O'Neil (Picture Cube). **7B:** R. Lyons. **Chapter 2□10T:** R. Purse (PRI). **10B:** E. Degginger. **13L:** L. Dwight (Arnold). **13R:** E. Degginger. **14:** J. Wyckoff. **16:** R.D. Ullman (Taurus Photos). **18TR:** R. Kinne (PRI). **18TI:** R. Knauft (PRI). **18C:** M. Abbey (PRI). **18B:** E. Degginger. **19TR:** W. Ferguson. **19BL:** M. Rotker (Taurus). **19BR:** Dr. Burgess (PRI). **20L:** Dr. G. Schatten (PRI). **20R:** D. Scharf (Arnold). **21:** Brinkmann Instruments, Inc./Sybron Corp. **22:** Science Photo Library (PRI). **Chapter 3□26:** W. Ferguson. **27T:** E. Degginger. **27B:** R. Kinne (PRI). **31T:** M. Napper (VU). **31B:** L. Appel, M.D. **37:** Malachuk (Taurus). **38:** K. Karp. **40:** K. Karp. **41:** T. McHugh (PRI). **43:** E. Steele. **44:** W. Williams (Taurus). **Chapter 4□48:** E. Degginger. **54:** J. White (Berg Assoc.). **58L,R:** T. Cordingley. **62L:** M. Rotker (Taurus). **62R:** A. Pasieka (Taurus). **Chapter 5□66:** E. Degginger. **67:** P. Chandoha. **71:** R. Kesse. **72:** M. Ledbetter. **73:** K.G. Murti (VU). **74:** M. Powell (VU). **75T:** K.R. Porter. **75B:** M. Schliwa (VU). **76:** K.R. Porter. **77:** LBL (VU). **78:** K. Porter (University of Maryland). **79:** D. McCoy (Rainbow). **84T,B:** G. Bakacs. **85:** E. Degginger. **Chapter 6□90:** G. Bakacs. **91L:** A. Brilliant (Picture Cube). **91R:** W. Ferguson. **93,** clockwise from top: H. Reinhard (Coleman); J. Burton (Coleman); M. Reed and B. Reed (AA); H. Reinhard (Coleman); B. Coleman; B. Calhoun and C. Calhoun (Coleman); and S. Krasemann (PRI). **96L,R:** B. Kent (Earth Scenes). **98T:** Walker (PRI). **98B:** K. Taylor (Coleman). **99T:** M. Rodriguez. **99B:** D. Hochreich. **105:** T. Cordingley.

UNIT 2□106-107: E. Degginger. Detail repeated in Table of Contents. **Chapter 7□108:** S. Pantovic (PRI). **109:** J. Lepore (PRI). **112:** B. Isear (PRI). **115L:** G. Bakacs. **115R:** U.S. Brewers Association. **120:** R. Goldstein (PRI). **Chapter 8□124:** M. Stouffer (AA). **128:** K. Williamson. **129TL,TR:** E. Grave (PRI). **129B:** M. Abbey (PRI). **130:** K. Taylor (Coleman). **133:** T. Cordingley. **Chapter 9□144:** from *Tissues and Organs: A Text-Atlas of Scanning Electron Microscopy*, by R.G. Kessel and R.H. Kardon. New York: W.H. Freeman and Co., 1979. **148:** from *Tissues and Organs*. **151:** D. Goldberg (Sygma). **152:** M. Rotker (Taurus). **153:** W. McIntyre (PRI). **Chapter 10□162:** E. Grave (PRI). **163T:** M. Rotker (Taurus). **163B, 164, 165:** from *Tissues and Organs*. **171:** Institute Pasteur (Sygma). **173LR:** Courtesy of Green Cross Corp. **174:** Runk/Schoenberger (Heilman). **Chapter 11□178:** *Focus on Sports*. **181:** L.L. Rue III (PRI). **182:** W. Ferguson. **184, 185:** from *Tissues and Organs*. **188:** E. Degginger. **189:** L.T. Rhodes (Taurus). **Chapter 12□194:** Gennaro (PRI). **202:** E. Degginger. **204:** I. Wyman (Sygma). **Chapter 13□208:** M. Kage (Arnold). **209T:** Z. Leszczynski (AA). **209B:** T. McHugh (PRI). **213T:** AA. **213B:** H. Vible (PRI). **214:** J. Nettis (PRI). **215:** from *Tissues and Organs*. **216:** B. Bartholomew. **Chapter 14□224:** M. Kage (Arnold). **225:** M. Thompson (Picture Cube). **228:** from *Tissues and Organs*. **233:** J.P. Laffont (Sygma). **235:** Courtesy of Dr. D. Stein, Brain Research Laboratory, Clark University. **Chapter 15□242:** Turner (Image Bank). **253:** E.R. Lewis, Y.Y. Zeevi, and F.S. Werblin. **254:** R. Isear (PRI). **258:** from *Tissues and Organs*. **261:** Dr. Leonard Holman. **Chapter 16□266:** M. Kage (Arnold). **276:** A. Reininger (DPI). **277:** P. Chandoha. **281:** Porterfield-Chickering (PRI).

UNIT 3□282-283: G. Heilman. Detail repeated in Table of Contents. **Chapter 17□284:** E. Degginger. **285:** J. Wyckoff. **286:** Runk/Schoenberger (Heilman). **288L,R:** G. Heilman. **289:** *Popular Science*. **293L:** J. Dermid. **293LR:** E. Anderson (VU). **294, 295T,B:** Runk/Schoenberger (Heilman). **Chapter 18□298:** G. Bakacs. **299:** L. Rhodes (Earth Scenes). **301T:** W. Ferguson. **301BL,BC:** Runk/Schoenberger. **301BR:** G. Heilman. **302L:** Runk/Schoenberger (Heilman). **302R:** G. Bakacs. **304:** N. Schenck (VU). **305:** Runk/Schoenberger (Heilman). **306:** J. Cunningham (VU). **307:** Runk/Schoenberger (Heilman). **310:** R. Mitchell. **Chapter 19□314:** Wexler (PRI). **315:** Cunningham (VU). **319:** R. Mitchell. **320:** G. Bakacs. **321:** R. Frerck (Odyssey). **322:** G. Bakacs. **323T,B:** R. Lyons. **327:** P. Menzel (Stock, Boston).

UNIT 4□328-329: W. Ferguson. Detail repeated in Table of Contents. **Chapter 20□330:** E. Reschter (Arnold). **331:** Carolina BSC. **333, 334, 335T:** M. Abbey (PRI). **335BL:** E. Reschke (Arnold). **335BR:** R. Knauft (PRI). **336:** Carolina BSC. **337:** D. McCoy (Rainbow). **339:** Oxford Science Films (AA). **340:** E. Degginger. **341:** Carolina BSC. **342:** M. Rodriguez (Heilman). **343L:** G. Bakacs. **343R:** J. Wexler (PRI). **343B:** G. Heilman. **344:** R. Mitchell. **Chapter 21□348:** M. Abbey (PRI). **354, 355:** Carolina BSC. **356:** Runk/Schoenberger (Heilman). **360:** Dr. L. Shettles. **361:** S. Ramels (Heilman). **362:** R. Hitchings (PRI). **Chapter 22□366:** M. Ederegger (DRK Photo). **370:** B. Stauer, *Discover*. **371:** Dr. J. Saunders. **372T:** D. Hochreich. **372B:** G. Heilman. **373TL, TR:** K. Taylor (Coleman). **373BL:** Runk/Schoenberger (Heilman). **373BR:** K. Taylor (Coleman). **374:** E. Degginger. **375:** T. McHugh (PRI). **Chapter 23□378:** J. Running. **383:** S. Krasemann (PRI). **384:** L. Mulvehill (PRI). **386T:** J. Boughton (Stock, Boston). **386B:** E. Stone (Arnold). **Chapter 24□390:** R. Parker (PRI). **393:** G. Bakacs. **394:** W. Ferguson. **395:** G. Bakacs. **396:** K. Williamson. **399:** Runk/Lefever (Heilman). **400** (A),(C), (D): G. Bakacs. **400** (B),(E),(F): R. Mitchell. **403L:** A. Davies (Coleman). **403R:** G. Bakacs. **407:** J. Myers (Stock, Boston).

UNIT 5□408-409: J. Dermid. Detail repeated in Table of Contents. **Chapter 25□410:** P. Scott (PRI). **411:** Runk/Schoenberger (Heilman). **414L:** E. Degginger. **414R:** Dept. of Plant Biology, Univ. of Illinois. **416:** R. Kinne (PRI). **423:** R. Kinne. **Chapter 26□426:** J. O'Neil. **428:** R. Rickanscrud (PRI). **430:** T. Cordingley. **434:** Courtesy Carnegie Institute. **435T:** M. Sherman (Coleman). **435B:** W. Ferguson. **437:** SL (PRI). **438:** U. Welsch. **Chapter 27□442:** Dr. Kafefuda (PRI). **448:** Fungal Genetics Institute. **455:** J. Brandenburg (DRK Photo). **456T:** M. Abbey (PRI). **456B:** M. Walker (PRI). **457:** M. Ledbetter. **458:** M. Kage (Arnold). **460:** DNAP. **463:** T. O'Keefe (Coleman).

UNIT 6□464-465: W. Ferguson. Detail repeated in Table of Contents. **Chapter 28□466:** E. Degginger. **467:** Carolina BSC. **468T:** E. Degginger. **468B:** R. Frear (National Park Service). **469:** Courtesy of James Farlow. **470:** R. Frerck (Odyssey). **476:** W. Ferguson. **479T:** M. Fairchild (Arnold). **479B:** J. Rotman (P. Arnold). **480, 481:** E. Degginger. **Chapter 29□486:** R. Mitchell. **487:** J. Bova (PRI). **488:** H. Sund. **489:** R. Mitchell. **491:** W. Ferguson. **492T:** J. Bartlett and D. Bartlett (Coleman). **492BL:** N. Sefton (DPI). **492BR:** Stouffer Productions (AA). **493TL,BR:** W. Ferguson. **493TR:** Brass (BRI). **493BL:** M. Rodriguez. **495:** R. Mitchell. **496:** S. Krasemann (DRK). **497L,R:** M. Tweedie (PRI). **500:** E. Degginger. **507:** Institute of Materials Science, Univ. of Connecticut. **511:** J. Fields (PRI).

UNIT 7□512-513: C. Seaborn (Odyssey). Detail repeated in Table of Contents. **Chapter 30□514:** M. Abbey (PRI). **516T:** B. Knauft (PRI). **516B:** E. Degginger (Coleman). **518:** P. Chandoha. **522:** Oxford (AA). **523T:** E. Grave. **523B:** M. Kage (Arnold). **524T:** M. Kage (Arnold). **524B:** E. Graves (PRI). **527:** R. Knauft (PRI). **529:** Courtesy of T.O. Diener, U.S. Dept. of Agriculture. **Chapter 31□532:** M. Rodriguez (PRI). **534TL:** Chesher (PRI). **534TR:** T. McHugh (PRI). **534C:** N. Sefton (PRI). **534BL:** B. Evans (Arnold). **534BR:** W. Hodge (Arnold). **535T:** B. Evans (Arnold). **535C:** W.H. Amos (Coleman). **535B:** J.M. Conrader (PRI). **536T:** R. Orenstein (Earth Scenes). **536B:** M. Rodriguez. **537T:** P. Grace (PRI). **537BL,BR:** M. Rodriguez. **538:** W. Ferguson. **539:** G. Bryce (Earth Scenes). **451:** P. Ward (Coleman). **543:** M. Rodriguez. **544T:** S. Hawn (Taurus). **544B:** M. Rodriguez. **545L,C:** M. Rodriguez. **545R:** G. Bakacs. **Chapter 32□548:** C. Roessler (AA). **548B:** M. Kage (Arnold). **549:** C. Roessler (AA). **550T:** Z. Leszczynski (AA). **550B:** M. Schick (AA). **551:** W. Ferguson. **552:** W. Amos

(Coleman). **553T:** S. Earley (AA). **553C:** T. Rocke (AA). **560:** W. Chandoha. **563:** Oxford (AA). **564T:** Z. Leszczynski (AA). **564B:** J. Fields (PRI). **566L:** Oxford (AA). **566R:** M. Rodriguez. **567:** Z. Leszczynski (AA). **Chapter 33□570:** R. Mendez (AA). **571:** T. McHugh (PRI). **572L:** Z. Leszczynski (AA). **572R:** Oxford (AA). **576L,R:** B. Kent (AA). **577T:** W. Ferguson. **577B:** Z. Leszczynski (AA). **578L:** M. Rodriguez. **578R:** W. Ferguson. **578B:** Z. Leszczynski (AA). **579L:** M. Rodriguez. **579R:** G. Kelly (PRI). **580T:** H. Schonglicker (Arnold). **580B:** G. Bakacs. **581:** B. MacDonald (AA). **582TL,TR:** G. Bakacs. **582C:** D.J. Hochreich. **582B:** M. Rodriguez. **583:** R. Mendez (AA). **584:** W. Ferguson. **585,** top to bottom: R. Coleman (PRI); Dr. A.C. Twomey (PRI); P. Metzger (PRI); F.E. Toman (Taurus). **588:** W. Ferguson. **589L:** Z. Leszczynski (AA). **589R:** J. Rotman. **591T,B:** J. Rotman. **Chapter 34□594:** Z. Leszczynski (AA). **595:** J. Rotman. **597:** T. McHugh (PRI). **598:** J. Rotman (Arnold). **600T:** R. Hermes (PRI). **600BL:** R. Kinne (PRI). **600BR:** C. Seaborn (Odyssey). **601:** H. Reinhard (Coleman). **602:** P. Chandoha. **603T:** J. Burniey (PRI). **603C:** R. Kinne (PRI). **603B:** M. Rodriguez. **605:** M. Fogen (Coleman). **609TL,TR,BL:** Oxford (AA). **609BR:** R. Erwin (PRI). **610T:** D. Bartlett (Coleman). **610B:** T. McHugh: (PRI). **611T:** E. Degginger. **611B.** M. Rodriguez. **612L:** J. Collins (PRI). **612R:** C. Belinsky (PRI). **613TL:** T. McHugh (PRI). **613TR:** R.J. Ashworth (PRI). **613C:** T. McHugh (PRI). **613B:** W. Ferguson. **614:** T. McHugh (PRI). **Chapter 35□618:** T. McHugh (PRI). **619TL:** T. McHugh (PRI). **619TR:** Ferrara (PRI). **619B:** R. Willocks (PRI). **620T:** T. McHugh (PRI). **620B:** P. Lynch (PRI). **623:** T. Cordingley. **624:** L.L. Rue III (DPI). **625TL:** S. Krasemann (Arnold). **625TR:** P. Dotson (DPI). **625C:** J. Burton (Coleman). **625B:** M. Rodriguez. **626T:** G. Grant (PRI). **626B:** L. Georgia (PRI). **627L:** B. Kent (AA). **627R:** P. Dotson (DPI). **628TL:** J.C. Stevenson (AA). **628TR:** AA. **628BL:** B. Smith (AA). **628BR:** AA. **629TL:** D.C. Fritts. **629TR:** L.L. Rue III (AA). **629BL:** Z. Leszczynski (AA). **629BR:** M. Austerman (AA). **630:** M. Crabtree (Courtesy of AAAS). **631:** R. Frerck (Odyssey). **632T:** American Museum of Natural History. **632B:** Cleveland Museum of Natural History. **633T,C:** M. Crabtree (Courtesy of AAAS). **633B:** D. Bartlett (Coleman). **634T:** M. Crabtree (Courtesy of AAAS). **634C,BL:** American Museum of Natural History. **634BR:** Gallery of Prehistoric Art. **635TL,BL,R:** R. Frerck/Odyssey (Courtesy of the Field Museum of Chicago). **Chapter 36□640:** E. Degginger. **641T,B:** Tweedie (PRI). **642T:** Oxford (AA). **642B:** A. Blank (Coleman). **643T:** K. Ammann (Coleman). **643B:** G. Heilman. **644T,B:** B. Calhoun and C. Calhoun (Coleman). **646L,R:** W. Hodge (Arnold). **649T:** S. Krasemann (PRI). **649B:** A. Moreton (PRI). **654TL:** S. Seitz (Woodfin Camp Assoc.) **654TR,BL:** W. Chandoha. **654BR:** N. Leen (*Life,* 1948). **655:** Dr. H. Topoff. **657:** T. Martin (PRI). **658T:** PRI. **658B:** F. Miller (PRI). **659:** Courtesy of Katherine Payne. **660:** VanNostrand (PRI). **661:** Lowrie (PRI). **662:** N. Lightfoot (PRI). **667:** Seitz (Woodfin Camp Assoc.)

UNIT 8□668–669: S. Rannels (Heilman). Detail repeated in Table of Contents. **Chapter 37□670:** R. Frerck (Odyssey). **672:** E. Degginger. **675:** E. Bauer and P. Bauer (Coleman). **676T:** B. Kent (Earth Scenes). **676B:** J. Foott (Coleman). **684:** P. Lesson and T. Lesson (PRI). **686.** G. Bakacs. **Chapter 38□690:** M. Male (PRI). **692T:** W. Ruth (Coleman). **692B:** N. Simmerman (Coleman). **693T:** P. Degginger (Coleman). **693B:** G. Bakacs. **694L:** B. Milne (AA). **694R:** H. Ehgels (AA). **695L:** E. Degginger. **695R:** J. VanWormer (Coleman). **696:** D.W. Frith. **697TL:** M.P.L. Fogler (Coleman). **697TR:** J. Jangoux (Arnold). **697BL:** L.A. McIntire. **697BR:** J. Markham (Coleman). **699:** C. Seaborn (Odyssey). **701:** Courtesy of J. Donnelly (Woods Hole Oceanographic Institute). **702:** W. W. Bacon III (PRI). **Chapter 39□706:** M. Yamashita (Woodfin Camp Assoc.). **708:** W. Hodge (Arnold). **709T:** W. Chandoha. **709B:** P. Stephanus (DPI). **710:** P. Chandoha. **711:** J.A. Langley (DPI). **714:** N. Dudley (Stock, Boston). **715:** J. Whitmer (Nawrocki Stock Photo). **717T:** Domico (Earth Images). **718.** May (Biological Photo Service). **723:** G. Holton (PRI).

Any photo acknowledgement inadvertently omitted will be amended upon notification.